P9-BJL-459

EIGHTH EDITION

# Elementary Statistics

## PICTURING THE WORLD

**Ron Larson**
The Pennsylvania State University
The Behrend College

Content Development: *Robert Carroll*
Content Management: *Suzanna Smith-Bainbridge, Amanda Brands Moschberger*
Content Production: *Noelle Saligumba, Peggy McMahon*
Product Management: *Karen Montgomery*
Product Marketing: *Demetrius Hall*
Rights and Permissions: *Tanvi Bhatia/Anjali Singh*
Please contact https://support.pearson.com/getsupport/s/ with any queries on this content
Cover images by Shutterstock.



**Library of Congress Control Number: 2021921349**

2 2022

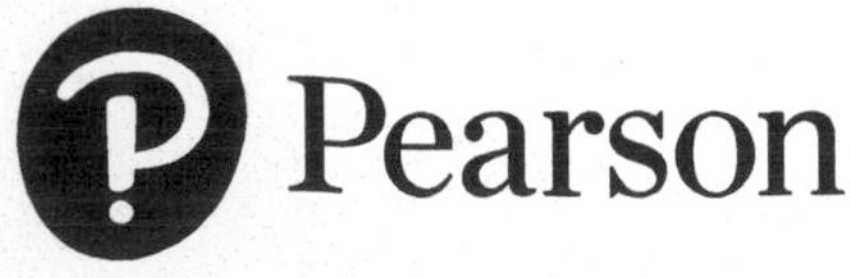


ISBN 10: 0-13-749332-0
ISBN 13: 978-0-13-749332-6

## Pearson's Commitment to Diversity, Equity, and Inclusion

Pearson is dedicated to creating bias-free content that reflects the diversity of all learners. We embrace the many dimensions of diversity, including but not limited to race, ethnicity, gender, socioeconomic status, ability, age, sexual orientation, and religious or political beliefs.

Education is a powerful force for equity and change in our world. It has the potential to deliver opportunities that improve lives and enable economic mobility. As we work with authors to create content for every product and service, we acknowledge our responsibility to demonstrate inclusivity and incorporate diverse scholarship so that everyone can achieve their potential through learning. As the world's leading learning company, we have a duty to help drive change and live up to our purpose to help more people create a better life for themselves and to create a better world.

Our ambition is to purposefully contribute to a world where:

- Everyone has an equitable and lifelong opportunity to succeed through learning.
- Our educational products and services are inclusive and represent the rich diversity of learners.
- Our educational content accurately reflects the histories and experiences of the learners we serve.
- Our educational content prompts deeper discussions with students and motivates them to expand their own learning (and worldview).

We are also committed to providing products that are fully accessible to all learners. As per Pearson's guidelines for accessible educational Web media, we test and retest the capabilities of our products against the highest standards for every release, following the WCAG guidelines in developing new products for copyright year 2022 and beyond. You can learn more about Pearson's commitment to accessibility at https://www.pearson.com/us/accessibility.html.

While we work hard to present unbiased, fully accessible contact, we want to hear from you about any concerns or needs with this Pearson product so that we can investigate and address them.

- Please contact us with concerns about any potential bias at https://www.pearson.com/report-bias.html.
- For accessibility-related issues, such as using assistive technology with Pearson products, alternative text requests, or accessibility documentation, email the Pearson Disability Support team at disability.support@pearson.com.

# CONTENTS



## PART 1 DESCRIPTIVE STATISTICS

### 1 Introduction to Statistics

### 2 Descriptive Statistics *38*

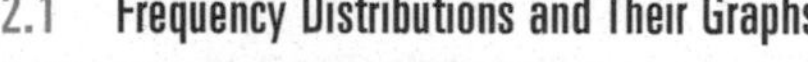

# PART 2 PROBABILITY AND PROBABILITY DISTRIBUTIONS

# 5 Normal Probability Distributions 232

## PART 3 STATISTICAL INFERENCE

# 6 Confidence Intervals 296

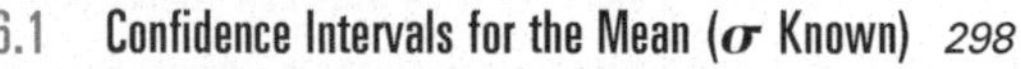

# 7 Hypothesis Testing with One Sample 346

# 8 Hypothesis Testing with Two Samples 416

# PART 4 MORE STATISTICAL INFERENCE

## Correlation and Regression 468

## Chi-Square Tests and the *F*-Distribution 524

# 11 Nonparametric Tests (Online Only)*

* Available in MyLab Statistics

# Appendices

# PREFACE

Welcome to *Elementary Statistics: Picturing the World*, Eighth Edition. You will find that this textbook is written with a balance of rigor and simplicity. It combines step-by-step instructions, real-life examples and exercises, carefully developed features, and technology that makes statistics accessible to all.

I am grateful for the overwhelming acceptance of the first seven editions. It is gratifying to know that my vision of combining theory, pedagogy, and design to exemplify how statistics is used to picture and describe the world has helped students learn about statistics and make informed decisions.

## What's New in This Edition

The goal of the Eighth Edition was a thorough update of the key features, examples, and exercises:

**Examples** This edition has 213 examples, nearly 50% of which are new or revised. Also, several of the examples now show an alternate solution or a check using technology.

**Try It Yourself** Over 40% of the 213 Try It Yourself exercises are new or revised.

**Picturing the World** Over 70% of these are new or revised.

**Screen Displays** In the examples, technology tips, and other features that show screen displays from Minitab®, Excel®, the TI-84 Plus, and StatCrunch®, the displays were revised as appropriate to make them more visually appealing, easy to follow, and reflective of the most up-to-date version of the software.

**Exercises** Over 30% of the more than 2300 exercises are new or revised.

**Extensive Chapter Feature Updates** A full 50% of the following key features are new or revised, making this edition fresh and relevant to today's students:

- Where You've Been and Where You're Going
- Uses and Abuses: Statistics in the Real World
- Real Statistics—Real Decisions: Putting it all together
- Chapter Technology Project

**References to Co-Requisite Help** Margin notes have been included at point-of-use locations throughout this edition to remind students that they can get help reviewing a particular area of mathematics in the Integrated Review in MyLab Statistics.

**Applet Activities** Revisions have been made to the applet activities throughout the text to reflect changes to the corresponding online applets they reference. Applet activities are discussed further on the next page.

**Study Strategies** At the bottom of each chapter summary page in Chapters 1 through 10, there are study strategies that students can use to help improve their performance in college. These include tips on improving reading skills, avoiding procrastination, preparing for a test, taking notes, and other areas.

## Features of the Eighth Edition

### Guiding Student Learning

**Where You've Been and Where You're Going** Each chapter begins with a two-page visual description of a real-life problem. *Where You've Been* connects the chapter to topics learned in earlier chapters. *Where You're Going* gives students an overview of the chapter.

**What You Should Learn** Each section is organized by learning objectives, presented in everyday language in *What You Should Learn.* The same objectives are then used as subsection titles throughout the section.

**Definitions and Formulas** are clearly presented in easy-to-locate boxes. They are often followed by **Guidelines**, which explain *In Words* and *In Symbols* how to apply the formula or understand the definition.

**Margin Features** help reinforce understanding:

- **Study Tips** show how to read a table, interpret a result, help drive home an important interpretation, or connect different concepts.
- **Tech Tips** show how to use Minitab, Excel, the TI-84 Plus, or StatCrunch to solve a problem.
- **References to Co-Requisite Help** point students to extra math help.
- **Picturing the World** is a "mini case study" in each section that illustrates the important concept or concepts of the section. Each Picturing the World concludes with a question and can be used for general class discussion or group work. The answers to these questions are included in the *Annotated Instructor's Edition.*

### Examples and Exercises

**Examples** Every concept in the text is clearly illustrated with one or more step-by-step examples. Most examples have an interpretation step that shows the student how the solution may be interpreted within the real-life context of the example and promotes critical thinking and writing skills. Each example, which is numbered and titled for easy reference, is followed by a similar exercise called **Try It Yourself** so students can immediately practice the skill learned. The answers to these exercises are in the back of the book and the worked-out solutions are available in MyLab Statistics in the *Student Solutions Manual.*

**Technology Examples** Many sections contain an example that shows how technology can be used to calculate formulas, perform tests, or display data. Screen displays from Minitab, Excel, the TI-84 Plus, and StatCrunch are shown. Additional screen displays are presented at the ends of selected chapters, and detailed instructions are given in separate technology manuals available with the book.

**Exercises** The exercises give students practice in performing calculations, making decisions, providing explanations, and applying results to a real-life setting. The section exercises are divided into three parts:

- **Building Basic Skills and Vocabulary** are short-answer, true-or-false, and vocabulary exercises carefully written to nurture student understanding.
- **Using and Interpreting Concepts** are skill or word problems that move from basic skill development to more challenging and interpretive problems.
- **Extending Concepts** go beyond the material presented in the section. They tend to be more challenging and are not required as prerequisites for subsequent sections.

**Technology Answers** Answers in the back of the book are found using calculations by hand and by tables. Answers found using technology (usually the TI-84 Plus) are also included when there are discrepancies due to rounding.

## Review and Assessment

**Chapter Summary** Each chapter concludes with a Chapter Summary that answers the question *What did you learn?* The objectives listed are correlated to Examples in the section as well as to the Review Exercises.

**Chapter Review Exercises** A set of Review Exercises follows each Chapter Summary. The order of the exercises follows the chapter organization. Answers to all odd-numbered exercises are given in the back of the book.

**Chapter Quizzes** Each chapter has a Chapter Quiz. The answers to all quiz questions are provided in the back of the book. For additional help, see the step-by-step video solutions available in MyLab Statistics.

**Chapter Tests** Each chapter has a Chapter Test. The questions are in random order. The answers to all test questions are provided in the *Annotated Instructor's Edition.*

**Cumulative Review** There is a Cumulative Review after Chapters 2, 5, 8, and 10. Exercises in the Cumulative Review are in random order and may incorporate multiple ideas. Answers to all odd-numbered exercises are given in the back of the book.

## Statistics in the Real World

**Uses and Abuses: Statistics in the Real World** Each chapter discusses how statistical techniques should be used, while cautioning students about common abuses. The discussion includes ethics, where appropriate. Exercises help students apply their knowledge.

**Applet Activities** Selected sections contain activities that encourage interactive investigation of concepts in the lesson with exercises that ask students to draw conclusions. The applets are available in MyLab Statistics and at **www.pearson.com/math-stats-resources.**

**Chapter Case Study** Each chapter has a full-page Case Study featuring actual data from a real-world context and questions that illustrate the important concepts of the chapter.

**Real Statistics—Real Decisions: Putting it all together** This feature encourages students to think critically and make informed decisions about real-world data. Exercises guide students from interpretation to drawing of conclusions.

**Chapter Technology Project** Each chapter has a Technology project using Minitab, Excel, and the TI-84 Plus that gives students insight into how technology is used to handle large data sets or real-life questions.

## Continued Strong Pedagogy from the Seventh Edition

**Versatile Course Coverage** The table of contents was developed to give instructors many options. For instance, the *Extending Concepts* exercises, applet activities, Real Statistics—Real Decisions, and Uses and Abuses provide sufficient content for the text to be used in a two-semester course. More commonly, I expect the text to be used in a three-credit semester course or a four-credit semester course that includes a lab component. In such cases, instructors will have to pare down the text's 46 sections.

**Graphical Approach** As with most introductory statistics texts, this text begins the descriptive statistics chapter (Chapter 2) with a discussion of different ways to display data graphically. A difference between this text and many others is that **it continues to incorporate the graphical display of data throughout the text.** For example, see the use of stem-and-leaf plots to display data on page 387. This emphasis on graphical displays is beneficial to all students, especially those utilizing visual learning strategies.

**Balanced Approach** The text strikes a **balance among computation, decision making, and conceptual understanding.** I have provided many Examples, Exercises, and Try It Yourself exercises that go beyond mere computation.

**Variety of Real-Life Applications** I have chosen real-life applications that are representative of the majors of students taking introductory statistics courses. I want statistics to come alive and appear relevant to students so they understand the importance of and rationale for studying statistics. I wanted the applications to be **authentic**—but they also need to be **accessible.** See the Index of Applications on page xvi.

**Data Sets and Source Lines** The data sets in the book were chosen for interest, variety, and their ability to illustrate concepts. Most of the **250-plus data sets** contain real data with source lines. The remaining data sets contain simulated data that are representative of real-life situations. All data sets containing 20 or more entries are available in a variety of formats in MyLab™ Statistics or at **www.pearson.com/math-stats-resources.** In the exercise sets, the data sets that are available electronically are indicated by the icon.

**Flexible Technology** Although most formulas in the book are illustrated with "hand" calculations, I assume that most students have access to some form of technology, such as Minitab, Excel, StatCrunch, or the TI-84 Plus. Because technology varies widely, the text is flexible. **It can be used in courses with no more technology than a scientific calculator—or it can be used in courses that require sophisticated technology tools.** Whatever your use of technology, I am sure you agree with me that the goal of the course is not computation. Rather, it is to help students gain an understanding of the basic concepts and uses of statistics.

**Prerequisites** Algebraic manipulations are kept to a minimum—often I display informal versions of formulas using words in place of or in addition to variables.

**Choice of Tables** My experience has shown that students find a **cumulative distribution function** (CDF) table easier to use than a "0-to-$z$" table. Using the CDF table to find the area under the standard normal curve is a topic of Section 5.1 on pages 237–241. Because some teachers prefer to use the "0-to-$z$" table, an alternative presentation of this topic is provided in Appendix A.

**Page Layout** Statistics instruction is more accessible when it is carefully formatted on each page with a consistent open layout. This text is the first college-level statistics book to be written so that, when possible, its features are not split from one page to the next. Although this process requires extra planning, the result is a presentation that is clean and clear.

## Meeting the Standards

**MAA, AMATYC, NCTM Standards** This text answers the call for a **student-friendly text that emphasizes the uses of statistics.** My goal is not to produce statisticians but to produce informed consumers of statistical reports. For this reason, I have included exercises that require students to interpret results, provide written explanations, find patterns, and make decisions.

**GAISE Recommendations** Funded by the American Statistical Association, the Guidelines for Assessment and Instruction in Statistics Education (GAISE) Project developed six recommendations for teaching introductory statistics in a college course. These recommendations are:

- Emphasize statistical literacy and develop statistical thinking.
- Use real data.
- Stress conceptual understanding rather than mere knowledge of procedures.
- Foster active learning in the classroom.
- Use technology for developing conceptual understanding and analyzing data.
- Use assessments to improve and evaluate student learning.

The examples, exercises, and features in this text embrace all of these recommendations.

## MyLab Statistics Resources for Success

MyLab Statistics is available to accompany Pearson's market-leading text options, including *Elementary Statistics: Picturing The World*, 8e (access code required).

MyLab™ is the teaching and learning platform that empowers you to reach every student. MyLab Statistics combines trusted author content—including full eText and assessment with immediate feedback—with digital tools and a flexible platform to personalize the learning experience and improve results for each student. Integrated with StatCrunch®, a web-based statistical software program, students learn the skills they need to interact with data in the real world.

MyLab Statistics supports all learners, regardless of their ability and background, to provide an equal opportunity for success. Accessible resources support learners for a more equitable experience no matter their abilities. And options to personalize learning and address individual gaps helps to provide each learner with the specific resources they need to achieve success.

### Student Resources

Each student learns at a different pace. Personalized learning pinpoints the precise areas where each student needs practice, giving all students the support they need—when and where they need it—to be successful.

StatCrunch® is integrated directly into MyLab Statistics. StatCrunch® is a powerful web-based statistical software that allows users to perform complex analyses, share data sets, and generate compelling reports of their data. The vibrant online community offers tens of thousands of shared data sets for students to analyze.

- **Collect** Users can upload their own data to StatCrunch or search a large library of publicly shared data sets, spanning almost any topic of interest. Data sets from the text and from online homework exercises can also be accessed and analyzed in StatCrunch. An online survey tool allows users to quickly collect data via web-based surveys.
- **Crunch** A full range of numerical and graphical methods allows users to analyze and gain insights from any data set. Interactive graphics help users understand statistical concepts, and are available for export to enrich reports with visual representations of data.
- **Communicate** Reporting options help users create a wide variety of visually appealing representations of their data.

StatCrunch can be accessed on your laptop, smartphone, or tablet when you visit the StatCrunch website from your device's browser. For more information, visit the StatCrunch website, or contact your Pearson representative.

**Exercises with Immediate Feedback** The exercises in MyLab Statistics reflect the approach and learning style of this text, and regenerate algorithmically to give student unlimited opportunity for practice and mastery. Most exercises include learning aids, such as guided solutions and sample problems, and they offer helpful feedback when students enter incorrect answers.

**Personalized Homework** With Personalized Homework, students take a quiz or test and receive a subsequent homework assignment that is personalized based on their performance. This way, students can focus on just the topics they have not yet mastered.

**Integrated Review** *Elementary Statistics, Picturing the World with Integrated Review* can be used in corequisite courses, or simply to help students who enter without a full understanding of prerequisite skills and concepts.

MyLab courses provide the full suite of supporting resources for the Statistics course, plus additional assignments and for study aids from select intermediate algebra topics for students who will benefit from remediation.

Assignments for the integrated review content are pre-assigned in MyLab, making it easier than ever to create your course.

**Mindset videos** and assignable, open-ended **exercises** foster a growth mindset in students. This material encourages them to maintain a positive attitude about learning, value their own ability to grow, and view mistakes as learning opportunities—so often a hurdle for math students.

**Personal Inventory Assessments** are a collection of online exercises designed to promote self reflection and metacognition in students. These 33 assessments include topics such as a Stress Management Assessment, Diagnosing Poor Performance and Enhancing Motivation, and Time Management Assessment.

## Instructor Resources

Your course is unique. So whether you'd like to build your own assignments, teach multiple sections, or set prerequisites, MyLab gives you the flexibility to easily create your course to fit your needs.

### MyLab Features

**Performance Analytics** enable instructors to see and analyze student performance across multiple courses. Based on their current course progress, the student's performance is identified as above, at, or below expectations through a variety of graphs and visualizations.

**Conceptual Question Library** There are 1000 questions in the Assignment Manager that require students to apply their statistical understanding.

**PowerPoint Presentations** include lecture content and key graphics from the textbook. Accessible PowerPoint slides are also available and are built to align with WCAG 2.0 AA standards and Section 508 guidelines.

**TestGen®** (www.pearsoned.com/testgen) enables instructors to build, edit, print, and administer tests using a computerized bank of questions developed to cover the objectives of the text.

**Test Bank** features printable PDF containing all the test exercises available in TestGen.

**Accessibility** Pearson works continuously to ensure our products are as accessible as possible to all students. Currently we work toward achieving WCAG 2.0 AA for our existing products (2.1 AA for future products) and Section 508 standards, as expressed in the Pearson Guidelines for Accessible Educational Web Media (https://www.pearson.com/accessibility-guidelines.html).

## Minitab

Minitab™ makes learning statistics easy and provide students with a skill-set that is in demand in today's data driven workforce. Bundling Minitab software with educational materials ensures students have access to the software they need in the classroom, around campus, and at home. And having 12-month access to Minitab ensures students can use the software for the duration of their course. ISBN 13: 978-0-13-445640-9 ISBN 10: 0-13-445640-8 (access card only; not sold as stand alone)

## JMP Student Edition

JMP® Student Edition is an easy-to-use, streamlined version of JMP desktop statistical discovery software from SAS Institute, Inc. and is available for bundling with the text. ISBN-13: 978-0-13-467979-2 ISBN-10: 0-13-467979-2

## XLSTAT

XLSTAT™ is an Excel add-in that enhances the analytical capabilities of Excel. XLSTAT is used by leading businesses and universities around the world. It is available to bundle with this text. For more information, go to **www.pearsonhighered.com/xlstat.** ISBN-13: 978-0-321-75932-0; ISBN-10: 0-321-75932-X

# ACKNOWLEDGMENTS

I owe a debt of gratitude to the many reviewers who helped me shape and refine *Elementary Statistics: Picturing the World,* Eighth Edition.

## Reviewers of the Current Edition

Chris Bendixen, Lake Michigan College
Seunghee Lee, Pellissippi State Community College
Nancy Liu, Miami Dade College
Lohuwa Mamadu, University of South Florida
Ashley Nicoloff, Glendale Community College
Jason Samuels, Borough of Manhattan Community College

## Reviewers of the Previous Editions

Rosalie Abraham, Florida Community College at Jacksonville
Ahmed Adala, Metropolitan Community College
Olcay Akman, College of Charleston
Polly Amstutz, University of Nebraska, Kearney
John J. Avioli, Christopher Newport University
Karen Benway, University of Vermont
David P. Benzel, Montgomery College
John Bernard, University of Texas—Pan American
B.K. Brinkley, Tidewater Community College
G. Andy Chang, Youngstown State University
Keith J. Craswell, Western Washington University
Carol Curtis, Fresno City College
Christine Curtis, Hillsborough Community College–Dale Mabry
Dawn Dabney, Northeast State Community College
Cara DeLong, Fayetteville Technical Community College
Ginger Dewey, York Technical College
David DiMarco, Neumann College
Gary Egan, Monroe Community College
Charles Ehler, Anne Arundel Community College
Carrie Elledge, San Juan College
Harold W. Ellingsen, Jr., SUNY—Potsdam
Michael Eurgubian, Santa Rosa Jr. College
Jill Fanter, Walters State Community College
Patricia Foard, South Plains College
Douglas Frank, Indiana University of Pennsylvania
Frieda Ganter, California State University
David Gilbert, Santa Barbara City College
Donna Gorton, Butler Community College
Larry Green, Lake Tahoe Community College
Sonja Hensler, St. Petersburg Jr. College
Sandeep Holay, Southeast Community College, Lincoln Campus
Lloyd Jaisingh, Morehead State
Nancy Johnson, Manatee Community College
Martin Jones, College of Charleston
David Kay, Moorpark College
Mohammad Kazemi, University of North Carolina—Charlotte
Jane Keller, Metropolitan Community College
Susan Kellicut, Seminole Community College
Hyune-Ju Kim, Syracuse University
Rita Kolb, Cantonsville Community College
Rowan Lindley, Westchester Community College
Jeffrey Linek, St. Petersburg Jr. College
Benny Lo, DeVry University, Fremont
Diane Long, College of DuPage
Austin Lovenstein, Pulaski Technical College
Rhonda Magel, North Dakota State University
Jason Malozzi, Lower Columbia College
Mike McGann, Ventura Community College
Cynthia McGinnis, Northwest Florida State College
Vicki McMillian, Ocean County College
Lynn Meslinsky, Erie Community College
Larry Musolino, Pennsylvania State University
Lyn A. Noble, Florida Community College at Jacksonville— South Campus
Julie Norton, California State University—Hayward
Lynn Onken, San Juan College
Lindsay Packer, College of Charleston
Nishant Patel, Northwest Florida State
Jack Plaggemeyer, Little Big Horn College
Eric Preibisius, Cuyamaca Community College
Melonie Rasmussen, Pierce College
Cyndi Roemer, Union County College
Neal Rogness, Grand Valley State University
Jean Rowley, American Public University and DeVry University
Elisabeth Schuster, Benedictine University
Jean Sells, Sacred Heart University
John Seppala, Valdosta State University
Carole Shapero, Oakton Community College
Abdullah Shuaibi, Harry S. Truman College
Aileen Solomon, Trident Technical College
Sandra L. Spain, Thomas Nelson Community College
Michelle Strager-McCarney, Penn State—Erie, The Behrend College
Jennifer Strehler, Oakton Community College
Deborah Swiderski, Macomb Community College
William J. Thistleton, SUNY—Institute of Technology, Utica
Millicent Thomas, Northwest University
Agnes Tuska, California State University—Fresno
Clark Vangilder, DeVry University
Ting-Xiu Wang, Oakton Community
Heidi Webb, Horry Georgetown Technical College
Dex Whittinghall, Rowan University
Cathleen Zucco-Teveloff, Rider University

Many thanks to Betsy Farber for her significant contributions to previous editions of the text.

I would also like to thank the staff of Larson Texts, Inc., who assisted with the production of the book. On a personal level, I am grateful to my spouse, Deanna Gilbert Larson, for her love, patience, and support. Also, a special thanks goes to R. Scott O'Neil.

I have worked hard to make this text a clean, clear, and enjoyable one from which to teach and learn statistics. Despite my best efforts to ensure accuracy and ease of use, many users will undoubtedly have suggestions for improvement. I welcome your suggestions.

Ron Larson

Ron Larson, odx@psu.edu

# INDEX OF APPLICATIONS

### Demographics



### Earth Science



### Economics and Finance



### Education

## Engineering



## Entertainment



## Food and Nutrition

### Government and Political Science



### Health and Medicine



### Housing and Construction



### Law



### Miscellaneous

### Mortality



### Motor Vehicles and Transportation



### Psychology

## Sports



## Work

CHAPTER 1

# Introduction to Statistics

During 2020, the fastest-growing state in the United States was Idaho. In the same year, the Idaho cities of Meridian and Nampa were among the 10 fastest-growing cities in the United States.

## Where You've Been

You are already familiar with many of the practices of statistics, such as taking surveys, collecting data, and describing populations. What you may not know is that collecting accurate statistical data is often difficult and costly. Consider, for instance, the monumental task of counting and describing the entire population of the United States. If you were in charge of such a census, how would you do it? How would you ensure that your results are accurate? These and many more concerns are the responsibility of the United States Census Bureau, which conducts the census every decade.

## Where You're Going

In Chapter 1, you will be introduced to the basic concepts and goals of statistics. For instance, statistics were used to construct the figures below, which show the fastest-growing U.S. states from 2019 to 2020 by the percent increase in population and by the numerical increase in population, along with the regions where these states are located.

For the 2010 Census, the Census Bureau sent short forms to every household. Short forms ask all members of every household such things as their gender, age, race, and ethnicity. Previously, a long form, which covered additional topics, was sent to about 17% of the population. But for the first time since 1940, the long form was replaced by the American Community Survey, which surveys more than 3.5 million households a year throughout the decade. These households form a sample. In this course, you will learn how the data collected from a sample are used to infer characteristics about the entire population.

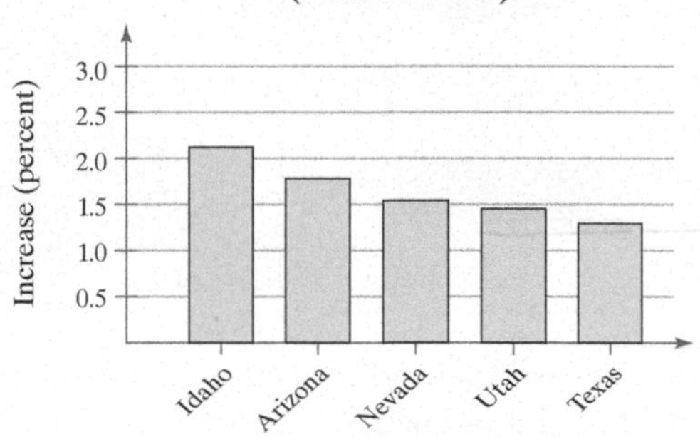


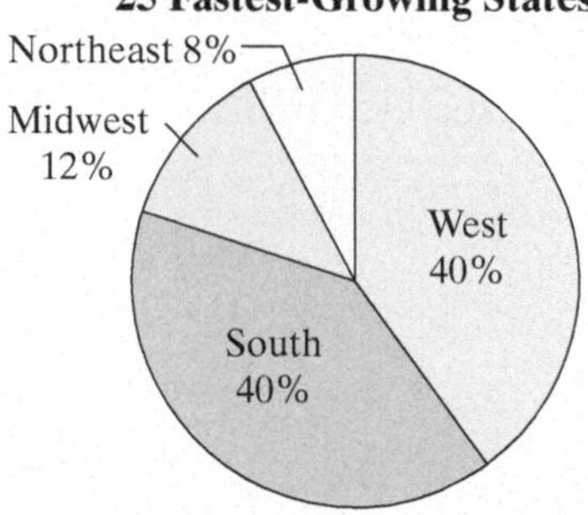


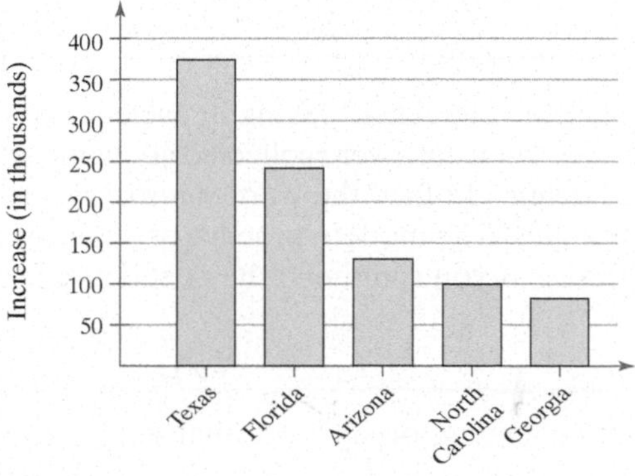


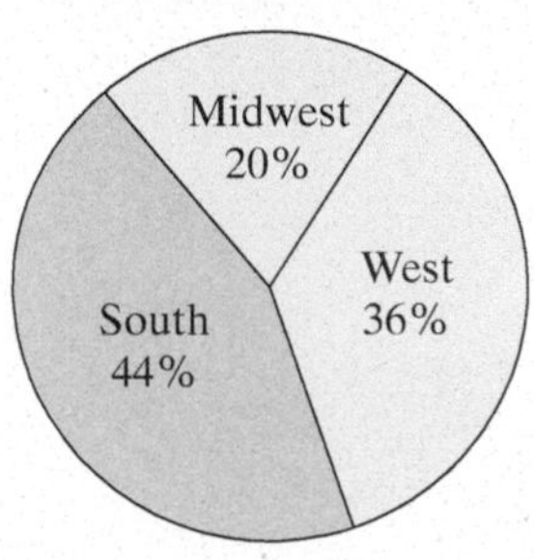

# 1.1 An Overview of Statistics

### What You Should Learn

- A definition of statistics
- How to distinguish between a population and a sample and between a parameter and a statistic
- How to distinguish between descriptive statistics and inferential statistics

A Definition of Statistics ■ Data Sets ■ Branches of Statistics

## A Definition of Statistics

Almost every day you are exposed to statistics. For instance, consider the next two statements.

- "7 in 10 Americans believe the arts unify their communities, and 2 in 5 Americans have changed an opinion or perception based on an arts experience." *(Source: Americans for the Arts)*
- "Notably, 21% of 8–11 year-olds have a social media profile." *(Source: Smart Insights, Ltd.)*

By learning the concepts in this text, you will gain the tools to become an informed consumer, understand statistical studies, conduct statistical research, and sharpen your critical thinking skills.

Many statistics are presented graphically. For instance, consider the figure shown below.

For help with percents and reading graphs, see *Integrated Review* at

MyLab® Statistics

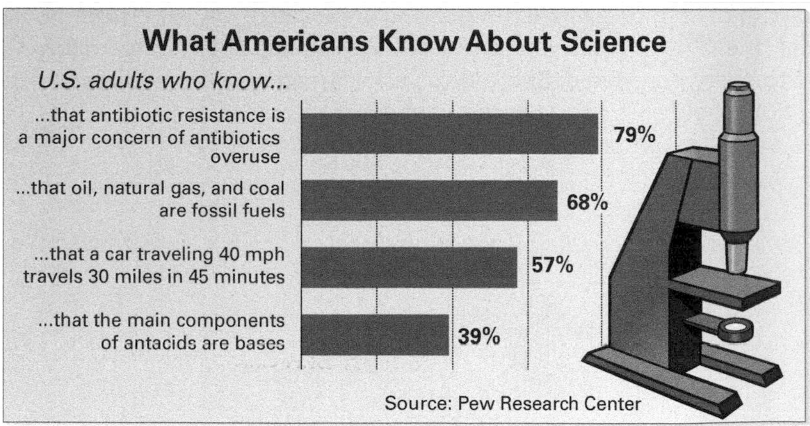


The information in the figure is based on the collection of **data.** In this instance, the data are based on the results of a science quiz given to 4464 U.S. adults.

**DEFINITION**

**Data** consist of information coming from observations, counts, measurements, or responses.

The use of statistics dates back to census taking in ancient Babylonia, Egypt, and later in the Roman Empire, when data were collected about matters concerning the state, such as births and deaths. In fact, the word *statistics* is derived from the Latin word *status*, meaning "state." The modern practice of statistics involves more than counting births and deaths, as you can see in the next definition.

**DEFINITION**

**Statistics** is the science of collecting, organizing, analyzing, and interpreting data to make decisions.

## Data Sets

There are two types of data sets you will use when studying statistics. These data sets are called **populations** and **samples.**

**Study Tip**

A *census* consists of data from an entire population. But, unless a population is small, it is usually impractical to obtain all the population data. In most studies, information must be obtained from a random sample.

**DEFINITION**

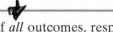

A **population** is the collection of *all* outcomes, responses, measurements, or counts that are of interest. A **sample** is a subset, or part, of a population.

A sample is used to gain information about a population. For instance, to estimate the unemployment rate for the *population* of the United States, the U.S. Bureau of Labor Statistics uses a *sample* of about 60,000 households.

A sample should be representative of a population so that sample data can be used to draw conclusions about that population. Sample data must be collected using an appropriate method, such as *random sampling*. When sample data are collected using an *inappropriate* method, the data cannot be used to draw conclusions about the population. (You will learn more about random sampling and data collection in Section 1.3.)

**EXAMPLE 1**

### Identifying Data Sets

In a survey, 751 employees in the United States were asked how stressed they feel at work. Of the 751 respondents, 616 said that they feel at least a little stressed at work. Identify the population and the sample. Describe the sample data set. *(Adapted from The Marlin Company)*

**SOLUTION**

The population consists of the responses of all employees in the United States. The sample consists of the responses of the 751 employees in the survey. In the Venn diagram below, notice that the sample is a subset of the responses of all employees in the United States. Also, the sample data set consists of 616 employees who said that they feel at least a little stressed at work and 135 who said that they do not feel stressed at work.

**Responses of All Employees (population)**

Responses of employees in survey (sample)

Responses of employees *not* in the survey

**TRY IT YOURSELF 1**

In a survey of 1516 teens in the United States, 1228 said "mental health is a significant issue for young people in the U.S." Identify the population and the sample. Describe the sample data set. *(Adapted from National 4-H Council)*

*Answer: Page A35*

Whether a data set is a population or a sample usually depends on the context of the real-life situation. For instance, in Example 1, the population is the set of responses of all employees in the United States. Depending on the purpose of the survey, the population could have been the set of responses of all employees who live in California or who work in the health care industry.

**Study Tip**

To remember the terms *parameter* and *statistic,* try using the mnemonic device of matching the first letters in *population parameter* and the first letters in *sample statistic.*

Two important terms that are used throughout this course are **parameter** and **statistic.**

**DEFINITION**

A **parameter** is a numerical description of a *population* characteristic.

A **statistic** is a numerical description of a *sample* characteristic.

It is important to note that a sample statistic can differ from sample to sample, whereas a population parameter is constant for a population. For instance, consider the survey in Example 1. The results showed that 616 of 751 employees surveyed feel at least a little stressed at work. Another sample may have a different number of employees who say they feel at least a little stressed at work. For the population, however, the number of employees who feel at least a little stressed at work does not change.

## Picturing the World

What is the cost of the U.S. Census? According to estimates, it has been escalating with each decade. The cost of the 1950 Census was approximately $91.5 million. The most recent U.S. Census, taken in 2020, was estimated to cost a staggering $15.6 billion. (Source: U.S. Census Bureau and U.S. Government Accountability Office)

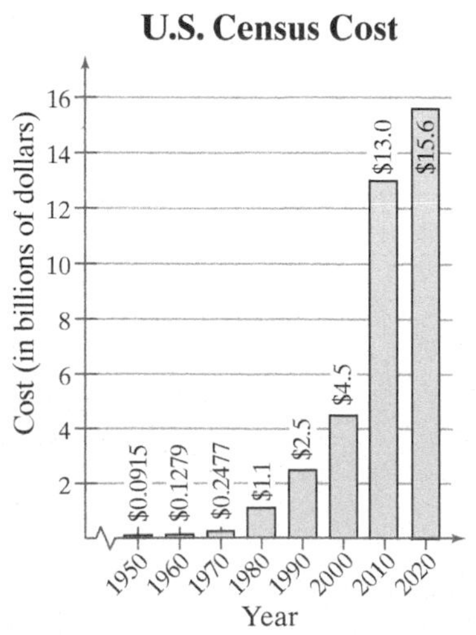


**What are some of the costs involved in taking a census?**

**EXAMPLE 2**

### Distinguishing Between a Parameter and a Statistic

Determine whether each number describes a population parameter or a sample statistic. Explain your reasoning.

1. In the United States, a survey of about 9400 individuals aged 15 and over found that such individuals spent an average of 5.19 hours per day engaged in leisure and sports activities. *(Source: U.S. Bureau of Labor Statistics)*
2. The freshman class at a university has an average SAT math score of 514.
3. In a random check of several hundred retail stores, the Food and Drug Administration found that 34% of the stores were not storing fish at the proper temperature.

**SOLUTION**

1. Because the average of 5.19 hours per day is based on a subset of the population, it is a sample statistic.
2. Because the average SAT math score of 514 is based on the entire freshman class, it is a population parameter.
3. Because 34% is based on a subset of the population, it is a sample statistic.

**TRY IT YOURSELF 2**

Determine whether each number describes a population parameter or a sample statistic. Explain your reasoning.

**a.** Last year, a small company spent a total of $5,150,694 on employees' salaries.

**b.** In the United States, a survey of more than 1000 adults aged 65–80 found that 47% who report listening to loud or very loud music in their youth now report being hard of hearing. *(Source: The Harris Poll)*

*Answer: Page A35*

In this course, you will see how the use of statistics can help you make informed decisions. Consider the census that the U.S. government takes every decade. The Census Bureau attempts to contact everyone living in the United States. Although it is impossible to count everyone, it is important that the census be as accurate as it can be because public officials make many decisions based on the census information. Data collected in the census will determine how to assign congressional seats and how to distribute public funds.

## Branches of Statistics

The study of statistics has two major branches: **descriptive statistics** and **inferential statistics.**

**DEFINITION**

**Descriptive statistics** is the branch of statistics that involves the organization, summarization, and display of data.

**Inferential statistics** is the branch of statistics that involves using a sample to draw conclusions about a population. A basic tool in the study of inferential statistics is probability. (You will learn more about probability in Chapter 3.)

**EXAMPLE 3**

### Descriptive and Inferential Statistics

For each study, identify the population and the sample. Then determine which part of the study represents the descriptive branch of statistics. What conclusions might be drawn from the study using inferential statistics?

1. A study of 1502 U.S. adults found that 18% of adults from households earning less than \$30,000 annually do not use the Internet, as shown in the figure at the left. *(Source: Pew Research Center)*
2. A study of 1000 U.S. 401(k) retirement plan participants found that the percentage who do not know how many years their retirement savings might last is 32%. *(Source: Charles Schwab & Co., Inc.)*

**Not Online**
U.S. adults who do not use the Internet by household income

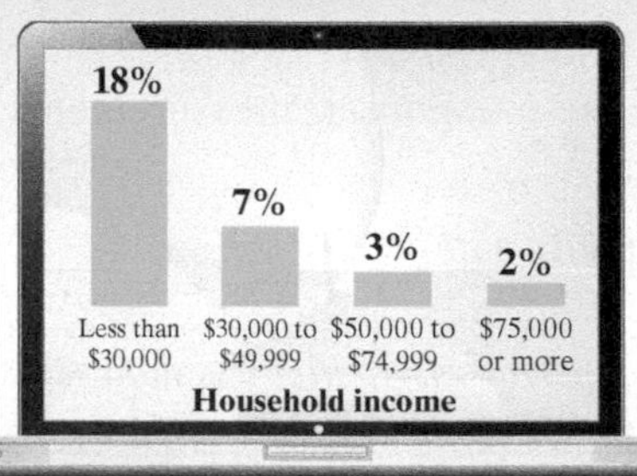


**SOLUTION**

1. The population consists of the responses of all U.S. adults, and the sample consists of the responses of the 1502 U.S. adults in the study. The part of this study that represents the descriptive branch of statistics involves the statement "18% of adults from households earning less than \$30,000 annually do not use the Internet." Also, the figure represents the descriptive branch of statistics. A possible inference drawn from the study is that the Internet has been made inaccessible to lower-income households.
2. The population consists of the responses of all U.S. 401(k) retirement plan participants, and the sample consists of the responses of the 1000 U.S. 401(k) retirement plan participants in the study. The part of this study that represents the descriptive branch of statistics involves the statement "the percentage [of U.S. 401(k) retirement plan participants] who do not know how many years their retirement savings might last is 32%." A possible inference drawn from the study is that the amount of money a person needs for retirement is difficult to determine.

**TRY IT YOURSELF 3**

A study of 513 respondents to an Internet-wide survey found that 97% of the respondents said music is important to them, and 83% of the respondents said they actively look for new music. *(Source: Medium)*

a. Identify the population and the sample.
b. Determine which part of the study represents the descriptive branch of statistics.
c. What conclusions might be drawn from the study using inferential statistics?

*Answer: Page A35*

**Study Tip**

Throughout this course you will see applications of both branches of statistics. A major theme in this course will be how to use sample statistics to make inferences about unknown population parameters.

# 1.1 EXERCISES

For Extra Help: MyLab Statistics

## Building Basic Skills and Vocabulary

1. How is a sample related to a population?
2. Why is a sample used more often than a population?
3. What is the difference between a parameter and a statistic?
4. What are the two main branches of statistics? 

**True or False?** *In Exercises 5–10, determine whether the statement is true or false. If it is false, rewrite it as a true statement.*

5. A statistic is a numerical description of a population characteristic.
6. A sample is a subset of a population.
7. It is impossible to obtain all the census data about the U.S. population.
8. Inferential statistics involves using a population to draw a conclusion about a corresponding sample.
9. A population is the collection of some outcomes, responses, measurements, or counts that are of interest.

10. A sample statistic will not change from sample to sample.

**Classifying a Data Set** *In Exercises 11–20, determine whether the data set is a population or a sample. Explain your reasoning.*

11. The salary of each employee of an advertising firm
12. The amount of energy collected from every solar panel on a photovoltaic power plant
13. A survey of 250 members from an organized union of over 20,000 members
14. The annual revenue of each team in a pro sports league
15. The carbon monoxide levels of 12 of 49 people who escaped a burning building
16. The number of electoral college votes for each state in the U.S. and the District of Columbia
17. The number of guests in each room of a hotel
18. The amount spent by every tenth person cashing out at a store

19. The nationality of every person passing through a customs station 
20. The precipitation amounts at 15 locations in a county

**Graphical Analysis** *In Exercises 21–24, use the Venn diagram to identify the population and the sample.*

21. **Parties of Registered Voters**

| Parties of registered voters who respond to a survey |
|---|
| Parties of registered voters who do not respond to a survey |

22. **Meal Plan Choices of College Students**

| Meal plan choices of freshmen |
|---|
| Meal plan choices of all college students other than freshmen |

**23.** **Ages of Adults in the United States Who Own Moter Vehicles**

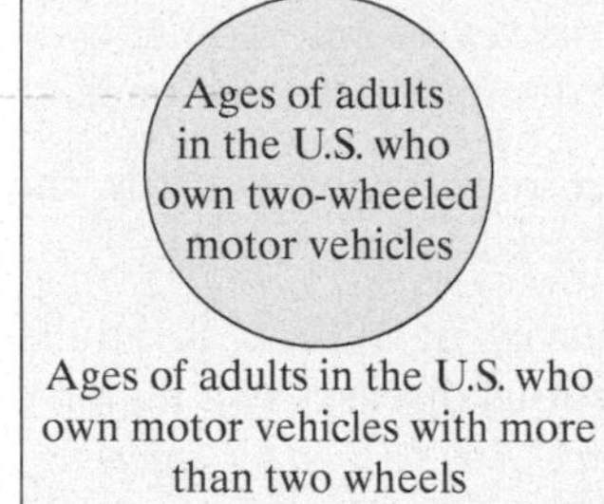


**24.** **Incomes of Adults in Nevada**

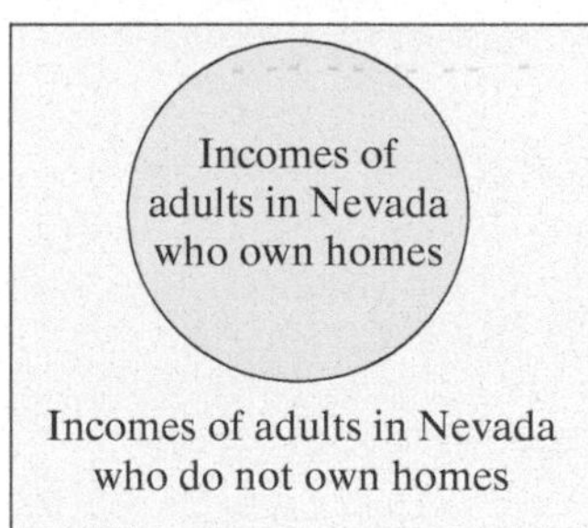


## Using and Interpreting Concepts

**Identifying Data Sets** *In Exercises 25–34, identify the population and the sample. Describe the sample data set.*

**25.** A survey of 1021 U.S. adults found that 45% have a favorable view of Cuba. *(Source: Gallup)*

**26.** A study of 227 U.S. infants was conducted to explore norms of the gut microbiomes of healthy infants. *(Source: Scientific Reports)*

**27.** A survey of 1500 U.S. adults found that 59% have never had a vaccine reaction. *(Source: SingleCare)*

**28.** A survey of 1028 U.S. adults found that 7% of respondents have never heard of organ and tissue donation. *(Source: Research!America)*

**29.** A survey of 2111 U.S. small business owners found that 54% oppose increasing the minimum wage. *(Source: CNBC)*

**30.** A survey of 214 of the seniors graduating with a bachelor of science degree from a university found that 15% planned to obtain entry-level jobs in the health field.

**31.** A survey of 1001 U.S. adults found that 47% of respondents typically feel well rested on weekdays. *(Source: National Sleep Foundation)*

**32.** A survey of 366 automobile owners who purchased extended warranties found that 44% never used the warranty.

**33.** To gather information about starting salaries at companies listed in the Standard & Poor's 500, a researcher contacts 74 of the 500 companies.

**34.** In a survey of 679 members of a local children's museum about parenting attitudes, 575 of the participants were female and 423 of the participants were parents of two or more children. *(Source: University of California Press)*

**Distinguishing Between a Parameter and a Statistic** *In Exercises 35–42, determine whether the number describes a population parameter or a sample statistic. Explain your reasoning.*

**35.** The average salary for 24 of a hospital's 82 registered nurses is $71,000.

**36.** A survey of 919 college board members found that 89% think that their institution is a good place for members of racial and ethnic minorities. *(Source: Association of Governing Boards of Universities and Colleges)*

**37.** Sixty-two of the 97 passengers aboard the *Hindenburg* airship survived its explosion.

**38.** In January 2021, 54% of the governors of the 50 states in the United States were Republicans. *(Source: National Governors Association)*

**39.** In a survey of automobile owners, 6% said they had to change their engine control module at least once.

**40.** Voter registration records show that 47% of all voters in a county are registered as Democrats.

**41.** A survey of 1000 U.S. adults found that 79% think that the spread of infectious diseases is a major threat to the well-being of the United States. *(Source: Pew Research Center)*

**42.** In a recent year, the average math score on the ACT for all graduates was 20.2. *(Source: ACT, Inc.)*

**43. Descriptive and Inferential Statistics** Which part of the survey described in Exercise 31 represents the descriptive branch of statistics? What conclusions might be drawn from the survey using inferential statistics?

**44. Descriptive and Inferential Statistics** Which part of the survey described in Exercise 32 represents the descriptive branch of statistics? What conclusions might be drawn from the survey using inferential statistics?

## Extending Concepts

**45. Identifying Data Sets in Articles** Find an article that describes a survey.

(a) Identify the sample used in the survey.

(b) What is the population?

(c) Make an inference about the population based on the results of the survey.

**46. Writing** Write an essay about the importance of statistics for one of the following.

- A study on the effectiveness of a new drug
- An analysis of a manufacturing process
- Drawing conclusions about voter opinions using surveys

**47. Exercise and Immunity** A study showed the same level of T cell production in senior citizens who are amateur cyclists as in young adults, but a significantly lower level of T cell production in senior citizens who do not exercise regularly. Is it appropriate to infer that exercise stimulates T cell production? Explain. *(Source: University of Birmingham)*

**48. Weight Loss and High Blood Pressure** A study showed an association between intentional weight loss and a decreased risk of high blood pressure. Is it appropriate to infer from this study that weight loss causes a decreased risk of high blood pressure? Explain. *(Source: European Association for the Study of Obesity)*

**49. Sleep and Student Achievement** A study of college students showed that participants earned higher scores on quizzes and midterm exams with better sleep. *(Source: The American Journal of Managed Care)*

(a) Identify the sample used in the study.

(b) What is the population?

(c) Which part of the study represents the descriptive branch of statistics?

(d) Make an inference about the population based on the results of the study.

# 1.2 Data Classification

## What You Should Learn

- How to distinguish between qualitative data and quantitative data
- How to classify data with respect to the four levels of measurement: nominal, ordinal, interval, and ratio

Types of Data ■ Levels of Measurement

## Types of Data

When conducting a study, it is important to know the kind of data involved. The type of data you are working with will determine which statistical procedures can be used. In this section, you will learn how to classify data by type and by level of measurement. Data sets can consist of two types of data: **qualitative data** and **quantitative data.**

**DEFINITION**

**Qualitative data** consist of attributes, labels, or nonnumerical entries.

**Quantitative data** consist of numbers that are measurements or counts.

**EXAMPLE 1**

### Classifying Data by Type

The table shows a partial list of vulnerable, endangered, or critically endangered species and the approximate numbers of each species remaining. Which data are qualitative data and which are quantitative data? Explain your reasoning. *(Source: World Wildlife Fund)*

**Vulnerable, Endangered, or Critically Endangered Species**

| Common species name | Number remaining |
|---|---|
| African elephant | 415,000 |
| Black-footed ferret | 370 |
| Giant panda | 1864 |
| Indus river dolphin | 1816 |
| Javan rhinoceros | 60 |
| North Atlantic right whale | 400 |
| Sunda tiger | 400 |
| Tapanuli orangutan | 800 |
| Vaquita | 10 |

**SOLUTION**

The information shown in the table can be separated into two data sets. One data set contains the common species names and the other contains the numbers remaining. The names are nonnumerical entries, so these are qualitative data. The numbers remaining are numerical entries, so these are quantitative data.

**TRY IT YOURSELF 1**

The populations of several U.S. cities are shown in the table. Which data are qualitative data and which are quantitative data? Explain your reasoning. *(Source: U.S. Census Bureau)*

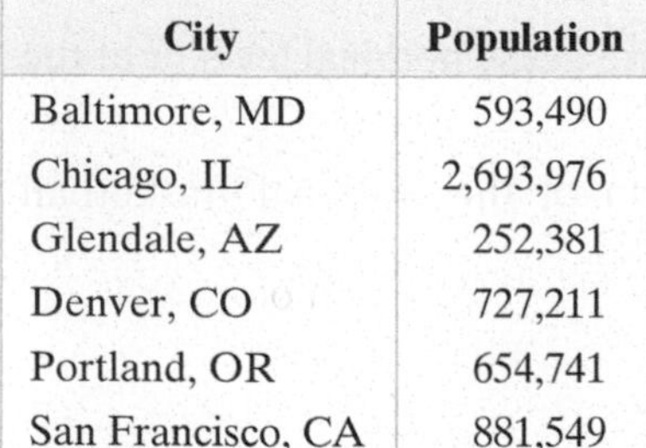

| City | Population |
|---|---|
| Baltimore, MD | 593,490 |
| Chicago, IL | 2,693,976 |
| Glendale, AZ | 252,381 |
| Denver, CO | 727,211 |
| Portland, OR | 654,741 |
| San Francisco, CA | 881,549 |

*Answer: Page A35*

## Levels of Measurement

Another characteristic of data is their level of measurement. The level of measurement determines which statistical calculations are meaningful. The four levels of measurement, in order from lowest to highest, are **nominal, ordinal, interval,** and **ratio.**

**DEFINITION**

Data at the **nominal level of measurement** are qualitative only. Data at this level are categorized using names, labels, or qualities. No mathematical computations can be made at this level.

Data at the **ordinal level of measurement** are qualitative or quantitative. Data at this level can be arranged in order, or ranked, but differences between data entries are not meaningful.

When numbers are at the nominal level of measurement, they simply represent a label. Examples of numbers used as labels include Social Security numbers and numbers on sports jerseys. For instance, it would not make sense to add the numbers on the players' jerseys for the Chicago Bears.

**Picturing the World**

For more than 30 years, The Harris Poll has conducted an annual study to determine the strongest brands, based on consumer response, in several industries. A recent study determined the top five health nonprofit brands, as shown in the table. (Source: The Harris Poll)

| Top five health nonprofit brands |
|---|
| **1.** St. Jude Children's Research Hospital |
| **2.** Make-A-Wish |
| **3.** American Cancer Society |
| **4.** Shriners Hospital for Children |
| **5.** The Breast Cancer Research Foundation |

**In this list, what is the level of measurement?**

**EXAMPLE 2**

### Classifying Data by Level

For each data set, determine whether the data are at the nominal level or at the ordinal level. Explain your reasoning. *(Source: U.S. Bureau of Labor Statistics)*

**1.**

| Top five U.S. occupations with the most job growth (projected 2029) |
|---|
| **1.** Home health and personal care aides |
| **2.** Fast food and counter workers |
| **3.** Restaurant cooks |
| **4.** Software developers and software quality assurance analysts and testers |
| **5.** Registered nurses |

**2.**

| Movie genres |
|---|
| Action |
| Adventure |
| Comedy |
| Drama |
| Horror |

**SOLUTION**

1. This data set lists the ranks of the five fastest-growing occupations in the U.S. over the next few years. The data set consists of the ranks 1, 2, 3, 4, and 5. Because the ranks can be listed in order, these data are at the ordinal level. Note that the difference between a rank of 1 and 5 has no mathematical meaning.
2. This data set consists of the names of movie genres. No mathematical computations can be made with the names, and the names cannot be ranked, so these data are at the nominal level.

**TRY IT YOURSELF 2**

For each data set, determine whether the data are at the nominal level or at the ordinal level. Explain your reasoning.

1. The final standings for the Pacific Division of the National Basketball Association
2. A collection of phone numbers

*Answer: Page A35*

The two highest levels of measurement consist of quantitative data only.

**DEFINITION**

Data at the **interval level of measurement** can be ordered, and meaningful differences between data entries can be calculated. At the interval level, a zero entry simply represents a position on a scale; the entry is not an inherent zero.

Data at the **ratio level of measurement** are similar to data at the interval level, with the added property that a zero entry is an inherent zero. A ratio of two data entries can be formed so that one data entry can be meaningfully expressed as a multiple of another.

For help with basic mathematical symbols and Greek letters and addition and subtraction of integers, see *Integrated Review* at MyLab Statistics

An *inherent zero* is a zero that implies "none." For instance, the amount of money you have in a savings account could be zero dollars. In this case, the zero represents no money; it is an inherent zero. In contrast, a temperature of 0°C does not represent a condition in which no heat is present. The 0°C temperature is simply a position on the Celsius scale; it is not an inherent zero.

To distinguish between data at the interval level and at the ratio level, determine whether the expression "twice as much" has any meaning in the context of the data. For instance, $2 is twice as much as $1, so these data are at the ratio level. In contrast, 2°C is not twice as warm as 1°C, so these data are at the interval level.

**EXAMPLE 3**

### Classifying Data by Level

Two data sets are shown at the left. Which data set consists of data at the interval level? Which data set consists of data at the ratio level? Explain your reasoning. *(Source: Major League Baseball)*

| New York Yankees' World Series victories (years) |
|---|
| 1923, 1927, 1928, 1932, 1936, 1937, 1938, 1939, 1941, 1943, 1947, 1949, 1950, 1951, 1952, 1953, 1956, 1958, 1961, 1962, 1977, 1978, 1996, 1998, 1999, 2000, 2009 |

| 2020 American League home run totals (by team) | |
|---|---|
| Baltimore | 77 |
| Boston | 81 |
| Chicago | 96 |
| Cleveland | 59 |
| Detroit | 62 |
| Houston | 69 |
| Kansas City | 68 |
| Los Angeles | 85 |
| Minnesota | 91 |
| New York | 94 |
| Oakland | 71 |
| Seattle | 60 |
| Tampa Bay | 80 |
| Texas | 62 |
| Toronto | 88 |

**SOLUTION**

Both of these data sets contain quantitative data. Consider the dates of the Yankees' World Series victories. It makes sense to find differences between specific dates. For instance, the time between the Yankees' first and last World Series victories is

$$2009 - 1923 = 86 \text{ years.}$$

But it does not make sense to say that one year is a multiple of another. So, these data are at the interval level. However, using the home run totals, you can find differences *and* write ratios. For instance, Boston hit 22 more home runs than Cleveland hit because $81 - 59 = 22$ home runs. Also, Chicago hit about 1.25 times as many home runs as Baltimore hit because

$$\frac{96}{77} \approx 1.25.$$

So, these data are at the ratio level.

**TRY IT YOURSELF 3**

For each data set, determine whether the data are at the interval level or at the ratio level. Explain your reasoning.

1. The body temperatures (in degrees Fahrenheit) of an athlete during an exercise session
2. The heart rates (in beats per minute) of an athlete during an exercise session

*Answer: Page A35*

The tables below summarize which operations are meaningful at each of the four levels of measurement. When identifying a data set's level of measurement, use the highest level that applies.

| Level of measurement | Put data in categories | Arrange data in order | Subtract data entries | Determine whether one data entry is a multiple of another |
|---|---|---|---|---|
| Nominal | Yes | No | No | No |
| Ordinal | Yes | Yes | No | No |
| Interval | Yes | Yes | Yes | No |
| Ratio | Yes | Yes | Yes | Yes |

**Summary of Four Levels of Measurement**

| | Example of a data set | Meaningful calculations |
|---|---|---|
| **Nominal level**<br>(Qualitative data) | *Types of Shows Televised by a Network*<br>Comedy, Documentaries<br>Drama, Cooking<br>Reality Shows, Soap Operas<br>Sports, Talk Shows | *Put in a category.*<br>For instance, a show televised by the network could be put into one of the eight categories shown. |
| **Ordinal level**<br>(Qualitative or quantitative data) | *Motion Picture Association of America Ratings Description*<br>G General Audiences<br>PG Parental Guidance Suggested<br>PG-13 Parents Strongly Cautioned<br>R Restricted<br>NC-17 No One 17 and Under Admitted | Put in a category and *put in order.*<br>For instance, a PG rating has a stronger restriction than a G rating. |
| **Interval level**<br>(Quantitative data) | *Average Monthly Temperatures (in degrees Fahrenheit) for Denver, CO*<br>Jan 30.9, Jul 73.6<br>Feb 32.8, Aug 71.5<br>Mar 40.0, Sep 62.4<br>Apr 47.5, Oct 50.3<br>May 57.2, Nov 38.6<br>Jun 67.0, Dec 30.0<br>*(Source: National Oceanic and Atmospheric Administration)* | Put in a category, put in order, and *find differences between data entries.*<br>For instance, $71.5 - 62.4 = 9.1°F$. So, August is 9.1°F warmer than September. |
| **Ratio level**<br>(Quantitative data) | *Average Monthly Precipitation (in inches) for Orlando, FL*<br>Jan 2.35, Jul 7.27<br>Feb 2.38, Aug 7.13<br>Mar 3.77, Sep 6.06<br>Apr 2.68, Oct 3.31<br>May 3.45, Nov 2.17<br>Jun 7.58, Dec 2.58<br>*(Source: National Oceanic and Atmospheric Administration)* | Put in a category, put in order, find differences between data entries, and *find ratios of data entries.*<br>For instance, $\frac{7.58}{3.77} \approx 2.$<br>So, there is about twice as much precipitation in June as in March. |

# 1.2 EXERCISES

For Extra Help: MyLab Statistics

## Building Basic Skills and Vocabulary

1. Name each level of measurement for which data can be qualitative.
2. Name each level of measurement for which data can be quantitative.

**True or False?** *In Exercises 3–6, determine whether the statement is true or false. If it is false, rewrite it as a true statement.*

3. Data at the ordinal level are quantitative only.
4. For data at the interval level, you cannot calculate meaningful differences between data entries.
5. More types of calculations can be performed with data at the nominal level than with data at the interval level.
6. Data at the ratio level cannot be put in order.

## Using and Interpreting Concepts

**Classifying Data by Type** *In Exercises 7–14, determine whether the data are qualitative or quantitative. Explain your reasoning.*

7. Nationalities of passengers on a plane
8. Zip codes
9. Ages of dogs at a rescue facility
10. Capacities of commercial freezers
11. Types of flowers
12. Names of towns where branch campuses of a college are located
13. Distances of track events
14. Response times for a customer service representative

**Classifying Data By Level** *In Exercises 15–20, determine the level of measurement of the data set. Explain your reasoning.*

15. **Comedy Series** The years that a television show on ABC won the Emmy for best comedy series are listed. *(Source: Academy of Television Arts and Sciences)*

| 1955 | 1979 | 1980 | 1981 | 1982 | 1988 |
|---|---|---|---|---|---|
| 2010 | 2011 | 2012 | 2013 | 2014 | |

16. **Business Schools** The top ten colleges in terms of value for the money according to *U.S. News & World Report* are listed. *(Source: U.S. News & World Report)*

| | |
|---|---|
| **1.** Harvard | **6.** Columbia |
| **2.** Princeton | **7.** Stanford |
| **3.** Gallaudet | **8.** Rice |
| **4.** Yale | **9.** Vanderbilt |
| **5.** MIT | **10.** Dartmouth |

**17. Automobiles** The lengths (in centimeters) of 22 Ford automobiles are listed. *(Source: Automobiledimension.com)*

| | | | | | | | |
|---|---|---|---|---|---|---|---|
| 404 | 407 | 410 | 416 | 421 | 438 | 440 | 443 |
| 461 | 467 | 471 | 478 | 480 | 483 | 483 | 485 |
| 487 | 487 | 497 | 505 | 534 | 536 | | |

**18. Classrooms** The room numbers of the classrooms in a college science building are listed.

| | | | | | | |
|---|---|---|---|---|---|---|
| 112 | 113 | 114 | 116 | 117 | 118 | 122 |
| 212 | 213 | 214 | 215 | 216 | 217 | 219 |

**19. Best Sellers List** The top ten fiction hardcover books on *The New York Times* Best Sellers List based on sales in the week ending March 6, 2021, are listed. *(Source: The New York Times)*

1. *Life After Death*
2. *The Four Winds*
3. *Klara and the Sun*
4. *Dark Sky*
5. *The Affair*
6. *The Midnight Library*
7. *The Lost Apothecary*
8. *The Vanishing Half*
9. *Infinite Country*
10. *A Court of Silver Flames*

**20. Bell Schedule** The times from a high school bell schedule are listed.

| | | | | |
|---|---|---|---|---|
| 8:00 A.M. | 8:52 A.M. | 8:56 A.M. | 9:48 A.M. | 9:52 A.M. |
| 10:44 A.M. | 10:48 A.M. | 11:40 A.M. | 11:44 A.M. | 1:08 P.M. |
| 1:12 P.M. | 2:04 P.M. | 2:08 P.M. | 3:00 P.M. | |

## Graphical Analysis

*In Exercises 21–24, determine the level of measurement of the data listed on the horizontal and vertical axes in the figure.*

**21.** **What Platform Do You Prefer for Getting News?**

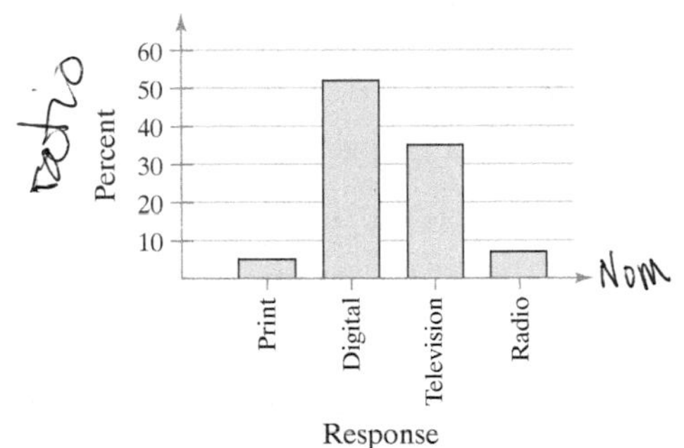


*(Source: Pew Research Center)*

**22.** **What Ages of Children Participate a Lot in Your Vacation Planning?**

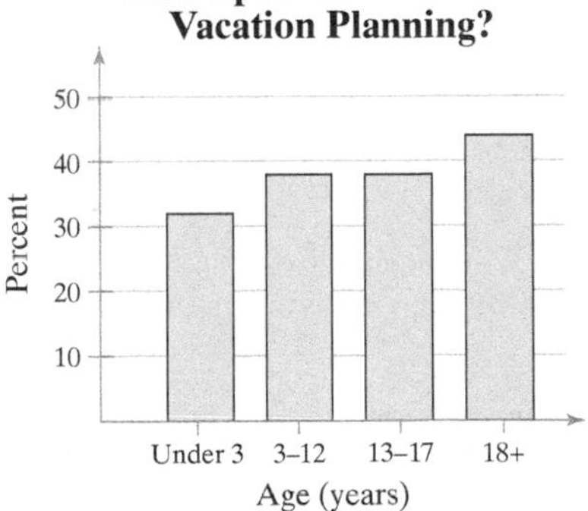


*(Source: Marriott Bonvoy Bold from Chase)*

**23.** **Gender Profile of the 117th Congress**

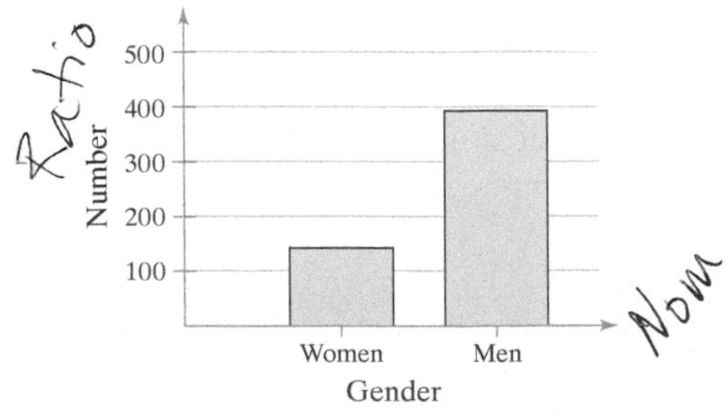


*(Source: Center for American Women and Politics)*

**24.** **Motor Vehicle Fatalities by Year**

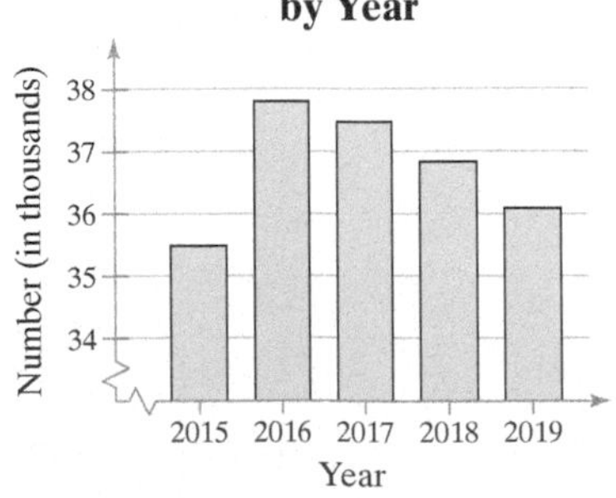


*(Source: National Highway Traffic Safety Administration)*

**25.** The items below appear on a physician's intake form. Determine the level of measurement of the data for each category.

(a) Temperature
(b) Allergies
(c) Weight
(d) Pain level (scale of 0 to 10)

**26.** The items below appear on an employment application. Determine the level of measurement of the data for each category.

(a) Highest grade level completed
(b) Gender
(c) Year of college graduation
(d) Number of years at last job

**Classifying Data by Type and Level** *In Exercises 27–32, determine whether the data are qualitative or quantitative, and determine the level of measurement of the data set.*

**27. Football** The top ten teams in the final college football poll released in January 2021 are listed. *(Source: Associated Press)*

**1.** Alabama
**2.** Ohio State
**3.** Clemson
**4.** Texas A&M
**5.** Notre Dame
**6.** Oklahoma
**7.** Georgia
**8.** Cincinnati
**9.** Iowa State
**10.** Northwestern

**28. Coffee** Four principal types of coffee beans are listed.

Arabica Robusta Liberica Excelsa

**29. Census Regions** The four geographical regions of the United States recognized by the U.S. Census Bureau are listed.

Northeast South
Midwest West

**30. Figure Skating** The top six final scores at the 2021 U.S. Women's Figure Skating Championships are listed. *(Source: NBC Sports)*

232.61 215.33 214.98
213.39 199.95 178.89

**31. Richest People** The ten richest people in the world as of March 30, 2021, are listed. *(Source: Bloomberg Reporting)*

**1.** Jeff Bezos
**2.** Elon Musk
**3.** Bill Gates
**4.** Bernard Arnault
**5.** Mark Zuckerberg
**6.** Warren Buffett
**7.** Larry Page
**8.** Sergey Brin
**9.** Steve Ballmer
**10.** Larry Ellison

**32. Numbers of Performances** The numbers of performances for the 10 longest-running original runs of Broadway shows as of March 15, 2020, are listed. *(Source: Playbill)*

13,370 9692 9302 7485 6836
6680 6137 5959 5758 5461

## Extending Concepts

**33. Writing** What is an inherent zero? Describe three examples of data sets that have inherent zeros and three that do not.

**34.** Describe two examples of data sets for each of the four levels of measurement. Justify your answer.

CASE STUDY

# Reputations of Companies in the U.S.

For more than 50 years, The Harris Poll has conducted surveys using a representative sample of people in the United States. The surveys have been used to represent the opinions of people in the United States on many subjects, such as health, politics, the U.S. economy, and sports.

Since 1999, The Harris Poll has conducted an annual survey to measure the reputations of the most visible companies in the United States, as perceived by U.S. adults. The Harris Poll used a sample of 34,026 U.S. adults for the 2020 survey. The survey respondents rate companies according to key attributes that are classified into seven categories: (1) trust, (2) vision, (3) growth, (4) products and services, (5) culture, (6) ethics, and (7) citizenship. This information is used to determine the reputation of a company as Excellent, Very Good, Good, Fair, Poor, or Very Poor. The reputations (along with some additional information) of 10 companies are shown in the table.

**All U.S. Adults**

U.S. adults in The Harris Poll sample (about 34,026 U.S. adults)

U.S. adults *not* in The Harris Poll sample (about 257.9 million U.S. adults)

**Reputations of 10 Companies in the U.S.**

| Company Name | Year Company Formed | Reputation | Industry | Number of Employees |
|---|---|---|---|---|
| Amazon.com | 1994 | Excellent | Retail | 798,000 |
| Netflix, Inc. | 1999 | Very Good | Digital television | 8,600 |
| Apple, Inc. | 1977 | Very Good | Computers and peripherals | 147,000 |
| The Kraft Heinz Co. | 2015 | Very Good | Food products | 37,000 |
| Chipotle Mexican Grill, Inc. | 1993 | Good | Restaurant | 83,000 |
| Exxon Mobil Corp. | 1999 | Good | Petroleum (integrated) | 71,000 |
| The Boeing Co. | 1916 | Fair | Aircraft | 161,000 |
| Comcast Corp. | 1963 | Poor | Cable television | 168,000 |
| Wells Fargo & Co. | 1998 | Poor | Banking | 263,000 |
| Facebook, Inc. | 2004 | Poor | Internet | 45,000 |

(Source: The Harris Poll; Amazon.com; Netflix, Inc.; Apple, Inc.; The Kraft Heinz Co.; Chipotle Mexican Grill, Inc.; Exxon Mobil Corp.; The Boeing Co.; Comcast Corp.; Wells Fargo & Co.; Facebook, Inc.)

## EXERCISES

1. **Sampling Percent** What percentage of the total number of U.S. adults did The Harris Poll sample for its survey? (Assume the total number of U.S. adults is 257.9 million.)
2. **Nominal Level of Measurement** Identify any column in the table with data at the nominal level.
3. **Ordinal Level of Measurement** Identify any column in the table with data at the ordinal level. Describe two ways that the data can be ordered.
4. **Interval Level of Measurement** Identify any column in the table with data at the interval level. How can these data be ordered?
5. **Ratio Level of Measurement** Identify any column in the table with data at the ratio level.
6. **Inferences** What decisions can be made on the basis of The Harris Poll survey that measures the reputations of the most visible companies in the United States?

# 1.3 Data Collection and Experimental Design

## What You Should Learn

- How to design a statistical study and how to distinguish between an observational study and an experiment
- How to collect data by using a survey or a simulation
- How to design an experiment
- How to create a sample using random sampling, simple random sampling, stratified sampling, cluster sampling, and systematic sampling and how to identify a biased sample

Design of a Statistical Study ■ Data Collection ■ Experimental Design ■ Sampling Techniques

## Design of a Statistical Study

The goal of every statistical study is to collect data and then use the data to make a decision. Any decision you make using the results of a statistical study is only as good as the process used to obtain the data. When the process is flawed, the resulting decision is questionable.

Although you may never have to develop a statistical study, it is likely that you will have to interpret the results of one. Before interpreting the results of a study, however, you should determine whether the results are reliable. In other words, you should be familiar with how to design a statistical study.

**GUIDELINES**

**Designing a Statistical Study**

1. Identify the variable(s) of interest (the focus) and the population of the study.
2. Develop a detailed plan for collecting data. If you use a sample, make sure the sample is representative of the population.
3. Collect the data.
4. Describe the data, using descriptive statistics techniques.
5. Interpret the data and make decisions about the population using inferential statistics.
6. Identify any possible errors.

A statistical study can usually be categorized as an observational study or an experiment. In an **observational study,** a researcher does not influence the responses. In an **experiment,** a researcher deliberately applies a treatment before observing the responses. Here is a brief summary of these types of studies.

- In an **observational study,** a researcher observes and measures characteristics of interest of part of a population but does not change existing conditions. For instance, an observational study was conducted in which researchers measured the amount of time people spent doing various activities, such as volunteering, paid work, childcare, and socializing. *(Source: U.S. Bureau of Labor Statistics)*
- In performing an **experiment,** a **treatment** is applied to part of a population, called a **treatment group,** and responses are observed. Another part of the population may be used as a **control group,** in which no treatment is applied. (The subjects in both groups are called **experimental units.**) In many cases, subjects in the control group are given a **placebo,** which is a harmless, fake treatment that is made to look like the real treatment. The responses of both groups can then be compared and studied. In most cases, it is a good idea to use the same number of subjects for each group. For instance, an experiment was performed in which rats in a treatment group were given trimethylamine oxide, a substance present in seafood, while rats in a control group were given water. After performing testing, researchers concluded that trimethylamine oxide reduced mortality related to heart disease in rats that had heart disease. *(Source: eLife)*

**EXAMPLE 1**

### Distinguishing Between an Observational Study and an Experiment

Determine whether each study is an observational study or an experiment.

1. Researchers study the effect of vitamin $D_3$ supplementation among patients who were newly diagnosed with a viral infection. To perform the study, researchers give 2700 U.S. adults either a daily vitamin $D_3$ supplement or a placebo for four weeks. *(Source: U.S. National Library of Medicine)*
2. Researchers conduct a study to determine how confident Americans are in the U.S. economy. To perform the study, researchers call 1019 U.S. adults and ask them to rate current U.S. economic conditions and whether the U.S. economy is getting better or worse. *(Source: Gallup)*

**SOLUTION**

1. Because the study applies a treatment (vitamin $D_3$) to the subjects, the study is an experiment.
2. Because the study does not attempt to influence the responses of the subjects (there is no treatment), the study is an observational study.

**TRY IT YOURSELF 1**

The Pennsylvania Game Commission conducted a study to determine the percentage of the Pennsylvania elk population in each age and sex class. The commission captured and released elk during each year of the study and found an overall average of 16% branched bulls, 7% spike bulls, 56% adult cows, and 21% calves. Is this study an observational study or an experiment? *(Source: Pennsylvania Game Commission)*

*Answer: Page A35*

## Data Collection

There are several ways to collect data. Often, the focus of the study dictates the best way to collect data. Here is a brief summary of two methods of data collection.

- A **simulation** is the use of a mathematical or physical model to reproduce the conditions of a situation or process. Collecting data often involves the use of computers. Simulations allow you to study situations that are impractical or even dangerous to create in real life, and often they save time and money. For instance, automobile manufacturers use simulations with dummies to study the effects of crashes on humans. Throughout this course, you will have the opportunity to use applets that simulate statistical processes on a computer.
- A **survey** is an investigation of one or more characteristics of a population. Most often, surveys are carried out on *people* by asking them questions. The most common types of surveys are done by interview, Internet, phone, or mail. In designing a survey, it is important to word the questions so that they do not lead to biased results, which are not representative of a population. For instance, a survey is conducted on a sample of physicians to determine whether the primary reason for their career choice is financial stability. In designing the survey, it would be acceptable to make a list of reasons and ask each individual in the sample to select their first choice.

## Experimental Design

To produce meaningful unbiased results, experiments should be carefully designed and executed. It is important to know what steps should be taken to make the results of an experiment valid. Three key elements of a well-designed experiment are *control*, *randomization*, and *replication*.

Because experimental results can be ruined by a variety of factors, being able to control these influential factors is important. One such factor is a **confounding variable.**

**DEFINITION**

A **confounding variable** occurs when an experimenter cannot tell the difference between the effects of different factors on the variable.

**Study Tip**

The *Hawthorne effect* occurs in an experiment when subjects change their behavior simply because they know they are participating in an experiment.

For instance, to attract more customers, a coffee shop owner experiments by remodeling the shop using bright colors. At the same time, a shopping mall nearby has its grand opening. If business at the coffee shop increases, it cannot be determined whether it is because of the new colors or the new shopping mall. The effects of the colors and the shopping mall have been confounded.

Another factor that can affect experimental results is the *placebo effect.* The **placebo effect** occurs when a subject reacts favorably to a placebo when in fact the subject has been given a fake treatment. To help control or minimize the placebo effect, a technique called **blinding** can be used.

**DEFINITION**

**Blinding** is a technique in which the subjects do not know whether they are receiving a treatment or a placebo. In a **double-blind experiment,** neither the experimenter nor the subjects know whether the subjects are receiving a treatment or a placebo. The experimenter is informed after all the data have been collected. This type of experimental design is preferred by researchers.

One challenge for experimenters is assigning subjects to groups so the groups have similar characteristics (such as age, height, weight, and so on). When treatment and control groups are similar, experimenters can conclude that any differences between groups are due to the treatment. To form groups with similar characteristics, experimenters use **randomization.**

**DEFINITION**

**Randomization** is a process of randomly assigning subjects to different treatment groups.

In a **completely randomized design,** subjects are assigned to different treatment groups through random selection. In some experiments, it may be necessary for the experimenter to use **blocks,** which are groups of subjects with similar characteristics. A commonly used experimental design is a **randomized block design.** To use a randomized block design, the experimenter divides the subjects with similar characteristics into blocks, and then, within each block, randomly assign subjects to treatment groups. For instance, an experimenter who is testing the effects of a new weight loss drink may first divide the subjects into age categories such as 30–39 years old, 40–49 years old, and over 50 years old, and then, within each age group, randomly assign subjects to either the treatment group or the control group (see figure at the left).

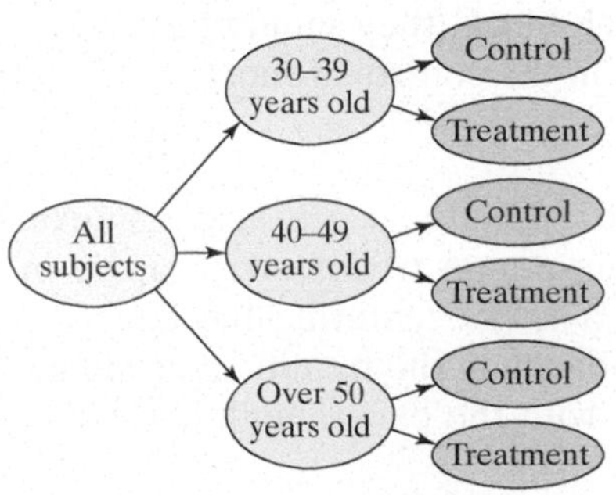


Randomized Block Design

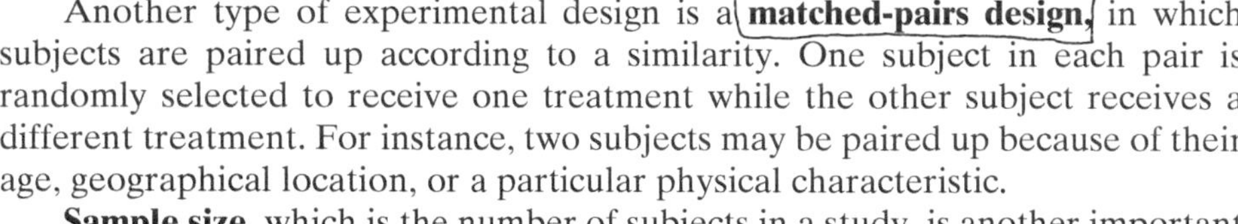

Another type of experimental design is a **matched-pairs design,** in which subjects are paired up according to a similarity. One subject in each pair is randomly selected to receive one treatment while the other subject receives a different treatment. For instance, two subjects may be paired up because of their age, geographical location, or a particular physical characteristic.

**Sample size,** which is the number of subjects in a study, is another important part of experimental design. To improve the validity of experimental results, **replication** is required.

### Study Tip

The *validity* of an experiment refers to the accuracy and reliability of the experimental results. The results of a valid experiment are more likely to be accepted in the scientific community.

### DEFINITION

**Replication** is the repetition of an experiment under the same or similar conditions.

For instance, suppose an experiment is designed to test a vaccine against a strain of influenza. In the experiment, 10,000 people are given the vaccine and another 10,000 people are given a placebo. Because of the sample size, the effectiveness of the vaccine would most likely be observed. But, if the subjects in the experiment are not selected so that the two groups are similar (according to age and gender), the results are of less value.

## EXAMPLE 2

### Analyzing an Experimental Design

A company wants to test the effectiveness of a new gum developed to help people quit smoking. Identify a potential problem with each experimental design and suggest a way to improve it.

1. The company identifies ten adults who are heavy smokers. Five of the subjects are given the new gum and the other five subjects are given a placebo. After two months, the subjects are evaluated and it is found that the five subjects using the new gum have quit smoking.
2. The company identifies 1000 adults who are heavy smokers. The subjects are divided into blocks according to gender. Females are given the new gum and males are given the placebo. After two months, a significant number of the female subjects have quit smoking.

#### SOLUTION

1. The sample size being used is not large enough to validate the results of the experiment. The experiment must be replicated to improve the validity.
2. The groups are not similar. The new gum may have a greater effect on women than on men, or vice versa. The subjects can be divided into blocks according to gender, but then, within each block, they should be randomly assigned to be in the treatment group or in the control group.

#### TRY IT YOURSELF 2

The company in Example 2 identifies 240 adults who are heavy smokers. The subjects are randomly assigned to be in a gum treatment group or in a control group. Each subject is also given a DVD featuring the dangers of smoking. After four months, most of the subjects in the treatment group have quit smoking. Identify a potential problem with the experimental design and suggest a way to improve it.

*Answer: Page A35*

**Study Tip**

A *biased sample* is one that is not representative of the population from which it is drawn. For instance, a sample consisting of only 18- to 22-year-old U.S. college students would not be representative of the entire 18- to 22-year-old population in the United States.

To explore this topic further, see **Activity 1.3** on page 27.

**Tech Tip**

You can use technology such as Minitab, Excel, StatCrunch, or the TI-84 Plus to generate random numbers. (Detailed instructions for using Minitab, Excel, and the TI-84 Plus are shown in the technology manuals that accompany this text.) For instance, here are instructions for using the random integer generator on a TI-84 Plus for Example 3.

MATH

Choose the PRB menu.

5: randInt(

1 , 7 3 1 , 8 )

ENTER

```
randInt(1,731,8)
        {537 33 249 728...
```

Continuing to press ENTER will generate more random samples of 8 integers.

## Sampling Techniques

A **census** is a count or measure of an *entire* population. Taking a census provides complete information, but it is often costly and difficult to perform. A **sampling** is a count or measure of *part* of a population and is more commonly used in statistical studies. To collect unbiased data, a researcher must ensure that the sample is representative of the population. Appropriate sampling techniques must be used to ensure that inferences about the population are valid. Remember that when a study is done with faulty data, the results are questionable. Even with the best methods of sampling, a **sampling error** may occur. A sampling error is the difference between the results of a sample and those of the population. When you learn about inferential statistics, you will learn techniques of controlling sampling errors.

A **random sample** is one in which every member of the population has an equal chance of being selected. A **simple random sample** is a sample in which every possible sample of the same size has the same chance of being selected. One way to collect a simple random sample is to assign a different number to each member of the population and then use a random number table such as Table 1 in Appendix B. Responses, counts, or measures for members of the population whose numbers correspond to those generated using the table would be in the sample. Calculators and computer software programs are also used to generate random numbers (see page 36).

**Table 1—Random Numbers**

| | | | | | | | |
|---|---|---|---|---|---|---|---|
| 92630 | 78240 | 19267 | 95457 | 53497 | 23894 | 37708 | 79862 |
| 79445 | 78735 | 71549 | 44843 | 26104 | 67318 | 00701 | 34986 |
| 59654 | 71966 | 27386 | 50004 | 05358 | 94031 | 29281 | 18544 |
| 31524 | 49587 | 76612 | 39789 | 13537 | 48086 | 59483 | 60680 |
| 06348 | 76938 | 90379 | 51392 | 55887 | 71015 | 09209 | 79157 |

Portion of Table 1 found in Appendix B

Consider a study of the number of people who live in West Ridge County. To use a simple random sample to count the number of people who live in West Ridge County households, you could assign a different number to each household, use a technology tool or table of random numbers to generate a sample of numbers, and then count the number of people living in each selected household.

**EXAMPLE 3**

### Using a Simple Random Sample

There are 731 students currently enrolled in a statistics course at your school. You wish to form a sample of eight students to answer some survey questions. Select the students who will belong to the simple random sample.

**SOLUTION**

Assign numbers 1 to 731 to the students in the course. In the table of random numbers, choose a starting place at random and read the digits in groups of three (because 731 is a three-digit number). For instance, if you started in the third row of the table at the beginning of the second column, you would group the numbers as follows:

719|66 2|738|6 50|004| 053|58 9|403|1 29|281| 185|44

Ignoring numbers greater than 731, the first eight numbers are 719, 662, 650, 4, 53, 589, 403, and 129. The students assigned these numbers will make up the sample. To find the sample using a TI-84 Plus, follow the instructions shown at the left.

**TRY IT YOURSELF 3**

A company employs 79 people. Choose a simple random sample of five to survey.

*Answer: Page A35*

When you choose members of a sample, you should decide whether it is acceptable to have the same population member selected more than once. If it is acceptable, then the sampling process is said to be *with replacement*. If it is not acceptable, then the sampling process is said to be *without replacement*.

There are several other commonly used sampling techniques. Each has advantages and disadvantages.

- ***Stratified Sample*** When it is important for the sample to have members from each segment of the population, you should use a stratified sample. Depending on the focus of the study, members of the population are divided into two or more subsets, called *strata*, that share a similar characteristic such as age, gender, ethnicity, or even political preference. A sample is then randomly selected from each of the strata. Using a stratified sample ensures that each segment of the population is represented. For instance, to collect a stratified sample of the number of people who live in West Ridge County households, you could divide the households into socioeconomic categories and then randomly select households from each category. In using a stratified sample, care must be taken to ensure that all strata are sampled in proportion to their actual percentages of occurrence in the population. For instance, if 40% of the people in West Ridge County belong to the low-income group, then the proportion of the sample should have 40% from this group.

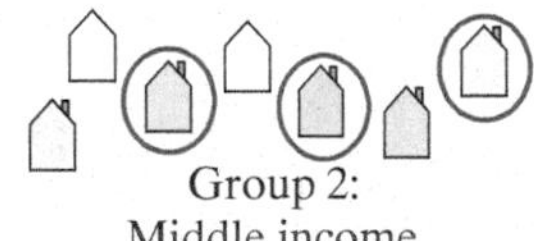


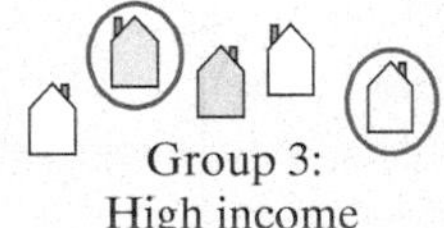


Stratified Sampling

**Study Tip**

Be sure you understand that stratified sampling randomly selects a *sample of members* from *all* strata. Cluster sampling uses *all members* from a randomly selected sample of *clusters* (but not all, so some clusters will not be part of the sample). For instance, in the figure for "Stratified Sampling" at the right, a *sample of households* in West Ridge County is randomly selected from *all* three income groups. In the figure for "Cluster Sampling," *all households* in a randomly selected *cluster* (Zone 1) are used. (Notice that the other zones are not part of the sample.)

- ***Cluster Sample*** When the population falls into naturally occurring subgroups, each having similar characteristics, a cluster sample may be the most appropriate. To select a cluster sample, divide the population into groups, called *clusters*, and select all of the members in one or more (but not all) of the clusters. Examples of clusters could be different sections of the same course or different branches of a bank. For instance, to collect a cluster sample of the number of people who live in West Ridge County households, divide the households into groups according to zip codes, then select all the households in one or more, but not all, zip codes and count the number of people living in each household. In using a cluster sample, care must be taken to ensure that all clusters have similar characteristics. For instance, if one of the zip code clusters has a greater proportion of high-income people, the data might not be representative of the population.

**Zip Code Zones in West Ridge County**

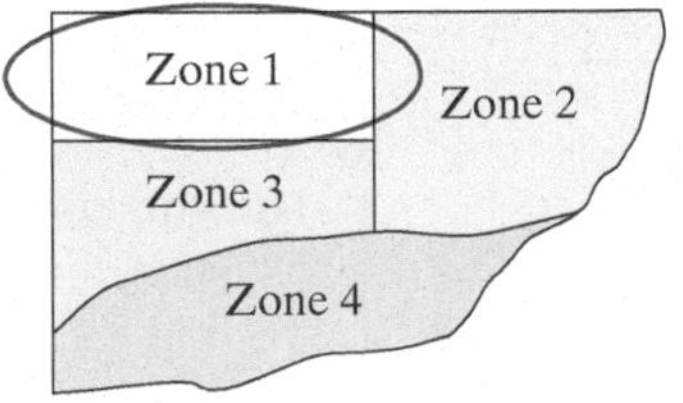


Cluster Sampling

## Picturing the World

The research firm Gallup conducts many polls (or surveys) regarding the president, Congress, and political and nonpolitical issues. A commonly cited Gallup poll is the public approval rating of the president. For instance, the approval ratings for President Donald Trump for selected months in 2020 are shown in the figure. (Each rating is from the poll conducted at the end of the indicated month.)

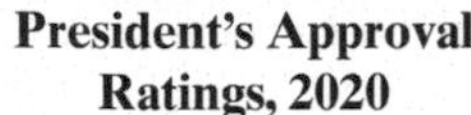


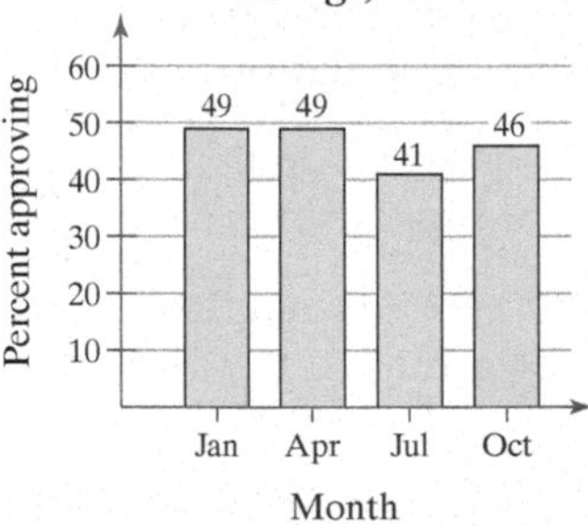


**Discuss some ways that Gallup could select a biased sample to conduct a poll. How could Gallup select a sample that is unbiased?**

- ***Systematic Sample*** A systematic sample is a sample in which each member of the population is assigned a number. The members of the population are ordered in some way, a starting number is randomly selected, and then sample members are selected at regular intervals from the starting number. (For instance, every 3rd, 5th, or 100th member is selected.) For instance, to collect a systematic sample of the number of people who live in West Ridge County households, you could assign a different number to each household, randomly choose a starting number, select every 100th household, and count the number of people living in each. An advantage of systematic sampling is that it is easy to use. In the case of any regularly occurring pattern in the data, however, this type of sampling should be avoided.

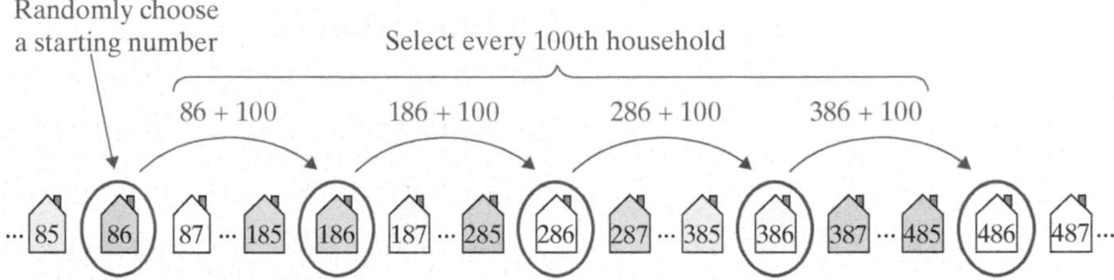


Systematic Sampling

A type of sample that often leads to biased studies (so it is not recommended) is a **convenience sample.** A convenience sample consists only of members of the population that are easy to access.

## EXAMPLE 4

### Identifying Sampling Techniques

You are doing a study to determine the opinions of students at your school regarding stem cell research. Identify the sampling technique you are using when you select the samples listed. Discuss potential sources of bias (if any).

1. You divide the student population with respect to majors and randomly select and question some students in each major.
2. You assign each student a number and generate random numbers. You then question each student whose number is randomly selected.
3. You select students who are in your biology class.

**SOLUTION**

1. Because students are divided into strata (majors) and a sample is selected from each major, this is a stratified sample.
2. Each sample of the same size has an equal chance of being selected and each student has an equal chance of being selected, so this is a simple random sample.
3. Because the sample is taken from students who are readily available, this is a convenience sample. The sample may be biased because biology students may be more familiar with stem cell research than other students and may have stronger opinions.

**TRY IT YOURSELF 4**

You want to determine the opinions of students regarding stem cell research. Identify the sampling technique you are using when you select these samples.

1. You select a class at random and question each student in the class.
2. You assign each student a number and, after choosing a starting number, question every 25th student.

*Answer: Page A35*

# 1.3 EXERCISES

For Extra Help: **MyLab Statistics**

## Building Basic Skills and Vocabulary

1. What is the difference between an observational study and an experiment?
2. What is the difference between a census and a sampling?
3. What is the difference between a random sample and a simple random sample?
4. What is replication in an experiment? Why is replication important?

**True or False?** *In Exercises 5–10, determine whether the statement is true or false. If it is false, rewrite it as a true statement.*

5. A placebo is an actual treatment.
6. A double-blind experiment is used to increase the placebo effect.
7. Using a systematic sample guarantees that members of each group within a population will be sampled.
8. A convenience sample is always representative of a population.
9. The method for selecting a stratified sample is to order a population in some way and then select members of the population at regular intervals.
10. To select a cluster sample, divide a population into groups and then select all of the members in at least one (but not all) of the groups.

**Distinguishing Between an Observational Study and an Experiment** *In Exercises 11–14, determine whether the study is an observational study or an experiment. Explain.*

11. A research study compared the memory retention of subjects when a learning activity was followed by a brief period of wakeful rest and when a learning activity was followed by a brief period of distraction. *(Source: Springer Nature)*
12. In a survey of U.S. employees, 42% of black women say they are uncomfortable sharing thoughts about racial inequality. *(Source: McKinsey & Company)*
13. A study used periodic blood pressure readings and brain MRIs of adults to find that adults with long periods of high blood pressure were more likely to develop cerebral small blood vessel disease. *(Source: American Heart Association)*
14. To study the effects of music on body image, researchers played a song with a body-positive message or a song with a body-negative message to different groups of women. *(Source: Psychology of Popular Media)*

15. **Random Number Table** Use the sixth row of Table 1 in Appendix B to generate 12 random numbers between 1 and 99.
16. **Random Number Table** Use the tenth row of Table 1 in Appendix B to generate 10 random numbers between 1 and 920.

**Random Numbers** *In Exercises 17 and 18, use technology to generate the random numbers.*

17. Fifteen numbers between 1 and 150
18. Nineteen numbers between 1 and 1000

## Using and Interpreting Concepts

**19. Acne Treatment** A company wants to test the effectiveness of a new acne cream. The company recruits 500 girls ages 13 to 17 who have acne. The subjects are randomly assigned into two groups. One group is given the acne cream and the other is given a placebo that looks exactly like the acne cream. Both groups apply the cream daily for two months. Facial photos are taken at the beginning and end of the treatment to compare results.

(a) Identify the experimental units and treatments used in this experiment.

(b) Identify a potential problem with the experimental design being used and suggest a way to improve it.

(c) How could this experiment be designed to be double-blind?

**20. Social Anxiety Disorder** Researchers in Japan tested the effect of cannabidiol (CBD) in treating late teenagers with social anxiety disorder (SAD). Thirty-seven 18- to 19-year-old teenagers with SAD took part in the study. The patients were assigned at random to receive a daily dose of either CBD or a placebo for 4 weeks. Symptoms were measured using The Fear of Negative Evaluation Questionnaire and the Liebowitz Social Anxiety Scale at the beginning and end of the treatment. *(Source: Frontiers in Psychology)*

(a) Identify the experimental units and treatments used in this experiment.

(b) Identify a potential problem with the experimental design being used and suggest a way to improve it.

(c) The experiment is described as a placebo-controlled, double-blind study. Explain what this means.

(d) How could blocking be used in designing this experiment?

**21. Sleep Deprivation** A researcher wants to study the effects of sleep deprivation on motor skills. Eighteen people volunteer for the experiment: Jake, Arya, Xavier, Nyla, Shaniece, Chen, Juan, Hana, Nia, Ansel, Liam, Bruno, Mei, Zoey, Kayla, Liam, Sofia, and Kai. Use a random number generator to choose nine subjects for the treatment group. The other nine subjects will go into the control group. List the subjects in each group. Tell which method you used to generate the random numbers.

**22. Using a Simple Random Sample** Volunteers for an experiment are numbered from 1 to 90. The volunteers are to be randomly assigned to two different treatment groups. Use a random number generator different from the one you used in Exercise 21 to choose 45 subjects for the treatment group. The other 45 subjects will go into the control group. List the subjects, according to number, in each group. Tell which method you used to generate the random numbers.

**Identifying Sampling Techniques** *In Exercises 23–28, identify the sampling technique used, and discuss potential sources of bias (if any). Explain.*

**23.** Selecting students at random from a campus directory, researchers contact 300 people and ask what obstacles (partying is mentioned as an example) keep them from completing their homework.

**24.** Questioning university students as they leave a college cafeteria, a researcher asks 342 students about their eating habits.

**25.** After a hurricane, a disaster area is divided into 200 equal grids. Thirty of the grids are selected, and every occupied household in the grid is interviewed to help focus relief efforts on what residents require the most.

**26.** Every tenth person using a mall entrance is asked to name their favorite store.

**27.** Soybeans are planted on a 48-acre field. The field is divided into one-acre subplots. A sample is taken from each subplot to estimate the harvest.

**28.** By making calls to randomly generated telephone numbers, 1012 respondents are asked if they rent or own their residences.

**Choosing Between a Census and a Sampling** *In Exercises 29 and 30, determine whether you would take a census or use a sampling. If you would use a sampling, determine which sampling technique you would use. Explain.*

**29.** The average GPA of the 85 students on a college football team roster

**30.** The average distance traveled to a stadium by 55,000 spectators

**Recognizing a Biased Question** *In Exercises 31–34, determine whether the survey question is biased. If the question is biased, suggest a better wording.*

**31.** Why does eating whole-grain foods improve your health?

**32.** Why does text messaging while driving increase the risk of a crash?

**33.** How much do you exercise during an average week?

**34.** How does the media influence the opinions of voters?

## Extending Concepts

**35. Analyzing a Study** Find an article or a news story that describes a statistical study.

(a) Identify the population and the sample.

(b) Classify the data as qualitative or quantitative. Determine the level of measurement.

(c) Is the study an observational study or an experiment? If it is an experiment, identify the treatment.

(d) Identify the sampling technique used to collect the data.

**36. Designing and Analyzing a Study** Design a study for a subject that interests you. Answer parts (a)–(d) of Exercise 35 for this study.

**37. Open and Closed Questions** Two types of survey questions are open questions and closed questions. An open question allows for any kind of response; a closed question allows for only a fixed response, such as a "yes" or "no" response, or a multiple choice response. An open question and a closed question are given below. List an advantage and a disadvantage of each type of question.

*Open Question* What can be done to get students to eat healthier foods?

*Closed Question* Would a mandatory nutrition course be an effective way to get students to eat healthier foods?

**38. Natural Experiments** Observational studies are sometimes referred to as *natural experiments*. Explain, in your own words, what this means.

# 1.3 ACTIVITY Random Numbers

You can find the interactive applet for this activity at MyLab Statistics.

The *Random numbers* applet is designed to allow you to generate random numbers from a range of values. You can specify integer values for the **Minimum, Maximum,** and **Sample Size.** You should not use decimal points when filling in the fields. When **Sample** is clicked, the applet generates random values, which are displayed as a list in the text field.

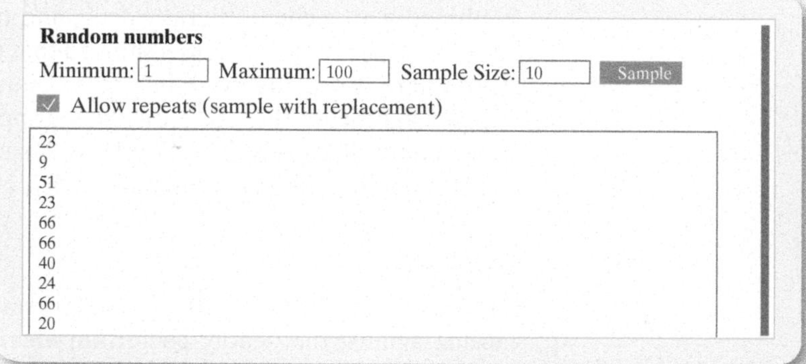


## EXPLORE

**Step 1** Specify a **Minimum** value.
**Step 2** Specify a **Maximum** value.
**Step 3** Specify the **Sample Size.**
**Step 4** Click **Sample** to generate a list of random values.

## DRAW CONCLUSIONS

1. Specify the **Minimum, Maximum,** and **Sample Size** to be 1, 20, and 8, respectively, as shown. Run the applet. Continue generating lists until you obtain one that shows that the random sample is taken with replacement. Write down this list. How do you know that the list is a random sample taken with replacement? Explain how the samples will change when you uncheck **Allow repeats.**

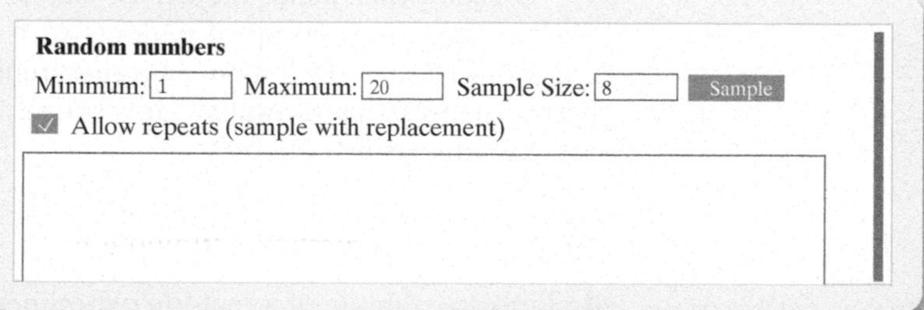


2. Use the applet to repeat Example 3 on page 21. What values did you use for the **Minimum, Maximum,** and **Sample Size?** Which method do you prefer? Explain.

# USES AND ABUSES Statistics in the Real World

## Uses

An experiment studied 321 women with advanced breast cancer. All of the women had been previously treated with other drugs, but the cancer had stopped responding to the medications. The women were then given the opportunity to take a new drug combined with a chemotherapy drug.

The subjects were divided into two groups, one that took the new drug combined with a chemotherapy drug, and one that took only the chemotherapy drug. After three years, results showed that the new drug in combination with the chemotherapy drug delayed the progression of cancer in the subjects. The results were so significant that the study was stopped, and the new drug was offered to all women in the study. The Food and Drug Administration has since approved use of the new drug in conjunction with a chemotherapy drug.

## Abuses

For four years, 180,000 teenagers in Norway were used as subjects to test a new vaccine against the deadly bacterium *meningococcus b*. A brochure describing the possible effects of the vaccine stated, "it is unlikely to expect serious complications," while information provided to the Norwegian Parliament stated, "serious side effects can not be excluded." The vaccine trial had some disastrous results: More than 500 side effects were reported, with some considered serious, and several of the subjects developed serious neurological diseases. The results showed that the vaccine was providing immunity in only 57% of the cases. This result was not sufficient for the vaccine to be added to Norway's vaccination program. Compensations have since been paid to the vaccine victims.

## Ethics

Experiments help us further understand the world that surrounds us. But, in some cases, they can do more harm than good. In the vaccine experiment in Norway, several ethical questions arise. Was the experiment unethical if the best interests of the subjects were neglected? When should the experiment have been stopped? Should it have been conducted at all? When serious side effects are not reported and are withheld from subjects, there is no ethical question—it is just wrong.

On the other hand, the breast cancer researchers would not want to deny the new drug to a group of patients with a life-threatening disease. But again, questions arise. How long must a researcher continue an experiment that shows better-than-expected results? How soon can a researcher conclude a drug is safe for the subjects involved?

## EXERCISES

1. Find an example of a real-life experiment other than the one described above that may be considered an "abuse." What could have been done to avoid the outcome of the experiment?
2. ***Stopping an Experiment*** In your opinion, what are some problems that may arise when clinical trials of a new experimental drug or vaccine are stopped early and then the drug or vaccine is distributed to other subjects or patients?

# 1 Chapter Summary

| What Did You Learn? | Example(s) | Review Exercises |
|---|---|---|
| **Section 1.1** | | |
| ▶ How to distinguish between a population and a sample | 1 | 1–4 |
| ▶ How to distinguish between a parameter and a statistic | 2 | 5–8 |
| ▶ How to distinguish between descriptive statistics and inferential statistics | 3 | 9, 10 |
| **Section 1.2** | | |
| ▶ How to distinguish between qualitative data and quantitative data | 1 | 11–14 |
| ▶ How to classify data with respect to the four levels of measurement: nominal, ordinal, interval, and ratio | 2, 3 | 15–18 |
| **Section 1.3** | | |
| ▶ How to design a statistical study and how to distinguish between an observational study and an experiment | 1 | 19, 20 |
| ▶ How to design an experiment | 2 | 21, 22 |
| ▶ How to create a sample using random sampling, simple random sampling, stratified sampling, cluster sampling, and systematic sampling and how to identify a biased sample | 3, 4 | 23–29 |

## Study Strategies

**College Transition** You may wonder how you are going to fit into the culture of your college. College culture typically consists of the rules and expectations of the institution, and the behaviors, attitudes, and values of your college's community. Understanding your college's culture will increase your chances to transition effectively, be better prepared, and connect readily to people and resources. All of this will start you on your path to success.

- One difference between high school and college is that in college, you are expected to learn not only from in-class lectures, but from other sources such as independent reading and research, laboratory work, papers, and projects. What you are expected to learn in college increases in difficulty level, pace, and volume when compared to high school, so time management is important.
- College tests focus more on critical thinking than on memorizing formulas, facts, people, and dates. Although tests may include assessment of how well you remember certain things, college instructors focus on expecting you to compare or contrast, evaluate material, support your opinions, apply concepts to new situations, and make recommendations or judgments.
- The biggest difference between high school and college is how much personal responsibility you will need for your education. Taking personal responsibility can help you develop skills that transfer to the workplace, such as working well in a group, solving problems by thinking critically, managing your time to get your class work done, and dealing with people who are different from you.

For more information, visit Skills for Success in the accompanying MyLab course.

# 1 Review Exercises

## Section 1.1

*In Exercises 1–4, identify the population and the sample. Describe the sample data set.*

**1.** A survey of 1025 U.S. adults found that they had visited the library an average of 10.5 times in the past 12 months. *(Source: Gallup)*

**2.** Eighty-three doctors working in the St. Louis area were surveyed concerning their opinions on health care reform.

**3.** In a survey of 23,503 U.S. adults, 59% said that if they were single, they would look up someone on the Internet before going on a date with them. *(Source: YouGov)*

**4.** A survey of 1508 U.S. adults ages 40–64 found that 32% had provided regular support to their parents in the past year. *(Source: AARP)*

*In Exercises 5–8, determine whether the number describes a population parameter or a sample statistic. Explain your reasoning.*

**5.** In 2019, the United States imported more than $4.8 billion worth of personal protective equipment. *(Source: Office of Textiles and Apparel)*

**6.** In a survey of 1000 household food purchasers, 24.7% say that they avoid meat, dairy, and eggs produced by animals living in confined conditions. *(Source: FoodPrint)*

**7.** In a sample of 2061 U.S. workers, 39% say that they are engaged in their work. *(Source: Gallup)*

**8.** The students receiving bachelor of science degrees from a university include 52 biology majors.

**9.** Which part of the survey described in Exercise 3 represents the descriptive branch of statistics? Make an inference based on the results of the survey.

**10.** Which part of the survey described in Exercise 4 represents the descriptive branch of statistics? Make an inference based on the results of the survey.

## Section 1.2

*In Exercises 11–14, determine whether the data are qualitative or quantitative. Explain your reasoning.*

**11.** The ages of a sample of 350 employees of a software company

**12.** The zip codes of a sample of 200 customers at a sporting goods store

**13.** The revenues of the companies on the Fortune 500 list

**14.** The marital statuses of the employees of a casino

*In Exercises 15–18, determine the level of measurement of the data set. Explain.*

**15.** The daily high temperatures (in degrees Fahrenheit) for Phoenix, Arizona, for a week in March are listed. *(Source: NOAA)*

89 87 80 70 69 59 61

16. The vehicle size classes for a sample of sedans are listed.

Minicompact Subcompact Compact Mid-size Large

17. The four departments of a printing company are listed.

Administration Sales Production Billing

18. The total compensations (in millions of dollars) of the ten highest-paid CEOs at U.S. public companies are listed. *(Source: 24/7 Wall St.)*

280.6 66.9 42.9 36.5 34.3 31.6 31.6 28.8 26.4 25.8

## Section 1.3

*In Exercises 19 and 20, determine whether the study is an observational study or an experiment. Explain.*

19. Researchers conduct a study to determine whether a medication based on fish oil known as omega-3 carboxylic acids is effective in reducing the risk of cardiac events in people already at risk. In the study, 13,078 patients are randomly chosen to receive either omega-3 carboxylic acids or a placebo of corn oil daily. Researchers compare the number of cardiac events of the two groups over similar follow-up periods of time. *(Source: American Heart Association)*

20. Researchers conduct a study to compare attitudes of first- and last-year medical students toward mental illness. To perform the study, researchers surveyed 111 first and last year students from the Faculty of Medicine of the University of Porto, Portugal. *(Source: Porto Biomedical Journal)*

*In Exercises 21 and 22, 200 students volunteer for an experiment to test the effects of sleep deprivation on memory recall. The students will be placed in one of five different treatment groups, including the control group.*

21. Explain how you could design an experiment so that it uses a randomized block design.

22. Explain how you could design an experiment so that it uses a completely randomized design.

*In Exercises 23–28, identify the sampling technique used, and discuss potential sources of bias (if any). Explain.*

23. Using random digit dialing, researchers ask 987 U.S. adults whether they feel comfortable with their current financial plans for retirement.

24. A student asks 18 friends to participate in a psychology experiment.

25. A study in a district of Northern Ethiopia is designed to investigate the level of awareness among pregnant women of the danger signs of obstetrics. Researchers interview all pregnant women in eleven randomly selected neighborhoods in the district. *(Source: Springer Nature)*

26. Law enforcement officials stop and check the driver of every third vehicle for blood alcohol content.

27. Twenty-five students are randomly selected from each grade level at a high school and surveyed about their study habits.

28. A journalist interviews 154 people waiting at an airport baggage claim and asks them how safe they feel during air travel.

29. You want to know the favorite spring break destination among 15,000 students at a university. Determine whether you would take a census or use a sampling. If you would use a sampling, determine which sampling technique you would use. Explain your reasoning.

# 1 Chapter Quiz

*Take this quiz as you would take a quiz in class. After you are done, check your work against the answers given in the back of the book.*

**1.** A study of 1622 high school seniors from four public high schools in the northeastern United States compared high school grade point averages to SAT and ACT scores as predictors of on-time college graduation. Identify the population and the sample in the study. *(Source: SAGE Journals)*

**2.** Determine whether each number describes a population parameter or a sample statistic. Explain your reasoning.

(a) A survey of 1301 U.S. adults found that 42% would feel safer getting into a driverless car if they were given a demonstration first. *(Source: AAA)*

(b) At a college, 90% of the members of the Board of Trustees approved the contract of the new president.

(c) A survey of 500 small business owners found that 48% no longer feel they need a physical store. *(Source: Entrepreneur)*

**3.** Determine whether the data are qualitative or quantitative. Explain.

(a) A list of debit card personal identification numbers

(b) The final scores on a video game

**4.** Determine the level of measurement of the data set. Explain your reasoning.

(a) A list of badge numbers of police officers at a precinct

(b) The horsepowers of racing car engines

(c) The top 10 grossing films released in a year

(d) The years of birth for the runners in the Boston Marathon

**5.** Determine whether the study is an observational study or an experiment. Explain.

(a) Researchers conduct a study to determine whether cataract surgery patients experience different comfort levels during their first and second surgeries. Researchers based their results on a verbal questionnaire. *(Source: Medicine)*

(b) In a study about smoking and vaping cues, researchers randomly assign 936 current or former smokers or vapers to watch a video that involves smoking, vaping, or neither. The subjects are then asked to report their level of desire to smoke or vape. *(Source: Springer Nature)*

**6.** An experiment is performed to test the effects of a new drug on attention-deficit/hyperactivity disorder (ADHD). The experimenter identifies 320 people ages 7 to 44 with ADHD to participate in the experiment. The subjects are divided into equal groups according to age. Within each group, subjects are then randomly selected to be in either the treatment group or the control group. What type of experimental design is being used for this experiment?

**7.** Identify the sampling technique used in each study. Explain your reasoning.

(a) A journalist asks people at a campground about air pollution.

(b) For quality assurance, every tenth machine part is selected from an assembly line and measured for accuracy.

(c) A study on attitudes about smoking is conducted at a college. The students are divided by class (freshman, sophomore, junior, and senior). Then a random sample is selected from each class and interviewed.

**8.** Which technique used in Exercise 7 could lead to a biased study? Explain.

# 1 Chapter Test

*Take this test as you would take a test in class.*

**1.** Determine whether you would take a census or use a sampling. If you would use a sampling, determine which sampling technique you would use. Explain.

(a) The most popular type of investment among investors in New Jersey

(b) The average age of the 30 employees of a company

**2.** Determine whether each number describes a population parameter or a sample statistic. Explain.

(a) A survey of 4272 U.S. adults found that 27% of smart watch or fitness tracker owners are college graduates. *(Source: Pew Research Center)*

(b) In a recent year, the average evidence-based reading and writing score on the SAT was 528. *(Source: College Board)*

**3.** Identify the sampling technique used, and discuss potential sources of bias (if any). Explain.

(a) Chosen at random, 200 male and 200 female high school students are asked about their plans after high school.

(b) Chosen at random, 625 customers at an electronics store are contacted and asked their opinions of the service they received.

(c) Questioning teachers as they leave a faculty lounge, a researcher asks 45 of them about their teaching styles.

**4.** Determine whether the data are qualitative or quantitative, and determine the level of measurement of the data set. Explain your reasoning.

(a) The numbers of employees at fast-food restaurants in a city are listed.

| | | | | | | | | | |
|---|---|---|---|---|---|---|---|---|---|
| 20 | 11 | 6 | 31 | 17 | 23 | 12 | 18 | 40 | 22 |
| 13 | 8 | 18 | 14 | 37 | 32 | 25 | 27 | 25 | 18 |

(b) The grade point averages (GPAs) for a class of students are listed.

| | | | | | | | |
|---|---|---|---|---|---|---|---|
| 3.6 | 3.2 | 2.0 | 3.8 | 3.0 | 3.5 | 1.7 | 3.2 |
| 2.2 | 4.0 | 2.5 | 1.9 | 2.8 | 3.6 | 2.5 | 3.7 |

**5.** Determine whether the survey question is biased. If the question is biased, suggest a better wording.

(a) How many hours of sleep do you get on a normal night?

(b) Do you agree that the town's ban on skateboarding in parks is unfair?

**6.** In a study, researchers surveyed 17,461 U.S. physicians, asking for the information below. *(Source: Medscape from WebMD)*

gender (male or female)　　age (years)
location (region of the U.S.)　　income (dollars)
employment status (private practice or an employee)
specialty (cardiology, family medicine, radiology, etc.)
time spent seeing patients per week (hours)
Would you choose medicine again? (yes or no)

(a) Identify the population and the sample.

(b) Are the data collected qualitative, quantitative, or both? Explain your reasoning.

(c) Determine the level of measurement for each item above.

(d) Is the study an observational study or an experiment? Explain.

# REAL STATISTICS REAL DECISIONS

# Putting it all together

You are a researcher for a professional research firm. Your firm has won a contract to conduct a study for a technology publication. The editors of the publication would like to know their readers' thoughts on using smartphones for making and receiving payments, for redeeming coupons, and as tickets to events. They would also like to know whether people are interested in using smartphones as digital wallets that store data from their drivers' licenses, health insurance cards, and other cards.

The editors have given you their readership database and 20 questions they would like to ask (two sample questions from a previous study are given at the right). You know that it is too expensive to contact all of the readers, so you need to determine a way to contact a representative sample of the entire readership population.

**Mobile payment app users: How does your current mobile payment behavior compare to this time last year?**

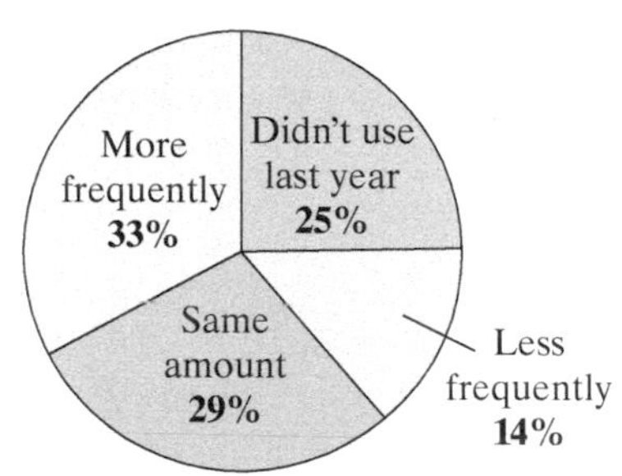


(Source: Fluent Pulse)

**Mobile payment app users: How frequently do you use mobile payment apps?**

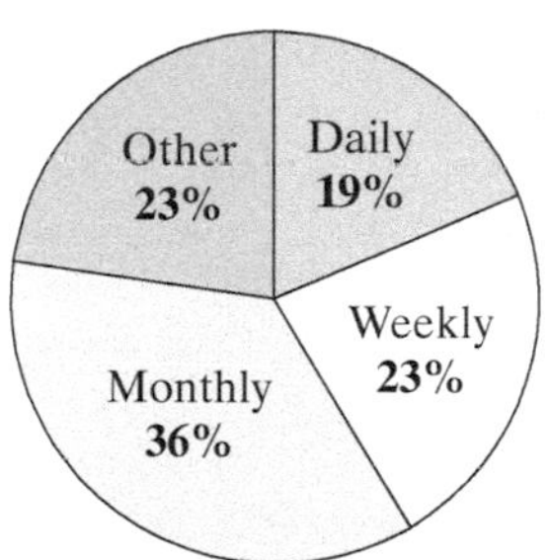


(Source: Fluent Pulse)

## EXERCISES

1. ***How Would You Do It?***
   (a) What sampling technique would you use to select the sample for the study? Why?
   (b) Will the technique you chose in part (a) give you a sample that is representative of the population?
   (c) Describe the method for collecting data.
   (d) Identify possible flaws or biases in your study.

2. ***Data Classification***
   (a) What type of data do you expect to collect: qualitative, quantitative, or both? Why?
   (b) At what levels of measurement do you think the data in the study will be? Why?
   (c) Will the data collected for the study represent a population or a sample?
   (d) Will the numerical descriptions of the data be parameters or statistics?

3. ***How They Did It***
   When Fluent Pulse did a study about the use of mobile payment apps, it used an Internet survey.
   (a) Describe some possible errors in collecting data by Internet surveys.
   (b) Compare your method for collecting data in Exercise 1 to this method.

# HISTORY OF STATISTICS–TIMELINE

## 17TH CENTURY

**John Graunt** (1620–1674)

Studied records of deaths in London in the early 1600s. The first to make extensive statistical observations from massive amounts of data (Chapter 2), his work laid the foundation for modern statistics.

**Blaise Pascal** (1623–1662)
**Pierre de Fermat** (1601–1665)

Pascal and Fermat corresponded about basic probability problems (Chapter 3)—especially those dealing with gaming and gambling.

## 18TH CENTURY

**Pierre Laplace** (1749–1827)

Studied probability (Chapter 3) and is credited with putting probability on a sure mathematical footing.

► **Carl Friedrich Gauss** (1777–1855)

Studied regression and the method of least squares (Chapter 9) through astronomy. In his honor, the normal distribution (Chapter 5) is sometimes called the Gaussian distribution.

## 19TH CENTURY

**Lambert Quetelet** (1796–1874)

Used descriptive statistics (Chapter 2) to analyze crime and mortality data and studied census techniques. Described normal distributions (Chapter 5) in connection with human traits such as height.

◄ **Florence Nightingale** (1820–1910)

A nurse during the Crimean War, she was one of the first to advocate the importance of sanitation in hospitals. One of the first statisticians to use descriptive statistics (Chapter 2) as a way to argue for social change and credited with having developed the Coxcomb chart.

**Francis Galton** (1822–1911)

Used regression and correlation (Chapter 9) to study genetic variation in humans. Credited with discovering the Central Limit Theorem (Chapter 5).

## 20TH CENTURY

**Karl Pearson** (1857–1936)

Studied natural selection using correlation (Chapter 9). Formed first academic department of statistics and helped develop chi-square analysis (Chapter 6).

**William Gosset** (1876–1937)

Studied process of brewing and developed *t*-test to correct problems connected with small sample sizes (Chapter 6).

**Charles Spearman** (1863–1945)

British psychologist who was one of the first to develop intelligence testing using factor analysis (Chapter 10).

**Ronald Fisher** (1890–1962)

Studied biology and natural selection and developed ANOVA (Chapter 10), stressed the importance of experimental design (Chapter 1), and was the first to identify the null and alternative hypotheses (Chapter 7).

## 20TH CENTURY (later)

**Frank Wilcoxon** (1892–1965)

Biochemist, used statistics to study plant pathology. Introduced two-sample tests (Chapter 8), which led to development of nonparametric statistics.

**John Tukey** (1915–2000)

Worked at Princeton during World War II. Introduced exploratory data analysis techniques such as stem-and-leaf plots (Chapter 2). Also, worked at Bell Laboratories and is best known for his work in inferential statistics (Chapters 6–11).

◄ **David Blackwell** (1919–2010)

Worked at Universities of Howard and California Berkeley. Significant contributions to Bayesian statistics, game theory, and probability theory (Chapter 3), and various other areas of mathematics. Authored one of the first texts on Bayesian statistics. Co-creator of the Rao-Blackwell Theorem.

TECHNOLOGY

MINITAB EXCEL TI-84 PLUS

# Using Technology in Statistics

With large data sets, you will find that calculators or computer software programs can help perform calculations and create graphics. These calculations can be performed on many calculators and statistical software programs, such as Minitab, Excel, and the TI-84 Plus.

The following example shows a sample generated by each of these three technologies to generate a list of random numbers. This list of random numbers can be used to select sample members or perform simulations.

**EXAMPLE**

### Generating a List of Random Numbers

A quality control department inspects a random sample of 15 of the 167 cars that are assembled at an auto plant. How should the cars be chosen?

**SOLUTION**

One way to choose the sample is to first number the cars from 1 to 167. Then you can use technology to form a list of random numbers from 1 to 167. Each of the technology tools shown requires different steps to generate the list. Each, however, does require that you identify the minimum value as 1 and the maximum value as 167. Check your user's manual for specific instructions.

**MINITAB**

| ↓ | C1 |
|---|---|
| | |
| 1 | 167 |
| 2 | 11 |
| 3 | 74 |
| 4 | 160 |
| 5 | 18 |
| 6 | 70 |
| 7 | 80 |
| 8 | 56 |
| 9 | 37 |
| 10 | 6 |
| 11 | 82 |
| 12 | 126 |
| 13 | 98 |
| 14 | 104 |
| 15 | 137 |

**EXCEL**

| | A |
|---|---|
| 1 | 41 |
| 2 | 16 |
| 3 | 91 |
| 4 | 58 |
| 5 | 151 |
| 6 | 36 |
| 7 | 96 |
| 8 | 154 |
| 9 | 2 |
| 10 | 113 |
| 11 | 157 |
| 12 | 103 |
| 13 | 64 |
| 14 | 135 |
| 15 | 90 |

**TI-84 PLUS**

```
randInt (1, 167, 15)
{17 42 152 59 5 116
125 64 122 55 58 60
82 152 105}
```

Recall that when you generate a list of random numbers, you should decide whether it is acceptable to have numbers that repeat. If it is acceptable, then the sampling process is said to be with replacement. If it is not acceptable, then the sampling process is said to be without replacement.

With each of the three technology tools shown on page 36, you have the capability of sorting the list so that the numbers appear in order. Sorting helps you see whether any of the numbers in the list repeat. If it is not acceptable to have repeats, you should specify that the tool generate more random numbers than you need.

## EXERCISES

1. The SEC (Securities and Exchange Commission) is investigating a financial services company. The company being investigated has 86 brokers. The SEC decides to review the records for a random sample of 10 brokers. Describe how this investigation could be done. Then use technology to generate a list of 10 random numbers from 1 to 86 and order the list.
2. A quality control department is testing 25 smartphones from a shipment of 300 smartphones. Describe how this test could be done. Then use technology to generate a list of 25 random numbers from 1 to 300 and order the list.
3. Consider the population of ten digits: 0, 1, 2, 3, 4, 5, 6, 7, 8, and 9. Select three random samples of five digits from this list. Find the average of each sample. Compare your results with the average of the entire population. Comment on your results. (Hint: To find the average, sum the data entries and divide the sum by the number of entries.)
4. Consider the population of 41 whole numbers from 0 to 40. What is the average of these numbers? Select three random samples of seven numbers from this list. Find the average of each sample. Compare your results with the average of the entire population. Comment on your results. (Hint: To find the average, sum the data entries and divide the sum by the number of entries.)
5. Use random numbers to simulate rolling a six-sided die 60 times. How many times did you obtain each number from 1 to 6? Are the results what you expected?
6. You rolled a six-sided die 60 times and got the following tally.

   20 ones
   20 twos
   15 threes
   3 fours
   2 fives
   0 sixes

   Does this seem like a reasonable result? What inference might you draw from the result?
7. Use random numbers to simulate tossing a coin 100 times. Let 0 represent heads, and let 1 represent tails. How many times did you obtain each number? Are the results what you expected?
8. You tossed a coin 100 times and got 77 heads and 23 tails. Does this seem like a reasonable result? What inference might you draw from the result?
9. A political analyst would like to survey a sample of the registered voters in a county. The county has 47 election districts. How could the analyst use random numbers to obtain a cluster sample?

Extended solutions are given in the technology manuals that accompany this text. Technical instruction is provided for Minitab, Excel, and the TI-84 Plus.

CHAPTER 2

# Descriptive Statistics

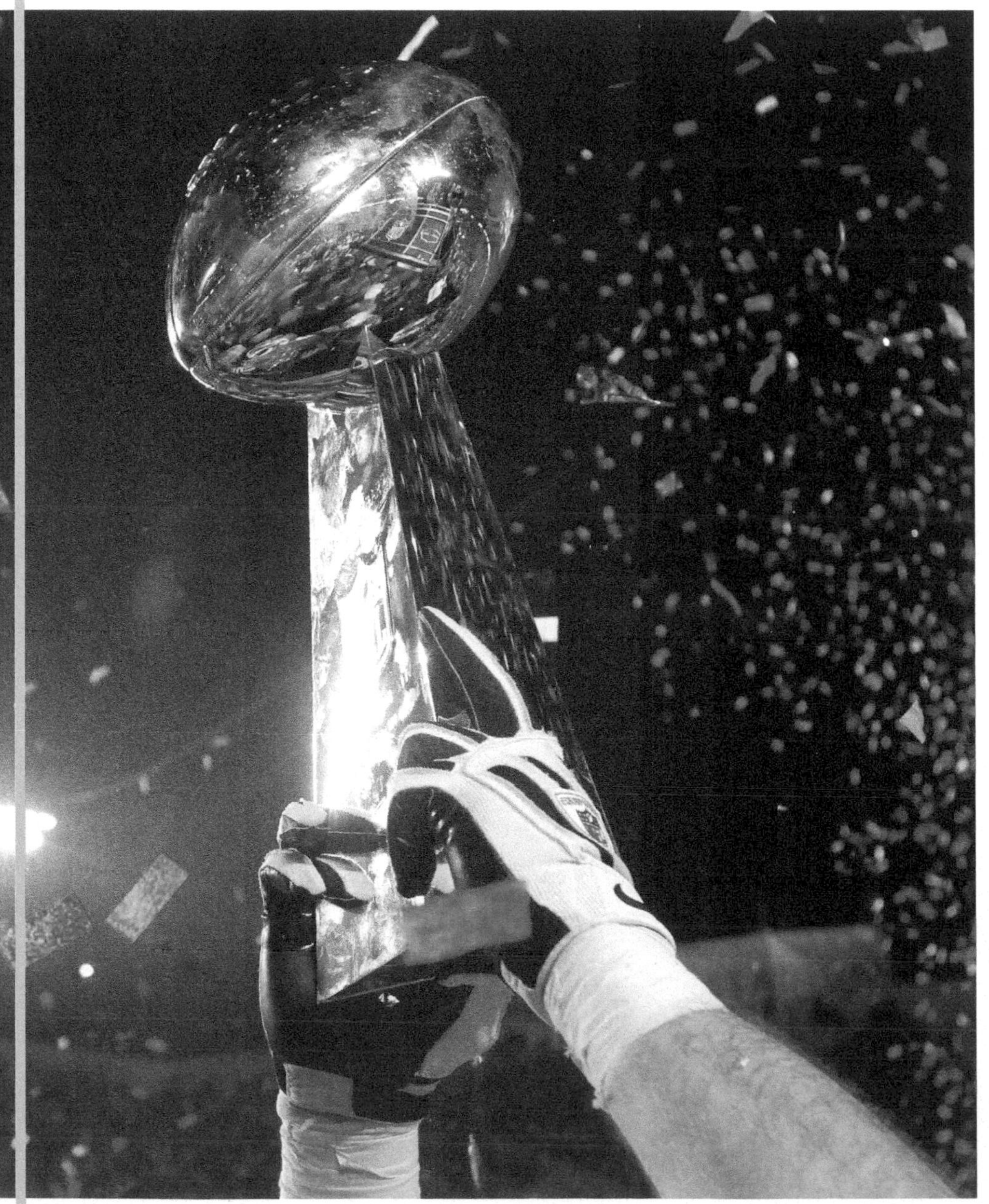

Since the 1966 season, the National Football League has determined its champion in the Super Bowl. The winning team receives the Lombardi Trophy.

## Where You've Been

In Chapter 1, you learned that there are many ways to collect data. Usually, researchers must work with sample data in order to analyze populations, but occasionally it is possible to collect all the data for a given population. For instance, the data at the right represent the points scored by the winning teams in the first 55 Super Bowls. *(Source: ESPN.com)*

35, 33, 16, 23, 16, 24, 14, 24, 16, 21, 32, 27, 35, 31, 27, 26, 27, 38, 38, 46, 39, 42, 20, 55, 20, 37, 52, 30, 49, 27, 35, 31, 34, 23, 34, 20, 48, 32, 24, 21, 29, 17, 27, 31, 31, 21, 34, 43, 28, 24, 34, 41, 13, 31, 31

## Where You're Going

In Chapter 2, you will learn ways to organize and describe data sets. The goal is to make the data easier to understand by describing trends, averages, and variations. For instance, in the raw data showing the points scored by the winning teams in the first 55 Super Bowls, it is not easy to see any patterns or special characteristics. Here are some ways you can organize and describe the data.

Make a frequency distribution.

| Class | Frequency, $f$ |
|---|---|
| 13–19 | 6 |
| 20–26 | 13 |
| 27–33 | 17 |
| 34–40 | 11 |
| 41–47 | 4 |
| 48–54 | 3 |
| 55–61 | 1 |

Draw a histogram.

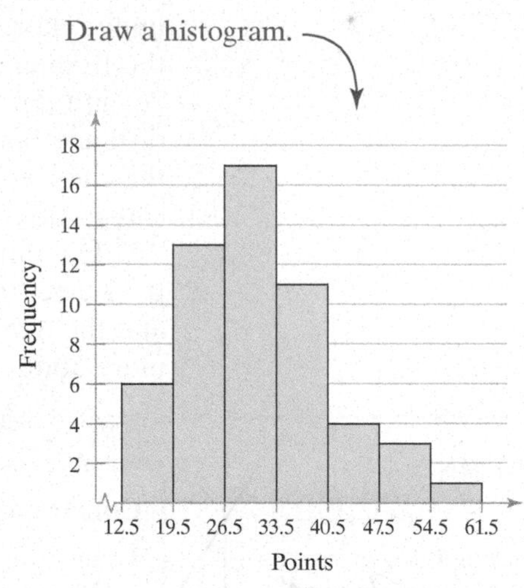


$$\text{Mean} = \frac{35 + 33 + 16 + 23 + 16 + \cdots + 41 + 13 + 31 + 31}{55}$$
$$= \frac{1657}{55}$$
$$\approx 30.1 \text{ points}$$

Find an average.

$$\text{Range} = 55 - 13$$
$$= 42 \text{ points}$$

Find how the data vary.

# 2.1 Frequency Distributions and Their Graphs

## What You Should Learn

- How to construct a frequency distribution, including limits, midpoints, relative frequencies, cumulative frequencies, and boundaries
- How to construct frequency histograms, frequency polygons, relative frequency histograms, and ogives

Frequency Distributions ■ Graphs of Frequency Distributions

## Frequency Distributions

There are many ways to organize and describe a data set. Important characteristics to look for when organizing and describing a data set are its **center,** its **variability** (or spread), and its **shape.** Measures of center and shapes of distributions are covered in Section 2.3. Measures of variability are covered in Section 2.4.

When a data set has many entries, it can be difficult to see patterns. In this section, you will learn how to organize data sets by grouping the data into **intervals** called **classes** and forming a **frequency distribution.** You will also learn how to use frequency distributions to construct graphs.

**DEFINITION**

A **frequency distribution** is a table that shows **classes** or **intervals** of data entries with a count of the number of entries in each class. The **frequency** $f$ of a class is the number of data entries in the class.

**Example of a Frequency Distribution**

| Class | Frequency, $f$ |
|---|---|
| 1–5 | 5 |
| 6–10 | 8 |
| 11–15 | 6 |
| 16–20 | 8 |
| 21–25 | 5 |
| 26–30 | 4 |

In the frequency distribution shown at the left, there are six classes. The frequencies for each of the six classes are 5, 8, 6, 8, 5, and 4. Each class has a **lower class limit,** which is the least number that can belong to the class, and an **upper class limit,** which is the greatest number that can belong to the class. In the frequency distribution shown, the lower class limits are 1, 6, 11, 16, 21, and 26, and the upper class limits are 5, 10, 15, 20, 25, and 30. The **class width** is the distance between lower (or upper) limits of consecutive classes. For instance, the class width in the frequency distribution shown is $6 - 1 = 5$. Notice that the classes do not overlap.

The difference between the maximum and minimum data entries is called the **range.** In the frequency table shown, suppose the maximum data entry is 29, and the minimum data entry is 1. The range then is $29 - 1 = 28$. You will learn more about the range of a data set in Section 2.4.

**Study Tip**

In general, the frequency distributions shown in this text will use the minimum data entry for the lower limit of the first class. Sometimes it may be more convenient to choose a lower limit that is slightly less than the minimum data entry. The frequency distribution produced will vary slightly.

**GUIDELINES**

**Constructing a Frequency Distribution from a Data Set**

1. Decide on the number of classes to include in the frequency distribution. The number of classes should be between 5 and 20; otherwise, it may be difficult to detect any patterns.
2. Find the class width as follows. Determine the range of the data, divide the range by the number of classes, and *round up to the next convenient number.*
3. Find the class limits. You can use the minimum data entry as the lower limit of the first class. To find the remaining lower limits, add the class width to the lower limit of the preceding class. Then find the upper limit of the first class. Remember that classes cannot overlap. Find the remaining upper class limits.
4. Make a tally mark for each data entry in the row of the appropriate class.
5. Count the tally marks to find the total frequency $f$ for each class.

**EXAMPLE 1**

## Constructing a Frequency Distribution from a Data Set

The data set lists the cell phone screen times (in minutes) for 30 U.S. adults on a recent day. Construct a frequency distribution that has seven classes.

| | | | | | | | | | |
|---|---|---|---|---|---|---|---|---|---|
| 200 | 239 | 155 | 252 | 384 | 165 | 296 | 405 | 303 | 400 |
| 307 | 241 | 256 | 315 | 330 | 317 | 352 | 266 | 276 | 345 |
| 238 | 306 | 290 | 271 | 345 | 312 | 293 | 195 | 168 | 342 |

**SOLUTION**

1. The number of classes (7) is stated in the problem.
2. The minimum data entry is 155 and the maximum data entry is 405, so the range is 405 − 155 = 250. Divide the range by the number of classes and round up to find the class width.

$$\text{Class width} = \frac{250}{7} \qquad \frac{\text{Range}}{\text{Number of classes}}$$

$$\approx 35.71 \qquad \text{Round up to the next convenient number, 36.}$$

3. The minimum data entry is a convenient lower limit for the first class. To find the lower limits of the remaining six classes, add the class width of 36 to the lower limit of each previous class. So, the lower limits of the other classes are 155 + 36 = 191, 191 + 36 = 227, and so on. The upper limit of the first class is 190, which is one less than the lower limit of the second class. The upper limits of the other classes are 190 + 36 = 226, 226 + 36 = 262, and so on. The lower and upper limits for all seven classes are shown at the left.
4. Make a tally mark for each data entry in the appropriate class. For instance, the data entry 168 is in the 155–190 class, so make a tally mark in that class. Continue until you have made a tally mark for each of the 30 data entries.
5. The number of tally marks for a class is the frequency of that class.

The frequency distribution is shown below. The first class, 155–190, has three tally marks. So, the frequency of this class is 3. Notice that the sum of the frequencies is 30, which is the number of entries in the data set. The sum is denoted by $\Sigma f$ where $\Sigma$ is the uppercase Greek letter **sigma.**

**Study Tip**

If you obtain a whole number when calculating the class width of a frequency distribution, use the next whole number as the class width. Doing this ensures that you will have enough space in your frequency distribution for all the data entries.

| Lower limit | Upper limit |
|---|---|
| 155 | 190 |
| 191 | 226 |
| 227 | 262 |
| 263 | 298 |
| 299 | 334 |
| 335 | 370 |
| 371 | 406 |

**Study Tip**

The uppercase Greek letter sigma ($\Sigma$) is used throughout statistics to indicate a summation of values.

**Frequency Distribution for Cell Phone Screen Times (in minutes)**

Times → Class; Number of adults → Frequency, $f$

| Class | Tally | Frequency, $f$ |
|---|---|---|
| 155–190 | \|\|\| | 3 |
| 191–226 | \|\| | 2 |
| 227–262 | ~~\|\|\|\|~~ | 5 |
| 263–298 | ~~\|\|\|\|~~ \| | 6 |
| 299–334 | ~~\|\|\|\|~~ \|\| | 7 |
| 335–370 | \|\|\|\| | 4 |
| 371–406 | \|\|\| | 3 |
| | | $\Sigma f = 30$ |

Check that the sum of the frequencies equals the number in the sample.

**TRY IT YOURSELF 1**

Construct a frequency distribution using the points scored by the 55 winning teams listed on page 39. Use six classes. *Answer: Page A35*

**Population of Iowa**

| Ages | Frequency |
|---|---|
| 0–9 | 396,037 |
| 10–19 | 418,823 |
| 20–29 | 422,774 |
| 30–39 | 399,314 |
| 40–49 | 363,809 |
| 50–59 | 392,536 |
| 60–69 | 385,737 |
| 70–79 | 229,536 |
| 80 and older | 146,504 |

The last class, 80 and older, is open-ended.
(Source: U.S. Census Bureau)

Note in Example 1 that the classes do not overlap, so each of the original data entries belongs to exactly one class. Also, the classes are of equal width. In general, all classes in a frequency distribution have the same width. However, this may not always be possible because a class can be *open-ended.* For instance, the frequency distribution for the population of Iowa shown at the left has an open-ended class, "80 and older."

After constructing a standard frequency distribution such as the one in Example 1, you can include several additional features that will help provide a better understanding of the data. These features (the **midpoint, relative frequency,** and **cumulative frequency** of each class) can be included as additional columns in your table.

For help with evaluating formulas, order of operations, multiplication and division of integers, operations with fractions and decimals, and significant digits and rounding, see *Integrated Review* at

MyLab® Statistics

## DEFINITION

The **midpoint** of a class is the sum of the lower and upper limits of the class divided by two. The midpoint is sometimes called the *class mark.*

$$\text{Midpoint} = \frac{(\text{Lower class limit}) + (\text{Upper class limit})}{2}$$

The **relative frequency** of a class is the portion, or percentage, of the data that falls in that class. To find the relative frequency of a class, divide the frequency $f$ by the sample size $n$.

$$\text{Relative frequency} = \frac{\text{Class frequency}}{\text{Sample size}} = \frac{f}{n} \qquad \text{Note that } n = \Sigma f.$$

The **cumulative frequency** of a class is the sum of the frequencies of that class and all previous classes. The cumulative frequency of the last class is equal to the sample size $n$.

You can use the formula shown above to find the midpoint of each class, or after finding the first midpoint, you can find the remaining midpoints by adding the class width to the previous midpoint. For instance, the midpoint of the first class in Example 1 is

$$\text{Midpoint} = \frac{155 + 190}{2} = 172.5. \qquad \text{Midpoint of first class.}$$

Using the class width of 36, the remaining midpoints are

$172.5 + 36 = 208.5$ — Midpoint of second class.

$208.5 + 36 = 244.5$ — Midpoint of third class.

$244.5 + 36 = 280.5$ — Midpoint of fourth class.

and so on.

You can write the relative frequency as a fraction, decimal, or percent. The sum of the relative frequencies of all the classes should be equal to 1, or 100%. Due to rounding, the sum may be slightly less than or greater than 1. So, values such as 0.99 and 1.01 are sufficient.

EXAMPLE 2

## Finding Midpoints, Relative Frequencies, and Cumulative Frequencies

Using the frequency distribution constructed in Example 1, find the midpoint, relative frequency, and cumulative frequency of each class. Describe any patterns.

**SOLUTION**

The midpoints, relative frequencies, and cumulative frequencies of the first five classes are calculated as follows.

| Class | $f$ | Midpoint | Relative frequency | Cumulative frequency |
|---|---|---|---|---|
| 155–190 | 3 | $\frac{155 + 190}{2} = 172.5$ | $\frac{3}{30} = 0.1$ | 3 |
| 191–226 | 2 | $\frac{191 + 226}{2} = 208.5$ | $\frac{2}{30} \approx 0.07$ | $3 + 2 = 5$ |
| 227–262 | 5 | $\frac{227 + 262}{2} = 244.5$ | $\frac{5}{30} \approx 0.17$ | $5 + 5 = 10$ |
| 263–298 | 6 | $\frac{263 + 298}{2} = 280.5$ | $\frac{6}{30} = 0.2$ | $10 + 6 = 16$ |
| 299–334 | 7 | $\frac{299 + 334}{2} = 316.5$ | $\frac{7}{30} \approx 0.23$ | $16 + 7 = 23$ |

The remaining midpoints, relative frequencies, and cumulative frequencies are shown in the expanded frequency distribution below.

**Frequency Distribution for Cell Phone Screen Times (in minutes)**

Times → Class; Number of adults → Frequency, $f$; Portion of adults → Relative frequency

| Class | Frequency, $f$ | Midpoint | Relative frequency | Cumulative frequency |
|---|---|---|---|---|
| 155–190 | 3 | 172.5 | 0.1 | 3 |
| 191–226 | 2 | 208.5 | 0.07 | 5 |
| 227–262 | 5 | 244.5 | 0.17 | 10 |
| 263–298 | 6 | 280.5 | 0.2 | 16 |
| 299–334 | 7 | 316.5 | 0.23 | 23 |
| 335–370 | 4 | 352.5 | 0.13 | 27 |
| 371–406 | 3 | 388.5 | 0.1 | 30 |
| | $\Sigma f = 30$ | | $\Sigma \frac{f}{n} = 1$ | |

For help with summation, see *Integrated Review* at

MyLab Statistics

***Interpretation*** There are several patterns in the data set. For instance, the most common range for the times is 299 to 334 minutes. Also, about half of the times are less than 299 minutes.

**TRY IT YOURSELF 2**

Using the frequency distribution constructed in Try It Yourself 1, find the midpoint, relative frequency, and cumulative frequency of each class. Describe any patterns.

*Answer: Page A35*

## Graphs of Frequency Distributions

Sometimes it is easier to discover patterns in a data set by looking at a graph of the frequency distribution. One such graph is a **frequency histogram.**

### DEFINITION

A **frequency histogram** uses bars to represent the frequency distribution of a data set. A histogram has the following properties.

1. The horizontal scale is quantitative and measures the data entries.
2. The vertical scale measures the frequencies of the classes.
3. Consecutive bars must touch.

Because consecutive bars of a histogram must touch, bars must begin and end at class boundaries instead of class limits. **Class boundaries** are the numbers that separate classes *without* forming gaps between them. For data that are integers, subtract 0.5 from each lower limit to find the lower class boundaries. To find the upper class boundaries, add 0.5 to each upper limit. The upper boundary of a class will equal the lower boundary of the next higher class.

### EXAMPLE 3

### Constructing a Frequency Histogram

Draw a frequency histogram for the frequency distribution in Example 2. Describe any patterns.

**SOLUTION**

First, find the class boundaries. Because the data entries are integers, subtract 0.5 from each lower limit to find the lower class boundaries and add 0.5 to each upper limit to find the upper class boundaries. So, the lower and upper boundaries of the first class are as follows.

First class lower boundary $= 155 - 0.5 = 154.5$

First class upper boundary $= 190 + 0.5 = 190.5$

| Class | Class boundaries | Frequency, $f$ |
|---|---|---|
| 155–190 | 154.5–190.5 | 3 |
| 191–226 | 190.5–226.5 | 2 |
| 227–262 | 226.5–262.5 | 5 |
| 263–298 | 262.5–298.5 | 6 |
| 299–334 | 298.5–334.5 | 7 |
| 335–370 | 334.5–370.5 | 4 |
| 371–406 | 370.5–406.5 | 3 |

The boundaries of the remaining classes are shown in the table at the left. To construct the histogram, choose possible frequency values for the vertical scale. You can mark the horizontal scale either at the midpoints or at the class boundaries. Both histograms are shown below.

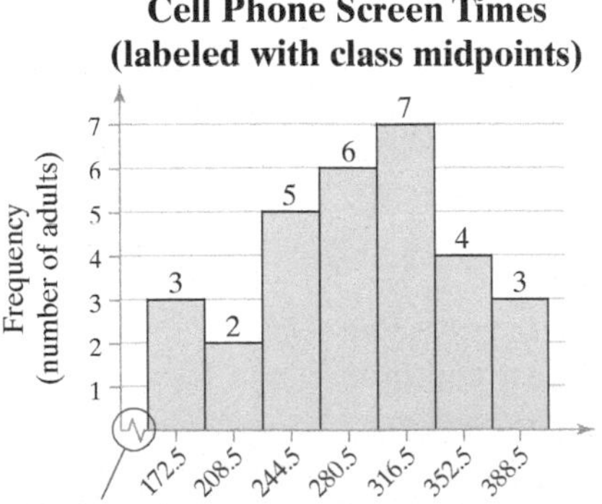


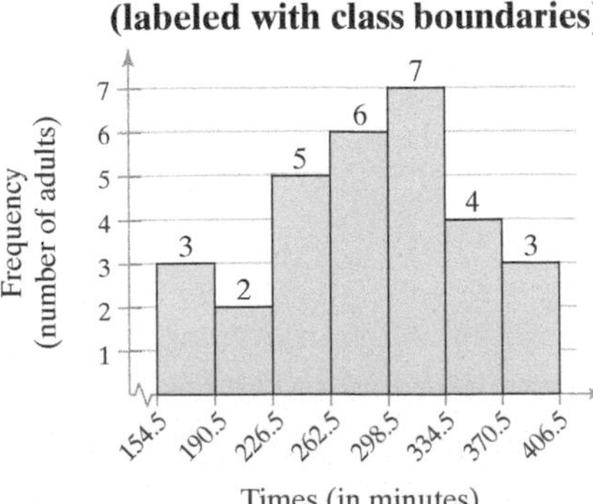


***Interpretation*** From either histogram, you can determine that two thirds of the adults are spending more than 262.5 minutes each day using their cell phones.

**Study Tip**

It is customary in bar graphs to have spaces between the bars, whereas with histograms, it is customary that the bars have no spaces between them.

**TRY IT YOURSELF 3**

Use the frequency distribution from Try It Yourself 2 to construct a frequency histogram that represents the points scored by the 55 winning teams listed on page 39. Describe any patterns. *Answer: Page A35*

Another way to graph a frequency distribution is to use a frequency polygon. A **frequency polygon** is a line graph that emphasizes the continuous change in frequencies.

**EXAMPLE 4**

## Constructing a Frequency Polygon

Draw a frequency polygon for the frequency distribution in Example 2. Describe any patterns.

**SOLUTION**

For help with the *xy*-plane and point plotting, see *Integrated Review* at

MyLab Statistics

To construct the frequency polygon, use the same horizontal and vertical scales that were used in the histogram labeled with class midpoints in Example 3. Then plot points that represent the midpoint and frequency of each class and connect the points in order from left to right with line segments. Because the graph should begin and end on the horizontal axis, extend the left side to one class width before the first class midpoint and extend the right side to one class width after the last class midpoint.

**Cell Phone Screen Times**

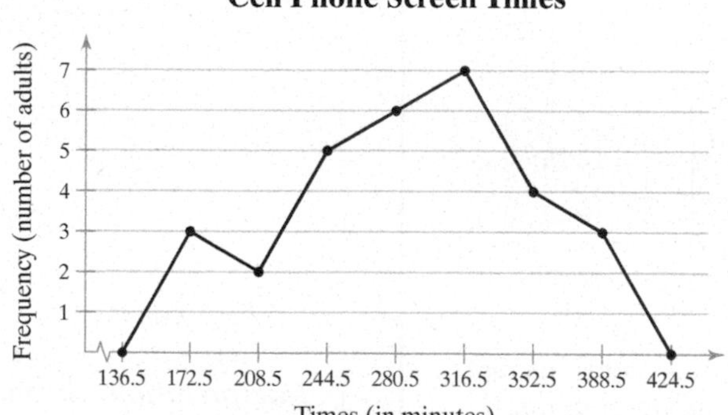


You can check your answer using technology, as shown below.

**TI-84 PLUS**

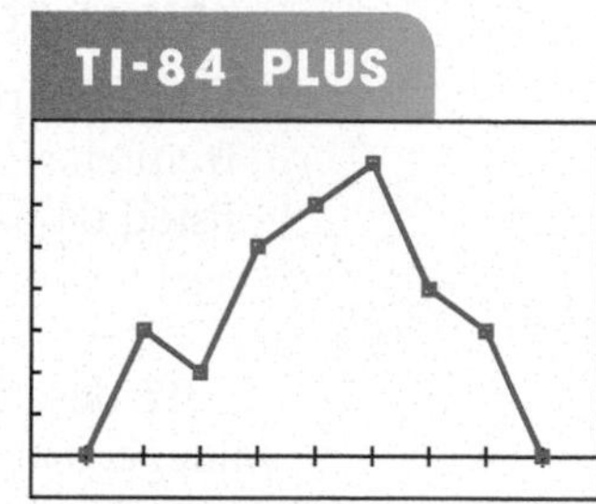

***Interpretation*** You can see that the frequency of adults increases up to a time of 316.5 minutes and then the frequency decreases.

**TRY IT YOURSELF 4**

Use the frequency distribution from Try It Yourself 2 to construct a frequency polygon that represents the points scored by the 55 winning teams listed on page 39. Describe any patterns.

*Answer: Page A36*

**EXCEL**

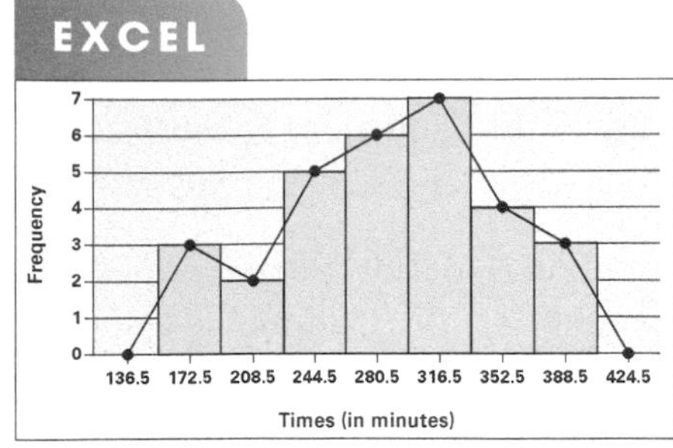


A histogram and its corresponding frequency polygon are often drawn together, as shown at the left using Excel. To do this by hand, first construct the frequency polygon by choosing appropriate horizontal and vertical scales. The horizontal scale should consist of the class midpoints, and the vertical scale should consist of appropriate frequency values. Then plot the points that represent the midpoint and frequency of each class. After connecting the points with line segments, finish by drawing the bars for the histogram.

A **relative frequency histogram** has the same shape and the same horizontal scale as the corresponding frequency histogram. The difference is that the vertical scale measures the *relative* frequencies, not frequencies.

## Picturing the World

Old Faithful, a geyser at Yellowstone National Park, erupts on a regular basis. The time spans of a sample of eruptions are shown in the relative frequency histogram. (Source: Yellowstone National Park)

**Old Faithful Eruptions**

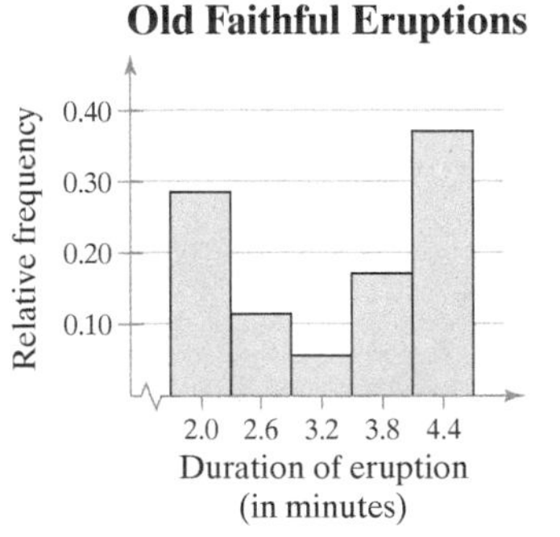


**About 50% of the eruptions last less than how many minutes?**

**EXAMPLE 5**

### Constructing a Relative Frequency Histogram

Draw a relative frequency histogram for the frequency distribution in Example 2.

**SOLUTION**

The relative frequency histogram is shown. Notice that the shape of the histogram is the same as the shape of the frequency histogram constructed in Example 3. The only difference is that the vertical scale measures the relative frequencies.

**Cell Phone Screen Times**

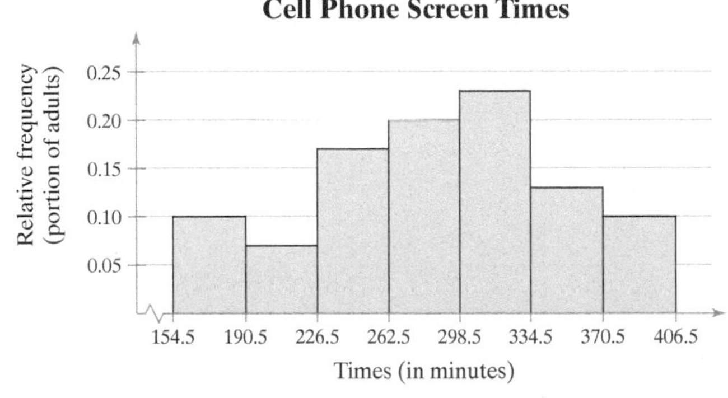


***Interpretation*** From this graph, you can quickly see that 0.2, or 20%, of the adults have screen times between 262.5 minutes and 298.5 minutes, which is not immediately obvious from the frequency histogram in Example 3.

**TRY IT YOURSELF 5**

Use the frequency distribution in Try It Yourself 2 to construct a relative frequency histogram that represents the points scored by the 55 winning teams listed on page 39.

*Answer: Page A36*

To describe the number of data entries that are less than or equal to a certain value, construct a **cumulative frequency graph.**

**DEFINITION**

A **cumulative frequency graph,** or **ogive** (pronounced ō′jīve), is a line graph that displays the cumulative frequency of each class at its upper class boundary. The upper boundaries are marked on the horizontal axis, and the cumulative frequencies are marked on the vertical axis.

## GUIDELINES

**Constructing an Ogive (Cumulative Frequency Graph)**

1. Construct a frequency distribution that includes cumulative frequencies as one of the columns.
2. Specify the horizontal and vertical scales. The horizontal scale consists of upper class boundaries, and the vertical scale measures cumulative frequencies.
3. Plot points that represent the upper class boundaries and their corresponding cumulative frequencies.
4. Connect the points in order from left to right with line segments.
5. The graph should start at the lower boundary of the first class (cumulative frequency is 0) and should end at the upper boundary of the last class (cumulative frequency is equal to the sample size).

## EXAMPLE 6

### Constructing an Ogive

Draw an ogive for the frequency distribution in Example 2.

**SOLUTION**

Using the cumulative frequencies, you can construct the ogive shown. The upper class boundaries, frequencies, and cumulative frequencies are shown in the table. Notice that the graph starts at 154.5, where the cumulative frequency is 0, and the graph ends at 406.5, where the cumulative frequency is 30.

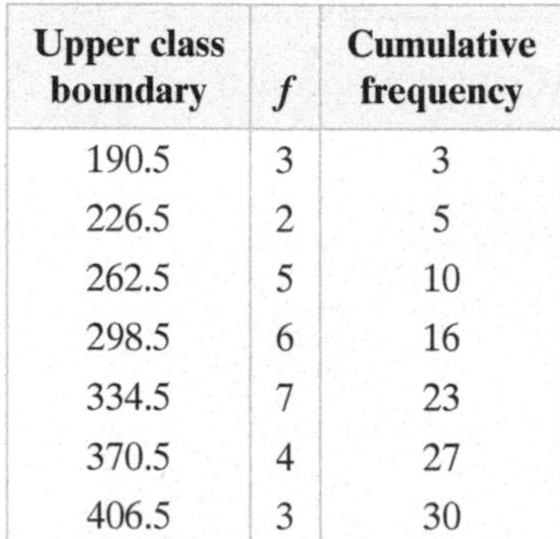

| Upper class boundary | $f$ | Cumulative frequency |
|---|---|---|
| 190.5 | 3 | 3 |
| 226.5 | 2 | 5 |
| 262.5 | 5 | 10 |
| 298.5 | 6 | 16 |
| 334.5 | 7 | 23 |
| 370.5 | 4 | 27 |
| 406.5 | 3 | 30 |

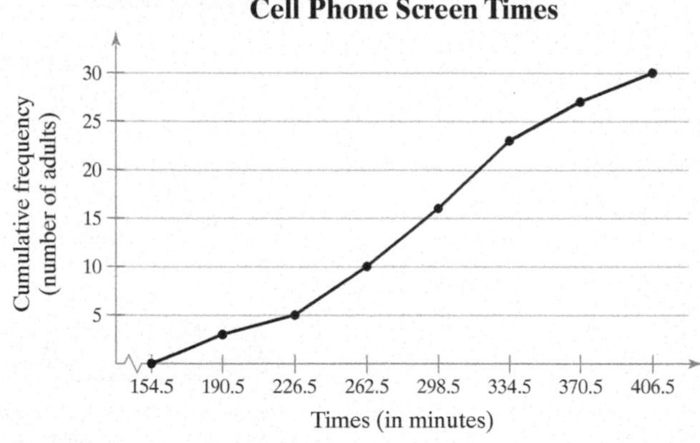


***Interpretation*** From the ogive, you can see that 10 adults had screen times of 262.5 minutes or less. Also, the greatest increase in cumulative frequency occurs between 298.5 minutes and 334.5 minutes because the line segment is steepest between these two class boundaries.

**TRY IT YOURSELF 6**

Use the frequency distribution from Try It Yourself 2 to construct an ogive that represents the points scored by the 55 winning teams listed on page 39.

*Answer: Page A36*

Another type of ogive uses percent as the vertical axis instead of frequency (see Example 5 in Section 2.5).

If you have access to technology such as Minitab, Excel, StatCrunch, or the TI-84 Plus, you can use it to draw the graphs discussed in this section.

**EXAMPLE 7**

### Using Technology to Construct Histograms

Use technology to construct a histogram for the frequency distribution in Example 2.

**SOLUTION**

Using the instructions for a TI-84 Plus shown in the Tech Tip at the left, you can draw a histogram similar to the one below on the left. To investigate the graph, you can use the *trace* feature. After pressing TRACE, the midpoint and the frequency of the first class are displayed, as shown in the figure on the right. Use the right and left arrow keys to move through each bar.

**TI-84 PLUS**

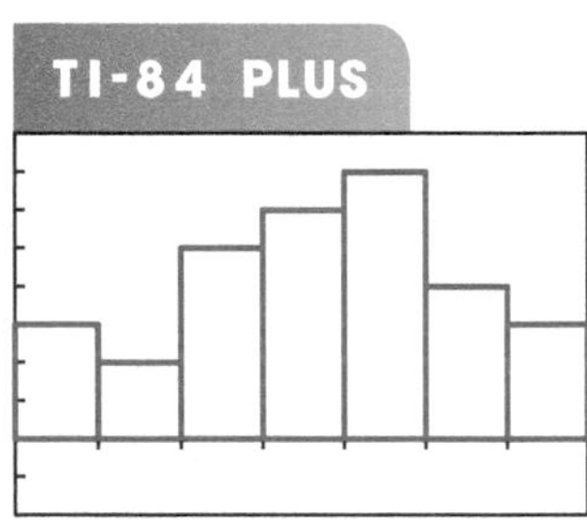

**TI-84 PLUS**

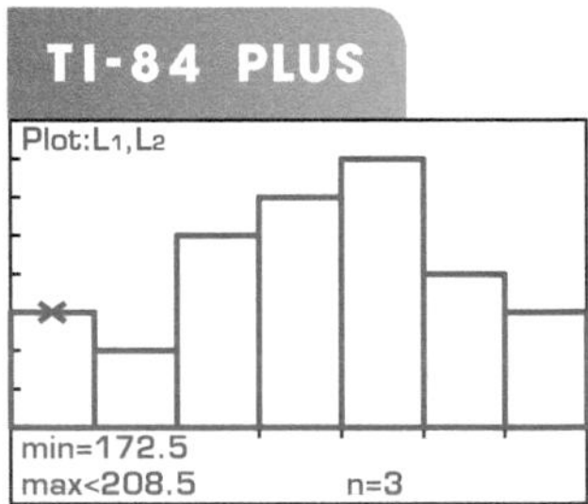


Histograms made using Minitab, Excel, and StatCrunch are shown below.

**MINITAB**

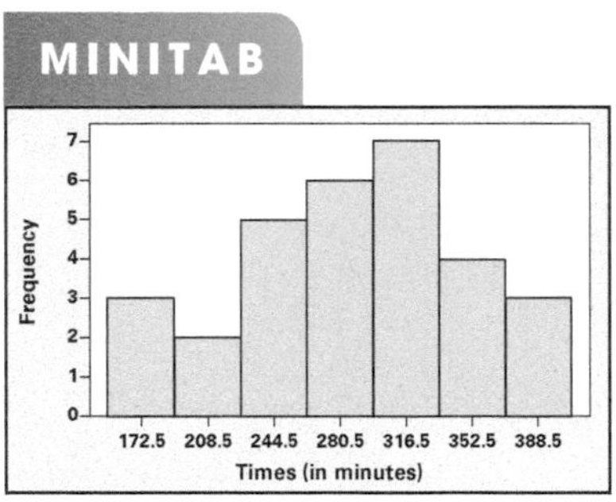


**EXCEL**

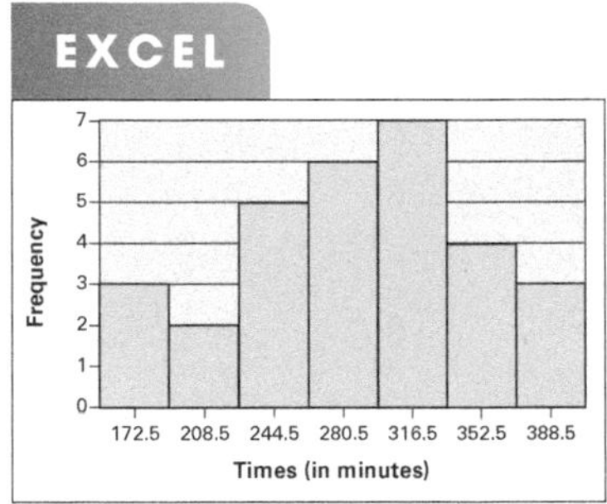


**STATCRUNCH**

155 191 227 263 299 335 371 407

Times (in minutes)

**TRY IT YOURSELF 7**

Use technology and the frequency distribution from Try It Yourself 2 to construct a frequency histogram that represents the points scored by the 55 winning teams listed on page 39.

*Answer: Page A36*

**Tech Tip**

You can use technology such as Minitab, Excel, StatCrunch, or the TI-84 Plus to create a histogram. (Detailed instructions for using Minitab, Excel, and the TI-84 Plus are shown in the technology manuals that accompany this text.) For instance, here are instructions for creating a histogram on a TI-84 Plus.

STAT ENTER

Enter midpoints in L1.
Enter frequencies in L2.

2nd STAT PLOT

Turn on Plot 1.
Highlight Histogram.

Xlist: L1

Freq: L2

ZOOM 9

# 2.1 EXERCISES

For Extra Help: MyLab Statistics

## Building Basic Skills and Vocabulary

1. What are some benefits of representing data sets using frequency distributions? What are some benefits of using graphs of frequency distributions?
2. Why should the number of classes in a frequency distribution be between 5 and 20?
3. What is the difference between class limits and class boundaries?
4. What is the difference between relative frequency and cumulative frequency?
5. After constructing an expanded frequency distribution, what should the sum of the relative frequencies be? Explain.
6. What is the difference between a frequency polygon and an ogive?

**True or False?** *In Exercises 7–10, determine whether the statement is true or false. If it is false, rewrite it as a true statement.*

7. In a frequency distribution, the class width is the distance between the lower and upper limits of a class.
8. The difference between two consecutive midpoints is equal to the class width.
9. A graph of the cumulative frequencies can decrease from left to right.
10. Class boundaries ensure that consecutive bars of a histogram touch.

*In Exercises 11–14, use the given information about the data set and the number of classes to find the class width, the lower class limits, and the upper class limits.*

11. min = 9, max = 64, 7 classes
12. min = 12, max = 88, 6 classes
13. min = 17, range = 118, 8 classes
14. max = 247, range = 93, 10 classes

**Reading a Frequency Distribution** *In Exercises 15 and 16, use the frequency distribution to find the (a) class width, (b) class midpoints, and (c) class boundaries.*

15. **Travel Time to Work (in minutes)**

| Class | Frequency, $f$ |
|---|---|
| 0–10 | 188 |
| 11–21 | 372 |
| 22–32 | 264 |
| 33–43 | 205 |
| 44–54 | 83 |
| 55–65 | 76 |
| 66–76 | 32 |

16. **Toledo, OH, Average Normal Temperatures (°F)**

| Class | Frequency, $f$ |
|---|---|
| 25–32 | 86 |
| 33–40 | 39 |
| 41–48 | 41 |
| 49–56 | 48 |
| 57–64 | 43 |
| 65–72 | 68 |
| 73–80 | 40 |

17. Use the frequency distribution in Exercise 15 to construct an expanded frequency distribution, as shown in Example 2.
18. Use the frequency distribution in Exercise 16 to construct an expanded frequency distribution, as shown in Example 2.

**Graphical Analysis** *In Exercises 19 and 20, use the frequency histogram to*

*(a) determine the number of classes.*

*(b) estimate the greatest and least frequencies.*

*(c) determine the class width.*

*(d) describe any patterns with the data.*

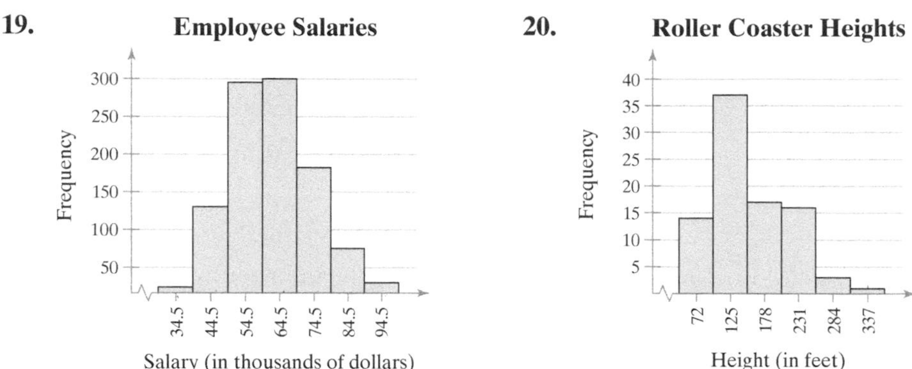


**Graphical Analysis** *In Exercises 21 and 22, use the frequency polygon to identify the class with the greatest, and the class with the least, frequency.*

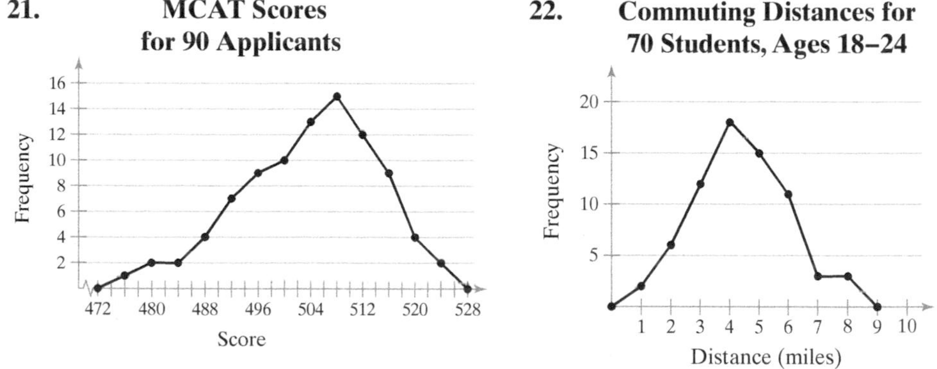


**Graphical Analysis** *In Exercises 23 and 24, use the relative frequency histogram to*

*(a) identify the class with the greatest, and the class with the least, relative frequency.*

*(b) approximate the greatest and least relative frequencies.*

*(c) describe any patterns with the data.*

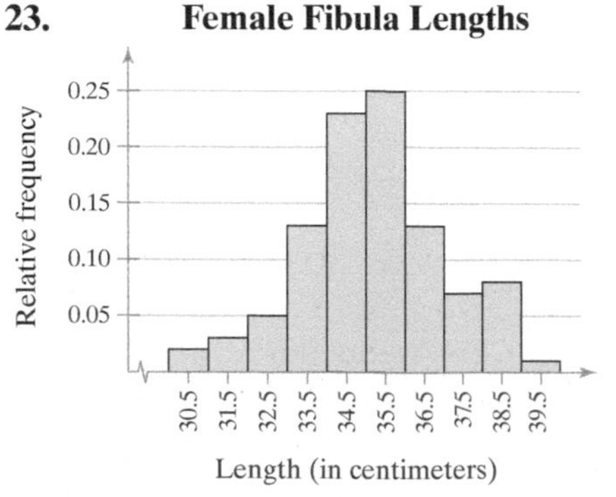


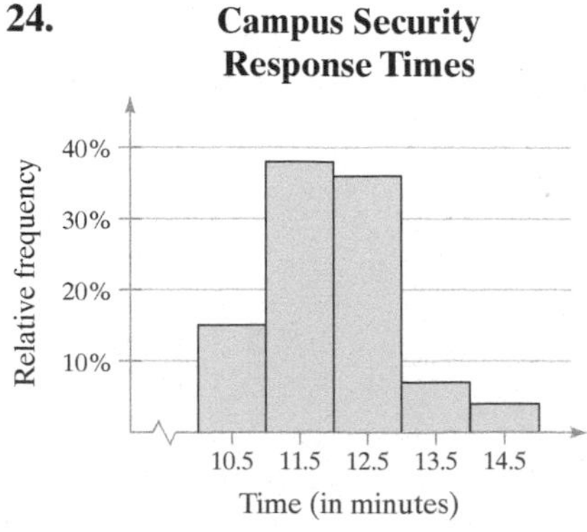

**Graphical Analysis** *In Exercises 25 and 26, use the ogive to approximate*

*(a) the number in the sample.*

*(b) the location of the greatest increase in frequency.*

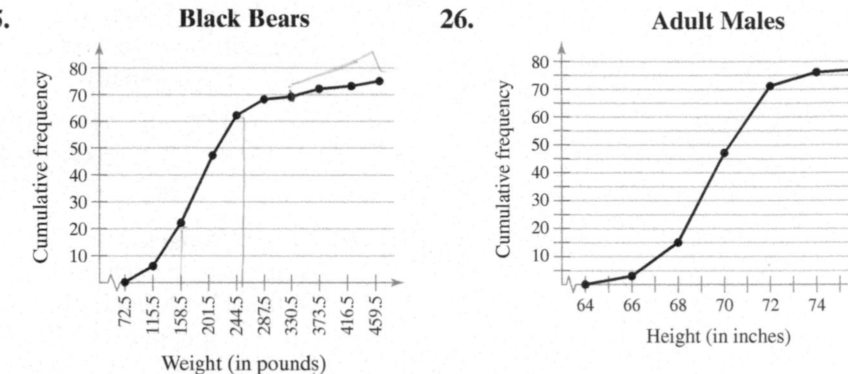


**27.** Use the ogive in Exercise 25 to approximate

(a) the cumulative frequency for a weight of 201.5 pounds.

(b) the weight for which the cumulative frequency is 68.

(c) the number of black bears that weigh between 158.5 pounds and 244.5 pounds.

(d) the number of black bears that weigh more than 330.5 pounds.

**28.** Use the ogive in Exercise 26 to approximate

(a) the cumulative frequency for a height of 72 inches.

(b) the height for which the cumulative frequency is 15.

(c) the number of adult males that are between 68 and 72 inches tall.

(d) the number of adult males that are taller than 70 inches.

## Using and Interpreting Concepts

**Constructing a Frequency Distribution** *In Exercises 29 and 30, construct a frequency distribution for the data set using the indicated number of classes. In the table, include the midpoints, relative frequencies, and cumulative frequencies. Which class has the greatest class frequency and which has the least class frequency?*

 **29. YouTube Watching Times**

Number of classes: 5

Data set: Times (in minutes) spent watching YouTube videos in a day

| | | | | | | | | | | | |
|---|---|---|---|---|---|---|---|---|---|---|---|
| 100 | 32 | 125 | 164 | 123 | 149 | 73 | 88 | 87 | 104 | 110 | 98 |
| 122 | 28 | 177 | 69 | 90 | 68 | 125 | 90 | 118 | 123 | 139 | 175 |

 **30. Textbook Spending**

Number of classes: 6

Data set: Amounts (in dollars) spent on textbooks for a semester

| | | | | | | | | | |
|---|---|---|---|---|---|---|---|---|---|
| 91 | 472 | 279 | 249 | 530 | 376 | 188 | 341 | 266 | 199 |
| 142 | 273 | 189 | 130 | 489 | 266 | 248 | 101 | 375 | 486 |
| 190 | 398 | 188 | 269 | 43 | 30 | 127 | 354 | 84 | 319 |

---

indicates that the data set for this exercise is available within MyStatLab or at *www.pearsonhighered.com/mathstatsresources.*

## Constructing a Frequency Distribution and a Frequency Histogram

*In Exercises 31–34, construct a frequency distribution and a frequency histogram for the data set using the indicated number of classes. Describe any patterns.*

 **31. Sales**

Number of classes: 6

Data set: July sales (in dollars) for 21 sales representatives at a company

| | | | | | | |
|---|---|---|---|---|---|---|
| 2114 | 2468 | 7119 | 1876 | 4105 | 3183 | 1932 |
| 1355 | 4278 | 2000 | 1077 | 5835 | 1512 | 1697 |
| 2478 | 3981 | 1643 | 1858 | 1500 | 4608 | 1000 |

 **32. Pepper Pungencies**

Number of classes: 5

Data set: Pungencies (in thousands of Scoville units) of 24 tabasco peppers

| | | | | | | | | | | | |
|---|---|---|---|---|---|---|---|---|---|---|---|
| 35 | 51 | 44 | 42 | 37 | 38 | 36 | 39 | 44 | 43 | 40 | 40 |
| 32 | 39 | 41 | 38 | 42 | 39 | 40 | 46 | 37 | 35 | 41 | 39 |

 **33. Reaction Times**

Number of classes: 8

Data set: Reaction times (in milliseconds) of 30 adult females to an auditory stimulus

| | | | | | | | | | |
|---|---|---|---|---|---|---|---|---|---|
| 507 | 389 | 305 | 291 | 336 | 310 | 514 | 442 | 373 | 428 |
| 387 | 454 | 323 | 441 | 388 | 426 | 411 | 382 | 320 | 450 |
| 309 | 416 | 359 | 388 | 307 | 337 | 469 | 351 | 422 | 413 |

 **34. Finishing Times**

Number of classes: 8

Data set: Finishing times (in seconds) of 21 participants in a 10K race

| | | | | | | |
|---|---|---|---|---|---|---|
| 3449 | 2645 | 3255 | 3712 | 4183 | 3896 | 3760 |
| 5008 | 3983 | 2855 | 3789 | 3176 | 2923 | 2281 |
| 2574 | 2252 | 4223 | 2588 | 2243 | 2837 | 3292 |

## Constructing a Frequency Distribution and a Frequency Polygon

*In Exercises 35 and 36, construct a frequency distribution and a frequency polygon for the data set using the indicated number of classes. Describe any patterns.*

 **35. Ages of the Presidents**

Number of classes: 7

Data set: Ages of the U.S. presidents at Inauguration *(Source: The White House)*

| | | | | | | | | | | | | | | | |
|---|---|---|---|---|---|---|---|---|---|---|---|---|---|---|---|
| 57 | 61 | 57 | 57 | 58 | 57 | 61 | 54 | 68 | 51 | 49 | 64 | 50 | 48 | 65 | 52 |
| 56 | 46 | 54 | 49 | 51 | 47 | 55 | 55 | 54 | 42 | 51 | 56 | 55 | 51 | 54 | 51 |
| 60 | 62 | 43 | 55 | 56 | 61 | 52 | 69 | 64 | 46 | 54 | 47 | 70 | 78 | | |

 **36. Declaration of Independence**

Number of classes: 5

Data set: Number of children of those who signed the Declaration of Independence *(Source: The U.S. National Archives & Records Administration)*

| | | | | | | | | | | | | | |
|---|---|---|---|---|---|---|---|---|---|---|---|---|---|
| 5 | 2 | 12 | 18 | 7 | 4 | 10 | 8 | 16 | 3 | 3 | 7 | 3 | 1 |
| 2 | 7 | 13 | 0 | 8 | 3 | 7 | 5 | 2 | 6 | 0 | 6 | 7 | 9 |
| 0 | 11 | 9 | 10 | 7 | 8 | 13 | 5 | 8 | 3 | 5 | 0 | 3 | 13 |
| 3 | 15 | 5 | 6 | 3 | 2 | 5 | 2 | 0 | 3 | 7 | 12 | 4 | 1 |

**Constructing a Frequency Distribution and a Relative Frequency Histogram** *In Exercises 37–40, construct a frequency distribution and a relative frequency histogram for the data set using five classes. Which class has the greatest relative frequency and which has the least relative frequency?*

**37. Taste Test**

Data set: Ratings from 1 (lowest) to 10 (highest) provided by 36 people after taste-testing a new flavor of protein bar

| | | | | | | | | |
|---|---|---|---|---|---|---|---|---|
| 2 | 6 | 9 | 2 | 9 | 9 | 6 | 10 | 5 |
| 8 | 7 | 6 | 5 | 10 | 1 | 4 | 9 | 3 |
| 4 | 5 | 3 | 6 | 5 | 2 | 4 | 9 | 2 |
| 9 | 3 | 3 | 6 | 5 | 1 | 9 | 4 | 2 |

**38. Years of Service**

Data set: Years of service of 28 Ohio state government employees

| | | | | | | |
|---|---|---|---|---|---|---|
| 13 | 8 | 10 | 9 | 10 | 9 | 13 |
| 11 | 10 | 11 | 7 | 9 | 14 | 13 |
| 11 | 12 | 8 | 15 | 13 | 10 | 9 |
| 11 | 10 | 12 | 14 | 9 | 15 | 19 |

**39. Fijian Banded Iguanas**

Data set: Lengths (in centimeters) of 28 adult Fijian banded iguanas

| | | | | | | |
|---|---|---|---|---|---|---|
| 68 | 65 | 70 | 61 | 60 | 60 | 69 |
| 61 | 64 | 74 | 64 | 62 | 70 | 70 |
| 63 | 75 | 74 | 71 | 70 | 66 | 72 |
| 64 | 67 | 66 | 70 | 73 | 72 | 70 |

**40. Triglyceride Levels**

Data set: Triglyceride levels (in milligrams per deciliter of blood) of 28 patients

| | | | | | | |
|---|---|---|---|---|---|---|
| 209 | 140 | 155 | 170 | 265 | 138 | 180 |
| 295 | 250 | 320 | 270 | 225 | 215 | 390 |
| 420 | 462 | 150 | 200 | 400 | 295 | 240 |
| 200 | 190 | 145 | 160 | 175 | 195 | 223 |

**Constructing a Cumulative Frequency Distribution and an Ogive**

*In Exercises 41 and 42, construct a cumulative frequency distribution and an ogive for the data set using six classes. Then describe the location of the greatest increase in frequency.*

**41. Retirement Ages**

Data set: Retirement ages of 35 English professors

| | | | | | | |
|---|---|---|---|---|---|---|
| 72 | 62 | 55 | 61 | 53 | 62 | 65 |
| 66 | 69 | 55 | 66 | 63 | 67 | 69 |
| 55 | 65 | 67 | 57 | 67 | 68 | 73 |
| 75 | 65 | 54 | 71 | 57 | 52 | 58 |
| 58 | 71 | 72 | 67 | 63 | 65 | 61 |

**42. Saturated Fat Intakes**

Data set: Daily saturated fat intakes (in grams) of 28 people

| | | | | | | |
|---|---|---|---|---|---|---|
| 18 | 12 | 14 | 19 | 20 | 26 | 12 |
| 17 | 19 | 13 | 8 | 20 | 25 | 16 |
| 13 | 14 | 22 | 16 | 11 | 13 | 17 |
| 14 | 15 | 11 | 13 | 15 | 23 | 7 |

*In Exercises 43 and 44, use the data set and the indicated number of classes to construct (a) an expanded frequency distribution, (b) a frequency histogram, (c) a frequency polygon, (d) a relative frequency histogram, and (e) an ogive.*

**43. Pulse Rates**

Number of classes: 6

Data set: Pulse rates of all students in a class

68 105 95 80 90 100 75 70 84 98 102 70
65 88 90 75 78 94 110 120 95 80 76 108

**44. Hospitals**

Number of classes: 8

Data set: Number of hospitals in each of the 50 U.S. states and 5 inhabited territories *(Source: American Hospital Directory)*

10 90 51 1 77 341 56 34 8 214 111
3 14 40 18 142 102 55 75 108 72 53
19 105 55 83 1 69 19 108 10 27 14
78 37 31 186 146 90 37 177 52 11 67
25 100 361 35 91 2 7 61 78 33 14

## Extending Concepts

**45. What Would You Do?** You work at a bank and are asked to recommend the amount of cash to put in an ATM each day. You do not want to put in too much (which would cause security concerns) or too little (which may create customer irritation). The daily withdrawals (in hundreds of dollars) for 30 days are listed.

72 84 61 76 104 76 86 92 80 88 98 76 97 82 84
67 70 81 82 89 74 73 86 81 85 78 82 80 91 83

(a) Construct a relative frequency histogram for the data. Use 8 classes.

(b) If you put $9000 in the ATM each day, what percent of the days in a month should you expect to run out of cash? Explain.

(c) If you are willing to run out of cash on 10% of the days, how much cash should you put in the ATM each day? Explain.

**46. What Would You Do?** The admissions department for a college is asked to recommend the minimum SAT scores that the college will accept for full-time students. The SAT scores of 50 applicants are listed.

1170 1000 910 870 1070 1290 920 1470 1080 1180
770 900 1120 1070 1370 1160 970 930 1240 1270
1250 1330 1010 1010 1410 1130 1210 1240 960 820
650 1010 1190 1500 1400 1270 1310 1050 950 1150
1450 1290 1310 1100 1330 1410 840 1040 1090 1080

(a) Construct a relative frequency histogram for the data. Use 10 classes.

(b) If you set the minimum score at 1070, what percent of the applicants will meet this requirement? Explain.

(c) If you want to accept the top 88% of the applicants, what should the minimum score be? Explain.

**47. Writing** Use the data set listed and technology to create frequency histograms with 5, 10, and 20 classes. Which graph displays the data best? Explain.

2 7 3 2 11 3 15 8 4 9 10 13 9
7 11 10 1 2 12 5 6 4 2 9 15 14

# 2.2 More Graphs and Displays

## What You Should Learn

- How to graph and interpret quantitative data sets using stem-and-leaf plots and dot plots
- How to graph and interpret qualitative data sets using pie charts and Pareto charts
- How to graph and interpret paired data sets using scatter plots and time series charts

Graphing Quantitative Data Sets ■ Graphing Qualitative Data Sets ■ Graphing Paired Data Sets

## Graphing Quantitative Data Sets

In Section 2.1, you learned several ways to display quantitative data graphically. In this section, you will learn more ways to display quantitative data, beginning with **stem-and-leaf plots.** Stem-and-leaf plots are examples of **exploratory data analysis (EDA),** which was developed by John Tukey in 1977.

In a stem-and-leaf plot, each number is separated into a **stem** (for instance, the entry's leftmost digits) and a **leaf** (for instance, the rightmost digit). You should have as many leaves as there are entries in the original data set and the leaves should be single digits. A stem-and-leaf plot is similar to a histogram but has the advantage that the graph still contains the original data. Another advantage of a stem-and-leaf plot is that it provides an easy way to sort data.

**EXAMPLE 1**

### Constructing a Stem-and-Leaf Plot

The data set at the left lists the number of text messages sent in one day by 50 U.S. adults. Display the data in a stem-and-leaf plot. Describe any patterns.

| Number of Text Messages Sent | | | | |
|---|---|---|---|---|
| 75 | 49 | 104 | 59 | 88 |
| 123 | 75 | 109 | 68 | 81 |
| 66 | 80 | 78 | 69 | 55 |
| 76 | 114 | 98 | 73 | 18 |
| 42 | 84 | 46 | 52 | 25 |
| 25 | 26 | 33 | 25 | 20 |
| 32 | 24 | 43 | 17 | 49 |
| 27 | 32 | 29 | 29 | 40 |
| 23 | 33 | 30 | 41 | 35 |
| 38 | 36 | 54 | 30 | 148 |

**SOLUTION**

Because the data entries go from a low of 17 to a high of 148, you should use stem values from 1 to 14. To construct the plot, list these stems to the left of a vertical line. For each data entry, list a leaf to the right of its stem. For instance, the entry 104 has a stem of 10 and a leaf of 4. Make the plot with the leaves in increasing order from left to right. Be sure to include a key.

**Number of Text Messages Sent**

| Stem | Leaves |
|---|---|
| 1 | 7 8     Key: 10\|4 = 104 |
| 2 | 0 3 4 5 5 5 6 7 9 9 |
| 3 | 0 0 2 2 3 3 5 6 8 |
| 4 | 0 1 2 3 6 9 9 |
| 5 | 2 4 5 9 |
| 6 | 6 8 9 |
| 7 | 3 5 5 6 8 |
| 8 | 0 1 4 8 |
| 9 | 8 |
| 10 | 4 9 |
| 11 | 4 |
| 12 | 3 |
| 13 | |
| 14 | 8 |

***Interpretation*** From the display, you can see that more than 50% of the cell phone users sent between 20 and 50 text messages.

**Study Tip**

It is important to include a key for a stem-and-leaf plot to identify the data entries. This is done by showing an entry represented by a stem and one leaf.

**Tech Tip**

You can use technology such as Minitab, StatCrunch, or Excel (with the XLSTAT add-in) to construct a stem-and-leaf plot. For instance, a StatCrunch stem-and-leaf plot for the data in Example 1 is shown below.

**STATCRUNCH**

**Variable: Number of text messages sent**

```
Decimal point is 1 digit(s)
to the right of the colon.
Leaf unit = 1
 1 : 78
 2 : 0345556799
 3 : 002233568
 4 : 0123699
 5 : 2459
 6 : 689
 7 : 35568
 8 : 0148
 9 : 8
10 : 49
11 : 4
12 : 3
13 :
14 : 8
```

**Study Tip**

You can use stem-and-leaf plots to identify unusual data entries called *outliers*. In Examples 1 and 2, the data entry 148 is an outlier. You will learn more about outliers in Section 2.3.

**TRY IT YOURSELF 1**

Use a stem-and-leaf plot to organize the points scored by the 55 winning teams listed on page 39. Describe any patterns. *Answer: Page A36*

## EXAMPLE 2

### Constructing Variations of Stem-and-Leaf Plots

Organize the data set in Example 1 using a stem-and-leaf plot that has two rows for each stem. Describe any patterns.

**SOLUTION**

Use the stem-and-leaf plot from Example 1, except now list each stem twice. Use the leaves 0, 1, 2, 3, and 4 in the first stem row and the leaves 5, 6, 7, 8, and 9 in the second stem row. The revised stem-and-leaf plot is shown. Notice that by using two rows per stem, you obtain a more detailed picture of the data.

**Number of Text Messages Sent**

| Stem | Leaves |
|---|---|
| 1 | Key: 10\|4 = 104 |
| 1 | 7 8 |
| 2 | 0 3 4 |
| 2 | 5 5 5 6 7 9 9 |
| 3 | 0 0 2 2 3 3 |
| 3 | 5 6 8 |
| 4 | 0 1 2 3 |
| 4 | 6 9 9 |
| 5 | 2 4 |
| 5 | 5 9 |
| 6 | |
| 6 | 6 8 9 |
| 7 | 3 |
| 7 | 5 5 6 8 |
| 8 | 0 1 4 |
| 8 | 8 |
| 9 | |
| 9 | 8 |
| 10 | 4 |
| 10 | 9 |
| 11 | 4 |
| 11 | |
| 12 | 3 |
| 12 | |
| 13 | |
| 13 | |
| 14 | |
| 14 | 8 |

***Interpretation*** From the display, you can see that most of the cell phone users sent between 20 and 80 text messages.

**TRY IT YOURSELF 2**

Using two rows for each stem, revise the stem-and-leaf plot you constructed in Try It Yourself 1. Describe any patterns. *Answer: Page A36*

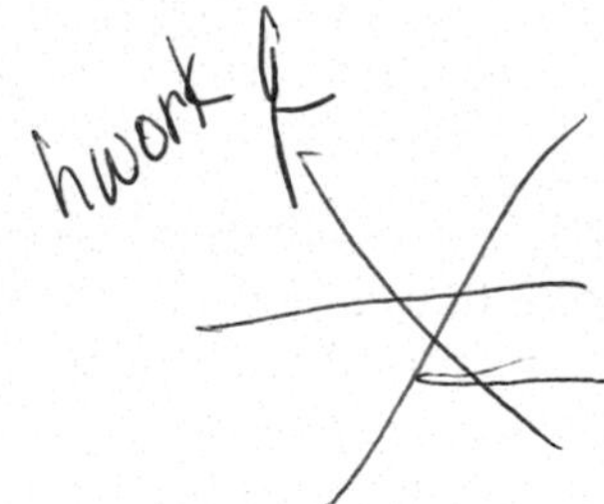

You can also use a dot plot to graph quantitative data. In a **dot plot,** each data entry is plotted, using a point, above a horizontal axis. Like a stem-and-leaf plot, a dot plot allows you to see how data are distributed, to determine specific data entries, and to identify unusual data entries.

**EXAMPLE 3**

### Constructing a Dot Plot

Use a dot plot to organize the data set in Example 1. Describe any patterns.

| Number of Text Messages Sent | | | | | | | | | |
|---|---|---|---|---|---|---|---|---|---|
| 75 | 49 | 104 | 59 | 88 | 123 | 75 | 109 | 68 | 81 |
| 66 | 80 | 78 | 69 | 55 | 76 | 114 | 98 | 73 | 18 |
| 42 | 84 | 46 | 52 | 25 | 25 | 26 | 33 | 25 | 20 |
| 32 | 24 | 43 | 17 | 49 | 27 | 32 | 29 | 29 | 40 |
| 23 | 33 | 30 | 41 | 35 | 38 | 36 | 54 | 30 | 148 |

**SOLUTION**

So that each data entry is included in the dot plot, the horizontal axis should include numbers between 15 and 150. To represent a data entry, plot a point above the entry's position on the axis. When an entry is repeated, plot another point above the previous point.

**Number of Text Messages Sent**

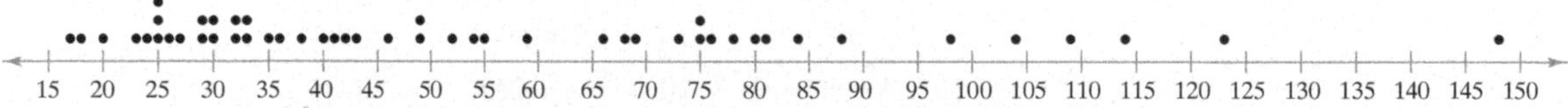


For help with the number line and ordering numbers, see *Integrated Review* at

MyLab Statistics

***Interpretation*** From the dot plot, you can see that most entries occur between 20 and 80 and only five people sent more than 100 text messages. You can also see that 148 is an unusual data entry.

**TRY IT YOURSELF 3**

Use a dot plot to organize the points scored by the 55 winning teams listed on page 39. Describe any patterns.

*Answer: Page A36*

Technology can be used to construct dot plots. For instance, Minitab and StatCrunch dot plots for the text messaging data are shown below.

**MINITAB**

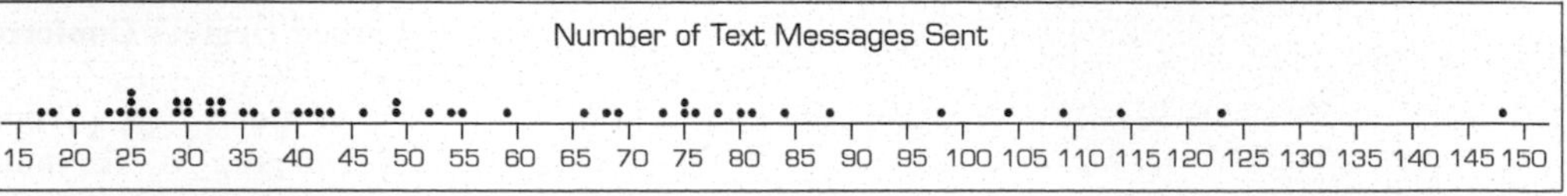


**STATCRUNCH**

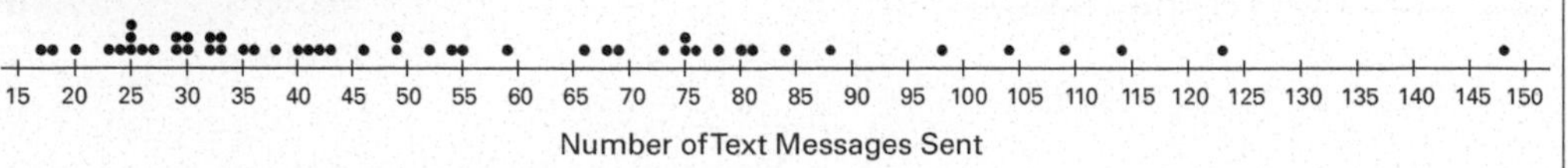

## Graphing Qualitative Data Sets

Pie charts provide a convenient way to present qualitative data graphically as percents of a whole. A **pie chart** is a circle that is divided into sectors that represent categories. The area of each sector is proportional to the frequency of each category. In most cases, you will be interpreting a pie chart or constructing one using technology. Example 4 shows how to construct a pie chart by hand.

**EXAMPLE 4**

### Constructing a Pie Chart

The number of earned degrees conferred (in thousands) in 2019 are shown in the table at the right. Use a pie chart to organize the data. *(Source: U.S. National Center for Education Statistics)*

**Earned Degrees Conferred in 2019**

| Type of degree | Number (in thousands) |
|---|---|
| Associate's | 1037 |
| Bachelor's | 2013 |
| Master's | 834 |
| Doctoral | 188 |

**SOLUTION**

Begin by finding the relative frequency, or percent, of each category. Then construct the pie chart using the central angle that corresponds to each category. To find the central angle, multiply 360° by the category's relative frequency. For instance, the central angle for associate's degrees is 360°(0.255) ≈ 91.8°.

| Type of degree | $f$ | Relative frequency | Angle |
|---|---|---|---|
| Associate's | 1037 | 0.255 | 91.8° |
| Bachelor's | 2013 | 0.494 | 177.8° |
| Master's | 834 | 0.205 | 73.8° |
| Doctoral | 188 | 0.046 | 16.6° |

**Earned Degrees Conferred in 2019**

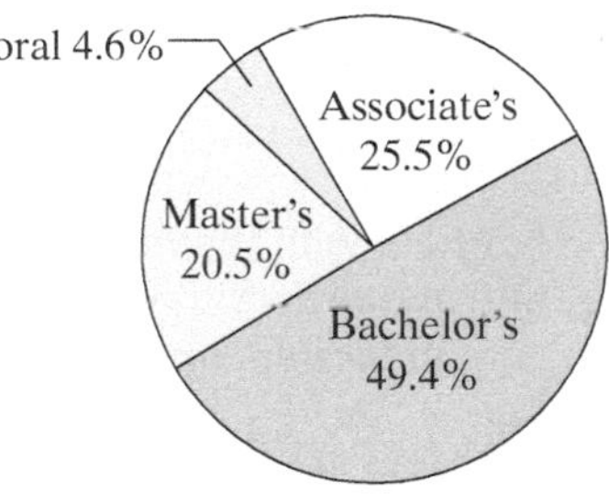


***Interpretation*** From the pie chart, you can see that almost one half of the degrees conferred in 2019 were bachelor's degrees.

**TRY IT YOURSELF 4**

The number of earned degrees conferred (in thousands) in 2010 are shown in the table. Use a pie chart to organize the data. Compare the 2010 data with the 2019 data. *(Source: U.S. National Center for Education Statistics)*

**Earned Degrees Conferred in 2010**

| Type of degree | Number (in thousands) |
|---|---|
| Associate's | 849 |
| Bachelor's | 1650 |
| Master's | 693 |
| Doctoral | 159 |

*Answer: Page A36*

**EXCEL**

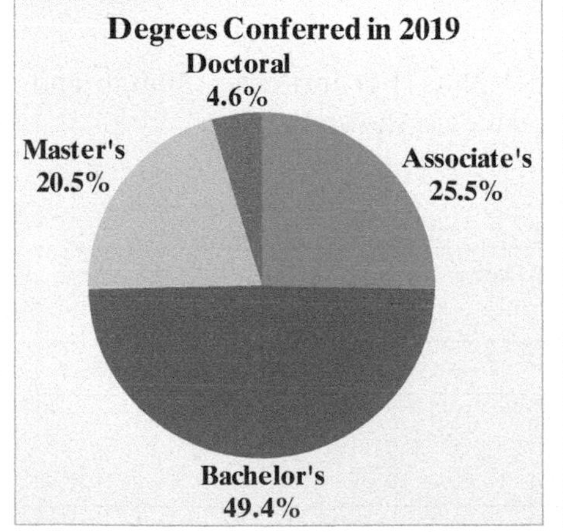


You can use technology to construct a pie chart. For instance, an Excel pie chart for the degrees conferred in 2019 is shown at the left.

Another way to graph qualitative data is to use a Pareto chart. A **Pareto chart** is a vertical bar graph in which the height of each bar represents frequency or relative frequency. The bars are positioned in order of decreasing height, with the tallest bar positioned at the left. Such positioning helps highlight important data and is used frequently in business.

## Picturing the World

According to data from the U.S. Bureau of Labor Statistics, earnings increase as educational attainment rises. The average weekly earnings data by educational attainment are shown in the Pareto chart. (Source: U.S. Bureau of Labor Statistics)

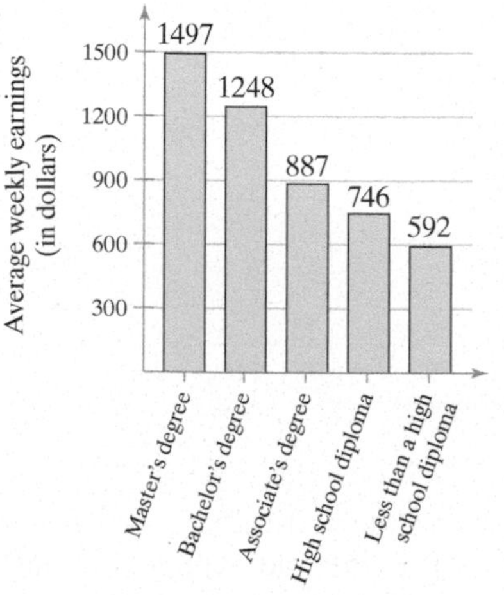


**The average employee with an associate's degree makes how much more in a year (52 weeks) than the average employee with a high school diploma?**

**EXAMPLE 5**

### Constructing a Pareto Chart

In 2019, these were the top five causes of death in the United States.

Accidents: 173,040

Cancer: 599,601

Chronic lower respiratory diseases: 156,979

Heart disease: 659,041

Stroke (cerebrovascular diseases): 150,005

Use a Pareto chart to organize the data. What was the leading cause of death in the United States in 2019? *(Source: National Center for Health Statistics)*

**SOLUTION**

Using frequencies for the vertical axis, you can construct the Pareto chart as shown.

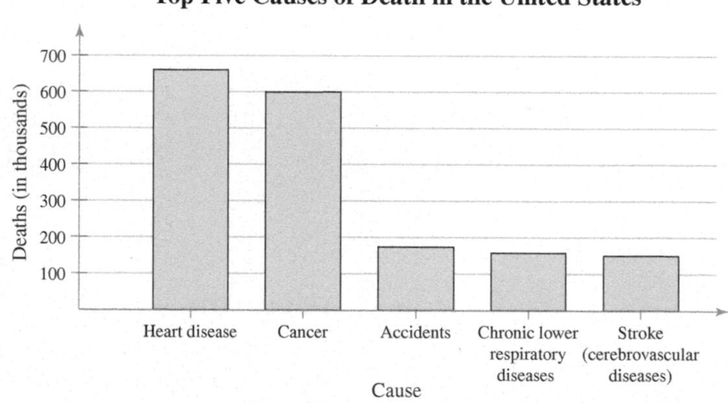


***Interpretation*** From the Pareto chart, you can see that the leading cause of death in the United States in 2019 was heart disease. Also, heart disease and cancer caused more deaths than the other three causes combined.

**TRY IT YOURSELF 5**

Every year, the Better Business Bureau (BBB) receives complaints from customers. Here are some complaints the BBB received in 2019.

5987 complaints about roofing contractors

14,878 complaints about collections agencies

10,871 complaints about insurance companies

23,848 complaints about new car dealers

1687 complaints about Internet marketing services

Use a Pareto chart to organize the data. Which of the industries listed is the greatest source of complaints? *(Source: Better Business Bureau)*

*Answer: Page A36*

## Graphing Paired Data Sets

When each entry in one data set corresponds to one entry in a second data set, the sets are called **paired data sets.** For instance, a data set contains the costs of an item and a second data set contains sales amounts for the item at each cost. Because each cost corresponds to a sales amount, the data sets are paired. One way to graph paired data sets is to use a **scatter plot,** where the ordered pairs are graphed as points in a coordinate plane. A scatter plot is used to show the relationship between two quantitative variables.

**EXAMPLE 6**

### Interpreting a Scatter Plot

The British statistician Ronald Fisher (see page 35) introduced a famous data set called Fisher's Iris data set. This data set describes various physical characteristics, such as petal length and petal width (in millimeters), for three species of iris. In the scatter plot shown, the petal lengths form the first data set and the petal widths form the second data set. As the petal length increases, what tends to happen to the petal width? *(Source: Fisher, R. A., 1936)*

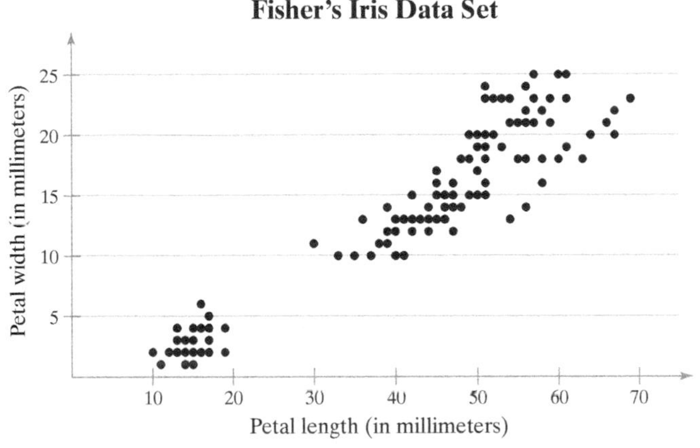


**SOLUTION**

The horizontal axis represents the petal length, and the vertical axis represents the petal width. Each point in the scatter plot represents the petal length and petal width of one flower.

***Interpretation*** From the scatter plot, you can see that as the petal length increases, the petal width also tends to increase.

**TRY IT YOURSELF 6**

The lengths of employment and the salaries of 10 employees are listed in the table below. Graph the data using a scatter plot. Describe any trends.

| Length of employment (in years) | 5 | 4 | 8 | 4 | 2 |
|---|---|---|---|---|---|
| Salary (in dollars) | 36,000 | 36,500 | 45,000 | 31,350 | 28,000 |

| Length of employment (in years) | 10 | 7 | 6 | 9 | 3 |
|---|---|---|---|---|---|
| Salary (in dollars) | 48,000 | 46,650 | 44,225 | 50,100 | 32,000 |

*Answer: Page A36*

You will learn more about scatter plots and how to analyze them in Chapter 9.

A data set that is composed of quantitative entries taken at regular intervals over a period of time is called a **time series.** For instance, the amount of precipitation measured each day for one month is a time series. You can use a **time series chart** to graph a time series.

## EXAMPLE 7

See Minitab and TI-84 Plus steps on pages 124 and 125.

### Constructing a Time Series Chart

The table lists the numbers of burglaries (in millions) and robberies (in thousands) in the United States for the years 2009 through 2019. Construct a time series chart for the number of burglaries. Describe any trends. *(Source: Federal Bureau of Investigation, Crime in the United States)*

| Year | Burglaries (in millions) | Robberies (in thousands) |
|---|---|---|
| 2009 | 2.20 | 409 |
| 2010 | 2.17 | 369 |
| 2011 | 2.19 | 355 |
| 2012 | 2.11 | 355 |
| 2013 | 1.93 | 345 |
| 2014 | 1.71 | 323 |
| 2015 | 1.59 | 328 |
| 2016 | 1.52 | 333 |
| 2017 | 1.40 | 321 |
| 2018 | 1.24 | 281 |
| 2019 | 1.12 | 268 |

**SOLUTION**

Let the horizontal axis represent the years and let the vertical axis represent the numbers of burglaries (in millions). Then plot the paired data and connect them with line segments

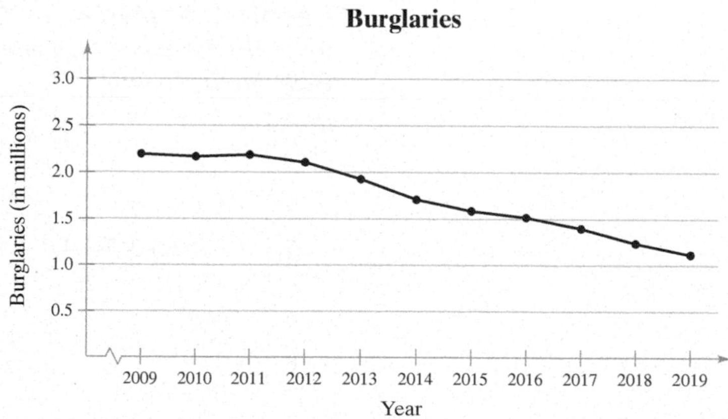


***Interpretation*** The time series chart shows that the number of burglaries remained about the same until 2011 and then decreased through 2019.

**TRY IT YOURSELF 7**

Use the table in Example 7 to construct a time series chart for the number of robberies for the years 2009 through 2019. Describe any trends.

*Answer: Page A36*

# 2.2 EXERCISES

For Extra Help: MyLab Statistics

## Building Basic Skills and Vocabulary

1. Name some ways to display quantitative data graphically. Name some ways to display qualitative data graphically.

2. What is an advantage of using a stem-and-leaf plot instead of a histogram? What is a disadvantage?

3. In terms of displaying data, how is a stem-and-leaf plot similar to a dot plot?

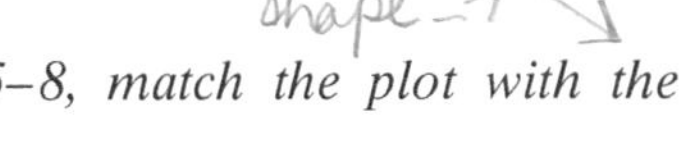

4. How is a Pareto chart different from a standard vertical bar graph?

**Putting Graphs in Context** *In Exercises 5–8, match the plot with the description of the sample.*

**5.** Key: 0|8 = 0.8

| | |
|---|---|
| 0 | 8 |
| 1 | 5 6 8 |
| 2 | 1 3 4 5 |
| 3 | 0 9 |
| 4 | 0 0 |

**6.** Key: 6|7 = 67

| | |
|---|---|
| 6 | 7 8 |
| 7 | 4 5 5 8 8 8 |
| 8 | 1 3 5 5 8 8 9 |
| 9 | 0 0 0 2 4 |

**7.**

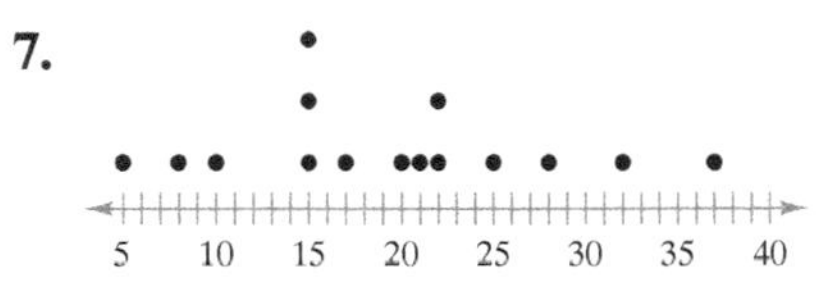


**8.**

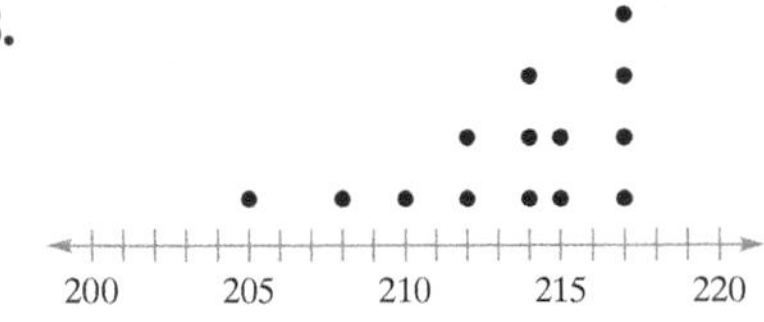


(a) Times (in minutes) it takes a sample of employees to drive to work

(b) Grade point averages of a sample of students with finance majors

(c) Top speeds (in miles per hour) of a sample of high-performance sports cars

(d) Ages (in years) of a sample of residents of a retirement home

**Graphical Analysis** *In Exercises 9–12, use the stem-and-leaf plot or dot plot to list the actual data entries. What is the maximum data entry? What is the minimum data entry?*

**9.** Key: 2|7 = 27

| | |
|---|---|
| 2 | 7 |
| 3 | 2 |
| 4 | 1 3 3 4 7 7 8 |
| 5 | 0 1 1 2 3 3 3 4 4 4 4 5 6 6 8 9 |
| 6 | 8 8 8 |
| 7 | 3 8 8 |
| 8 | 5 |

**10.**

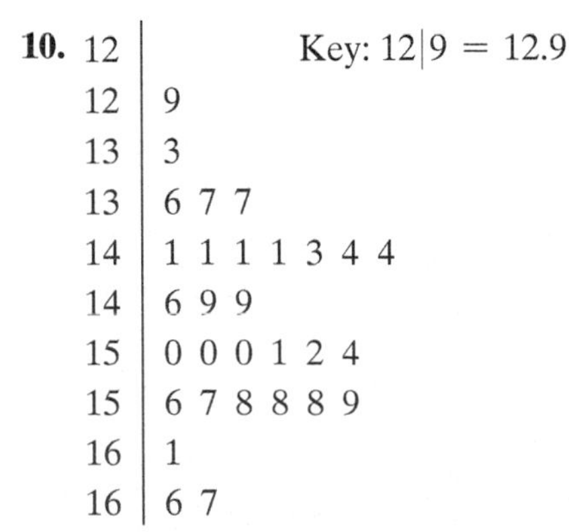

Key: 12|9 = 12.9

| | |
|---|---|
| 12 | |
| 12 | 9 |
| 13 | 3 |
| 13 | 6 7 7 |
| 14 | 1 1 1 1 3 4 4 |
| 14 | 6 9 9 |
| 15 | 0 0 0 1 2 4 |
| 15 | 6 7 8 8 8 9 |
| 16 | 1 |
| 16 | 6 7 |

**11.**

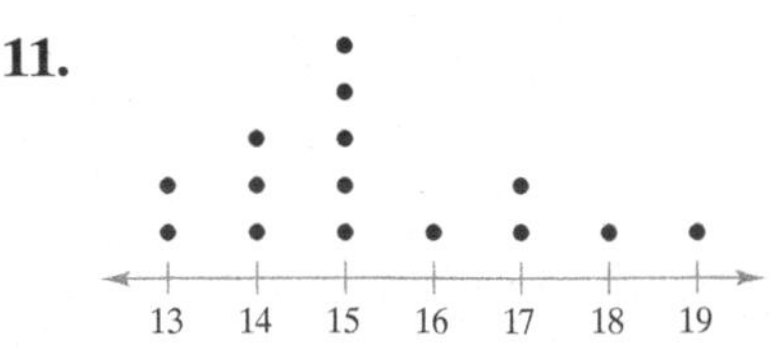


**12.**

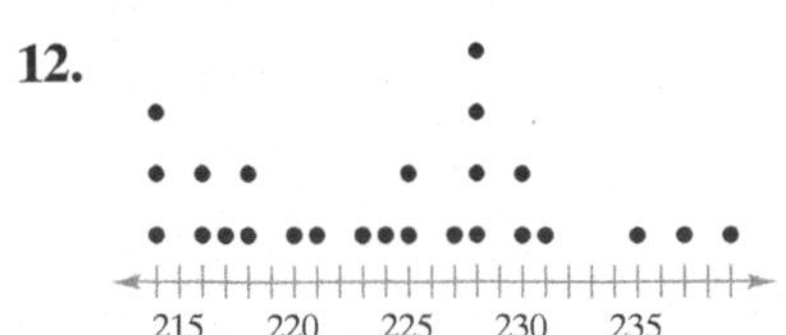

## Using and Interpreting Concepts

**Graphical Analysis** *In Exercises 13–16, give three observations that can be made from the graph.*

**13.**

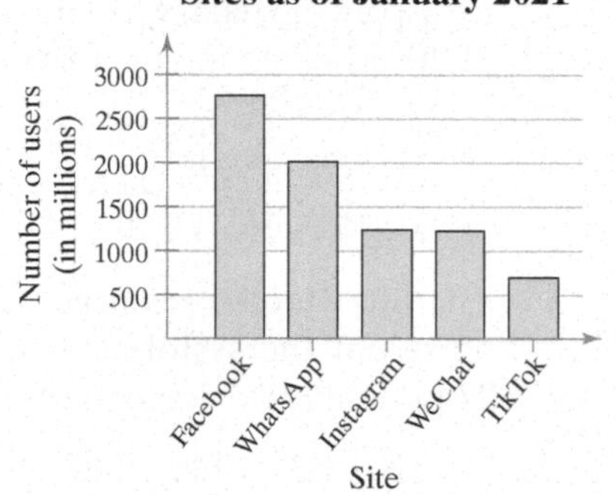


*(Source: Statista)*

**14.**

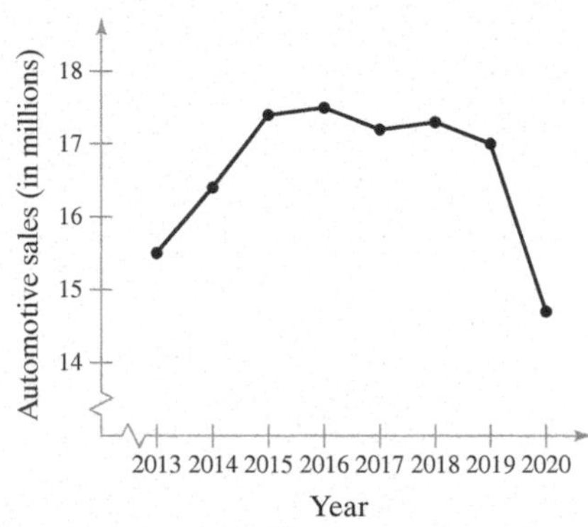


*(Source: U.S. Bureau of Economic Analysis)*

**15.**

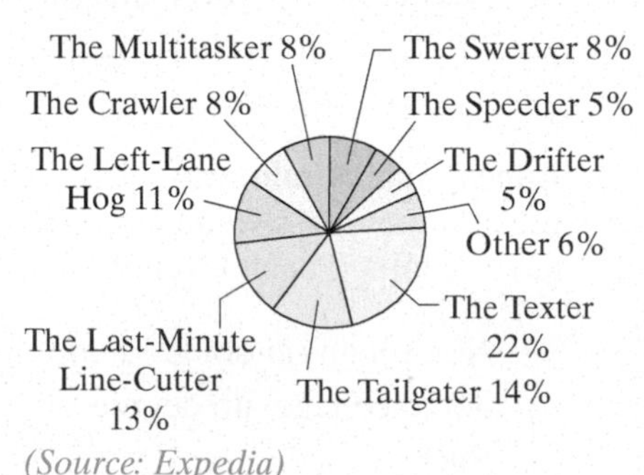


*(Source: Expedia)*

**16.**

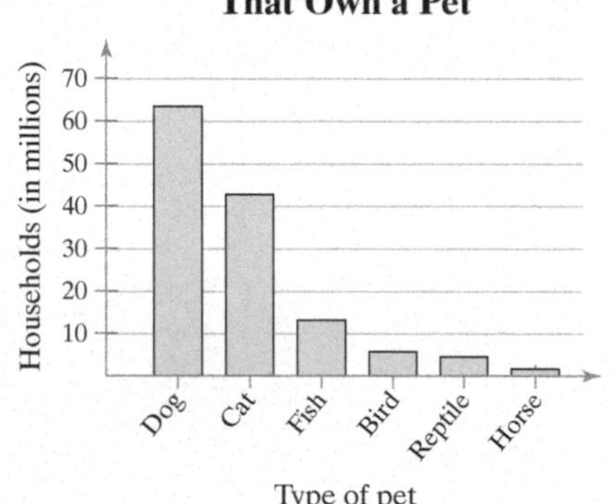


*(Source: American Pet Products Association)*

**Graphing Data Sets** *In Exercises 17–32, organize the data using the indicated type of graph. Describe any patterns.*

**17. Exam Scores** Use a stem-and-leaf plot to display the data, which represent the scores of a biology class on a midterm exam.

75 85 90 80 87 67 82 88 95 91 73 80
83 92 94 68 75 91 79 95 87 76 91 85

**18. Nursing** Use a stem-and-leaf plot to display the data, which represent the number of hours 24 nurses work per week.

40 40 35 48 38 40 36 50 32 36 40 35
30 24 40 36 40 36 40 39 33 40 32 38

**19. Ice Thickness** Use a stem-and-leaf plot to display the data, which represent the thicknesses (in centimeters) of ice measured at 20 different locations on a frozen lake.

5.8 6.4 6.9 7.2 5.1 4.9 4.3 5.8 7.0 6.8
8.1 7.5 7.2 6.9 5.8 7.2 8.0 7.0 6.9 5.9

**20. Tomato Prices** Use a stem-and-leaf plot to display the data shown in the table at the left, which represent the monthly average prices (in dollars per pound) charged by 30 retail outlets for fresh tomatoes.

| Tomato prices (in dollars per pound) | | | | |
|---|---|---|---|---|
| 1.71 | 1.60 | 1.83 | 1.64 | 2.07 |
| 2.08 | 1.54 | 1.78 | 1.82 | 1.91 |
| 1.57 | 1.64 | 1.74 | 1.87 | 1.61 |
| 2.13 | 1.63 | 1.79 | 2.07 | 1.68 |
| 1.97 | 1.61 | 1.93 | 1.98 | 1.66 |
| 2.11 | 1.77 | 1.89 | 1.86 | 1.78 |

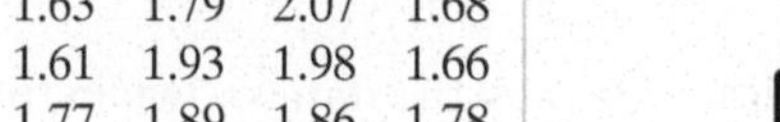

TABLE FOR EXERCISE 20

**21. Highest-Paid Athletes** Use a stem-and-leaf plot that has two rows for each stem to display the data, which represent the incomes (in millions) of the top 30 highest-paid athletes. *(Source: Forbes Media LLC)*

39 42 41 45 48 48 106 45 88 54 61 37 62 74 40
47 56 57 105 96 37 48 41 64 52 47 45 59 49 104

**22. Electoral Votes** Use a stem-and-leaf plot that has two rows for each stem to display the data, which represent the number of electoral votes for each of the 50 states and the District of Columbia. *(Source: U.S. Census Bureau)*

9 3 11 6 55 9 7 3 3 29 16 4 4 20 11 6 6
8 8 4 10 11 16 10 6 10 3 5 6 4 14 5 29 15
3 18 7 7 20 4 9 3 11 38 6 3 13 12 5 10 3

**23. Systolic Blood Pressures** Use a dot plot to display the data, which represent the systolic blood pressures (in millimeters of mercury) of 24 patients at a doctor's office.

120 135 140 145 130 150 120 170 145 125 130 110
160 180 200 150 200 135 140 120 130 170 165 140

**24. Life Spans of Houseflies** Use a dot plot to display the data, which represent the life spans (in days) of 30 houseflies.

9 9 4 11 10 5 13 9 7 11 6 8 14 10 6
10 10 7 14 11 7 8 6 13 10 14 14 8 13 10

**25. Educational Attainment** Use a pie chart to display the data, which represent the number of civilian noninstitutionalized U.S. adults (in millions) that have obtained each level of education. *(Source: U.S. Census Bureau)*

| | | | |
|---|---|---|---|
| Not a high school graduate | 26.6 | High school graduate | 70.9 |
| Some college, no degree | 45.0 | Associate's degree | 24.5 |
| Bachelor's degree | 53.3 | Master's degree | 22.5 |
| Doctoral or professional degree | 7.7 | | |

**26. London Marathon** Use a pie chart to display the data, which represent the number of men's London Marathon winners from each country through 2020. *(Source: Britannica)*

| | | | | | |
|---|---|---|---|---|---|
| United States | 2 | Norway | 1 | United Kingdom | 6 |
| Japan | 2 | Denmark | 1 | Kenya | 15 |
| Soviet Union | 1 | Portugal | 3 | Mexico | 3 |
| Spain | 1 | Morocco | 2 | Ethiopia | 4 |

**27. Smartphone Sales** The five best-selling smartphone manufacturers of 2020 were Apple (206.1 million units), Huawei (189.0 million units), Samsung (266.7 million units), vivo (111.7 million units), and Xiaomi (147.8 million units). Use a Pareto chart to display the data. *(Source: International Data Corporation)*

**28. Causes of Death** The top five causes of death worldwide from January 1, 2020 through March 11, 2021, were lower respiratory infections (about 2,971,000), stroke (about 7,809,000), chronic obstructive pulmonary disease (about 3,910,000), ischemic heart disease (about 10,890,000), and COVID-19 (about 3,068,000). Use a Pareto chart to display the data. *(Source: Institute for Health Metrics and Evaluation)*

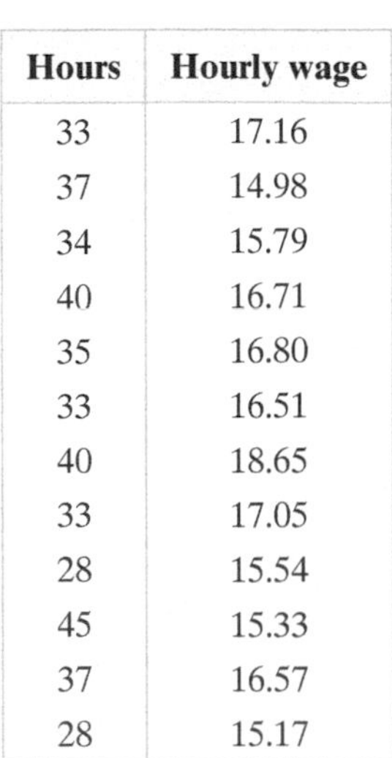

| Hours | Hourly wage |
|---|---|
| 33 | 17.16 |
| 37 | 14.98 |
| 34 | 15.79 |
| 40 | 16.71 |
| 35 | 16.80 |
| 33 | 16.51 |
| 40 | 18.65 |
| 33 | 17.05 |
| 28 | 15.54 |
| 45 | 15.33 |
| 37 | 16.57 |
| 28 | 15.17 |

TABLE FOR EXERCISE 29

**29. Hourly Wages** Use a scatter plot to display the data shown in the table at the left. The data represent the number of hours worked and the hourly wages (in dollars) of 12 production workers.

| Number of students per teacher | Average teacher's salary |
|---|---|
| 16.6 | 66.4 |
| 22.8 | 45.4 |
| 24.3 | 72.5 |
| 16.2 | 50.9 |
| 15.6 | 55.2 |
| 20.6 | 56.7 |
| 13.2 | 77.0 |
| 22.2 | 59.8 |
| 23.0 | 46.0 |
| 14.1 | 45.4 |

TABLE FOR EXERCISE 30

**30. Salaries** Use a scatter plot to display the data shown in the table at the left. The data represent the number of students per teacher and the average teacher salaries (in thousands of dollars) of 10 school districts.

**31. Engineering Degrees** Use a time series chart to display the data shown in the table. The data represent the number of bachelor's degrees in engineering (in thousands) conferred in the U.S. *(Source: U.S. Deapartment of Education)*

| **Year** | 2011 | 2012 | 2013 | 2014 | 2015 | 2016 | 2017 | 2018 | 2019 |
|---|---|---|---|---|---|---|---|---|---|
| **Degrees** | 93.1 | 98.7 | 103.0 | 109.0 | 115.1 | 123.9 | 133.8 | 140.7 | 146.3 |

**32. Manufacturing** Use a time series chart to display the data shown in the table. The data represent the percentages of the U.S. gross domestic product (GDP) that come from the manufacturing sector. *(Source: U.S. Bureau of Economic Analysis)*

| **Year** | 2008 | 2009 | 2010 | 2011 | 2012 | 2013 |
|---|---|---|---|---|---|---|
| **Percent** | 12.2% | 11.8% | 12.0% | 12.0% | 11.9% | 11.9% |

| **Year** | 2014 | 2015 | 2016 | 2017 | 2018 | 2019 |
|---|---|---|---|---|---|---|
| **Percent** | 11.7% | 11.7% | 11.2% | 11.2% | 11.2% | 10.9% |

**33. Basketball** Display the data below in a stem-and-leaf plot. Describe the differences in how the dot plot and the stem-and-leaf plot show patterns in the data.

**Heights of Players on a College Basketball Team**

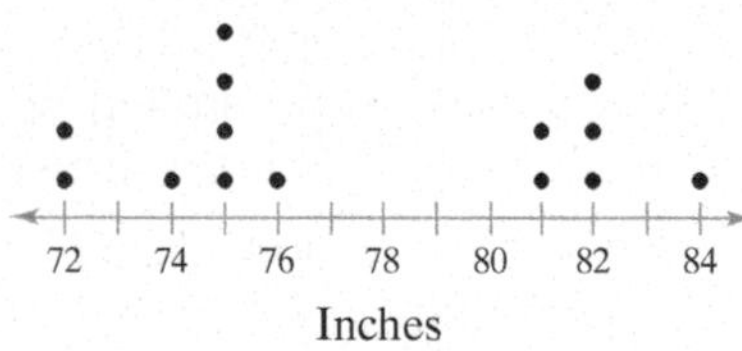


**34. Phone Screen Sizes** Display the data below in a dot plot. Describe the differences in how the stem-and-leaf plot and the dot plot show patterns in the data.

**Phone Screen Sizes (in inches)**

| | | |
|---|---|---|
| 5 | 0 0 | Key: 5\|0 = 5.0 |
| 5 | 5 5 5 6 7 8 8 9 | |
| 6 | 0 0 0 1 2 3 4 4 | |
| 6 | 5 5 6 8 8 9 | |
| 7 | 0 | |
| 7 | | |

**35. Favorite Season** Display the data below in a Pareto chart. Describe the differences in how the pie chart and the Pareto chart show patterns in the data. *(Source: Ipsos Public Affairs)*

**Favorite Season of U.S. Adults Ages 18 and Older**

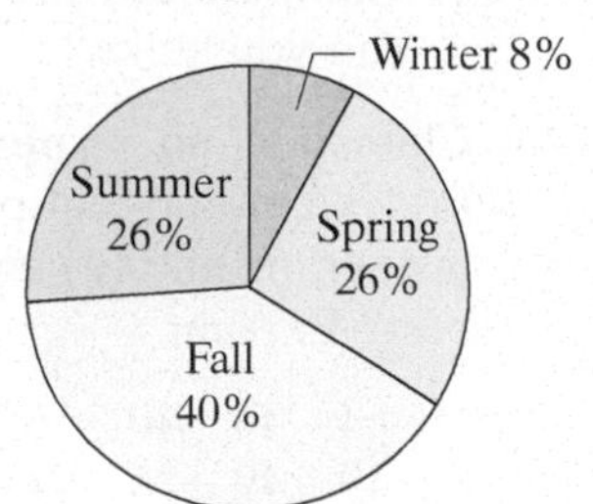


**36. Favorite Day of the Week** Display the data below in a pie chart. Describe the differences in how the Pareto chart and the pie chart show patterns in the data.

**Favorite Day of the Week**

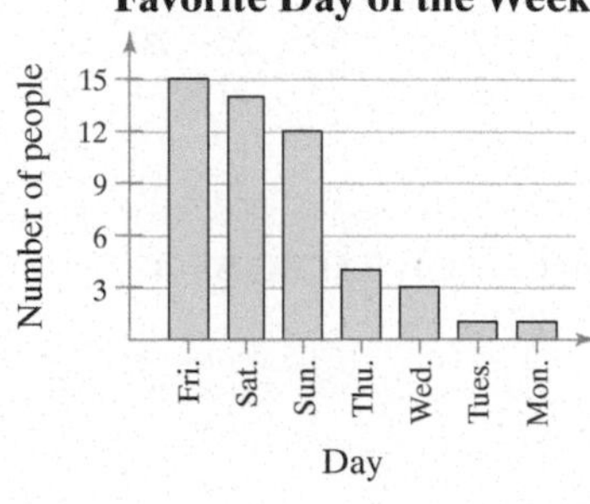

## Extending Concepts

**A Misleading Graph?** *A misleading graph is not drawn appropriately, which can misrepresent data and lead to false conclusions. In Exercises 37–40, (a) explain why the graph is misleading, and (b) redraw the graph so that it is not misleading.*

**37.**

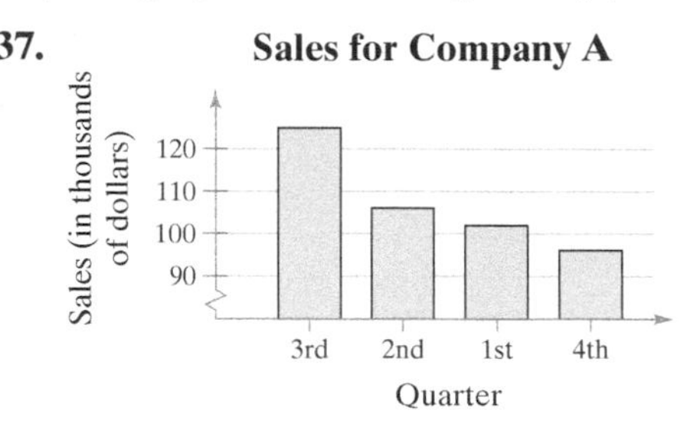


**38.**

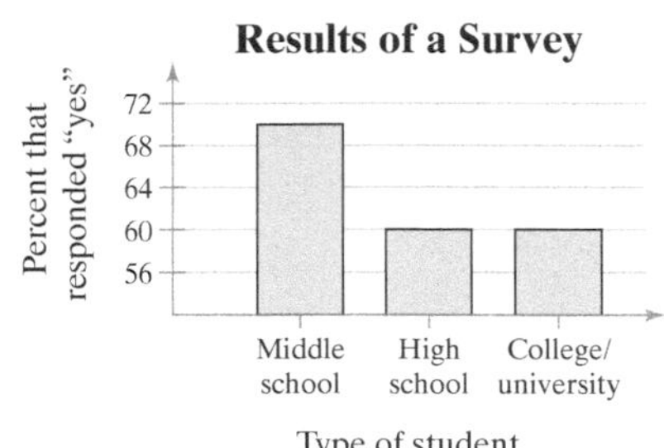


**39.**

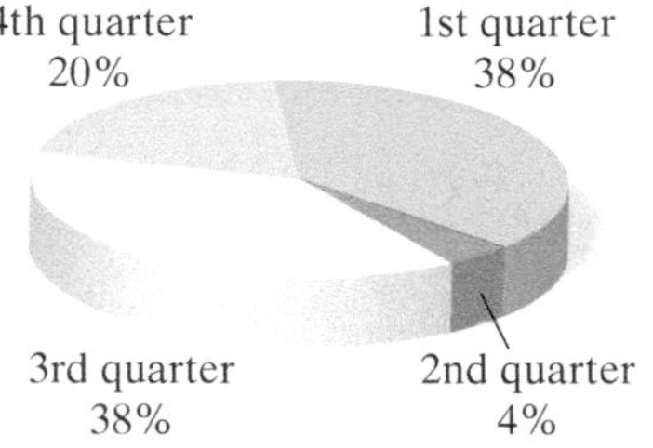


**40.**

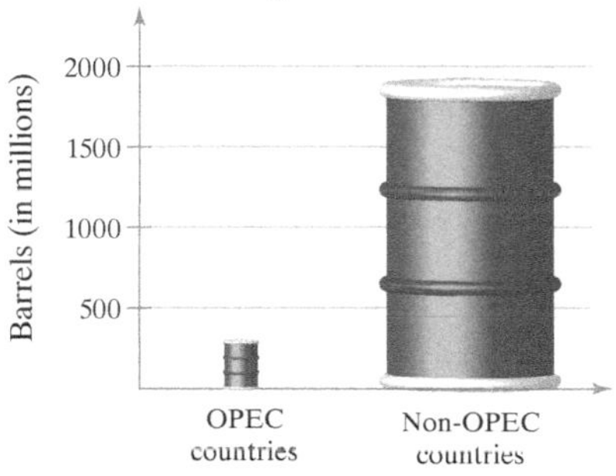


*(Source: U.S. Energy Information Administration)*

**41. Law Firm Salaries** A **back-to-back stem-and-leaf plot** compares two data sets by using the same stems for each data set. Leaves for the first data set are on one side while leaves for the second data set are on the other side. The back-to-back stem-and-leaf plot at the left shows the salaries (in thousands of dollars) of all lawyers at two small law firms.

(a) What are the lowest and highest salaries at Law Firm A? at Law Firm B? How many lawyers are in each firm?

(b) Compare the distribution of salaries at each law firm. What do you notice?

| Law Firm A | | Law Firm B |
|---|---|---|
| 5 0 | 9 | 0 3 |
| 8 5 2 2 2 | 10 | 5 7 |
| 9 9 7 0 0 | 11 | 0 0 5 |
| 1 1 | 12 | 0 3 3 5 |
| | 13 | 2 2 5 9 |
| | 14 | 1 3 3 3 9 |
| | 15 | 5 5 5 6 |
| | 16 | 4 9 9 |
| 9 9 5 1 0 | 17 | 1 2 5 |
| 5 5 5 2 1 | 18 | 9 |
| 9 9 8 7 5 | 19 | 0 |
| 3 | 20 | |

Key: 5|19|0 = \$195,000 for Law Firm A and \$190,000 for Law Firm B

FIGURE FOR EXERCISE 41

**42. Yoga Classes** The data sets at the left show the ages of all participants in two yoga classes.

(a) Make a back-to-back stem-and-leaf plot as described in Exercise 41 to display the data.

(b) What are the lowest and highest ages of participants in the 3:00 P.M. class? in the 8:00 P.M. class? How many participants are in each class?

(c) Compare the distribution of ages in each class. What observation(s) can you make?

| 3:00 P.M. class | | | | 8:00 P.M. class | | | |
|---|---|---|---|---|---|---|---|
| 40 | 60 | 73 | 77 | 19 | 18 | 20 | 29 |
| 51 | 68 | 68 | 35 | 39 | 43 | 71 | 56 |
| 68 | 53 | 64 | 75 | 44 | 44 | 18 | 19 |
| 76 | 69 | 59 | 55 | 19 | 18 | 18 | 20 |
| 38 | 57 | 68 | 84 | 25 | 29 | 25 | 22 |
| 75 | 62 | 73 | 75 | 31 | 24 | 24 | 23 |
| 85 | 77 | | | 19 | 19 | 18 | 28 |
| | | | | 20 | 31 | | |

TABLE FOR EXERCISE 42

**43. Choosing an Appropriate Display** Use technology to create (a) a stem-and-leaf plot, (b) a dot plot, (c) a pie chart, (d) a frequency histogram, and (e) an ogive for the data. Which graph displays the data best? Explain.

| | | | | | | | | | |
|---|---|---|---|---|---|---|---|---|---|
| 64 | 46 | 40 | 55 | 70 | 31 | 47 | 44 | 55 | 63 |
| 49 | 49 | 26 | 72 | 64 | 55 | 44 | 71 | 45 | 72 |

# 2.3 Measures of Central Tendency

### What You Should Learn

- How to find the mean, median, and mode of a population and of a sample
- How to find a weighted mean of a data set, and how to estimate the sample mean of grouped data
- How to describe the shape of a distribution as symmetric, uniform, or skewed, and how to compare the mean and median for each

Mean, Median, and Mode ■ Weighted Mean and Mean of Grouped Data ■ The Shapes of Distributions

## Mean, Median, and Mode

In Sections 2.1 and 2.2, you learned about the graphical representations of quantitative data. In Sections 2.3 and 2.4, you will learn how to supplement graphical representations with numerical statistics that describe the center and variability of a data set.

A **measure of central tendency** is a value that represents a typical, or central, entry of a data set. The three most commonly used measures of central tendency are the **mean,** the **median,** and the **mode.**

**DEFINITION**

The **mean** of a data set is the sum of the data entries divided by the number of entries. To find the mean of a data set, use one of these formulas.

Population Mean: $\mu = \dfrac{\Sigma x}{N}$ Sample Mean: $\bar{x} = \dfrac{\Sigma x}{n}$

The lowercase Greek letter $\mu$ (mu) represents the population mean and $\bar{x}$ (read as "$x$ bar") represents the sample mean. Note that $N$ represents the number of entries in a *population* and $n$ represents the number of entries in a *sample.* Recall that the uppercase Greek letter $\Sigma$ (sigma) indicates a summation of values.

For help with operations and summations, see *Integrated Review* at

MyLab Statistics

**EXAMPLE 1**

### Finding a Sample Mean

The weights (in pounds) for a sample of adults before starting a weight-loss study are listed. What is the mean weight of the adults?

274 235 223 268 290 285 235

**SOLUTION** The sum of the weights is

$$\Sigma x = 274 + 235 + 223 + 268 + 290 + 285 + 235 = 1810.$$

There are 7 adults in the sample, so $n = 7$. To find the mean weight, divide the sum of the weights by the number of adults in the sample.

$$\bar{x} = \frac{\Sigma x}{n} = \frac{1810}{7} \approx 258.6.$$

Round the last calculation to one more decimal place than the original data.

So, the mean weight of the adults is about 258.6 pounds.

**TRY IT YOURSELF 1**

The points scored by the winning teams in the Super Bowls for the National Football League's 2005 through 2020 seasons are listed. Find the mean.

21 29 17 27 31 31 21 34
43 28 24 34 41 13 31 31

*Answer: Page A36*

### Study Tip

Notice that the mean in Example 1 has one more decimal place than the original set of data entries. When the mean needs to be rounded, this *round-off rule* will be used in the text. Another important *round-off rule* is that rounding should not be done until the last calculation.

**DEFINITION**

The **median** of a data set is the value that lies in the middle of the data when the data set is ordered. The median measures the center of an ordered data set by dividing it into two equal parts. When the data set has an odd number of entries, the median is the middle data entry. When the data set has an even number of entries, the median is the mean of the two middle data entries.

**Tech Tip**

You can use technology such as Minitab, Excel, StatCrunch, or the TI-84 Plus to find the mean and median of a data set. For instance, to find the mean and median of the weights listed in Example 1 on a TI-84 Plus, enter the data in L1. Next, press 2nd LIST and from the MATH menu choose *mean*. Then press 2nd LIST and from the MATH menu choose *median*.

**TI-84 PLUS**

```
mean(L1)
                258.5714286
median(L1)
                        268
```

**EXAMPLE 2**

### Finding the Median

Find the median of the weights listed in Example 1.

**SOLUTION** To find the median weight, first order the data.

223 235 235 268 274 285 290

Because there are seven entries (an odd number), the median is the middle, or fourth, entry. So, the median weight is 268 pounds.

**TRY IT YOURSELF 2**

Find the median of the points scored by the 55 winning teams listed on page 39.

*Answer: Page A36*

In a data set, the number of data entries above the median is the same as the number below the median. For instance, in Example 2, three of the weights are below 268 pounds and three are above 268 pounds.

**EXAMPLE 3**

### Finding the Median

In Example 2, the adult weighing 285 pounds decides to not participate in the study. What is the median weight of the remaining adults?

**SOLUTION** The remaining weights, in order, are

223 235 235 268 274 290.

Because there are six entries (an even number), the median is the mean of the two middle entries.

$$\text{Median} = \frac{235 + 268}{2} = 251.5$$

So, the median weight of the remaining adults is 251.5 pounds. You can check your answer using technology, as shown below using Excel.

**EXCEL**

| | A | B | C | D | E | F |
|---|---|---|---|---|---|---|
| 1 | 223 | 235 | 235 | 268 | 274 | 290 |
| 2 | | | | | | 251.5 |

← =MEDIAN(A1:F1)

**TRY IT YOURSELF 3**

The points scored by the winning teams in the Super Bowls for the National Football League's 2005 through 2020 seasons are listed. Find the median.

21 29 17 27 31 31 21 34

43 28 24 34 41 13 31 31

*Answer: Page A36*

**DEFINITION**

The **mode** of a data set is the data entry that occurs with the greatest frequency. A data set can have one mode, more than one mode, or no mode. When no entry is repeated, the data set has no mode. When two entries occur with the same greatest frequency, each entry is a mode and the data set is called **bimodal.**

**EXAMPLE 4**

### Finding the Mode

Find the mode of the weights listed in Example 1.

**SOLUTION**

To find the mode, first order the data.

223 235 235 268 274 285 290

From the ordered data, you can see that the entry 235 occurs twice, whereas the other data entries occur only once. So, the mode of the weights is 235 pounds.

**TRY IT YOURSELF 4**

Find the mode of the points scored by the 55 winning teams listed on page 39.

*Answer: Page A36*

**EXAMPLE 5**

### Finding the Mode

At a political debate, a sample of audience members was asked to name the political party to which they belonged. Their responses are shown in the table. What is the mode of the responses?

| Political party | Frequency, $f$ |
|---|---|
| Democrat | 46 |
| Republican | 34 |
| Independent | 39 |
| Other/don't know | 5 |

**SOLUTION**

The response occurring with the greatest frequency is Democrat. So, the mode is Democrat.

***Interpretation*** In this sample, there were more Democrats than people of any other single affiliation.

**TRY IT YOURSELF 5**

In a survey, 12,648 adults were asked, "How much confidence, if any, do you have in elected officials to act in the best interests of the public?" Of those surveyed, 531 said "a great deal," 4073 said "a fair amount," 5970 said "not too much," 1922 said "none at all," and 152 did not provide an answer. What is the mode of the responses? *(Adapted from Pew Research Center)* *Answer: Page A36*

The mode is the only measure of central tendency that can be used to describe data at the nominal level of measurement. But when working with quantitative data, the mode is rarely used.

Although the mean, the median, and the mode each describe a typical entry of a data set, there are advantages and disadvantages of using each. The mean is a reliable measure because it takes into account every entry of a data set. The mean can be greatly affected, however, when the data set contains **outliers.**

## DEFINITION

An **outlier** is a data entry that is far removed from the other entries in the data set. (You will learn a formal way for determining an outlier in Section 2.5.)

While some outliers are valid data, other outliers may occur due to data-recording errors. A data set can have one or more outliers, causing **gaps** in a distribution. Conclusions that are drawn from a data set that contains outliers may be flawed.

| Ages in a class | | | | | | |
|---|---|---|---|---|---|---|
| 20 | 20 | 20 | 20 | 20 | 20 | 21 |
| 21 | 21 | 21 | 22 | 22 | 22 | 23 |
| 23 | 23 | 23 | 24 | 24 | 65 | |

## Picturing the World

The National Association of Realtors keeps track of existing home sales. One list uses the *median* price of existing homes sold and another uses the *mean* price of existing homes sold. The median and mean sales prices of existing homes over a three-month span are shown in the double-bar graph. (Source: National Association of Realtors)

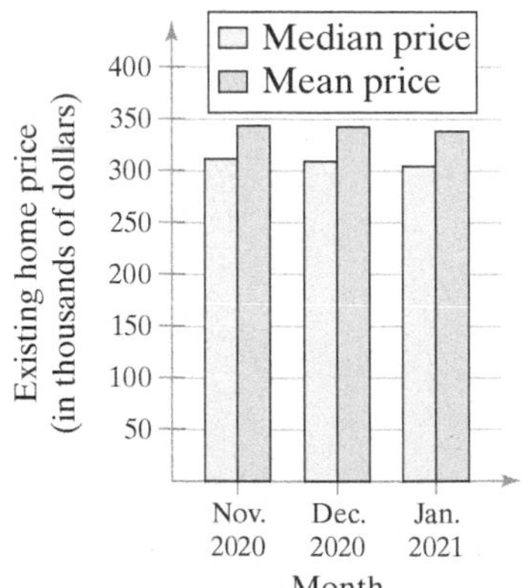


**Notice in the graph that each month, the mean price is more than the median price. Identify a factor that would cause the mean price to be greater than the median price.**

## EXAMPLE 6

### Comparing the Mean, the Median, and the Mode

The table at the left shows the sample ages of students in a class. Find the mean, median, and mode of the ages. Are there any outliers? Which measure of central tendency best describes a typical entry of this data set?

**SOLUTION**

From the histogram below, it appears that the data entry 65 is an outlier because it is far removed from the other ages in the class.

Mean: $\bar{x} = \dfrac{\Sigma x}{n} = \dfrac{475}{20} \approx 23.8$ years

Median: Median $= \dfrac{21 + 22}{2} = 21.5$ years

Mode: The entry occurring with the greatest frequency is 20 years.

***Interpretation*** The mean takes every entry into account but is influenced by the outlier of 65. The median also takes every entry into account, and it is not affected by the outlier. In this case the mode exists, but it does not appear to represent a typical entry. Sometimes a graphical comparison can help you decide which measure of central tendency best represents a data set. The histogram shows the distribution of the data and the locations of the mean, the median, and the mode. In this case, it appears that the median best describes the data set.

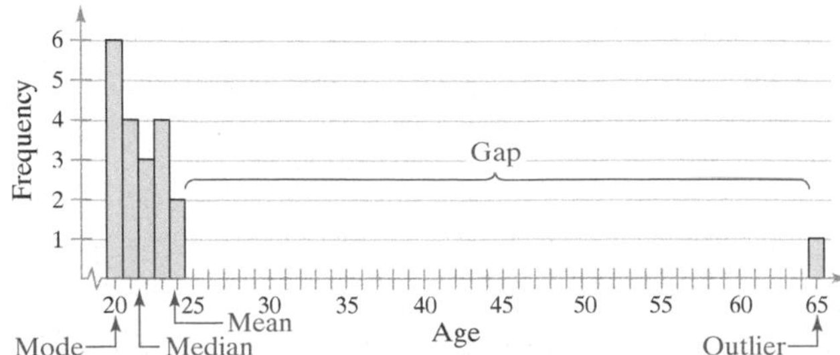


**TRY IT YOURSELF 6**

Remove the data entry 65 from the data set in Example 6. Then rework the example. How does the absence of this outlier change each of the measures?

*Answer: Page A36*

## Weighted Mean and Mean of Grouped Data

Sometimes data sets contain entries that have a greater effect on the mean than do other entries. To find the mean of such a data set, you must find the **weighted mean.**

### DEFINITION

A **weighted mean** is the mean of a data set whose entries have varying weights. The weighted mean is given by

$$\bar{x} = \frac{\Sigma xw}{\Sigma w} \qquad \frac{\text{Sum of the products of the entries and the weights}}{\text{Sum of the weights}}$$

where $w$ is the weight of each entry $x$.

### Tech Tip

You can use technology such as Minitab, Excel, StatCrunch, or the TI-84 Plus to find the weighted mean. For instance, to find the weighted mean in Example 7 on a TI-84 Plus, enter the points in L1 and the credit hours in L2. Then, use the *1-Var Stats* feature with L1 as the list and L2 as the frequency list to calculate the mean (and other statistics), as shown below.

**TI-84 PLUS**

```
1-Var Stats
x̄=2.5  ←—— Mean
Σx=40
Σx²=112
Sx=.894427191
σx=.8660254038
↓n=16
```

### EXAMPLE 7

### Finding a Weighted Mean

Your grades from last semester are in the table. The grading system assigns points as follows: A = 4, B = 3, C = 2, D = 1, F = 0. Determine your grade point average (weighted mean).

| Final grade | Credit hours |
|---|---|
| C | 3 |
| C | 4 |
| D | 1 |
| A | 3 |
| C | 2 |
| B | 3 |

**SOLUTION**

Let $x$ be the points assigned to the letter grade and $w$ be the credit hours. You can organize the points and hours in a table.

| Points, $x$ | Credit hours, $w$ | $xw$ |
|---|---|---|
| 2 | 3 | 6 |
| 2 | 4 | 8 |
| 1 | 1 | 1 |
| 4 | 3 | 12 |
| 2 | 2 | 4 |
| 3 | 3 | 9 |
| | $\Sigma w = 16$ | $\Sigma(x \cdot w) = 40$ |

$$\bar{x} = \frac{\Sigma xw}{\Sigma w} = \frac{40}{16} = 2.5$$

Last semester, your grade point average was 2.5.

**TRY IT YOURSELF 7**

In Example 7, your grade in the two-credit course is changed to a B. What is your new weighted mean?

*Answer: Page A36*

For data presented in a frequency distribution, you can estimate the mean as shown in the next definition.

### Study Tip

For a frequency distribution that represents a population, the mean of the frequency distribution is estimated by

$$\mu = \frac{\Sigma xf}{N}$$

where $N = \Sigma f$.

### DEFINITION

The **mean of a frequency distribution** for a sample is estimated by

$$\bar{x} = \frac{\Sigma xf}{n} \qquad \text{Note that } n = \Sigma f.$$

where $x$ and $f$ are the midpoint and frequency of each class, respectively.

### GUIDELINES

**Finding the Mean of a Frequency Distribution**

| In Words | In Symbols |
|---|---|
| **1.** Find the midpoint of each class. | $x = \frac{(\text{Lower limit}) + (\text{Upper limit})}{2}$ |
| **2.** Find the sum of the products of the midpoints and the frequencies. | $\Sigma xf$ |
| **3.** Find the sum of the frequencies. | $n = \Sigma f$ |
| **4.** Find the mean of the frequency distribution. | $\bar{x} = \frac{\Sigma xf}{n}$ |

### EXAMPLE 8

#### Finding the Mean of a Frequency Distribution

The frequency distribution at the left shows the cell phone screen times (in minutes) for 30 U.S. adults on a recent day. Use the frequency distribution to estimate the mean screen time. Using the sample mean formula from page 67 with the original data set (see Example 1 in Section 2.1), the mean screen time is about 285.5 minutes. Compare this with the estimated mean.

| Class midpoint, $x$ | Frequency, $f$ | $xf$ |
|---|---|---|
| 172.5 | 3 | 517.5 |
| 208.5 | 2 | 417.0 |
| 244.5 | 5 | 1222.5 |
| 280.5 | 6 | 1683.0 |
| 316.5 | 7 | 2215.5 |
| 352.5 | 4 | 1410.0 |
| 388.5 | 3 | 1165.5 |
| | $n = 30$ | $\Sigma = 8631$ |

**SOLUTION**

$$\bar{x} = \frac{\Sigma xf}{n} = \frac{8631}{30} = 287.7$$

***Interpretation*** The mean screen time is 287.7 minutes. This value is an estimate because it is based on class midpoints instead of the original data set. Although it is not substantially different, the mean of about 285.5 minutes found using the original data set is a more accurate result.

**TRY IT YOURSELF 8**

Use a frequency distribution to estimate the mean of the points scored by the 55 winning teams listed on page 39. (See Try It Yourself 2 on page 43.) Using the population mean formula from page 67 with the original data set, the mean is about 30.1 points. Compare this with the estimated mean.

*Answer: Page A36*

## The Shapes of Distributions

A graph reveals several characteristics of a frequency distribution. One such characteristic is the shape of the distribution.

**Study Tip**

The graph of a symmetric distribution is not always bell-shaped (see below). Some of the other possible shapes for the graph of a symmetric distribution are U-, M-, or W-shaped.

**DEFINITION**

A frequency distribution is **symmetric** when a vertical line can be drawn through the middle of a graph of the distribution and the resulting halves are approximately mirror images.

A frequency distribution is **uniform** (or **rectangular**) when all entries, or classes, in the distribution have equal or approximately equal frequencies. A uniform distribution is also symmetric.

A frequency distribution is skewed when the "tail" of the graph elongates more to one side than to the other. A distribution is **skewed left (negatively skewed)** when its tail extends to the left. A distribution is **skewed right (positively skewed)** when its tail extends to the right.

**2.3** To explore this topic further, see **Activity 2.3** on page 81.

When a distribution is symmetric and unimodal, the mean, median, and mode are equal. When a distribution is skewed left, the mean is less than the median and the median is usually less than the mode. When a distribution is skewed right, the mean is greater than the median and the median is usually greater than the mode. Examples of these commonly occurring distributions are shown.

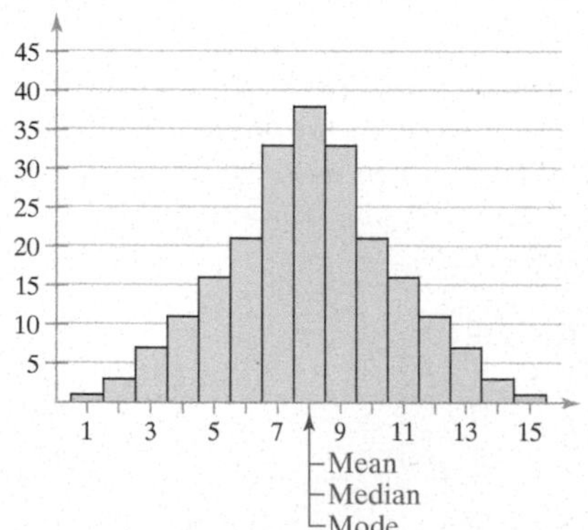


Symmetric Distribution

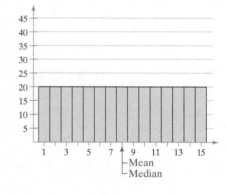

45
40
35
30
25
20
15
10
5
1 3 5 7 9 11 13 15
Mean
Median

Uniform Distribution

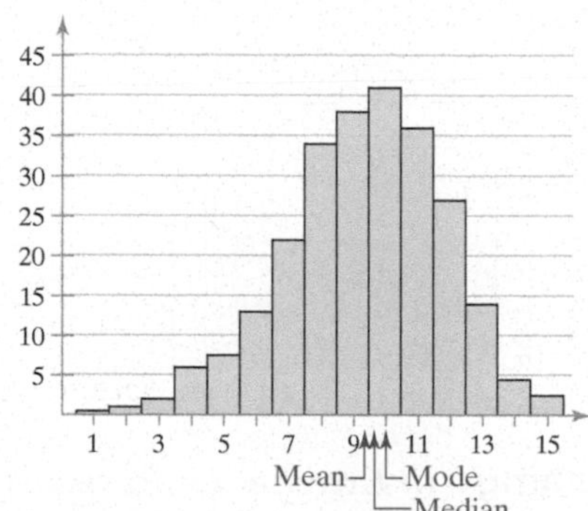


Skewed Left Distribution

45
40
35
30
25
20
15
10
5
1 3 5 7 9 11 13 15
Mode
Mean
Median

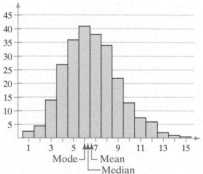

Skewed Right Distribution

**Study Tip**

Be aware that there are many different shapes of distributions. In some cases, the shape cannot be classified as symmetric, uniform, or skewed. A distribution can have several gaps caused by outliers or *clusters* of data. Clusters may occur when several types of data entries are used in a data set. For instance, a data set of gas mileages for trucks (which get low gas mileage) and hybrid cars (which get high gas mileage) would have two clusters.

The mean will always fall in the direction in which the distribution is skewed. For instance, when a distribution is skewed left, the mean is to the left of the median.

# 2.3 EXERCISES

For Extra Help: MyLab Statistics

## Building Basic Skills and Vocabulary

**True or False?** *In Exercises 1–4, determine whether the statement is true or false. If it is false, rewrite it as a true statement.*

1. The mean is the measure of central tendency most likely to be affected by an outlier.
2. Some quantitative data sets do not have medians.
3. A data set can have the same mean, median, and mode.
4. When each data class has the same frequency, the distribution is symmetric.

**Constructing Data Sets** *In Exercises 5–8, construct the described data set. The entries in the data set cannot all be the same.*

5. Median and mode are the same.
6. Mean and median are the same and the data is bimodal.
7. Mean is *not* representative of a typical number in the data set.
8. Mean, median, and mode are the same.

**Graphical Analysis** *In Exercises 9–12, determine whether the approximate shape of the distribution in the histogram is symmetric, uniform, skewed left, skewed right, or none of these. Justify your answer.*

9.

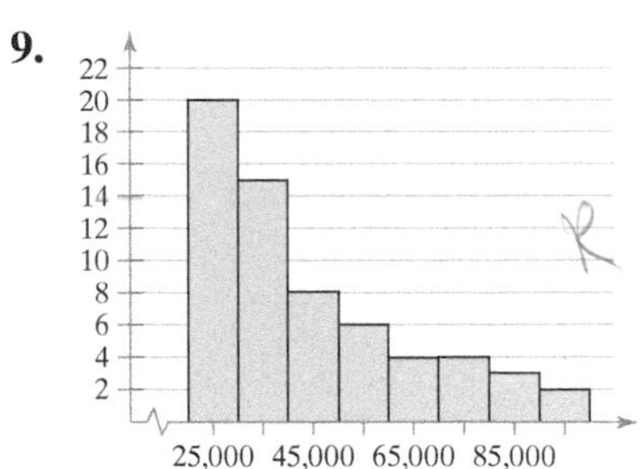


10.

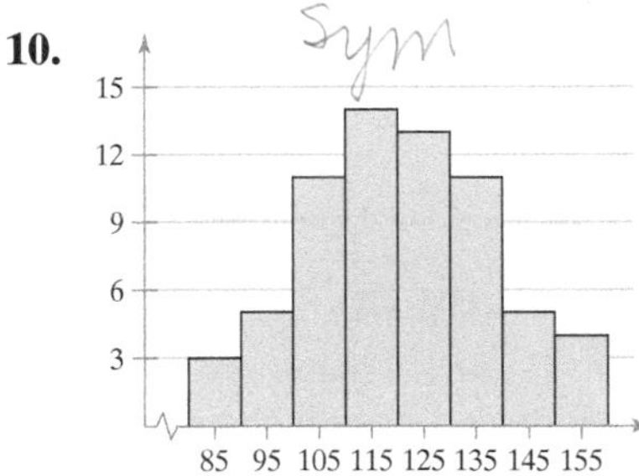


11.

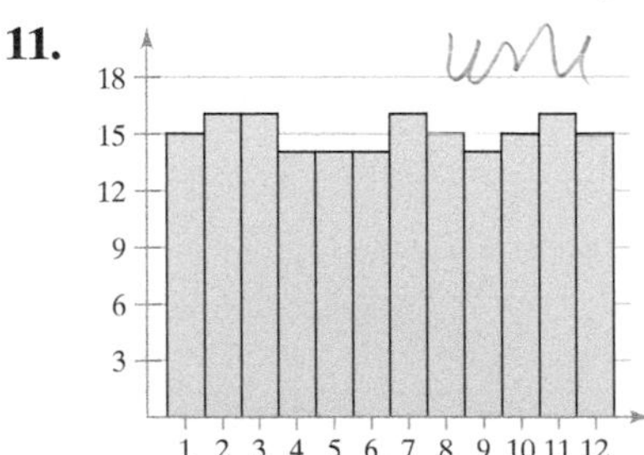


12.

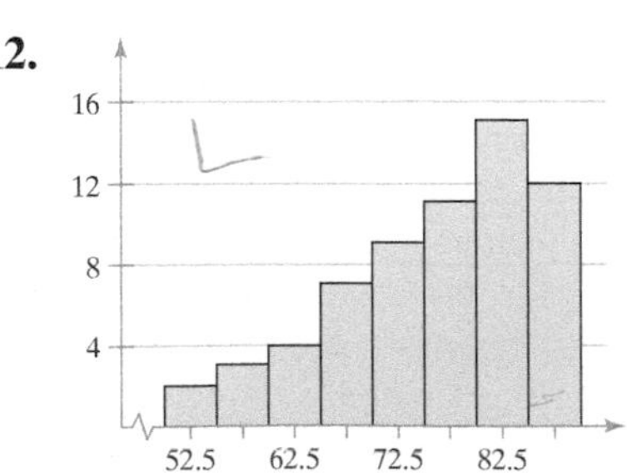


**Matching** *In Exercises 13–16, match the distribution with one of the graphs in Exercises 9–12. Justify your decision.*

13. The frequency distribution of 180 rolls of a dodecagon (a 12-sided die)
14. The frequency distribution of mileages of service vehicles at a business where a few vehicles have much higher mileages than the majority of vehicles
15. The frequency distribution of scores on a 90-point test where a few students scored much lower than the majority of students
16. The frequency distribution of weights for a sample of seventh-grade boys

## Using and Interpreting Concepts

**Finding and Discussing the Mean, Median, and Mode** *In Exercises 17–34, find the mean, the median, and the mode of the data, if possible. If any measure cannot be found or does not represent the center of the data, explain why.*

**17. College Credits** The number of credits being taken by a sample of 14 full-time college students for a semester

12 14 16 15 13 14 15
18 16 16 12 16 15 17

**18. LSAT Scores** The Law School Admission Test (LSAT) scores for a sample of seven students accepted into a law school

174 172 169 176 169 170 175

**19. Video Durations** The lengths (in minutes) of seven educational videos from the Public Broadcasting Service (PBS) *(Source: PBS)*

83 67 90 55 56 119 52

**20. Page Counts** The lengths (in pages) of the 10 best-selling books of 2020 on Amazon *(Source: Amazon)*

768 240 384 84 672 352 34 192 320 592

**21. Tuition** The 2020–2021 tuition and fees (in thousands of dollars) for the 14 top-ranked universities in the U.S. according to U.S. News & World Report *(Source: U.S. News & World Report)*

54 54 64 54 58 56 59
60 57 57 59 60 59 61

**22. Cholesterol** The cholesterol levels of a sample of 10 female employees

154 240 171 188 235 203 184 173 181 275

**23. Ports of Entry** The maximum number of passenger vehicle lanes at 16 Canadian border ports of entry *(Source: U.S. Customs and Border Protection)*

8 7 10 3 9 17 1 2
2 6 1 10 4 19 10 5

**24. Treatment of Depression** The number of patients who responded to various combinations of electroconvulsive therapy, medication, and cognitive-behavioral therapy to treat acute depression over different time periods *(Source: Adapted from Bipolar Network News)*

42 15 8 9 13 6 7

**25. Power Failures** The durations (in minutes) of power failures at a residence in the last 10 years

18 26 45 75 125 80 33
40 44 49 89 80 96 125
12 61 31 63 103 28 19

**26. Number One Songs** The number of weeks the 39 longest leading Hot 100 songs remained at number 1 as of March 24, 2020 *(Source: Billboard)*

10 10 13 14 11 14 16 14 11 11 14 10 11
13 12 10 11 10 10 12 12 14 10 10 11 19
10 12 14 10 12 10 14 12 10 10 12 16 12

| Where online harassment takes place | Frequency, $f$ |
|---|---|
| Social media site | 3104 |
| Forum/discussion site | 1035 |
| Texting/messaging app | 993 |
| Online gaming | 662 |
| Email account | 455 |
| Online dating | 414 |

TABLE FOR EXERCISE 27

**Biggest Benefit of Remote Work**

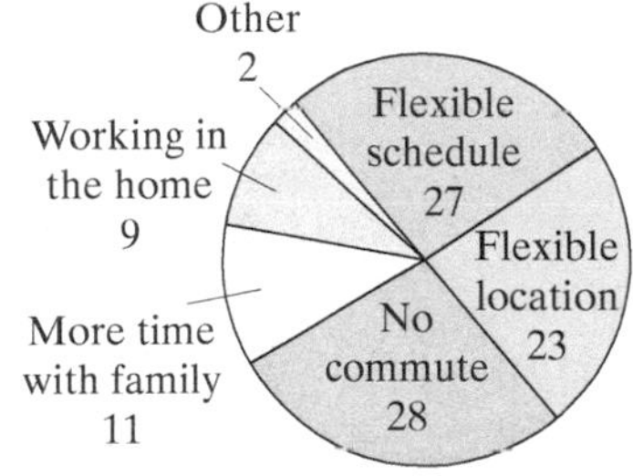


FIGURE FOR EXERCISE 30

**27. Online Harassment** A sample of 4138 U.S. adults who have been harassed online were asked in what environment the harassment took place. The responses are shown in the table at the left. *(Source: Adapted from Pew Research)*

**28. Judicial System** The responses of a sample of 34 young adult United Kingdom males in custodial sentences who were asked what is affected by such sentences *(Adapted from User Vo ice)*

Mental health: 8
Trust: 3
Education: 8
Personal development: 5
Family: 3
Future opportunities: 3
Other: 4

**29. Class Level** The class levels of 25 students in a physics course

Freshman: 8% Junior: 40%
Sophomore: 20% Senior: 32%

**30. Remote Work** The pie chart at the left shows the responses of employees working from home due to COVID-19 who were asked about the biggest benefit of working remotely. *(Source: Buffer)*

**31.** **Weights (in pounds) of Packages on a Delivery Truck**

Key: 3|0 = 30

| Stem | Leaves |
|---|---|
| 0 | 5 8 |
| 1 | 0 1 3 6 |
| 2 | 1 3 3 3 6 7 7 |
| 3 | 0 1 2 4 4 4 5 7 8 |
| 4 | 3 4 5 6 9 |
| 5 | 2 |

**32.** **Grade Point Averages of Students in a Class**

Key: 0|8 = 0.8

| Stem | Leaves |
|---|---|
| 0 | 8 |
| 1 | 5 6 8 |
| 2 | 1 3 4 5 |
| 3 | 0 9 |
| 4 | 0 0 |

**33.** **Times (in minutes) It Takes Employees to Drive to Work**

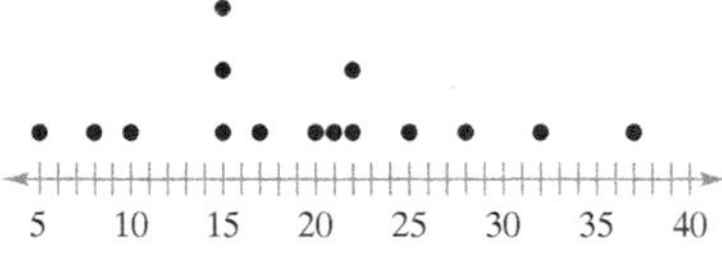


**34.** **Prices (in dollars) of Flights from Chicago to Alanta**

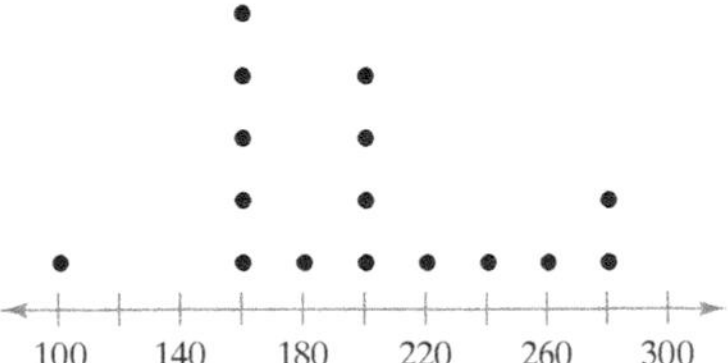


**Graphical Analysis** *In Exercises 35 and 36, identify any clusters, gaps, or outliers.*

**35.** **Model Year 2020 Plug-In Hybrid Electric Vehicles**

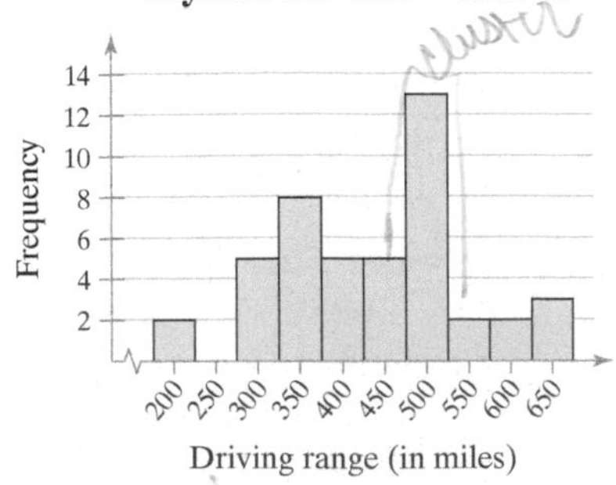

Frequency

14 12 10 8 6 4 2

200 250 300 350 400 450 500 550 600 650

Driving range (in miles)

*(Source: United States Environmental Protection Agency)*

**36.** **Model Year 2020 All-Electric Vehicles**

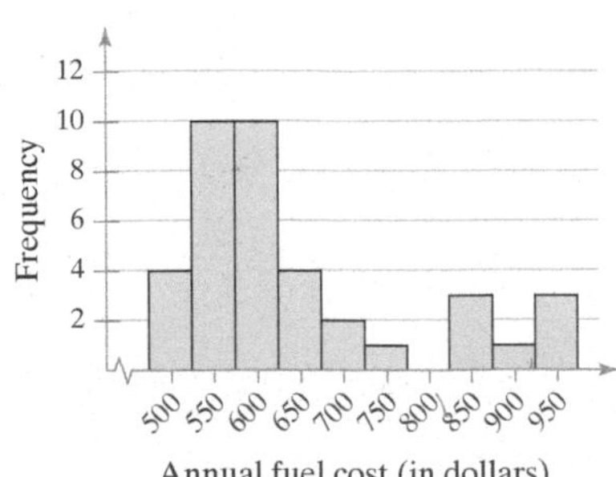


*(Source: United States Environmental Protection Agency)*

*In Exercises 37–40, without performing any calculations, determine which measure of central tendency best represents the graphed data. Explain your reasoning.*

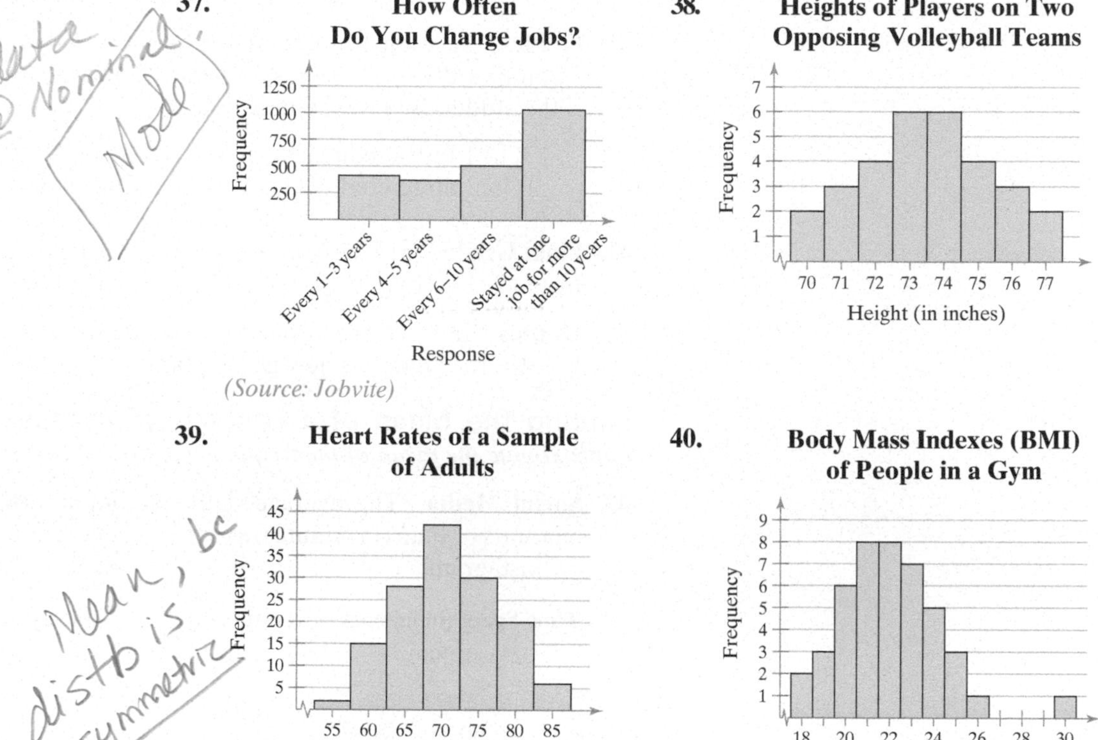


**Finding a Weighted Mean** *In Exercises 41–46, find the weighted mean of the data.*

**41. Final Grade** The scores and their percents of the final grade for a statistics student are shown below. What is the student's mean score?

| | Score | Percent of final grade |
|---|---|---|
| Homework | 85 | 5% |
| Quizzes | 80 | 35% |
| Project/Speech | 100 | 35% |
| Final exam | 93 | 25% |

**42. Final Grade** The scores and their percents of the final grade for an archaeology student are shown below. What is the student's mean score?

| | Score | Percent of final grade |
|---|---|---|
| Quizzes | 100 | 20% |
| Midterm exam | 89 | 30% |
| Student lecture | 100 | 10% |
| Final exam | 92 | 40% |

**43. Account Balance** For the month of April, a checking account has a balance of \$523 for 24 days, \$2415 for 2 days, and \$250 for 4 days. What is the account's mean daily balance for April?

**44. Credit Card Balance** For the month of October, a credit card has a balance of \$115.63 for 12 days, \$637.19 for 6 days, \$1225.06 for 7 days, \$0 for 2 days, and \$34.88 for 4 days. What is the account's mean daily balance for October?

**45. Scores** The mean scores for students in a statistics course (by major) are shown below. What is the mean score for the class?

9 engineering majors: 85 5 math majors: 90 13 business majors: 81

**46. Grades** A student receives the grades shown below, with an A worth 4 points, a B worth 3 points, a C worth 2 points, and a D worth 1 point. What is the student's grade point average?

A in 1 four-credit class
B in 2 three-credit classes
C in 1 three-credit class
D in 1 two-credit class

**47. Final Grade** In Exercise 41, an error was made in grading your final exam. Instead of getting 93, you scored 85. What is your new weighted mean?

**48. Grades** In Exercise 46, one of the student's B grades gets changed to an A. What is the student's new grade point average?

## Finding the Mean of a Frequency Distribution *In Exercises 49–52, approximate the mean of the frequency distribution.*

**49. Social Media** The average daily amounts of time (in minutes) spent on Instagram

| Time Spent (in minutes) | Frequency |
|---|---|
| 0–29 | 9 |
| 30–59 | 23 |
| 60–89 | 12 |
| 90–119 | 6 |

**50. Social Media** The average daily amounts of time (in minutes) spent on Snapchat

| Time Spent (in minutes) | Frequency |
|---|---|
| 0–19 | 8 |
| 20–39 | 8 |
| 40–59 | 15 |
| 60–79 | 10 |
| 80–99 | 7 |

**51. Ages** The ages (in years) of the residents of a small town in 2021

| Age (in years) | Frequency |
|---|---|
| 0–9 | 78 |
| 10–19 | 97 |
| 20–29 | 54 |
| 30–39 | 63 |
| 40–49 | 69 |
| 50–59 | 86 |
| 60–69 | 73 |
| 70–79 | 53 |
| 80–89 | 43 |
| 90–99 | 15 |

**52. Populations** The populations (in thousands) of the counties in Montana in 2019 *(Source: U.S. Census Bureau)*

| Population (in thousands) | Frequency |
|---|---|
| 0–19 | 46 |
| 20–39 | 3 |
| 40–59 | 1 |
| 60–79 | 1 |
| 80–99 | 1 |
| 100–119 | 3 |
| 120–139 | 0 |
| 140–159 | 1 |

## Identifying the Shape of a Distribution *In Exercises 53–56, construct a frequency distribution and a frequency histogram for the data set using the indicated number of classes. Describe the shape of the histogram as symmetric, uniform, negatively skewed, positively skewed, or none of these.*

**53. Hospital Beds**
Number of classes: 5
Data set: The number of beds in a sample of 20 hospitals

167 162 127 130 180 160 167 221 145 137
194 207 150 254 262 244 297 137 204 180

**54. Emergency Room**
Number of classes: 6
Data set: The number of patients visiting an emergency room per day over a two-week period

| | | | | | | |
|---|---|---|---|---|---|---|
| 256 | 317 | 237 | 182 | 382 | 106 | 162 |
| 112 | 162 | 264 | 104 | 194 | 236 | 227 |

**55. Heights of Males**
Number of classes: 5
Data set: The heights (to the nearest inch) of 30 males

| | | | | | | | | | |
|---|---|---|---|---|---|---|---|---|---|
| 67 | 76 | 69 | 68 | 72 | 68 | 65 | 63 | 75 | 69 |
| 66 | 72 | 67 | 66 | 69 | 73 | 64 | 62 | 71 | 73 |
| 68 | 72 | 71 | 65 | 69 | 66 | 74 | 72 | 68 | 69 |

**56. Six-Sided Die**
Number of classes: 6
Data set: The results of rolling a six-sided die 30 times

| | | | | | | | | | |
|---|---|---|---|---|---|---|---|---|---|
| 1 | 4 | 6 | 1 | 5 | 3 | 2 | 5 | 4 | 6 |
| 1 | 2 | 4 | 3 | 5 | 6 | 3 | 2 | 1 | 1 |
| 5 | 6 | 2 | 4 | 4 | 3 | 1 | 6 | 2 | 4 |

**57. Protein Powder** During a quality assurance check, the actual contents (in grams) of six containers of protein powder were recorded as 1525, 1526, 1502, 1516, 1529, and 1511.

(a) Find the mean and the median of the contents.

(b) The third value was incorrectly measured and is actually 1520. Find the mean and the median of the contents again.

(c) Which measure of central tendency, the mean or the median, was affected more by the data entry error?

| U.S. trade deficits (in billions of dollars) | |
|---|---|
| China: 310.8 | Taiwan: 29.9 |
| Mexico: 112.7 | Italy: 29.5 |
| Vietnam: 69.7 | Thailand: 26.4 |
| Germany: 57.3 | South Korea: 24.8 |
| Switzerland: 56.7 | India: 23.8 |
| Ireland: 55.9 | France: 15.6 |
| Japan: 55.4 | Canada: 15.2 |
| Malaysia: 31.7 | Indonesia: 12.8 |
| Russian Federation: 12.0 | |
| Denmark: 8.6 | |

TABLE FOR EXERCISE 58

**58. U.S. Trade Deficits** The table at the left shows the U.S. trade deficits (in billions of dollars) with 18 countries in 2020. *(Source: U.S. Department of Commerce)*

(a) Find the mean and the median of the trade deficits.

(b) Find the mean and the median without the Chinese trade deficit. Which measure of central tendency, the mean or the median, was affected more by the elimination of the Chinese trade deficit?

(c) The Austrian trade deficit was \$8.2 billion. Find the mean and the median with the Austrian trade deficit added to the original data set. Which measure of central tendency was affected more?

**Graphical Analysis** *In Exercises 59 and 60, the letters A, B, and C are marked on the horizontal axis. Describe the shape of the data. Then determine which is the mean, which is the median, and which is the mode. Justify your answers.*

**59.**

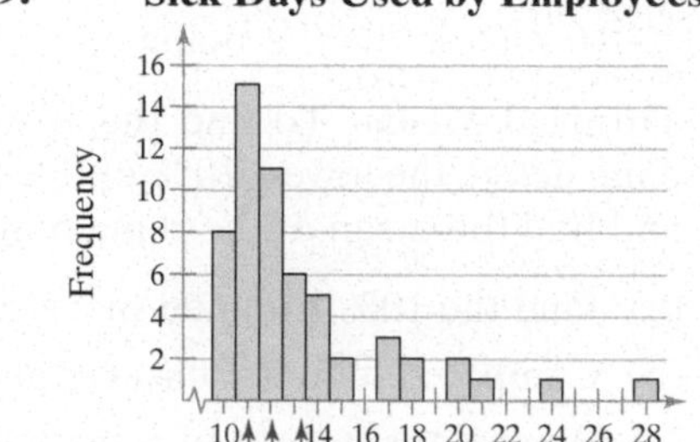


**60.**

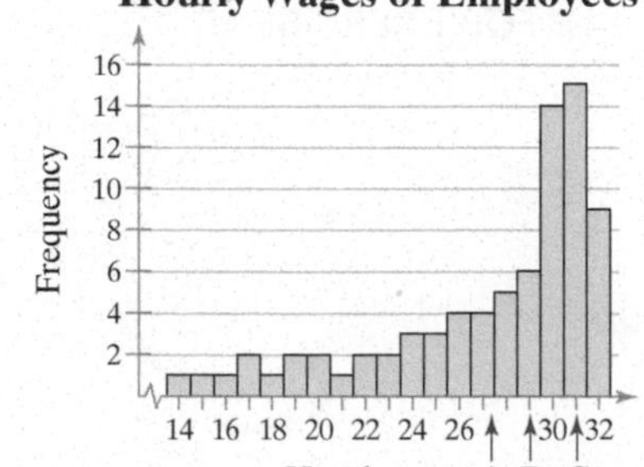

## Extending Concepts

**61. Writing** In an academic year, a student receives the grades shown below, with an A worth 4 points, a B worth 3 points, and a C worth 2 points.

A in 2 four-credit classes and 3 three-credit classes
B in 2 three-credit classes and 2 two-credit classes
C in 1 two-credit class

The student can increase one of the Bs or Cs by one letter grade. Which one should the student choose? Explain your reasoning.

**62. Golf** The distances (in yards) for nine holes of a golf course are listed.

336 393 408 522 147 504 177 375 360

(a) Find the mean and the median of the data.

(b) Convert the distances to feet. Then rework part (a).

(c) Compare the measures you found in part (b) with those found in part (a). What do you notice?

(d) Use your results from part (c) to explain how to quickly find the mean and the median of the original data set when the distances are converted to inches.

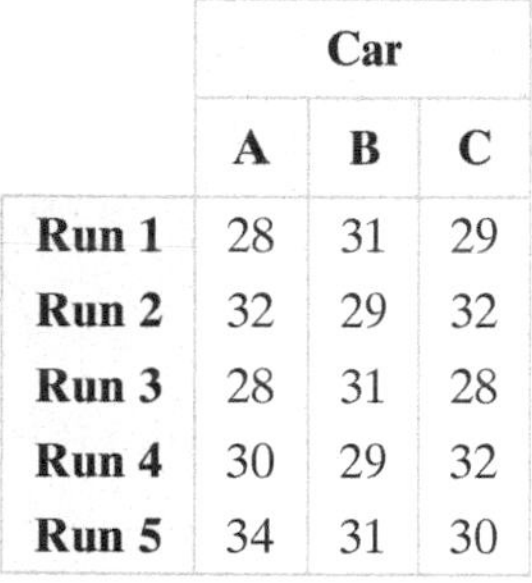

| | Car | | |
|---|---|---|---|
| | A | B | C |
| **Run 1** | 28 | 31 | 29 |
| **Run 2** | 32 | 29 | 32 |
| **Run 3** | 28 | 31 | 28 |
| **Run 4** | 30 | 29 | 32 |
| **Run 5** | 34 | 31 | 30 |

TABLE FOR EXERCISE 63

**63. Data Analysis** A consumer testing service obtained the gas mileages (in miles per gallon) shown in the table at the left in five test runs performed with three types of compact cars.

(a) The manufacturer of Car A wants to advertise that its car performed best in this test. Which measure of central tendency—mean, median, or mode—should be used for its claim? Explain your reasoning.

(b) The manufacturer of Car B wants to advertise that its car performed best in this test. Which measure of central tendency—mean, median, or mode—should be used for its claim? Explain your reasoning.

(c) The manufacturer of Car C wants to advertise that its car performed best in this test. Which measure of central tendency—mean, median, or mode—should be used for its claim? Explain your reasoning.

**64. Midrange** Another measure of central tendency, which is rarely used, is the **midrange.** It can be found by using the formula

$$\text{Midrange} = \frac{(\text{Maximum data entry}) + (\text{Minimum data entry})}{2}.$$

Which of the manufacturers in Exercise 63 would prefer to use the midrange statistic in their ads? Explain your reasoning.

| Test scores | | | | | | | |
|---|---|---|---|---|---|---|---|
| 44 | 51 | 11 | 90 | 76 | 36 | 64 | 37 |
| 43 | 72 | 53 | 62 | 36 | 74 | 51 | 72 |
| 37 | 28 | 38 | 61 | 47 | 63 | 36 | 41 |
| 22 | 37 | 51 | 46 | 85 | 13 | | |

TABLE FOR EXERCISE 65

**65. Data Analysis** Students in an experimental psychology class did research on depression as a sign of stress. A test was administered to a sample of 30 students. The scores are shown in the table at the left.

(a) Find the mean and the median of the data.

(b) Draw a stem-and-leaf plot for the data using one row per stem. Locate the mean and the median on the display.

(c) Describe the shape of the distribution.

**66. Trimmed Mean** To find the 10% **trimmed mean** of a data set, order the data, delete the lowest 10% of the entries and the highest 10% of the entries, and find the mean of the remaining entries.

(a) Find the 10% trimmed mean for the data in Exercise 65.

(b) Compare the four measures of central tendency, including the midrange.

(c) What is the benefit of using a trimmed mean versus using a mean found using all data entries? Explain your reasoning.

# 2.3 ACTIVITY Mean Versus Median

APPLET

You can find the interactive applet for this activity at MyLab Statistics.

The *Mean versus median* applet is designed to allow you to investigate interactively the mean and the median as measures of the center of a data set. You can generate a data set by entering a **Sample size** and clicking **Simulate.** You can also generate data values by clicking **Add point** or by clicking above the horizontal axis. The mean of the points is shown as a green arrow and the median is shown as a red arrow. When the two values are the same, a single green arrow is displayed. Numeric values for the mean and the median are shown in the table at the right. Remove a data value by dragging the corresponding point outside the axis range. Remove all the data values and their corresponding points from the data set by clicking **Reset.**

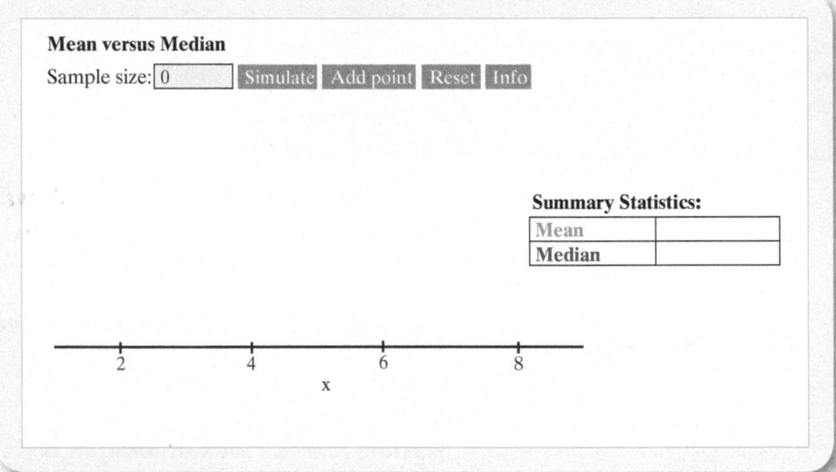


## EXPLORE

**Step 1** Specify a **Sample size.**
**Step 2** Click **Simulate.**
**Step 3** Add and remove various points to and from the plot.
**Step 4** Remove all the points from the plot.

## DRAW CONCLUSIONS

APPLET

1. Simulate several data sets using a **Sample size** of 5. Do you notice any tendencies of the plotted points in a data set when the mean and the median are the same (or very close)? Do you notice any tendencies of the plotted points in a data set when the mean and the median are not very close? Explain.

2. Create a plot of 10 data points that are symmetric about the value $x = 5$. What do you notice about the mean and the median of the data set? Is it possible to add a single point without changing the mean or median? Explain. Is it possible to add a single point to *any* data set without changing the mean or median? Explain.

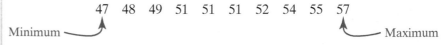

# 2.4 Measures of Variation

**What You Should Learn**

- How to find the range of a data set
- How to find the variance and standard deviation of a population and of a sample
- How to use the Empirical Rule and Chebychev's Theorem to interpret standard deviation
- How to estimate the sample standard deviation for grouped data
- How to use the coefficient of variation to compare variation in different data sets

Range ■ Variance and Standard Deviation ■ Interpreting Standard Deviation ■ Standard Deviation for Grouped Data ■ Coefficient of Variation

## Range

In this section, you will learn different ways to measure the variation (or spread) of a data set. The simplest measure is the **range** of the set.

**DEFINITION**

The **range** of a data set is the difference between the maximum and minimum data entries in the set. To find the range, the data must be quantitative.

Range = (Maximum data entry) − (Minimum data entry)

**EXAMPLE 1**

### Finding the Range of a Data Set

Two corporations each hired 10 graduates. The starting salaries for each graduate are shown. Find the range of the starting salaries for Corporation A.

**Starting Salaries for Corporation A (in thousands of dollars)**

| **Salary** | 51 | 48 | 49 | 55 | 57 | 51 | 54 | 51 | 47 | 52 |
|---|---|---|---|---|---|---|---|---|---|---|

**Starting Salaries for Corporation B (in thousands of dollars)**

| **Salary** | 50 | 33 | 51 | 60 | 59 | 42 | 51 | 39 | 62 | 68 |
|---|---|---|---|---|---|---|---|---|---|---|

**SOLUTION**

Ordering the data helps to find the least and greatest salaries.

47 48 49 51 51 51 52 54 55 57

Minimum (47) — Maximum (57)

Range = (Maximum salary) − (Minimum salary)
= 57 − 47
= 10

So, the range of the starting salaries for Corporation A is 10, or $10,000.

**TRY IT YOURSELF 1**

Find the range of the starting salaries for Corporation B. Compare the result to the one in Example 1. *Answer: Page A37*

**Corporation A**

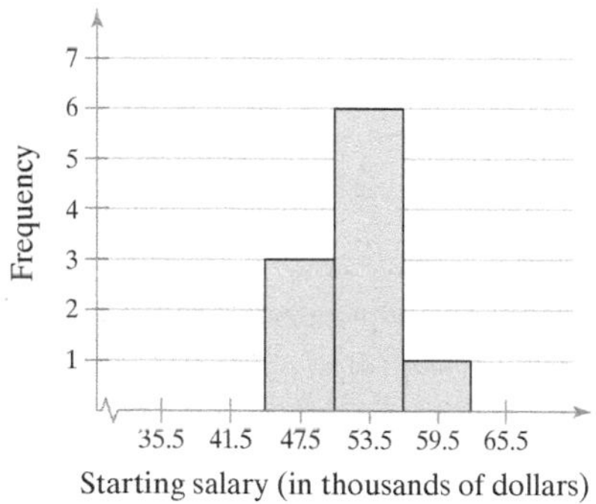


**Corporation B**

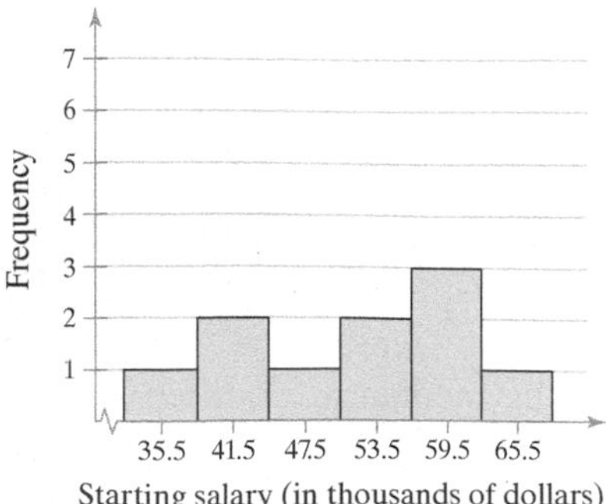


Both data sets in Example 1 have a mean of 51.5, or $51,500, a median of 51, or $51,000, and a mode of 51, or $51,000. And yet the two sets differ significantly. The difference is that the entries in the second set have greater variation. As you can see in the figures at the left, the starting salaries for Corporation B are more spread out than those for Corporation A.

## Variance and Standard Deviation

As a measure of variation, the range has the advantage of being easy to compute. Its disadvantage, however, is that it uses only two entries from the data set. Two measures of variation that use all the entries in a data set are the *variance* and the *standard deviation.* Before you learn about these measures of variation, you need to know what is meant by the **deviation** of an entry in a data set.

**DEFINITION**

The **deviation** of an entry $x$ in a population data set is the difference between the entry and the mean $\mu$ of the data set.

Deviation of $x = x - \mu$

**Deviations of Starting Salaries for Corporation A**

| Salary (in 1000s of dollars) $x$ | Deviation (in 1000s of dollars) $x - \mu$ |
|---|---|
| 51 | −0.5 |
| 48 | −3.5 |
| 49 | −2.5 |
| 55 | 3.5 |
| 57 | 5.5 |
| 51 | −0.5 |
| 54 | 2.5 |
| 51 | −0.5 |
| 47 | −4.5 |
| 52 | 0.5 |
| $\Sigma x = 515$ | $\Sigma(x - \mu) = 0$ |

The sum of the deviations is 0.

Consider the starting salaries for Corporation A in Example 1. The mean starting salary is $\mu = 515/10 = 51.5$, or $51,500. The table at the left lists the deviation of each salary from the mean. For instance, the deviation of 51 is $51 - 51.5 = -0.5$. Notice that the sum of the deviations is 0. In fact, the sum of the deviations for *any* data set is 0, so it does not make sense to find the average of the deviations. To overcome this problem, take the square of each deviation. The sum of the squares of the deviations, or **sum of squares,** is denoted by $SS_x$. In a population data set, the average of the squares of the deviations is the **population variance.**

**DEFINITION**

The **population variance** of a population data set of $N$ entries is

$$\text{Population variance} = \sigma^2 = \frac{\Sigma(x - \mu)^2}{N}.$$

The symbol $\sigma$ is the lowercase Greek letter sigma.

As a measure of variation, one disadvantage with the variance is that its units are different from those of the data set. For instance, the variance for the starting salaries (in thousands of dollars) in Example 1 is measured in "square thousands of dollars." To overcome this problem, take the square root of the variance to get the **standard deviation.**

**DEFINITION**

The **population standard deviation** of a population data set of $N$ entries is the square root of the population variance.

$$\text{Population standard deviation} = \sigma = \sqrt{\sigma^2} = \sqrt{\frac{\Sigma(x - \mu)^2}{N}}$$

Here are some observations about the standard deviation.

- The standard deviation measures the variation of the data set about the mean and has the same units of measure as the data set.
- The standard deviation is always greater than or equal to 0. When $\sigma = 0$, the data set has no variation and all entries have the same value.
- As the entries get farther from the mean (that is, more spread out), the value of $\sigma$ increases.

For help with exponents, operations with square roots, and division involving powers and square roots, see *Integrated Review* at

MyLab Statistics

To find the variance and standard deviation of a population data set, use these guidelines.

**GUIDELINES**

**Finding the Population Variance and Standard Deviation**

| In Words | In Symbols |
|---|---|
| **1.** Find the mean of the population data set. | $\mu = \dfrac{\Sigma x}{N}$ |
| **2.** Find the deviation of each entry. | $x - \mu$ |
| **3.** Square each deviation. | $(x - \mu)^2$ |
| **4.** Add to get the sum of squares. | $SS_x = \Sigma(x - \mu)^2$ |
| **5.** Divide by $N$ to get the population variance. | $\sigma^2 = \dfrac{\Sigma(x - \mu)^2}{N}$ |
| **6.** Find the square root of the variance to get the population standard deviation. | $\sigma = \sqrt{\dfrac{\Sigma(x - \mu)^2}{N}}$ |

**Sum of Squares of Starting Salaries for Corporation A**

| Salary $x$ | Deviation $x - \mu$ | Squares $(x - \mu)^2$ |
|---|---|---|
| 51 | −0.5 | 0.25 |
| 48 | −3.5 | 12.25 |
| 49 | −2.5 | 6.25 |
| 55 | 3.5 | 12.25 |
| 57 | 5.5 | 30.25 |
| 51 | −0.5 | 0.25 |
| 54 | 2.5 | 6.25 |
| 51 | −0.5 | 0.25 |
| 47 | −4.5 | 20.25 |
| 52 | 0.5 | 0.25 |
| $\Sigma x = 515$ | | $SS_x = 88.5$ |

**EXAMPLE 2**

## Finding the Population Variance and Standard Deviation

Find the population variance and standard deviation of the starting salaries for Corporation A listed in Example 1.

**SOLUTION**

For this data set, $N = 10$ and $\Sigma x = 515$. The mean is

$$\mu = \frac{515}{10} = 51.5. \qquad \text{Mean}$$

The table at the left summarizes the steps used to find $SS_x$. Because

$$SS_x = 88.5 \qquad \text{Sum of squares}$$

you can find the variance and standard deviation as shown.

$$\sigma^2 = \frac{88.5}{10} \approx 8.9 \qquad \text{Round to one more decimal place than the original data.}$$

$$\sigma = \sqrt{\frac{88.5}{10}} \approx 3.0 \qquad \text{Round to one more decimal place than the original data.}$$

So, the population variance is about 8.9, and the population standard deviation is about 3.0, or $3000.

**TRY IT YOURSELF 2**

Find the population variance and standard deviation of the starting salaries for Corporation B in Example 1.

*Answer: Page A37*

**Study Tip**

Notice that the variance and standard deviation in Example 2 have one more decimal place than the original set of data entries. This is the same *round-off rule* that was used to calculate the mean.

The formulas shown on the next page for the sample variance $s^2$ and sample standard deviation $s$ of a sample data set differ slightly from those of a population. For instance, to find $s$, the formula uses $\bar{x}$. Also, $SS_x$ is divided by $n - 1$. Why divide by one less than the number of entries? In many cases, a statistic is calculated to estimate the corresponding parameter, such as using $\bar{x}$ to estimate $\mu$. Statistical theory has shown that the best estimates of $\sigma^2$ and $\sigma$ are obtained when dividing $SS_x$ by $n - 1$ in the formulas for $s^2$ and $s$.

## DEFINITION

The **sample variance** and **sample standard deviation** of a sample data set of $n$ entries are listed below.

$$\text{Sample variance} = s^2 = \frac{\Sigma(x - \bar{x})^2}{n - 1}$$

$$\text{Sample standard deviation} = s = \sqrt{s^2} = \sqrt{\frac{\Sigma(x - \bar{x})^2}{n - 1}}$$

**Symbols in Variance and Standard Deviation Formulas**

| | Population | Sample |
|---|---|---|
| **Variance** | $\sigma^2$ | $s^2$ |
| **Standard deviation** | $\sigma$ | $s$ |
| **Mean** | $\mu$ | $\bar{x}$ |
| **Number of entries** | $N$ | $n$ |
| **Deviation** | $x - \mu$ | $x - \bar{x}$ |
| **Sum of squares** | $\Sigma(x - \mu)^2$ | $\Sigma(x - \bar{x})^2$ |

## GUIDELINES

**Finding the Sample Variance and Standard Deviation**

| In Words | In Symbols |
|---|---|
| **1.** Find the mean of the sample data set. | $\bar{x} = \frac{\Sigma x}{N}$ |
| **2.** Find the deviation of each entry. | $x - \bar{x}$ |
| **3.** Square each deviation. | $(x - \bar{x})^2$ |
| **4.** Add to get the sum of squares. | $SS_x = \Sigma(x - \bar{x})^2$ |
| **5.** Divide by $n - 1$ to get the sample variance. | $s^2 = \frac{\Sigma(x - \bar{x})^2}{n - 1}$ |
| **6.** Find the square root of the variance to get the sample standard deviation. | $s = \sqrt{\frac{\Sigma(x - \bar{x})^2}{n - 1}}$ |

## EXAMPLE 3

See Minitab and TI-84 Plus steps on pages 124 and 125.

### Finding the Sample Variance and Standard Deviation

In a study of high school football players who sustained concussions, researchers placed the players in two groups. Players who recovered from their concussions in 14 days or less were placed in Group 1. Those who took more than 14 days were placed in Group 2. The recovery times (in days) for Group 1 are listed below. Find the sample variance and standard deviation of the recovery times. *(Adapted from The American Journal of Sports Medicine)*

8 10 4 6 7 7 9 10 7 6 5 11

| Time $x$ | Deviation $x - \bar{x}$ | Squares $(x - \bar{x})^2$ |
|---|---|---|
| 8 | 0.5 | 0.25 |
| 10 | 2.5 | 6.25 |
| 4 | −3.5 | 12.25 |
| 6 | −1.5 | 2.25 |
| 7 | −0.5 | 0.25 |
| 7 | −0.5 | 0.25 |
| 9 | 1.5 | 2.25 |
| 10 | 2.5 | 6.25 |
| 7 | −0.5 | 0.25 |
| 6 | −1.5 | 2.25 |
| 5 | −2.5 | 6.25 |
| 11 | 3.5 | 12.25 |
| $\Sigma x = 90$ | | $SS_x = 51$ |

**SOLUTION**

For this data set, $n = 12$ and $\Sigma x = 90$. The mean is $\bar{x} = 90/12 = 7.5$. To calculate $s^2$ and $s$, note that $n - 1 = 12 - 1 = 11$.

$SS_x = 51$ Sum of squares (see table at left)

$s^2 = \frac{51}{11} \approx 4.6$ Sample variance (divide $SS_x$ by $n - 1$)

$s = \sqrt{\frac{51}{11}} \approx 2.2$ Sample standard deviation

So, the sample variance is about 4.6, and the sample standard deviation is about 2.2 days.

**TRY IT YOURSELF 3**

Refer to the study in Example 3. The recovery times (in days) for Group 2 are listed below. Find the sample variance and standard deviation of the recovery times.

53 25 41 36 19 22 42 34

*Answer: Page A37*

## EXAMPLE 4

### Using Technology to Find the Standard Deviation

Sample office rental rates (in dollars per square foot per year) for Los Angeles are shown in the table at the left. Use technology to find the mean rental rate and the sample standard deviation. *(Source: LoopNet.com)*

| Office rental rates | | |
|---|---|---|
| 42 | 14 | 46 |
| 30 | 23 | 50 |
| 26 | 39 | 13 |
| 48 | 42 | 24 |
| 30 | 35 | 36 |
| 45 | 23 | 72 |
| 35 | 34 | 30 |
| 60 | 30 | 64 |
| 14 | 36 | 23 |
| 42 | 35 | 72 |

**SOLUTION**

Minitab, Excel, and the TI-84 Plus each have features that calculate the means and the standard deviations of data sets. Use such technology to find the mean and the standard deviation of the office rental rates. From the displays, you can see that

$\bar{x} = 37.1$ and $s \approx 15.5$.

**MINITAB**

**Descriptive Statistics: Rental Rates**

| Variable | N | Mean | SE Mean | StDev | Minimum |
|---|---|---|---|---|---|
| Rental Rates | 30 | 37.10 | 2.83 | 15.48 | 13.00 |

| Variable | Q1 | Median | Q3 | Maximum |
|---|---|---|---|---|
| Rental Rates | 26.00 | 35.00 | 45.00 | 72.00 |

**EXCEL**

| | A | B |
|---|---|---|
| 1 | Mean | 37.1 |
| 2 | Standard Error | 2.826943 |
| 3 | Median | 35 |
| 4 | Mode | 30 |
| 5 | Standard Deviation | 15.48381 |
| 6 | Sample Variance | 239.7483 |
| 7 | Kurtosis | 0.2787 |
| 8 | Skewness | 0.689938 |
| 9 | Range | 59 |
| 10 | Minimum | 13 |
| 11 | Maximum | 72 |
| 12 | Sum | 1113 |
| 13 | Count | 30 |

**TI-84 PLUS**

1-Var Stats
$\bar{x}$=37.1
Σx=1113
Σx²=48245
Sx=15.48380689
σx=15.22355631
↓n=30

Sample Mean

Sample Standard Deviation

**TRY IT YOURSELF 4**

Sample office rental rates (in dollars per square foot per year) for Dallas are listed. Use technology to find the mean rental rate and the sample standard deviation. *(Adapted from LoopNet.com)*

29 27 25 32 14 18 24 26 25 17
15 19 16 19 14 14 13 26 24 20
22 20 14 15 16 38 26 26 25 6

*Answer: Page A37*

## Interpreting Standard Deviation

When interpreting the standard deviation, remember that it is a measure of the typical amount an entry deviates from the mean. The more the entries are spread out, the greater the standard deviation.

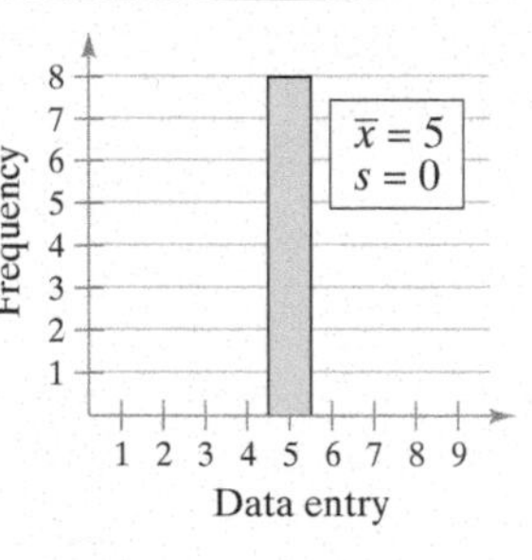


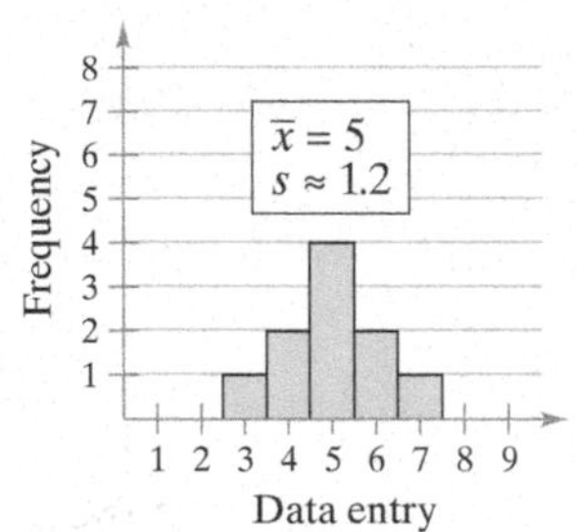


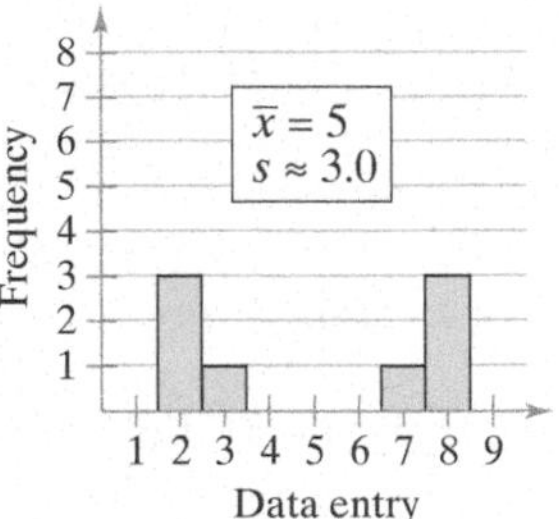

### Study Tip

You can use standard deviation to compare variation in data sets that use the same units of measure and have means that are about the same. For instance, in the data sets with $\bar{x} = 5$ shown at the right, the data set with $s \approx 3.0$ is more spread out than the other data sets. Not all data sets, however, use the same units of measure or have approximately equal means. To compare variation in these data sets, use the *coefficient of variation,* which is discussed later in this section.

**EXAMPLE 5**

### Estimating Standard Deviation

Without calculating, estimate the population standard deviation of each data set.

**1.**

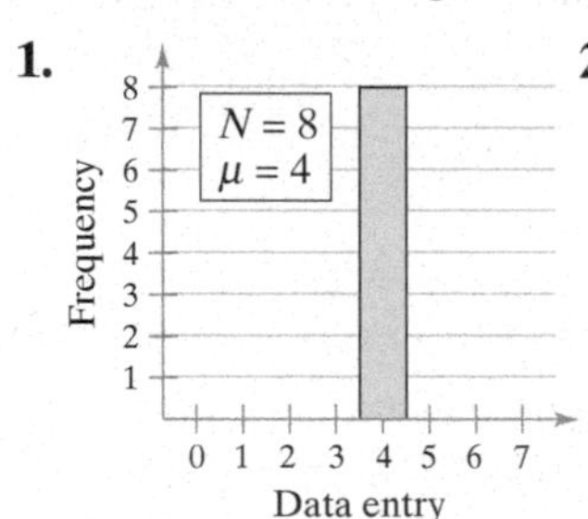


**2.**

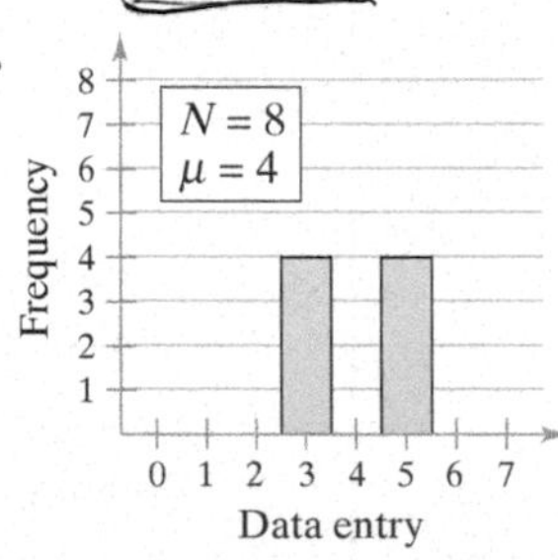


**3.**

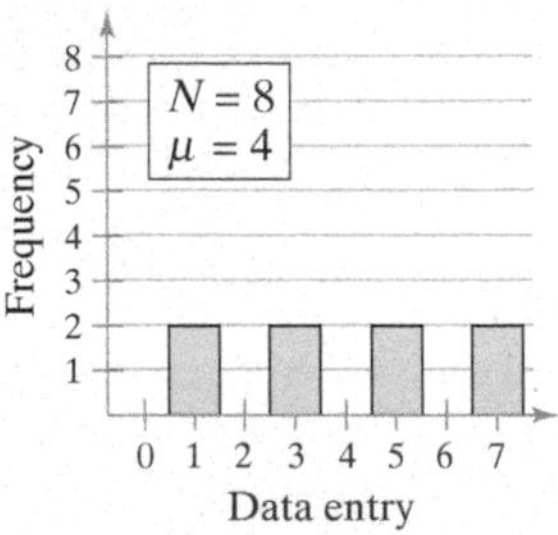


**2.4** To explore this topic further, see **Activity 2.4** on page 100.

**SOLUTION**

**1.** Each of the eight entries is 4. The deviation of each entry is 0, so

$\sigma = 0.$ Standard deviation

**2.** Each of the eight entries has a deviation of $\pm 1$. So, the population standard deviation should be 1. By calculating, you can see that

$\sigma = 1.$ Standard deviation

**3.** Each of the eight entries has a deviation of $\pm 1$ or $\pm 3$. So, the population standard deviation should be about 2. By calculating, you can see that $\sigma$ is greater than 2, with

$\sigma \approx 2.2.$ Standard deviation

**TRY IT YOURSELF 5**

Write a data set that has 10 entries, a mean of 10, and a population standard deviation that is approximately 3. (There are many correct answers.)

*Answer: Page A37*

| Entry $x$ | Deviation $x - \mu$ | Squares $(x - \mu)^2$ |
|---|---|---|
| 1 | −3 | 9 |
| 3 | −1 | 1 |
| 5 | 1 | 1 |
| 7 | 3 | 9 |

Data entries that lie more than two standard deviations from the mean are considered unusual, while those that lie more than three standard deviations from the mean are very unusual. Unusual and very unusual entries have a greater influence on the standard deviation than entries closer to the mean. This happens because the deviations are squared. Consider the data entries from Example 5, part 3 (see table at the left). The squares of the deviations of the entries farther from the mean (1 and 7) have a greater influence on the value of the standard deviation than those closer to the mean (3 and 5).

## Picturing the World

A survey was conducted by the National Center for Health Statistics to find the mean height of men in the United States. The histogram shows the distribution of heights for a sample of men ages 20–29. In this group, the mean was 69.2 inches and the standard deviation was 2.8 inches. (Adapted from National Center for Health Statistics)

**Heights of Men in the U.S. Ages 20–29**

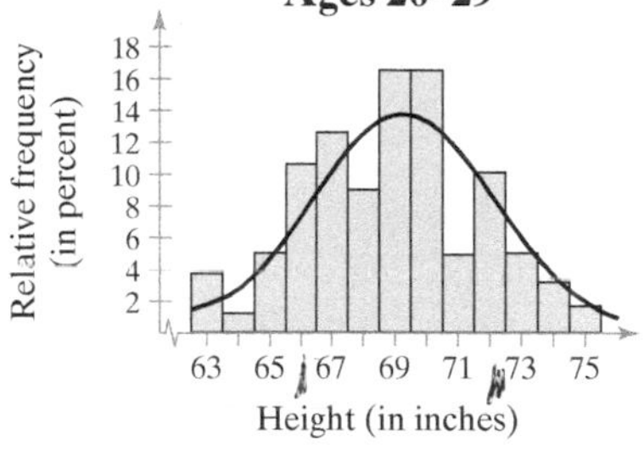


**Estimate which two heights contain the middle 95% of the data. The height of a twenty-five-year-old man is 74 inches. Is this height unusual? Why or why not?**

Many real-life data sets have distributions that are approximately symmetric and bell-shaped (see figure below). For instance, the distributions of men's and women's heights in the United States are approximately symmetric and bell-shaped (see the figures at the left and bottom left). Later in the text, you will study bell-shaped distributions in greater detail. For now, however, the **Empirical Rule** can help you see how valuable the standard deviation can be as a measure of variation.

**Bell-Shaped Distribution**

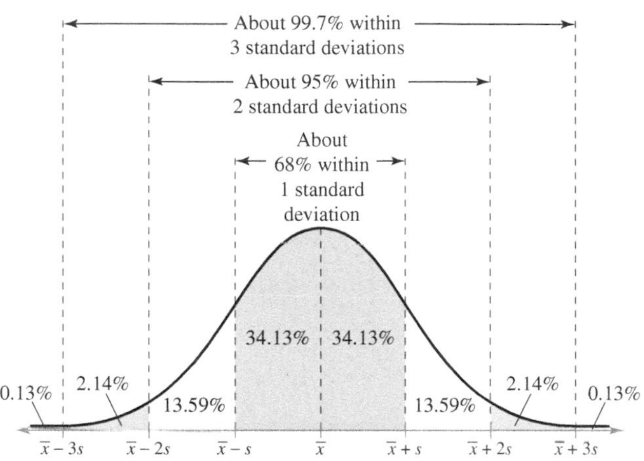


### Empirical Rule (or 68-95-99.7 Rule)

For data sets with distributions that are approximately symmetric and bell-shaped (see figure above), the standard deviation has these characteristics.

1. About 68% of the data lie within one standard deviation of the mean.
2. About 95% of the data lie within two standard deviations of the mean.
3. About 99.7% of the data lie within three standard deviations of the mean.

## EXAMPLE 6

### Using the Empirical Rule

A survey was conducted by the National Center for Health Statistics to find the mean height of women in the United States. For a sample of women ages 20–29, the mean height was 64.1 inches and the standard deviation was 2.6 inches. Estimate the percent of women whose heights are between 58.9 and 64.1 inches. *(Adapted from National Center for Health Statistics)*

**Heights of Women in the U.S. Ages 20–29**

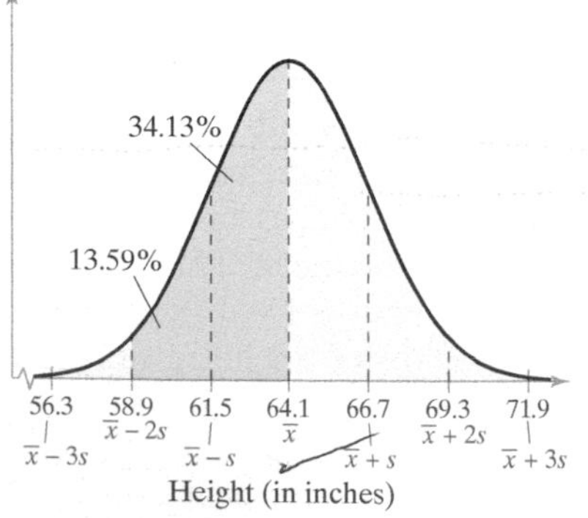


#### SOLUTION

The distribution of women's heights is shown at the left. Because the distribution is bell-shaped, you can use the Empirical Rule. The mean height is 64.1, so when you subtract two standard deviations from the mean height, you get

$$\bar{x} - 2s = 64.1 - 2(2.6) = 58.9.$$

Because 58.9 is two standard deviations below the mean height, the percent of the heights between 58.9 and 64.1 inches is about 13.59% + 34.13% = 47.72%.

***Interpretation*** So, about 47.72% of women are between 58.9 and 64.1 inches tall.

#### TRY IT YOURSELF 6

Estimate the percent of women ages 20–29 whose heights are between 64.1 inches and 66.7 inches.

*Answer: Page A37*

The Empirical Rule applies only to (symmetric) bell-shaped distributions. What if the distribution is not bell-shaped, or what if the shape of the distribution is not known? The next theorem gives an inequality statement that applies to *all* distributions. It is named after the Russian statistician Pafnuti Chebychev (1821–1894).

## Chebychev's Theorem

The portion of any data set lying within $k$ standard deviations ($k > 1$) of the mean is at least

$$1 - \frac{1}{k^2}.$$

- $k = 2$: In any data set, at least $1 - \frac{1}{2^2} = \frac{3}{4}$, or 75%, of the data lie within 2 standard deviations of the mean.
- $k = 3$: In any data set, at least $1 - \frac{1}{3^2} = \frac{8}{9}$, or about 88.9%, of the data lie within 3 standard deviations of the mean.

## EXAMPLE 7

### Using Chebychev's Theorem

The age distributions for Georgia and Iowa are shown in the histograms. Apply Chebychev's Theorem to the data for Georgia using $k = 2$. What can you conclude? Is an age of 90 unusual for a Georgia resident? Explain. *(Source: Based on U.S. Census Bureau)*

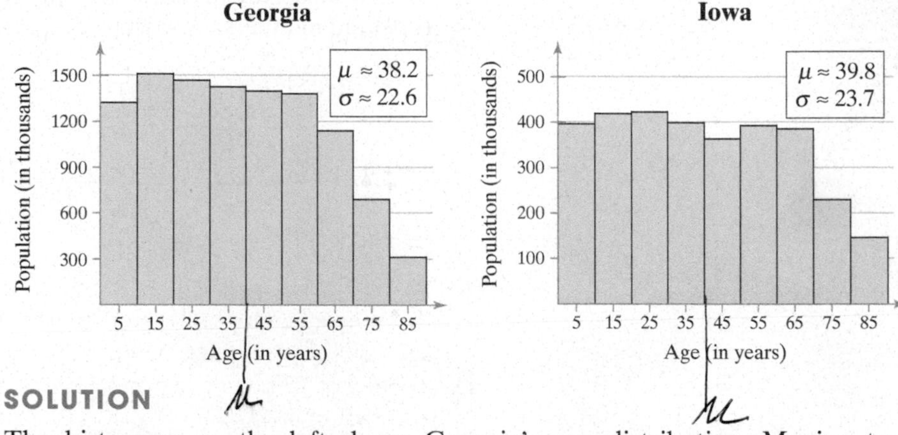


**SOLUTION**

The histogram on the left shows Georgia's age distribution. Moving two standard deviations to the left of the mean puts you below 0, because $\mu - 2\sigma \approx 38.2 - 2(22.6) = -7.0$. Moving two standard deviations to the right of the mean puts you at

$$\mu + 2\sigma \approx 38.2 + 2(22.6) = 83.4.$$

By Chebychev's Theorem, you can say that at least 75% of the population of Georgia is between birth (0) and 83.4 years old. Also, because $90 > 83.4$, an age of 90 lies more than two standard deviations from the mean. So, this age is unusual.

**TRY IT YOURSELF 7**

Apply Chebychev's Theorem to the data for Iowa using $k = 2$. What can you conclude? Is an age of 80 unusual for an Iowa resident? Explain.

*Answer: Page A37*

### Study Tip

In Example 7, Chebychev's Theorem gives you an inequality statement that says at least 75% of the population of Georgia is under the age of 83.4. This is a true statement, but it is not nearly as strong a statement as could be made from reading the histogram. In general, Chebychev's Theorem gives the minimum percent of data entries that fall within the given number of standard deviations of the mean. Depending on the distribution, there is probably a higher percent of data falling in the given range.

**Study Tip**

Remember that formulas for grouped data require you to multiply by the frequencies.

## Standard Deviation for Grouped Data

In Section 2.1, you learned that large data sets are usually best represented by frequency distributions. The formula for the sample standard deviation for a frequency distribution is

$$\text{Sample standard deviation} = s = \sqrt{\frac{\Sigma(x - \bar{x})^2 f}{n - 1}}$$

where $n = \Sigma f$ is the number of entries in the data set.

**EXAMPLE 8**

### Finding the Standard Deviation for Grouped Data

You collect a random sample of the number of children per household in a region. The results are listed below. Find the sample mean and the sample standard deviation of the data set.

1 3 1 1 1 1 2 2 1 0
1 1 0 0 0 1 5 0 3 6
3 0 3 1 1 1 1 6 0 1
3 6 6 1 2 2 3 0 1 1
4 1 1 2 2 0 3 0 2 4

**SOLUTION**

These data could be treated as 50 individual entries, and you could use the formulas for mean and standard deviation. Because there are so many repeated numbers, however, it is easier to use a frequency distribution.

| $x$ | $f$ | $xf$ |
|---|---|---|
| 0 | 10 | 0 |
| 1 | 19 | 19 |
| 2 | 7 | 14 |
| 3 | 7 | 21 |
| 4 | 2 | 8 |
| 5 | 1 | 5 |
| 6 | 4 | 24 |
| | $\Sigma = 50$ | $\Sigma = 91$ |

| $x - \bar{x}$ | $(x - \bar{x})^2$ | $(x - \bar{x})^2 f$ |
|---|---|---|
| −1.82 | 3.3124 | 33.1240 |
| −0.82 | 0.6724 | 12.7756 |
| 0.18 | 0.0324 | 0.2268 |
| 1.18 | 1.3924 | 9.7468 |
| 2.18 | 4.7524 | 9.5048 |
| 3.18 | 10.1124 | 10.1124 |
| 4.18 | 17.4724 | 69.8896 |
| | | $\Sigma = 145.38$ |

$$\bar{x} = \frac{\Sigma xf}{n} = \frac{91}{50} = 1.82 \approx 1.8$$ Sample mean

Use the sum of squares to find the sample standard deviation.

$$s = \sqrt{\frac{\Sigma(x - \bar{x})^2 f}{n - 1}} = \sqrt{\frac{145.38}{49}} \approx 1.7$$ Sample standard deviation

So, the sample mean is about 1.8 children, and the sample standard deviation is about 1.7 children.

**TRY IT YOURSELF 8**

Change three of the 6's in the data set to 4's. How does this change affect the sample mean and sample standard deviation? *Answer: Page A37*

When a frequency distribution has classes, you can estimate the sample mean and the sample standard deviation by using the midpoint of each class.

## EXAMPLE 9

### Using Midpoints of Classes

The figure below shows the price ranges (in thousands of dollars) and corresponding number of homes recently listed for sale in a mid-sized U.S. city. Make a frequency distribution for the data. Then use the table to estimate the sample mean and the sample standard deviation of the data set. *(Adapted from National Association of Realtors and Move, Inc.)*

**Sales Prices of Homes**
(in thousands of dollars) in a mid-sized city

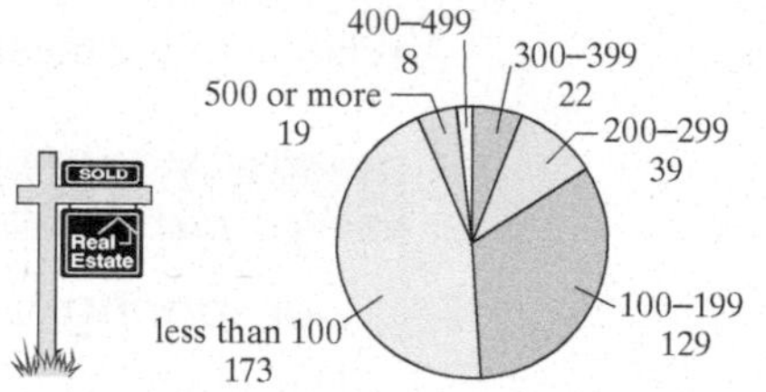


**SOLUTION**

Begin by using a frequency distribution to organize the data. Because the class of \$500 thousand or more is open-ended, you must choose a value to represent the midpoint, such as 599.5 thousand.

| Sales price (in thousands of dollars) | $x$ | $f$ | $xf$ |
|---|---|---|---|
| 0–99 | 49.5 | 173 | 8563.5 |
| 100–199 | 149.5 | 129 | 19,285.5 |
| 200–299 | 249.5 | 39 | 9730.5 |
| 300–399 | 349.5 | 22 | 7689.0 |
| 400–499 | 449.5 | 8 | 3596.0 |
| 500+ | 599.5 | 19 | 11,390.5 |
| | | $\Sigma = 390$ | $\Sigma = 60{,}255.0$ |

| $x - \bar{x}$ | $(x - \bar{x})^2$ | $(x - \bar{x})^2 f$ |
|---|---|---|
| −105 | 11,025 | 1,907,325 |
| −5 | 25 | 3225 |
| 95 | 9025 | 351,975 |
| 195 | 38,025 | 836,550 |
| 295 | 87,025 | 696,200 |
| 445 | 198,025 | 3,762,475 |
| | | $\Sigma = 7{,}557{,}750$ |

$$\bar{x} = \frac{\Sigma xf}{n} = \frac{60{,}255.0}{390} = 154.5 \qquad \text{Sample mean}$$

Use the sum of squares to find the sample standard deviation.

$$s = \sqrt{\frac{\Sigma(x - \bar{x})^2 f}{n - 1}} = \sqrt{\frac{7{,}557{,}750}{389}} \approx 139.4 \qquad \text{Sample standard deviation}$$

So, an estimate for the sample mean is \$154,500 per year, and an estimate for the sample standard deviation is \$139,400.

**TRY IT YOURSELF 9**

In the frequency distribution in Example 9, 599.5 was chosen as the midpoint for the class of \$500 or more. How does the sample mean and standard deviation change when the midpoint of this class is 650?

*Answer: Page A37*

## Coefficient of Variation

To compare variation in different data sets, you can use standard deviation when the data sets use the same units of measure and have means that are about the same. For data sets with different units of measure or different means, use the **coefficient of variation.**

Quiz # 18

**DEFINITION**

The **coefficient of variation ($CV$)** of a data set describes the standard deviation as a percent of the mean.

Population: $CV = \frac{\sigma}{\mu} \cdot 100\%$ Sample: $CV = \frac{s}{\bar{x}} \cdot 100\%$

Note that the coefficient of variation measures the variation of a data set relative to the mean of the data.

**EXAMPLE 10**

### Comparing Variation in Different Data Sets

The table below shows the population heights (in inches) and weights (in pounds) of the members of a basketball team. Find the coefficient of variation for the heights and the weights. Then compare the results.

**Heights and Weights of a Basketball Team**

| **Heights** | 72 | 74 | 68 | 76 | 74 | 69 | 72 | 79 | 70 | 69 | 77 | 73 |
|---|---|---|---|---|---|---|---|---|---|---|---|---|
| **Weights** | 180 | 168 | 225 | 201 | 189 | 192 | 197 | 162 | 174 | 171 | 185 | 210 |

**SOLUTION**

The mean height is $\mu \approx 72.8$ inches with a standard deviation of $\sigma \approx 3.3$ inches. The coefficient of variation for the heights is

$$\begin{aligned} CV_{\text{height}} &= \frac{\sigma}{\mu} \cdot 100\% \\ &= \frac{3.3}{72.8} \cdot 100\% \\ &\approx 4.5\%. \end{aligned}$$

The mean weight is $\mu \approx 187.8$ pounds with a standard deviation of $\sigma \approx 17.7$ pounds. The coefficient of variation for the weights is

$$\begin{aligned} CV_{\text{weight}} &= \frac{\sigma}{\mu} \cdot 100\% \\ &= \frac{17.7}{187.8} \cdot 100\% \\ &\approx 9.4\%. \end{aligned}$$

***Interpretation*** The weights (9.4%) are more variable than the heights (4.5%).

**TRY IT YOURSELF 10**

Find the coefficient of variation for the office rental rates in Los Angeles (see Example 4) and for those in Dallas (see Try It Yourself 4). Then compare the results.

*Answer: Page A37*

# 2.4 EXERCISES

For Extra Help: MyLab Statistics

## Building Basic Skills and Vocabulary

1. Explain how to find the range of a data set. What is an advantage of using the range as a measure of variation? What is a disadvantage?
2. Explain how to find the deviation of an entry in a data set. What is the sum of all the deviations in any data set?
3. Why is the standard deviation used more frequently than the variance?
4. Explain the relationship between variance and standard deviation. Can either of these measures be negative? Explain.
5. Describe the difference between the calculation of population standard deviation and that of sample standard deviation.
6. Given a data set, how do you know whether to calculate $\sigma$ or $s$?
7. Discuss the similarities and the differences between the Empirical Rule and Chebychev's Theorem.
8. What must you know about a data set before you can use the Empirical Rule?

## Using and Interpreting Concepts

**Finding the Range of a Data Set** *In Exercises 9 and 10, find the range of the data set represented by the graph.*

**9.** **Median Annual Income by State**

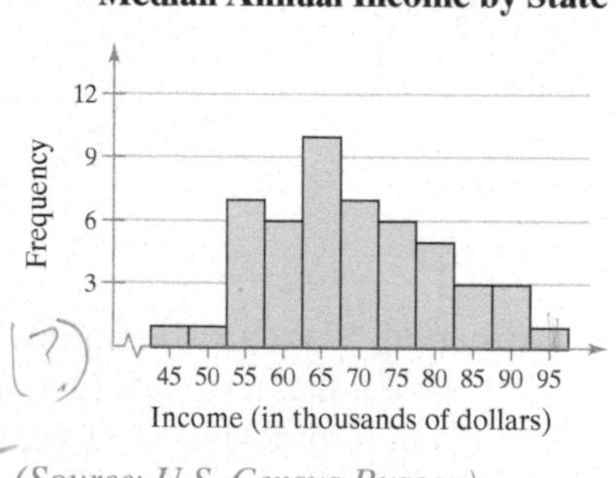


*(Source: U.S. Census Bureau)*

**10.**

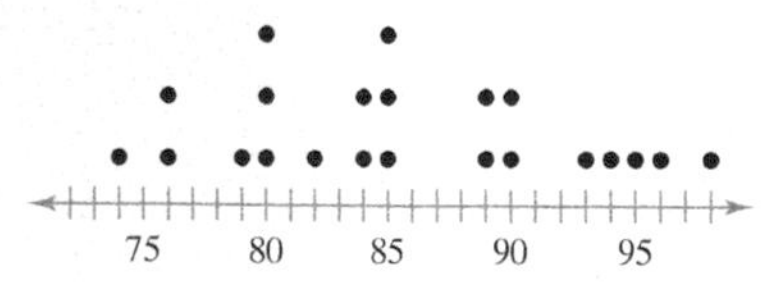


11. **Archaeology** The depths (in inches) at which 10 artifacts are found are listed.

    20.7 24.8 30.5 26.2 36.0 34.3 30.3 29.5 27.0 38.5

    (a) Find the range of the data set.

    (b) Change 38.5 to 60.5 and find the range of the new data set.

12. In Exercise 11, compare your answer to part (a) with your answer to part (b). How do outliers affect the range of a data set?

**Finding Population Statistics** *In Exercises 13 and 14, find the range, mean, variance, and standard deviation of the population data set.*

13. **Drunk Driving** The number of alcohol-impaired crash fatalities (in thousands) per year from 2010 through 2019 *(Source: National Highway Traffic Safety Administration)*

    10.1 9.9 10.3 10.1 9.9 10.3 11.0 10.9 10.7 10.1

**14. Density** The densities (in kilograms per cubic meter) of the ten most abundant elements by weight in Earth's crust

| | | | | |
|---|---|---|---|---|
| 1.4 | 2330 | 2700 | 7870 | 1500 |
| 970 | 900 | 1740 | 4500 | 0.09 |

**Finding Sample Statistics** *In Exercises 15 and 16, find the range, mean, variance, and standard deviation of the sample data set.*

**15. Ages of Students** The ages (in years) of a random sample of students in a campus dining hall

| | | | | | | | | | |
|---|---|---|---|---|---|---|---|---|---|
| 19 | 20 | 17 | 19 | 17 | 21 | 23 | 21 | 17 | 17 |
| 19 | 19 | 17 | 20 | 23 | 18 | 18 | 18 | 18 | 19 |

**16. Pregnancy Durations** The durations (in days) of pregnancies for a random sample of pregnant people

| | | | | | | |
|---|---|---|---|---|---|---|
| 277 | 291 | 295 | 280 | 268 | 278 | 291 |
| 277 | 282 | 279 | 296 | 285 | 269 | 293 |
| 267 | 281 | 286 | 269 | 264 | 299 | 275 |

**17. Estimating Standard Deviation** Both data sets shown in the histograms have a mean of 50. One has a standard deviation of 2.4, and the other has a standard deviation of 5. By looking at the histograms, which is which? Explain your reasoning.

(a)

Frequency

20
15
10
5

42 45 48 51 54 57 60

Data entry

(b)

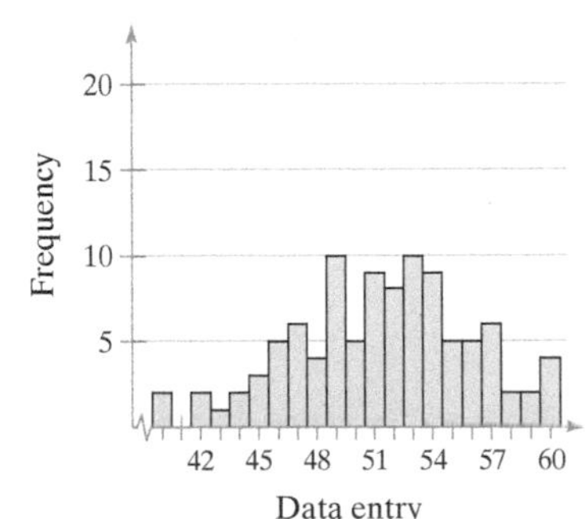


**18. Estimating Standard Deviation** Both data sets shown in the stem-and-leaf plots have a mean of 165. One has a standard deviation of 16, and the other has a standard deviation of 24. By looking at the stem-and-leaf plots, which is which? Explain your reasoning.

(a) Key: 12|8 = 128

| Stem | Leaves |
|---|---|
| 12 | 8 9 |
| 13 | 5 5 8 |
| 14 | 1 2 |
| 15 | 0 0 6 7 |
| 16 | 4 5 9 |
| 17 | 1 3 6 8 |
| 18 | 0 8 9 |
| 19 | 6 |
| 20 | 3 5 7 |

(b) Key: 13|1 = 131

| Stem | Leaves |
|---|---|
| 12 | |
| 13 | 1 |
| 14 | 2 3 5 |
| 15 | 0 4 5 6 8 |
| 16 | 1 1 2 3 3 3 |
| 17 | 1 5 8 8 |
| 18 | 2 3 4 5 |
| 19 | 0 2 |
| 20 | |

**19. Salary Offers** You are applying for jobs at two companies. Company A offers starting salaries with $\mu = \$41,000$ and $\sigma = \$1000$. Company B offers starting salaries with $\mu = \$41,000$ and $\sigma = \$5000$. From which company are you more likely to get an offer of \$43,000 or more? Explain your reasoning.

**20. Salary Offers** You are applying for jobs at two companies. Company C offers starting salaries with $\mu = \$59{,}000$ and $\sigma = \$1500$. Company D offers starting salaries with $\mu = \$59{,}000$ and $\sigma = \$1000$. From which company are you more likely to get an offer of \$62,000 or more? Explain your reasoning.

**Graphical Analysis** *In Exercises 21–24, you are asked to compare three data sets. (a) Without calculating, determine which data set has the greatest sample standard deviation and which has the least sample standard deviation. Explain your reasoning. (b) How are the data sets the same? How do they differ? (c) Estimate the sample standard deviations. Then determine how close each of your estimates is by finding the sample standard deviations.*

**21.** (i)

(ii)

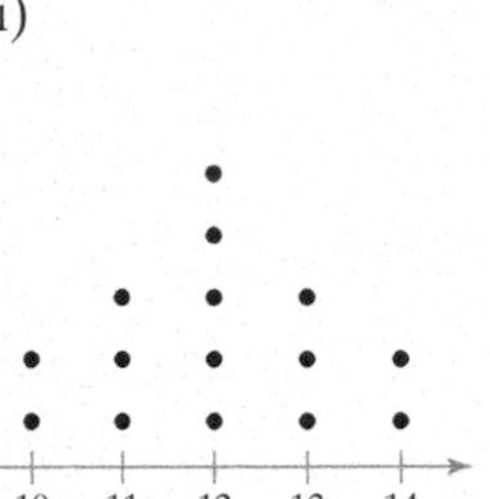

(iii)

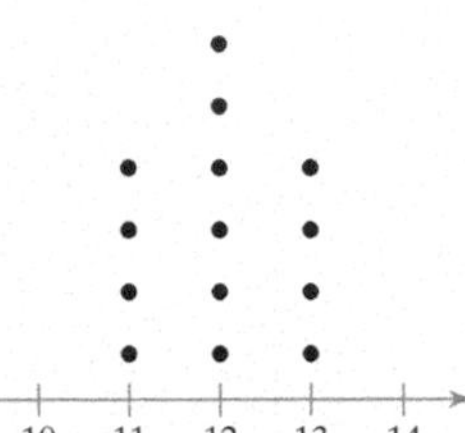

**22.** (i)

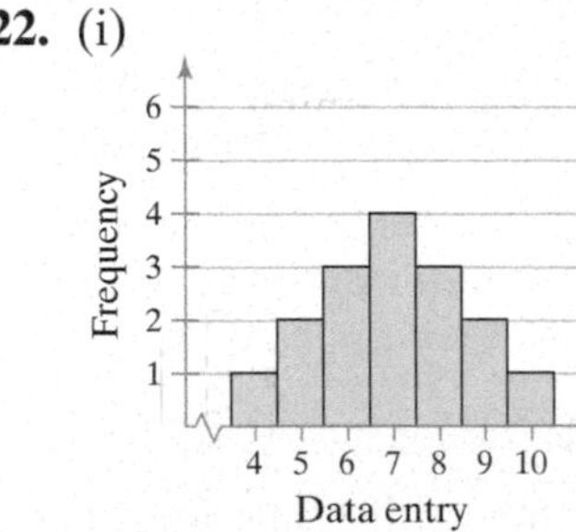

(ii)

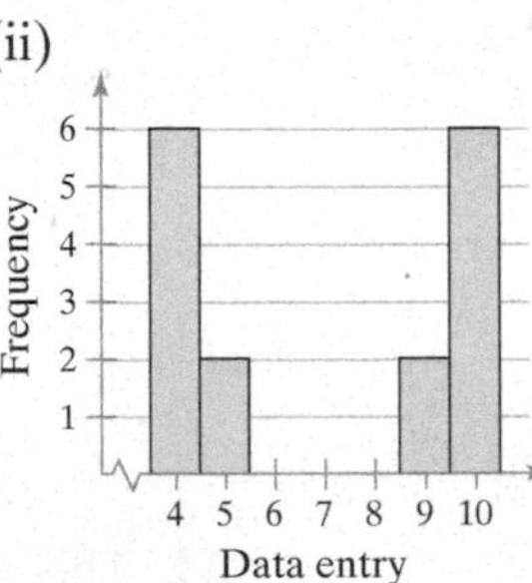

(iii)

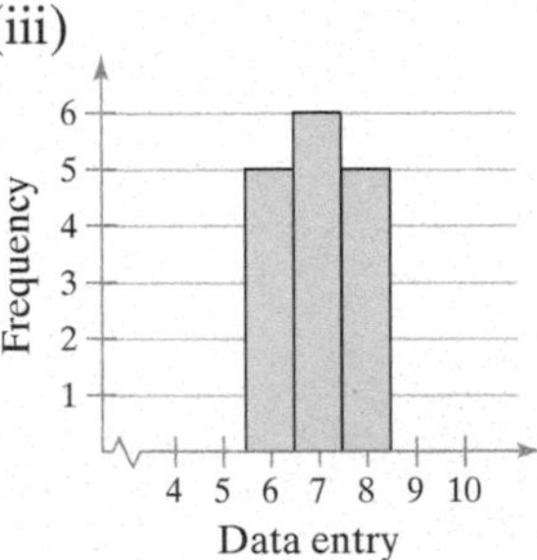

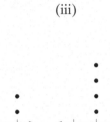

**23.** (i)

| | |
|---|---|
| 0 | 9 |
| 1 | 5 8 |
| 2 | 3 3 7 7 |
| 3 | 2 5 |
| 4 | 1 |

Key: 1|5 = 15

(ii)

| | |
|---|---|
| 0 | 9 |
| 1 | 5 |
| 2 | 3 3 3 7 7 7 |
| 3 | 5 |
| 4 | 1 |

Key: 1|5 = 15

(iii)

| | |
|---|---|
| 0 | |
| 1 | 5 |
| 2 | 3 3 3 3 7 7 7 7 |
| 3 | 5 |
| 4 | |

Key: 1|5 = 15

**24.** (i)

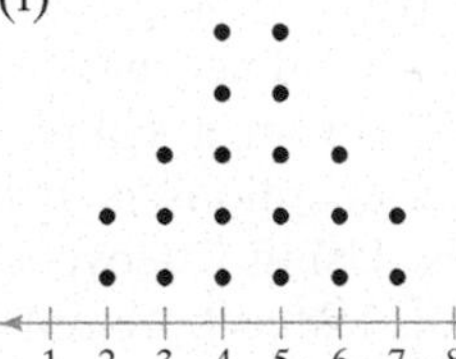

(ii)

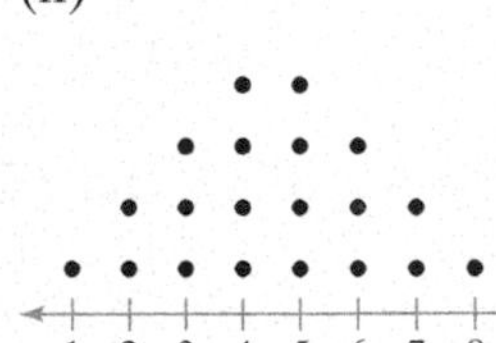

(iii)

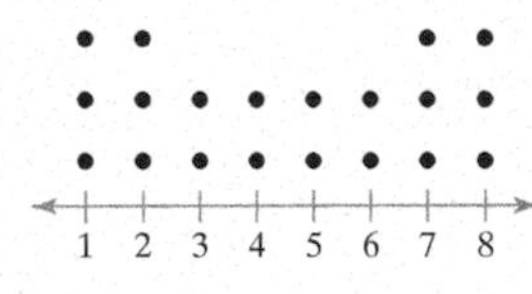

**Constructing Data Sets** *In Exercises 25–28, construct a data set that has the given statistics.*

**25.** $N = 6$

$\mu = 5$

$\sigma \approx 2$

**26.** $N = 8$

$\mu = 6$

$\sigma \approx 3$

**27.** $n = 7$

$\bar{x} = 9$

$s = 0$

**28.** $n = 6$

$\bar{x} = 7$

$s = 2$

**Using the Empirical Rule** *In Exercises 29–34, use the Empirical Rule.*

**29.** The mean speed of a sample of vehicles along a stretch of highway is 67 miles per hour, with a standard deviation of 4 miles per hour. Estimate the percent of vehicles whose speeds are between 63 miles per hour and 71 miles per hour. (Assume the data set has a bell-shaped distribution.)

**30.** The mean monthly utility bill for a sample of households in a city is \$70, with a standard deviation of \$8. Between what two values do about 95% of the data lie? (Assume the data set has a bell-shaped distribution.)

**31.** Use the sample statistics from Exercise 29 and assume the number of vehicles in the sample is 75.

(a) Estimate the number of vehicles whose speeds are between 63 miles per hour and 71 miles per hour.

(b) In a sample of 25 additional vehicles, about how many vehicles would you expect to have speeds between 63 miles per hour and 71 miles per hour?

**32.** Use the sample statistics from Exercise 30 and assume the number of households in the sample is 40.

(a) Estimate the number of households whose monthly utility bills are between \$54 and \$86.

(b) In a sample of 20 additional households, about how many households would you expect to have monthly utility bills between \$54 and \$86?

**33.** The speeds for eight vehicles are listed. Using the sample statistics from Exercise 29, determine which of the data entries are unusual. Are any of the data entries very unusual? Explain your reasoning.

70, 78, 62, 71, 65, 76, 82, 64

**34.** The monthly utility bills for eight households are listed. Using the sample statistics from Exercise 30, determine which of the data entries are unusual. Are any of the data entries very unusual? Explain your reasoning.

\$65, \$52, \$63, \$83, \$77, \$98, \$84, \$70

**35. Using Chebychev's Theorem** You are conducting a survey on the number of pets per household in your region. From a sample with $n = 40$, the mean number of pets per household is 2 pets and the standard deviation is 1 pet. Using Chebychev's Theorem, determine at least how many of the households have 0 to 4 pets.

**36. Using Chebychev's Theorem** Old Faithful is a famous geyser at Yellowstone National Park. From a sample with $n = 100$, the mean interval between Old Faithful's eruptions is 101.56 minutes and the standard deviation is 42.69 minutes. Using Chebychev's Theorem, determine at least how many of the intervals lasted between 16.18 minutes and 186.94 minutes. *(Adapted from Geyser Times)*

**37. Using Chebychev's Theorem** The mean score on a Statistics exam is 82 points, with a standard deviation of 3 points. Apply Chebychev's Theorem to the data using $k = 4$. Interpret the results.

**38. Using Chebychev's Theorem** The mean number of runs per game scored by the Los Angeles Dodgers during the 2020 World Series was 5.3 runs, with a standard deviation of 1.8 runs. Apply Chebychev's Theorem to the data using $k = 2$. Interpret the results. *(Source: Major League Baseball)*

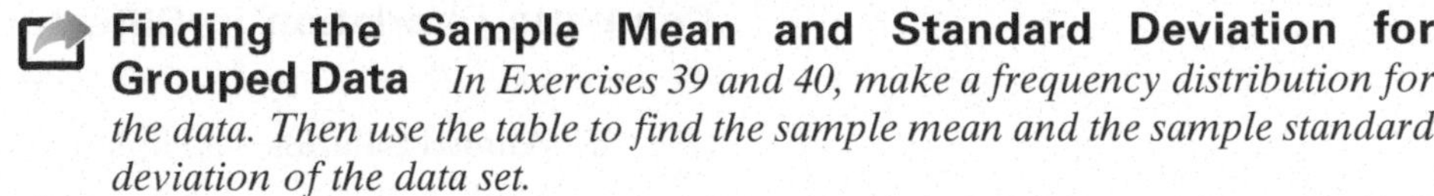

**Finding the Sample Mean and Standard Deviation for Grouped Data** *In Exercises 39 and 40, make a frequency distribution for the data. Then use the table to find the sample mean and the sample standard deviation of the data set.*

**39.** 3 3 5 3 8 0 3 9 6 6 7 1 6 3 2 6 9 1 8 5 0 2 3 4 9
5 8 1 9 7 6 9 6 7 0 6 3 8 6 8 7 3 8 9 3 7 2 4 4 1

**40.** 1 1 1 0 0 0 0 0 1 0 1 0 0 1 0 1 1 0 0 0 0 1 0 0 1
1 1 0 0 1 1 0 0 0 0 0 1 0 1 1 1 0 0 0 0 1 1 0 0 0

**Estimating the Sample Mean and Standard Deviation for Grouped Data** *In Exercises 41–44, make a frequency distribution for the data. Then use the table to estimate the sample mean and the sample standard deviation of the data set.*

**41. College Expenses** The distribution of the tuitions, fees, and room and board charges of a random sample of public 4-year degree-granting postsecondary institutions is shown in the pie chart. Use $28,249.50 as the midpoint for "$27,000 or more."

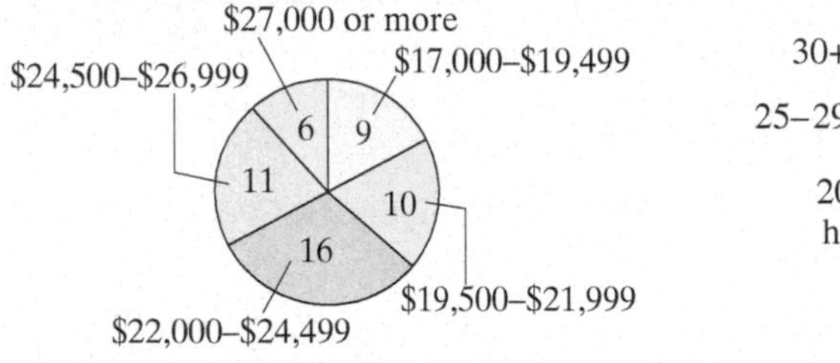


FIGURE FOR EXERCISE 41

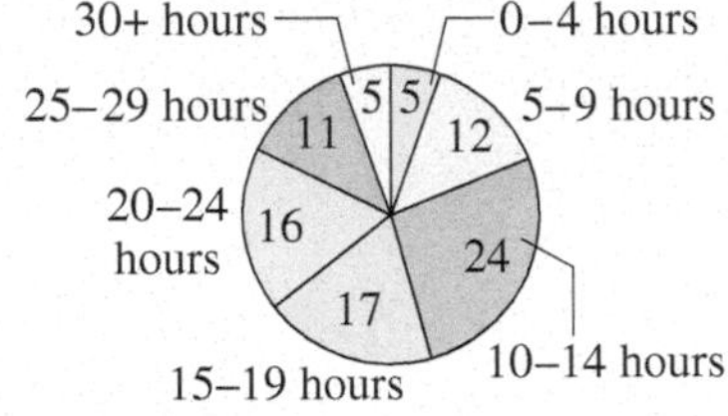


FIGURE FOR EXERCISE 42

**42. Weekly Study Hours** The distribution of the number of hours that a random sample of college students study per week is shown in the pie chart. Use 32 as the midpoint for "30+ hours."

**43. Teaching Load** The number of courses taught per semester by a random sample of university professors are shown in the histogram.

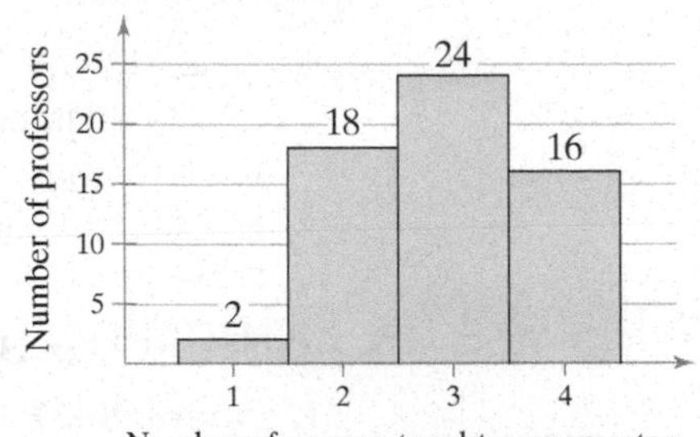


**44. Amounts of Caffeine** The amounts of caffeine in a sample of five-ounce servings of brewed coffee are shown in the histogram.

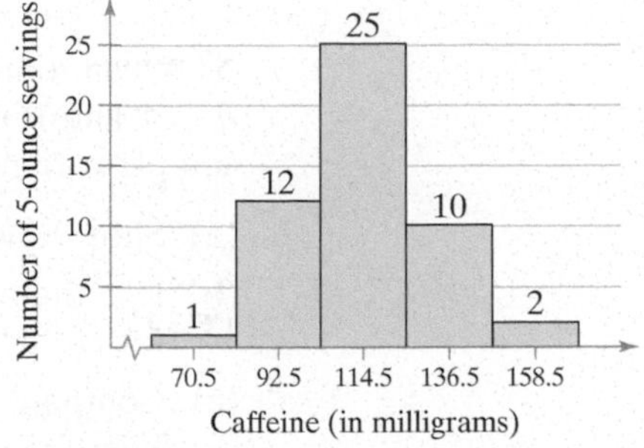

**Comparing Variation in Different Data Sets** *In Exercises 45–50, find the coefficient of variation for each of the two data sets. Then compare the results.*

**45. Annual Salaries** Sample annual salaries (in thousands of dollars) for entry level architects in Denver, CO, and Los Angeles, CA, are listed.

| | | | | | | |
|---|---|---|---|---|---|---|
| **Denver** | 55.2 | 55.8 | 53.8 | 50.1 | 60.9 | 48.9 |
| | 53.6 | 62.5 | 54.2 | 61.0 | 50.7 | 58.4 |
| **Los Angeles** | 68.4 | 62.3 | 67.7 | 60.2 | 67.4 | 67.3 |
| | 59.3 | 68.0 | 59.8 | 58.0 | 63.6 | 72.9 |

**46. Annual Salaries** Sample annual salaries (in thousands of dollars) for entry level software engineers in Raleigh, NC, and Wichita, KS, are listed.

| | | | | | | | | | |
|---|---|---|---|---|---|---|---|---|---|
| **Raleigh** | 69.5 | 74.2 | 65.1 | 56.5 | 65.6 | 62.1 | 79.5 | 72.4 | 58.3 |
| **Wichita** | 59.7 | 76.0 | 57.1 | 79.7 | 55.2 | 70.7 | 80.0 | 78.8 | 64.2 |

**47. Ages and Caps** The ages (in years) and caps (number of matches played) of all members of the 2021 Women's U.S. soccer team are listed. *(Source: U.S. Soccer)*

| | | | | | | | | | | | | |
|---|---|---|---|---|---|---|---|---|---|---|---|---|
| **Ages** | 26 | 23 | 27 | 22 | 28 | 28 | 26 | 25 | 38 | 21 | 30 | 28 |
| | 31 | 24 | 32 | 32 | 32 | 25 | 35 | 35 | 20 | 27 | 27 | |
| **Caps** | 5 | 2 | 65 | 28 | 109 | 108 | 91 | 51 | 299 | 3 | 21 | 70 |
| | 173 | 0 | 67 | 134 | 142 | 6 | 173 | 182 | 3 | 51 | 33 | |

**48. Heights and Weights** The heights (in inches) and weights (in pounds) of every France national soccer team player that started the 2018 FIFA Men's World Cup final are listed. *(Source: ESPN)*

| | | | | | | | | | | | |
|---|---|---|---|---|---|---|---|---|---|---|---|
| **Heights** | 74 | 73 | 75 | 72 | 72 | 76 | 66 | 70 | 69 | 69 | 76 |
| **Weights** | 181 | 168 | 179 | 163 | 168 | 183 | 150 | 161 | 161 | 152 | 203 |

**49. SAT Scores** Sample SAT scores for eight males and eight females are listed.

| | | | | | | | | |
|---|---|---|---|---|---|---|---|---|
| **Males** | 1010 | 1170 | 1410 | 920 | 1320 | 1100 | 690 | 1140 |
| **Females** | 1190 | 1010 | 1000 | 1300 | 1470 | 1250 | 840 | 1060 |

**50. Grade Point Averages** Sample grade point averages for ten male students and ten female students are listed.

| | | | | | | | | | | |
|---|---|---|---|---|---|---|---|---|---|---|
| **Males** | 2.4 | 3.7 | 3.8 | 3.9 | 2.8 | 2.6 | 3.6 | 3.3 | 4.0 | 1.9 |
| **Females** | 2.8 | 3.7 | 2.1 | 3.9 | 3.6 | 4.0 | 2.0 | 3.9 | 3.7 | 2.3 |

## Extending Concepts

**51. Alternative Formula** You used $SS_x = \Sigma(x - \bar{x})^2$ when calculating variance and standard deviation. An alternative formula that is sometimes more convenient for hand calculations is

$$SS_x = \Sigma x^2 - \frac{(\Sigma x)^2}{n}.$$

You can find the sample variance by dividing the sum of squares by $n - 1$ and the sample standard deviation by finding the square root of the sample variance.

(a) Show how to obtain the alternative formula.

(b) Use the alternative formula to calculate the sample standard deviation for the data set in Exercise 15.

(c) Compare your result with the sample standard deviation obtained in Exercise 15.

**52. Mean Absolute Deviation** Another useful measure of variation for a data set is the **mean absolute deviation (MAD).** It is calculated by the formula

$$MAD = \frac{\Sigma|x - \bar{x}|}{n}.$$

For help with absolute value, see *Integrated Review* at

MyLab Statistics

(a) Find the mean absolute deviation of the data set in Exercise 15. Compare your result with the sample standard deviation obtained in Exercise 15.

(b) Find the mean absolute deviation of the data set in Exercise 16. Compare your result with the sample standard deviation obtained in Exercise 16.

**53. Scaling Data** Sample annual salaries (in thousands of dollars) for employees at a company are listed.

42 36 48 51 39 39 42
36 48 33 39 42 45 50

(a) Find the sample mean and the sample standard deviation.

(b) Each employee in the sample receives a 5% raise. Find the sample mean and the sample standard deviation for the revised data set.

(c) Find each monthly salary. Then find the sample mean and the sample standard deviation for the monthly salaries.

(d) What can you conclude from the results?

**54. Shifting Data** Sample annual salaries (in thousands of dollars) for employees at a company are listed.

40 35 49 53 38 39 40
37 49 34 38 43 47 35

(a) Find the sample mean and the sample standard deviation.

(b) Each employee in the sample receives a $1000 raise. Find the sample mean and the sample standard deviation for the revised data set.

(c) Each employee in the sample takes a pay cut of $2000 from their original salary. Find the sample mean and the sample standard deviation for the revised data set.

(d) What can you conclude from the results of (a), (b), and (c)?

**55. Pearson's Index of Skewness** The English statistician Karl Pearson (1857–1936) introduced a formula for the skewness of a distribution.

$$P = \frac{3(\bar{x} - \text{median})}{s} \qquad \text{Pearson's index of skewness}$$

Most distributions have an index of skewness between −3 and 3. When $P > 0$, the data are skewed right. When $P < 0$, the data are skewed left. When $P = 0$, the data are symmetric. Calculate the coefficient of skewness for each distribution. Describe the shape of each.

(a) $\bar{x} = 17, s = 2.3, \text{median} = 19$

(b) $\bar{x} = 32, s = 5.1, \text{median} = 25$

(c) $\bar{x} = 9.2, s = 1.8, \text{median} = 9.2$

(d) $\bar{x} = 42, s = 6.0, \text{median} = 40$

(e) $\bar{x} = 155, s = 20.0, \text{median} = 175$

**56. Chebychev's Theorem** At least 99% of the data in any data set lie within how many standard deviations of the mean? Explain how you obtained your answer.

# 2.4 ACTIVITY Standard Deviation

APPLET

You can find the interactive applet for this activity at MyLab Statistics.

The *Standard deviation* applet is designed to allow you to investigate interactively the standard deviation as a measure of spread for a data set. You can generate a data set by entering a **Sample size** and clicking **Simulate;** you can generate data values by clicking **Add point** or by clicking above the horizontal axis. The mean of the points is shown as a green arrow and the median is shown as a red arrow. A blue line segment covering the range from one standard deviation below the mean to one standard deviation above the mean is shown below the horizontal axis. Numeric values for the standard deviation and the other summary statistics are shown in the table at the right. Remove a data value by dragging the corresponding point outside the axis range. Remove all the data values and their corresponding points from the data set by clicking **Reset.**

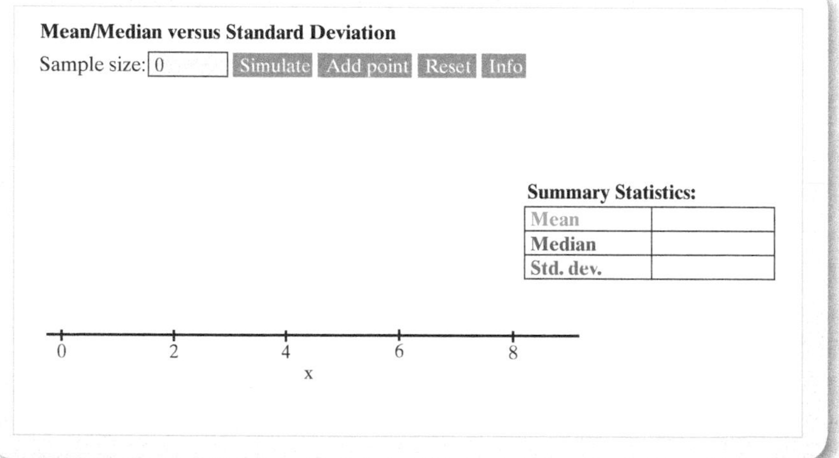


## EXPLORE

**Step 1** Specify a **Sample size.**
**Step 2** Click **Simulate.**
**Step 3** Add and remove various points to and from the plot.
**Step 4** Remove all the points from the plot.

## DRAW CONCLUSIONS

APPLET

1. Plot 10 points that have a mean of about 5 and a standard deviation of about 1. Write the estimates of the values of the points. Plot a point with a value of 15. What happens to the mean and standard deviation? Plot a point with a value of 20. What happens to the mean and standard deviation?

2. How can you plot eight points so that the points have the greatest possible standard deviation? Use the applet to plot the set of points and then use the formula for standard deviation to confirm the value given in the applet. How can you plot eight points so that the points have the least possible standard deviation? Explain.

# CASE STUDY Business Size

The number of employees at businesses can vary from a single employee to more than 1000 employees. The data shown below are the number of manufacturing businesses for nine states in a recent year. *(Source: U.S. Census Bureau)*

| State | Number of manufacturing businesses |
|---|---|
| California | 37,849 |
| Illinois | 13,154 |
| Indiana | 8,045 |
| Michigan | 12,400 |
| New York | 15,488 |
| Ohio | 13,902 |
| Pennsylvania | 13,502 |
| Texas | 19,764 |
| Wisconsin | 8,817 |

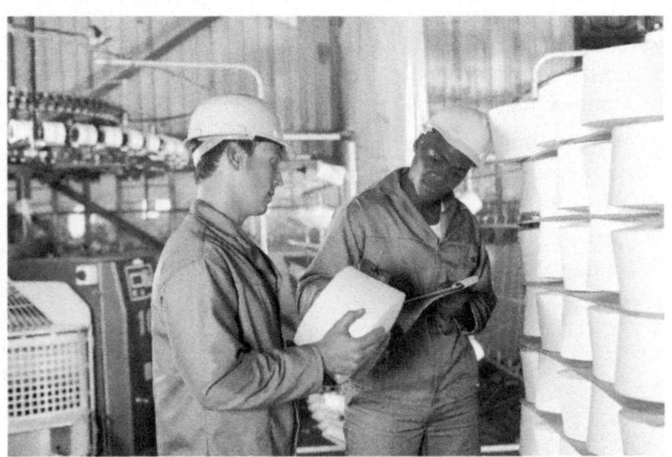

**Number of Manufacturing Businesses by Number of Employees**

| State | 1–4 | 5–9 | 10–19 | 20–49 | 50–99 | 100–249 | 250–499 | 500–999 | 1000+ |
|---|---|---|---|---|---|---|---|---|---|
| California | 15,464 | 6,929 | 5,690 | 5,253 | 2,212 | 1,599 | 456 | 161 | 85 |
| Illinois | 4,513 | 2,239 | 2,000 | 2,105 | 1,074 | 839 | 257 | 92 | 35 |
| Indiana | 2,213 | 1,288 | 1,266 | 1,370 | 797 | 701 | 244 | 120 | 46 |
| Michigan | 4,007 | 2,062 | 2,043 | 1,952 | 1,039 | 858 | 282 | 105 | 52 |
| New York | 6,809 | 2,726 | 2,245 | 2,030 | 838 | 565 | 188 | 60 | 27 |
| Ohio | 4,079 | 2,410 | 2,283 | 2,370 | 1,266 | 989 | 326 | 126 | 53 |
| Pennsylvania | 4,323 | 2,374 | 2,213 | 2,269 | 1,054 | 879 | 274 | 82 | 34 |
| Texas | 7,171 | 3,472 | 2,990 | 3,157 | 1,376 | 1,079 | 312 | 140 | 67 |
| Wisconsin | 2,581 | 1,371 | 1,311 | 1,520 | 900 | 757 | 241 | 102 | 34 |

## EXERCISES

*Use the information given in the above tables.*

1. **Employees** Which state has the greatest number of manufacturing employees? Explain your reasoning.
2. **Mean Business Size** Estimate the mean number of employees at a manufacturing business for each state. Use 1500 as the midpoint for "1000+."
3. **Employees** Which state has the greatest number of employees per manufacturing business? Explain your reasoning.
4. **Standard Deviation** Estimate the standard deviation for the number of employees at a manufacturing business for each state. Use 1500 as the midpoint for "1000+."
5. **Standard Deviation** Which state has the greatest standard deviation? Explain your reasoning.
6. **Distribution** Describe the distribution of the number of employees at manufacturing businesses for each state.

# 2.5 Measures of Position

### What You Should Learn

- How to find the first, second, and third quartiles of a data set, how to find the interquartile range of a data set, and how to represent a data set graphically using a box-and-whisker plot
- How to interpret other fractiles such as percentiles, and how to find percentiles for a specific data entry
- How to find and interpret the standard score ($z$-score)

Quartiles ■ Percentiles and Other Fractiles ■ The Standard Score

## Quartiles

In this section, you will learn how to use fractiles to specify the position of a data entry within a data set. **Fractiles** are numbers that partition, or divide, an ordered data set into equal parts (each part has the same number of data entries). For instance, the median is a fractile because it divides an ordered data set into two equal parts.

**DEFINITION**

The three **quartiles,** $Q_1$, $Q_2$, and $Q_3$, divide an ordered data set into four equal parts. About one quarter of the data fall on or below the **first quartile** $Q_1$. About one half of the data fall on or below the **second quartile** $Q_2$ (the second quartile is the same as the median of the data set). About three quarters of the data fall on or below the **third quartile** $Q_3$.

**EXAMPLE 1**

### Finding the Quartiles of a Data Set

The amounts of fuel (in gallons per year) that automobile commuters waste due to traffic congestion in the 15 largest U.S. urban areas (where the populations are over 3 million) are listed. Find the first, second, and third quartiles of the data set. What do you observe? *(Source: Texas A&M Transportation Institute)*

34 30 31 31 25 31 25 24 38 26 39 26 38 31 35

**SOLUTION**

First, order the data set and find the median $Q_2$. The first quartile $Q_1$ is the median of the data entries to the left of $Q_2$. The third quartile $Q_3$ is the median of the data entries to the right of $Q_2$.

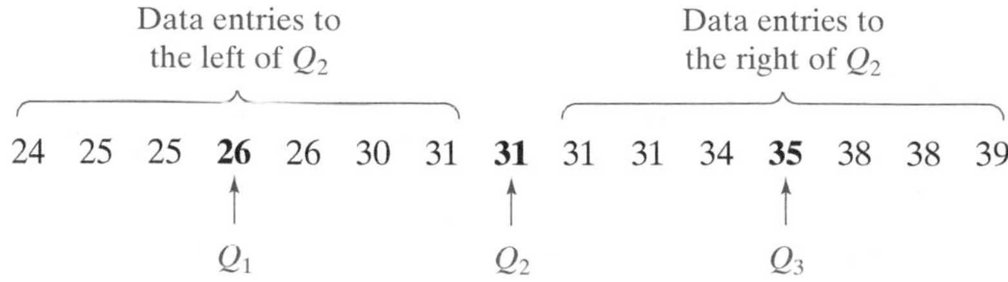


***Interpretation*** In about one quarter of the large urban areas, auto commuters waste 26 gallons of fuel or less, about one half waste 31 gallons or less, and about three quarters waste 35 gallons or less.

**TRY IT YOURSELF 1**

Find the first, second, and third quartiles for the points scored by the 55 winning teams using the data set listed on page 39. What do you observe?

*Answer: Page A37*

## EXAMPLE 2

### Using Technology to Find Quartiles

The costs of tuition and fees (in thousands of dollars) for 25 liberal arts colleges are listed. Use technology to find the first, second, and third quartiles. What do you observe? *(Source: U.S. News & World Report)*

55 59 55 56 57 55 60 59 61 58 57 61 59

48 44 30 39 58 48 46 19 55 45 48 48

**SOLUTION**

Minitab and the TI-84 Plus, for instance, each have features that calculate quartiles. Use such technology to find the first, second, and third quartiles of the tuition data. From the displays, you can see that

$Q_1 = 47$, $Q_2 = 55$, and $Q_3 = 58.5$.

**MINITAB**

**Descriptive Statistics: Tuition**

| Variable | N | Mean | SE Mean | StDev | Minimum |
|---|---|---|---|---|---|
| Tuition | 25 | 51.20 | 2.04 | 10.18 | 19.00 |

| Variable | Q1 | Median | Q3 | Maximum |
|---|---|---|---|---|
| Tuition | 47.00 | 55.00 | 58.50 | 61.00 |

**TI-84 PLUS**

1-Var Stats
↑n=25
minX=19
$Q_1$=47
Med=55
$Q_3$=58.5
maxX=61

**STATCRUNCH**

**Summary statistics:**

| Column | Q1 | Median | Q3 |
|---|---|---|---|
| Tuition | 48 | 55 | 58 |

***Interpretation*** About one quarter of these colleges charge tuition of $47,000 or less; about one half charge $55,000 or less; and about three quarters charge $58,500 or less.

**TRY IT YOURSELF 2**

The costs of tuition and fees (in thousands of dollars) for 25 universities are listed. Use technology to find the first, second, and third quartiles. What do you observe? *(Source: U.S. News & World Report)*

58 35 49 11 31 56 25 18 36 31 10 32 35

19 39 49 33 27 55 33 55 46 28 54 57

*Answer: Page A37*

**Tech Tip**

Note that you may get results that differ slightly when comparing results obtained by different technology tools. For instance, in Example 2, the first quartile, as determined by Minitab, the TI-84 Plus, and the Quartile.exc function of Excel, is 47, whereas the result using StatCrunch and the Quartile.inc function of Excel is 48.

**EXCEL**

| | A | B | |
|---|---|---|---|
| 1 | 55 | 47 | ←=Quartile.exc(A1:A25,1) |
| 2 | 59 | | |
| 3 | 55 | 55 | ←=Quartile.exc(A1:A25,2) |
| 4 | 56 | | |
| 5 | 57 | 58.5 | ←=Quartile.exc(A1:A25,3) |
| 6 | 55 | | |
| 7 | 60 | 48 | ←=Quartile.inc(A1:A25,1) |
| 8 | 59 | | |
| 9 | 61 | 55 | ←=Quartile.inc(A1:A25,2) |
| 10 | 58 | | |
| 11 | 57 | 58 | ←=Quartile.inc(A1:A25,3) |
| 12 | 61 | | |
| 13 | 59 | | |
| 14 | 48 | | |
| 15 | 44 | | |
| 16 | 30 | | |
| 17 | 39 | | |
| 18 | 58 | | |
| 19 | 48 | | |
| 20 | 46 | | |
| 21 | 19 | | |
| 22 | 55 | | |
| 23 | 45 | | |
| 24 | 48 | | |
| 25 | 48 | | |

The median (the second quartile) is a measure of central tendency based on position. A measure of variation that is based on position is the **interquartile range.** The interquartile range tells you the spread of the middle half of the data, as shown in the next definition.

**DEFINITION**

The **interquartile range (IQR)** of a data set is a measure of variation that gives the range of the middle portion (about half) of the data. The IQR is the difference between the third and first quartiles.

$$\text{IQR} = Q_3 - Q_1$$

In Section 2.3, an outlier was described as a data entry that is far removed from the other entries in the data set. One way to identify outliers is to use the interquartile range.

**GUIDELINES**

**Using the Interquartile Range to Identify Outliers**

1. Find the first $(Q_1)$ and third $(Q_3)$ quartiles of the data set.
2. Find the interquartile range: $\text{IQR} = Q_3 - Q_1$.
3. Multiply IQR by 1.5: $1.5(\text{IQR})$.
4. Subtract $1.5(\text{IQR})$ from $Q_1$. Any data entry less than $Q_1 - 1.5(\text{IQR})$ is an outlier.
5. Add $1.5(\text{IQR})$ to $Q_3$. Any data entry greater than $Q_3 + 1.5(\text{IQR})$ is an outlier.

**EXAMPLE 3**

### Using the Interquartile Range to Identify an Outlier

Find the interquartile range of the data set in Example 2. Are there any outliers?

**SOLUTION**

From Example 2, you know that $Q_1 = 47$ and $Q_3 = 58.5$. So, the interquartile range is $\text{IQR} = Q_3 - Q_1 = 58.5 - 47 = 11.5$. To identify any outliers, first note that $1.5(\text{IQR}) = 1.5(11.5) = 17.25$. There is a data entry, 19, that is less than

$$Q_1 - 1.5(\text{IQR}) = 47 - 17.25 \quad \text{Subtract } 1.5(\text{IQR}) \text{ from } Q_1.$$
$$= 29.75 \quad \text{A data entry less than 29.75 is an outlier.}$$

but there are no data entries greater than

$$Q_3 + 1.5(\text{IQR}) = 58.5 + 17.25 \quad \text{Add } 1.5(\text{IQR}) \text{ from } Q_3.$$
$$= 75.75. \quad \text{A data entry greater than 75.75 is an outlier.}$$

So, 19 is an outlier.

***Interpretation*** The costs of tuition and fees for the liberal arts colleges listed in the middle of the data set varies by at most $17,250. Notice that the outlier, 19 (or $19,000), does not affect the IQR.

**TRY IT YOURSELF 3**

Find the interquartile range for the points scored by the 55 winning teams listed on page 39. Are there any outliers?

*Answer: Page A37*

Another important application of quartiles is to represent data sets using box-and-whisker plots. A **box-and-whisker plot** (or **boxplot**) is an exploratory data analysis tool that highlights the important features of a data set. To graph a box-and-whisker plot, you must know the values shown at the top of the next page.

## Picturing the World

From 1970 through 2019, there were 2939 fatalities in the United States attributed to lightning strikes. The box-and-whisker plot summarizes the fatalities for each of these years. (Source: National Weather Service)

**Lightning Fatalities**

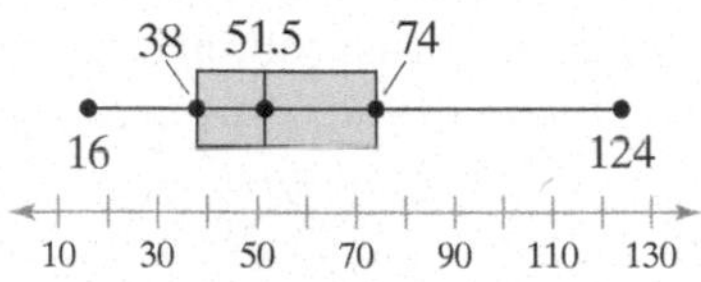


Fatalities per year from 1970 through 2019

**About how many fatalities are represented by the right whisker? There were 20 lightning fatalities in 2019. Into what quartile does this number of fatalities fall?**

### Study Tip

For data sets that have outliers, you can represent them graphically using a modified box-and-whisker plot. A *modified box-and-whisker plot* is a box-and-whisker plot that uses symbols (such as an asterisk or a point) to indicate outliers. The horizontal line of a modified box-and-whisker plot extends as far as the minimum data entry that is not an outlier and the maximum data entry that is not an outlier. For instance, on pages 124 and 125, Minitab and the TI-84 Plus were used to draw modified box-and-whisker plots that represent the data set in Example 2. Compare these results with the one in Example 4.

**1.** The minimum entry
**2.** The first quartile $Q_1$
**3.** The median $Q_2$
**4.** The third quartile $Q_3$
**5.** The maximum entry

These five numbers are called the **five-number summary** of the data set.

**GUIDELINES**

**Drawing a Box-and-Whisker Plot**

1. Find the five-number summary of the data set.
2. Construct a horizontal scale that spans the range of the data.
3. Plot the five numbers above the horizontal scale.
4. Draw a box above the horizontal scale from $Q_1$ to $Q_3$ and draw a vertical line segment in the box at $Q_2$.
5. Draw whiskers from the box to the minimum and maximum entries.

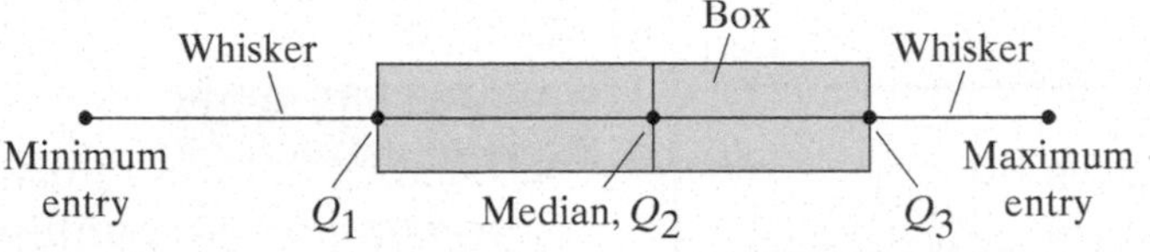


**EXAMPLE 4**

See Minitab and TI-84 Plus steps on pages 124 and 125.

### Drawing a Box-and-Whisker Plot

Draw a box-and-whisker plot that represents the data set in Example 2. What do you observe?

**SOLUTION** Here is the five-number summary of the data set.

Minimum = 19 $\quad Q_1 = 47 \quad Q_2 = 55 \quad Q_3 = 58.5 \quad$ Maximum = 61

Using these five numbers, you can construct the box-and-whisker plot shown.

**Tuition and Fees**

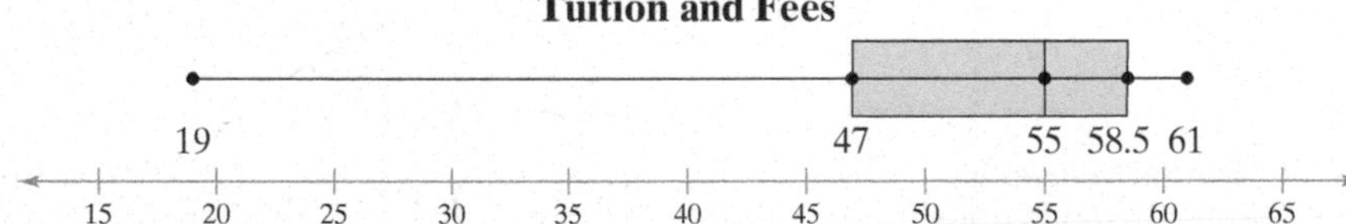


***Interpretation*** The box represents about half of the data, which means about 50% of the data entries are between 47 and 58.5. The left whisker represents about one quarter of the data, so about 25% of the data entries are less than 47. The right whisker represents about one quarter of the data, so about 25% of the data entries are greater than 58.5. Also, the length of the left whisker is much longer than the right one. This indicates that the data set has a possible outlier to the left. (You already know from Example 3 that the data entry of 19 is an outlier).

**TRY IT YOURSELF 4**

Draw a box-and-whisker plot that represents the points scored by the 55 winning teams listed on page 39. What do you observe?

*Answer: Page A37*

You can use a box-and-whisker plot to determine the shape of a distribution. Notice that the box-and-whisker plot in Example 4 represents a distribution that is skewed left.

**Study Tip**

Notice that the 25th percentile is the same as $Q_1$; the 50th percentile is the same as $Q_2$, or the median; and the 75th percentile is the same as $Q_3$.

## Percentiles and Other Fractiles

In addition to using quartiles to specify a measure of position, you can also use percentiles and deciles. Here is a summary of these common fractiles.

| Fractiles | Summary | Symbols |
|---|---|---|
| Quartiles | Divide a data set into 4 equal parts. | $Q_1, Q_2, Q_3$ |
| Deciles | Divide a data set into 10 equal parts. | $D_1, D_2, D_3, \ldots, D_9$ |
| Percentiles | Divide a data set into 100 equal parts. | $P_1, P_2, P_3, \ldots, P_{99}$ |

Percentiles are often used in education and health-related fields to indicate how one individual compares with others in a group. Percentiles can also be used to identify unusually high or unusually low values. For instance, children's growth measurements are often expressed in percentiles. Measurements in the 95th percentile and above are unusually high, while those in the 5th percentile and below are unusually low.

**Study Tip**

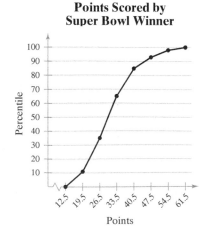

Be sure you understand what a percentile means. For instance, the weight of a six-month-old infant is at the 78th percentile. This means the infant weighs the same as or more than 78% of all six-month-old infants. It does not mean that the infant weighs 78% of some ideal weight.

**EXAMPLE 5**

### Interpreting Percentiles

The ogive at the right represents the cumulative frequency distribution for SAT scores of college-bound students in a recent year. What score represents the 90th percentile? *(Source: College Board)*

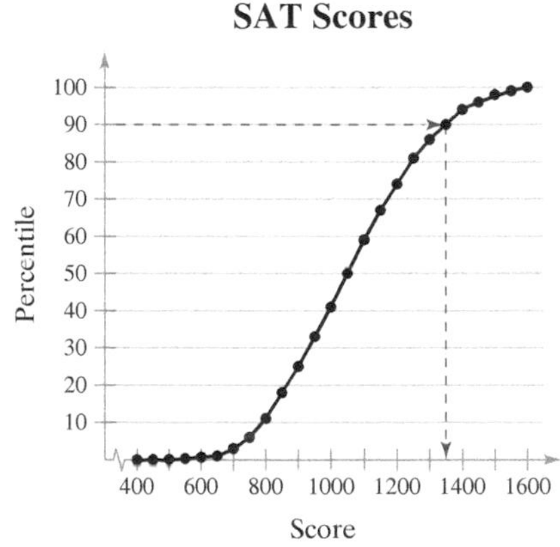


**SOLUTION**

From the ogive, you can see that the 90th percentile corresponds to a score of 1350.

***Interpretation*** This means that approximately 90% of the students had an SAT score of 1350 or less.

**TRY IT YOURSELF 5**

The points scored by the 55 winning teams in the Super Bowl (see page 39) are represented in the ogive at the left. What score represents the 65th percentile? How should you interpret this?

*Answer: Page A37*

**Points Scored by Super Bowl Winner**

Percentile: 100, 90, 80, 70, 60, 50, 40, 30, 20, 10

Points: 12.5, 19.5, 26.5, 33.5, 40.5, 47.5, 54.5, 61.5

In Example 5, you used an ogive to approximate a data entry that corresponds to a percentile. You can also use an ogive to approximate a percentile that corresponds to a data entry. Another way to find a percentile is to use a formula.

**DEFINITION**

To find the **percentile that corresponds to a specific data entry *x*,** use the formula

$$\text{Percentile of } x = \frac{\text{number of data entries less than } x}{\text{total number of data entries}} \cdot 100$$

and then round to the nearest whole number.

## EXAMPLE 6

### Finding a Percentile

For the data set in Example 2, find the percentile that corresponds to $57,000.

**SOLUTION**

The costs of tuition and fees are in thousands of dollars, so $57,000 is the data entry 57. Begin by ordering the data.

19 30 39 44 45 46 48 48 48 48 55 55 55
55 56 57 57 58 58 59 59 59 60 61 61

There are 15 data entries less than 57 and the total number of data entries is 25.

$$\text{Percentile of } 57 = \frac{\text{Number of data entries less than } 57}{\text{Total number of entries}} \cdot 100$$
$$= \frac{15}{25} \cdot 100$$
$$= 60$$

The cost of $57,000 corresponds to the 60th percentile.

***Interpretation*** The cost of $57,000 is greater than 60% of the other tuition costs.

**TRY IT YOURSELF 6**

For the data set in Try It Yourself 2, find the percentile that corresponds to $31,000, which is the data entry 31.

*Answer: Page A37*

## The Standard Score

When you know the mean and standard deviation of a data set, you can measure the position of an entry in the data set with a **standard score,** or **$z$-score.**

### DEFINITION

The **standard score,** or **$z$-score,** represents the number of standard deviations a value $x$ lies from the mean $\mu$. To find the $z$-score for a value, use the formula

$$z = \frac{\text{Value} - \text{Mean}}{\text{Standard deviation}} = \frac{x - \mu}{\sigma}.$$

A $z$-score can be negative, positive, or zero. When $z$ is negative, the corresponding $x$-value is less than the mean. When $z$ is positive, the corresponding $x$-value is greater than the mean. For $z = 0$, the corresponding $x$-value is equal to the mean. A $z$-score can be used to identify an unusual value of a data set that is approximately bell-shaped.

When a distribution is approximately bell-shaped, you know from the Empirical Rule that about 95% of the data lie within 2 standard deviations of the mean. So, when this distribution's values are transformed to $z$-scores, about 95% of the $z$-scores should fall between $-2$ and 2. A $z$-score outside of this range will occur about 5% of the time and would be considered unusual. So, according to the Empirical Rule, a $z$-score less than $-3$ or greater than 3 would be very unusual, with such a score occurring about 0.3% of the time.

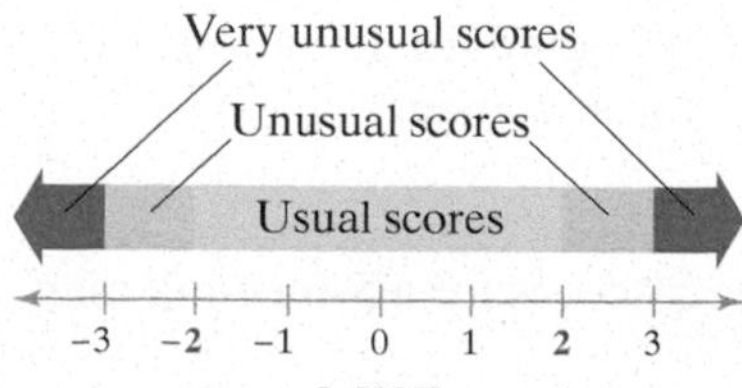

**EXAMPLE 7**

### Finding z-Scores

The mean speed of vehicles along a stretch of highway is 56 miles per hour with a standard deviation of 4 miles per hour. You measure the speeds of three cars traveling along this stretch of highway as 62 miles per hour, 47 miles per hour, and 56 miles per hour. Find the $z$-score that corresponds to each speed. Assume the distribution of the speeds is approximately bell-shaped.

**SOLUTION** The $z$-score that corresponds to each speed is calculated below.

$x = 62$ mph $\qquad x = 47$ mph $\qquad x = 56$ mph

$$z = \frac{62 - 56}{4} = 1.5 \qquad z = \frac{47 - 56}{4} = -2.25 \qquad z = \frac{56 - 56}{4} = 0$$

***Interpretation*** From the $z$-scores, you can conclude that a speed of 62 miles per hour is 1.5 standard deviations above the mean; a speed of 47 miles per hour is 2.25 standard deviations below the mean; and a speed of 56 miles per hour is equal to the mean. The car traveling 47 miles per hour is said to be traveling unusually slowly, because its speed corresponds to a $z$-score of $-2.25$.

**TRY IT YOURSELF 7**

The monthly utility bills in a city have a mean of \$70 and a standard deviation of \$8. Find the $z$-scores that correspond to utility bills of \$60, \$71, and \$92. Assume the distribution of the utility bills is approximately bell-shaped.

*Answer: Page A37*

**EXAMPLE 8**

### Comparing z-Scores from Different Data Sets

The table shows the mean heights and standard deviations for a population of men and a population of women. Compare the $z$-scores for a 6-foot-tall man and a 6-foot-tall woman. Assume the distributions of the heights are approximately bell-shaped.

| Men's heights | Women's heights |
|---|---|
| $\mu = 69.9$ in. | $\mu = 64.3$ in. |
| $\sigma = 3.0$ in. | $\sigma = 2.6$ in. |

**SOLUTION** Note that 6 feet = 72 inches. Find the $z$-score for each height.

**$z$-score for 6-foot-tall man** $\qquad$ **$z$-score for 6-foot-tall woman**

$$z = \frac{x - \mu}{\sigma} = \frac{72 - 69.9}{3.0} = 0.7 \qquad z = \frac{x - \mu}{\sigma} = \frac{72 - 64.3}{2.6} \approx 3.0$$

***Interpretation*** The $z$-score for the 6-foot-tall man is within 1 standard deviation of the mean (69.9 inches). This is among the typical heights for a man. The $z$-score for the 6-foot-tall woman is about 3 standard deviations from the mean (64.3 inches). This is an unusual height for a woman.

**TRY IT YOURSELF 8**

Use the information in Example 8 to compare the $z$-scores for a 5-foot-tall man and a 5-foot-tall woman.

*Answer: Page A37*

# 2.5 EXERCISES

For Extra Help: MyLab Statistics

## Building Basic Skills and Vocabulary

1. The length of a guest lecturer's talk represents the third quartile for talks in a guest lecture series. Make an observation about the length of the talk.
2. A motorcycle's fuel efficiency represents the ninth decile of vehicles in its class. Make an observation about the motorcycle's fuel efficiency.
3. A student's grade on the Fundamentals of Engineering exam has a $z$-score of $-0.5$. Make an observation about the student's grade.
4. A student's IQ score is in the 91st percentile on the Weschler Adult Intelligence Scale. Make an observation about the student's IQ score.
5. Explain how to identify outliers using the interquartile range.
6. Describe the relationship between quartiles and percentiles.

**True or False?** *In Exercises 7–10, determine whether the statement is true or false. If it is false, rewrite it as a true statement.*

7. On a box-and-whisker plot, one quarter of a data set lies on the left whisker.
8. The second quartile is the mean of an ordered data set.
9. An outlier is any number above $Q_3$ or below $Q_1$.
10. It is impossible to have a $z$-score of 0.

## Using and Interpreting Concepts

**Finding Quartiles, Interquartile Range, and Outliers** *In Exercises 11 and 12, (a) find the quartiles, (b) find the interquartile range, and (c) identify any outliers.*

**11.** 56 63 51 60 57 60 60 54 63 59 80 63 60 62 65

**12.** 22 25 22 24 20 24 19 22 29 21
21 20 23 25 23 23 21 25 23 22

**Graphical Analysis** *In Exercises 13 and 14, use the box-and-whisker plot to identify the five-number summary.*

**13.** **14.**

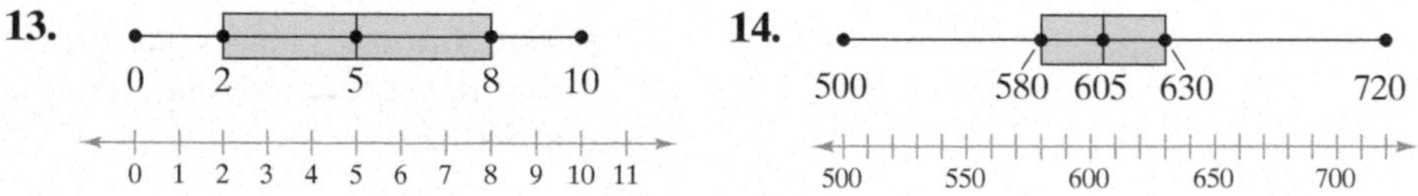


**Drawing a Box-and-Whisker Plot** *In Exercises 15–18, (a) find the five-number summary, and (b) draw a box-and-whisker plot that represents the data set.*

**15.** 39 36 30 27 26 24 28 35 39 60 50 41 35 32 51

**16.** 171 176 182 150 178 180 173 170 174 178 181 180

**17.** 4 7 7 5 2 9 7 6 8 5 8 4 1 5 2 8 7 6 6 9

**18.** 2 7 1 3 1 2 8 9 9 2 5 4 7 3 7 5 4
2 3 5 9 5 6 3 9 3 4 9 8 8 2 3 9 5

**Graphical Analysis** *In Exercises 19–22, use the box-and-whisker plot to determine whether the shape of the distribution represented is symmetric, skewed left, skewed right, or none of these. Justify your answer.*

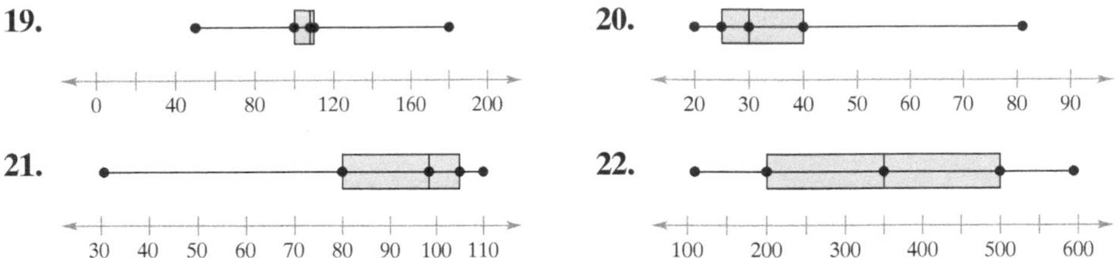


**Using Technology to Find Quartiles and Draw Graphs** *In Exercises 23–26, use technology to draw a box-and-whisker plot that represents the data set.*

**23. Studying** The number of hours spent studying per day by a sample of 28 students

| | | | | | | | | | | | | | |
|---|---|---|---|---|---|---|---|---|---|---|---|---|---|
| 2 | 8 | 7 | 2 | 3 | 3 | 3 | 2 | 2 | 7 | 8 | 3 | 5 | 1 |
| 1 | 2 | 6 | 1 | 5 | 7 | 3 | 8 | 5 | 3 | 3 | 7 | 6 | 2 |

**24. Vacation Days** The number of vacation days used by a sample of 20 employees in a recent year

| | | | | | | | | | |
|---|---|---|---|---|---|---|---|---|---|
| 3 | 9 | 2 | 1 | 7 | 5 | 3 | 2 | 2 | 6 |
| 4 | 0 | 10 | 0 | 3 | 5 | 7 | 8 | 6 | 5 |

**25. Commuting Distances** The commuting distances (in miles) of a sample of 30 employees

| | | | | | | | | | |
|---|---|---|---|---|---|---|---|---|---|
| 7 | 6 | 7 | 5 | 2 | 1 | 1 | 2 | 3 | 8 |
| 15 | 24 | 3 | 8 | 9 | 19 | 12 | 17 | 45 | 4 |
| 4 | 3 | 11 | 26 | 10 | 4 | 21 | 1 | 5 | 12 |

**26. Hourly Earnings** The hourly earnings (in dollars) of a sample of 21 employees at a consulting firm

| | | | | | | |
|---|---|---|---|---|---|---|
| 25.89 | 27.09 | 31.76 | 28.28 | 26.19 | 27.43 | 24.06 |
| 25.61 | 22.56 | 29.76 | 18.01 | 23.66 | 38.24 | 37.27 |
| 32.70 | 31.12 | 25.87 | 15.06 | 23.12 | 30.62 | 19.85 |

**27. Studying** Refer to the data set in Exercise 23 and the box-and-whisker plot you drew that represents the data set.

(a) About 75% of the students studied no more than how many hours per day?

(b) What percent of the students studied more than 3 hours per day?

(c) You randomly select one student from the sample. What is the likelihood that the student studied less than 2 hours per day? Write your answer as a percent.

**28. Hourly Earnings** Refer to the data set in Exercise 26 and the box-and-whisker plot you drew that represents the data set.

(a) About 50% of the employees made less than what amount per hour?

(b) What percent of the employees made more than \$23.39 per hour?

(c) What percent of the employees made between \$23.39 and \$38.24 per hour?

(d) You randomly select one employee from the sample. What is the likelihood that the employee made more than \$30.87 per hour? Write your answer as a percent.

**Interpreting Percentiles** *In Exercises 29–32, use the ogive, which represents the cumulative frequency distribution for quantitative reasoning scores on the Graduate Record Examination in a recent range of years.* (Adapted from Educational Testing Service)

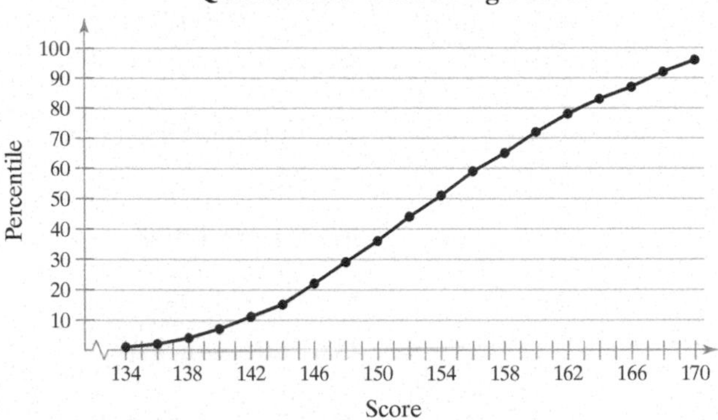


**29.** What score represents the 65th percentile? How should you interpret this?

**30.** Which score represents the 50th percentile? How should you interpret this?

**31.** What percentile is a score of 140? How should you interpret this?

**32.** What percentile is a score of 170? How should you interpret this?

**Finding a Percentile** *In Exercises 33–36, use the data set, which represents the ages of 30 executives.*

| 43 | 57 | 65 | 47 | 57 | 41 | 56 | 53 | 61 | 54 |
|---|---|---|---|---|---|---|---|---|---|
| 56 | 50 | 66 | 56 | 50 | 61 | 47 | 40 | 50 | 43 |
| 54 | 41 | 48 | 45 | 28 | 35 | 38 | 43 | 42 | 44 |

**33.** Find the percentile that corresponds to an age of 40 years old.

**34.** Find the percentile that corresponds to an age of 56 years old.

**35.** Which ages are above the 75th percentile?

**36.** Which ages are below the 25th percentile?

**Finding and Interpreting Percentiles** *In Exercises 37–40, use the data set, which represents wait times (in minutes) for various services at a state's Department of Motor Vehicles locations.*

| 6 | 10 | 1 | 22 | 23 | 10 | 6 | 7 | 2 | 1 | 6 | 6 | 2 | 4 | 14 | 15 | 16 | 4 |
|---|---|---|---|---|---|---|---|---|---|---|---|---|---|---|---|---|---|
| 19 | 3 | 19 | 26 | 5 | 3 | 4 | 7 | 6 | 10 | 9 | 10 | 20 | 18 | 3 | 20 | 10 | 13 |
| 14 | 11 | 14 | 17 | 4 | 27 | 4 | 8 | 4 | 3 | 26 | 18 | 21 | 1 | 3 | 3 | 5 | 5 |

**37.** Draw an ogive to show corresponding percentiles for the data.

**38.** Which wait time represents the 50th percentile? How would you interpret this?

**39.** Find the percentile that corresponds to a wait time of 20 minutes.

**40.** Which wait times are between the 25th and 75th percentiles?

**Graphical Analysis** *In Exercises 41 and 42, the midpoints A, B, and C are marked on the histograms at the left. Match them with the indicated z-scores. Which z-scores, if any, would be considered unusual?*

**41.** $z = 0, z = 2.14, z = -1.43$

**42.** $z = 0.77, z = 1.54, z = -1.54$

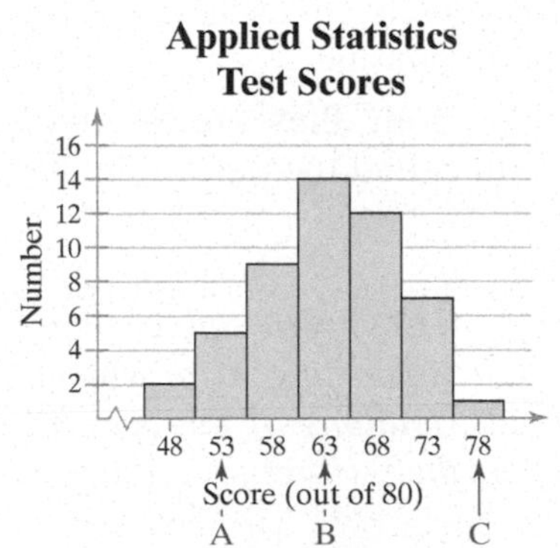


FIGURE FOR EXERCISE 41

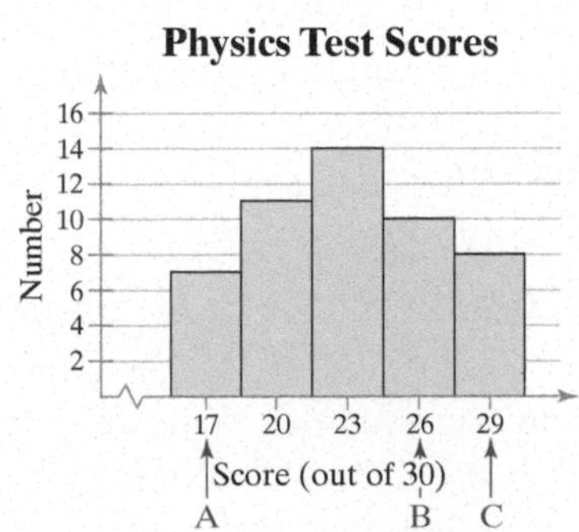


FIGURE FOR EXERCISE 42

**Finding *z*-Scores** *The distribution of the ages of the winners of the Tour de France from 1903 to 2020 is approximately bell-shaped. The mean age is 27.9 years, with a standard deviation of 3.4 years. In Exercises 43–48, use the corresponding z-score to determine whether the age is unusual. Explain your reasoning.* *(Source: Le Tour de France)*

| | Winner | Year | Age |
|---|---|---|---|
| **43.** | Christopher Froome | 2016 | 31 |
| **44.** | Jan Ullrich | 1997 | 24 |
| **45.** | Antonin Magne | 1931 | 27 |
| **46.** | Firmin Lambot | 1922 | 36 |
| **47.** | Henri Cornet | 1904 | 20 |
| **48.** | Tadej Pogačar | 2020 | 21 |

**49. Life Spans of Tires** A brand of automobile tire has a mean life span of 35,000 miles, with a standard deviation of 2250 miles. Assume the life spans of the tires have a bell-shaped distribution.

(a) The life spans of three randomly selected tires are 34,000 miles, 37,000 miles, and 30,000 miles. Find the $z$-score that corresponds to each life span. Determine whether any of these life spans are unusual.

(b) The life spans of three randomly selected tires are 30,500 miles, 37,250 miles, and 35,000 miles. Using the Empirical Rule, find the percentile that corresponds to each life span.

**50. Life Spans of Fruit Flies** The life spans of a species of fruit fly have a bell-shaped distribution, with a mean of 33 days and a standard deviation of 4 days.

(a) The life spans of three randomly selected fruit flies are 34 days, 30 days, and 42 days. Find the $z$-score that corresponds to each life span. Determine whether any of these life spans are unusual.

(b) The life spans of three randomly selected fruit flies are 29 days, 41 days, and 25 days. Using the Empirical Rule, find the percentile that corresponds to each life span.

**Comparing *z*-Scores from Different Data Sets** *The table shows population statistics for the ages of Best Actor and Best Supporting Actor winners at the Academy Awards from 1929 to 2020. The distributions of the ages are approximately bell-shaped. In Exercises 51–54, compare the z-scores for the actors.*

| Best actor | Best supporting actor |
|---|---|
| $\mu \approx$ 43.8 yr | $\mu \approx$ 50.2 yr |
| $\sigma \approx$ 8.7 yr | $\sigma \approx$ 13.5 yr |

**51.** Best Actor 2018: Gary Oldman, Age: 59
Best Supporting Actor 2018: Sam Rockwell, Age: 49

**52.** Best Actor 2005: Jamie Foxx, Age: 37
Best Supporting Actor 2005: Morgan Freeman, Age: 67

**53.** Best Actor 1970: John Wayne, Age: 62
Best Supporting Actor 1970: Gig Young, Age: 56

**54.** Best Actor 1982: Henry Fonda, Age: 76
Best Supporting Actor 1982: John Gielgud, Age: 77

## Extending Concepts

**Midquartile** *Another measure of position is called the* ***midquartile.*** *You can find the midquartile of a data set by using the formula below.*

$$\text{Midquartile} = \frac{Q_1 + Q_3}{2}$$

*In Exercises 55 and 56, find the midquartile of the data set.*

**55.** 5 7 1 2 3 10 8 7 5 3

**56.** 23 36 47 33 34 40 39 24 32 22 38 41

**57. Song Lengths** **Side-by-side box-and-whisker plots** can be used to compare two or more different data sets. Each box-and-whisker plot is drawn on the same number line to compare the data sets more easily. The lengths (in seconds) of songs played at two different concerts are shown.

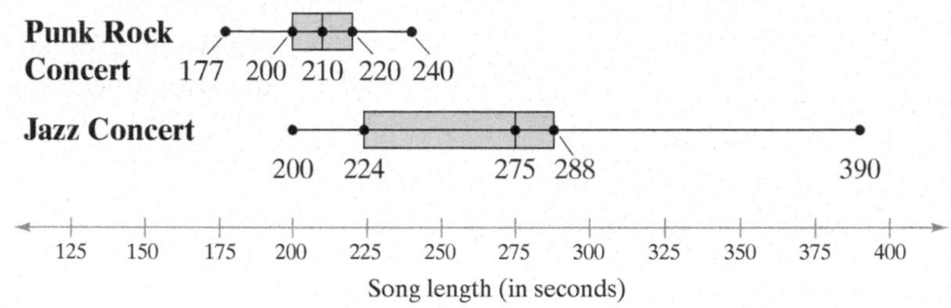


(a) Describe the shape of each distribution. Which concert has less variation in song lengths?

(b) Which distribution is more likely to have outliers? Explain.

(c) Which concert do you think has a standard deviation of 16.3? Explain.

(d) Can you determine which concert lasted longer? Explain.

**58. Credit Card Purchases** The credit card purchases (rounded to the nearest dollar) over the last three months for you and a friend are listed.

**You** 60 95 102 110 130 130 162 200 215 120 124 28 58 40 102 105 141 160 130 210 145 90 46 76

**Friend** 100 125 132 90 85 75 140 160 180 190 160 105 145 150 151 82 78 115 170 158 140 130 165 125

Use technology to draw side-by-side box-and-whisker plots that represent the data sets. Then describe the shapes of the distributions.

**Modified Box-and-Whisker Plot** *In Exercises 59–62, (a) identify any outliers and (b) draw a modified box-and-whisker plot that represents the data set. Use asterisks (*) to identify outliers.*

**59.** 16 9 11 12 8 10 12 13 11 10 24 9 2 15 7

**60.** 75 78 80 75 62 72 74 75 80 95 76 72

**61.** 47 29 59 83 46 1 46 23 52 53 35 37 49

**62.** 36 38 47 50 53 54 19 27 30 47 48 50 56 60 90 62

**63. Project** Find a real-life data set and use the techniques of Chapter 2, including graphs and numerical quantities, to discuss the center, variation, and shape of the data set. Describe any patterns.

# USES AND ABUSES Statistics in the Real World

## Uses

Descriptive statistics help you see trends or patterns in a set of raw data. A good description of a data set consists of (1) a measure of the center of the data, (2) a measure of the variability (or spread) of the data, and (3) the shape (or distribution) of the data. When you read reports, news items, or advertisements prepared by other people, you are rarely given the raw data used for a study. Instead, you see graphs, measures of central tendency, and measures of variability. To be a discerning reader, you need to understand the terms and techniques of descriptive statistics.

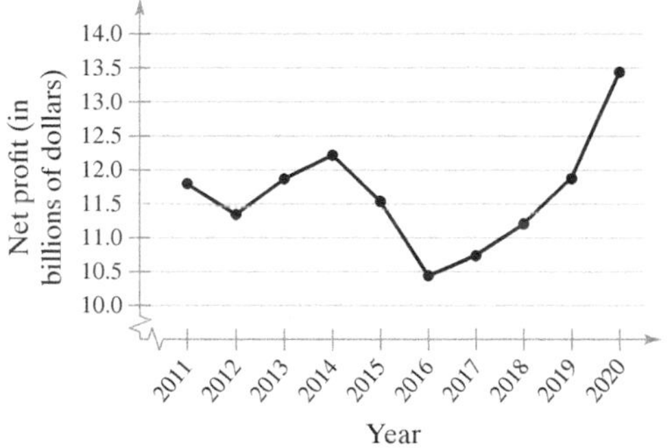


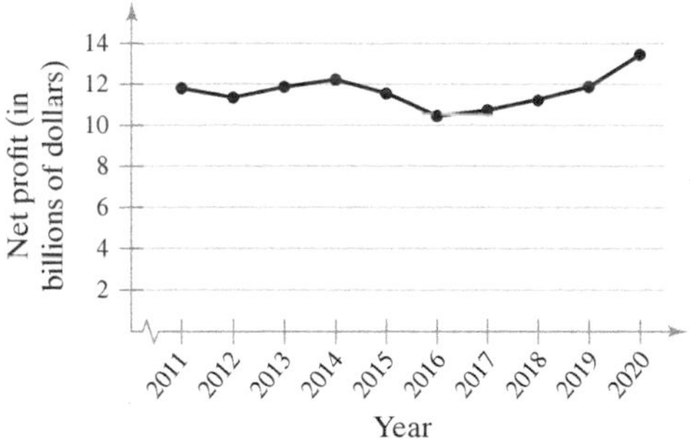


## Abuses

Knowing how statistics are calculated can help you analyze questionable statistics. For instance, you are interviewing for a sales position and the company reports that the average yearly commission earned by the five people in its sales force is \$60,000. This is a misleading statement if it is based on four commissions of \$25,000 and one of \$200,000. The median would more accurately describe the yearly commission, but the company used the mean because it is a greater amount.

Statistical graphs can also be misleading. Compare the two time series charts at the left, which show the net profits for the Procter & Gamble Corporation from 2011 through 2020. The data are the same for each chart. The first time series chart, however, has a cropped vertical axis, which makes it appear that the net profit decreased greatly from 2011 to 2012 and from 2014 to 2016, and increased greatly from 2012 to 2014 and from 2016 to 2020. In the second time series chart, the scale on the vertical axis begins at zero. This time series chart correctly shows that the net profit changed modestly during this time period and has been steadily increasing in recent years. *(Source: Procter & Gamble Corporation)*

## Ethics

Mark Twain helped popularize the saying, "There are three kinds of lies: lies, damned lies, and statistics." In short, even the most accurate statistics can be used to support studies or statements that are incorrect. Unscrupulous people can use misleading statistics to "prove" their point. Being informed about how statistics are calculated and questioning the data are ways to avoid being misled.

### EXERCISES

1. Use the Internet or some other resource to find an example of a graph that might lead to incorrect conclusions.
2. You are publishing an article that discusses how drinking red wine can help prevent heart disease. Because drinking red wine might help people at risk for heart disease, you include a graph that exaggerates the effects of drinking red wine and preventing heart disease. Do you think it is ethical to publish this graph? Explain.

# 2 Chapter Summary

| What Did You Learn? | Example(s) | Review Exercises |
|---|---|---|
| **Section 2.1** | | |
| ▶ How to construct frequency distributions, frequency histograms, frequency polygons, relative frequency histograms, and ogives | 1–7 | 1–6 |
| **Section 2.2** | | |
| ▶ How to graph and interpret (1) quantitative data sets using stem-and-leaf plots and dot plots, (2) qualitative data sets using pie charts and Pareto charts, and (3) paired data sets using scatter plots and time series charts | 1–7 | 7–12 |
| **Section 2.3** | | |
| ▶ How to find the mean, median, and mode of a population and of a sample | 1–6 | 13, 14 |
| ▶ How to find a weighted mean of a data set, and how to estimate the sample mean of grouped data | 7, 8 | 15–18 |
| ▶ How to describe the shape of a distribution as symmetric, uniform, or skewed, and how to compare the mean and median for each | | 19–24 |
| **Section 2.4** | | |
| ▶ How to find the range of a data set, and how to find the variance and standard deviation of a population and of a sample | 1–4 | 25–28 |
| ▶ How to use the Empirical Rule and Chebychev's Theorem to interpret standard deviation | 5–7 | 29–32 |
| ▶ How to estimate the sample standard deviation for grouped data | 8, 9 | 33, 34 |
| ▶ How to use the coefficient of variation to compare variation in different data sets | 10 | 35, 36 |
| **Section 2.5** | | |
| ▶ How to find the first, second, and third quartiles of a data set, how to find the interquartile range of a data set, and how to represent a data set graphically using a box-and-whisker plot | 1–4 | 37–42 |
| ▶ How to interpret other fractiles such as percentiles, and how to find percentiles for a specific data entry | 5, 6 | 43, 44 |
| ▶ How to find and interpret the standard score ($z$-score) | 7, 8 | 45–48 |

## Study Strategies

**Basic Reading Strategies** Reading is an important skill for your college courses. You can improve your reading skills if you are motivated and willing to practice.

- Find an environment that is as distraction-free as possible. Read in short sessions to increase retention.
- Preview what you are about to read. Adjust your reading strategy based on the material you are reading.
- To promote understanding, ask questions while reading. Take notes or make annotations. Connect to information you already know. Use imagery and find examples to illustrate concepts. Re-read material you do not understand.

For more information, visit Skills for Success in the accompanying MyLab course.

# 2 Review Exercises

## Section 2.1

*In Exercises 1 and 2, use the data set, which represents the overall average class sizes for 20 national universities.* (Adapted from Public University Honors)

37 34 42 44 39 40 41 51 49 31
52 26 31 40 30 27 36 43 48 35

1. Construct a frequency distribution for the data set using five classes. Include class limits, midpoints, boundaries, frequencies, relative frequencies, and cumulative frequencies.

2. Construct a relative frequency histogram using the frequency distribution in Exercise 1. Then determine which class has the greatest relative frequency and which has the least relative frequency.

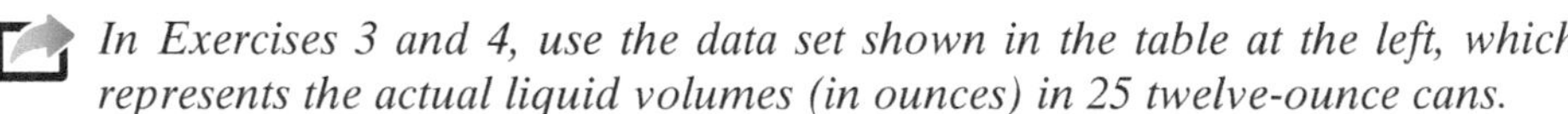

*In Exercises 3 and 4, use the data set shown in the table at the left, which represents the actual liquid volumes (in ounces) in 25 twelve-ounce cans.*

| Volumes (in ounces) | | | | |
|---|---|---|---|---|
| 11.95 | 11.91 | 11.86 | 11.94 | 12.00 |
| 11.93 | 12.00 | 11.94 | 12.10 | 11.95 |
| 11.99 | 11.94 | 11.89 | 12.01 | 11.99 |
| 11.94 | 11.92 | 11.98 | 11.88 | 11.94 |
| 11.98 | 11.92 | 11.95 | 11.93 | 12.04 |

TABLE FOR EXERCISES 3 AND 4

3. Construct a frequency histogram for the data set using seven classes.

4. Construct a relative frequency histogram for the data set using seven classes.

*In Exercises 5 and 6, use the data set, which represents the number of rooms reserved during one night's business at a sample of hotels.*

153 104 118 166 89 104 100 79 93 96 116
94 140 84 81 96 108 111 87 126 101 111
122 108 126 93 108 87 103 95 129 93 124

5. Construct a frequency distribution for the data set with six classes and draw a frequency polygon.

6. Construct an ogive for the data set using six classes.

## Section 2.2

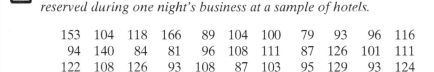

*In Exercises 7 and 8, use the data set shown in the table at the left, which represents the pollution indices (a unitless measure of pollution ranging from 0 to 100) for 24 U.S. cities.* (Adapted from Numbeo)

| Pollution indices | | | | | | | |
|---|---|---|---|---|---|---|---|
| 52 | 63 | 31 | 27 | 30 | 45 | 25 | 50 |
| 45 | 43 | 36 | 42 | 47 | 30 | 32 | 23 |
| 39 | 31 | 45 | 29 | 44 | 20 | 37 | 39 |

TABLE FOR EXERCISES 7 AND 8

7. Use a stem-and-leaf plot to display the data set. Describe any patterns.

8. Use a dot plot to display the data set. Describe any patterns.

*In Exercises 9 and 10, use the data set, which represents the results of a survey that asked U.S. full-time university and college students about their activities and time use on an average weekday.* (Source: Bureau of Labor Statistics)

| **Response** | Sleeping | Leisure and Sports | Working | Educational Activities | Other |
|---|---|---|---|---|---|
| **Time (in hours)** | 8.8 | 4.0 | 2.3 | 3.5 | 5.4 |

9. Use a pie chart to display the data set. Describe any patterns.

10. Use a Pareto chart to display the data set. Describe any patterns.

**11.** The heights (in feet) and the number of stories of the ten tallest buildings in New York City are listed. Use a scatter plot to display the data. Describe any patterns. *(Source: Emporis)*

| Height (in feet) | 1776 | 1550 | 1428 | 1401 | 1397 | 1270 | 1250 | 1200 | 1079 | 1050 |
|---|---|---|---|---|---|---|---|---|---|---|
| Stories | 104 | 95 | 84 | 59 | 85 | 73 | 102 | 54 | 71 | 77 |

**12.** The U.S. real unemployment rates over a 12-year period are listed. Use a time series chart to display the data. Describe any patterns. *(Source: U.S. Bureau of Labor Statistics)*

| Year | 2010 | 2011 | 2012 | 2013 | 2014 | 2015 |
|---|---|---|---|---|---|---|
| Rate | 16.7% | 16.2% | 15.2% | 14.5% | 12.7% | 11.3% |

| Year | 2016 | 2017 | 2018 | 2019 | 2020 | 2021 |
|---|---|---|---|---|---|---|
| Rate | 9.9% | 9.4% | 8.2% | 8.1% | 6.9% | 11.1% |

## Section 2.3

*In Exercises 13 and 14, find the mean, the median, and the mode of the data, if possible. If any measure cannot be found or does not represent the center of the data, explain why.*

**13.** The vertical jumps (in inches) of a sample of 10 college basketball players at the 2020 NBA Draft Combine *(Source: National Basketball Association)*

37.5 30.0 31.5 29.5 24.0 29.0 29.0 30.0 30.0 28.0

**14.** The responses of 1019 adults who were asked how much money they think they will spend on Christmas gifts in a recent year *(Adapted from Gallup)*

$1000 or more: 306 $250–999: 336 Less than $250: 234
Not sure: 51 None/do not celebrate Christmas: 92

**15.** For the six test scores 78, 72, 86, 91, 87, and 80, the first 5 test scores are 15% of the final grade and the last test score is 25% of the final grade. Find the weighted mean of the test scores.

**16.** For the four test scores 96, 85, 91, and 86, the first 3 test scores are 20% of the final grade, and the last test score is 40% of the final grade. Find the weighted mean of the test scores.

**17.** Estimate the mean of the frequency distribution you made in Exercise 1.

**18.** The frequency distribution shows the number of magazine subscriptions per household for a sample of 60 households. Find the mean number of subscriptions per household.

| Number of magazines | 0 | 1 | 2 | 3 | 4 | 5 | 6 |
|---|---|---|---|---|---|---|---|
| Frequency | 13 | 9 | 19 | 8 | 5 | 2 | 4 |

**19.** Describe the shape of the distribution for the histogram you made in Exercise 3 as symmetric, uniform, skewed left, skewed right, or none of these.

**20.** Describe the shape of the distribution for the histogram you made in Exercise 4 as symmetric, uniform, skewed left, skewed right, or none of these.

*In Exercises 21 and 22, determine whether the approximate shape of the distribution in the histogram is symmetric, uniform, skewed left, skewed right, or none of these.*

**21.**

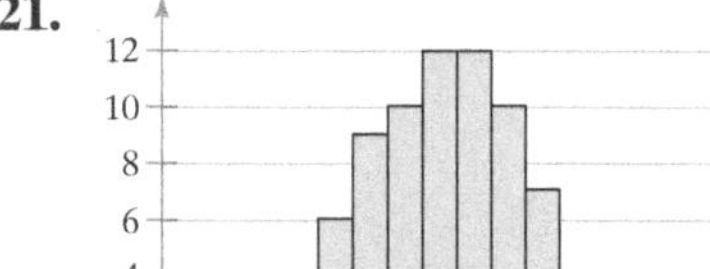


**22.**

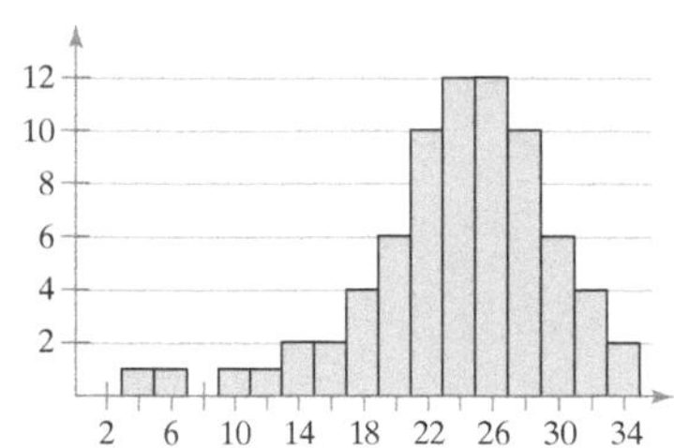


**23.** For the histogram in Exercise 21, which is greater, the mean or the median? Explain your reasoning.

**24.** For the histogram in Exercise 22, which is greater, the mean or the median? Explain your reasoning.

## Section 2.4

*In Exercises 25 and 26, find the range, mean, variance, and standard deviation of the population data set.*

**25.** The mileages (in thousands of miles) for a rental car company's fleet.

4 2 9 12 15 3 6 8 1 4 14 12 3 3

**26.** The ages of the Supreme Court justices as of April 7, 2021 *(Source: Supreme Court of the United States)*

66 56 72 49 82 71 66 60 53

*In Exercises 27 and 28, find the range, mean, variance, and standard deviation of the sample data set.*

**27.** Dormitory room charges (in dollars) for one school year for a random sample of four-year universities

5816 6045 5612 6341 6106 7361 6320 6265
7220 7439 5395 6908 5561 5710 5538 6632

**28.** Salaries (in dollars) of a random sample of teachers

62,222 56,719 50,259 45,120 47,692 45,985 53,489 71,534

*In Exercises 29 and 30, use the Empirical Rule.*

**29.** The mean charge for electricity for a sample of households was \$110.00 per month, with a standard deviation of \$17.50 per month. Between what two values do 95% of the data lie? (Assume the data set has a bell-shaped distribution.)

**30.** The mean charge for satellite television for a sample of households was \$87.50 per month, with a standard deviation of \$14.50 per month. Estimate the percent of satellite television charges between \$73.00 and \$102.00. (Assume the data set has a bell-shaped distribution.)

**31.** The mean sale per customer for 40 customers at a gas station is \$32.00, with a standard deviation of \$4.00. Using Chebychev's Theorem, determine at least how many of the customers spent between \$24.00 and \$40.00.

**32.** The mean duration of the 135 space shuttle flights was about 9.9 days, and the standard deviation was about 3.8 days. Using Chebychev's Theorem, determine at least how many of the flights lasted between 2.3 days and 17.5 days. *(Source: NASA)*

**33.** From a random sample of households, the number of televisions are listed. Find the sample mean and the sample standard deviation of the data.

| **Number of televisions** | 0 | 1 | 2 | 3 | 4 | 5 |
|---|---|---|---|---|---|---|
| **Number of households** | 1 | 8 | 13 | 10 | 5 | 3 |

**34.** From a random sample of airplanes, the number of defects found in their fuselages are listed. Find the sample mean and the sample standard deviation of the data.

| **Number of defects** | 0 | 1 | 2 | 3 | 4 | 5 | 6 |
|---|---|---|---|---|---|---|---|
| **Number of airplanes** | 4 | 5 | 2 | 9 | 1 | 3 | 1 |

*In Exercises 35 and 36, find the coefficient of variation for each of the two data sets. Then compare the results.*

**35.** Sample grade point averages for freshmen and seniors are listed.

| **Freshmen** | 2.8 | 1.8 | 4.0 | 3.8 | 2.4 | 2.0 | 0.9 | 3.6 | 1.8 |
|---|---|---|---|---|---|---|---|---|---|
| **Seniors** | 2.3 | 3.3 | 1.8 | 4.0 | 3.1 | 2.7 | 3.9 | 2.6 | 2.9 |

**36.** The ages and years of experience for all lawyers at a firm are listed.

| **Ages** | 66 | 54 | 47 | 61 | 36 | 59 | 50 | 33 |
|---|---|---|---|---|---|---|---|---|
| **Years of experience** | 37 | 20 | 23 | 32 | 14 | 29 | 22 | 8 |

## Section 2.5

*In Exercises 37–40, use the data set, which represents the model 2020 vehicles with the highest fuel economies (in miles per gallon) in the most popular classes.* *(Source: U.S. Environmental Protection Agency)*

36 30 30 45 31 113 113 33 33 33 52 141 56 117 58
118 50 26 23 23 27 48 22 22 22 121 41 105 35 35

**37.** Find the five-number summary of the data set.

**38.** Find the interquartile range of the data set.

**39.** Draw a box-and-whisker plot that represents the data set.

**40.** About how many vehicles fall on or below the third quartile?

**41.** Find the interquartile range of the data set from Exercise 13.

**42.** The weights (in pounds) of the defensive players on a high school football team are shown below. Draw a box-and-whisker plot that represents the data set and describe the shape of the distribution.

173 145 205 192 197 227 156 240 172
208 185 190 167 212 228 190 184 195

**43.** A student's test grade of 75 represents the 65th percentile of the grades. What percent of students scored higher than 75?

**44.** As of April 2021, there were 682 top-40 radio stations in the United States. One station finds that 115 stations have a larger daily audience than it has. What percentile does this station come closest to in the daily audience rankings? *(Source: Radio-Locator.com)*

*The towing capacities (in pounds) of all the pickup trucks at a dealership have a bell-shaped distribution, with a mean of 11,830 pounds and a standard deviation of 2370 pounds. In Exercises 45–48, use the corresponding z-score to determine whether the towing capacity is unusual. Explain your reasoning.*

**45.** 16,500 pounds **46.** 5500 pounds **47.** 18,000 pounds **48.** 11,300 pounds

# 2 Chapter Quiz

*Take this quiz as you would take a quiz in class. After you are done, check your work against the answers given in the back of the book.*

**1.** The data set represents the number of minutes a sample of 27 people exercise each week.

| | | | | | | | | |
|---|---|---|---|---|---|---|---|---|
| 108 | 139 | 120 | 123 | 120 | 132 | 123 | 131 | 131 |
| 157 | 150 | 124 | 111 | 101 | 135 | 119 | 116 | 117 |
| 127 | 128 | 139 | 119 | 118 | 114 | 127 | 142 | 130 |

(a) Construct a frequency distribution for the data set using five classes. Include class limits, midpoints, boundaries, frequencies, relative frequencies, and cumulative frequencies.

(b) Display the data using a frequency histogram and a frequency polygon on the same axes.

(c) Display the data using a relative frequency histogram.

(d) Describe the shape of the distribution as symmetric, uniform, skewed left, skewed right, or none of these.

(e) Display the data using an ogive.

(f) Display the data using a stem-and-leaf plot. Use one line per stem.

(g) Display the data using a box-and-whisker plot.

**2.** Use frequency distribution formulas to approximate the sample mean and the sample standard deviation of the data set in Exercise 1.

**3.** The elements with known properties can be classified as metals (55 elements), metalloids (6 elements), halogens (5 elements), noble gases (6 elements), rare earth elements (30 elements), and other nonmetals (7 elements). Display the data using (a) a pie chart and (b) a Pareto chart.

**4.** Weekly salaries (in dollars) for a sample of construction workers are listed.

| | | | | | | | |
|---|---|---|---|---|---|---|---|
| 1100 | 720 | 1384 | 1124 | 1255 | 976 | 718 | 1316 |
| 749 | 1062 | 1248 | 891 | 969 | 790 | 860 | 1100 |

(a) Find the mean, median, and mode of the salaries. Which best describes a typical salary?

(b) Find the range, variance, and standard deviation of the data set.

(c) Find the coefficient of variation of the data set.

**5.** The mean price of new homes from a sample of houses is \$180,000 with a standard deviation of \$15,000. The data set has a bell-shaped distribution. Using the Empirical Rule, between what two prices do 95% of the houses fall?

**6.** Refer to the sample statistics from Exercise 5 and determine whether any of the house prices below are unusual. Explain your reasoning.

(a) \$225,000 (b) \$80,000 (c) \$200,000 (d) \$147,000

**7.** The number of regular season wins for each Major League Baseball team in 2020 are listed. Display the data using a box-and-whisker plot. *(Source: Major League Baseball)*

| | | | | | | | | | |
|---|---|---|---|---|---|---|---|---|---|
| 43 | 25 | 26 | 26 | 23 | 27 | 31 | 32 | 36 | 40 |
| 30 | 26 | 35 | 31 | 26 | 26 | 29 | 24 | 29 | 29 |
| 22 | 36 | 19 | 35 | 25 | 37 | 33 | 28 | 35 | 34 |

# 2 Chapter Test

*Take this test as you would take a test in class.*

**1.** The overall averages of 12 students in a statistics class prior to taking the final exam are listed.

67 72 88 73 99 85 81 87 63 94 68 87

(a) Find the mean, median, and mode of the data set. Which best represents the center of the data?

(b) Find the range, variance, and standard deviation of the sample data set.

(c) Find the coefficient of variation of the data set.

(d) Display the data in a stem-and-leaf plot. Use one line per stem.

**2.** The data set represents the number of movies that a sample of 20 people watched in a year.

121 148 94 142 170 88 221 106 18 67
149 28 60 101 134 168 92 154 53 66

(a) Construct a frequency distribution for the data set using six classes. Include class limits, midpoints, boundaries, frequencies, relative frequencies, and cumulative frequencies.

(b) Display the data using a frequency histogram and a frequency polygon on the same axes.

(c) Display the data using a relative frequency histogram.

(d) Describe the shape of the distribution as symmetric, uniform, skewed left, skewed right, or none of these.

(e) Display the data using an ogive.

**3.** Use frequency distribution formulas to estimate the sample mean and the sample standard deviation of the data set in Exercise 2.

**4.** For the data set in Exercise 2, find the percentile that corresponds to 149 movies watched in a year.

**5.** The table lists the number of albums by The Beatles that received sales certifications. Display the data using (a) a pie chart and (b) a Pareto chart. *(Source: Recording Industry Association of America)*

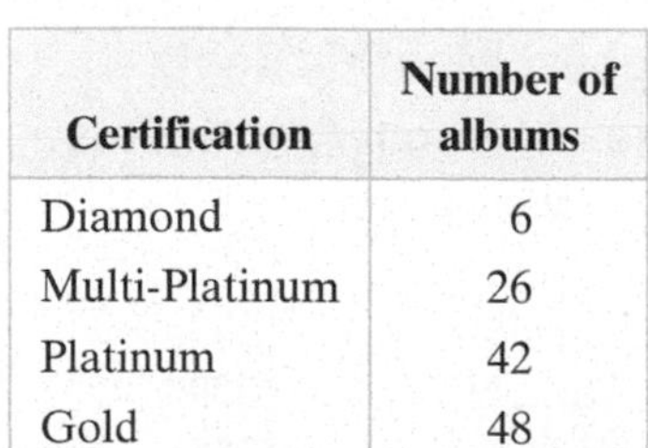

| Certification | Number of albums |
|---|---|
| Diamond | 6 |
| Multi-Platinum | 26 |
| Platinum | 42 |
| Gold | 48 |

TABLE FOR EXERCISE 5

**6.** The number of minutes it took 12 students in a statistics class to complete the final exam are listed. Use a scatter plot to display this data set and the data set in Exercise 1. The data sets are in the same order. Describe any patterns.

61 85 67 48 54 61 59 80 67 55 88 84

**7.** The data set represents the ages of 15 college professors.

46 51 60 58 37 65 40 55 30 68 28 62 56 42 59

(a) Display the data in a box-and-whisker plot.

(b) About what percent of the professors are over the age of 40?

**8.** The mean gestational length of a sample of 208 horses is 343.7 days, with a standard deviation of 10.4 days. The data set has a bell-shaped distribution.

(a) Estimate the number of gestational lengths between 333.3 and 354.1 days.

(b) Determine whether a gestational length of 318.4 days is unusual.

# REAL STATISTICS REAL DECISIONS

# Putting it all together

You are a member of your local apartment association. The association represents rental housing owners and managers who operate residential rental property throughout the greater metropolitan area. Recently, the association has received several complaints from tenants in a particular area of the city who feel that their monthly rental fees are much higher compared to other parts of the city.

You want to investigate the rental fees. You gather the data shown in the table at the right. Area A represents the area of the city where tenants are unhappy about their monthly rents. The data represent the monthly rents paid by a random sample of tenants in Area A and three other areas of similar size. Assume all the apartments represented are approximately the same size with the same amenities.

**The Monthly Rents (in dollars) Paid by 12 Randomly Selected Apartment Tenants in 4 Areas of Your City**

| Area A | Area B | Area C | Area D |
|---|---|---|---|
| 1435 | 1265 | 1221 | 1044 |
| 1249 | 1074 | 931 | 1234 |
| 1097 | 917 | 893 | 970 |
| 970 | 1213 | 1317 | 827 |
| 1171 | 949 | 1034 | 898 |
| 1122 | 839 | 1061 | 914 |
| 1259 | 896 | 851 | 1387 |
| 1022 | 918 | 861 | 1166 |
| 1002 | 1056 | 911 | 1123 |
| 1187 | 1218 | 1148 | 1029 |
| 968 | 844 | 799 | 1131 |
| 1097 | 791 | 872 | 1047 |

## EXERCISES

1. ***How Would You Do It?***
   (a) How would you investigate the complaints from renters who are unhappy about their monthly rents?
   (b) Which statistical measure do you think would best represent the data sets for the four areas of the city?
   (c) Calculate the measure from part (b) for each of the four areas.
2. ***Displaying the Data***
   (a) What type of graph would you choose to display the data? Explain your reasoning.
   (b) Construct the graph from part (a).
   (c) Based on your data displays, does it appear that the monthly rents in Area A are higher than the rents in the other areas of the city? Explain.
3. ***Measuring the Data***
   (a) What other statistical measures in this chapter could you use to analyze the monthly rent data?
   (b) Calculate the measures from part (a).
   (c) Compare the measures from part (b) with the graph you constructed in Exercise 2. Do the measurements support your conclusion in Exercise 2? Explain.
4. ***Discussing the Data***
   (a) Do you think the complaints in Area A are legitimate? How do you think they should be addressed?
   (b) What reasons might you give as to why the rents vary among different areas of the city?

Highest Monthly Rents
For One-Bedroom Apartments
MEDIAN PER CITY
San Francisco, CA $3500
New York, NY $3000
Boston, MA $2590
Oakland, CA $2500
San Jose, CA $2450

(Source: FortuneBuilders)

# TECHNOLOGY

MINITAB EXCEL TI-84 PLUS

## Parking Tickets

According to data from the city of Toronto, Ontario, Canada, there were nearly 112,000 parking infractions in the city for December 2020, with fines totaling over 5,500,000 Canadian dollars.

The fines (in Canadian dollars) for a random sample of 105 parking infractions in Toronto, Ontario, Canada, for December 2020 are listed below. *(Source: City of Toronto)*

| | | | | | | |
|---|---|---|---|---|---|---|
| 30 | 250 | 100 | 40 | 30 | 30 | 100 |
| 30 | 30 | 50 | 100 | 100 | 30 | 30 |
| 100 | 100 | 30 | 30 | 100 | 30 | 30 |
| 30 | 30 | 40 | 50 | 50 | 40 | 50 |
| 40 | 50 | 30 | 30 | 30 | 30 | 30 |
| 30 | 40 | 100 | 150 | 30 | 50 | 40 |
| 50 | 30 | 60 | 40 | 30 | 40 | 150 |
| 50 | 100 | 30 | 50 | 100 | 40 | 30 |
| 30 | 30 | 30 | 100 | 150 | 30 | 150 |
| 30 | 50 | 50 | 50 | 30 | 50 | 30 |
| 30 | 40 | 30 | 40 | 30 | 100 | 50 |
| 30 | 40 | 30 | 50 | 50 | 30 | 30 |
| 50 | 40 | 30 | 50 | 40 | 30 | 30 |
| 30 | 40 | 30 | 100 | 100 | 30 | 50 |
| 30 | 50 | 30 | 40 | 150 | 30 | 30 |

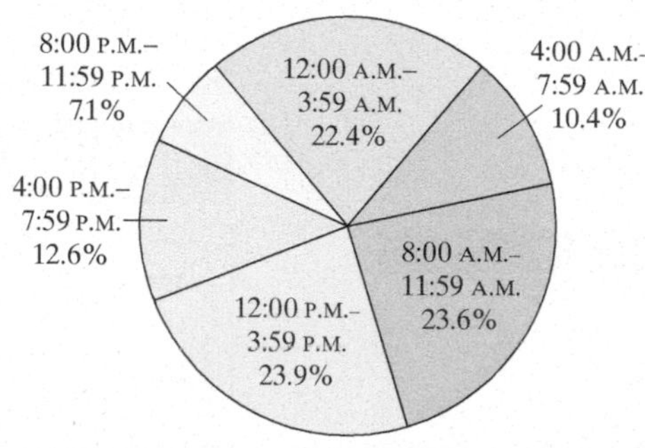


(Source: City of Toronto)

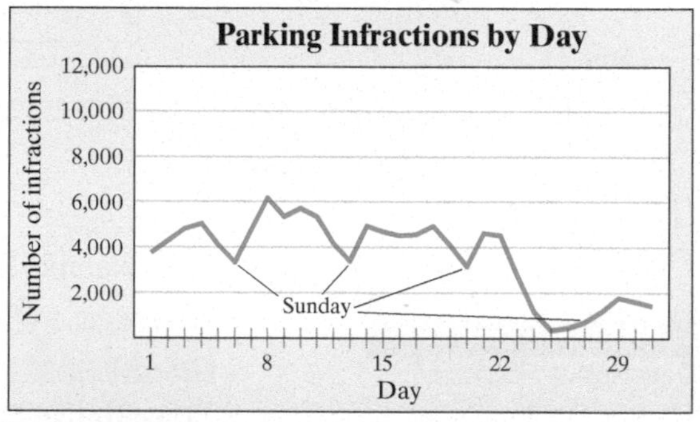


(Source: City of Toronto)

The figures above show parking infractions in Toronto, Ontario, Canada, for December 2020 by time of day and by day.

### EXERCISES

*In Exercises 1–5, use technology. If possible, print your results.*

**1.** Find the sample mean of the data.

**2.** Find the sample standard deviation of the data.

**3.** Find the five-number summary of the data.

**4.** Make a frequency distribution for the data. Use a class width of 15.

**5.** Draw a histogram for the data. Does the distribution appear to be bell-shaped?

**6.** What percent of the distribution lies within one standard deviation of the mean? Within two standard deviations of the mean? Within three standard deviations of the mean?

**7.** Does it make sense to estimate the answers for Exercise 6 using the Empirical Rule? If so, compare the estimates to your answers. If not, explain why.

**8.** Does it make sense to estimate the answers for Exercise 6 using Chebychev's Theorem? If so, compare the estimates to your answers. If not, explain why.

**9.** Use the frequency distribution in Exercise 4 to estimate the sample mean and sample standard deviation of the data. Do the formulas for grouped data give results that are as accurate as the individual entry formulas? Explain.

**10. Writing** Do you think the mean or the median better represents the data? Explain your reasoning.

Extended solutions are given in the technology manuals that accompany this text. Technical instruction is provided for Minitab, Excel, and the TI-84 Plus.

# 2 Using Technology to Determine Descriptive Statistics

Here are some Minitab and TI-84 Plus printouts for three examples in this chapter.

See Example 7, page 61.

Bar Chart...
Pie Chart...
Time Series Plot...
Area Graph...
Contour Plot...
3D Scatterplot...
3D Surface Plot...

MINITAB

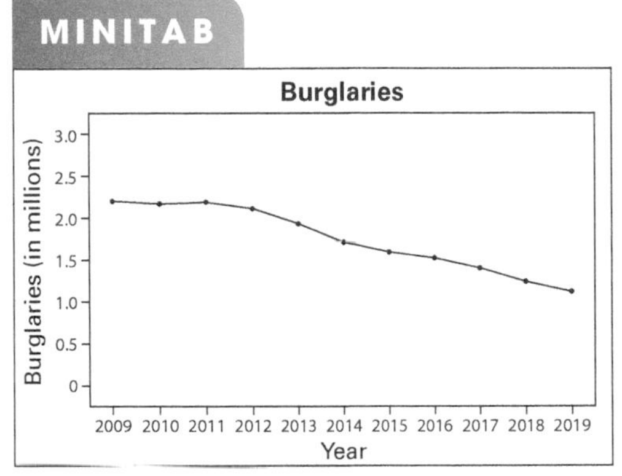


See Example 3, page 85.

Display Descriptive Statistics...
Store Descriptive Statistics...
Graphical Summary...
1-Sample Z...
1-Sample t...
2-Sample t...
Paired t...

MINITAB

**Descriptive Statistics: Recovery times**

| Variable | N | Mean | SE Mean | StDev | Minimum |
|---|---|---|---|---|---|
| Recovery times | 12 | 7.500 | 0.622 | 2.153 | 4.000 |

| Variable | Q1 | Median | Q3 | Maximum |
|---|---|---|---|---|
| Recovery times | 6.000 | 7.000 | 9.750 | 11.000 |

See Example 4, page 105.

Empirical CDF...
Probability Distribution Plot ...
Boxplot...
Interval Plot...
Individual Value Plot...
Line Plot...

MINITAB

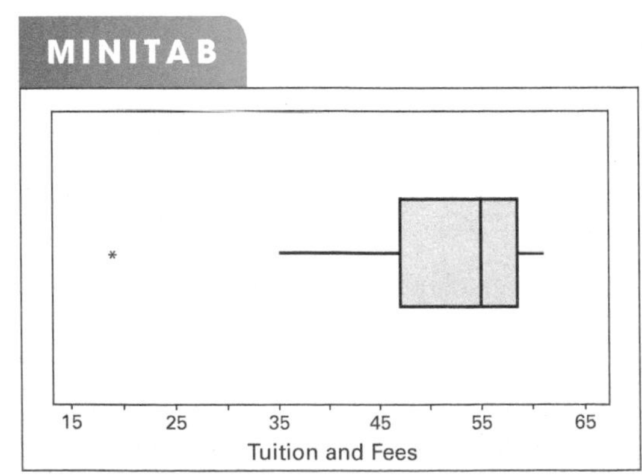

See Example 7, page 61.

**TI-84 PLUS**

```
STAT PLOTS
1: Plot1...Off
   L1 L2 ▫
2: Plot2...Off
   L1 L2 ▫
3: Plot3...Off
   L1 L2 ▫
4↓ PlotsOff
```

**TI-84 PLUS**

```
Plot1 Plot2 Plot3
On Off
Type:
Xlist: L1
Ylist: L2
Mark: ▫ + .
```

**TI-84 PLUS**

```
ZOOM MEMORY
4↑ ZDecimal
5: ZSquare
6: ZStandard
7: ZTrig
8: ZInteger
9: ZoomStat
0↓ ZoomFit
```

**TI-84 PLUS**

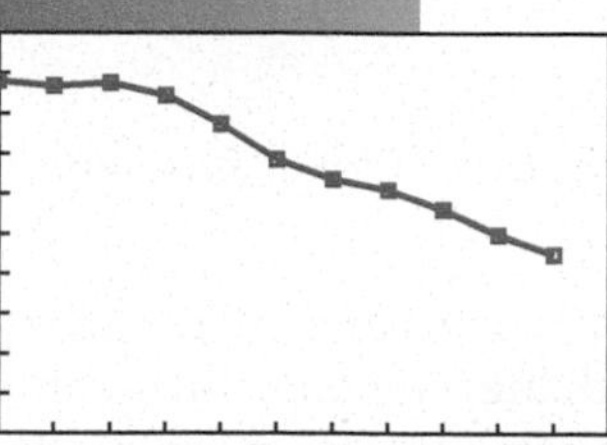

See Example 3, page 85.

**TI-84 PLUS**

```
EDIT CALC TESTS
1: 1-Var Stats
2: 2-Var Stats
3: Med-Med
4: LinReg(ax+b)
5: QuadReg
6: CubicReg
7↓ QuartReg
```

**TI-84 PLUS**

```
1-Var Stats
List:L1
FreqList:
Calculate
```

**TI-84 PLUS**

```
1-Var Stats
x̄=7.5
Σx=90
Σx²=726
Sx=2.153221688
σx=2.061552813
↓n=12
```

See Example 4, page 105.

**TI-84 PLUS**

```
STAT PLOTS
1: Plot1...Off
   L1 L2 ▫
2: Plot2...Off
   L1 L2 ▫
3: Plot3...Off
   L1 L2 ▫
4↓ PlotsOff
```

**TI-84 PLUS**

```
Plot1 Plot2 Plot3
On Off
Type:
Xlist: L1
Freq: 1
Mark: ▫ + .
```

**TI-84 PLUS**

```
ZOOM MEMORY
4↑ ZDecimal
5: ZSquare
6: ZStandard
7: ZTrig
8: ZInteger
9: ZoomStat
0↓ ZoomFit
```

**TI-84 PLUS**

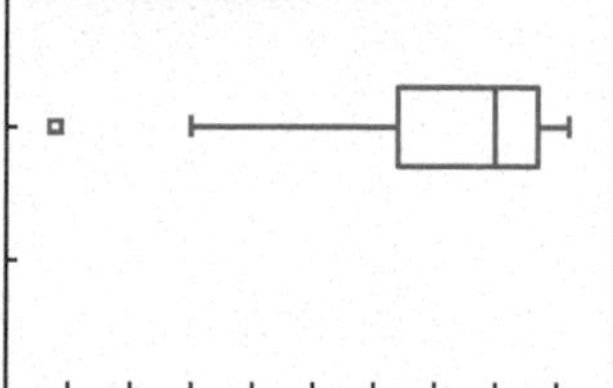

# CHAPTERS 1&2 CUMULATIVE REVIEW

*In Exercises 1 and 2, identify the sampling technique used, and discuss potential sources of bias (if any). Explain.*

**1.** For quality assurance, every fortieth toothbrush is taken from each of four assembly lines and tested to make sure the bristles stay in the toothbrush.

**2.** Using random digit dialing, researchers asked 1090 U.S. adults their level of education.

**3.** In 2020, a worldwide study of workplace fraud found that initial detections of fraud resulted from a tip (43%), an internal audit (15%), management review (12%), by accident (5%), account reconciliation (4%), external audit (4%), document examination (3%), surveillance/monitoring (3%), notified by law enforcement (2%), IT controls (2%), confession (1%), or some other means (6%). Use a Pareto chart to organize the data. *(Source: Association of Certified Fraud Examiners)*

*In Exercises 4 and 5, determine whether the number is a parameter or a statistic. Explain your reasoning.*

**4.** In 2021, the median annual salary of a first-year chemist was $58,700.

**5.** In a survey of 1002 U.S. adults, 64% said that fake news has caused a great deal of confusion or some confusion. *(Source: Pew Research Center)*

**6.** The mean annual salary for a sample of electrical engineers is $86,500, with a standard deviation of $1500. The data set has a bell-shaped distribution.

(a) Use the Empirical Rule to estimate the percent of electrical engineers whose annual salaries are between $83,500 and $89,500.

(b) The salaries of three randomly selected electrical engineers are $93,500, $85,600, and $82,750. Find the $z$-score that corresponds to each salary. Determine whether any of these salaries are unusual.

*In Exercises 7 and 8, identify the population and the sample.*

**7.** A survey of 3941 college students in bachelor's degree programs found that 49% think that the COVID-19 pandemic is likely to negatively impact their ability to complete their degree. *(Source: Gallup)*

**8.** A survey of 182 undergraduate and graduate students found that 60% have had difficulty coping with stress in a healthy way. *(Source: The JED Foundation)*

*In Exercises 9 and 10, determine whether the study is an observational study or an experiment. Explain.*

**9.** To study the effect of using digital devices in the classroom on exam performance, researchers divided 726 undergraduate students into three groups, including a group that was allowed to use digital devices, a group that had restricted access to tablets, and a control group that was "technology-free." *(Source: Massachusetts Institute of Technology)*

**10.** In a study of 7847 children in grades 1 through 5, 15.5% have attention deficit hyperactivity disorder. *(Source: Journal of Attention Disorders)*

*In Exercises 11 and 12, determine whether the data are qualitative or quantitative, and determine the level of measurement of the data set.*

**11.** The amounts of time (in months) that 16 stars of *The Bachelorette* and their chosen partner stayed together as of April 2021 are listed.

208 12 3 12 18 94 3 75 8 36 75 20 24 0 4 5

**12.** The six top-earning states in 2019 by median household income are listed. *(Source: U.S. Census Bureau)*

| | | |
|---|---|---|
| 1. Maryland | 2. New Jersey | 3. Hawaii |
| 4. Massachusetts | 5. Connecticut | 6. Alaska |

**13.** The number of tornadoes by state in 2020 are listed. (a) Draw a box-and-whisker plot that represents the data set and (b) describe the shape of the distribution. *(Source: National Oceanic and Atmospheric Administration)*

| | | | | | | | | | |
|---|---|---|---|---|---|---|---|---|---|
| 78 | 0 | 4 | 41 | 7 | 34 | 6 | 7 | 65 | 75 |
| 0 | 0 | 71 | 18 | 28 | 27 | 23 | 55 | 2 | 21 |
| 3 | 2 | 69 | 127 | 27 | 2 | 35 | 0 | 2 | 5 |
| 6 | 10 | 54 | 22 | 19 | 31 | 3 | 6 | 0 | 57 |
| 21 | 38 | 102 | 0 | 0 | 15 | 2 | 0 | 22 | 1 |

**14.** Five test scores are shown below. The first 4 test scores are 15% of the final grade, and the last test score is 40% of the final grade. Find the weighted mean of the test scores.

85 92 84 89 91

**15.** Tail lengths (in feet) for a sample of American alligators are listed.

6.5 3.4 4.2 7.1 5.4 6.8 7.5 3.9 4.6

(a) Find the mean, median, and mode of the tail lengths. Which best describes a typical American alligator tail length? Explain your reasoning.

(b) Find the range, variance, and standard deviation of the data set.

**16.** A study shows that life expectancies for Americans have increased or remained stable every year for the past five years.

(a) Make an inference based on the results of the study.

(b) What is wrong with this type of reasoning?

*In Exercises 17–19, use the data set, which represents the points recorded by each player on the Winnipeg Jets in the 2019–2020 NHL season. (Source: National Hockey League)*

| | | | | | | | |
|---|---|---|---|---|---|---|---|
| 8 | 8 | 8 | 6 | 0 | 73 | 26 | 1 |
| 0 | 5 | 58 | 1 | 7 | 5 | 10 | 63 |
| 0 | 5 | 10 | 0 | 31 | 5 | 15 | 45 |
| 16 | 29 | 10 | 73 | 5 | 3 | 0 | 65 |

**17.** Construct a frequency distribution for the data set using eight classes. Include class limits, midpoints, boundaries, frequencies, relative frequencies, and cumulative frequencies.

**18.** Describe the shape of the distribution.

**19.** Construct a relative frequency histogram using the frequency distribution in Exercise 17. Then determine which class has the greatest relative frequency and which has the least relative frequency.

CHAPTER 3

# Probability

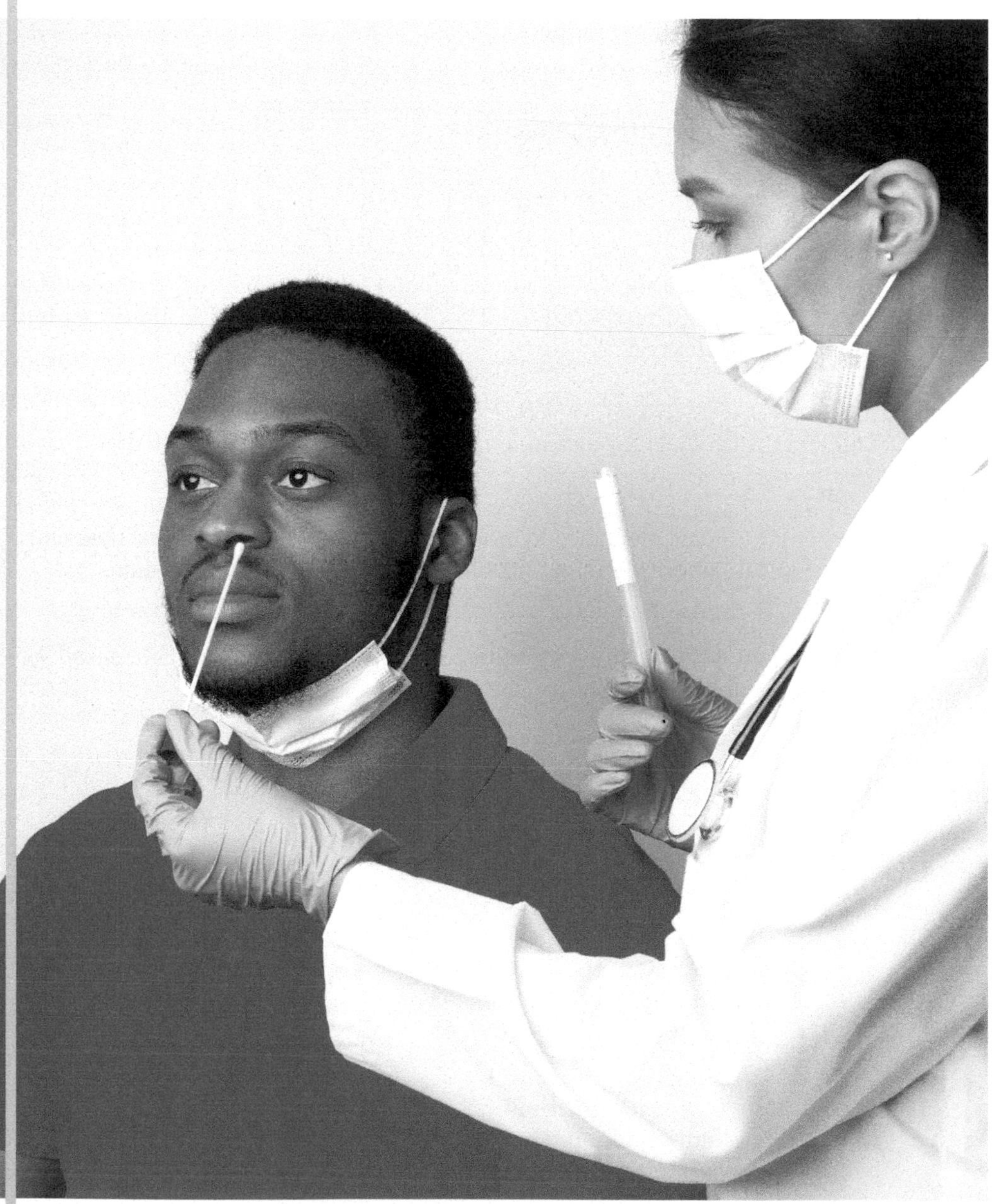

The coronavirus pandemic hit the United States in early 2020. By May of 2021, over 400 million tests for coronavirus had been administered in the United States.

## Where You've Been

In Chapters 1 and 2, you learned how to collect and describe data. Once the data are collected and described, you can use the results to write summaries, draw conclusions, and make decisions. For instance, during the early stages of the coronavirus disease 2019 (COVID-19) pandemic, testing was the primary means of minimizing the spread of the disease by identifying people who were infected and having them isolate. Like most lab tests, COVID-19 tests have a chance of producing false results. By collecting and analyzing data, scientists determined the accuracy of various tests to help decide which tests to use in different situations.

## Where You're Going

In Chapter 3, you will learn how to determine the probability of an event. For instance, you will study *conditional probability* in Section 3.2. An important conditional probability in COVID-19 testing is the probability $P(\text{negative test}|\text{infected})$ that a person tests negative for COVID-19 given that the person is infected. This is known as a false negative result. False negative results allow people to believe they are not contagious when they are.

The probability of a false negative result is affected by both the sensitivity of the test and the percentage of people infected. One test for COVID-19 has a sensitivity of about 75%, which means that 75% of infected people test positive for infection. The remaining 25% of infected people have false negative results.

For a test sensitivity of 75%, the table shows how the probability that a person is infected affects the probability of a false negative result. The last column shows how many false negative results you can expect for 100 tests.

| $P(\text{infected})$ | $P(\text{negative test}|\text{infected})$ | False negatives expected for 100 tests |
|---|---|---|
| 0.2 | 0.05 | 5 |
| 0.4 | 0.10 | 10 |
| 0.6 | 0.15 | 15 |
| 0.8 | 0.20 | 20 |

# 3.1 Basic Concepts of Probability and Counting

### What You Should Learn

- How to identify the sample space of a probability experiment and how to identify simple events
- How to use the Fundamental Counting Principle to find the number of ways two or more events can occur
- How to distinguish among classical probability, empirical probability, and subjective probability
- How to find the probability of the complement of an event
- How to use a tree diagram and the Fundamental Counting Principle to find probabilities

Probability Experiments ■ The Fundamental Counting Principle ■ Types of Probability ■ Complementary Events ■ Probability Applications

## Probability Experiments

When weather forecasters say that there is a 90% chance of rain or a physician says there is a 35% chance for a successful surgery, they are stating the likelihood, or *probability*, that a specific event will occur. Decisions such as "should you go golfing" or "should you proceed with surgery" are often based on these probabilities. In the preceding chapter, you learned about the role of the descriptive branch of statistics. The second branch, inferential statistics, has probability as its foundation, so it is necessary to learn about probability before proceeding.

**DEFINITION**

A **probability experiment** is an action, or trial, through which specific results (counts, measurements, or responses) are obtained. The result of a single trial in a probability experiment is an **outcome.** The set of all possible outcomes of a probability experiment is the **sample space.** An **event** is a subset of the sample space. It may consist of one or more outcomes.

**Study Tip**

Here is a simple example of the use of the terms *probability experiment, sample space, event,* and *outcome.*

Probability Experiment:
Roll a six-sided die.

Sample Space:
{1, 2, 3, 4, 5, 6}

Event:
Roll an even number, {2, 4, 6}.

Outcome:
Roll a 2, {2}.

**EXAMPLE 1**

### Identifying the Sample Space of a Probability Experiment

A survey consists of asking people for their blood types (O, A, B, and AB), including whether they are Rh-positive or Rh-negative. Determine the number of outcomes and identify the sample space.

**SOLUTION**

There are four blood types: O, A, B, and AB. For each person, they are either Rh-positive or Rh-negative. A **tree diagram** gives a visual display of the outcomes of a probability experiment by using branches that originate from a starting point. It can be used to find the number of possible outcomes in a sample space as well as individual outcomes.

**Tree Diagram for Blood Types**

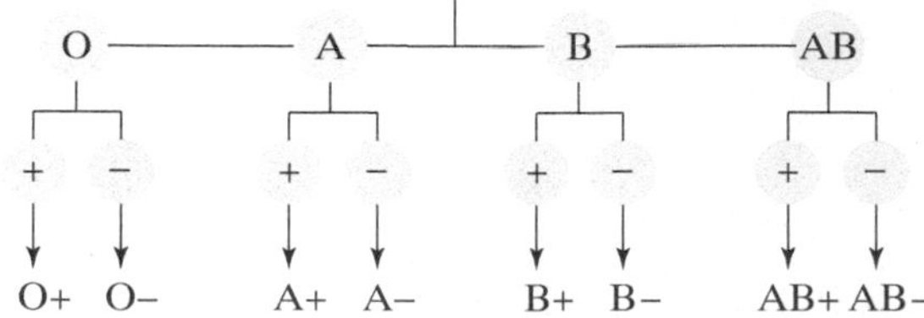


From the tree diagram, you can see that the sample space has eight possible outcomes, which are listed below.

{O+, O−, A+, A−, B+, B−, AB+, AB−} Sample space

**SURVEY**

Does your favorite team's win or loss affect your mood?

Check one response:

☐ Yes
☐ No
☑ Not sure

**TRY IT YOURSELF 1**

For each probability experiment, determine the number of outcomes and identify the sample space.

1. A probability experiment consists of recording a response to the survey question at the left and the gender of the respondent.
2. A probability experiment consists of recording a response to the survey question at the left and the age (18–34, 35–49, 50 and older) of the respondent.
3. A probability experiment consists of recording a response to the survey question at the left and the geographic location (Northeast, South, Midwest, West) of the respondent.

*Answer: Page A37*

**Diagram for Coin and Die Experiment**

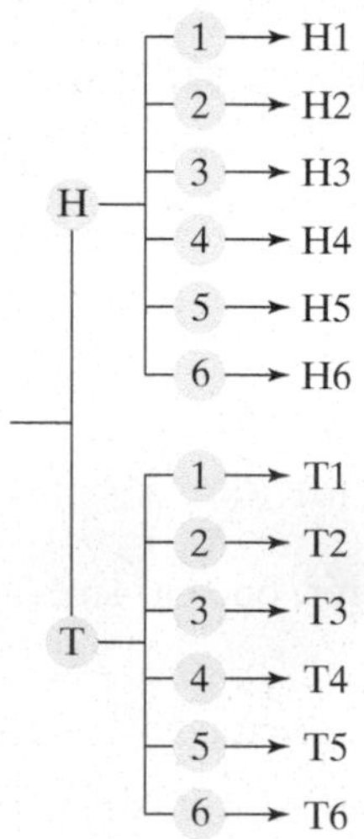


In this chapter, you will learn how to calculate the probability or likelihood of an event. Events are often represented by uppercase letters, such as $A$, $B$, and $C$. An event that consists of a single outcome is called a **simple event.** For instance, consider a probability experiment that consists of tossing a coin and then rolling a six-sided die, as shown in the tree diagram at the left. The event "tossing heads and rolling a 3" is a simple event and can be represented as

$A = \{\text{H3}\}$. Event $A$ has one outcome, so it is a simple event.

In contrast, the event "tossing heads and rolling an even number" is not simple because it consists of three possible outcomes and can be represented as

$B = \{\text{H2, H4, H6}\}$. Event $B$ has more than one outcome, so it is not simple.

## EXAMPLE 2

### Identifying Simple Events

Determine the number of outcomes in each event. Then decide whether each event is simple or not. Explain your reasoning.

1. For quality assurance, you randomly select a machine part from a batch that has been manufactured that day. Event $A$ is selecting a specific defective machine part.
2. You roll a six-sided die. Event $B$ is rolling at least a 4.

**SOLUTION**

1. Event $A$ has only one outcome: choosing the specific defective machine part. So, the event is a simple event.
2. Event $B$ has three outcomes: rolling a 4, a 5, or a 6. Because the event has more than one outcome, it is not simple.

**TRY IT YOURSELF 2**

You ask for a student's age at their last birthday. Determine the number of outcomes in each event. Then decide whether each event is simple or not. Explain your reasoning.

1. Event $C$: The student's age is between 18 and 23, inclusive.
2. Event $D$: The student's age is 20.

*Answer: Page A37*

## The Fundamental Counting Principle

In some cases, an event can occur in so many different ways that it is not practical to write out all the outcomes. When this occurs, you can rely on the Fundamental Counting Principle. The **Fundamental Counting Principle** can be used to find the number of ways two or more events can occur in sequence.

### The Fundamental Counting Principle

If one event can occur in $m$ ways and a second event can occur in $n$ ways, then the number of ways the two events can occur in sequence is $m \cdot n$. This rule can be extended to any number of events occurring in sequence.

In words, the number of ways that events can occur in sequence is found by multiplying the number of ways one event can occur by the number of ways the other event(s) can occur.

### EXAMPLE 3

#### Using the Fundamental Counting Principle

You are purchasing a new car. The possible manufacturers, car sizes, and colors are listed in the table.

| Manufacturer | Car size | Color |
|---|---|---|
| Ford | compact | white (W) |
| GM | midsize | red (R) |
| Honda | | black (B) |
| | | green (G) |

How many different ways can you select one manufacturer, one car size, and one color? Use a tree diagram to check your result.

**SOLUTION**

There are three choices of manufacturers, two choices of car sizes, and four choices of colors. Using the Fundamental Counting Principle, you can determine that the number of ways to select one manufacturer, one car size, and one color is

$$3 \cdot 2 \cdot 4 = 24 \text{ ways.}$$

Using a tree diagram, you can see why there are 24 options.

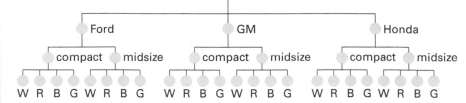

**Tree Diagram for Car Selections**



**TRY IT YOURSELF 3**

You add another manufacturer, Toyota, and another color, tan, to the choices in Example 3. How many different ways can you select one manufacturer, one car size, and one color? Use a tree diagram to check your result.

*Answer: Page A38*

## EXAMPLE 4

### Using the Fundamental Counting Principle

The access code for a car's security system consists of four digits. Each digit can be any number from 0 through 9.

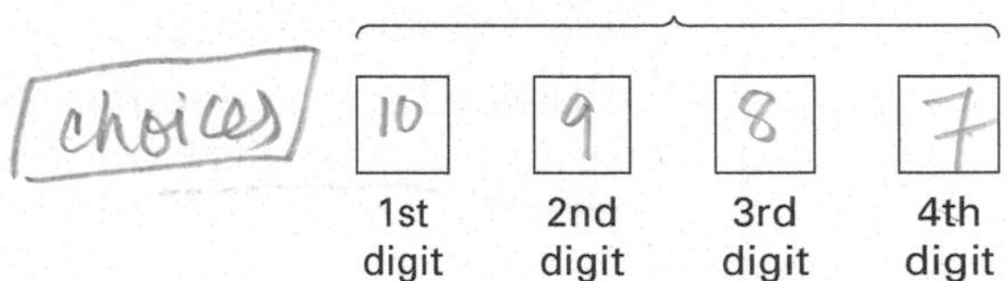


How many access codes are possible when

1. each digit can be used only once and not repeated?
2. each digit can be repeated?
3. each digit can be repeated but the first digit cannot be 0 or 1?

**SOLUTION**

1. Because each digit can be used only once, there are 10 choices for the first digit, 9 choices left for the second digit, 8 choices left for the third digit, and 7 choices left for the fourth digit. Using the Fundamental Counting Principle, you can conclude that there are

   $$10 \cdot 9 \cdot 8 \cdot 7 = 5040$$

   possible access codes.

2. Because each digit can be repeated, there are 10 choices for each of the four digits. So, there are

   $$10 \cdot 10 \cdot 10 \cdot 10 = 10^4$$
   $$= 10{,}000$$

   possible access codes.

3. Because the first digit cannot be 0 or 1, there are 8 choices for the first digit. Then there are 10 choices for each of the other three digits. So, there are

   $$8 \cdot 10 \cdot 10 \cdot 10 = 8000$$

   possible access codes.

Remember that you can use technology to check your answers. For instance, at the left, a TI-84 Plus was used to check the results in Example 4.

For help with multiplication and division, see *Integrated Review* at

MyLab® Statistics

**TI-84 PLUS**

```
10*9*8*7
                5040
10^4
               10000
8*10*10*10
                8000
```

**TRY IT YOURSELF 4**

How many license plates can you make when a license plate consists of

1. six (out of 26) alphabetical letters, each of which can be repeated?
2. six (out of 26) alphabetical letters, each of which cannot be repeated?
3. six (out of 26) alphabetical letters, each of which can be repeated but the first letter cannot be A, B, C, or D?
4. one digit (any number 1 through 9) and five (out of 26) alphabetical letters, each of which can be repeated?

*Answer: Page A38*

## Types of Probability

The method you will use to calculate a probability depends on the type of probability. There are three types of probability: **classical probability, empirical probability,** and **subjective probability.** The probability that event $E$ will occur is written as $P(E)$ and is read as "the probability of event $E$."

**Study Tip**

Probabilities can be written as fractions, decimals, or percents. In Example 5, the probabilities are written as reduced fractions and decimals, with decimals rounded to three places when possible. For very small probabilities, round to the first nonzero digit. For example, 0.0000271 would be 0.00003. In general, these *round-off rules* will be used throughout the text. (Note that some results may be rounded differently for accuracy.)

**DEFINITION**

**Classical** (or **theoretical**) **probability** is used when each outcome in a sample space is equally likely to occur. The classical probability for an event $E$ is given by

$$P(E) = \frac{\text{Number of outcomes in event } E}{\text{Total number of outcomes in sample space}}.$$

**EXAMPLE 5**

### Finding Classical Probabilities

You roll a six-sided die. Find the probability of each event.

1. Event $A$: rolling a 3
2. Event $B$: rolling a 7
3. Event $C$: rolling a number less than 5

**SOLUTION**

When a six-sided die is rolled, the sample space consists of six outcomes: $\{1, 2, 3, 4, 5, 6\}$. Because each outcome in the sample space is equally likely to occur, you can use the formula for classical probability.

1. There is one outcome in event $A = \{3\}$. So,

$$P(\text{rolling a 3}) = \frac{1}{6} \approx 0.167. \quad \text{Round to three decimal places.}$$

The probability of rolling a 3 is $\frac{1}{6}$, or about 0.167.

2. Because 7 is not in the sample space, there are no outcomes in event $B$. So,

$$P(\text{rolling a 7}) = \frac{0}{6} = 0. \quad \text{Event is not possible.}$$

The probability of rolling a 7 is 0, so it is not possible for the event to occur.

3. There are four outcomes in event $C = \{1, 2, 3, 4\}$. So,

$$P(\text{rolling a number less than 5}) = \frac{4}{6} = \frac{2}{3} \approx 0.667.$$

The probability of rolling a number less than 5 is $\frac{2}{3}$, or about 0.667.

**TRY IT YOURSELF 5**

You select a card from a standard deck of playing cards (see figure). Find the probability of each event.

1. Event $D$: Selecting the nine of clubs
2. Event $E$: Selecting a heart
3. Event $F$: Selecting a diamond, heart, club, or spade

*Answer: Page A38*

**Standard Deck of Playing Cards**

| Hearts | Diamonds | Spades | Clubs |
|---|---|---|---|
| A ♥ | A ♦ | A ♠ | A ♣ |
| K ♥ | K ♦ | K ♠ | K ♣ |
| Q ♥ | Q ♦ | Q ♠ | Q ♣ |
| J ♥ | J ♦ | J ♠ | J ♣ |
| 10 ♥ | 10 ♦ | 10 ♠ | 10 ♣ |
| 9 ♥ | 9 ♦ | 9 ♠ | 9 ♣ |
| 8 ♥ | 8 ♦ | 8 ♠ | 8 ♣ |
| 7 ♥ | 7 ♦ | 7 ♠ | 7 ♣ |
| 6 ♥ | 6 ♦ | 6 ♠ | 6 ♣ |
| 5 ♥ | 5 ♦ | 5 ♠ | 5 ♣ |
| 4 ♥ | 4 ♦ | 4 ♠ | 4 ♣ |
| 3 ♥ | 3 ♦ | 3 ♠ | 3 ♣ |
| 2 ♥ | 2 ♦ | 2 ♠ | 2 ♣ |

When an experiment is repeated many times, regular patterns are formed. These patterns make it possible to find empirical probability. Empirical probability can be used even when each outcome of an event is not equally likely to occur.

## Picturing the World

It seems that no matter how unlikely an event is, somebody wants to know the probability that it will occur. The table below lists the probabilities that some rare events will happen. (Adapted from *Life: The Odds* by Gregory Arthur Baer)

| Event | Probability |
|---|---|
| Being audited by the IRS | 0.6% |
| Writing a *New York Times* best seller | 0.005 |
| Winning an Academy Award | 0.00009 |
| Having your identity stolen | 0.5% |
| Spotting a UFO | 0.0000003 |

**Which of these events is most likely to occur? Least likely?**

**3.1** To explore this topic further, see **Activity 3.1** on page 146.

### DEFINITION

**Empirical** (or **statistical**) **probability** is based on observations obtained from probability experiments. The empirical probability of an event $E$ is the relative frequency of event $E$.

$$P(E) = \frac{\text{Frequency of event } E}{\text{Total frequency}}$$

$$= \frac{f}{n} \qquad \text{Note that } n = \Sigma f.$$

### EXAMPLE 6

### Finding Empirical Probabilities

A research organization is conducting a survey of randomly selected U.S. adults to determine how they read books during the past year, if at all. So far, 1502 adults have been surveyed. The pie chart shows the results. (Note that digital books include ebooks as well as audio books.) What is the probability that the next adult surveyed read only print books during the last year? *(Adapted from Pew Research Center)*

**Book Reading by U.S. Adults**

**SOLUTION**

Note that the responses are *not* equally likely to occur and are based on observations. So, you *cannot* use the formula for classical probability, but you can use the formula for empirical probability. The event is a response of "read only print books." The frequency of this event is 560. The total of the frequencies is

$$n = 560 + 108 + 425 + 409 \qquad \text{Add frequency of each response.}$$

$$= 1502. \qquad \text{Total frequency}$$

The empirical probability that the response of the next adult is "read only print books" is

$$P(\text{read only print books}) = \frac{560}{1502} \qquad \text{Find empirical probability.}$$

$$\approx 0.373. \qquad \text{Round to three decimal places.}$$

**TRY IT YOURSELF 6**

In Example 6, determine the probability that the next adult surveyed read only digital books during the last year. *Answer: Page A38*

| Ages | Frequency, $f$ |
|---|---|
| 13 to 17 | 84 |
| 18 to 24 | 459 |
| 25 to 34 | 765 |
| 35 to 44 | 546 |
| 45 to 54 | 432 |
| 55 to 64 | 369 |
| 65 and over | 345 |
| | $\Sigma f = 3000$ |

## EXAMPLE 7

### Using a Frequency Distribution to Find Probabilities

A research organization is conducting a survey of randomly selected individuals to determine the ages of users of a social media application. So far, 3000 users of the application have been surveyed. The frequency distribution at the left shows the results. What is the probability that the next user surveyed is 25 to 34 years old? *(Adapted from Statista)*

**SOLUTION**

Because the responses are *not* equally likely to occur and are based on observations, use the formula for empirical probability. The event is a response of "25 to 34 years old." The frequency of this event is 765. Because the total of the frequencies is 3000, the empirical probability that the next user is 25 to 34 years old is

$$P(\text{age 25 to 34}) = \frac{765}{3000} = 0.255.$$

**TRY IT YOURSELF 7**

Find the probability that the next user surveyed is 35 to 44 years old.

*Answer: Page A38*

As you increase the number of times a probability experiment is repeated, the empirical probability (relative frequency) of an event approaches the theoretical probability of the event. This is known as the **law of large numbers.**

### Law of Large Numbers

As an experiment is repeated over and over, the empirical probability of an event approaches the theoretical (actual) probability of the event.

As an example of this law, suppose you want to determine the probability of tossing a head with a fair coin. You toss the coin 10 times and get 3 heads, so you obtain an empirical probability of $\frac{3}{10}$. Because you tossed the coin only a few times, your empirical probability is not representative of the theoretical probability, which is $\frac{1}{2}$. The law of large numbers tells you that the empirical probability after tossing the coin several thousand times will be very close to the theoretical or actual probability.

The scatter plot below shows the results of simulating a coin toss 150 times. Notice that, as the number of tosses increases, the probability of tossing a head gets closer and closer to the theoretical probability of 0.5.

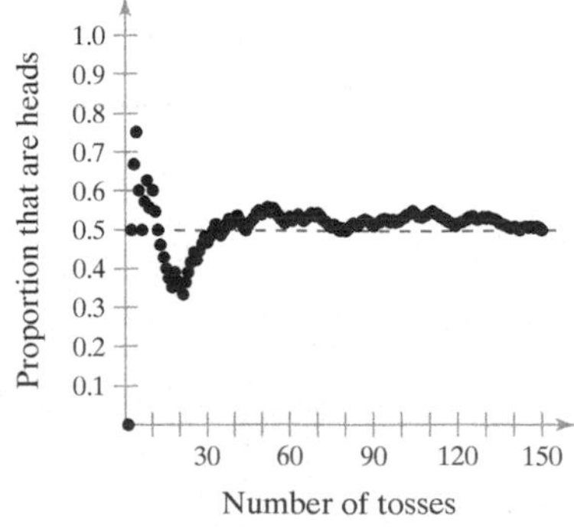

The third type of probability is **subjective probability.** Subjective probabilities result from intuition, educated guesses, and estimates. For instance, given a patient's health and extent of injuries, a doctor may feel that the patient has a 90% chance of a full recovery. Or a business analyst may predict that the chance of the employees of a certain company going on strike is 0.25.

## EXAMPLE 8

### Classifying Types of Probability

Classify each statement as an example of classical probability, empirical probability, or subjective probability. Explain your reasoning.

1. The probability that you will get an A on your next test is 0.9.
2. The probability that a voter chosen at random will be younger than 35 years old is 0.3.
3. The probability of winning a 1000-ticket raffle with one ticket is $\frac{1}{1000}$.

**SOLUTION**

1. This probability is most likely based on an educated guess. It is an example of subjective probability.
2. This statement is most likely based on a survey of a sample of voters, so it is an example of empirical probability.
3. Because you know the number of outcomes and each is equally likely, this is an example of classical probability.

**TRY IT YOURSELF 8**

Based on previous counts, the probability of a salmon successfully passing through a dam on the Columbia River is 0.85. Is this statement an example of classical probability, empirical probability, or subjective probability? *(Source: Army Corps of Engineers)*

*Answer: Page A38*

A probability cannot be negative or greater than 1, as stated in the rule below.

**Range of Probabilities Rule**

The probability of an event $E$ is between 0 and 1, inclusive. That is,

$$0 \leq P(E) \leq 1.$$

For help with double inequalities, see *Integrated Review* at

MyLab Statistics

When the probability of an event is 1, the event is certain to occur. When the probability of an event is 0, the event is impossible. A probability of 0.5 indicates that an event has an even chance of occurring or not occurring.

The figure below shows the possible range of probabilities and their meanings.

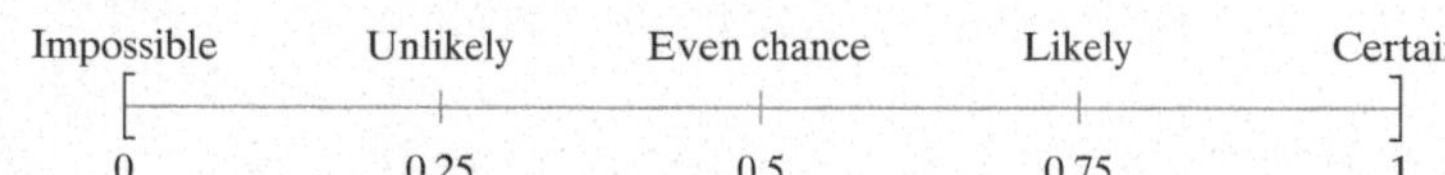


An event that occurs with a probability of 0.05 or less is typically considered unusual. Unusual events are highly unlikely to occur. Later in this course you will identify unusual events when studying inferential statistics.

## Complementary Events

The sum of the probabilities of all outcomes in a sample space is 1, or 100%. An important result of this fact is that when you know the probability of an event $E$, you can find the probability of the **complement of event $E$.**

**Sample Space**

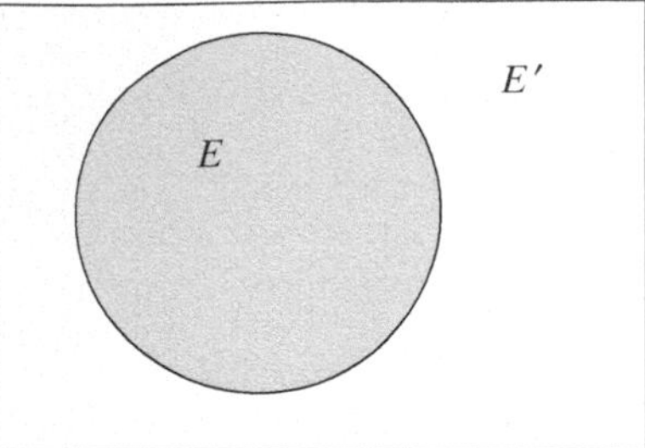


The area of the rectangle represents the total probability of the sample space ($1 = 100\%$). The area of the circle represents the probability of event $E$, and the area outside the circle represents the probability of the complement of event $E$.

### DEFINITION

The **complement of event $E$** is the set of all outcomes in a sample space that is not included in event $E$. The complement of event $E$ is denoted by $E'$ and is read as "$E$ prime." The Venn diagram at the left illustrates the relationship between the sample space, event $E$, and its complement $E'$.

For instance, when you roll a die and let $E$ be the event "the number is at least 5," the complement of $E$ is the event "the number is less than 5." In symbols, $E = \{5, 6\}$ and $E' = \{1, 2, 3, 4\}$.

Using the definition of the complement of an event and the fact that the sum of the probabilities of all outcomes is 1, you can determine the formulas below.

$$P(E) + P(E') = 1$$

$$P(E) = 1 - P(E')$$

$$P(E') = 1 - P(E)$$

### EXAMPLE 9

#### Finding the Probability of the Complement of an Event

The frequency distribution from Example 7 is shown below. Find the probability of randomly selecting a user of a social media application who is not 25 to 34 years old.

| Ages | Frequency, $f$ |
|---|---|
| 13 to 17 | 84 |
| 18 to 24 | 459 |
| 25 to 34 | 765 |
| 35 to 44 | 546 |
| 45 to 54 | 432 |
| 55 to 64 | 369 |
| 65 and over | 345 |
| | $\Sigma f = 3000$ |

**SOLUTION**

From Example 7, you know that

$$P(\text{age 25 to 34}) = \frac{765}{3000} = 0.255.$$

So, the probability that a user is not 25 to 34 years old is

$$P(\text{age is not 25 to 34}) = 1 - \frac{765}{3000} = 1 - 0.255 = 0.745.$$

**TRY IT YOURSELF 9**

Use the frequency distribution in Example 7 to find the probability of randomly selecting a user who is not 18 to 24 years old. *Answer: Page A38*

## Probability Applications

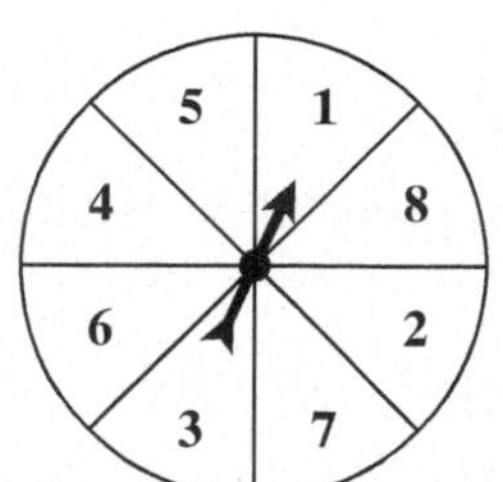


### EXAMPLE 10

#### Using a Tree Diagram

A probability experiment consists of tossing a coin and spinning the spinner shown at the left. The spinner is equally likely to land on each number. Use a tree diagram to find the probability of each event.

1. Event $A$: tossing a tail and spinning an odd number
2. Event $B$: tossing a head or spinning a number greater than 3

**SOLUTION**

Tree Diagram for Coin and Spinner Experiment

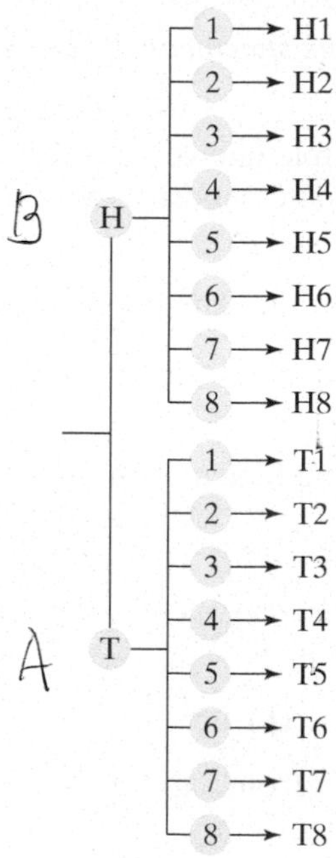


From the tree diagram at the left, you can see that there are 16 outcomes. The outcomes are equally likely to occur, so use the formula for classical probability.

1. There are four outcomes in event $A = \{T1, T3, T5, T7\}$. So,

$$P(\text{tossing a tail and spinning an odd number}) = \frac{4}{16} = \frac{1}{4} = 0.25.$$

2. There are 13 outcomes in event $B = \{H1, H2, H3, H4, H5, H6, H7, H8, T4, T5, T6, T7, T8\}$. So,

$$P(\text{tossing a head or spinning a number greater than 3}) = \frac{13}{16} \approx 0.813.$$

**TRY IT YOURSELF 10**

Find the probability of tossing a tail and spinning a number less than 6.

*Answer: Page A38*

### EXAMPLE 11

#### Using the Fundamental Counting Principle

Your college identification number consists of eight digits. Each digit can be 0 through 9 and each digit can be repeated. What is the probability of getting your college identification number when randomly generating eight digits?

**SOLUTION**

Because each digit can be repeated, there are 10 choices for each of the 8 digits. So, using the Fundamental Counting Principle, there are

$$10 \cdot 10 \cdot 10 \cdot 10 \cdot 10 \cdot 10 \cdot 10 \cdot 10 = 10^8 = 100{,}000{,}000$$

possible identification numbers. But only one of those numbers corresponds to your college identification number. So, the probability of randomly generating 8 digits and getting your college identification number is

$$\frac{1}{100{,}000{,}000}, \text{ or } 0.00000001.$$

**TRY IT YOURSELF 11**

Your college identification number consists of nine digits. The first two digits of the number will be the last two digits of the year you are scheduled to graduate. The other digits can be any number from 0 through 9, and each digit can be repeated. What is the probability of getting your college identification number when randomly generating the other seven digits?

*Answer: Page A38*

# 3.1 EXERCISES

For Extra Help: MyLab Statistics

## Building Basic Skills and Vocabulary

**1.** What is the difference between an outcome and an event?

**2.** Determine whether each number could represent the probability of an event. Explain your reasoning.

(a) $\frac{25}{25}$ (b) 333.3% (c) 2.3 (d) $-0.0004$ (e) 0 (f) $\frac{320}{105}$

**3.** Explain why the statement is incorrect: *The probability of rain is 150%.*

**4.** When you use the Fundamental Counting Principle, what are you counting?

**5.** Describe the law of large numbers in your own words. Give an example.

**6.** List the three formulas that can be used to describe complementary events.

**True or False?** *In Exercises 7–10, determine whether the statement is true or false. If it is false, rewrite it as a true statement.*

**7.** You are taking a test that has true or false and multiple choice questions. The event "choosing false on a true or false question and choosing A or B on a multiple choice question" is a simple event.

**8.** You toss a fair coin nine times and it lands tails up each time. The probability it will land heads up on the tenth toss is greater than 0.5.

**9.** A probability of $\frac{1}{10}$ indicates an unusual event.

**10.** When an event is almost certain to happen, its complement will be an unusual event.

**Matching Probabilities** *In Exercises 11–16, match the event with its probability.*

(a) 0.95 (b) 0.005 (c) 0.25 (d) 0 (e) 0.375 (f) 0.5

**11.** A random number generator is used to select a number from 1 to 100. What is the probability of selecting the number 153?

**12.** A random number generator is used to select a number from 1 to 100. What is the probability of selecting an even number?

**13.** You randomly select a number from 0 to 9 and then randomly select a number from 0 to 19. What is the probability of selecting a 3 both times?

**14.** A game show contestant must randomly select a door. One door doubles her money while the other three doors leave her with no winnings. What is the probability she selects the door that doubles her money?

**15.** Five of the 100 digital video recorders (DVRs) in an inventory are known to be defective. What is the probability you randomly select a DVR that is not defective?

**16.** You toss a coin four times. What is the probability of tossing tails exactly half of the time?

**Finding the Probability of the Complement of an Event** *In Exercises 17–20, the probability that an event will happen is given. Find the probability that the event will not happen.*

**17.** $P(E) = \frac{5}{6}$ **18.** $P(E) = 0.55$ **19.** $P(E) = 0.03$ **20.** $P(E) = \frac{2}{7}$

**Finding the Probability of an Event** *In Exercises 21–24, the probability that an event will not happen is given. Find the probability that the event will happen.*

**21.** $P(E') = 0.95$ **22.** $P(E') = 0.13$ **23.** $P(E') = \frac{3}{4}$ **24.** $P(E') = \frac{21}{61}$

## Using and Interpreting Concepts

**Identifying the Sample Space of a Probability Experiment** *In Exercises 25–32, identify the sample space of the probability experiment and determine the number of outcomes in the sample space. Draw a tree diagram when appropriate.*

**25.** Guessing the initial of a student's middle name

**26.** Guessing a student's letter grade (A, B, C, D, F) in a class

**27.** Drawing one card from a standard deck of cards

**28.** Identifying a person's eye color (brown, blue, green, hazel, gray, other) and hair color (black, brown, blonde, red, other).

**29.** Tossing two coins

**30.** Tossing three coins

**31.** Rolling a pair of six-sided dice

**32.** Rolling a six-sided die, tossing two coins, and spinning the fair spinner shown

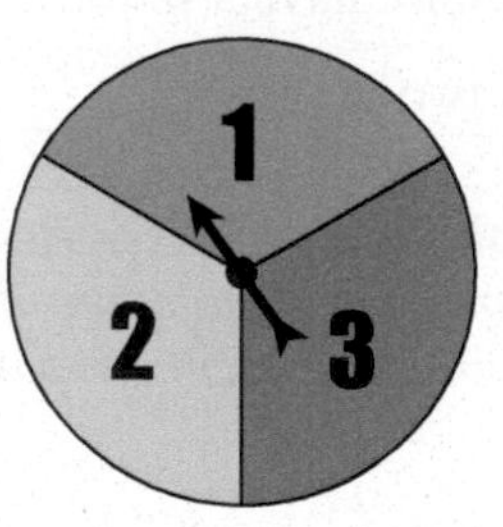

FIGURE FOR EXERCISE 32

**Identifying Simple Events** *In Exercises 33–36, determine the number of outcomes in the event. Then decide whether the event is a simple event or not. Explain your reasoning.*

**33.** A spreadsheet is used to randomly generate a number from 1 to 2000. Event $A$ is generating the number 253.

**34.** A spreadsheet is used to randomly generate a number from 1 to 4000. Event $B$ is generating a number less than 500.

**35.** You randomly select one card from a standard deck of 52 playing cards. Event $A$ is selecting a diamond.

**36.** You randomly select one card from a standard deck of 52 playing cards. Event B is selecting the ace of spades.

**Using the Fundamental Counting Principle** *In Exercises 37–40, use the Fundamental Counting Principle.*

**37. Menu** A restaurant offers a $15 dinner special that lets you choose from 6 appetizers, 12 entrées, and 8 desserts. How many different meals are available when you select an appetizer, an entrée, and a dessert?

**38. Tablet** A tablet has four choices for an operating system, three choices for a screen size, four choices for a processor, six choices for memory size, and three choices for a battery. How many ways can you customize the tablet?

**39. Realty** A realtor uses a programmable lock box to store the keys to a house that is for sale. The access code for the lock box consists of four digits. The first digit cannot be zero and the last digit must be even. How many different codes are available?

**40. True or False Quiz** Assuming that no questions are left unanswered, in how many ways can a six-question true or false quiz be answered?

**Finding Classical Probabilities** *In Exercises 41–46, a probability experiment consists of rolling a 12-sided die numbered 1 to 12. Find the probability of the event.*

**41.** Event $A$: rolling a 2

**42.** Event $B$: rolling a 10

**43.** Event $C$: rolling a number greater than 4

**44.** Event $D$: rolling a number less than 8

**45.** Event $E$: rolling a number divisible by 3

**46.** Event $F$: rolling a number divisible by 5

| Response | Number of times, $f$ |
|---|---|
| None | 704 |
| One | 131 |
| Two | 57 |
| Three | 34 |
| Four or more | 79 |

TABLE FOR EXERCISES 47 AND 48

**Finding Empirical Probabilities** *A survey asked U.S. adults how many tattoos they have. The frequency distribution at the left shows the results. In Exercises 47 and 48, use the frequency distribution.* (Source: Ipsos)

**47.** What is the probability that the next person asked does not have a tattoo?

**48.** What is the probability that the next person asked has two tattoos?

| Ages | Frequency, $f$ (in millions) |
|---|---|
| Under 18 | 73.0 |
| 18 to 24 | 30.2 |
| 25 to 44 | 87.6 |
| 45 to 64 | 83.3 |
| 65 and over | 54.1 |

TABLE FOR EXERCISES 49–52

**Using a Frequency Distribution to Find Probabilities** *In Exercises 49–52, use the frequency distribution at the left, which shows the population of the United States by age group, to find the probability that a U.S. resident chosen at random is in the age range.* (Source: U.S. Census Bureau)

**49.** 18 to 24 years old

**50.** 25 to 44 years old

**51.** 45 to 64 years old

**52.** 65 years old and older

**Classifying Types of Probability** *In Exercises 53–58, classify the statement as an example of classical probability, empirical probability, or subjective probability. Explain your reasoning.*

**53.** According to company records, the probability that an automobile will need covered repairs during its three-year warranty period is 0.46.

**54.** The probability of choosing 6 numbers from 1 to 40 that match the 6 numbers drawn by a state lottery is $1/3{,}838{,}380 \approx 0.00000026$.

**55.** An analyst feels that the probability of a team winning an upcoming game is 60%.

**56.** According to a survey, the probability that a randomly chosen high school counselor will say that significant changes are needed in U.S. schools is 55%.

**57.** The probability that a randomly selected number from 1 to 100 is divisible by 6 is 0.16.

**58.** You estimate that the probability of getting all the classes you want on your next schedule is about 25%.

| Ages | Frequency, $f$ |
|---|---|
| 0–17 | 2416 |
| 18–24 | 16,598 |
| 25–39 | 5293 |
| 40–54 | 2726 |
| 55–69 | 2140 |
| 70 and over | 1396 |

TABLE FOR EXERCISES 59–62

**Finding the Probability of the Complement of an Event** *The age distribution of the residents of Ithaca, New York, is shown at the left. In Exercises 59–62, find the probability of the event.* (Source: U.S. Census Bureau)

**59.** Event $A$: A randomly chosen resident of Ithaca is not 18 to 24 years old.

**60.** Event $B$: A randomly chosen resident of Ithaca is not 25 to 39 years old.

**61.** Event $C$: A randomly chosen resident of Ithaca is not less than 18 years old.

**62.** Event $D$: A randomly chosen resident of Ithaca is not 70 years old or older.

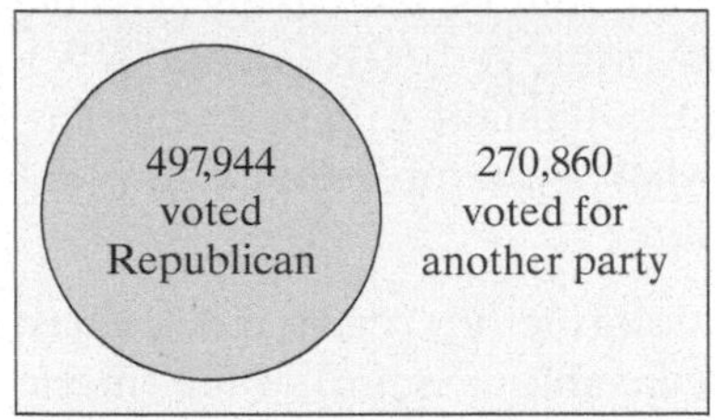


FIGURE FOR EXERCISE 63

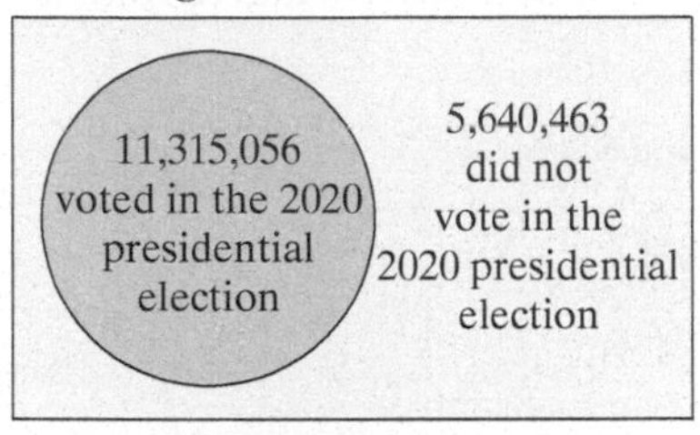


FIGURE FOR EXERCISE 64

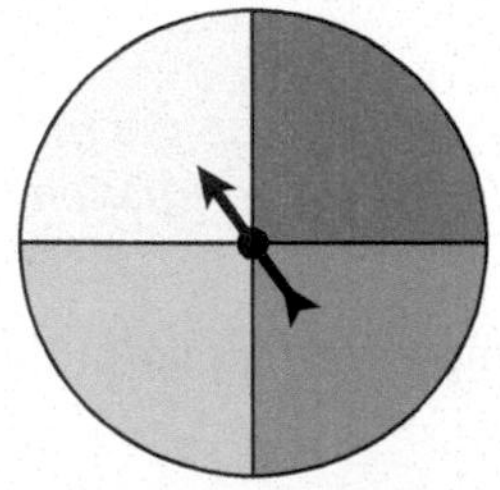

FIGURE FOR EXERCISES 67–70

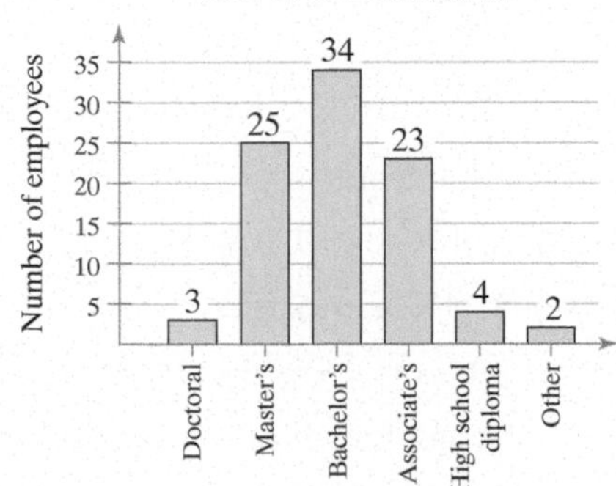


FIGURE FOR EXERCISES 75–78

**Graphical Analysis** *In Exercises 63 and 64, use the diagram at the left.*

**63.** What is the probability that a voter from West Virginia chosen at random voted Republican in the 2020 governor's election? *(Source: West Virginia State)*

**64.** What is the probability that a registered voter in Texas chosen at random did not vote in the 2020 presidential election? *(Source: Texas Secretary of State)*

**65. Access Code** An access code consists of three digits. Each digit can be any number from 0 through 9, and each digit can be repeated.

(a) What is the probability of randomly selecting the correct access code on the first try?

(b) What is the probability of not selecting the correct access code on the first try?

**66. Access Code** An access code consists of six characters. For each character, any letter or number can be used, with the exceptions that the first character cannot be 0 and the last two characters must be odd numbers.

(a) What is the probability of randomly selecting the correct access code on the first try?

(b) What is the probability of not selecting the correct access code on the first try?

**Using a Tree Diagram** *In Exercises 67–70, a probability experiment consists of rolling a six-sided die and spinning the spinner shown at the left. The spinner is equally likely to land on each color. Use a tree diagram to find the probability of the event. Then explain whether the event can be considered unusual.*

**67.** Event $A$: rolling a 5 and the spinner landing on blue

**68.** Event $B$: rolling an odd number and the spinner landing on green

**69.** Event $C$: rolling a number less than 6 and the spinner landing on yellow

**70.** Event $D$: not rolling a number less than 6 and the spinner landing on yellow

**Boy or Girl?** *In Exercises 71–74, a couple plans to have three children. Each child is equally likely to be a boy or a girl.*

**71.** What is the probability that all three children are girls?

**72.** What is the probability that all three children are boys?

**73.** What is the probability that exactly one child is a girl?

**74.** What is the probability that at least one child is a boy?

**Using a Bar Graph to Find Probabilities** *In Exercises 75–78, use the bar graph at the left, which shows the highest level of education received by employees of a company. Find the probability that the highest level of education for an employee chosen at random is*

**75.** a doctorate.

**76.** an associate's degree.

**77.** a master's degree.

**78.** a high school diploma.

**79. Unusual Events** Can any of the events in Exercises 49–52 be considered unusual? Explain.

**80. Unusual Events** Can any of the events in Exercises 75–78 be considered unusual? Explain.

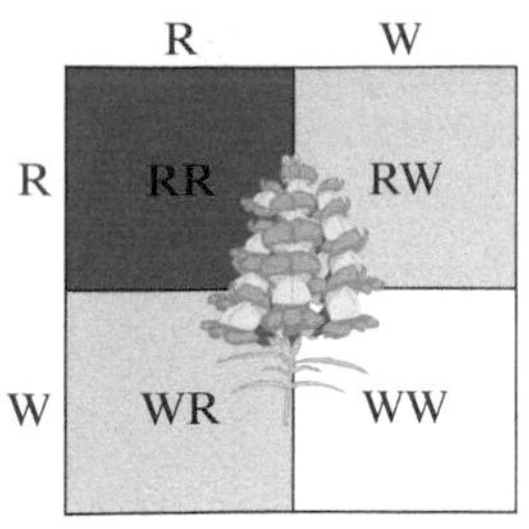


FIGURE FOR EXERCISE 81

**81. Genetics** A *Punnett square* is a diagram that shows all possible gene combinations in a cross of parents whose genes are known. When two pink snapdragon flowers (RW) are crossed, there are four equally likely possible outcomes for the genetic makeup of the offspring: red (RR), pink (RW), pink (WR), and white (WW), as shown in the Punnett square at the left. When two pink snapdragons are crossed, what is the probability that the offspring will be (a) pink, (b) red, and (c) white?

**82. Genetics** There are six basic types of coloring in registered collies: sable (SSmm), tricolor (ssmm), trifactored sable (Ssmm), blue merle (ssMm), sable merle (SSMm), and trifactored sable merle (SsMm). The Punnett square below shows the possible coloring of the offspring of a trifactored sable merle collie and a trifactored sable collie. What is the probability that the offspring will have the same coloring as one of its parents?

**Parents: Ssmm and SsMm**

| | SM | Sm | sM | sm |
|---|---|---|---|---|
| **Sm** | SSMm | SSmm | SsMm | Ssmm |
| **Sm** | SSMm | SSmm | SsMm | Ssmm |
| **sm** | SsMm | Ssmm | ssMm | ssmm |
| **sm** | SsMm | Ssmm | ssMm | ssmm |

## Using a Pie Chart to Find Probabilities

*In Exercises 83–86, use the pie chart at the left, which shows the number of workers (in millions) by occupation for the United States. (Source: U.S. Bureau of Labor Statistics)*

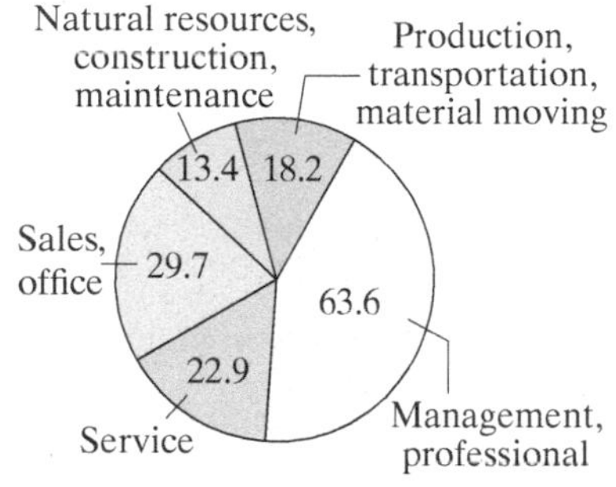


FIGURE FOR EXERCISES 83–86

**83.** Find the probability that a worker chosen at random is employed in a natural resources, construction, or maintenance occupation.

**84.** Find the probability that a worker chosen at random is not employed in a service occupation.

**85.** Find the probability that a worker chosen at random is employed in a sales or office occupation.

**86.** Find the probability that a worker chosen at random is not employed in a production, transportation, or material moving occupation..

**87. College Football** A stem-and-leaf plot for the numbers of touchdowns allowed by the 127 NCAA Division I Football Bowl Subdivision teams in the 2020–2021 season is shown. Find the probability that a team chosen at random allowed (a) at least 51 touchdowns, (b) from 21 to 31 touchdowns, and (c) fewer than 14 touchdowns. Are any of these events unusual? Explain. *(Source: National Collegiate Athletic Association)*

Key: 1|1 = 11

| | |
|---|---|
| 0 | 6 |
| 1 | 1 1 2 3 4 4 4 5 5 6 6 6 7 7 8 8 8 9 9 9 |
| 2 | 0 0 1 1 1 1 1 2 2 3 3 3 3 3 3 4 5 5 5 6 6 6 6 6 7 7 7 7 7 7 8 8 8 8 8 9 9 9 |
| 3 | 0 0 0 0 0 0 0 0 1 1 1 2 2 3 3 3 3 4 4 4 4 4 4 5 5 5 6 6 7 7 7 7 7 8 8 9 9 9 |
| 4 | 0 1 1 1 2 2 2 2 3 3 3 4 4 4 5 5 5 5 5 5 6 7 7 8 |
| 5 | 0 2 3 6 6 8 8 |

**88. Individual Stock Price** An individual stock is selected at random from the portfolio represented by the box-and-whisker plot shown. Find the probability that the stock price is (a) less than \$21, (b) between \$21 and \$50, and (c) \$30 or more.

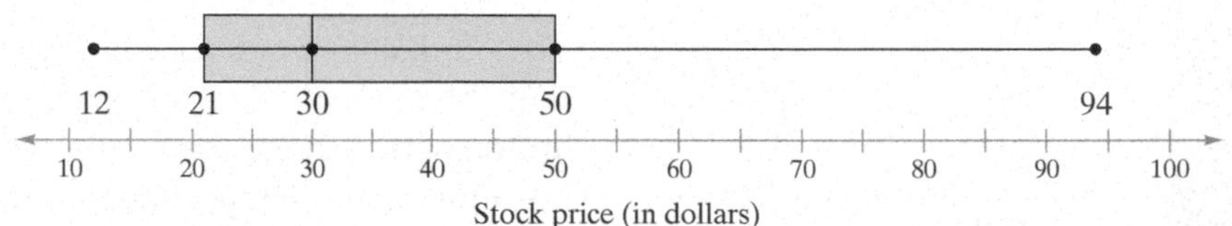


**Writing** *In Exercises 89 and 90, write a statement that represents the complement of the probability.*

**89.** The probability of randomly choosing a person who smokes whose mother also smoked from the population of all people who smoke

**90.** The probability of randomly choosing a car with more than one cause for showing its "CHECK ENGINE" light from the population of vehicles showing "CHECK ENGINE" lights

## Extending Concepts

**Odds** *The chances of winning are often written in terms of odds rather than probabilities. The* ***odds of winning*** *is the ratio of the number of successful outcomes to the number of unsuccessful outcomes. The* ***odds of losing*** *is the ratio of the number of unsuccessful outcomes to the number of successful outcomes. For example, when the number of successful outcomes is 2 and the number of unsuccessful outcomes is 3, the odds of winning are 2:3 (read "2 to 3"). In Exercises 91–96, use this information about odds.*

**91.** A beverage company puts game pieces under the caps of its drinks and claims that one in six game pieces wins a prize. The official rules of the contest state that the odds of winning a prize are 1:6. Is the claim "one in six game pieces wins a prize" correct? Explain your reasoning.

**92.** The probability of winning an instant prize game is $\frac{1}{10}$. The odds of winning a different instant prize game are 1 : 10. You want the best chance of winning. Which game should you play? Explain your reasoning.

**93.** The odds of an event occurring are 4:5. Find (a) the probability that the event will occur and (b) the probability that the event will not occur.

**94.** A card is picked at random from a standard deck of 52 playing cards. Find the odds that it is a spade.

**95.** A card is picked at random from a standard deck of 52 playing cards. Find the odds that it is not a spade.

**96.** The odds of winning an event $A$ are $p : q$. Show that the probability of event $A$ is given by $P(A) = \dfrac{p}{p + q}$.

**97. Rolling a Pair of Dice** You roll a pair of six-sided dice and record the sum.

(a) List all of the possible sums and determine the probability of rolling each sum.

(b) Use technology to simulate rolling a pair of dice and record the sum 100 times. Make a tally of the 100 sums and use these results to list the probability of rolling each sum.

(c) Compare the probabilities in part (a) with the probabilities in part (b). Explain any similarities or differences.

# 3.1 ACTIVITY Simulating the Stock Market

APPLET

You can find the interactive applet for this activity at MyLab Statistics.

The *Simulating the stock market* applet allows you to investigate the probability that the stock market will go up on any given day. When the **1 day** or **5 days** buttons are clicked, the results of the corresponding number of daily outcomes are added to the **Days** column. For each day, a green arrow indicates the market going up and a red arrow indicates the market going down. Clicking the **1000 days** button will add the 1000 daily outcomes as fast as possible by skipping the animation. The cumulative results of the daily outcomes are given in the plot showing the cumulative proportion of up outcomes versus the total number of days. The tallied results are also stored in the table above the graph. The green line in the plot reflects the true probability of the market going up on any given day, which is set to $1/2 = 0.5$. In this case, the market has a 50% chance of going up on any given day. As more and more outcomes are simulated, the cumulative proportion of "up" days should converge to this value.

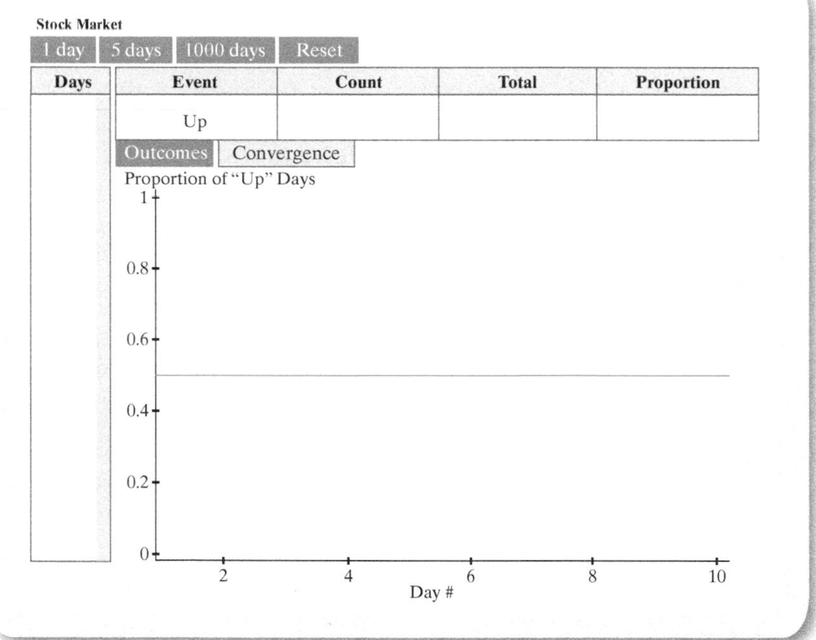


## EXPLORE

**Step 1** Click **1 day** twelve times. Click **Outcomes** and **Convergence.**
**Step 2** Click **Reset.**
**Step 3** Click **5 days** four times. Click **Reset.**
**Step 4** Click **1000 days** four times.

## DRAW CONCLUSIONS

APPLET

1. Run a simulation by clicking **1 day** several times without clicking **Reset.** How many days did it take until there were three straight days on which the stock market went up? three straight days on which the stock market went down?

2. Run a simulation of the stock market for 35 business days. Find the empirical probability that the market goes up on day 36.

# 3.2 Conditional Probability and the Multiplication Rule

**What You Should Learn**

- How to find the probability of an event given that another event has occurred
- How to distinguish between independent and dependent events
- How to use the Multiplication Rule to find the probability of two or more events occurring in sequence and to find conditional probabilities

Conditional Probability ■ Independent and Dependent Events ■ The Multiplication Rule

## Conditional Probability

In this section, you will learn how to find the probability that two events occur in sequence. Before you can find this probability, however, you must know how to find **conditional probabilities.**

**DEFINITION**

A **conditional probability** is the probability of an event occurring, given that another event has already occurred. The conditional probability of event $B$ occurring, given that event $A$ has occurred, is denoted by $P(B|A)$ and is read as "probability of $B$, given $A$."

**EXAMPLE 1**

### Finding Conditional Probabilities

1. Two cards are selected in sequence from a standard deck of 52 playing cards. Find the probability that the second card is a queen, given that the first card is a king. (Assume that the king is not replaced.)
2. The table at the left shows the results of a survey in which 970 U.S. adults were asked whether they have ever ridden as a passenger in a self-driving vehicle. Find the probability that an adult is 18 to 64 years old, given that the adult has ridden as a passenger in a self-driving vehicle. *(Adapted from The Harris Poll)*

| | Have you ever ridden as a passenger in a self-driving vehicle? | | |
|---|---|---|---|
| **Age** | **Yes** | **No** | **Total** |
| **18–64** | 202 | 549 | 751 |
| **65+** | 23 | 196 | 219 |
| **Total** | 225 | 745 | 970 |

**SOLUTION**

1. Because the first card is a king and is not replaced, the remaining deck has 51 cards, 4 of which are queens. So,

$$P(B|A) = \frac{4}{51} \approx 0.078.$$

The probability that the second card is a queen, given that the first card is a king, is about 0.078.

2. There are 225 adults who said they have ridden as a passenger in a self-driving vehicle. So, the sample space consists of these 225 adults, as shown at the left. Of these, 202 are 18 to 64 years old. So,

**Sample Space**

| Age | Yes |
|---|---|
| **18–64** | 202 |
| **65+** | 23 |
| **Total** | 225 |

$$P(B|A) = \frac{202}{225} \approx 0.898.$$

The probability that an adult is 18 to 64 years old, given that the adult has ridden as a passenger in a self-driving vehicle, is about 0.898.

**TRY IT YOURSELF 1**

Refer to the survey in the second part of Example 1. Find the probability that an adult is 65 years old or older, given that the adult has not ridden as a passenger in a self-driving vehicle.

*Answer: Page A38*

## Picturing the World

Truman Collins, a probability and statistics enthusiast, wrote a program that finds the probability of landing on each square of a Monopoly® board during a game. Collins explored various scenarios, including the effects of the Chance and Community Chest cards and the various ways of landing in or getting out of jail. Interestingly, Collins discovered that the length of each jail term affects the probabilities. (Note that the probabilities are rounded to more than three decimal places so that it is easier to see how going to jail affects the probabilities.)

| Monopoly square | Probability given short jail term | Probability given long jail term |
|---|---|---|
| Go | 0.0310 | 0.0291 |
| Chance | 0.0087 | 0.0082 |
| In Jail | 0.0395 | 0.0946 |
| Free Parking | 0.0288 | 0.0283 |
| Park Place | 0.0219 | 0.0206 |
| B&O RR | 0.0307 | 0.0289 |
| Water Works | 0.0281 | 0.0265 |

**Why do the probabilities depend on how long you stay in jail?**

## Independent and Dependent Events

In some experiments, one event does not affect the probability of another. For instance, when you roll a die and toss a coin, the outcome of the roll of the die does not affect the probability of the coin landing heads up. These two events are *independent*. The question of the independence of two or more events is important to researchers in fields such as marketing, medicine, and psychology. You can use conditional probabilities to determine whether events are **independent.**

### DEFINITION

Two events are **independent** when the occurrence of one of the events does not affect the probability of the occurrence of the other event. Two events $A$ and $B$ are independent when

$P(B|A) = P(B)$ — Occurrence of $A$ does not affect probability of $B$

or when

$P(A|B) = P(A).$ — Occurrence of $B$ does not affect probability of $A$

Events that are not independent are **dependent.**

To determine whether $A$ and $B$ are independent, first calculate $P(B)$, the probability of event $B$. Then calculate $P(B|A)$, the probability of $B$, given $A$. If the values are equal, then the events are independent. If $P(B) \neq P(B|A)$, then $A$ and $B$ are dependent events.

### EXAMPLE 2

### Classifying Events as Independent or Dependent

Determine whether the events are independent or dependent.

1. Selecting a king $(A)$ from a standard deck of 52 playing cards, not replacing it, and then selecting a queen $(B)$ from the deck
2. Tossing a coin and getting a head $(A)$, and then rolling a six-sided die and obtaining a 6 $(B)$
3. Driving over 85 miles per hour $(A)$, and then getting in a car accident $(B)$

**SOLUTION**

1. $P(B) = \frac{4}{52}$ and $P(B|A) = \frac{4}{51}$. The occurrence of $A$ changes the probability of the occurrence of B, so the events are dependent.
2. $P(B) = \frac{1}{6}$ and $P(B|A) = \frac{1}{6}$. The occurrence of $A$ does not change the probability of the occurrence of $B$, so the events are independent.
3. Driving over 85 miles per hour increases the chances of getting in an accident, so these events are dependent.

**TRY IT YOURSELF 2**

Determine whether the events are independent or dependent.

1. Smoking a pack of cigarettes per day $(A)$ and developing emphysema, a chronic lung disease $(B)$
2. Tossing a coin and getting a head $(A)$, and then tossing the coin again and getting a tail $(B)$

*Answer: Page A38*

## The Multiplication Rule

To find the probability of two events occurring in sequence, you can use the **Multiplication Rule.**

**Study Tip**

In words, to use the Multiplication Rule,

1. find the probability that the first event occurs,
2. find the probability that the second event occurs given that the first event has occurred, and
3. multiply these two probabilities.

### The Multiplication Rule for the Probability of *A* and *B*

The probability that two events $A$ and $B$ will occur in sequence is

$$P(A \text{ and } B) = P(A) \cdot P(B|A). \qquad \text{Events } A \text{ and } B \text{ are dependent.}$$

If events $A$ and $B$ are independent, then the rule can be simplified to

$$P(A \text{ and } B) = P(A) \cdot P(B). \qquad \text{Events } A \text{ and } B \text{ are independent.}$$

This simplified rule can be extended to any number of independent events.

### EXAMPLE 3

#### Using the Multiplication Rule to Find Probabilities

1. Two cards are selected, without replacing the first card, from a standard deck of 52 playing cards. Find the probability of selecting a king and then selecting a queen.
2. A coin is tossed and a die is rolled. Find the probability of tossing a head and then rolling a 6.

**SOLUTION**

1. Because the first card is not replaced, the events are dependent.

$$\begin{aligned} P(K \text{ and } Q) &= P(K) \cdot P(Q|K) \\ &= \frac{4}{52} \cdot \frac{4}{51} \\ &= \frac{16}{2652} \\ &\approx 0.006 \end{aligned}$$

So, the probability of selecting a king and then a queen without replacement is about 0.006.

**Study Tip**

Recall from Section 3.1 that a probability of 0.05 or less is typically considered unusual. In the first part of Example 3, $0.006 < 0.05$. This means that selecting a king and then a queen (without replacement) from a standard deck is an unusual event.

2. The events are independent.

$$\begin{aligned} P(H \text{ and } 6) &= P(H) \cdot P(6) \\ &= \frac{1}{2} \cdot \frac{1}{6} \\ &= \frac{1}{12} \\ &\approx 0.083 \end{aligned}$$

So, the probability of tossing a head and then rolling a 6 is about 0.083.

**TRY IT YOURSELF 3**

1. The probability that a salmon swims successfully through a dam is 0.85. Find the probability that two salmon swim successfully through the dam.
2. Two cards are selected from a standard deck of 52 playing cards without replacement. Find the probability that they are both hearts.

*Answer: Page A38*

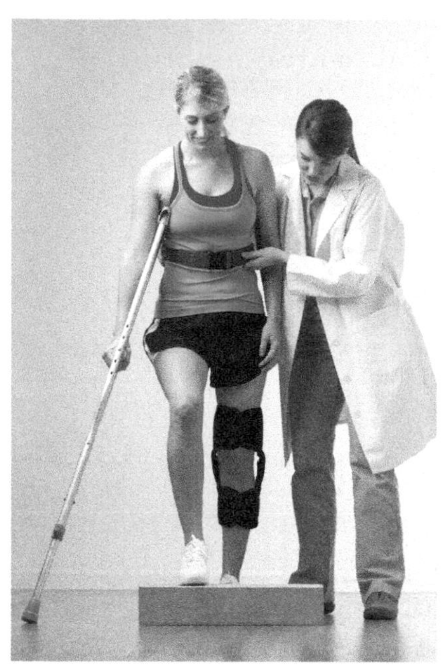

For help with translating verbal phrases, see *Integrated Review* at

MyLab Statistics

**EXAMPLE 4**

### Using the Multiplication Rule to Find Probabilities

For anterior cruciate ligament (ACL) reconstructive surgery, the probability that the surgery is successful is 0.95. *(Source: The Orthopedic Center of St. Louis)*

1. Find the probability that three ACL surgeries are successful.
2. Find the probability that none of three ACL surgeries are successful.
3. Find the probability that at least one of three ACL surgeries is successful.

**SOLUTION**

1. The probability that each ACL surgery is successful is 0.95. The chance of success for one surgery is independent of the chances for the other surgeries.

$$P(\text{three surgeries are successful}) = (0.95)(0.95)(0.95) \approx 0.857$$

So, the probability that all three surgeries are successful is about 0.857.

2. Because the probability of success for one surgery is 0.95, the probability of failure for one surgery is $1 - 0.95 = 0.05$.

$$P(\text{none of three are successful}) = (0.05)(0.05)(0.05) \approx 0.0001$$

So, the probability that none of three surgeries are successful is about 0.0001. Note that because 0.0001 is less than 0.05, this can be considered an unusual event.

3. The phrase "at least one" means one or more. The complement to the event "at least one is successful" is the event "none are successful." Use the complement found in part 2 to find the probability. (To avoid rounding in the second step below, use (0.05)(0.05)(0.05), not the rounded result.)

$$\begin{aligned} P(\text{at least one is successful}) &= 1 - P(\text{none are successful}) \\ &= 1 - (0.05)(0.05)(0.05) \\ &\approx 0.9999. \end{aligned}$$

So, the probability that at least one of three surgeries is successful is about 0.9999. Note that this probability is not rounded to three decimal places because the result would be 1.000, which implies the event is certain. Even though it is highly likely that at least one of the three surgeries is successful, it is not a certain event.

**TRY IT YOURSELF 4**

The probability that a particular rotator cuff surgery is successful is 0.9. *(Source: The Orthopedic Center of St. Louis)*

1. Find the probability that three rotator cuff surgeries are successful.
2. Find the probability that none of three rotator cuff surgeries are successful.
3. Find the probability that at least one of three rotator cuff surgeries is successful.

*Answer: Page A38*

In Example 4, you were asked to find a probability using the phrase "at least one." Notice that it was easier to find the probability of its complement, "none," and then subtract the probability of its complement from 1. In general, this probability can be written as

$$P(\text{at least one occurrence of event } A) = 1 - P(\text{no occurrence of event } A).$$

## EXAMPLE 5

### Using the Multiplication Rule to Find Probabilities

In a recent year, there were 19,326 U.S. MD medical school seniors who applied to first-year post-graduate residency programs and submitted their residency program choices. Of these seniors, 18,108 were matched with residency positions, with about 75.6% getting one of their top three choices. Medical students rank the residency programs in their order of preference, and program directors in the United States rank the students. The term "match" refers to the process whereby a student's preference list and a program director's preference list overlap, resulting in the placement of the student in a residency position. *(Source: National Resident Matching Program)*

1. Find the probability that a randomly selected senior was matched with a residency position *and* it was one of the senior's top three choices.
2. Find the probability that a randomly selected senior who was matched with a residency position did *not* get matched with one of the senior's top three choices.
3. Would it be unusual for a randomly selected senior to be matched with a residency position *and* that it was one of the senior's top three choices?

**SOLUTION**

Let $A = \{\text{matched with residency position}\}$ and $B = \{\text{matched with one of top three choices}\}$. So,

$$P(A) = \frac{18{,}108}{19{,}326} \quad \text{and} \quad P(B|A) = 0.756.$$

1. The events are dependent.

$$P(A \text{ and } B) = P(A) \cdot P(B|A) = \left(\frac{18{,}108}{19{,}326}\right)(0.756) \approx 0.708$$

So, the probability that a randomly selected senior was matched with one of the senior's top three choices is about 0.708.

2. To find this probability, use the complement.

$$P(B'|A) = 1 - P(B|A) = 1 - 0.756 = 0.244$$

So, the probability that a randomly selected senior was matched with a residency position that was not one of the senior's top three choices is 0.244.

3. It is not unusual because the probability of a senior being matched with a residency position that was one of the senior's top three choices is about 0.708, which is greater than 0.05. In fact, with a probability of 0.708, this event is *likely* to happen.

**TRY IT YOURSELF 5**

In a jury selection pool, 65% of the people are female. Of these 65%, one out of four works in a health field.

1. Find the probability that a randomly selected person from the jury pool is female and works in a health field. Is this event unusual?
2. Find the probability that a randomly selected person from the jury pool is female and does not work in a health field. Is this event unusual?

*Answer: Page A38*

# 3.2 EXERCISES

For Extra Help: MyLab Statistics

## Building Basic Skills and Vocabulary

1. What is the difference between independent and dependent events?
2. Give an example of
   (a) two events that are independent.
   (b) two events that are dependent.
3. What does the notation $P(B|A)$ mean?
4. Explain how to use the complement to find the probability of getting at least one item of a particular type.

**True or False?** *In Exercises 5 and 6, determine whether the statement is true or false. If it is false, rewrite it as a true statement.*

5. If two events are independent, then $P(A|B) = P(B)$.
6. If events $A$ and $B$ are dependent, then $P(A \text{ and } B) = P(A) \cdot P(B)$.

## Using and Interpreting Concepts

**Finding Conditional Probabilities** *In Exercises 7 and 8, use the table to find each conditional probability.*

7. **Business Degrees** The table shows the numbers of male and female students in the United States who received bachelor's degrees in business and nonbusiness fields in a recent year. *(Source: National Center for Educational Statistics)*

| | Business degrees | Nonbusiness degrees | Total |
|---|---|---|---|
| **Male** | 204,839 | 640,121 | 844,960 |
| **Female** | 181,362 | 954,322 | 1,135,684 |
| **Total** | 386,201 | 1,594,443 | 1,980,644 |

   (a) Find the probability that a randomly selected bachelor's degree-earning student is male, given that the degree is in business.
   (b) Find the probability that a randomly selected bachelor's degree-earning student received a business degree, given that the student is female.

8. **Retirement Savings** The table shows the results of a survey in which 250 male and 250 female workers ages 25 to 64 were asked if they contribute to a retirement savings plan at work.

| | Contribute | Do not contribute | Total |
|---|---|---|---|
| **Male** | 116 | 134 | 250 |
| **Female** | 143 | 107 | 250 |
| **Total** | 259 | 241 | 500 |

   (a) Find the probability that a randomly selected worker contributes to a retirement savings plan at work, given that the worker is male.
   (b) Find the probability that a randomly selected worker is female, given that the worker contributes to a retirement savings plan at work.

**Classifying Events as Independent or Dependent** *In Exercises 9–14, determine whether the events are independent or dependent. Explain your reasoning.*

**9.** Selecting a king from a standard deck of 52 playing cards, replacing it, and then selecting a queen from the deck

**10.** A father having hazel eyes and a daughter having hazel eyes

**11.** Returning a rented movie after the due date and receiving a late fee

**12.** Not putting money in a parking meter and getting a parking ticket

**13.** Rolling a six-sided die and then rolling the die a second time so that the sum of the two rolls is five

**14.** A ball is selected from a bin of balls numbered from 1 through 52. It is replaced, and then a second numbered ball is selected from the bin.

**Classifying Events Based on Studies** *In Exercises 15–18, identify the two events described in the study. Do the results indicate that the events are independent or dependent? Explain your reasoning.*

**15.** A study was conducted to debunk the idea that abilities in music and math are related. Instead, the study showed a strong relationship between achievements in music and math. *(Source: University of Kansas)*

**16.** A study found no significant association between the use of talc powder and the incidence of ovarian cancer in women. *(Source: JAMA)*

**17.** A study found that there is no relationship between playing violent video games and aggressive or bullying behavior in teenagers. *(Source: The Royal Society Publishing)*

**18.** A study found that business executives with high levels of self-leadership traits are more likely to attribute successes to their own efforts. *(Source: Pollack Peacebuilding Systems)*

**Using the Multiplication Rule** *In Exercises 19–32, use the Multiplication Rule.*

**19. Cards** Two cards are selected from a standard deck of 52 playing cards. The first card is not replaced before the second card is selected. Find the probability of selecting a heart and then selecting a club.

**20. Coin and Die** A coin is tossed and a die is rolled. Find the probability of tossing a tail and then rolling a number greater than 2.

**21. BRCA1 Gene** Research has shown that approximately 1 woman in 400 carries a mutation of the BRCA1 gene. About 64% of women with this mutation develop breast cancer. Find the probability that a randomly selected woman will carry the mutation of the BRCA1 gene and will develop breast cancer. *(Source: National Cancer Institute)*

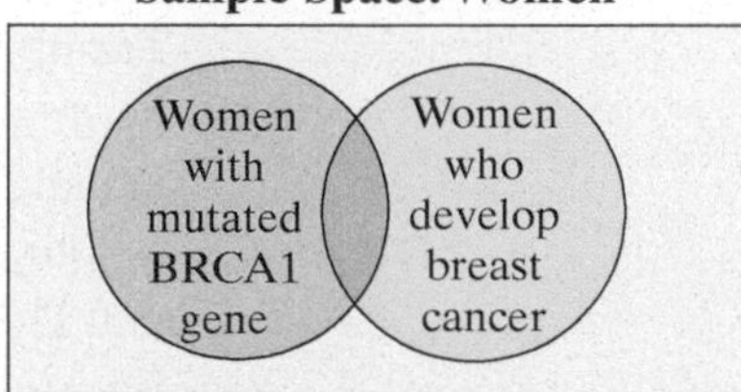

**22. Pickup Trucks** In a survey, 510 U.S. adults were asked whether they drive a pickup truck and whether they drive a Ford. The results showed that three in twenty adults surveyed drive a Ford. Of the adults surveyed that drive Fords, nine in twenty drive a pickup truck. Find the probability that a randomly selected adult drives a Ford and drives a pickup truck.

**Sample Space: U.S. Adults**

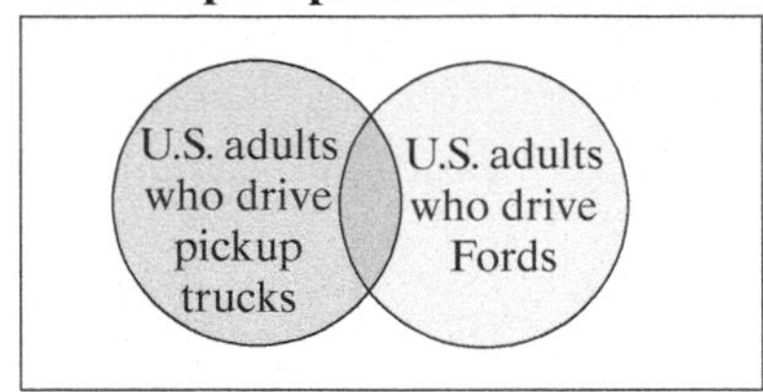


**23. Celebrities as Role Models** In a sample of 1103 probable voters, three out of four say they would like entertainers to address social and political issues. Two probable voters are selected at random. *(Source: The Hollywood Reporter)*

(a) Find the probability that both probable voters would like entertainers to address social and political issues.

(b) Find the probability that neither probable voter would like entertainers to address social and political issues.

(c) Find the probability that at least one of the two probable voters would like entertainers to address social and political issues.

**24. Knowing a Person Who Was Murdered** In a sample of 11,771 children ages 2 to 17, 8% have lost a friend or relative to murder. Four children are selected at random. *(Adapted from University of New Hampshire)*

(a) Find the probability that all four have lost a friend or relative to murder.

(b) Find the probability that none of the four has lost a friend or relative to murder.

(c) Find the probability that at least one of the four has lost a friend or relative to murder.

**25. Best President** In a sample of 1500 adult U.S. citizens, 270 said that Barack Obama was the best president in U.S. history. Two adult U.S. citizens are selected at random. *(Adapted from YouGov)*

(a) Find the probability that both adult U.S. citizens say that Barack Obama was the best president in U.S. history.

(b) Find the probability that neither adult U.S. citizen says that Barack Obama was the best president in U.S. history.

(c) Find the probability that at least one of the two adult U.S. citizens says that Barack Obama was the best president in U.S. history.

(d) Which of the events can be considered unusual? Explain.

**26. Worst President** In a sample of 1500 adult U.S. citizens, 690 said that Donald Trump was the worst president in U.S. history. Three adult U.S. citizens are selected at random. *(Adapted from YouGov)*

(a) Find the probability that all three adult U.S. citizens say that Donald Trump was the worst president in U.S. history.

(b) Find the probability that none of the three adult U.S. citizens say that Donald Trump was the worst president in U.S. history.

(c) Find the probability that at most two of the three adult U.S. citizens say that Donald Trump was the worst president in U.S. history.

(d) Which of the events can be considered unusual? Explain.

**27. Blood Types** The probability that a person of Asian descent in the United States has type O+ blood is 39%. At random, six people of Asian descent in the United States are selected. *(Source: American National Red Cross)*

(a) Find the probability that all six have type O+ blood.

(b) Find the probability that none of the six have type O+ blood.

(c) Find the probability that at least one of the six has type O+ blood.

(d) Which of the events can be considered unusual? Explain.

**28. Blood Types** The probability that a Latinx American person in the United States has type A+ blood is 29%. Four Latinx American people in the United States are selected at random. *(Source: American National Red Cross)*

(a) Find the probability that all four have type A+ blood.

(b) Find the probability that none of the four have type A+ blood.

(c) Find the probability that at least one of the four has type A+ blood.

(d) Which of the events can be considered unusual? Explain.

**29. In Vitro Fertilization** In a recent year, about 1.9% of all infants born in the U.S. were conceived through assisted reproductive technology (ART). Of the ART deliveries, about 26.4% resulted in multiple births. *(Source: Morbidity and Mortality Weekly Report)*

(a) Find the probability that a randomly selected infant was conceived through ART *and* was part of a multiple birth.

(b) Find the probability that a randomly selected infant conceived through ART was *not* part of a multiple birth.

(c) Would it be unusual for a randomly selected infant to have been conceived through ART and to have been part of a multiple birth? Explain.

**30. Standardized Test Scores** According to a survey, 57.8% of college-seeking high school seniors say they have taken one of the standardized tests for potential college students. Of these, 35.6% say they do *not* plan to submit their score with their college applications. *(Adapted from Niche)*

(a) Find the probability that a randomly selected college-seeking high school senior took one of the standardized tests and does *not* plan to submit this score with their college applications.

(b) Find the probability that a randomly selected college-seeking high school senior took one of the standardized tests *and* plans to submit this score with their college applications.

(c) Would either of the events in part (a) or (b) be considered unusual? Explain.

**31. Using Social Media to Explore Colleges** According to a survey of over 31,000 college-seeking high school seniors, 31.2% have never used social media to look up a college. Of those who *have* used social media to look up a college, 89% have used Instagram. Find the probability that a randomly selected college-seeking high school senior has used Instagram to look up a college. *(Adapted from Niche)*

**32. Surviving Surgery** A patient has a 60% chance of surviving bypass surgery after a heart attack. If the patient survives the surgery, then the patient has a 70% chance of making a full recovery. Find the probability that the patient survives surgery but does not make a full recovery.

## Extending Concepts

*According to **Bayes' Theorem,** the probability of event A, given that event B has occurred, is*

$$P(A|B) = \frac{P(A) \cdot P(B|A)}{P(A) \cdot P(B|A) + P(A') \cdot P(B|A')}.$$

*In Exercises 33–38, use Bayes' Theorem to find* $P(A|B)$.

**33.** $P(A) = \frac{2}{3}$, $P(A') = \frac{1}{3}$, $P(B|A) = \frac{1}{5}$, and $P(B|A') = \frac{1}{2}$

**34.** $P(A) = \frac{3}{8}$, $P(A') = \frac{5}{8}$, $P(B|A) = \frac{2}{3}$, and $P(B|A') = \frac{3}{5}$

**35.** $P(A) = 0.25$, $P(A') = 0.75$, $P(B|A) = 0.3$, and $P(B|A') = 0.5$

**36.** $P(A) = 0.62$, $P(A') = 0.38$, $P(B|A) = 0.41$, and $P(B|A') = 0.17$

**37.** $P(A) = 73\%$, $P(A') = 17\%$, $P(B|A) = 46\%$, and $P(B|A') = 52\%$

**38.** $P(A) = 12\%$, $P(A') = 88\%$, $P(B|A) = 66\%$, and $P(B|A') = 19\%$

**39. Reliability of Testing** A virus infects one in every 200 people. A test used to detect the virus in a person is positive 80% of the time when the person has the virus and 5% of the time when the person does not have the virus. (This 5% result is called a *false positive*.) Let $A$ be the event "the person is infected" and $B$ be the event "the person tests positive."

(a) Using Bayes' Theorem, when a person tests positive, determine the probability that the person is infected.

(b) Using Bayes' Theorem, when a person tests negative, determine the probability that the person is *not* infected.

**40. Birthday Problem** You are in a class that has 24 students. You want to find the probability that at least two of the students have the same birthday.

(a) Find the probability that each student has a different birthday.

(b) Use the result of part (a) to find the probability that at least two students have the same birthday.

(c) Use technology to simulate the "Birthday Problem" by generating 24 random numbers from 1 to 365. Repeat the simulation 10 times. How many times did you get at least two people with the same birthday?

**The Multiplication Rule and Conditional Probability** *By rewriting the formula for the Multiplication Rule, you can write a formula for finding conditional probabilities. The conditional probability of event B occurring, given that event A has occurred, is*

$$P(B|A) = \frac{P(A \text{ and } B)}{P(A)}.$$

*In Exercises 41 and 42, use the information below.*

- *The probability that an airplane flight departs on time is 0.89.*
- *The probability that a flight arrives on time is 0.87.*
- *The probability that a flight departs and arrives on time is 0.83.*

**41.** Find the probability that a flight departed on time given that it arrives on time.

**42.** Find the probability that a flight arrives on time given that it departed on time.

# 3.3 The Addition Rule

## What You Should Learn

- How to determine whether two events are mutually exclusive
- How to use the Addition Rule to find the probability of two events

Mutually Exclusive Events ■ The Addition Rule ■ A Summary of Probability

## Mutually Exclusive Events

In Section 3.2, you learned how to find the probability of two events, $A$ and $B$, occurring in sequence. Such probabilities are denoted by $P(A \text{ and } B)$. In this section, you will learn how to find the probability that at least one of two events will occur. Probabilities such as these are denoted by $P(A \text{ or } B)$ and depend on whether the events are **mutually exclusive.**

**DEFINITION**

Two events $A$ and $B$ are **mutually exclusive** when $A$ and $B$ cannot occur at the same time. That is, $A$ and $B$ have no outcomes in common.

### Study Tip

In probability and statistics, the word *or* is mostly used as an "inclusive or" rather than an "exclusive or." For instance, there are three ways for "event $A$ or $B$" to occur.

(1) $A$ occurs and $B$ does not occur.

(2) $B$ occurs and $A$ does not occur.

(3) $A$ and $B$ both occur.

The Venn diagrams show the relationship between events that are mutually exclusive and events that are not mutually exclusive. Note that when events $A$ and $B$ are mutually exclusive, they have no outcomes in common, so $P(A \text{ and } B) = 0$.

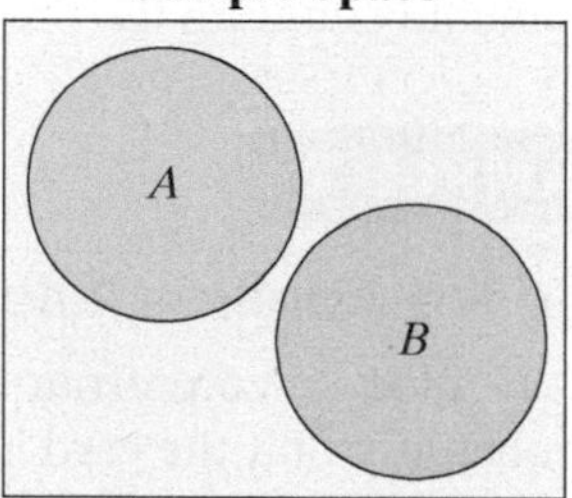


$A$ and $B$ are mutually exclusive.

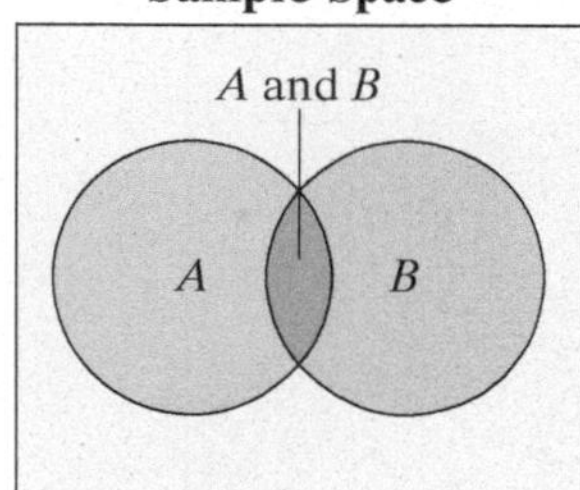


$A$ and $B$ are not mutually exclusive.

**EXAMPLE 1**

### Recognizing Mutually Exclusive Events

Determine whether the events are mutually exclusive. Explain your reasoning.

1. Event $A$: Roll a 3 on a die.
   Event $B$: Roll a 4 on a die.
2. Event $A$: Randomly select a male student.
   Event $B$: Randomly select a nursing major.
3. Event $A$: Randomly select a blood donor with type O blood.
   Event $B$: Randomly select a female blood donor.

**SOLUTION**

1. Event $A$ has one outcome, a 3. Event $B$ also has one outcome, a 4. These outcomes cannot occur at the same time, so the events are mutually exclusive.
2. Because the student can be a male nursing major, the events are not mutually exclusive.
3. Because the donor can be a female with type O blood, the events are not mutually exclusive.

**TRY IT YOURSELF 1**

Determine whether the events are mutually exclusive. Explain your reasoning.

1. Event $A$: Randomly select a jack from a standard deck of 52 playing cards.
   Event $B$: Randomly select a face card from a standard deck of 52 playing cards.

2. Event $A$: Randomly select a vehicle that is a Ford.
   Event $B$: Randomly select a vehicle that is a Toyota.

*Answer: Page A38*

**3.3** To explore this topic further, see **Activity 3.3** on page 166.

## The Addition Rule

**The Addition Rule for the Probability of *A* or *B***

The probability that event $A$ or $B$ will occur, $P(A \text{ or } B)$, is given by

$$P(A \text{ or } B) = P(A) + P(B) - P(A \text{ and } B).$$

If events $A$ and $B$ are mutually exclusive, then the rule can be simplified to

$$P(A \text{ or } B) = P(A) + P(B). \quad \text{Events } A \text{ and } B \text{ are mutually exclusive.}$$

This simplified rule can be extended to any number of mutually exclusive events.

Outcomes here are double counted by $P(A) + P(B)$

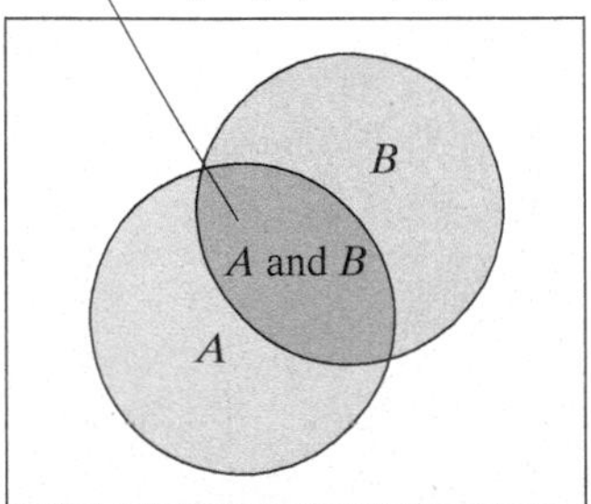


In words, to find the probability that one event or the other will occur, add the individual probabilities of each event and subtract the probability that they both occur. As shown in the Venn diagram at the left, subtracting $P(A \text{ and } B)$ avoids double counting the probability of outcomes that occur in both $A$ and $B$.

**EXAMPLE 2**

### Using the Addition Rule to Find Probabilities

1. You select a card from a standard deck of 52 playing cards. Find the probability that the card is a 4 or an ace.
2. You roll a die. Find the probability of rolling a number less than 3 or rolling an odd number.

**SOLUTION**

1. A card that is a 4 cannot be an ace. So, the events are mutually exclusive, as shown in the Venn diagram. The probability of selecting a 4 or an ace is

$$P(4 \text{ or ace}) = P(4) + P(\text{ace}) = \frac{4}{52} + \frac{4}{52} = \frac{8}{52} = \frac{2}{13} \approx 0.154.$$

**Deck of 52 Cards**

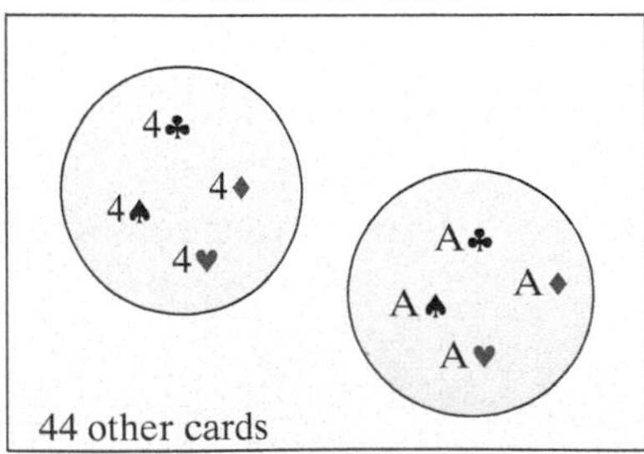


2. The events are not mutually exclusive because 1 is an outcome of both events, as shown in the Venn diagram. So, the probability of rolling a number less than 3 or an odd number is

$$\begin{aligned} P(\text{less than 3 or odd}) &= P(\text{less than 3}) + P(\text{odd}) - P(\text{less than 3 and odd}) \\ &= \frac{2}{6} + \frac{3}{6} - \frac{1}{6} \\ &= \frac{4}{6} \\ &= \frac{2}{3} \\ &\approx 0.667. \end{aligned}$$

**Roll a Die**

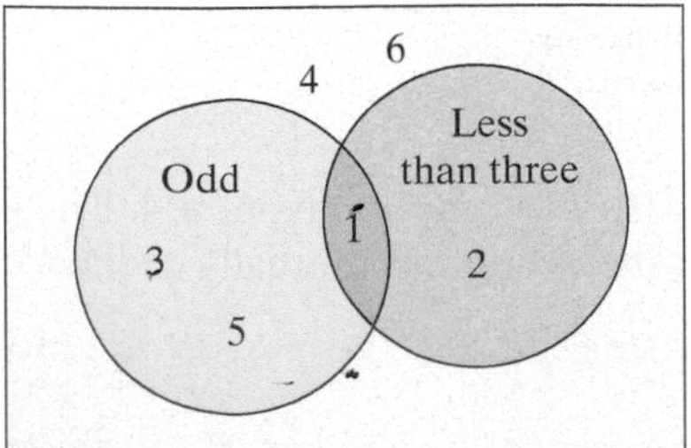

## Picturing the World

A survey of 10,121 adults asked them how often they have had trouble sleeping in a recent span of seven days. Overall, 37% said less than one day; 30% said one to two days; 19% said three to four days; and 14% said five to seven days, as shown in the pie chart. (Source: Pew Research)

**How often have you had trouble sleeping in the past seven days?**

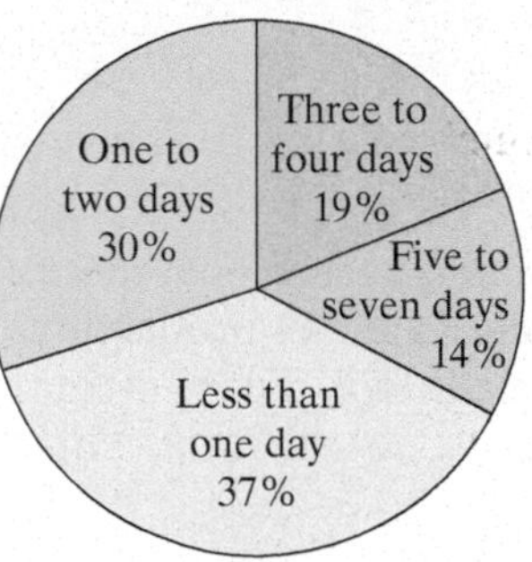


**A U.S. adult is selected at random. What is the probability that when asked how often the adult has had trouble sleeping in the past seven days, the response will be "less than one day" or "one to two days?"**

**TRY IT YOURSELF 2**

1. A die is rolled. Find the probability of rolling a 6 or an odd number.
2. A card is selected from a standard deck of 52 playing cards. Find the probability that the card is a face card or a heart.

*Answer: Page A38*

**EXAMPLE 3**

### Finding Probabilities of Mutually Exclusive Events

The frequency distribution shows volumes of sales (in dollars) and the number of months in which a sales representative reached each sales level during the past three years. Using this sales pattern, find the probability that the sales representative will sell between \$75,000 and \$124,999 next month.

| Sales volume (in dollars) | Months |
|---|---|
| 0–24,999 | 3 |
| 25,000–49,999 | 5 |
| 50,000–74,999 | 6 |
| 75,000–99,999 | 7 |
| 100,000–124,999 | 9 |
| 125,000–149,999 | 2 |
| 150,000–174,999 | 3 |
| 175,000–199,999 | 1 |

**SOLUTION**

To solve this problem, define events $A$ and $B$ as

$A = \{\text{monthly sales between \$75,000 and \$99,999}\}$

and

$B = \{\text{monthly sales between \$100,000 and \$124,999}\}.$

The events are mutually exclusive, as shown in the Venn diagram.

**Monthly Sales Volume**

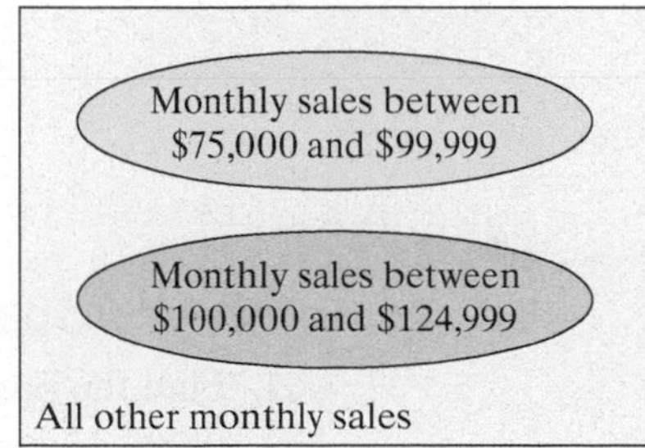


Because events $A$ and $B$ are mutually exclusive, the probability that the sales representative will sell between \$75,000 and \$124,999 next month is

$$P(A \text{ or } B) = P(A) + P(B) = \frac{7}{36} + \frac{9}{36} = \frac{16}{36} = \frac{4}{9} \approx 0.444.$$

**TRY IT YOURSELF 3**

Find the probability that the sales representative will sell between \$0 and \$49,999.

*Answer: Page A38*

## EXAMPLE 4

### Using the Addition Rule to Find Probabilities

A blood bank catalogs the types of blood, including whether it is Rh-positive or Rh-negative, given by donors during the last five days. The number of donors who gave each blood type is shown in the table.

1. Find the probability that a donor selected at random has type O or type A blood.
2. Find the probability that a donor selected at random has type B blood or is Rh-negative.

| | | Blood type | | | | |
|---|---|---|---|---|---|---|
| | | **O** | **A** | **B** | **AB** | **Total** |
| **Rh-factor** | **Positive** | 156 | 139 | 37 | 12 | 344 |
| | **Negative** | 28 | 25 | 8 | 4 | 65 |
| | **Total** | 184 | 164 | 45 | 16 | 409 |

**SOLUTION**

1. Because a donor cannot have type O blood and type A blood, these events are mutually exclusive. So, using the Addition Rule, the probability that a randomly chosen donor has type O or type A blood is

$$\begin{aligned} P(\text{type O or type A}) &= P(\text{type O}) + P(\text{type A}) \\ &= \frac{184}{409} + \frac{164}{409} \\ &= \frac{348}{409} \\ &\approx 0.851. \end{aligned}$$

2. Because a donor can have type B blood and be Rh-negative, these events are not mutually exclusive. So, using the Addition Rule, the probability that a randomly chosen donor has type B blood or is Rh-negative is

$$\begin{aligned} P(\text{type B or Rh-neg}) &= P(\text{type B}) + P(\text{Rh-neg}) - P(\text{type B and Rh-neg}) \\ &= \frac{45}{409} + \frac{65}{409} - \frac{8}{409} \\ &= \frac{102}{409} \\ &\approx 0.249. \end{aligned}$$

**TRY IT YOURSELF 4**

1. Find the probability that a donor selected at random has type B or type AB blood.
2. Find the probability that a donor selected at random does not have type O or type A blood.
3. Find the probability that a donor selected at random has type O blood or is Rh-positive.
4. Find the probability that a donor selected at random has type A blood or is Rh-negative.

*Answer: Page A38*

## A Summary of Probability

| Type of probability and probability rules | In words | In symbols |
|---|---|---|
| **Classical Probability** | The number of outcomes in the sample space is known and each outcome is equally likely to occur. | $P(E) = \dfrac{\text{Number of outcomes in event } E}{\text{Number of outcomes in sample space}}$ |
| **Empirical Probability** | The frequency of each outcome in the sample space is estimated from experimentation. | $P(E) = \dfrac{\text{Frequency of event } E}{\text{Total frequency}} = \dfrac{f}{n}$ |
| **Range of Probabilities Rule** | The probability of an event is between 0 and 1, inclusive. | $0 \le P(E) \le 1$ |
| **Complementary Events** | The complement of event $E$ is the set of all outcomes in a sample space that are not included in $E$, and is denoted by $E'$. | $P(E') = 1 - P(E)$ |
| **Multiplication Rule** | The Multiplication Rule is used to find the probability of two events occurring in sequence. | $P(A \text{ and } B) = P(A) \cdot P(B\|A)$ Dependent events<br>$P(A \text{ and } B) = P(A) \cdot P(B)$ Independent events |
| **Addition Rule** | The Addition Rule is used to find the probability of at least one of two events occurring. | $P(A \text{ or } B) = P(A) + P(B) - P(A \text{ and } B)$<br>$P(A \text{ or } B) = P(A) + P(B)$ Mutually exclusive events |

**EXAMPLE 5**

### Combining Rules to Find Probabilities

Use the figure at the right to find the probability that a randomly selected draft pick is not a running back or a wide receiver.

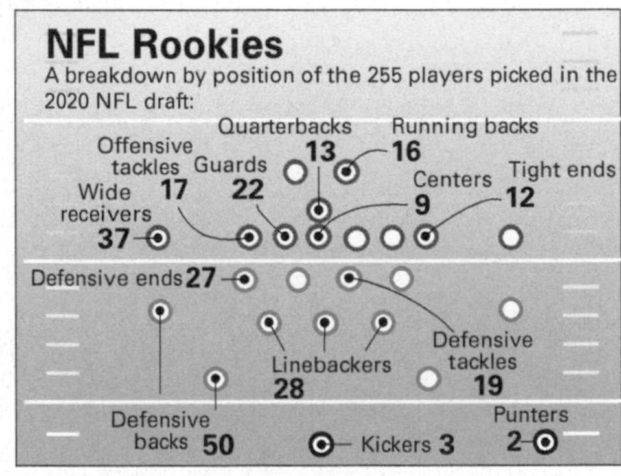


(Source: National Football League)

**SOLUTION**

Define events A and B.

$A$: Draft pick is a running back.
$B$: Draft pick is a wide receiver.

These events are mutually exclusive, so the probability that the draft pick is a running back or wide receiver is

$$P(A \text{ or } B) = P(A) + P(B) = \frac{16}{255} + \frac{37}{255} = \frac{53}{255}.$$

By taking the complement of $P(A \text{ or } B)$, you can determine that the probability of randomly selecting a draft pick who is not a running back or wide receiver is

$$1 - P(A \text{ or } B) = 1 - \frac{53}{255} = \frac{202}{255} \approx 0.792.$$

**TRY IT YOURSELF 5**

Find the probability that a randomly selected draft pick is not a linebacker or a quarterback.

*Answer: Page A38*

# 3.3 EXERCISES

For Extra Help: MyLab Statistics

## Building Basic Skills and Vocabulary

1. When two events are mutually exclusive, why is $P(A \text{ and } B) = 0$?
2. Give an example of (a) two events that are mutually exclusive and (b) two events that are not mutually exclusive.

**True or False?** *In Exercises 3–6, determine whether the statement is true or false. If it is false, explain why.*

3. When two events are mutually exclusive, they have no outcomes in common.
4. When two events are independent, they are also mutually exclusive.
5. The probability that event $A$ or event $B$ will occur is

   $$P(A \text{ or } B) = P(A) + P(B) + P(A \text{ and } B).$$

6. If events $A$ and $B$ are mutually exclusive, then

   $$P(A \text{ or } B) = P(A) + P(B).$$

**Graphical Analysis** *In Exercises 7 and 8, determine whether the events shown in the Venn diagram are mutually exclusive. Explain your reasoning.*

7. **Sample Space: Clothes**

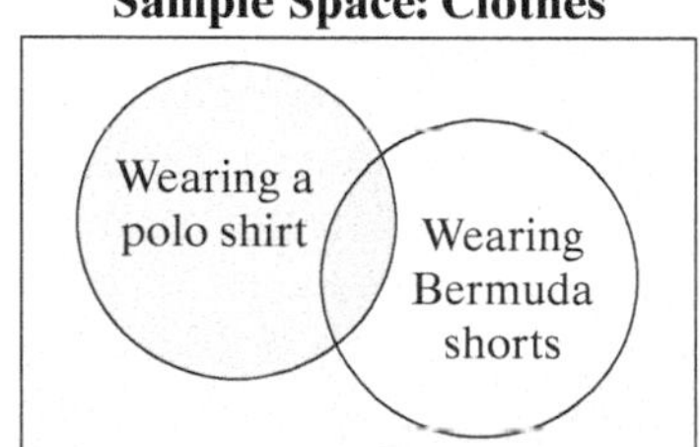


8. **Sample Space: Grades**

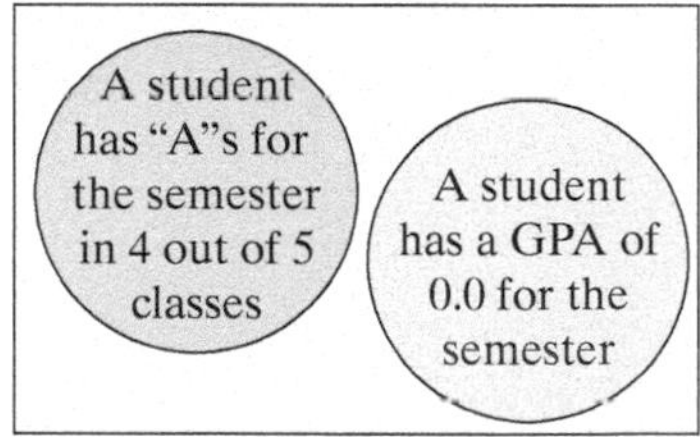


## Using and Interpreting Concepts

**Recognizing Mutually Exclusive Events** *In Exercises 9–12, determine whether the events are mutually exclusive. Explain your reasoning.*

9. Event $A$: Randomly select a freshman music major.
   Event $B$: Randomly select a music major who is 20 years old.
10. Event $A$: Randomly select a student with a birthday in April.
    Event $B$: Randomly select a student with a birthday in May.
11. Event $A$: Randomly select a voter who is a registered Republican.
    Event $B$: Randomly select a voter who is a registered Democrat.
12. Event $A$: Randomly select a member of the U.S. Congress.
    Event $B$: Randomly select a male U.S. Senator.

13. **Students** A physics class has 40 students. Of these, 12 students are physics majors and 16 students are minoring in math. Of the physics majors, three are minoring in math. Find the probability that a randomly selected student is minoring in math or a physics major.
14. **Conference** A teaching conference has an attendance of 6855 people. Of these, 3120 are college professors and 3595 are male. Of the college professors, 1505 are male. Find the probability that a randomly selected attendee is male or a college professor.

15. **Carton Defects** Of the cartons produced by a company, 5% have a puncture, 8% have a smashed corner, and 0.4% have both a puncture and a smashed corner. Find the probability that a randomly selected carton has a puncture or a smashed corner.

16. **Can Defects** Of the cans produced by a company, 96% do not have a puncture, 93% do not have a smashed edge, and 89.3% have neither a puncture nor a smashed edge. Find the probability that a randomly selected can does not have a puncture or a smashed edge.

17. **Selecting a Card** A card is selected at random from a standard deck of 52 playing cards. Find the probability of each event.
    (a) Randomly selecting a club or a 3
    (b) Randomly selecting a red suit or a king
    (c) Randomly selecting a 9 or a face card

18. **Rolling a Die** You roll a die. Find the probability of each event.
    (a) Rolling a 5 or a number greater than 3
    (b) Rolling a 2 or an odd number
    (c) Rolling a number less than 4 or an even number

19. **U.S. Age Distribution** The projected percent distribution of the U.S. population for 2025 is shown in the pie chart. Find the probability of each event. *(Source: U.S. Census Bureau)*
    (a) Randomly selecting someone who is under 10 years old
    (b) Randomly selecting someone who is 50 years or over
    (c) Randomly selecting someone who is not 60 years or over
    (d) Randomly selecting someone who is not 20 to 39 years old

**U.S. Age Distribution**

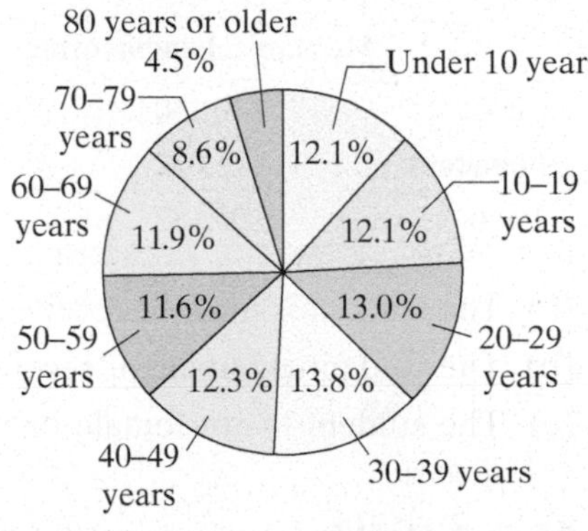


FIGURE FOR EXERCISE 19

**Last Marijuana Use**

FIGURE FOR EXERCISE 20



20. **Marijuana Use** The percent distribution of the last marijuana use (either medical or nonmedical) for a sample of 13,373 college students is shown in the pie chart. Find the probability of each event. *(Source: American College Health Association)*
    (a) Randomly selecting a student who never used marijuana
    (b) Randomly selecting a student who used marijuana
    (c) Randomly selecting a student who used marijuana within the last 30 days
    (d) Randomly selecting a student who has not used marijuana within the last 12 months

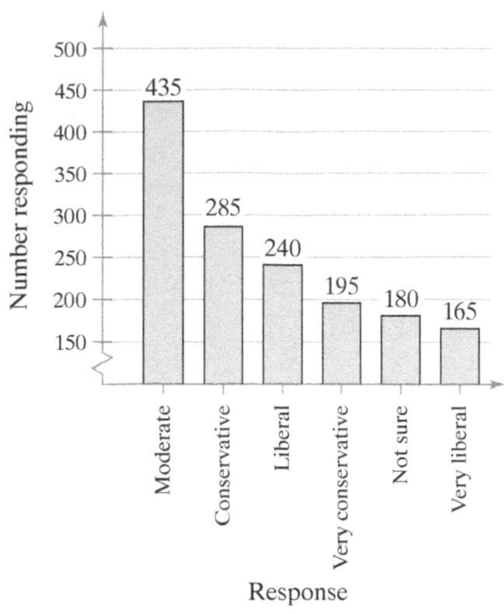


FIGURE FOR EXERCISE 21

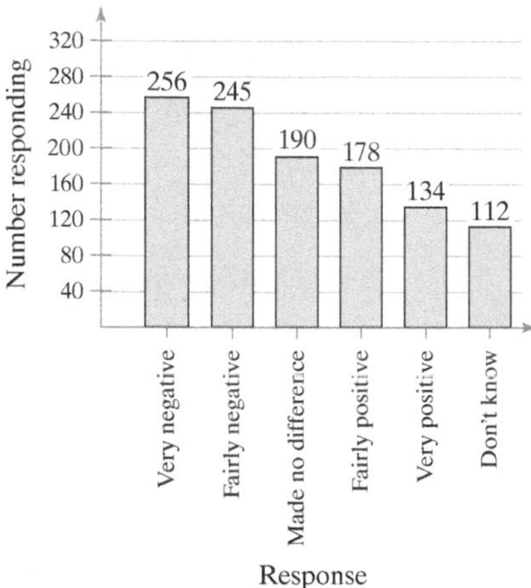


FIGURE FOR EXERCISE 22

**21. Politics** The responses of 1500 U.S. adults to a survey that asked them to state their own political viewpoints are shown in the Pareto chart. Find the probability of each event. *(Adapted from YouGov)*

(a) Randomly selecting a person from the sample who does not consider themselves liberal or very liberal

(b) Randomly selecting a person from the sample who is conservative or very conservative

(c) Randomly selecting a person from the sample who is not very liberal or very conservative

(d) Randomly selecting a person from the sample who is either unsure or moderate

**22. Brexit** A survey asked 1115 British adults how Britain's decision to leave the European Union has impacted the country. The results are shown in the Pareto chart. Find the probability of each event. *(Adapted from Ipsos)*

(a) Randomly selecting a British adult who feels that the move has made no difference

(b) Randomly selecting a British adult who feels that the move has had a very negative impact on Great Britain

(c) Randomly selecting a British adult who feels that the move has *not* had a very positive impact on Great Britain

(d) Randomly selecting a British adult who feels that the move has had a fairly positive or very positive impact on Great Britain

**23. Engineering Degrees** The table shows the numbers of male and female students in the U.S. who received B.S. degrees in engineering in a recent year. A student earning a B.S. degree in engineering during that year is selected at random. Find the probability of each event. *(Source: National Center for Educational Statistics)*

| | Mechanical engineering | Engineering (all other) | Total |
|---|---|---|---|
| **Males** | 30,150 | 64,697 | 94,847 |
| **Females** | 5,032 | 22,077 | 27,109 |
| **Total** | 35,182 | 86,774 | 121,956 |

(a) The student is male or received a mechanical engineering degree.

(b) The student is female or received a mechanical engineering degree.

(c) The student is not female or did not receive a mechanical engineering degree.

**24. Mental Health** A survey asks 4805 parents the severity of the mental issues they experienced from the coronavirus pandemic. The results are shown in the table. A parent is randomly selected from the sample. Find the probability of each event. *(Adapted from Kaiser Family Foundation)*

| | Major | Moderate | Minor | None | Total |
|---|---|---|---|---|---|
| **Mothers** | 415 | 1048 | 514 | 1684 | 3661 |
| **Fathers** | 76 | 144 | 180 | 744 | 1144 |
| **Total** | 491 | 1192 | 694 | 2428 | 4805 |

(a) The parent was unaffected mentally or is a father.

(b) The parent had major mental health issues or is a mother.

(c) The parent did not have major mental health issues or is a mother.

**25. Working from Home** The table shows the results of a survey that asked 1811 people how often they work from home. A person is selected at random from the sample. Find the probability of each event.

| | Frequently | Occasionally | Not at all | Total |
|---|---|---|---|---|
| **Males** | 346 | 297 | 441 | 1084 |
| **Females** | 217 | 198 | 312 | 727 |
| **Total** | 563 | 495 | 753 | 1811 |

(a) The person is male or frequently works from home.
(b) The person is female or does not work from home.
(c) The person frequently or occasionally works from home.
(d) The person is female or does not frequently work from home.

**26. Eye Survey** The table shows the results of a survey that asked 3203 people whether they wore contacts or glasses. A person is selected at random from the sample. Find the probability of each event.

| | Only contacts | Only glasses | Both | Neither | Total |
|---|---|---|---|---|---|
| **Males** | 64 | 841 | 177 | 456 | 1538 |
| **Females** | 189 | 427 | 368 | 681 | 1665 |
| **Total** | 253 | 1268 | 545 | 1137 | 3203 |

(a) The person wears only contacts or only glasses.
(b) The person is male or wears both contacts and glasses.
(c) The person is female or wears neither contacts nor glasses.
(d) The person is male or does not wear glasses.

## Extending Concepts

**Addition Rule for Three Events** *The Addition Rule for the probability that event $A$ or $B$ or $C$ will occur, $P(A \text{ or } B \text{ or } C)$, is given by*

$$P(A \text{ or } B \text{ or } C) = P(A) + P(B) + P(C) - P(A \text{ and } B) - P(A \text{ and } C) - P(B \text{ and } C) + P(A \text{ and } B \text{ and } C).$$

*In the Venn diagram shown at the left, $P(A \text{ or } B \text{ or } C)$ is represented by the blue areas. In Exercises 27 and 28, find $P(A \text{ or } B \text{ or } C)$.*

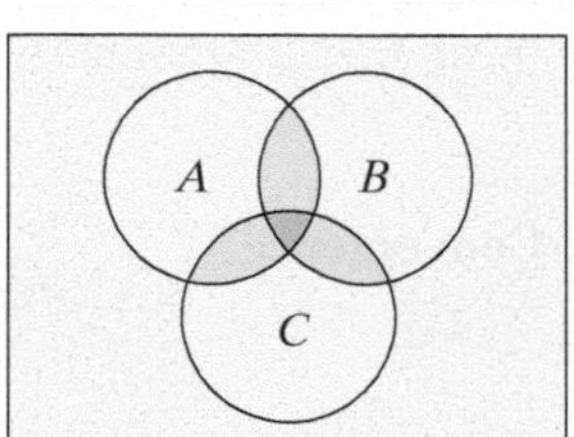

FIGURE FOR EXERCISES 27 AND 28

**27.** $P(A) = 0.40$, $P(B) = 0.10$, $P(C) = 0.50$, $P(A \text{ and } B) = 0.05$, $P(A \text{ and } C) = 0.25$, $P(B \text{ and } C) = 0.10$, $P(A \text{ and } B \text{ and } C) = 0.03$

**28.** $P(A) = 0.38$, $P(B) = 0.26$, $P(C) = 0.14$, $P(A \text{ and } B) = 0.12$, $P(A \text{ and } C) = 0.03$, $P(B \text{ and } C) = 0.09$, $P(A \text{ and } B \text{ and } C) = 0.01$

**29.** Explain, in your own words, why in the Addition Rule for $P(A \text{ or } B \text{ or } C)$, $P(A \text{ and } B \text{ and } C)$ is added at the end of the formula.

**30. Writing** Can two events with nonzero probabilities be both independent and mutually exclusive? Explain your reasoning.

# 3.3 ACTIVITY Simulating the Probability of Rolling a 3 or 4

APPLET

You can find the interactive applet for this activity at MyLab Statistics.

The *Simulating the probability of rolling a 3 or 4* applet allows you to investigate the probability of rolling a 3 or a 4 on a fair die. When the **1 roll** or **5 rolls** buttons are clicked, the results of the corresponding number of simulated die rolls are added to the **Rolls** column. Clicking the **1000 rolls** button will add the results of the 1000 rolls as fast as possible by skipping the animation. The cumulative results of the rolls are given in the plot showing the cumulative proportion of times a 3 or 4 was rolled versus the total number of rolls. The tallied results are also stored in the table above the graph. The green line in the plot reflects the true probability of rolling a 3 or 4, which is $1/3 \approx 0.333333$. As the virtual die is rolled more and more times, the cumulative proportion of times a 3 or 4 is rolled should converge to this value.

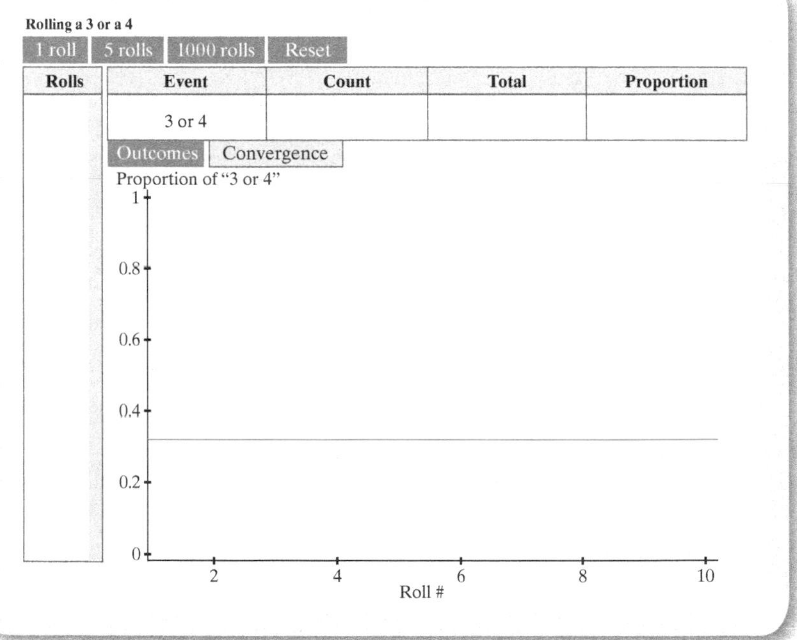


## EXPLORE

**Step 1** Click **1 roll** eight times. Click **Outcomes.** Click **Convergence.**
**Step 2** Click **Reset.**
**Step 3** Click **5 rolls** four times. Click **Reset.**
**Step 4** Click **1000 rolls** four times.

## DRAW CONCLUSIONS

APPLET

1. Run a simulation of **1 roll,** a simulation of **5 rolls,** and a simulation of **1000 rolls.** Clear the results after each simulation. Compare the cumulative proportion of "3 or 4" for each trial with the theoretical probability of rolling a 3 or 4.

2. You reprogram the applet to find the probability of rolling a number less than 4. How should you change the green line?

# CASE STUDY United States Congress

Congress is made up of the House of Representatives and the Senate. Members of the House of Representatives serve two-year terms and represent a district in a state. The number of representatives for each state is determined by population. States with larger populations have more representatives than states with smaller populations. The total number of representatives is set by law at 435. Members of the Senate serve six-year terms and represent a state. Each state has 2 senators, for a total of 100 senators. The tables show the makeup of the 117th Congress by gender and political party as of January 21, 2021. The House of Representatives had 3 vacant seats.

**House of Representatives**

| | | Political party | | | |
|---|---|---|---|---|---|
| | | **Republican** | **Democrat** | **Independent** | **Total** |
| **Gender** | **Male** | 182 | 132 | 0 | 314 |
| | **Female** | 29 | 89 | 0 | 118 |
| | **Total** | 211 | 221 | 0 | 432 |

**Senate**

| | | Political party | | | |
|---|---|---|---|---|---|
| | | **Republican** | **Democrat** | **Independent** | **Total** |
| **Gender** | **Male** | 42 | 32 | 2 | 76 |
| | **Female** | 8 | 16 | 0 | 24 |
| | **Total** | 50 | 48 | 2 | 100 |

## EXERCISES

**1.** Find the probability that a randomly selected representative is female. Find the probability that a randomly selected senator is female.

**2.** Compare the probabilities from Exercise 1.

**3.** A representative is selected at random. Find the probability of each event.

(a) The representative is male.

(b) The representative is a Republican.

(c) The representative is male given that the representative is a Republican.

(d) The representative is female and a Democrat.

**4.** Among members of the House of Representatives, are the events "being female" and "being a Democrat" independent or dependent events? Explain.

**5.** A senator is selected at random. Find the probability of each event.

(a) The senator is male.

(b) The senator is not a Democrat.

(c) The senator is female or a Republican.

(d) The senator is male or a Democrat.

**6.** Among members of the Senate, are the events "being female" and "being an Independent" mutually exclusive? Explain.

**7.** Using the same row and column headings as the tables above, create a combined table for Congress.

**8.** A member of Congress is selected at random. Use the table from Exercise 7 to find the probability of each event.

(a) The member is Independent.

(b) The member is female and a Republican.

(c) The member is male or a Democrat.

# 3.4 Additional Topics in Probability and Counting

Permutations ■ Combinations ■ Applications of Counting Principles

### What You Should Learn

- How to find the number of ways a group of objects can be arranged in order
- How to find the number of ways to choose several objects from a group without regard to order
- How to use counting principles to find probabilities

## Permutations

In Section 3.1, you learned that the Fundamental Counting Principle is used to find the number of ways two or more events can occur in sequence. An application of the Fundamental Counting Principle is finding the number of ways that $n$ objects can be arranged in order. An ordering of $n$ objects is called a **permutation.**

**DEFINITION**

A **permutation** is an ordered arrangement of objects. The number of different permutations of $n$ distinct objects is $n!$.

**Study Tip**

Notice that small values of $n$ can produce very large values of $n!$. For instance, $10! = 3{,}628{,}800$. Be sure you know how to use the factorial key on your calculator.

The expression $n!$ is read as ***n* factorial.** If $n$ is a positive integer, then $n!$ is defined as follows.

$$n! = n \cdot (n-1) \cdot (n-2) \cdot (n-3) \cdots 3 \cdot 2 \cdot 1$$

As a special case, $0! = 1$. Here are several other values of $n!$.

$$1! = 1 \qquad 2! = 2 \cdot 1 = 2 \qquad 3! = 3 \cdot 2 \cdot 1 = 6 \qquad 4! = 4 \cdot 3 \cdot 2 \cdot 1 = 24$$

For help with factorials, see *Integrated Review* at MyLab Statistics

**EXAMPLE 1**

### Finding the Number of Permutations of *n* Objects

The objective of a $9 \times 9$ Sudoku number puzzle is to fill the grid so that each row, each column, and each $3 \times 3$ grid contain the digits 1 through 9 without repetition. How many different ways can the first row of a blank $9 \times 9$ Sudoku grid be filled?

**Sudoku Number Puzzle**

| | | | | | | | | |
|---|---|---|---|---|---|---|---|---|
| 6 | 7 | 1 | | | | 2 | 4 | 9 |
| 8 | | | 7 | | 2 | | | 1 |
| 2 | | | | 6 | | | | 3 |
| | 5 | | 6 | | 3 | | 2 | |
| | | 8 | | | | 7 | | |
| | 1 | | 8 | | 4 | | 6 | |
| 9 | | | | 1 | | | | 6 |
| 1 | | | 5 | | 9 | | | 7 |
| 5 | 8 | 7 | | | | 9 | 1 | 2 |

**SOLUTION**

The number of permutations is

$$9! = 9 \cdot 8 \cdot 7 \cdot 6 \cdot 5 \cdot 4 \cdot 3 \cdot 2 \cdot 1 = 362{,}880.$$

So, there are 362,880 different ways the first row can be filled.

**TRY IT YOURSELF 1**

The Big 12 is a collegiate athletic conference with 10 schools: Baylor, Iowa State, Kansas, Kansas State, Oklahoma, Oklahoma State, Texas, Texas Christian, Texas Tech, and West Virginia. How many different final standings are possible for the Big 12's football teams? *Answer: Page A38*

You may want to choose some of the objects in a group and put them in order. Such an ordering is called a **permutation of *n* objects taken *r* at a time.**

**Permutations of *n* Objects Taken *r* at a Time**

The number of permutations of $n$ distinct objects taken $r$ at a time is

$${}_nP_r = \frac{n!}{(n-r)!}, \text{ where } r \leq n.$$

**Tech Tip**

You can use technology such as Minitab, Excel, StatCrunch, or the TI-84 Plus to find the number of permutations of $n$ objects taken $r$ at a time. For instance, here is how to find $_nP_r$ in Example 2 on a TI-84 Plus.

Enter the total number of objects, $n = 10$.

MATH

Choose the PRB menu.

2: nPr

Enter the number of objects taken, $r = 4$.

ENTER

**TI-84 PLUS**

```
10 nPr 4
                5040
```

## EXAMPLE 2

### Finding $_nP_r$

Find the number of ways of forming four-digit codes in which no digit is repeated.

**SOLUTION**

To form a four-digit code with no repeating digits, you need to select 4 digits from a group of 10, so $n = 10$ and $r = 4$.

$$\begin{aligned} {}_nP_r &= {}_{10}P_4 \\ &= \frac{10!}{(10-4)!} \\ &= \frac{10!}{6!} \\ &= \frac{10 \cdot 9 \cdot 8 \cdot 7 \cdot \cancel{6!}}{\cancel{6!}} \\ &= 5040 \end{aligned}$$

So, there are 5040 possible four-digit codes that do not have repeating digits.

**TRY IT YOURSELF 2**

A psychologist shows a list of eight activities to a subject in an experiment. How many ways can the subject pick a first, second, and third activity?

*Answer: Page A38*

## EXAMPLE 3

### Finding $_nP_r$

Each year, 33 race cars start the Indianapolis 500. How many ways can the cars finish first, second, and third?

**SOLUTION**

You need to select three race cars from a group of 33, so

$n = 33$ and $r = 3$.

Because the order is important, the number of ways the cars can finish first, second, and third is

$$_nP_r = {}_{33}P_3 = \frac{33!}{(33-3)!} = \frac{33!}{30!} = \frac{33 \cdot 32 \cdot 31 \cdot \cancel{30!}}{\cancel{30!}} = 32{,}736.$$

**TRY IT YOURSELF 3**

The board of directors of a company has 12 members. One member is the president, another is the vice president, another is the secretary, and another is the treasurer. How many ways can these positions be assigned?

*Answer: Page A38*

For help with operations with factorials and scientific notation, see *Integrated Review* at

MyLab Statistics

In Example 3, note that the Fundamental Counting Principle can be used to obtain the same result. There are 33 choices for first place, 32 choices for second place, and 31 choices for third place. So, there are

$$33 \cdot 32 \cdot 31 = 32{,}736$$

ways the cars can finish first, second, and third.

You may want to order a group of $n$ objects in which some of the objects are the same. For instance, consider the group of letters

AAAABBC.

This group has four A's, two B's, and one C. How many ways can you order such a group? Using the formula for $_nP_r$, you might conclude that there are

$$_7P_7 = 7! = 5040$$

possible orders. However, because some of the objects are the same, not all of these permutations are *distinguishable*. How many distinguishable permutations are possible? The answer can be found using the formula for the number of **distinguishable permutations.**

### Distinguishable Permutations

The number of **distinguishable permutations** of $n$ objects, where $n_1$ are of one type, $n_2$ are of another type, and so on, is

$$\frac{n!}{n_1! \cdot n_2! \cdot n_3! \cdots n_k!}$$

where

$$n_1 + n_2 + n_3 + \cdots + n_k = n.$$

Using the formula for distinguishable permutations, you can determine that the number of distinguishable permutations of the letters AAAABBC is

$$\frac{7!}{4! \cdot 2! \cdot 1!} = \frac{7 \cdot 6 \cdot 5}{2}$$
$$= 105 \text{ distinguishable permutations.}$$

## EXAMPLE 4

### Finding the Number of Distinguishable Permutations

A building contractor is planning to develop a subdivision. The subdivision is to consist of 6 one-story houses, 4 two-story houses, and 2 split-level houses. In how many distinguishable ways can the houses be arranged?

**SOLUTION**

There are to be 12 houses in the subdivision, 6 of which are of one type (one-story), 4 of another type (two-story), and 2 of a third type (split-level). So, there are

$$\frac{12!}{6! \cdot 4! \cdot 2!} = \frac{12 \cdot 11 \cdot 10 \cdot 9 \cdot 8 \cdot 7 \cdot 6!}{6! \cdot 4! \cdot 2!}$$
$$= 13{,}860 \text{ distinguishable ways.}$$

**TI-84 PLUS**

```
12!/(6!4!2!)
                    13860
```

You can check your answer using technology, as shown at the left on a TI-84 Plus.

***Interpretation*** There are 13,860 distinguishable ways to arrange the houses in the subdivision.

**TRY IT YOURSELF 4**

The contractor wants to plant six oak trees, nine maple trees, and five poplar trees along the subdivision street. The trees are to be spaced evenly. In how many distinguishable ways can they be planted?

*Answer: Page A38*

## Combinations

A state park manages five beaches labeled A, B, C, D, and E. Due to budget constraints, new restrooms will be built at only three beaches. There are 10 ways for the state to select the three beaches.

ABC, ABD, ABE, ACD, ACE, ADE, BCD, BCE, BDE, CDE

In each selection, order does not matter (ABC is the same as BAC). The number of ways to choose $r$ objects from $n$ objects without regard to order is called the number of **combinations of $n$ objects taken $r$ at a time.**

### Combinations of $n$ Objects Taken $r$ at a Time

The number of combinations of $r$ objects selected from a group of $n$ objects *without regard to order* is

$$_nC_r = \frac{n!}{(n-r)!r!}$$

where $r \leq n$.

You can think of a combination of $n$ objects chosen $r$ at a time as a permutation of $n$ objects in which the $r$ selected objects are alike and the remaining $n - r$ (not selected) objects are alike.

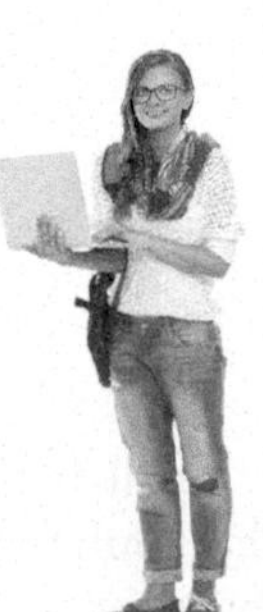

### Tech Tip

You can use technology such as Minitab, Excel, StatCrunch, or the TI-84 Plus to find the number of combinations of $n$ objects taken $r$ at a time. For instance, here is how to find $_nC_r$ in Example 5 on a TI-84 Plus.

Enter the total number of objects, $n = 16$.

MATH

Choose the PRB menu.

3: nCr

Enter the number of objects taken, $r = 4$.

ENTER

**TI-84 PLUS**

```
16 nCr 4
                    1820
```

### EXAMPLE 5

#### Finding the Number of Combinations

A state's department of transportation plans to develop a new section of interstate highway and receives 16 bids for the project. The state plans to hire four of the bidding companies. How many different combinations of four companies can be selected from the 16 bidding companies?

**SOLUTION**

The state is selecting four companies from a group of 16, so

$n = 16$ and $r = 4$.

Because order is not important, there are

$$\begin{aligned} _nC_r &= {}_{16}C_4 \\ &= \frac{16!}{(16-4)!4!} \\ &= \frac{16!}{12!4!} \\ &= \frac{16 \cdot 15 \cdot 14 \cdot 13 \cdot 12!}{12! \cdot 4!} \\ &= 1820 \text{ different combinations.} \end{aligned}$$

***Interpretation*** There are 1820 different combinations of four companies that can be selected from the 16 bidding companies.

**TRY IT YOURSELF 5**

The manager of an accounting department wants to form a three-person advisory committee from the 20 employees in the department. In how many ways can the manager form this committee?

*Answer: Page A38*

**Study Tip**

To solve a problem using a counting principle, be sure you choose the appropriate counting principle. To help you do this, consider these questions.

- *Are there two or more separate events?* Fundamental Counting Principle
- *Is the order of the objects important?* Permutation
- *Are the chosen objects from a larger group of objects in which order is not important?* Combination

Note that some problems may require you to use more than one counting principle (see Example 8).

## Applications of Counting Principles

The table summarizes the counting principles.

| Principle | Description | Formula |
|---|---|---|
| **Fundamental Counting Principle** | If one event can occur in $m$ ways and a second event can occur in $n$ ways, then the number of ways the two events can occur in sequence is $m \cdot n$. | $m \cdot n$ |
| **Permutations** | The number of permutations of $n$ distinct objects | $n!$ |
| | The number of permutations of $n$ distinct objects taken $r$ at a time, where $r \le n$ | ${}_nP_r = \dfrac{n!}{(n-r)!}$ |
| | The number of distinguishable permutations of $n$ objects where $n_1$ are of one type, $n_2$ are of another type, and so on, and $n_1 + n_2 + n_3 + \cdots + n_k = n$ | $\dfrac{n!}{n_1! \cdot n_2! \cdots n_k!}$ |
| **Combinations** | The number of combinations of $r$ objects selected from a group of $n$ objects without regard to order, where $r \le n$ | ${}_nC_r = \dfrac{n!}{(n-r)!r!}$ |

**EXAMPLE 6**

### Finding Probabilities

A student advisory board consists of 17 members. Three members will be chosen to serve as the board's chair, secretary, and webmaster. Each member is equally likely to serve in any of the positions. What is the probability of randomly selecting the three members who will be chosen for the board?

**SOLUTION**

Note that order is important because the positions (chair, secretary, and webmaster) are distinct objects. There is one favorable outcome and there are

$$ {}_{17}P_3 = \frac{17!}{(17-3)!} = \frac{17!}{14!} = \frac{17 \cdot 16 \cdot 15 \cdot 14!}{14!} = 17 \cdot 16 \cdot 15 = 4080 $$

ways the three positions can be filled. So, the probability of correctly selecting the three members who hold each position is

$$ P(\text{selecting the three members}) = \frac{1}{4080} \approx 0.0002. $$

You can check your answer using technology. For instance, using Excel's PERMUT command, you can find the probability of selecting the three members, as shown at the left.

**EXCEL**

| | A | |
|---|---|---|
| 1 | 4080 | ←=PERMUT(17,3) |
| 2 | 0.000245098 | ←=1/A2 |

**TRY IT YOURSELF 6**

A student advisory board consists of 20 members. Two members will be chosen to serve as the board's chair and secretary. Each member is equally likely to serve in either of the positions. What is the probability of randomly selecting the two members who will be chosen for the board?

*Answer: Page A38*

## Picturing the World

One of the largest lottery jackpots ever, $1.6 billion, was won in the Powerball lottery. When the jackpot was won, five different numbers were chosen from 1 to 69 and one number, the Powerball, was chosen from 1 to 26. The winning numbers are shown below.

In 2015, the lottery changed its rules. Previously, a player would choose five different numbers from 1 to 59 and one number from 1 to 35. A player wins the jackpot by matching all six winning numbers in a drawing.

**You purchase one ticket in the Powerball lottery. Find the probability of winning the jackpot using the old rules and the new rules. Which set of rules provides you with a better chance of winning the jackpot? How likely is your chance of winning?**

### EXAMPLE 7

#### Finding Probabilities

Find the probability of being dealt 5 diamonds from a standard deck of 52 playing cards.

**SOLUTION**

In a standard deck of playing cards, 13 cards are diamonds. Note that it does not matter in what order the cards are selected. The possible number of ways of choosing 5 diamonds out of 13 is ${}_{13}C_5$. The number of possible five-card hands is ${}_{52}C_5$. So, the probability of being dealt five diamonds is

$$\begin{aligned} P(5 \text{ diamonds}) &= \frac{{}_{13}C_5}{{}_{52}C_5} \\ &= \frac{1287}{2{,}598{,}960} \\ &\approx 0.0005. \end{aligned}$$

**TRY IT YOURSELF 7**

Find the probability of being dealt five diamonds from a standard deck of playing cards that also includes two jokers. In this case, the joker is considered to be a wild card that can be used to represent any card in the deck.

*Answer: Page A38*

### EXAMPLE 8

#### Finding Probabilities

A food manufacturer is analyzing a sample of 400 corn kernels for the presence of a toxin. In this sample, three kernels have dangerously high levels of the toxin. Four kernels are randomly selected from the sample. What is the probability that exactly one kernel contains a dangerously high level of the toxin?

**SOLUTION**

Note that it does not matter in what order the kernels are selected. The possible number of ways of choosing one toxic kernel out of three toxic kernels is ${}_3C_1$. The possible number of ways of choosing 3 nontoxic kernels from 397 nontoxic kernels is ${}_{397}C_3$. So, using the Fundamental Counting Principle, the number of ways of choosing one toxic kernel and three nontoxic kernels is

$${}_3C_1 \cdot {}_{397}C_3 = 3 \cdot 10{,}349{,}790 = 31{,}049{,}370.$$

The number of possible ways of choosing 4 kernels from 400 kernels is

$${}_{400}C_4 = 1{,}050{,}739{,}900.$$

So, the probability of selecting exactly one toxic kernel is

$$\begin{aligned} P(1 \text{ toxic kernel}) &= \frac{{}_3C_1 \cdot {}_{397}C_3}{{}_{400}C_4} \\ &= \frac{31{,}049{,}370}{1{,}050{,}739{,}900} \\ &\approx 0.030. \end{aligned}$$

**TRY IT YOURSELF 8**

A jury consists of five men and seven women. Three jury members are selected at random for an interview. Find the probability that all three are men.

*Answer: Page A38*

# 3.4 EXERCISES

For Extra Help: MyLab Statistics

## Building Basic Skills and Vocabulary

**1.** When you calculate the number of permutations of $n$ distinct objects taken $r$ at a time, what are you counting? Give an example.

**2.** When you calculate the number of combinations of $r$ objects taken from a group of $n$ objects, what are you counting? Give an example.

**True or False?** *In Exercises 3–6, determine whether the statement is true or false. If it is false, rewrite it as a true statement.*

**3.** A combination is an ordered arrangement of objects.

**4.** The number of different ordered arrangements of $n$ distinct objects is $n!$.

**5.** When you divide the number of permutations of 11 objects taken 3 at a time by 3!, you will get the number of combinations of 11 objects taken 3 at a time.

**6.** ${}_7C_5 = {}_7C_2$

*In Exercises 7–14, perform the indicated calculation.*

**7.** ${}_9P_5$

**8.** ${}_{14}P_3$

**9.** ${}_8C_3$

**10.** ${}_{21}C_8$

**11.** $\dfrac{{}_8C_4}{{}_{12}C_6}$

**12.** $\dfrac{{}_{10}C_7}{{}_{14}C_7}$

**13.** $\dfrac{{}_3P_2}{{}_{13}P_1}$

**14.** $\dfrac{{}_7P_3}{{}_{12}P_4}$

*In Exercises 15–18, determine whether the situation involves permutations, combinations, or neither. Explain your reasoning.*

**15.** The number of ways 16 floats can line up in a row for a parade

**16.** The number of ways a four-member committee can be chosen from 10 people

**17.** The number of ways 2 captains can be chosen from 28 players on a lacrosse team

**18.** The number of four-letter passwords that can be created when no letter can be repeated

## Using and Interpreting Concepts

**19. Video Games** You have seven different video games. How many different ways can you arrange the games side by side on a shelf?

**20. Skating** Eight people compete in a short track speed skating race. Assuming that there are no ties, in how many different orders can the skaters finish?

**21. Security Code** In how many ways can the letters A, B, C, D, E, and F be arranged for a six-letter security code?

**22. Starting Lineup** The starting lineup for a softball team consists of 10 players. How many different batting orders are possible using the starting lineup?

23. **Footrace** There are 72 runners in a 10-kilometer race. How many ways can the runners finish first, second, and third?

24. **Singing Competition** There are 16 finalists in a singing competition. The top five singers receive prizes. How many ways can the singers finish first through fifth?

25. **Playlist** A band is preparing a setlist of 21 songs for a concert. How many different ways can the band play the first six songs?

26. **Archaeology Club** An archaeology club has 38 members. How many different ways can the club select a president, vice president, treasurer, and secretary?

27. **Blood Donors** At a blood drive, eight donors with type O+ blood, six donors with type A+ blood, and three donors with type B+ blood arrive. In how many distinguishable ways can the donors stand in line?

28. **Necklaces** You are putting nine blue glass beads, three red glass beads, and seven green glass beads on a necklace. In how many distinguishable ways can the colored beads be put on the necklace?

29. **Letters** In how many distinguishable ways can the letters in the word *statistics* be written?

30. **Computer Science** A byte is a sequence of eight bits. A bit can be a 0 or a 1. In how many distinguishable ways can you have a byte with five 0's and three 1's?

31. **Experiment** A researcher is randomly selecting a treatment group of 10 human subjects from a group of 20 people taking part in an experiment. In how many different ways can the treatment group be selected?

32. **Jury Selection** From a group of 36 people, a jury of 12 people is selected. In how many different ways can a jury of 12 people be selected?

33. **Students** A class has 40 students. In how many different ways can three of the students be selected to work on a class project together? (Assume the order of the students is not important.)

34. **Lottery Number Selection** A lottery has 52 numbers. In how many different ways can six of the numbers be selected? (Assume the order of selection is not important.)

35. **Menu** A restaurant offers a dinner special that lets you choose from 10 entrées, 8 side dishes, and 13 desserts. The dinner special includes one entrée, two side dishes, and one dessert. Assume the side dishes are not the same. How many different meals are possible?

36. **Floral Arrangements** To create a floral arrangement with six different colored roses, three different colored carnations, and three different colored daisies, you choose from eight different colors of roses, six different colors of carnations, and seven different colors of daisies. How many different arrangements are possible?

37. **Water Pollution** An environmental agency is analyzing water samples from 80 lakes for pollution. Five of the lakes have dangerously high levels of dioxin. Six lakes are randomly selected from the sample. Use technology to find how many ways one polluted lake and five nonpolluted lakes can be chosen.

38. **Property Inspection** A property inspector is visiting 24 properties. Six of the properties are one acre or less in size, and the rest are greater than one acre in size. Eight properties are randomly selected. Use technology to find how many ways three properties that are each one acre or less and five properties that are each larger than one acre can be chosen.

**39. Zoning Board** The Saratoga Springs, New York, Zoning Board of Appeals has seven members. One member serves as board chair and another serves as vice chair. Given the names of the seven board members, what is the probability of randomly selecting the name of the chair and the name of the vice chair? *(Source: City of Saratoga Springs)*

**40. Board of Directors** The University of Colorado Board of Directors has 23 members. One member serves as board chair and another serves as vice chair. Given the names of the 23 board members, what is the probability of randomly selecting the name of the chair and the name of the vice chair? *(Source: University of Colorado)*

**41. Horse Race** A horse race has 10 entries. Given no information about the horses or jockeys, what is the probability of randomly selecting (in no particular order) the first three horses to finish the race?

**42. Pizza Toppings** A pizza shop offers nine toppings. No topping is used more than once. What is the probability that a random choice of three toppings is sausage, onions, and green peppers?

**43. Shuffle Play** You use a shuffle playback feature to randomly play songs in a playlist. The playlist of 56 songs includes 15 instrumental songs.

(a) What is the probability that the first three songs to play are instrumental songs? (Assume a song cannot be repeated.)

(b) What is the probability that the first three songs to play are *not* instrumental songs? (Assume a song cannot be repeated.)

**44. Officers** The offices of president, vice president, secretary, and treasurer for an environmental club will be filled from a pool of 14 candidates. Six of the candidates are members of the debate team.

(a) What is the probability that all of the offices are filled by members of the debate team?

(b) What is the probability that none of the offices are filled by members of the debate team?

**Finding New Music** *In Exercises 45–48, use the pie chart, which shows the results of a survey of 513 music listeners who were asked about their primary source for new music. (Source: The Sound of AI)*

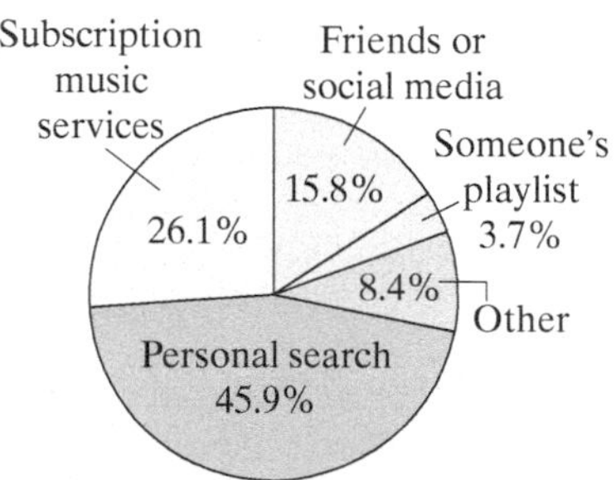


FIGURE FOR EXERCISES 45–48

**45.** You choose two music listeners at random. What is the probability that both say their primary source for new music is someone's playlist?

**46.** You choose three music listeners at random. What is the probability that all three say their primary source for new music is subscription music services?

**47.** You choose nine music listeners at random. What is the probability that none of them say their primary source for new music is friends or social media?

**48.** You choose five music listeners at random. What is the probability that none of them say their primary source for new music is personal search?

**49. Lottery** In a state lottery, you must correctly select 5 numbers (in any order) out of 40 to win the top prize. You purchase one lottery ticket. What is the probability that you will win the top prize?

**50. Investment Committee** A company has 200 employees, consisting of 144 women and 56 men. The company wants to select five employees to serve as an investment committee.

(a) Use technology to find the number of ways that 5 employees can be selected from 200.

(b) Use technology to find the number of ways that 5 employees can be selected from 56 males.

(c) Find the probability that no males will be selected by randomly selecting 5 of the 200 employees. Would this be a biased sample? Explain.

(d) Explain how the company can select a representative sample of the male and female population of employees.

**Warehouse** *In Exercises 51–54, a warehouse employs 24 workers on first shift, 17 workers on second shift, and 13 workers on third shift. Eight workers are chosen at random to be interviewed about the work environment.*

**51.** Find the probability of choosing five first-shift workers.

**52.** Find the probability of choosing three second-shift workers.

**53.** Find the probability of choosing four third-shift workers.

**54.** Find the probability of choosing two second-shift workers and two third-shift workers.

## Extending Concepts

**55. Defective Units** A shipment of 10 microwave ovens contains 2 defective units. A restaurant buys three units. What is the probability of the restaurant buying at least two nondefective units?

**56. Defective Disks** A pack of 100 recordable DVDs contains 5 defective disks. You select four disks. What is the probability of selecting at least three nondefective disks?

**57. Employee Selection** A company has eight sales representatives, two in each of four regions. The company randomly selects four of the eight representatives to participate in a training program. What is the probability that the four sales representatives chosen will be from only two of the four regions?

**58. Employee Selection** In Exercise 57, what is the probability that the four sales representatives chosen to participate in the training program will be from three of the four regions?

**Cards** *In Exercises 59–62, you are dealt a hand of five cards from a standard deck of 52 playing cards.*

**59.** Find the probability of being dealt two clubs and one of each of the other three suits.

**60.** Find the probability of being dealt four of a kind.

**61.** Find the probability of being dealt a full house (three of one kind and two of another kind).

**62.** Find the probability of being dealt three of a kind (the other two cards are different from each other).

# USES AND ABUSES Statistics in the Real World

## Uses

Probability affects decisions when the weather is forecast, when medications are selected, and even when players are selected for professional sports teams. Although intuition is often used for determining probabilities, you will be better able to assess the likelihood of an event by applying the rules of probability.

For instance, you work for a real estate company and are asked to estimate the likelihood that a particular house will sell for a particular price within the next 90 days. You could use your intuition, but you could better assess the probability by looking at sales records for similar houses.

## Abuses

One common abuse of probability is thinking that probabilities have "memories." For instance, the probability that a coin tossed eight times will land heads up every time is about 0.004. However, when seven heads have been tossed in a row, the probability that the eighth toss lands heads up is 0.5. Each toss is independent of all other tosses. The coin does not "remember" that it has already landed heads up seven times.

A famous instance of this abuse happened at a casino in Monte Carlo, Monaco, in 1913. After a roulette wheel landed on black 15 times in a row, people started rushing to bet on red, thinking that the wheel was bound to land on red soon. The wheel kept landing on black, and players doubled and tripled their bets, using the same reasoning. The wheel ended up landing on black a record 26 times in a row, costing players millions.

## Ethics

A study by economists Daniel Chen, Tobias Moskowitz, and Kelly Shue found evidence that the gambler's fallacy occasionally leads baseball umpires, loan officers, and judges in refugee asylum courts to make mistakes. For instance, when loan officers have approved five loan applications in a row, they might think that six deserving loans in a row are unlikely and reject the sixth application based on a minor flaw when objectively it should be approved. The study concluded that up to 9% of loan decisions are influenced by this fallacy.

Similarly, when judges are reviewing a request for asylum, they might be more likely to deny the case if they approved the last two cases. The authors of the study estimated that as many as 2% of asylum cases may be affected. Although not as serious an injustice as the first two examples, the study also found that baseball umpires are about 1.5% less likely to call a pitch a strike when they called the previous pitch a strike. For decision makers such as judges to make ethical decisions, they must attempt to view each case as independent from previous cases.

## EXERCISES

*A "Daily Number" lottery has a three-digit number from 000 to 999. You buy one ticket each day. The number you always play is 389.*

**1.** What is the probability of winning next Tuesday and Wednesday?

**2.** You won on Tuesday. What is the probability of winning on Wednesday?

**3.** You did not win on Tuesday. What is the probability of winning on Wednesday?

# 3 Chapter Summary

| What Did You Learn? | Example(s) | Review Exercises |
|---|---|---|
| **Section 3.1** | | |
| ▶ How to identify the sample space of a probability experiment and how to identify simple events | 1, 2 | 1–4 |
| ▶ How to use the Fundamental Counting Principle to find the number of ways two or more events can occur | 3, 4 | 5, 6 |
| ▶ How to distinguish among classical probability, empirical probability, and subjective probability | 5–8 | 7–12 |
| ▶ How to find the probability of the complement of an event and how to use a tree diagram and the Fundamental Counting Principle to find probabilities | 9–11 | 13–16 |
| **Section 3.2** | | |
| ▶ How to find the probability of an event given that another event has occurred | 1 | 17, 18 |
| ▶ How to distinguish between independent and dependent events | 2 | 19–22 |
| ▶ How to use the Multiplication Rule to find the probability of two or more events occurring in sequence and to find conditional probabilities | 3–5 | 23, 24 |
| **Section 3.3** | | |
| ▶ How to determine whether two events are mutually exclusive | 1 | 25, 26 |
| ▶ How to use the Addition Rule to find the probability of two events | 2–5 | 27–40 |
| **Section 3.4** | | |
| ▶ How to find the number of ways a group of objects can be arranged in order and the number of ways to choose several objects from a group without regard to order | 1–5 | 41–48 |
| ▶ How to use counting principles to find probabilities | 6–8 | 49–53 |

## Study Strategies

**Time Management** One of the biggest challenges you will face in college is managing your time. Learning some time-management skills can help you balance academic, work, and personal demands, all of which compete for your time.

- The syllabus for a course can be a valuable time-management tool. It typically provides you with quiz and test dates and assignments and their due dates. Read your syllabus carefully and highlight important due dates. Then use *backward planning* by marking a calendar with each due date and the tasks you need to complete to meet each due date. Be sure to include other responsibilities, such as your work schedule, on your calendar.
- To-do lists can also be valuable time-management tools. They are quick and easy to make, and you can easily update or change them. You can make a to-do list to cover the tasks for the day or for a week. You can include academic work or all your tasks. Pay attention to tasks that stay on your to-do list. These may indicate procrastination. Some tips for dealing with procrastination are given in the Chapter 4 Summary.
- Use an *ABC grid* to prioritize tasks. Category A includes tasks that must be completed in 24 hours. Category B includes tasks that can be completed in a day or two. Category C includes tasks that can be put off for several days.

For more information, visit Skills for Success in the accompanying MyLab course.

# 3 Review Exercises

## Section 3.1

*In Exercises 1–4, identify the sample space of the probability experiment and determine the number of outcomes in the event. Draw a tree diagram when appropriate.*

**1.** *Experiment:* Tossing four coins
*Event:* Getting three heads

**2.** *Experiment:* Rolling 2 six-sided dice
*Event:* Getting a sum of 4 or 5

**3.** *Experiment:* Choosing a month of the year
*Event:* Choosing a month that begins with the letter J

**4.** *Experiment:* Guessing the gender(s) of the three children in a family
*Event:* Guessing that the family has two boys

*In Exercises 5 and 6, use the Fundamental Counting Principle.*

**5.** A student must choose from seven classes to take at 8:00 A.M., four classes to take at 9:00 A.M., and three classes to take at 10:00 A.M. How many ways can the student arrange the schedule?

**6.** The state of Virginia's license plates have three letters and four digits. Assuming that any letter or digit can be used, how many different license plates are possible?

*In Exercises 7–12, classify the statement as an example of classical probability, empirical probability, or subjective probability. Explain your reasoning.*

**7.** On the basis of prior counts, a quality control officer says there is a 0.05 probability that a randomly chosen part is defective.

**8.** The probability of randomly selecting five cards of the same suit from a standard deck of 52 playing cards is about 0.002.

**9.** The chance that Corporation A's stock price will fall today is 75%.

**10.** The probability that a person can roll his or her tongue is 70%.

**11.** The probability of rolling 2 six-sided dice and getting a sum of 9 is $\frac{1}{9}$.

**12.** The chance that a randomly selected person in the United States is between 12 and 18 years old is about 8.9%. *(Source: U.S. Census Bureau)*

*In Exercises 13 and 14, use the table, which shows the approximate distribution of the sizes of firms for a recent year. (Adapted from North American Industry Classification System)*

| **Number of employees** | 1 to 4 | 5 to 9 | 10 to 19 | 20 to 99 | 100 or more |
|---|---|---|---|---|---|
| **Percent of firms** | 78.5% | 11.5% | 4.9% | 4.0% | 1.1% |

**13.** Find the probability that a randomly selected firm will have more than four employees.

**14.** Find the probability that a randomly selected firm will have fewer than 10 employees.

**Telephone Numbers** *The telephone numbers for a region of Pennsylvania have an area code of 570. The next seven digits represent the local telephone numbers for that region. These cannot begin with a 0 or 1. In Exercises 15 and 16, assume your cousin lives within the given area code.*

**15.** What is the probability of randomly generating your cousin's telephone number on the first try?

**16.** What is the probability of not randomly generating your cousin's telephone number on the first try?

## Section 3.2

*In Exercises 17 and 18, use the table, which shows the numbers of first-time and repeat U.S. nursing students taking the National Council Licensure Examination (NCLEX-RN® exam) to pass or fail in a recent year.* (Adapted from National Council Licensure Examinations)

| | Passed | Failed | Total |
|---|---|---|---|
| **First time** | 177,407 | 27,522 | 204,929 |
| **Repeat** | 44,983 | 59,775 | 104,758 |
| **Total** | 222,390 | 87,297 | 309,687 |

**17.** Find the probability that a student took the exam for the first time, given that the student failed.

**18.** Find the probability that a student passed, given that the student repeated the exam.

*In Exercises 19–22, determine whether the events are independent or dependent. Explain your reasoning.*

**19.** Tossing a coin four times and getting four heads, and then tossing it a fifth time and getting a head

**20.** Selecting an ace from a standard deck of 52 playing cards, and then selecting a jack from the deck without replacing the ace

**21.** Taking a driver's education course and passing the driver's license exam

**22.** Getting high grades and being awarded an academic scholarship

**23.** Your roommate asks you to buy toothpaste and dental rinse but does not tell you which brands to get. The store has eight brands of toothpaste and five brands of dental rinse. What is the probability that you will purchase the correct brands of both products? Is this an unusual event? Explain.

**24.** Your sock drawer has 18 folded pairs of socks, with 8 pairs of white, 6 pairs of black, and 4 pairs of blue. What is the probability, without looking in the drawer, that you will first select and remove a black pair, then select either a blue or a white pair? Is this an unusual event? Explain.

## Section 3.3

*In Exercises 25 and 26, determine whether the events are mutually exclusive. Explain your reasoning.*

**25.** Event $A$: Randomly select a red jelly bean from a jar.
Event $B$: Randomly select a yellow jelly bean from the jar.

**26.** Event $A$: Randomly select a person who loves cats.
Event $B$: Randomly select a person who owns a dog.

27. A random sample of 250 working adults found that 74% access the Internet at work, 88% access the Internet at home, and 72% access the Internet at both work and home. Find the probability that a person in this sample selected at random accesses the Internet at home or at work.

28. A sample of 6500 automobiles found that 1560 of the automobiles were black, 3120 of the automobiles were sedans, and 1170 of the automobiles were black sedans. Find the probability that a randomly chosen automobile from this sample is black or a sedan.

*In Exercises 29–32, find the probability.*

29. A card is randomly selected from a standard deck of 52 playing cards. Find the probability that the card is between 4 and 8, inclusive, or is a club.

30. A card is randomly selected from a standard deck of 52 playing cards. Find the probability that the card is red or a queen.

31. A 12-sided die, numbered 1 to 12, is rolled. Find the probability that the roll results in an odd number or a number less than 4.

32. The spinner shown at the left is spun. The spinner is equally likely to land on each number. Find the probability that the spinner lands on a multiple of 3 or a number greater than 5.

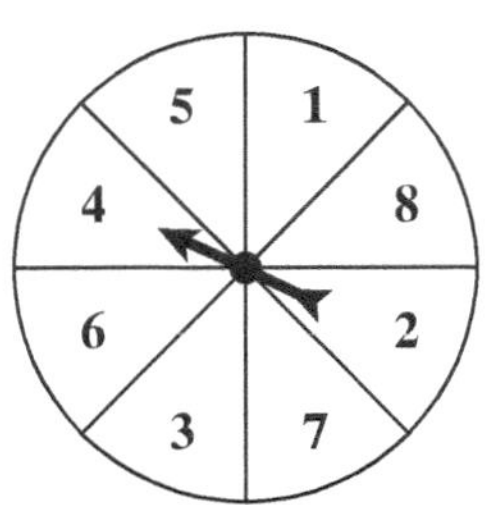


FIGURE FOR EXERCISE 32

*In Exercises 33 and 34, use the pie chart at the left, which shows the percent distribution of the number of students in U.S. public schools in a recent year. (Source: U.S. National Center for Education Statistics)*

33. Find the probability of randomly selecting a school with fewer than 500 students.

34. Find the probability of randomly selecting a school with 300 or more students.

**Students in Public Schools**

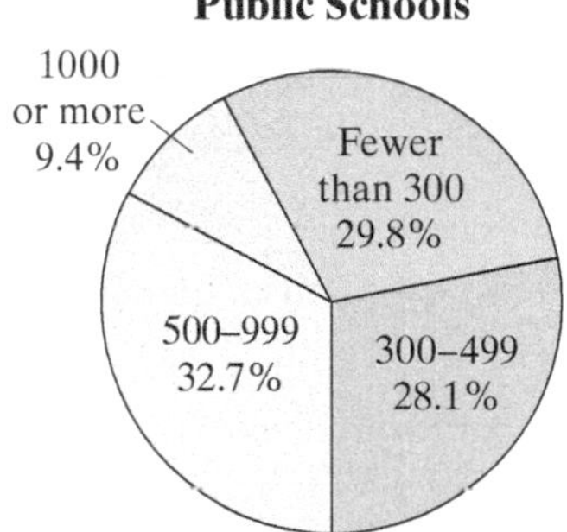


FIGURE FOR EXERCISES 33 AND 34

*In Exercises 35–38, the bar graph shows the results of a survey in which 8806 undergraduate students were asked how many hours they spend on studying and other academic activities outside of class in a typical week. (Source: American College Health Association)*

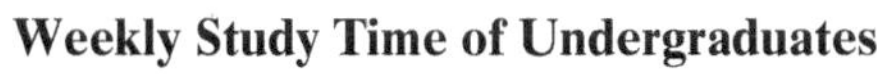


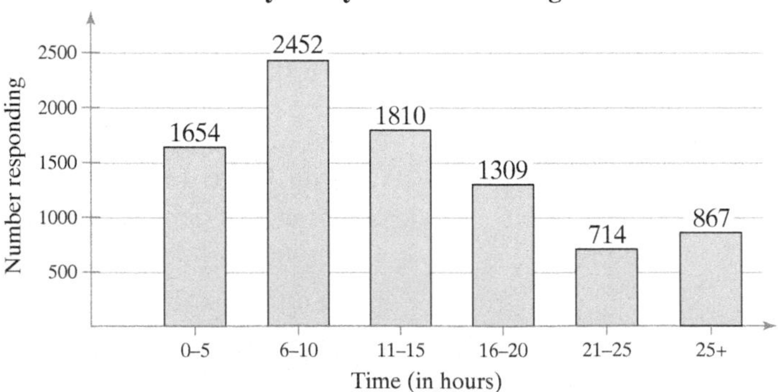


35. Find the probability of randomly selecting an undergraduate who studies more than 20 hours per week.

36. Find the probability of randomly selecting an undergraduate who studies less than 11 hours per week.

37. Find the probability of randomly selecting an undergraduate who does not study from 6 to 10 hours per week.

38. Find the probability of randomly selecting an undergraduate who does not study more than 15 hours per week.

**39.** You are given that $P(A) = 0.15$ and $P(B) = 0.40$. Do you have enough information to find $P(A \text{ or } B)$? Explain.

**40.** You are given that $P(A \text{ or } B) = 0.55$ and $P(A) + P(B) = 1$. Do you have enough information to find $P(A \text{ and } B)$? Explain.

## Section 3.4

*In Exercises 41–44, perform the indicated calculation.*

**41.** ${}_{11}P_2$ **42.** ${}_{8}P_6$ **43.** ${}_{7}C_4$ **44.** $\dfrac{{}_{5}C_3}{{}_{10}C_3}$

*In Exercises 45–48, use combinations and permutations.*

**45.** Fifteen cyclists enter a race. How many ways can the cyclists finish first, second, and third?

**46.** Five players on a basketball team must each choose one of the five players on the opposing team to defend. In how many ways can the players choose their defensive assignments?

**47.** A literary magazine editor must choose 4 short stories for this month's issue from 17 submissions. In how many ways can the editor choose this month's stories?

**48.** An employer must hire 2 people from a list of 13 applicants. In how many ways can the employer choose to hire the two people?

*In Exercises 49–53, use counting principles to find the probability.*

**49.** A full house consists of three of one kind and two of another kind. You are dealt a hand of five cards from a standard deck of 52 playing cards. Find the probability of being dealt a full house consisting of three kings and two queens.

**50.** A security code consists of three letters and one digit. The first letter cannot be A, B, or C. What is the probability of guessing the security code on the first try?

**51.** A shipment of 200 calculators contains 3 defective units. What is the probability that a sample of three calculators will have

(a) no defective calculators?

(b) all defective calculators?

(c) at least one defective calculator?

(d) at least one nondefective calculator?

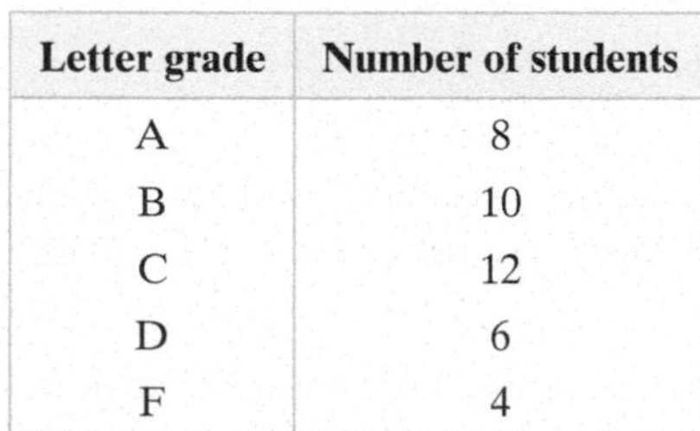

| Letter grade | Number of students |
|---|---|
| A | 8 |
| B | 10 |
| C | 12 |
| D | 6 |
| F | 4 |

TABLE FOR EXERCISE 52

**52.** A class of 40 students takes a statistics exam. The results are shown in the table at the left. Three students are selected at random. What is the probability that

(a) all three students received an A?

(b) all three students received a C or better?

(c) all three students received a D or an F?

(d) all three students received a B or a C?

**53.** A corporation has six male senior executives and four female senior executives. Four senior executives are chosen at random to attend a technology seminar. What is the probability of choosing

(a) four men? (b) four women?

(c) two men and two women? (d) one man and three women?

# 3 Chapter Quiz

*Take this quiz as you would take a quiz in class. After you are done, check your work against the answers given in the back of the book.*

1. The access code for a warehouse's security system consists of six digits. The first digit cannot be 0 and the last digit must be even. How many access codes are possible?

2. The table shows the numbers (in thousands) of earned degrees by level in two different fields, conferred in the United States in a recent year. *(Source: U.S. National Center for Education Statistics)*

| | | Field | | |
|---|---|---|---|---|
| | | **Natural sciences/ mathematics** | **Computer science/ engineering** | **Total** |
| **Level of degree** | **Bachelor's** | 175.5 | 220.3 | 395.8 |
| | **Master's** | 34.8 | 105.4 | 140.2 |
| | **Doctoral** | 16.4 | 13.0 | 29.4 |
| | **Total** | 226.7 | 338.7 | 565.4 |

A person who earned a degree in the year is randomly selected. Find the probability that the degree earned by the person is a

(a) bachelor's degree.

(b) bachelor's degree, given that the degree is in computer science/engineering.

(c) bachelor's degree, given that the degree is not in computer science/engineering.

(d) bachelor's degree or a master's degree.

(e) doctorate, given that the degree is in computer science/engineering.

(f) master's degree or the degree is in natural sciences/mathematics.

(g) bachelor's degree and the degree is in natural sciences/mathematics.

(h) degree in computer science/engineering, given that the person earned a bachelor's degree.

3. Which event(s) in Exercise 2 can be considered unusual? Explain.

4. Determine whether the events are mutually exclusive. Then determine whether the events are independent or dependent. Explain your reasoning.

Event $A$: A bowler having the highest game in a 40-game tournament
Event $B$: Losing the bowling tournament

5. From a pool of 40 club members, the offices of president, vice president, secretary, and treasurer will be filled. In how many different ways can the offices be filled?

6. A shipment of 250 netbooks contains 3 defective units. Determine how many ways a vending company can buy three of these units and receive

(a) no defective units. (b) all defective units. (c) at least one good unit.

7. In Exercise 6, find the probability of the vending company receiving

(a) no defective units. (b) all defective units. (c) at least one good unit.

# 3 Chapter Test

*Take this test as you would take a test in class.*

1. Your dorm enters 15 out of 65 plastic numbered ducks in a duck race. The ducks are all dumped into a stream and drift to the finish line. What is the probability that three of your dorm's ducks finish first, second, and third?

2. A person's building access code is their first and last initials and four digits.
   (a) What is the probability of randomly guessing a person's access code in one try?
   (b) What is the probability that a random try does not give the person's access code?
   (c) You know a person's first name only, and you know that the last digit is odd. What is the probability of guessing this person's code on the first try?
   (d) Are the statements in parts (a)–(c) examples of classical probability, empirical probability, or subjective probability? Explain your reasoning.

3. Determine whether the events are mutually exclusive. Explain your reasoning.
   Event $A$: Randomly select a student born on the 30th of a month
   Event $B$: Randomly select a student with a birthday in February

4. The table on the left shows the secondary school student enrollment levels (in thousands by grade) in Oklahoma and Texas schools in a recent year. *(Source: U.S. National Center for Education Statistics)*

| | Oklahoma | Texas | Total |
|---|---|---|---|
| **Ninth grade** | 52.3 | 437.2 | 489.5 |
| **Tenth grade** | 50.4 | 401.2 | 451.6 |
| **Eleventh grade** | 46.7 | 373.4 | 420.1 |
| **Twelfth grade** | 44.1 | 353.3 | 397.4 |
| **Total** | 193.5 | 1565.1 | 1758.6 |

TABLE FOR EXERCISE 4

   A student in one of the indicated grades and states is randomly selected. Find the probability of selecting a student who
   (a) is in ninth grade.
   (b) is in ninth or tenth grade.
   (c) is in eleventh grade, given that the student is enrolled in Oklahoma.
   (d) is enrolled in Texas, given that the student is in twelfth grade.
   (e) is in eleventh grade or is enrolled in Oklahoma.
   (f) is in twelfth grade and is enrolled in Oklahoma.

5. Which event(s) in Exercise 4 can be considered unusual? Explain your reasoning.

6. A person is selected at random from the sample in Exercise 4. Are the events "the student is in ninth grade" and "the student is enrolled in Texas" independent or dependent? Explain your reasoning.

7. There are 16 students giving final presentations in your history course.
   (a) Three students present on the first day. How many presentation orders are possible for the first day?
   (b) Presentation subjects are based on the units of the course. Unit B is covered by three students, Unit C is covered by five students, and Units A and D are each covered by four students. How many presentation orders are possible when presentations on the same unit are indistinguishable from each other?

# REAL STATISTICS REAL DECISIONS

# Putting it all together

You work in the security department of a bank's website. To access their accounts, customers of the bank must create an 8-digit password. It is your job to determine the password requirements for these accounts. Security guidelines state that for the website to be secure, the probability that an 8-digit password is guessed on one try must be less than $\frac{1}{60^8}$, assuming all passwords are equally likely.

Your job is to use the probability techniques you have learned in this chapter to decide what requirements a customer must meet when choosing a password, including what sets of characters are allowed, so that the website is secure according to the security guidelines.

**ACCOUNT REGISTRATION FORM**
register here to access your account

Select your username:

Create an 8-digit password:

Verify Password:

## EXERCISES

**1. *How Would You Do It?***

(a) How would you investigate the question of what password requirements you should set to meet the security guidelines?

(b) What statistical methods taught in this chapter would you use?

**2. *Answering the Question***

(a) What password requirements would you set? What characters would be allowed?

(b) Show that the probability that a password is guessed on one try is less than $\frac{1}{60^8}$, when the requirements in part (a) are used and all passwords are equally likely.

**3. *Additional Security***

For additional security, each customer creates a 5-digit PIN (personal identification number). The table on the right shows the 10 most commonly chosen 5-digit PINs. From the table, you can see that more than a third of all 5-digit PINs could be guessed by trying these 10 numbers. To discourage customers from using predictable PINs, you consider prohibiting PINs that use the same digit more than once.

(a) How would this requirement affect the number of possible 5-digit PINs?

(b) Would you decide to prohibit PINs that use the same digit more than once? Explain.

**Most Popular 5-Digit PINs**

| Rank | PIN | Percent |
|---|---|---|
| 1 | 12345 | 22.80% |
| 2 | 11111 | 4.48% |
| 3 | 55555 | 1.77% |
| 4 | 00000 | 1.26% |
| 5 | 54321 | 1.20% |
| 6 | 13579 | 1.11% |
| 7 | 77777 | 0.62% |
| 8 | 22222 | 0.45% |
| 9 | 12321 | 0.41% |
| 10 | 99999 | 0.40% |

(Source: Datagenetics.com)

# TECHNOLOGY

MINITAB | EXCEL | TI-84 PLUS

# Simulation: Composing Mozart Variations with Dice

Wolfgang Mozart (1756–1791) composed a wide variety of musical pieces. In his Musical Dice Game, he wrote a minuet with an almost endless number of variations. Each minuet has 16 bars. In the eighth and sixteenth bars, the player has a choice of two musical phrases. In each of the other 14 bars, the player has a choice of 11 phrases.

To create a minuet, Mozart suggested that the player toss 2 six-sided dice 16 times. For the eighth and sixteenth bars, choose Option 1 when the dice total is odd and Option 2 when it is even. For each of the other 14 bars, subtract 1 from the dice total. The minuet shown is the result of the following sequence of numbers.

| | | | | | | | |
|---|---|---|---|---|---|---|---|
| 5 | 7 | 1 | 6 | 4 | 10 | 5 | 1 |
| 6 | 6 | 2 | 4 | 6 | 8 | 8 | 2 |

## EXERCISES

1. How many phrases did Mozart write to create the Musical Dice Game minuet? Explain.
2. How many possible variations are there in Mozart's Musical Dice Game minuet? Explain.
3. Use technology to randomly select a number from 1 to 11.
   (a) What is the theoretical probability of each number from 1 to 11 occurring?
   (b) Use this procedure to select 100 integers from 1 to 11. Tally your results and compare them with the probabilities in part (a).
4. What is the probability of randomly selecting option 6, 7, or 8 for the first bar? For all 14 bars? Find each probability using (a) theoretical probability and (b) the results of Exercise 3(b).
5. Use technology to randomly select two numbers from 1 to 6. Find the sum and subtract 1 to obtain a total.
   (a) What is the theoretical probability of each total from 1 to 11?
   (b) Use this procedure to select 100 totals from 1 to 11. Tally your results and compare them with the probabilities in part (a).
6. Repeat Exercise 4 using the results of Exercise 5.

Extended solutions are given in the technology manuals that accompany this text. Technical instruction is provided for Minitab, Excel, and the TI-84 Plus.

CHAPTER 4

# Discrete Probability Distributions

The National Climatic Data Center (NCDC) is one of the world's largest active archives of weather data. NCDC archives weather data from the Coast Guard, Federal Aviation Administration, Military Services, the National Weather Service, and voluntary observers.

## Where You've Been

In Chapters 1 through 3, you learned how to collect and describe data and how to find the probability of an event. These skills are used in many different types of careers. For instance, data about climatic conditions are used to analyze and forecast the weather throughout the world. On a typical day, meteorologists use data from aircraft, National Weather Service cooperative observers, radar, remote sensing systems, satellites, ships, weather balloons, and a variety of other data-collection devices to forecast the weather. Even with this much data, meteorologists cannot forecast the weather with certainty. Instead, they assign probabilities to certain weather conditions. For instance, a meteorologist might determine that there is a 40% chance of rain (based on the relative frequency of rain under similar weather conditions).

## Where You're Going

In Chapter 4, you will learn how to create and use probability distributions. Knowing the shape, center, and variability of a probability distribution enables you to make decisions in inferential statistics. For example, consider a meteorologist working on a three-day forecast. Assuming that having rain on one day is independent of having rain on another day, the meteorologist determines that there is a 40% probability of rain (and a 60% probability of no rain) on each of the three days. What is the probability that it will rain on 0, 1, 2, or 3 of the days? To answer this, you can create a probability distribution for the possible outcomes.

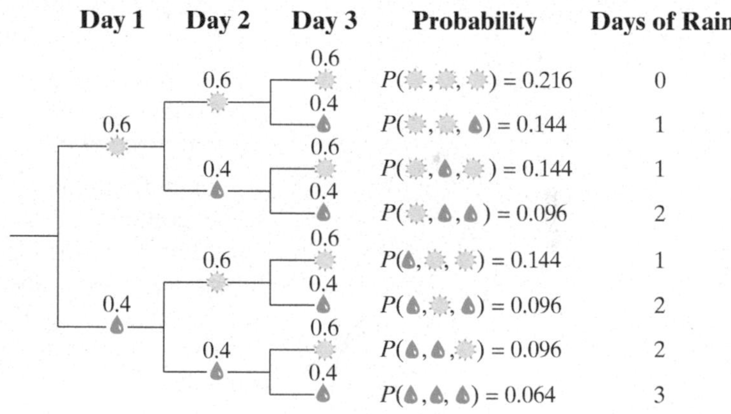


Using the *Multiplication and Addition Rules* with the probabilities in the tree diagram, you can determine the probabilities of having rain on various numbers of days. You can then use this information to construct and graph a probability distribution.

**Probability Distribution**

| Days of rain | Tally | Probability |
|---|---|---|
| 0 | 1 | 0.216 |
| 1 | 3 | 0.432 |
| 2 | 3 | 0.288 |
| 3 | 1 | 0.064 |

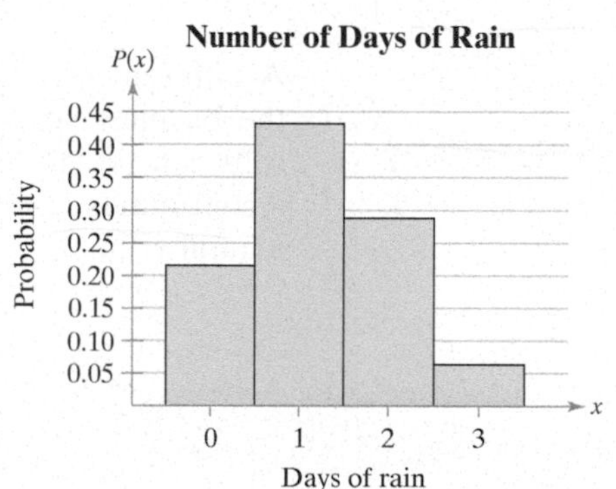

# 4.1 Probability Distributions

### What You Should Learn

- How to distinguish between discrete random variables and continuous random variables
- How to construct and graph a discrete probability distribution and how to determine whether a distribution is a probability distribution
- How to find the mean, variance, and standard deviation of a discrete probability distribution
- How to find the expected value of a discrete probability distribution

Random Variables ■ Discrete Probability Distributions ■ Mean, Variance, and Standard Deviation ■ Expected Value

## Random Variables

The outcome of a probability experiment is often a count or a measure. When this occurs, the outcome is called a **random variable.**

**DEFINITION**

A **random variable** $x$ represents a value associated with each outcome of a probability experiment.

The word *random* indicates that $x$ is determined by chance. There are two types of random variables: **discrete** and **continuous.**

**DEFINITION**

A random variable is **discrete** when it has a finite or countable number of possible outcomes that can be listed.

A random variable is **continuous** when it has an uncountable number of possible outcomes, represented by an interval on a number line.

In most applications, discrete random variables represent counted data, while continuous random variables represent measured data. For instance, consider the following example. You conduct a study of the number of calls a business makes in one day. The possible values of the random variable $x$ are 0, 1, 2, 3, 4, and so on. Because the set of possible outcomes $\{0, 1, 2, 3, \ldots\}$ can be listed, $x$ is a discrete random variable. You can represent its values as points on a number line.

**Number of Calls (Discrete)**

$x$ can be any whole number: 0, 1, 2, 3, . . .

A different way to conduct the study would be to measure the time (in hours) the business spends making calls in one day. Because the time spent making calls can be any number from 0 to 24 (including fractions and decimals), $x$ is a continuous random variable. You can represent its values with an interval on a number line.

**Hours Spent on Calls (Continuous)**

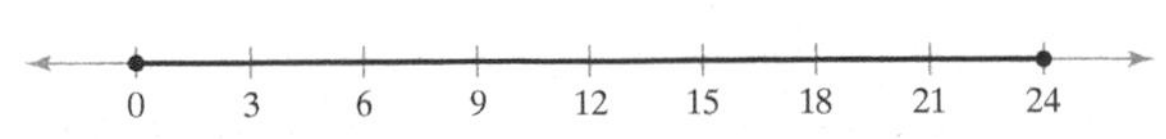


$x$ can be any value between 0 and 24.

When a random variable is discrete, you can list the possible values the variable can assume. However, it is impossible to list all values for a continuous random variable.

**EXAMPLE 1**

### Discrete Variables and Continuous Variables

Determine whether each random variable $x$ is discrete or continuous. Explain your reasoning.

1. Let $x$ represent the number of Fortune 500 companies that lost money in the previous year.
2. Let $x$ represent the volume of gasoline in a 21-gallon tank.

**Study Tip**

Values of variables such as volume, age, height, and weight are sometimes rounded to the nearest whole number. These values represent measured data, however, so they are continuous random variables.

**SOLUTION**

1. The number of Fortune 500 companies that lost money in the previous year can be counted. The set of possible outcomes is

   $$\{0, 1, 2, 3, \ldots, 500\}.$$

   So, $x$ is a *discrete* random variable.
2. The amount of gasoline in the tank can be any volume between 0 gallons and 21 gallons. So, $x$ is a *continuous* random variable.

**TRY IT YOURSELF 1**

Determine whether each random variable $x$ is discrete or continuous. Explain your reasoning.

1. Let $x$ represent the speed of a rocket.
2. Let $x$ represent the number of calves born on a farm in one year.
3. Let $x$ represent the number of days of rain for the next three days.

*Answer: Page A38*

It is important that you can distinguish between discrete and continuous random variables because different statistical techniques are used to analyze each. The remainder of this chapter focuses on discrete random variables and their probability distributions. Your study of continuous probability distributions will begin in Chapter 5.

## Discrete Probability Distributions

Each value of a discrete random variable can be assigned a probability. By listing each value of the random variable with its corresponding probability, you are forming a **discrete probability distribution.**

**DEFINITION**

A **discrete probability distribution** lists each possible value the random variable can assume, together with its probability. A discrete probability distribution must satisfy these conditions.

| In Words | In Symbols |
|---|---|
| **1.** The probability of each value of the discrete random variable is between 0 and 1, inclusive. | $0 \le P(x) \le 1$ |
| **2.** The sum of all the probabilities is 1. | $\Sigma P(x) = 1$ |

Because probabilities represent relative frequencies, a discrete probability distribution can be graphed with a relative frequency histogram.

**GUIDELINES**

**Constructing a Discrete Probability Distribution**

Let $x$ be a discrete random variable with possible outcomes $x_1, x_2, \ldots, x_n$.

1. Make a frequency distribution for the possible outcomes.
2. Find the sum of the frequencies.
3. Find the probability of each possible outcome by dividing its frequency by the sum of the frequencies.
4. Check that each probability is between 0 and 1, inclusive, and that the sum of all the probabilities is 1.

**Frequency Distribution**

| Score, $x$ | Frequency, $f$ |
|---|---|
| 1 | 24 |
| 2 | 33 |
| 3 | 42 |
| 4 | 30 |
| 5 | 21 |

**EXAMPLE 2**

## Constructing and Graphing a Discrete Probability Distribution

An industrial psychologist administered a personality inventory test for passive-aggressive traits to 150 employees. Each individual was given a whole number score from 1 to 5, where 1 is extremely passive and 5 is extremely aggressive. A score of 3 indicated neither trait. The results are shown at the left. Construct a discrete probability distribution for the random variable $x$. Then graph the distribution using a histogram.

**SOLUTION**

Divide the frequency of each score by the total number of individuals in the study to find the probability for each value of the random variable.

$$P(1) = \frac{24}{150} = 0.16 \qquad P(2) = \frac{33}{150} = 0.22 \qquad P(3) = \frac{42}{150} = 0.28$$

$$P(4) = \frac{30}{150} = 0.20 \qquad P(5) = \frac{21}{150} = 0.14$$

The discrete probability distribution is shown in the table below.

| $x$ | 1 | 2 | 3 | 4 | 5 |
|---|---|---|---|---|---|
| $P(x)$ | 0.16 | 0.22 | 0.28 | 0.20 | 0.14 |

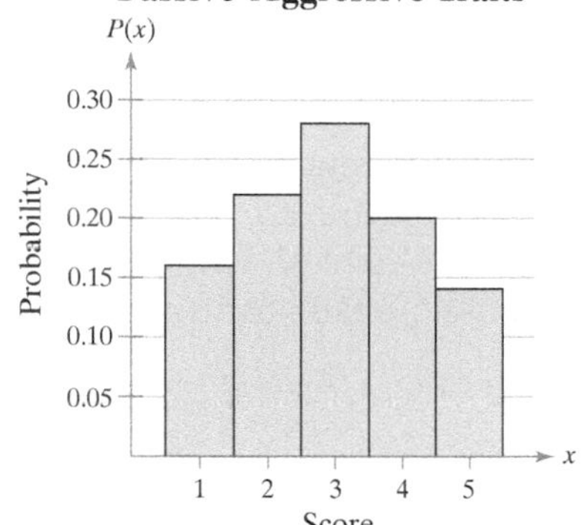


Note that the probability of each value of $x$ is between 0 and 1, and the sum of the probabilities is 1. So, the distribution is a probability distribution. The graph of the distribution is shown in the histogram at the left. Because the width of each bar is one, the area of each bar is equal to the probability of a particular outcome. Also, the probability of an event corresponds to the sum of the areas of the outcomes included in the event. For instance, the probability of the event "having a score of 2 or 3" is equal to the sum of the areas of the second and third bars.

$$(1)(0.22) + (1)(0.28) = 0.22 + 0.28 = 0.50$$

***Interpretation*** You can see that the distribution is approximately symmetric.

**TRY IT YOURSELF 2**

A company tracks the number of sales new employees make each day during a 100-day probationary period. The results for one new employee are shown at the left. Construct a probability distribution for the random variable $x$. Then graph the distribution using a histogram.

*Answer: Page A38*

**Frequency Distribution**

| Sales per day, $x$ | Number of days, $f$ |
|---|---|
| 0 | 16 |
| 1 | 19 |
| 2 | 15 |
| 3 | 21 |
| 4 | 9 |
| 5 | 10 |
| 6 | 8 |
| 7 | 2 |

## EXAMPLE 3

### Verifying a Probability Distribution

Verify that the distribution for the three-day forecast (see page 189) and the number of days of rain is a probability distribution.

| **Days of rain, $x$** | 0 | 1 | 2 | 3 |
|---|---|---|---|---|
| **Probability, $P(x)$** | 0.216 | 0.432 | 0.288 | 0.064 |

**SOLUTION**

If the distribution is a probability distribution, then (1) each probability is between 0 and 1, inclusive, and (2) the sum of all the probabilities equals 1.

1. Each probability is between 0 and 1.
2. $\Sigma P(x) = 0.216 + 0.432 + 0.288 + 0.064$
   $= 1.$

***Interpretation*** Because both conditions are met, the distribution is a probability distribution.

**TRY IT YOURSELF 3**

Verify that the distribution you constructed in Try It Yourself 2 is a probability distribution.

*Answer: Page A38*

### Picturing the World

A survey was conducted to determine how many credit cards people have. The results are shown in the histogram. (Adapted from YouGov Plc)

**How Many Credit Cards Do You Have?**

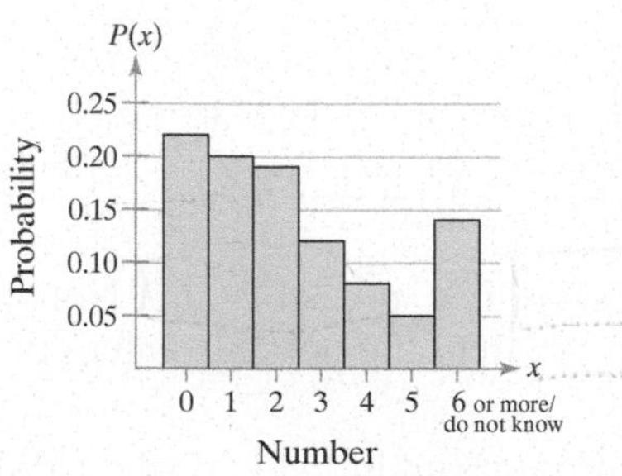


**Estimate the probability that a randomly selected person has two or three credit cards.**

## EXAMPLE 4

### Identifying Probability Distributions

Determine whether each distribution is a probability distribution. Explain your reasoning.

**1.**

| $x$ | 5 | 6 | 7 | 8 |
|---|---|---|---|---|
| $P(x)$ | 0.28 | 0.21 | 0.43 | 0.15 |

**2.**

| $x$ | 1 | 2 | 3 | 4 |
|---|---|---|---|---|
| $P(x)$ | $\frac{1}{2}$ | $\frac{1}{4}$ | $\frac{5}{4}$ | $-1$ |

**SOLUTION**

1. Each probability is between 0 and 1, but the sum of all the probabilities is 1.07, which is greater than 1. The sum of all the probabilities in a probability distribution always equals 1. So, this distribution is *not* a probability distribution.
2. The sum of all the probabilities is equal to 1, but $P(3)$ and $P(4)$ are not between 0 and 1. Probabilities can never be negative or greater than 1. So, this distribution is *not* a probability distribution.

**TRY IT YOURSELF 4**

Determine whether each distribution is a probability distribution. Explain your reasoning.

**1.**

| $x$ | 5 | 6 | 7 | 8 |
|---|---|---|---|---|
| $P(x)$ | $\frac{1}{16}$ | $\frac{5}{8}$ | $\frac{1}{4}$ | $\frac{1}{16}$ |

**2.**

| $x$ | 1 | 2 | 3 | 4 |
|---|---|---|---|---|
| $P(x)$ | 0.09 | 0.36 | 0.49 | 0.10 |

*Answer: Page A38*

## Mean, Variance, and Standard Deviation

You can measure the center of a probability distribution with its mean and measure the variability with its variance and standard deviation. The mean of a discrete random variable is defined as follows.

### Mean of a Discrete Random Variable

The **mean** of a discrete random variable is given by

$$\mu = \Sigma x P(x).$$

Each value of $x$ is multiplied by its corresponding probability and the products are added.

The mean of a random variable represents the "theoretical average" of a probability experiment and sometimes is not a possible outcome. If the experiment were performed many thousands of times, then the mean of all the outcomes would be close to the mean of the random variable.

### EXAMPLE 5

#### Finding the Mean of a Probability Distribution

The probability distribution for the personality inventory test for passive-aggressive traits discussed in Example 2 is shown below. Find the mean score.

| **Score, $x$** | 1 | 2 | 3 | 4 | 5 |
|---|---|---|---|---|---|
| **Probability, $P(x)$** | 0.16 | 0.22 | 0.28 | 0.20 | 0.14 |

**SOLUTION**

Use a table to organize your work, as shown below.

| $x$ | $P(x)$ | $xP(x)$ |
|---|---|---|
| 1 | 0.16 | $1(0.16) = 0.16$ |
| 2 | 0.22 | $2(0.22) = 0.44$ |
| 3 | 0.28 | $3(0.28) = 0.84$ |
| 4 | 0.20 | $4(0.20) = 0.80$ |
| 5 | 0.14 | $5(0.14) = 0.70$ |
| | $\Sigma P(x) = 1$ | $\Sigma xP(x) = 2.94 \approx 2.9$ ← Mean |

From the table, you can see that the mean score is $\mu = 2.94 \approx 2.9$. Note that the mean is rounded to one more decimal place than the possible values of the random variable $x$.

***Interpretation*** Recall that a score of 3 represents an individual who exhibits neither passive nor aggressive traits and the mean is slightly less than 3. So, the mean personality trait is neither extremely passive nor extremely aggressive, but is slightly closer to passive.

**Study Tip**

The mean in Example 5 was rounded to one decimal place because the mean of a probability distribution should be rounded to one more decimal place than was used for the random variable $x$. This *round-off rule* is also used for the variance and standard deviation of a probability distribution.

**TRY IT YOURSELF 5**

Find the mean of the probability distribution you constructed in Try It Yourself 2. What can you conclude?

*Answer: Page A38*

Although the mean of the random variable of a probability distribution describes a typical outcome, it gives no information about how the outcomes vary. To study the variation of the outcomes, you can use the variance and standard deviation of the random variable of a probability distribution.

### Study Tip

An alternative formula for the variance of a probability distribution is

$$\sigma^2 = \left[\Sigma x^2 P(x)\right] - \mu^2.$$

### Variance and Standard Deviation of a Discrete Random Variable

The **variance** of a discrete random variable is

$$\sigma^2 = \Sigma(x - \mu)^2 P(x).$$

The **standard deviation** is

$$\sigma = \sqrt{\sigma^2} = \sqrt{\Sigma(x - \mu)^2 P(x)}.$$

## EXAMPLE 6

### Finding the Variance and Standard Deviation

The probability distribution for the personality inventory test for passive-aggressive traits discussed in Example 2 is shown below. Find the variance and standard deviation of the probability distribution.

| **Score, $x$** | 1 | 2 | 3 | 4 | 5 |
|---|---|---|---|---|---|
| **Probability, $P(x)$** | 0.16 | 0.22 | 0.28 | 0.20 | 0.14 |

**SOLUTION**

To find the variance and standard deviation, note that from Example 5 the mean of the distribution before rounding is $\mu = 2.94$. (Use this value to avoid rounding until the last calculation.) Use a table to organize your work, as shown below.

| $x$ | $P(x)$ | $x - \mu$ | $(x - \mu)^2$ | $(x - \mu)^2 P(x)$ |
|---|---|---|---|---|
| 1 | 0.16 | −1.94 | 3.7636 | 0.602176 |
| 2 | 0.22 | −0.94 | 0.8836 | 0.194392 |
| 3 | 0.28 | 0.06 | 0.0036 | 0.001008 |
| 4 | 0.20 | 1.06 | 1.1236 | 0.224720 |
| 5 | 0.14 | 2.06 | 4.2436 | 0.594104 |
| | $\Sigma P(x) = 1$ | | | $\Sigma(x - \mu)^2 P(x) = 1.6164$ |

Variance

So, the variance is

$$\sigma^2 = 1.6164 \approx 1.6$$

and the standard deviation is

$$\sigma = \sqrt{\sigma^2} = \sqrt{1.6164} \approx 1.3.$$

***Interpretation*** "Usual" data values will be within $2(1.3) = 2.6$ of the mean.

**TRY IT YOURSELF 6**

Find the variance and standard deviation of the probability distribution constructed in Try It Yourself 2.

*Answer: Page A38*

### Tech Tip

You can use technology such as Minitab, Excel, StatCrunch, or the TI-84 Plus to find the mean and standard deviation of a discrete random variable. For instance, to find the mean and standard deviation of the discrete random variable in Example 6 on a TI-84 Plus, enter the possible values of the discrete random variable $x$ in L1. Next, enter the probabilities $P(x)$ in L2. Then, use the *1-Var Stats* feature with L1 as the list and L2 as the frequency list to calculate the mean and standard deviation (and other statistics), as shown below.

**TI-84 PLUS**

```
1-Var Stats
x̄=2.94
Σx=2.94
Σx²=10.26
Sx=
σx=1.271377206
↓n=1
```

## Expected Value

The mean of a random variable represents what you would expect to happen over thousands of trials. It is also called the **expected value.**

**DEFINITION**

The **expected value** of a discrete random variable is equal to the mean of the random variable.

$$\text{Expected Value} = E(x) = \mu = \Sigma xP(x)$$

In most applications, an expected value of 0 has a practical interpretation. For instance, in games of chance, an expected value of 0 implies that a game is fair (an unlikely occurrence). In a profit-and-loss analysis, an expected value of 0 represents the break-even point.

Although probabilities can never be negative, the expected value of a random variable can be negative, as shown in the next example.

**EXAMPLE 7**

### Finding an Expected Value

At a raffle, 1500 tickets are sold at \$2 each for four prizes of \$500, \$250, \$150, and \$75. You buy one ticket. Find the expected value and interpret its meaning.

**SOLUTION**

To find the gain for each prize, subtract the price of the ticket from the prize. For instance, your gain for the \$500 prize is

$$\$500 - \$2 = \$498$$

and your gain for the \$250 prize is

$$\$250 - \$2 = \$248.$$

Write a probability distribution for the possible gains (or outcomes). Note that a gain represented by a negative number is a loss.

| **Gain, $x$** | \$498 | \$248 | \$148 | \$73 | −\$2 |
|---|---|---|---|---|---|
| **Probability, $P(x)$** | $\frac{1}{1500}$ | $\frac{1}{1500}$ | $\frac{1}{1500}$ | $\frac{1}{1500}$ | $\frac{1496}{1500}$ |

−\$2 represents a loss of \$2

Then, using the probability distribution, you can find the expected value.

$$\begin{aligned} E(x) &= \Sigma xP(x) \\ &= \$498 \cdot \frac{1}{1500} + \$248 \cdot \frac{1}{1500} + \$148 \cdot \frac{1}{1500} + \$73 \cdot \frac{1}{1500} + (-\$2) \cdot \frac{1496}{1500} \\ &= -\$1.35 \end{aligned}$$

***Interpretation*** Because the expected value is negative, you can expect to lose an average of \$1.35 for each ticket you buy.

**TRY IT YOURSELF 7**

At a raffle, 2000 tickets are sold at \$5 each for five prizes of \$2000, \$1000, \$500, \$250, and \$100. You buy one ticket. Find the expected value and interpret its meaning.

*Answer: Page A38*

# 4.1 EXERCISES

For Extra Help: MyLab® Statistics

## Building Basic Skills and Vocabulary

1. What is a random variable? Give an example of a discrete random variable and a continuous random variable. Justify your answer.
2. What is a discrete probability distribution? What are the two conditions that a discrete probability distribution must satisfy?
3. Is the expected value of the probability distribution of a random variable always one of the possible values of $x$? Explain.
4. What does the mean of a probability distribution represent?

**True or False?** *In Exercises 5–8, determine whether the statement is true or false. If it is false, rewrite it as a true statement.*

5. In most applications, continuous random variables represent counted data, while discrete random variables represent measured data.
6. For a random variable $x$, the word *random* indicates that the value of $x$ is determined by chance.
7. The mean of the random variable of a probability distribution describes how the outcomes vary.
8. The expected value of a random variable can never be negative.

**Graphical Analysis** *In Exercises 9–12, determine whether the graph on the number line represents a discrete random variable or a continuous random variable. Explain your reasoning.*

9. The attendance at concerts for a rock group

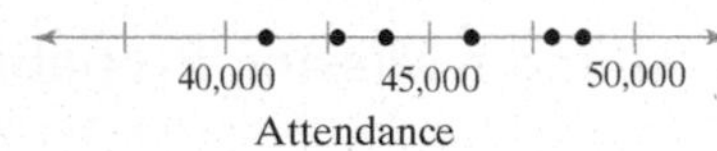


10. The length of time student musicians practice each week

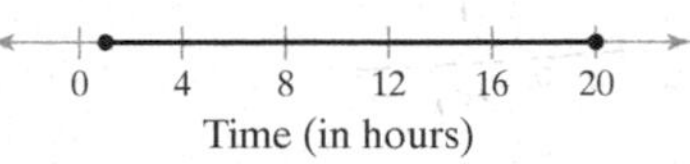


11. The distance a baseball travels after being hit

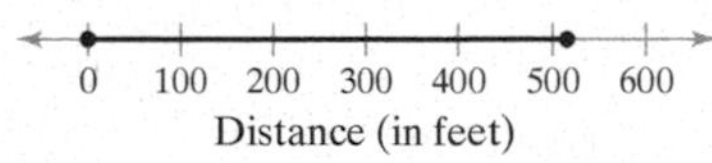


12. The total annual arrests (in millions) in the United States *(Source: U.S. Department of Justice)*

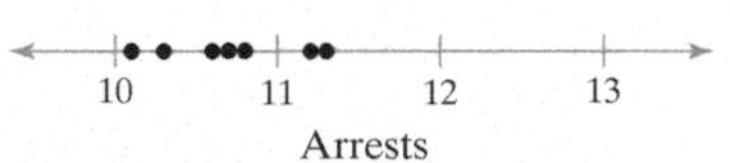


## Using and Interpreting Concepts

**Discrete Variables and Continuous Variables** *In Exercises 13–18, determine whether the random variable x is discrete or continuous. Explain.*

13. Let $x$ represent the number of cars in a university parking lot.
14. Let $x$ represent the length of time it takes to complete an exam.
15. Let $x$ represent the volume of blood drawn for a blood test.
16. Let $x$ represent the populations of the 50 U.S. states.
17. Let $x$ represent the fitted hat sizes of members of a softball team.
18. Let $x$ represent the snowfall (in inches) in Nome, Alaska, last winter.

**Constructing and Graphing Discrete Probability Distributions** *In Exercises 19 and 20, (a) construct a probability distribution, and (b) graph the probability distribution using a histogram and describe its shape.*

**19. Televisions** The number of high-definition (HD) televisions per household in a small town

| Televisions | 0 | 1 | 2 | 3 or more |
|---|---|---|---|---|
| Households | 56 | 511 | 679 | 754 |

**20. Overtime Hours** The number of overtime hours worked in one week per employee

| Overtime hours | 0 | 1 | 2 | 3 | 4 | 5 | 6 |
|---|---|---|---|---|---|---|---|
| Employees | 6 | 12 | 29 | 57 | 42 | 30 | 16 |

**21. Finding Probabilities** Use the probability distribution you made in Exercise 19 to find the probability of randomly selecting a household that has (a) one or two HD televisions, (b) two or more HD televisions, (c) from one to three HD televisions, and (d) at most two HD televisions.

**22. Finding Probabilities** Use the probability distribution you made in Exercise 20 to find the probability of randomly selecting an employee whose overtime is (a) one or two hours, (b) two hours or less, (c) from three to six hours, (d) from one to three hours, and (e) at most four hours.

**23. Unusual Events** In Exercise 19, would it be unusual for a household to have no HD televisions? Explain your reasoning.

**24. Unusual Events** In Exercise 20, would it be unusual for an employee to work two hours of overtime? Explain your reasoning.

**Determining a Missing Probability** *In Exercises 25 and 26, determine the missing probability for the probability distribution.*

**25.**

| $x$ | 0 | 1 | 2 | 3 | 4 |
|---|---|---|---|---|---|
| $P(x)$ | 0.06 | 0.12 | 0.18 | ? | 0.30 |

**26.**

| $x$ | 0 | 1 | 2 | 3 | 4 | 5 | 6 |
|---|---|---|---|---|---|---|---|
| $P(x)$ | 0.05 | ? | 0.23 | 0.21 | 0.17 | 0.11 | 0.08 |

**Identifying Probability Distributions** *In Exercises 27 and 28, determine whether the distribution is a probability distribution. If it is not a probability distribution, explain why.*

**27.**

| $x$ | 0 | 1 | 2 | 3 | 4 |
|---|---|---|---|---|---|
| $P(x)$ | 0.30 | 0.25 | 0.25 | 0.15 | 0.05 |

**28.**

| $x$ | 0 | 1 | 2 | 3 | 4 | 5 |
|---|---|---|---|---|---|---|
| $P(x)$ | $\frac{3}{4}$ | $\frac{1}{10}$ | $\frac{1}{20}$ | $\frac{1}{25}$ | $\frac{1}{50}$ | $\frac{1}{100}$ |

**Finding the Mean, Variance, and Standard Deviation** *In Exercises 29–34, (a) find the mean, variance, and standard deviation of the probability distribution, and (b) interpret the results.*

**29. Dogs** The number of dogs per household in a neighborhood

| Dogs | 0 | 1 | 2 | 3 | 4 | 5 |
|---|---|---|---|---|---|---|
| Probability | 0.686 | 0.195 | 0.077 | 0.022 | 0.013 | 0.007 |

**30. Baseball** The number of games played in each World Series from 1903 through 2020 *(Source: Major League Baseball)*

| Games played | 4 | 5 | 6 | 7 | 8 |
|---|---|---|---|---|---|
| Probability | 0.164 | 0.241 | 0.216 | 0.345 | 0.034 |

**31. Machine Parts** The number of defects per 1000 machine parts inspected

| Defects | 0 | 1 | 2 | 3 | 4 | 5 |
|---|---|---|---|---|---|---|
| Probability | 0.263 | 0.285 | 0.243 | 0.154 | 0.041 | 0.014 |

**32. Extracurricular Activities** The number of school-related extracurricular activities per student

| Activities | 0 | 1 | 2 | 3 | 4 | 5 | 6 | 7 |
|---|---|---|---|---|---|---|---|---|
| Probability | 0.059 | 0.122 | 0.163 | 0.178 | 0.213 | 0.128 | 0.084 | 0.053 |

**33. Hurricanes** The histogram shows the distribution of hurricanes that have hit the U.S. mainland from 1851 through 2019 by Saffir-Simpson category, where 1 is the weakest level and 5 is the strongest level. *(Source: National Oceanic & Atmospheric Administration)*

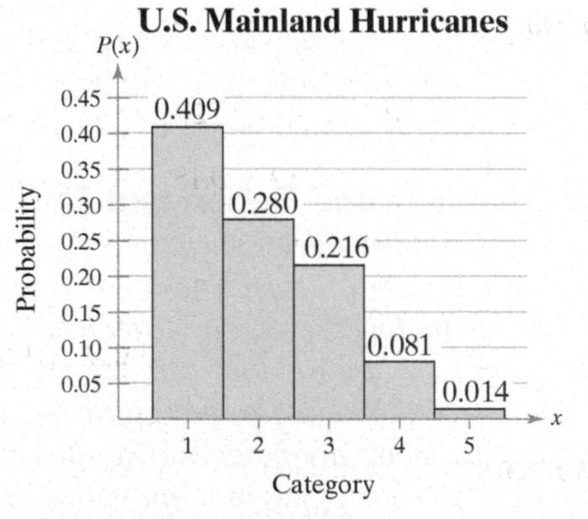


FIGURE FOR EXERCISE 33

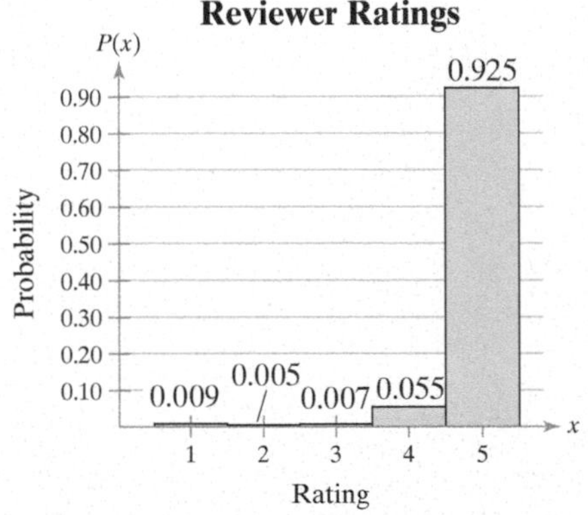


FIGURE FOR EXERCISE 34

**34. Reviewer Ratings** The histogram shows the reviewer ratings on a scale from 1 (lowest) to 5 (highest) of the Sony PlayStation 5. *(Source: Best Buy)*

**35. Writing** The expected value of an accountant's profit-and-loss analysis is 0. Explain what this means.

**36. Writing** In a game of chance, what is the relationship between a "fair bet" and its expected value? Explain.

**Finding an Expected Value** *In Exercises 37 and 38, find the expected value $E(x)$ to the player for one play of the game. If $x$ is the gain to a player in a game of chance, then $E(x)$ is usually negative. This value gives the average amount per game the player can expect to lose.*

**37.** In American roulette, the wheel has the 38 numbers, 00, 0, 1, 2, . . ., 34, 35, and 36, marked on equally spaced slots. If a player bets \$1 on a number and wins, then the player keeps the dollar and receives an additional \$35. Otherwise, the dollar is lost.

**38.** A high school basketball team is selling \$10 raffle tickets as part of a fund-raising program. The first prize is a trip to the Bahamas valued at \$5460, and the second prize is a weekend ski package valued at \$496. The remaining 18 prizes are \$100 gas cards. The number of tickets sold is 3500.

## Extending Concepts

**39. Writing** Find the area of each bar of the histogram you made in Exercise 19. Then find the sum of the areas. Interpret the results.

**40. Baseball** There were 116 World Series from 1903 to 2020. Use the probability distribution in Exercise 30 to find the number of World Series that had 4, 5, 6, 7, and 8 games. Find the population mean, variance, and standard deviation of the data using the traditional definitions. Compare to your answers in Exercise 30.

**Linear Transformation of a Random Variable** *In Exercises 41 and 42, use this information about linear transformations. For a random variable $x$, a new random variable $y$ can be created by applying a* ***linear transformation*** *$y = a + bx$, where $a$ and $b$ are constants. If the random variable $x$ has mean $\mu_x$ and standard deviation $\sigma_x$, then the mean, variance, and standard deviation of $y$ are given by the formulas $\mu_y = a + b\mu_x$, $\sigma_y^2 = b^2\sigma_x^2$, and $\sigma_y = |b|\sigma_x$.*

**41.** The mean annual salary of employees at an office is originally \$46,000. Each employee receives an annual bonus of \$600 and a 3% raise (based on salary). What is the new mean annual salary (including the bonus and raise)?

**42.** The mean annual salary of a firm's employees is \$44,000 with a variance of 18,000,000. What is the standard deviation of the salaries after each employee receives an annual bonus of \$1000 and a 3.5% raise (based on salary)?

**Independent and Dependent Random Variables** *Two random variables $x$ and $y$ are* ***independent*** *when the value of $x$ does not affect the value of $y$. When the variables are not independent, they are* ***dependent.*** *A new random variable can be formed by finding the sum or difference of random variables. If a random variable $x$ has mean $\mu_x$ and a random variable $y$ has mean $\mu_y$, then the means of the sum and difference of the variables are given by $\mu_{x+y} = \mu_x + \mu_y$ and $\mu_{x-y} = \mu_x - \mu_y$. If random variables are independent, then the variance and standard deviation of the sum or difference of the random variables can be found. So, if a random variable $x$ has variance $\sigma_x^2$ and a random variable $y$ has variance $\sigma_y^2$, then the variances of the sum and difference of the variables are given by $\sigma_{x+y}^2 = \sigma_x^2 + \sigma_y^2$ and $\sigma_{x-y}^2 = \sigma_x^2 + \sigma_y^2$.*

*In Exercises 43 and 44, the distribution of SAT mathematics scores for college-bound male seniors in 2020 has a mean of 531 and a standard deviation of 121. The distribution of SAT mathematics scores for college-bound female seniors in 2020 has a mean of 516 and a standard deviation of 112. One male and one female are randomly selected. Assume their scores are independent.* (Adapted from College Board)

**43.** Find the mean and standard deviation of the sum of their scores.

**44.** Find the mean and standard deviation of the difference of their scores. Compare to your answers in Exercise 43.

# 4.2 Binomial Distributions

## What You Should Learn

- How to determine whether a probability experiment is a binomial experiment
- How to find binomial probabilities using the binomial probability formula
- How to find binomial probabilities using technology, formulas, and a binomial probability table
- How to construct and graph a binomial distribution
- How to find the mean, variance, and standard deviation of a binomial probability distribution

Binomial Experiments ■ Binomial Probability Formula ■ Finding Binomial Probabilities ■ Graphing Binomial Distributions ■ Mean, Variance, and Standard Deviation

## Binomial Experiments

There are many probability experiments for which the results of each trial can be reduced to two outcomes: success and failure. For instance, when a basketball player attempts a free throw, the player either makes the basket or does not. Probability experiments such as these are called **binomial experiments.**

### DEFINITION

A **binomial experiment** is a probability experiment that satisfies these conditions.

1. The experiment has a fixed number of trials, where each trial is independent of the other trials.
2. There are only two possible outcomes of interest for each trial. Each outcome can be classified as a success (S) or as a failure (F).
3. The probability of a success is the same for each trial.
4. The random variable $x$ counts the number of successful trials.

### Notation for Binomial Experiments

| Symbol | Description |
|---|---|
| $n$ | The number of trials |
| $p$ | The probability of success in a single trial |
| $q$ | The probability of failure in a single trial $(q = 1 - p)$ |
| $x$ | The random variable represents a count of the number of successes in $n$ trials: $x = 0, 1, 2, 3, \ldots, n$. |

In a binomial experiment, success does not imply something good occurred. For instance, in an experiment a survey asks 1012 people about identity theft. A success is a person who was a victim of identity theft.

Here is an example of a binomial experiment. From a standard deck of cards, you pick a card, note whether it is a club or not, and replace the card. You repeat the experiment five times, so $n = 5$. The outcomes of each trial can be classified in two categories: S = selecting a club and F = selecting another suit. The probabilities of success and failure are

$$p = \frac{1}{4} \quad \text{and} \quad q = 1 - \frac{1}{4} = \frac{3}{4}.$$

The random variable $x$ represents the number of clubs selected in the five trials. So, the possible values of the random variable are $x = 0, 1, 2, 3, 4, 5$. For instance, if $x = 2$, then exactly two of the five cards are clubs and the other three are not clubs. An example of an experiment with $x = 2$ is shown at the left. Note that $x$ is a discrete random variable because its possible values can be counted.

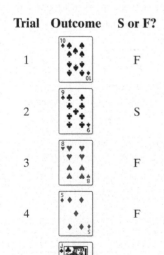

| Trial | Outcome | S or F? |
|---|---|---|
| 1 | 10 of spades | F |
| 2 | 9 of clubs | S |
| 3 | 8 of hearts | F |
| 4 | 5 of diamonds | F |
| 5 | Jack of clubs | S |

There are two successful outcomes. So, $x = 2$.

## Picturing the World

A survey of 2647 U.S. parents of a child age 11 and under was conducted to study the ways in which children use social media. One of the questions from the survey and the responses (either yes or no) are shown below. (Adapted from Pew Research Center)

**Survey question**: As far as you know, does this child ever watch videos on YouTube?

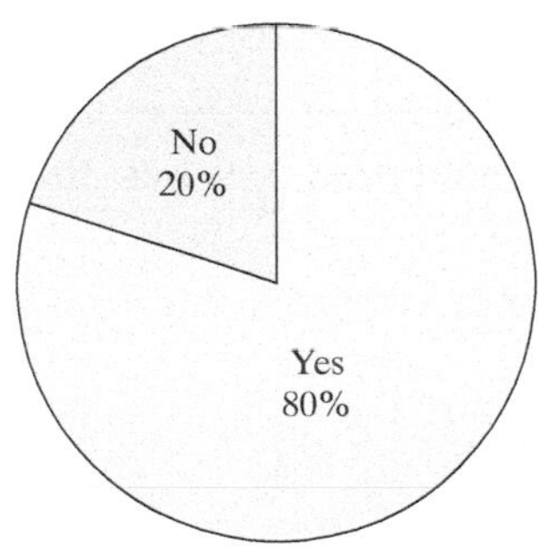


**Why is this a binomial experiment? Identify the probability of success *p*. Identify the probability of failure *q*.**

**EXAMPLE 1**

### Identifying and Understanding Binomial Experiments

Determine whether each experiment is a binomial experiment. If it is, specify the values of $n$, $p$, and $q$, and list the possible values of the random variable $x$. If it is not, explain why.

1. A certain surgical procedure has an 85% chance of success. A doctor performs the procedure on eight patients. The random variable represents the number of successful surgeries.
2. A jar contains five red marbles, nine blue marbles, and six green marbles. You randomly select three marbles from the jar, *without replacement.* The random variable represents the number of red marbles.

**SOLUTION**

1. The experiment is a binomial experiment because it satisfies the four conditions of a binomial experiment. In the experiment, each surgery represents one trial. There are eight surgeries, and each surgery is independent of the others. There are only two possible outcomes for each surgery—either the surgery is a success or it is a failure. Also, the probability of success for each surgery is 0.85. Finally, the random variable $x$ represents the number of successful surgeries.

   $n = 8$ Number of trials

   $p = 0.85$ Probability of success

   $q = 1 - 0.85$

   $= 0.15$ Probability of failure

   $x = 0, 1, 2, 3, 4, 5, 6, 7, 8$ Possible values of $x$

2. The experiment is not a binomial experiment because it does not satisfy all four conditions of a binomial experiment. In the experiment, each marble selection represents one trial, and selecting a red marble is a success. When the first marble is selected, the probability of success is 5/20. However, because the marble is not replaced, the probability of success for subsequent trials is no longer 5/20. So, the trials are not independent, and the probability of a success is not the same for each trial.

**TRY IT YOURSELF 1**

Determine whether the experiment is a binomial experiment. If it is, specify the values of $n$, $p$, and $q$, and list the possible values of the random variable $x$. If it is not, explain why.

A multiple-choice quiz consists of 10 questions. Each question has four possible answers, only one of which is correct. To complete the quiz, a student who did not study randomly guesses the answer to each question. The random variable represents the number of correct answers.

*Answer: Page A38*

For a random sample collected without replacement, such as in a survey, the events are dependent. However, you can treat this situation as a binomial experiment by treating the events as independent when the sample size is no more than 5% of the population. That is, $n \leq 0.05N$.

## Binomial Probability Formula

There are several ways to find the probability of $x$ successes in $n$ trials of a binomial experiment. One way is to use a tree diagram and the Multiplication Rule. Another way is to use the **binomial probability formula.**

### Study Tip

In the binomial probability formula, ${}_nC_x$ determines the number of ways of getting $x$ successes in $n$ trials, regardless of order.

$${}_nC_x = \frac{n!}{(n-x)!x!}$$

### Binomial Probability Formula

In a binomial experiment, the probability of exactly $x$ successes in $n$ trials is

$$P(x) = {}_nC_x p^x q^{n-x} = \frac{n!}{(n-x)!\,x!}p^x q^{n-x}.$$

Note that the number of failures is $n - x$.

## EXAMPLE 2

### Finding a Binomial Probability

Rotator cuff surgery has a 90% chance of success. The surgery is performed on three patients. Find the probability of the surgery being successful on exactly two patients. *(Source: The Orthopedic Center of St. Louis)*

### SOLUTION

**Method 1:** Draw a tree diagram and use the Multiplication Rule.

| 1st Surgery | 2nd Surgery | 3rd Surgery | Outcome | Number of Successes | Probability |
|---|---|---|---|---|---|
| S | S | S | SSS | 3 | $\frac{9}{10}\cdot\frac{9}{10}\cdot\frac{9}{10}=\frac{729}{1000}$ |
| S | S | F | SSF | 2 | $\frac{9}{10}\cdot\frac{9}{10}\cdot\frac{1}{10}=\frac{81}{1000}$ |
| S | F | S | SFS | 2 | $\frac{9}{10}\cdot\frac{1}{10}\cdot\frac{9}{10}=\frac{81}{1000}$ |
| S | F | F | SFF | 1 | $\frac{9}{10}\cdot\frac{1}{10}\cdot\frac{1}{10}=\frac{9}{1000}$ |
| F | S | S | FSS | 2 | $\frac{1}{10}\cdot\frac{9}{10}\cdot\frac{9}{10}=\frac{81}{1000}$ |
| F | S | F | FSF | 1 | $\frac{1}{10}\cdot\frac{9}{10}\cdot\frac{1}{10}=\frac{9}{1000}$ |
| F | F | S | FFS | 1 | $\frac{1}{10}\cdot\frac{1}{10}\cdot\frac{9}{10}=\frac{9}{1000}$ |
| F | F | F | FFF | 0 | $\frac{1}{10}\cdot\frac{1}{10}\cdot\frac{1}{10}=\frac{1}{1000}$ |

There are three outcomes that have exactly two successes, and each has a probability of $\frac{81}{1000}$. So, the probability of a successful surgery on exactly two patients is $3\left(\frac{81}{1000}\right) = 0.243$.

### Study Tip

Recall that $n!$ is read "$n$ factorial" and represents the product of all integers from $n$ to 1. For instance,

$$5! = 5\cdot4\cdot3\cdot2\cdot1 = 120.$$

**Method 2:** Use the binomial probability formula.

In this binomial experiment, the values of $n$, $p$, $q$, and $x$ are

$$n = 3, \quad p = \frac{9}{10}, \quad q = \frac{1}{10}, \quad \text{and} \quad x = 2.$$

The probability of exactly two successful surgeries is

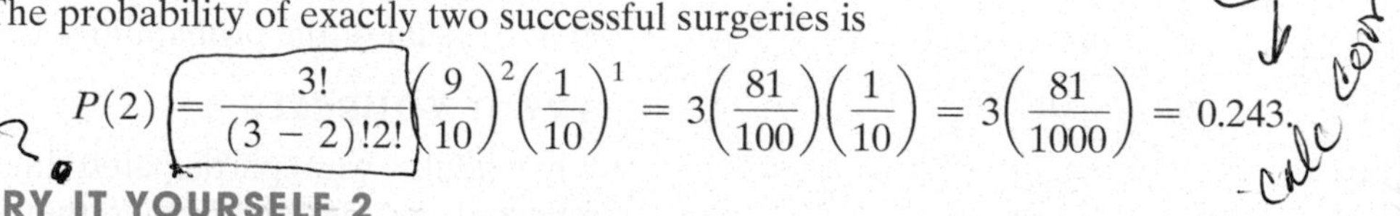

$$P(2) = \frac{3!}{(3-2)!2!}\left(\frac{9}{10}\right)^2\left(\frac{1}{10}\right)^1 = 3\left(\frac{81}{100}\right)\left(\frac{1}{10}\right) = 3\left(\frac{81}{1000}\right) = 0.243.$$

### TRY IT YOURSELF 2

A card is selected from a standard deck and replaced. This experiment is repeated a total of five times. Find the probability of selecting exactly three clubs.

*Answer: Page A38*

By listing the possible values of $x$ with the corresponding probabilities, you can construct a **binomial probability distribution.**

## EXAMPLE 3

### Constructing a Binomial Distribution

In a survey, U.S. adults were asked how often they go online. The results are shown in the figure. Six adults who participated in the survey are randomly selected and asked whether they go online several times a day. Construct a binomial probability distribution for the number who respond that they go online several times a day. *(Source: Pew Research Center)*

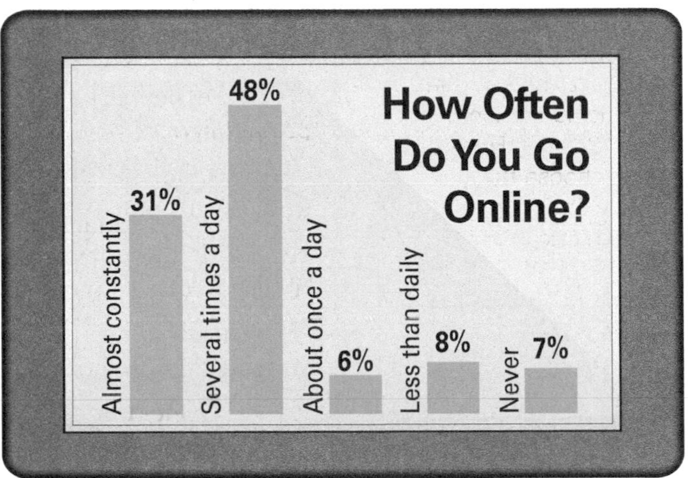


### SOLUTION

From the figure, you can see that 48% of adults go online several times a day. So, $p = 0.48$ and $q = 0.52$.

Because $n - 6$, the possible values of $x$ are 0, 1, 2, 3, 4, 5, and 6. The probabilities of each value of $x$ are

$$P(0) = {}_6C_0(0.48)^0(0.52)^6 = 1(0.48)^0(0.52)^6 \approx 0.020$$

$$P(1) = {}_6C_1(0.48)^1(0.52)^5 = 6(0.48)^1(0.52)^5 \approx 0.109$$

$$P(2) = {}_6C_2(0.48)^2(0.52)^4 = 15(0.48)^2(0.52)^4 \approx 0.253$$

$$P(3) = {}_6C_3(0.48)^3(0.52)^3 = 20(0.48)^3(0.52)^3 \approx 0.311$$

$$P(4) = {}_6C_4(0.48)^4(0.52)^2 = 15(0.48)^4(0.52)^2 \approx 0.215$$

$$P(5) = {}_6C_5(0.48)^5(0.52)^1 = 6(0.48)^5(0.52)^1 \approx 0.079$$

and

$$P(6) = {}_6C_6(0.48)^6(0.52)^0 = 1(0.48)^6(0.52)^0 \approx 0.012.$$

Notice in the table at the left that all the probabilities are between 0 and 1 and that the sum of the probabilities is about 1.

**Study Tip**

When probabilities are rounded to a fixed number of decimal places, the sum of the probabilities may differ slightly from 1.

| $x$ | $P(x)$ |
|---|---|
| 0 | 0.020 |
| 1 | 0.109 |
| 2 | 0.253 |
| 3 | 0.311 |
| 4 | 0.215 |
| 5 | 0.079 |
| 6 | 0.012 |
| | $\Sigma P(x) = 0.999$ |

### TRY IT YOURSELF 3

Five adults who participated in the survey in Example 3 are randomly selected and asked whether they go online almost constantly. Construct a binomial distribution for the number who respond that they go online almost constantly.

*Answer: Page A38*

## Finding Binomial Probabilities

In Examples 2 and 3, you used the binomial probability formula to find the probabilities. A more efficient way to find binomial probabilities is to use technology. For instance, you can find binomial probabilities using Minitab, Excel, StatCrunch, and the TI-84 Plus.

**Tech Tip**

You can use technology such as Minitab, Excel, StatCrunch, or the TI-84 Plus to find a binomial probability. For instance, here are instructions for finding a binomial probability on a TI-84 Plus. From the DISTR menu, choose the *binompdf(* feature. Enter the values of *n*, *p*, and *x*. Then calculate the probability.

**EXAMPLE 4**

### Finding a Binomial Probability Using Technology

A survey found that 75% of U.S. adults are experiencing digital device fatigue. (This is the state of mental exhaustion caused by concurrent and excessive use of digital devices such as smartphones and tablet computers.) You randomly select 100 adults. What is the probability that exactly 66 are experiencing digital device fatigue? Use technology to find the probability. *(Source: The Harris Poll)*

**SOLUTION**

Minitab, Excel, StatCrunch, and the TI-84 Plus each have features that allow you to find binomial probabilities. Use such technologies to obtain results similar to these displays.

**MINITAB**

**Probability Density Function**

Binomial with n = 100 and p = 0.75

| x | P(X = x) |
|---|---|
| 66 | 0.0111678 |

**STATCRUNCH**

**Binomial Calculator**

n:100 p:0.75

P(X = 66) = 0.01116782

**TI-84 PLUS**

binompdf(100, .75, 66)

.0111678235

**EXCEL**

| | A |
|---|---|
| 1 | 0.011167823 |

←=BINOM.DIST(66,100,0.75,FALSE)

*Interpretation* From these displays, you can see that the probability that exactly 66 adults are experiencing digital device fatigue is about 0.011. Because 0.011 is less than 0.05, this can be considered an unusual event.

**Study Tip**

Recall that a probability of 0.05 or less is considered unusual.

**TRY IT YOURSELF 4**

A survey found that 28% of U.S. employees will work from home full-time over the next few months. You randomly select 150 adults. What is the probability that exactly 30 will work from home full-time over the next few months? Use technology to find the probability. *(Source: The Harris Poll)*

*Answer: Page A38*

## EXAMPLE 5

### Finding Binomial Probabilities Using Formulas

A survey found that 22% of U.S. adults say that the economy, unemployment, and jobs are the most important problems facing the U.S. today. You randomly select four adults and ask them whether the economy, unemployment, and jobs are the most important problems facing the U.S. today. Find the probability that (1) exactly two of them respond yes, (2) at least two of them respond yes, and (3) fewer than two of them respond yes. *(Source: Ipsos)*

**SOLUTION**

1. Using $n = 4$, $p = 0.22$, $q = 0.78$, and $x = 2$, the probability that exactly two adults will respond yes is

$$P(2) = {}_4C_2(0.22)^2(0.78)^2 = 6(0.22)^2(0.78)^2 = 0.177.$$

2. To find the probability that at least two adults will respond yes, find the sum of $P(2)$, $P(3)$, and $P(4)$. Begin by using the binomial probability formula to write an expression for each probability.

$$P(2) = {}_4C_2(0.22)^2(0.78)^2 = 6(0.22)^2(0.78)^2$$
$$P(3) = {}_4C_3(0.22)^3(0.78)^1 = 4(0.22)^3(0.78)^1$$
$$P(4) = {}_4C_4(0.22)^4(0.78)^0 = 1(0.22)^4(0.78)^0$$

So, the probability that at least two will respond yes is

$$P(x \geq 2) = P(2) + P(3) + P(4) = 6(0.22)^2(0.78)^2 + 4(0.22)^3(0.78)^1 + (0.22)^4(0.78)^0 \approx 0.212.$$

3. To find the probability that fewer than two adults will respond yes, find the sum of $P(0)$ and $P(1)$. Begin by using the binomial probability formula to write an expression for each probability.

$$P(0) = {}_4C_0(0.22)^0(0.78)^4 = 1(0.22)^0(0.78)^4$$
$$P(1) = {}_4C_1(0.22)^1(0.78)^3 = 4(0.22)^1(0.78)^3$$

So, the probability that fewer than two will respond yes is

$$P(x < 2) = P(0) + P(1) = (0.22)^0(0.78)^4 + 4(0.22)^1(0.78)^3 \approx 0.788.$$

For help with translating verbal phrases, see *Integrated Review* at

**MyLab Statistics**

### Study Tip

The complement of "$x$ is at least 2" is "$x$ is less than 2." So, another way to find the probability in part 3 of Example 5 is

$$P(x < 2) = 1 - P(x \geq 2) \approx 1 - 0.212 = 0.788.$$

**TRY IT YOURSELF 5**

The survey in Example 5 found that 16% of U.S. adults say that public health, disease, and illness are the most important problems facing the U.S. today. You randomly select five adults and ask them whether public health, disease, and illness are the most important problems facing the U.S. today. Find the probability that (1) exactly two of them respond yes, (2) at least two of them respond yes, and (3) fewer than two of them respond yes. *(Source: Ipsos)*

*Answer: Page A38*

**TI-84 PLUS**

```
binompdf(4, 0.22, 2)
                .17667936
binomcdf(4, 0.22, 1)
                .78775632
```

You can use technology to check your answers. For instance, the TI-84 Plus screen at the left shows how to check parts 1 and 3 of Example 5. Note that the second entry uses the *binomial CDF* feature. A cumulative distribution function (CDF) computes the probability of "$x$ or fewer" successes by adding the areas for the given $x$-value and all those to its left.

Finding binomial probabilities with the binomial probability formula can be a tedious process. To make this process easier, you can use a binomial probability table. Table 2 in Appendix B lists the binomial probabilities for selected values of $n$ and $p$.

## EXAMPLE 6

### Finding a Binomial Probability Using a Table

About 5% of employees (ages 16 years and older) in the United States commute to their jobs by using public transportation (excluding taxicabs). You randomly select eight workers. What is the probability that exactly three of them use public transportation to get to work? Use a table to find the probability. *(Source: American Community Survey)*

**SOLUTION**

A portion of Table 2 in Appendix B is shown here. Using the distribution for $n = 8$ and $p = 0.05$, you can find the probability that $x = 3$, as shown by the highlighted areas in the table.

| | | *p* | | | | | | | | | | | | |
|---|---|---|---|---|---|---|---|---|---|---|---|---|---|---|
| *n* | *x* | .01 | .05 | .10 | .15 | .20 | .25 | .30 | .35 | .40 | .45 | .50 | .55 | .60 |
| 2 | 0 | .980 | .902 | .810 | .723 | .640 | .563 | .490 | .423 | .360 | .303 | .250 | .203 | .160 |
| | 1 | .020 | .095 | .180 | .255 | .320 | .375 | .420 | .455 | .480 | .495 | .500 | .495 | .480 |
| | 2 | .000 | .002 | .010 | .023 | .040 | .063 | .090 | .123 | .160 | .203 | .250 | .303 | .360 |
| 3 | 0 | .970 | .857 | .729 | .614 | .512 | .422 | .343 | .275 | .216 | .166 | .125 | .091 | .064 |
| | 1 | .029 | .135 | .243 | .325 | .384 | .422 | .441 | .444 | .432 | .408 | .375 | .334 | .288 |
| | 2 | .000 | .007 | .027 | .057 | .096 | .141 | .189 | .239 | .288 | .334 | .375 | .408 | .432 |
| | 3 | .000 | .000 | .001 | .003 | .008 | .016 | .027 | .043 | .064 | .091 | .125 | .166 | .216 |
| 8 | 0 | .923 | .663 | .430 | .272 | .168 | .100 | .058 | .032 | .017 | .008 | .004 | .002 | .001 |
| | 1 | .075 | .279 | .383 | .385 | .336 | .267 | .198 | .137 | .090 | .055 | .031 | .016 | .008 |
| | 2 | .003 | .051 | .149 | .238 | .294 | .311 | .296 | .259 | .209 | .157 | .109 | .070 | .041 |
| | 3 | .000 | .005 | .033 | .084 | .147 | .208 | .254 | .279 | .279 | .257 | .219 | .172 | .124 |
| | 4 | .000 | .000 | .005 | .018 | .046 | .087 | .136 | .188 | .232 | .263 | .273 | .263 | .232 |
| | 5 | .000 | .000 | .000 | .003 | .009 | .023 | .047 | .081 | .124 | .172 | .219 | .257 | .279 |
| | 6 | .000 | .000 | .000 | .000 | .001 | .004 | .010 | .022 | .041 | .070 | .109 | .157 | .209 |
| | 7 | .000 | .000 | .000 | .000 | .000 | .000 | .001 | .003 | .008 | .016 | .031 | .055 | .090 |
| | 8 | .000 | .000 | .000 | .000 | .000 | .000 | .000 | .000 | .001 | .002 | .004 | .008 | .017 |

According to the table, the probability is 0.005. You can check this result using technology. As shown at the right using Minitab, the probability is 0.0054165. After rounding to three decimal places, the probability is 0.005, which is the same value found using the table.

**MINITAB**

**Probability Density Function**

Binomial with n = 8 and p = 0.05

| x | P(X = x) |
|---|---|
| 3 | 0.0054165 |

4.2 To explore this topic further, see **Activity 4.2** on page 214.

***Interpretation*** So, the probability that exactly three of the eight employees use public transportation to get to work is 0.005. Because 0.005 is less than 0.05, this can be considered an unusual event.

**TRY IT YOURSELF 6**

About 85% of employees (ages 16 years and older) in the United States commute to their jobs by driving a car, truck, or van. You randomly select six workers. What is the probability that exactly four of them drive a car, truck, or van to work? Use a table to find the probability. *(Source: American Community Survey)*

*Answer: Page A38*

## Graphing Binomial Distributions

In Section 4.1, you learned how to graph discrete probability distributions. Because a binomial distribution is a discrete probability distribution, you can use the same process.

**EXAMPLE 7**

### Graphing a Binomial Distribution

Sixty-four percent of people who have survived cancer are 65 years of age or older. You randomly select six people who have survived cancer and ask them whether they are 65 years of age or older. Construct a probability distribution for the random variable $x$. Then graph the distribution. *(Source: American Cancer Society)*

**SOLUTION**

To construct the binomial distribution, find the probability for each value of $x$. Using $n = 6$, $p = 0.64$, and $q = 0.36$, you can obtain the following.

| $x$ | 0 | 1 | 2 | 3 | 4 | 5 | 6 |
|---|---|---|---|---|---|---|---|
| $P(x)$ | 0.002 | 0.023 | 0.103 | 0.245 | 0.326 | 0.232 | 0.069 |

Notice in the table that all the probabilities are between 0 and 1 and that the sum of the probabilities is 1. You can graph the probability distribution using a histogram as shown below.

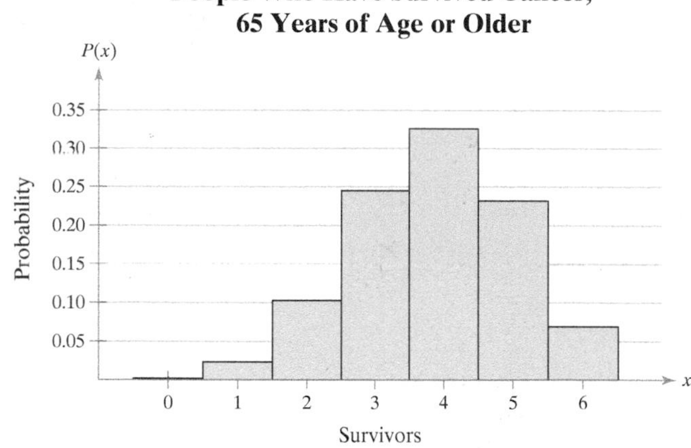


***Interpretation*** From the histogram, you can see that it would be unusual for none or only one of the people to be age 65 years or older because both probabilities are less than 0.05.

**TRY IT YOURSELF 7**

A recent study found that 27% of U.S. adults have not read a book in the past year. You randomly select four adults and ask them whether they have not read a book in the past year. Construct a probability distribution for the random variable $x$. Then graph the distribution. *(Source: Pew Research Center)*

*Answer: Page A39*

Notice in Example 7 that the histogram is skewed left. The graph of a binomial distribution with $p > 0.5$ is skewed left, whereas the graph of a binomial distribution with $p < 0.5$ is skewed right. The graph of a binomial distribution with $p = 0.5$ is symmetric.

## Mean, Variance, and Standard Deviation

Although you can use the formulas you learned in Section 4.1 for mean, variance, and standard deviation of a discrete probability distribution, the properties of a binomial distribution enable you to use much simpler formulas.

### Population Parameters of a Binomial Distribution

Mean: $\mu = np$

Variance: $\sigma^2 = npq$

Standard deviation: $\sigma = \sqrt{npq}$

### EXAMPLE 8

#### Finding and Interpreting Mean, Variance, and Standard Deviation

In Pittsburgh, Pennsylvania, about 56% of the days in a year are cloudy. Find the mean, variance, and standard deviation for the number of cloudy days during the month of June. Interpret the results and determine any unusual values. *(Source: National Oceanic and Atmospheric Administration)*

**SOLUTION**

There are 30 days in June. Using $n = 30$, $p = 0.56$, and $q = 0.44$, you can find the mean, variance, and standard deviation as shown below.

$$\begin{aligned}\mu &= np\\ &= 30 \cdot 0.56\\ &= 16.8 && \text{Mean}\end{aligned}$$

$$\begin{aligned}\sigma^2 &= npq\\ &= 30 \cdot 0.56 \cdot 0.44\\ &\approx 7.4 && \text{Variance}\end{aligned}$$

$$\begin{aligned}\sigma &= \sqrt{npq}\\ &= \sqrt{30 \cdot 0.56 \cdot 0.44}\\ &\approx 2.7 && \text{Standard deviation}\end{aligned}$$

Mean

***Interpretation*** On average, there are 16.8 cloudy days during the month of June. The standard deviation is about 2.7 days. Values that are more than two standard deviations from the mean are considered unusual. Because

$$16.8 - 2(2.7) = 11.4$$

a June with 11 cloudy days or less would be unusual. Similarly, because

$$16.8 + 2(2.7) = 22.2$$

a June with 23 cloudy days or more would also be unusual.

**TRY IT YOURSELF 8**

In San Francisco, California, about 44% of the days in a year are clear. Find the mean, variance, and standard deviation for the number of clear days during the month of May. Interpret the results and determine any unusual events. *(Source: National Oceanic and Atmospheric Administration)*

*Answer: Page A39*

# 4.2 EXERCISES

For Extra Help: MyLab Statistics

## Building Basic Skills and Vocabulary

**1.** In a binomial experiment, what does it mean to say that each trial is independent of the other trials?

**2.** In a binomial experiment with $n$ trials, what does the random variable measure?

**Graphical Analysis** *In Exercises 3–5, the histogram represents a binomial distribution with five trials. Match the histogram with the appropriate probability of success p. Explain your reasoning.*

(a) $p = 0.25$ (b) $p = 0.50$ (c) $p = 0.75$

**3.**
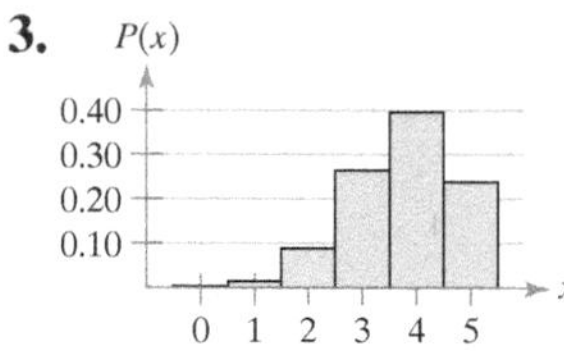


**4.**
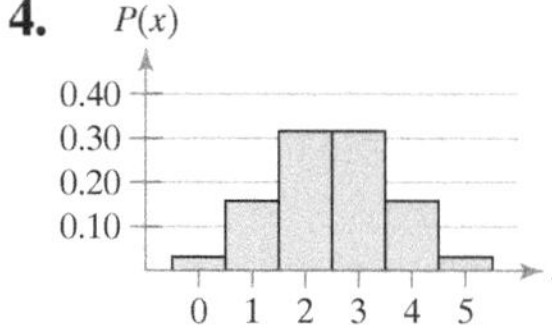


**5.**
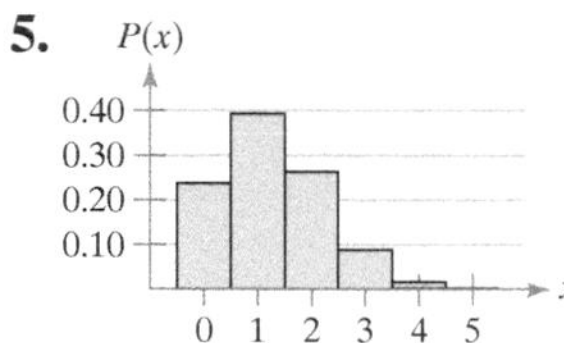


**Graphical Analysis** *In Exercises 6–8, the histogram represents a binomial distribution with probability of success p. Match the histogram with the appropriate number of trials n. Explain your reasoning. What happens as the value of n increases and p remains the same?*

(a) $n = 4$ (b) $n = 8$ (c) $n = 12$

**6.**
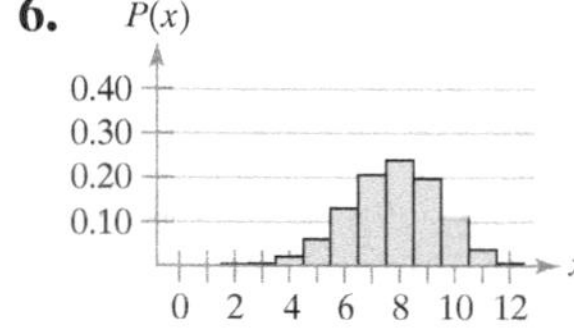


**7.**
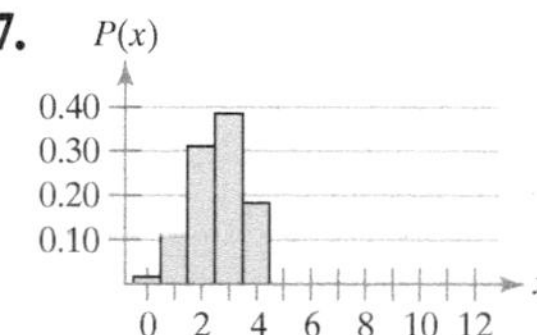


**8.**
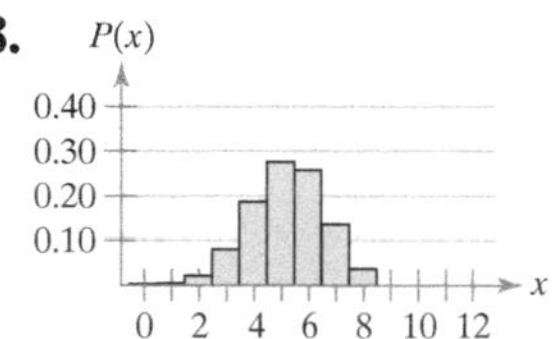


**9.** Which counting rule is used in the binomial probability formula?

**10.** Identify the unusual values of $x$ in each histogram in Exercises 6–8.

**Mean, Variance, and Standard Deviation** *In Exercises 11–14, find the mean, variance, and standard deviation of the binomial distribution with the given values of n and p.*

**11.** $n = 50, p = 0.4$

**12.** $n = 84, p = 0.65$

**13.** $n = 124, p = 0.26$

**14.** $n = 316, p = 0.82$

## Using and Interpreting Concepts

**Identifying and Understanding Binomial Experiments** *In Exercises 15–18, determine whether the experiment is a binomial experiment. If it is, identify a success; specify the values of n, p, and q; and list the possible values of the random variable x. If it is not a binomial experiment, explain why.*

**15. Video Games** A survey found that 29% of gamers own a virtual reality (VR) device. Ten gamers are randomly selected. The random variable represents the number who own a VR device. *(Source: Entertainment Software Association)*

16. **Cards** You draw five cards, one at a time, from a standard deck. You do not replace a card once it is drawn. The random variable represents the number of cards that are hearts.

17. **Lottery** A state lottery official randomly chooses 6 balls numbered from 1 through 40 without replacement. You choose six numbers and purchase a lottery ticket. The random variable represents the number of matches on your ticket to the numbers drawn in the lottery.

18. **Basketball** A'ja Wilson, the 2020 WNBA Most Valuable Player, makes a free throw shot about 78% of the time. The random variable represents the number of free throws that she makes on eight attempts. *(Source: Women's National Basketball Association)*

**Finding Binomial Probabilities** *In Exercises 19–26, find the indicated probabilities. If convenient, use technology or Table 2 in Appendix B.*

19. **Newspapers** Thirty-nine percent of U.S. adults have very little or no confidence in newspapers. You randomly select eight U.S. adults. Find the probability that the number who have very little or no confidence in newspapers is (a) exactly six and (b) exactly three. *(Source: Gallup)*

20. **Civil Rights** Fifty-nine percent of U.S. adults think that civil rights for Black Americans have improved during their lifetime. You randomly select seven U.S. adults. Find the probability that the number who think that civil rights for Black Americans have improved during their lifetime is (a) exactly one and (b) exactly five. *(Source: Gallup)*

21. **Actuarial Exam** Fifty-two percent of candidates taking actuarial Exam P pass the test. You randomly select 10 Exam P candidates. Find the probability that the number of candidates who pass is (a) exactly four, (b) at least seven, and (c) less than five. *(Source: Society of Actuaries)*

22. **Penalty Kicks** Argentine soccer player Lionel Messi converts 78% of his penalty kicks. Suppose Messi takes six penalty kicks next season. Find the probability that the number he converts is (a) exactly six, (b) at most three, and (c) more than three. *(Source: Transfermarkt)*

23. **Second-Hand Fashion** Fourteen percent of consumers have tried to purchase clothing second-hand rather than new in the past year. You randomly select 11 consumers. Find the probability that the number who have tried to purchase second-hand rather than new clothing is (a) exactly one, (b) at most five, and (c) more than three. *(Source: Fashion Revolution)*

24. **Responsible Consumption** Forty-five percent of consumers say it is important that the clothing they buy is made without child labor. You randomly select 16 consumers. Find the probability that the number of of consumers who say it is important that the clothing they buy is made without child labor is (a) exactly eight, (b) at least ten, and (c) less than twelve. *(Source: Fashion Revolution)*

25. **Workplace Drug Testing** Five percent of the U.S. workforce test positive for illicit drugs. You randomly select 14 workers. Find the probability that the number who test positive for illicit drugs is (a) exactly two, (b) more than two, and (c) from two to five. *(Source: Quest Diagnostics)*

26. **Pronunciation** Sixty-six percent of people pronounce pecan "puh-CON" instead of "PEA-can." You randomly select 15 people. Find the probability that the number of people who pronounce pecan "puh-CON" is (a) exactly seven, (b) more than seven, and (c) from seven to eleven. *(Source: American Pecans)*

**Constructing and Graphing Binomial Distributions** *In Exercises 27–30, (a) construct a binomial distribution, (b) graph the binomial distribution using a histogram and describe its shape, and (c) identify any values of the random variable x that you would consider unusual. Explain your reasoning.*

27. **College Acceptance** Pennsylvania State University accepts 49% of applicants. You randomly select seven Pennsylvania State University applicants. The random variable represents the number who are accepted. *(Source: US News & World Report)*

28. **Immigration** Thirty-three percent of immigrants to the United States ages 25 and older have a bachelor's degree or higher. You randomly select eight immigrants to the U.S. ages 25 and older. The random variable represents the number who have a bachelor's degree or higher. *(Source: Migration Policy Institute)*

29. **Living to Age 100** Seventy-seven percent of adults want to live to age 100. You randomly select five adults and ask them whether they want to live to age 100. The random variable represents the number who want to live to age 100. *(Source: Standford Center on Longevity)*

30. **Workplace Cleanliness** Fifty-seven percent of employees judge their peers by the cleanliness of their workspaces. You randomly select 10 employees and ask them whether they judge their peers by the cleanliness of their workspaces. The random variable represents the number who judge their peers by the cleanliness of their workspaces. *(Source: Adecco)*

**Finding and Interpreting Mean, Variance, and Standard Deviation** *In Exercises 31–36, find the mean, variance, and standard deviation of the binomial distribution for the given random variable. Interpret the results and determine any unusual values.*

31. **Penalty Shots** Thirty-three percent of penalty shots in the National Hockey League are converted. The random variable represents the number of penalty shots converted out of six randomly chosen attempts. *(Source: Hockey Reference)*

32. **SAT Test** Multiple choice questions on the SAT college admissions exam have four choices. The random variable represents the number of correct answers when you randomly guess the answer for seven questions.

33. **Life on Other Planets** Seventy-nine percent of U.S. adults believe that life on other planets is plausible. You randomly select eight U.S. adults and ask them whether they believe that life on other planets is plausible. The random variable represents the number who believe that life on other planets is plausible. *(Source: Ipsos)*

34. **Cloning** Eighty-five percent of U.S. adults believe cloning humans is morally wrong. You randomly select 10 U.S. adults and ask them whether they believe cloning humans is morally wrong. The random variable represents the number who believe cloning humans is morally wrong. *(Source: Gallup)*

35. **Late for Work** Thirty-one percent of U.S. employees who are late for work blame oversleeping. You randomly select 12 U.S. employees who are late for work and ask them whether they blame oversleeping. The random variable represents the number who are late for work and blame oversleeping. *(Source: CareerBuilder)*

36. **Supreme Court** Ten percent of college graduates think that Judge Judy serves on the Supreme Court. You randomly select 10 college graduates and ask them whether they think that Judge Judy serves on the Supreme Court. The random variable represents the number who think that Judge Judy serves on the Supreme Court. *(Source: CNN)*

**Unusual Events** *In Exercises 37 and 38, find the indicated probabilities. Then determine if the event is unusual. Explain your reasoning.*

**37. Rock-Paper-Scissors** The probability of winning a game of rock-paper-scissors is $\frac{1}{3}$. You play nine games of rock-paper-scissors. Find the probability that the number of games you win is (a) exactly five, (b) more than five, and (c) less than two.

**38. Marriage** Fifty-three percent of U.S. adults are currently married. You randomly select twelve U.S. adults. Find the probability that the number who are married is (a) exactly nine, (b) less than four, and (c) from eight to eleven. *(Source: Pew Research)*

## Extending Concepts

**Multinomial Experiments** *In Exercises 39 and 40, use the information below.*

A **multinomial experiment** satisfies these conditions.

- The experiment has a fixed number of trials $n$, where each trial is independent of the other trials.
- Each trial has $k$ possible mutually exclusive outcomes: $E_1, E_2, E_3, \ldots, E_k$.
- Each outcome has a fixed probability. So, $P(E_1) = p_1$, $P(E_2) = p_2$, $P(E_3) = p_3$, $\ldots$, $P(E_k) = p_k$. The sum of the probabilities for all outcomes is $p_1 + p_2 + p_3 + \cdots + p_k = 1$.
- The number of times $E_1$ occurs is $x_1$, the number of times $E_2$ occurs is $x_2$, the number of times $E_3$ occurs is $x_3$, and so on.
- The discrete random variable $x$ counts the number of times $x_1, x_2, x_3, \ldots, x_k$ that each outcome occurs in $n$ independent trials where $x_1 + x_2 + x_3 + \cdots + x_k = n$. The probability that $x$ will occur is

$$P(x) = \frac{n!}{x_1!x_2!x_3! \cdots x_k!} p_1^{x_1} p_2^{x_2} p_3^{x_3} \cdots p_k^{x_k}.$$

**39. Genetics** According to a theory in genetics, when tall and colorful plants are crossed with short and colorless plants, four types of plants will result: tall and colorful, tall and colorless, short and colorful, and short and colorless, with corresponding probabilities of $\frac{9}{16}$, $\frac{3}{16}$, $\frac{3}{16}$, and $\frac{1}{16}$. Ten plants are selected. Find the probability that 5 will be tall and colorful, 2 will be tall and colorless, 2 will be short and colorful, and 1 will be short and colorless.

**40. Genetics** Another proposed theory in genetics gives the corresponding probabilities for the four types of plants described in Exercise 39 as $\frac{5}{16}$, $\frac{4}{16}$, $\frac{1}{16}$, and $\frac{6}{16}$. Ten plants are selected. Find the probability that 5 will be tall and colorful, 2 will be tall and colorless, 2 will be short and colorful, and 1 will be short and colorless.

**41. Manufacturing** An assembly line produces 10,000 automobile parts. Twenty percent of the parts are defective. An inspector randomly selects 10 of the parts.

(a) Use the Multiplication Rule (discussed in Section 3.2) to find the probability that none of the selected parts are defective. (Note that the events are dependent.)

(b) Because the sample is only 0.1% of the population, treat the events as *independent* and use the binomial probability formula to approximate the probability that none of the selected parts are defective.

(c) Compare the results of parts (a) and (b).

# 4.2 ACTIVITY Binomial Distribution

APPLET

You can find the interactive applet for this activity at MyLab Statistics.

The *Binomial distribution* applet allows you to simulate values from a binomial distribution. You can specify the parameters for the binomial distribution (**n** and **p**) and the number of values to be simulated (**N**). When you click **Simulate, N** values from the specified binomial distribution will be plotted. The frequency of each outcome is shown in the plot.

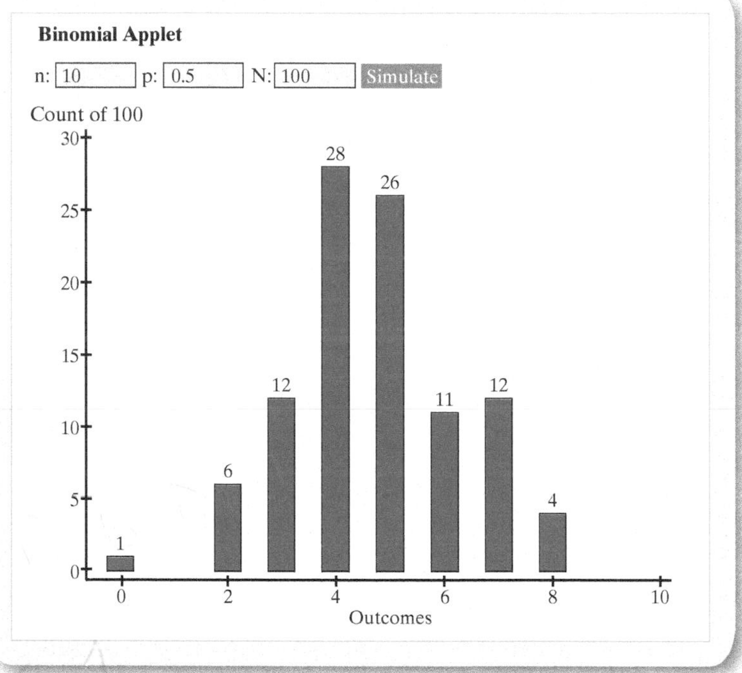


**EXPLORE**

**Step 1** Specify a value of **n.**

**Step 2** Specify a value of **p.**

**Step 3** Specify a value of **N.**

**Step 4** Click **Simulate.**

**DRAW CONCLUSIONS**

APPLET

1. During a presidential election year, 70% of a county's eligible voters cast a vote. Simulate selecting **n** = 10 eligible voters **N** = 10 times (for 10 communities in the county). Use the results to estimate the probability that the number who voted in this election is (a) exactly 5, (b) at least 8, and (c) at most 7.

2. During a non-presidential election year, 20% of the eligible voters in the same county as in Exercise 1 cast a vote. Simulate selecting **n** = 10 eligible voters **N** = 10 times (for 10 communities in the county). Use the results to estimate the probability that the number who voted in this election is (a) exactly 4, (b) at least 5, and (c) less than 4.

3. For the election in Exercise 1, simulate selecting **n** = 10 eligible voters **N** = 100 times. Estimate the probability that the number who voted in this election is exactly 5. Compare this result with the result in Exercise 1 part (a). Which of these is closer to the probability found using the binomial probability formula?

# CASE STUDY

# Distribution of Number of Hits in Baseball Games

The official website of Major League Baseball, *MLB.com,* records detailed statistics about players and games.

During the 2020 regular season, José Abreu of the Chicago White Sox had a batting average of 0.317. The graphs below show the number of hits he had in games in which he had different numbers of at-bats.

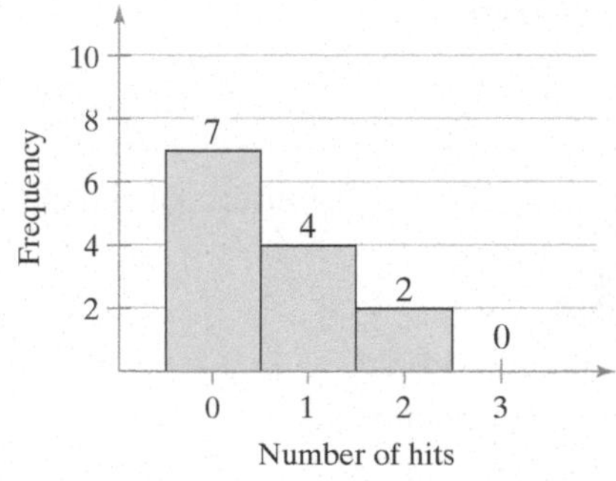


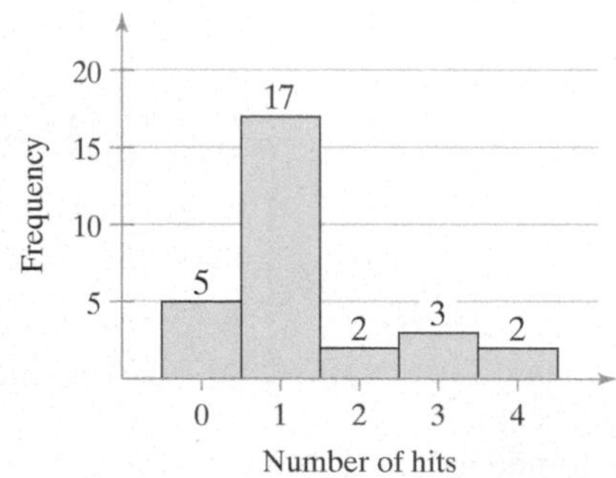


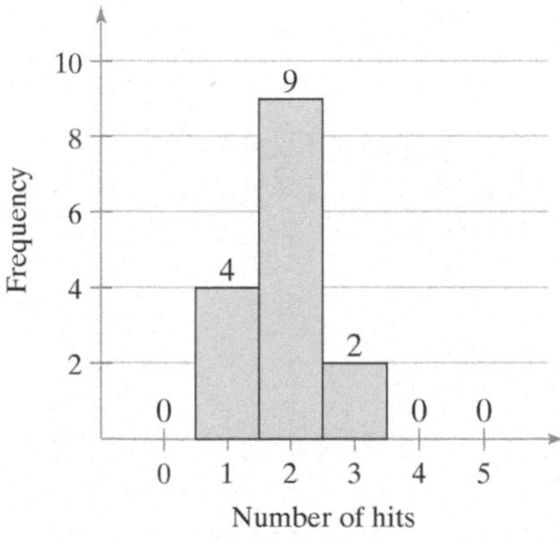


## EXERCISES

1. Construct a probability distribution for the number of hits in games with

   (a) 3 at-bats. (b) 4 at-bats. (c) 5 at-bats.

2. Construct binomial probability distributions for $p = 0.317$ and (a) $n = 3$, (b) $n = 4$, and (c) $n = 5$.

3. Compare your distributions from Exercise 1 and Exercise 2. Is a binomial distribution a good model for determining the numbers of hits in a baseball game for a given number of at-bats? Explain your reasoning and include a discussion of the four conditions for a binomial experiment.

4. During the 2020 regular season, Mookie Betts of the Los Angeles Dodgers had 11 games with 3 at-bats. Of these games, he had 3 games with no hits, 5 games with one hit, and 3 games with two hits.

   (a) Based on Abreu's and Betts's hits in games with three at-bats, which player do you think had the higher batting average?

   (b) Look up Betts's 2020 regular season batting average. Was your expectation from part (a) correct? If not, propose a reason why.

# 4.3 More Discrete Probability Distributions

## What You Should Learn

- How to find probabilities using the geometric distribution
- How to find probabilities using the Poisson distribution

The Geometric Distribution ■ The Poisson Distribution ■ Summary of Discrete Probability Distributions

## The Geometric Distribution

Many actions in life are repeated until a success occurs. For instance, you might have to call a number several times before someone answers. A situation such as this can be represented by a **geometric distribution.**

### DEFINITION

A **geometric distribution** is a discrete probability distribution of a random variable $x$ that satisfies these conditions.

1. A trial is repeated until a success occurs.
2. The repeated trials are independent of each other.
3. The probability of success $p$ is the same for each trial.
4. The random variable $x$ represents the number of the trial in which the first success occurs.

The probability that the first success will occur on trial number $x$ is

$$P(x) = pq^{x-1}, \text{ where } q = 1 - p.$$

For instance, when the first success occurs on the third trial, the outcome is FFS, and the probability is $P(3) = q \cdot q \cdot p$, or $P(3) = p \cdot q^2$.

### Tech Tip

You can use technology such as Minitab, Excel, StatCrunch, or the TI-84 Plus to find a geometric probability. For instance, here are instructions for finding a geometric probability on a TI-84 Plus. From the DISTR menu, choose the *geometpdf(* feature. Enter the values of $p$ and $x$. Then calculate the probability.

### EXAMPLE 1

#### Using the Geometric Distribution

A recent study found that the failure rate of businesses after five years is 50%. Four businesses that started five years ago are selected at random. Find the probability that the fourth business selected is the first one to have failed. *(Source: U.S. Bureau of Labor Statistics)*

**SOLUTION**

Using $p = 0.50$, $q = 0.50$, and $x = 4$, you have

$$\begin{aligned} P(4) &= 0.50(0.50)^{4-1} \\ &= (0.50)^4 \\ &\approx 0.063. \end{aligned}$$

So, the probability that the fourth business selected is the first one to have failed is about 0.063. You can use technology to check this result. For instance, using a TI-84 Plus, you can find $P(4)$, as shown below.

**TI-84 PLUS**

```
geometpdf(.5,4)
                    .0625
```

**TRY IT YOURSELF 1**

The study in Example 1 found that the failure rate of businesses after one year is 20%. Six businesses that started one year ago are selected at random. Find the probability that the sixth business selected is the first one to have failed. *(Source: U.S. Bureau of Labor Statistics)*

*Answer: Page A39*

Even though theoretically a success may never occur, the geometric distribution is a discrete probability distribution because the values of $x$ can be listed: 1, 2, 3, . . .. Notice that as $x$ becomes larger, $P(x)$ gets closer to zero. For instance, in Example 1, the probability that the thirtieth business selected is the first one to have failed is

$$P(30) = 0.50(0.50)^{30-1} = (0.50)^{30} \approx 0.0000000009.$$

## The Poisson Distribution

In a binomial experiment, you are interested in finding the probability of a specific number of successes in a given number of trials. Suppose instead that you want to know the probability that a specific number of occurrences takes place within a given unit of time, area, or volume. For instance, to determine the probability that an employee will take 15 sick days within a year, you can use the **Poisson distribution.**

**Tech Tip**

You can use technology such as Minitab, Excel, StatCrunch, or the TI-84 Plus to find a Poisson probability. For instance, here are instructions for finding a Poisson probability on a TI-84 Plus. From the DISTR menu, choose the *poissonpdf(* feature. Enter the values of $\mu$ and $x$. (Note that the TI-84 Plus uses the Greek letter lambda, $\lambda$, in place of $\mu$.) Then calculate the probability.

**DEFINITION**

The **Poisson distribution** is a discrete probability distribution of a random variable $x$ that satisfies these conditions.

1. The experiment consists of counting the number of times $x$ an event occurs in a given interval. The interval can be an interval of time, area, or volume.
2. The probability of the event occurring is the same for each interval.
3. The number of occurrences in one interval is independent of the number of occurrences in other intervals.

The probability of exactly $x$ occurrences in an interval is

$$P(x) = \frac{\mu^x e^{-\mu}}{x!}$$

where $e$ is an irrational number approximately equal to 2.71828 and $\mu$ is the mean number of occurrences per interval unit.

**EXAMPLE 2**

### Using the Poisson Distribution

The mean number of accidents per month at a certain intersection is three. What is the probability that in any given month four accidents will occur at this intersection?

**SOLUTION**

Using $x = 4$ and $\mu = 3$, the probability that 4 accidents will occur in any given month at the intersection is

$$P(4) \approx \frac{3^4(2.71828)^{-3}}{4!} \approx 0.168.$$

You can use technology to check this result. For instance, using a TI-84 Plus, you can find $P(4)$, as shown at the left.

**TI-84 PLUS**

```
poissonpdf(3,4)
         .1680313557
```

**TRY IT YOURSELF 2**

What is the probability that more than four accidents will occur in any given month at the intersection?

*Answer: Page A39*

In Example 2, you used a formula to determine a Poisson probability. You can also use a table to find Poisson probabilities. Table 3 in Appendix B lists the Poisson probabilities for selected values of $x$ and $\mu$. You can also use technology tools, such as Minitab, Excel, StatCrunch, and the TI-84 Plus, to find Poisson probabilities.

## EXAMPLE 3

### Finding a Poisson Probability Using a Table

A population count shows that the average number of rabbits per acre living in a field is 3.6. Use a table to find the probability that seven rabbits are found on any given acre of the field.

**SOLUTION**

A portion of Table 3 in Appendix B is shown here. Using the distribution for $\mu = 3.6$ and $x = 7$, you can find the Poisson probability as shown by the highlighted areas in the table.

| | $\mu$ | | | | | | |
|---|---|---|---|---|---|---|---|
| $x$ | 3.1 | 3.2 | 3.3 | 3.4 | 3.5 | 3.6 | 3.7 |
| 0 | .0450 | .0408 | .0369 | .0334 | .0302 | .0273 | .0247 |
| 1 | .1397 | .1304 | .1217 | .1135 | .1057 | .0984 | .0915 |
| 2 | .2165 | .2087 | .2008 | .1929 | .1850 | .1771 | .1692 |
| 3 | .2237 | .2226 | .2209 | .2186 | .2158 | .2125 | .2087 |
| 4 | .1734 | .1781 | .1823 | .1858 | .1888 | .1912 | .1931 |
| 5 | .1075 | .1140 | .1203 | .1264 | .1322 | .1377 | .1429 |
| 6 | .0555 | .0608 | .0662 | .0716 | .0771 | .0826 | .0881 |
| 7 | .0246 | .0278 | .0312 | .0348 | .0385 | .0425 | .0466 |
| 8 | .0095 | .0111 | .0129 | .0148 | .0169 | .0191 | .0215 |
| 9 | .0033 | .0040 | .0047 | .0056 | .0066 | .0076 | .0089 |
| 10 | .0010 | .0013 | .0016 | .0019 | .0023 | .0028 | .0033 |

According to the table, the probability is 0.0425. You can check this result using technology. As shown below using Excel, the probability is 0.042484. After rounding to four decimal places, the probability is 0.0425, which is the same value found using the table.

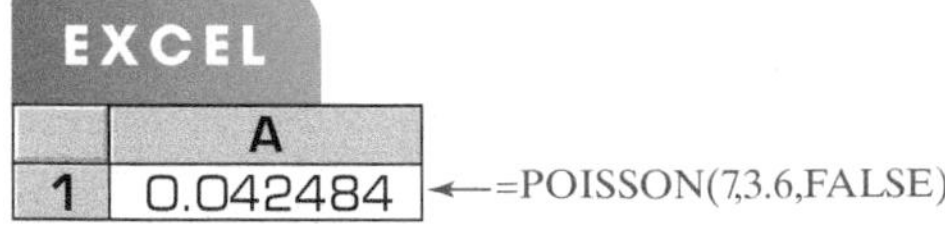


***Interpretation*** So, the probability that seven rabbits are found on any given acre is 0.0425. Because 0.0425 is less than 0.05, this can be considered an unusual event.

**TRY IT YOURSELF 3**

Two thousand brown trout are introduced into a small lake. The lake has a volume of 20,000 cubic meters. Use a table to find the probability that three brown trout are found in any given cubic meter of the lake.

*Answer: Page A39*

## Picturing the World

The Tacoma Narrows Bridge is a suspension bridge that spans the Tacoma Narrows in Washington State. The average occupancy of vehicles that travel across the bridge is 1.6. The probability distribution shown below represents the vehicle occupancy on the bridge during a five-day period. (Adapted from Washington State Department of Transportation)

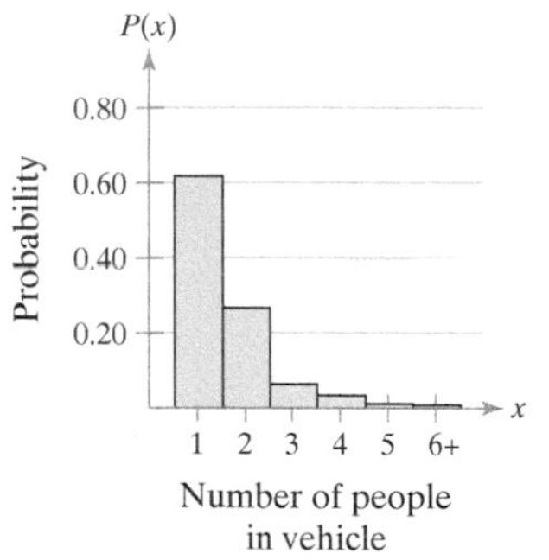


**During the five-day period, what is the probability that a randomly selected vehicle has two occupants or fewer?**

## Summary of Discrete Probability Distributions

The table summarizes the discrete probability distributions discussed in this chapter.

| Distribution | Summary | Formulas |
|---|---|---|
| **Binomial Distribution** | A binomial experiment satisfies these conditions.<br>**1.** The experiment has a fixed number $n$ of independent trials.<br>**2.** There are only two possible outcomes for each trial. Each outcome can be classified as a success or as a failure.<br>**3.** The probability of success $p$ is the same for each trial.<br>**4.** The random variable $x$ counts the number of successful trials.<br>The parameters of a binomial distribution are $n$ and $p$. | $n =$ the number of trials<br>$x =$ the number of successes in $n$ trials<br>$p =$ probability of success in a single trial<br>$q =$ probability of failure in a single trial<br>$q = 1 - p$<br>The probability of exactly $x$ successes in $n$ trials is<br>$P(x) = {}_nC_x p^x q^{n-x} = \frac{n!}{(n-x)!\,x!} p^x q^{n-x}.$<br>$\mu = np$<br>$\sigma^2 = npq$<br>$\sigma = \sqrt{npq}$ |
| **Geometric Distribution** | A geometric distribution is a discrete probability distribution of a random variable $x$ that satisfies these conditions.<br>**1.** A trial is repeated until a success occurs.<br>**2.** The repeated trials are independent of each other.<br>**3.** The probability of success $p$ is the same for each trial.<br>**4.** The random variable $x$ represents the number of the trial in which the first success occurs.<br>The parameter of a geometric distribution is $p$. | $x =$ the number of the trial in which the first success occurs<br>$p =$ probability of success in a single trial<br>$q =$ probability of failure in a single trial<br>$q = 1 - p$<br>The probability that the first success occurs on trial number $x$ is<br>$P(x) = pq^{x-1}.$ |
| **Poisson Distribution** | The Poisson distribution is a discrete probability distribution of a random variable $x$ that satisfies these conditions.<br>**1.** The experiment consists of counting the number of times $x$ an event occurs over a specified interval of time, area, or volume.<br>**2.** The probability of the event occurring is the same for each interval.<br>**3.** The number of occurrences in one interval is independent of the number of occurrences in other intervals.<br>The parameter of the Poisson distribution is $\mu$. | $x =$ the number of occurrences in the given interval<br>$\mu =$ the mean number of occurrences in a given interval unit<br>The probability of exactly $x$ occurrences in an interval is<br>$P(x) = \frac{\mu^x e^{-\mu}}{x!}.$ |

# 4.3 EXERCISES

For Extra Help: MyLab Statistics

## Building Basic Skills and Vocabulary

*In Exercises 1–4, find the indicated probability using the geometric distribution.*

**1.** Find $P(3)$ when $p = 0.65$.

**2.** Find $P(1)$ when $p = 0.45$.

**3.** Find $P(5)$ when $p = 0.09$.

**4.** Find $P(8)$ when $p = 0.28$.

*In Exercises 5–8, find the indicated probability using the Poisson distribution.*

**5.** Find $P(4)$ when $\mu = 5$.

**6.** Find $P(3)$ when $\mu = 6$.

**7.** Find $P(0)$ when $\mu = 1.5$.

**8.** Find $P(5)$ when $\mu = 9.8$.

**9.** In your own words, describe the difference between the value of $x$ in a binomial distribution and in a geometric distribution.

**10.** In your own words, describe the difference between the value of $x$ in a binomial distribution and in the Poisson distribution.

## Using and Interpreting Concepts

**Using a Distribution to Find Probabilities** *In Exercises 11–26, find the indicated probabilities using the geometric distribution, the Poisson distribution, or the binomial distribution. Then determine whether the events are unusual. If convenient, use a table or technology to find the probabilities.*

**11. Telephone Sales** The probability that you will make a sale on any given telephone call is 0.19. Find the probability that you (a) make your first sale on the first call, (b) make your first sale on the second call, and (c) make your first sale on the fifth call.

**12. Immigration** The mean number of people who immigrated to the United States per hour was about 5.5 in April 2021. Find the probability that the number of people who immigrate to the U.S. in a given hour in April 2021 was (a) zero, (b) exactly five, and (c) exactly eight. *(Source: U.S. Census Bureau)*

**13. Typographical Errors** A newspaper finds that the mean number of typographical errors per page is four. Find the probability that the number of typographical errors found on any given page is (a) exactly three, (b) at most three, and (c) more than three.

**14. Defective Parts** An auto parts seller finds that 1 in every 100 parts sold is defective. Find the probability that (a) the first defective part is the tenth part sold, (b) the first defective part is the first, second, or third part sold, and (c) none of the first 10 parts sold are defective.

**15. Pass Completions** NFL player Aaron Rodgers completes a pass 65.1% of the time. Find the probability that (a) the first pass he completes is the second pass, (b) the first pass he completes is the first or second pass, and (c) he does not complete his first two passes. *(Source: National Football League)*

**16. Pilot Test** The probability that a student passes the written test for a private pilot license is 0.75. Find the probability that (a) the first student that takes the test passes, (b) the second student to take the test is the first to pass, and (c) neither the first nor second student passes the test.

17. **Fossil Fuels** Sixty percent of U.S. adults favor establishing policies to reduce the use of fossil fuels. You randomly select eight U.S. adults. Find the probability that the number who favor establishing policies to reduce the use of fossil fuels is (a) exactly four, (b) less than five, and (c) at least three. *(Source: Gallup)*

18. **Living Donor Transplants** The mean number of organ transplants from living donors performed per day in the United States in 2020 was about 16. Find the probability that the number of organ transplants from living donors performed on any given day is (a) exactly 12, (b) at least eight, and (c) no more than 10. *(Source: Organ Procurement and Transplantation Network)*

19. **Hurricanes** The mean number of hurricanes to strike the U.S. mainland per year from 1851 through 2020 was about 1.8. Find the probability that the number of hurricanes striking the U.S. mainland in any given year from 1851 through 2020 is (a) exactly one, (b) at most one, and (c) more than one. *(Source: National Oceanic & Atmospheric Administration)*

20. **Reddit** Eighteen percent of U.S. adults say they use Reddit. You randomly select seven U.S. adults. Find the probability that the number who use Reddit is (a) exactly one, (b) more than three, and (c) from two to four. *(Source: Pew Research)*

21. **First Serve Points Won** When Japanese tennis player Naomi Osaka makes her first serve and does not fault, she wins the point 76% of the time. You randomly select ten of Osaka's non-fault first serves. Find the probability that the number of times she wins the point is (a) exactly 10, (b) more than seven, and (c) at most four. *(Source: Women's Tennis Association)*

22. **Winning a Prize** A cereal maker places a game piece in each of its cereal boxes. The probability of winning a prize in the game is 1 in 4. Find the probability that you (a) win your first prize with your fourth purchase, (b) win your first prize with your first, second, or third purchase, and (c) do not win a prize with your first four purchases.

23. **Precipitation** In Akron, Ohio, the mean number of days in April with 0.01 inch or more of precipitation is 14. Find the probability that the number of days in April with 0.01 inch or more of precipitation in Akron is (a) exactly 17 days, (b) at most 17 days, and (c) more than 17 days. *(Source: National Oceanic and Atmospheric Administration)*

24. **Paying for College Education** Sixty-eight percent of parents of children ages 8–14 say they are willing to get a second or part-time job to pay for their children's college eduction. You randomly select five parents. Find the probability that the number who say they are willing to get a second or part-time job to pay for their children's college eduction is (a) exactly three, (b) less than four, and (c) at least three. *(Source: T. Rowe Price Group, Inc.)*

25. **Glass Manufacturer** A glass manufacturer finds that 1 in every 500 glass items produced is warped. Find the probability that (a) the first warped glass item is the tenth item produced, (b) the first warped glass item is the first, second, or third item produced, and (c) none of the first 10 glass items produced are defective.

26. **Oil Tankers** In the month of June 2021, 240 oil tankers stop at a port city. No oil tanker visits more than once. Find the probability that the number of oil tankers that stop on any given day in June is (a) exactly eight, (b) at most three, and (c) more than eight.

## Extending Concepts

27. **Poisson Approximation of a Binomial Distribution** An automobile manufacturer finds that 1 in every 2500 automobiles produced has a specific manufacturing defect. (a) Use a binomial distribution to find the probability of finding 4 cars with the defect in a random sample of 6000 cars. (b) The Poisson distribution with a mean $\mu = np$ can be used to approximate the binomial distribution for large values of $n$ and small values of $p$. Repeat part (a) using the Poisson distribution and compare the results.

28. **Hypergeometric Distribution** Binomial experiments require that any sampling be done with replacement because each trial must be independent of the others. The **hypergeometric distribution** also has two outcomes: success and failure. The sampling, however, is done without replacement. For a population of $N$ items having $k$ successes and $N - k$ failures, the probability of selecting a sample of size $n$ that has $x$ successes and $n - x$ failures is given by

$$P(x) = \frac{({}_kC_x)({}_{N-k}C_{n-x})}{{}_NC_n}.$$

In a shipment of 15 microchips, 2 are defective and 13 are not defective. A sample of three microchips is chosen at random. Use the above formula to find the probability that (a) all three microchips are not defective, (b) one microchip is defective and two are not defective, and (c) two microchips are defective and one is not defective.

**Geometric Distribution: Mean and Variance** *In Exercises 29 and 30, use the fact that the mean of a geometric distribution is $\mu = 1/p$ and the variance is $\sigma^2 = q/p^2$.*

29. **Daily Lottery** A daily number lottery chooses three balls numbered 0 to 9. The probability of winning the lottery is 1/1000. Let $x$ be the number of times you play the lottery before winning the first time. (a) Find the mean, variance, and standard deviation. (b) How many times would you expect to have to play the lottery before winning? (c) The price to play is \$1 and winners are paid \$500. Would you expect to make or lose money playing this lottery? Explain.

30. **Paycheck Errors** A company assumes that 0.5% of the paychecks for a year were calculated incorrectly. The company has 200 employees and examines the payroll records from one month. (a) Find the mean, variance, and standard deviation. (b) How many employee payroll records would you expect to examine before finding one with an error?

**Poisson Distribution: Variance** *In Exercises 31 and 32, use the fact that the variance of the Poisson distribution is $\sigma^2 = \mu$.*

31. **Golf** In a recent year, the mean number of strokes per hole for golfer Bubba Watson was about 3.9. (a) Find the variance and standard deviation. Interpret the results. (b) Identify any numbers of strokes on a hole that you would consider unusual. *(Source: PGATour.com)*

32. **Bankruptcies** The mean number of bankruptcies filed per hour by businesses in the United States in 2020 was about 2.5. (a) Find the variance and the standard deviation. Interpret the results. (b) Identify any numbers of bankruptcies during an hour that you would consider unusual. *(Source: Administrative Office of the U.S. Courts)*

# USES AND ABUSES

# Statistics in the Real World

## Uses

There are countless occurrences of Poisson probability distributions in business, sociology, computer science, and many other fields.

For instance, suppose you work for the fire department in the city of Erie, Pennsylvania. You have to make sure the department has enough personnel and vehicles on hand to respond to fires, medical emergencies, and other situations where they provide aid. The fire department's records show that it responds to an average of 11 incidents per day, but one day the department responds to 15 incidents. Is this an unusual event? If so, the department may need to update the guidelines so that it is prepared to respond to more incidents.

Knowing the characteristics of the Poisson distribution will help you answer this type of question. By the time you have completed this course, you will be able make educated decisions about the reasonableness of the fire department's guidelines.

## Abuses

A common misuse of the Poisson distribution is to think that the "most likely" outcome is the outcome that will occur most of the time. For instance, suppose you are planning a typical day of responding to emergencies for the fire department. The most likely number of incidents the department will need to respond to is 11. Although this is the most likely outcome, the probability that it will occur is only about 0.119. There is about a 0.202 chance the department will respond to 12 or 13 incidents, and about a 0.219 chance of 14 or more incidents. So, it would be a mistake to simply plan for 11 incidents every day, thinking that days with fewer incidents and days with more incidents will balance out over time.

Citizens' safety and even lives can depend on the fire department, so it is important to be ready for any likely scenario. So, the fire department should be ready to respond to any number of incidents for which the cumulative probability of that many or more incidents is greater than 0.05.

### EXERCISES

*In Exercises 1–3, assume the fire department guidelines are correct and that the department responds to an average of 11 incidents per day. Use the graph of the Poisson distribution and technology to answer the questions. Explain your reasoning.*

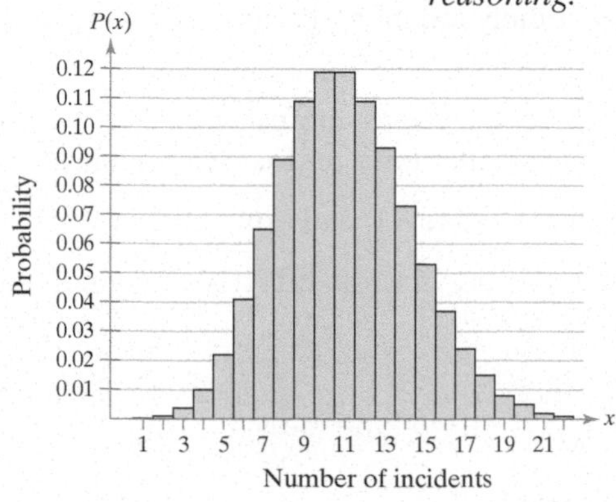


1. On a random day, what is more likely, 11 incidents or at least 16 incidents?

2. On a random day, what is more likely, 10 to 12 incidents or fewer than 10 incidents?

3. On the 4th of July, the fire department responds to 17 incidents. Is there reason to believe the guidelines should be adjusted for this holiday?

# 4 Chapter Summary

| What Did You Learn? | Example(s) | Review Exercises |
|---|---|---|
| **Section 4.1** | | |
| ▶ How to distinguish between discrete random variables and continuous random variables | 1 | 1, 2 |
| ▶ How to construct and graph a discrete probability distribution | 2 | 3, 4 |
| ▶ How to determine whether a distribution is a probability distribution | 3, 4 | 5, 6 |
| ▶ How to find the mean, variance, and standard deviation of a discrete probability distribution | 5, 6 | 7, 8 |
| $\mu = \Sigma xP(x)$ — Mean of a discrete random variable | | |
| $\sigma^2 = \Sigma(x - \mu)^2 P(x)$ — Variance of a discrete random variable | | |
| $\sigma = \sqrt{\sigma^2} = \sqrt{\Sigma(x - \mu)^2 P(x)}$ — Standard deviation of a discrete random variable | | |
| ▶ How to find the expected value of a discrete probability distribution | 7 | 9, 10 |
| **Section 4.2** | | |
| ▶ How to determine whether a probability experiment is a binomial experiment | 1 | 11, 12 |
| ▶ How to find binomial probabilities using the binomial probability formula, a binomial probability table, and technology | 2, 4–6 | 13–16, 23, 26 |
| ▶ How to construct and graph a binomial distribution | 3, 7 | 17, 18 |
| ▶ How to find the mean, variance, and standard deviation of a binomial probability distribution | 8 | 19, 20 |
| $\mu = np$ — Mean of a binomial distribution | | |
| $\sigma^2 = npq$ — Variance of a binomial distribution | | |
| $\sigma = \sqrt{npq}$ — Standard deviation of a binomial distribution | | |
| **Section 4.3** | | |
| ▶ How to find probabilities using the geometric distribution | 1 | 21, 24 |
| ▶ How to find probabilities using the Poisson distribution | 2, 3 | 22, 25 |

## Study Strategies

**Avoiding Procrastination** When you delay doing tasks or do not do tasks in a timely manner, you are *procrastinating.* Here are some tips to help you reduce how much you procrastinate.

- Address what is causing the procrastination. If you are afraid of failure because a task seems confusing or difficult, ask for clarification or help. If the task seems too large or overwhelming, break it into smaller tasks and set reasonable goals.
- Think about the long-term effects. Procrastinating can affect your sleep, your stress level, and your other work.
- Just get started. The simple act of starting a task makes it easier to continue. Putting in some effort, even a minimal amount, can produce positive results.
- Perform first the task you want to avoid doing the most.
- Know your distractions and avoid them until after you have finished your work.

For more information, visit Skills for Success in the accompanying MyLab course.

# 4 Review Exercises

## Section 4.1

*In Exercises 1 and 2, determine whether the random variable x is discrete or continuous. Explain.*

1. Let $x$ represent the grade on an exam worth a total of 100 points.
2. Let $x$ represent the weight of a truck at a weigh station.

*In Exercises 3 and 4, (a) construct a probability distribution, and (b) graph the probability distribution using a histogram and describe its shape.*

3. The number of hits per game played by a Major League Baseball player

| **Hits** | 0 | 1 | 2 | 3 | 4 | 5 |
|---|---|---|---|---|---|---|
| **Games** | 29 | 62 | 33 | 12 | 3 | 1 |

4. The number of hours students in a college class slept the previous night

| **Hours** | 4 | 5 | 6 | 7 | 8 | 9 | 10 |
|---|---|---|---|---|---|---|---|
| **Students** | 1 | 6 | 13 | 23 | 14 | 4 | 2 |

*In Exercises 5 and 6, determine whether the distribution is a probability distribution. If it is not a probability distribution, explain why.*

5. The random variable $x$ represents the number of tickets a police officer writes out each shift.

| $x$ | 0 | 1 | 2 | 3 | 4 | 5 |
|---|---|---|---|---|---|---|
| $P(x)$ | 0.09 | 0.23 | 0.29 | 0.16 | 0.21 | 0.02 |

6. The random variable $x$ represents the number of classes in which a student is enrolled in a given semester at a university.

| $x$ | 1 | 2 | 3 | 4 | 5 | 6 | 7 | 8 |
|---|---|---|---|---|---|---|---|---|
| $P(x)$ | $\frac{1}{80}$ | $\frac{2}{75}$ | $\frac{1}{10}$ | $\frac{12}{25}$ | $\frac{27}{20}$ | $\frac{1}{5}$ | $\frac{2}{25}$ | $\frac{1}{120}$ |

*In Exercises 7 and 8, (a) find the mean, variance, and standard deviation of the probability distribution, and (b) interpret the results.*

7. The number of cell phones per household in a small town

| **Cell phones** | 0 | 1 | 2 | 3 | 4 | 5 | 6 |
|---|---|---|---|---|---|---|---|
| **Probability** | 0.020 | 0.140 | 0.272 | 0.292 | 0.168 | 0.076 | 0.032 |

8. A television station sells advertising in 15-, 30-, 60-, 90-, and 120-second blocks. The distribution of sales for one 24-hour day is given.

| **Length (in seconds)** | 15 | 30 | 60 | 90 | 120 |
|---|---|---|---|---|---|
| **Probability** | 0.134 | 0.786 | 0.053 | 0.006 | 0.021 |

| Prize | Probability |
|---|---|
| \$100,000 | $\frac{1}{100,000}$ |
| \$100 | $\frac{1}{100}$ |
| \$50 | $\frac{1}{50}$ |

TABLE FOR EXERCISE 10

*In Exercises 9 and 10, find the expected net gain to the player for one play of the game.*

**9.** It costs \$25 to bet on a horse race. The horse has a $\frac{1}{8}$ chance of winning and a $\frac{1}{4}$ chance of placing second or third. You win \$125 if the horse wins and receive your money back if the horse places second or third.

**10.** A scratch-off lottery ticket costs \$5. The table at the left shows the probability of winning various prizes on the ticket.

## Section 4.2

*In Exercises 11 and 12, determine whether the experiment is a binomial experiment. If it is, identify a success; specify the values of n, p, and q; and list the possible values of the random variable x. If it is not a binomial experiment, explain why.*

**11.** Bags of milk chocolate M&M's produced in the Hackettstown, New Jersey, factory contain 12.5% green candies. One candy is selected from each of 12 bags. The random variable represents the number of green candies selected.

**12.** A fair coin is tossed repeatedly until 15 heads are obtained. The random variable $x$ counts the number of tosses.

*In Exercises 13–16, find the indicated binomial probabilities. If convenient, use technology or Table 2 in Appendix B.*

**13.** Fifty-three percent of U.S. adults support attempting to land an astronaut on Mars. You randomly select eight U.S. adults. Find the probability that the number who support attempting to land an astronaut on Mars is (a) exactly three, (b) at least three, and (c) more than three. *(Source: Gallup)*

**14.** Forty-two percent of U.S. adults have a gun in their home. You randomly select 12 U.S. adults. Find the probability that the number who have a gun in their home is (a) exactly two, (b) at least two, and (c) more than two. *(Source: Gallup)*

**15.** Seventy-two percent of U.S. civilian employees have access to medical care benefits. You randomly select nine civilian employees. Find the probability that the number who have access to medical care benefits is (a) exactly six, (b) at least six, and (c) more than six. *(Source: U.S. Bureau of Labor Statistics)*

**16.** Sixty-two percent of candidates taking the Texas Bar Exam pass the test. You randomly select five Texas Bar Exam candidates. Find the probability that the number who pass is (a) exactly two, (b) at least two, and (c) more than two. *(Source: National Conference of Bar Examiners)*

*In Exercises 17 and 18, (a) construct a binomial distribution, (b) graph the binomial distribution using a histogram and describe its shape, and (c) identify any values of the random variable x that you would consider unusual. Explain your reasoning.*

**17.** Seventy-two percent of U.S adults have read a book in any format in the past year. You randomly select five U.S adults and ask them whether they have read a book in any format in the past year. The random variable represents the number of adults who have read a book in any format in the past year. *(Source: Pew Research)*

**18.** Forty-nine percent of U.S adults answer correctly when asked "What is phishing?" You randomly select six U.S adults and ask them "What is phishing?" The random variable represents the number of adults who answer correctly. *(Source: Proofpoint)*

*In Exercises 19 and 20, find the mean, variance, and standard deviation of the binomial distribution for the given random variable. Interpret the results and determine any unusual values.*

**19.** About 13% of U.S. drivers are uninsured. You randomly select eight U.S. drivers and ask them whether they are uninsured. The random variable represents the number who are uninsured. *(Source: Insurance Research Council)*

**20.** Thirty-three percent of NCAA student-athletes have a job waiting for them when they graduate college. You randomly select ten NCAA student-athletes who are graduating and ask them whether they have a job waiting for them. The random variable represents the number who have a job waiting for them. *(Source: Gallup)*

## Section 4.3

*In Exercises 21–26, find the indicated probabilities using the geometric distribution, the Poisson distribution, or the binomial distribution. Then determine whether the events are unusual. If convenient, use a table or technology to find the probabilities.*

**21.** Fourteen percent of noninstitutionalized U.S. adults smoke cigarettes. After randomly selecting ten noninstitutionalized U.S. adults, you ask them whether they smoke cigarettes. Find the probability that the first adult who smokes cigarettes is (a) the third person selected, (b) the fourth or fifth person selected, and (c) not one of the first six persons selected. *(Source: National Center for Health Statistics)*

**22.** From 1940 to 2020, tornadoes killed about 0.26 people per day in the United States. Assume this rate holds true today and is constant throughout the year. Find the probability that the number of people in the United States killed by a tornado tomorrow is (a) exactly zero, (b) at most two, and (c) more than one. *(Source: National Weather Service)*

**23.** Thirty-six percent of Americans think there is still a need for the practice of changing their clocks for Daylight Savings Time. You randomly select seven Americans. Find the probability that the number who say there is still a need for changing their clocks for Daylight Savings Time is (a) exactly four, (b) less than two, and (c) at least six. *(Source: Rasmussen Reports)*

**24.** In a recent season, hockey player Evgeni Malkin scored 25 goals in 55 games he played. Assume that his goal production stayed at that level for the next season. Find the probability that he would get his first goal (a) in the first game of the season, (b) in the second game of the season, (c) within the first three games of the season, and (d) not within the first three games of the season. *(Source: National Hockey League)*

**25.** During a 10-year period, sharks killed an average of 6.4 people each year worldwide. Find the probability that the number of people killed by sharks next year is (a) exactly three, (b) more than six, and (c) at most five. *(Source: International Shark Attack File)*

**26.** Sixty-nine percent of U.S. adults plan to get a COVID-19 vaccine or already have. You randomly select ten U.S. adults and ask them whether they plan to get a COVID-19 vaccine or already have. Find the probability that the number who plan to get a COVID-19 vaccine or already have is (a) exactly seven, (b) more than eight, and (c) from two to four. *(Source: Pew Research)*

# 4 Chapter Quiz

*Take this quiz as you would take a quiz in class. After you are done, check your work against the answers given in the back of the book.*

**1.** Determine whether the random variable $x$ is discrete or continuous. Explain your reasoning.

(a) Let $x$ represent the number of lightning strikes that occur in Wyoming during the month of June.

(b) Let $x$ represent the amount of fuel (in gallons) used by a jet during takeoff.

(c) Let $x$ represent the final score in a game of bowling.

**2.** The table lists the number of wireless devices per household in a small town in the United States.

| **Wireless devices** | 0 | 1 | 2 | 3 | 4 | 5 |
|---|---|---|---|---|---|---|
| **Number of households** | 277 | 471 | 243 | 105 | 46 | 22 |

(a) Construct a probability distribution.

(b) Graph the probability distribution using a histogram and describe its shape.

(c) Find the mean, variance, and standard deviation of the probability distribution and interpret the results.

(d) Find the probability of randomly selecting a household that has at least four wireless devices.

**3.** In the past year, thirty-three percent of U.S. adults have put off medical treatment because of the cost. You randomly select nine U.S. adults. Find the probability that the number who have put off medical treatment because of the cost in the past year is (a) exactly three, (b) at most four, and (c) more than five. *(Source: Gallup)*

**4.** The five-year survival rate of people who undergo a liver transplant is 75%. The surgery is performed on six patients. *(Source: Mayo Clinic)*

(a) Construct a binomial distribution.

(b) Graph the binomial distribution using a histogram and describe its shape.

(c) Find the mean, variance, and standard deviation of the binomial distribution and interpret the results.

**5.** An online magazine finds that the mean number of typographical errors per page is five. Find the probability that the number of typographical errors found on any given page is (a) exactly five, (b) less than five, and (c) exactly zero.

**6.** Basketball player Stephen Curry makes a 3-pointer about 43% of the time. Find the probability that (a) the first 3-pointer he makes is the third shot, (b) the first 3-pointer he makes is the fourth or fifth shot, and (c) he does not make his first six shots. *(Source: ESPN)*

**7.** Which event(s) in Exercises 5 and 6 can be considered unusual? Explain your reasoning.

# 4 Chapter Test

*Take this test as you would take a test in class.*

*In Exercises 1–3, find the indicated probabilities using the geometric distribution, the Poisson distribution, or the binomial distribution. Then determine whether the events are unusual. If convenient, use a table or technology to find the probabilities.*

**1.** One out of every 42 tax returns for incomes over $1 million requires an audit. An auditor is examining tax returns for over $1 million. Find the probability that (a) the first return requiring an audit is the 25th return the tax auditor examines, (b) the first return requiring an audit is the first or second return the tax auditor examines, and (c) none of the first five returns the tax auditor examines require an audit. *(Source: Kiplinger)*

**2.** About 53% of U.S. full-time college students drank alcohol within a one-month period. You randomly select six U.S. full-time college students. Find the probability that the number who drank alcohol within a one-month period is (a) exactly two, (b) at least three, and (c) less than four. *(Source: National Center for Biotechnology Information)*

**3.** The mean increase in the U.S. population is about 1.5 people per minute. Find the probability that the increase in the U.S. population in any given minute is (a) exactly three people, (b) more than four, and (c) at most four people. *(Source: U.S. Census Bureau)*

**4.** Determine whether the distribution is a probability distribution. If it is not a probability distribution, explain why.

(a)

| $x$ | 0 | 5 | 10 | 15 | 20 |
|---|---|---|---|---|---|
| $P(x)$ | 0.03 | 0.09 | 0.19 | 0.32 | 0.37 |

(b)

| $x$ | 1 | 2 | 3 | 4 | 5 | 6 |
|---|---|---|---|---|---|---|
| $P(x)$ | $\frac{1}{20}$ | $\frac{1}{10}$ | $\frac{2}{5}$ | $\frac{3}{10}$ | $\frac{1}{5}$ | $\frac{1}{25}$ |

**5.** The table shows the ages of students in a freshman orientation course.

| Age | 17 | 18 | 19 | 20 | 21 | 22 |
|---|---|---|---|---|---|---|
| Students | 2 | 13 | 4 | 3 | 2 | 1 |

(a) Construct a probability distribution.

(b) Graph the probability distribution using a histogram and describe its shape.

(c) Find the mean, variance, and standard deviation of the probability distribution and interpret the results.

(d) Find the probability that a randomly selected student is less than 20 years old.

**6.** Fifty-six percent of federal student loans are in repayment. You randomly select five student loans and determine whether they are in repayment. The random variable represents the number that are in repayment. *(Source: U.S. Department of Education)*

(a) Construct a probability distribution.

(b) Graph the probability distribution using a histogram and describe its shape.

(c) Find the mean, variance, and standard deviation of the probability distribution and interpret the results.

# REAL STATISTICS REAL DECISIONS

# Putting it all together

The Centers for Disease Control and Prevention (CDC) is required by law to publish a report on assisted reproductive technology (ART). ART includes all fertility treatments in which both the egg and the sperm are used. These procedures generally involve removing eggs from a patient's ovaries, combining them with sperm in the laboratory, and returning them to the patient's body or giving them to another patient.

You are helping to prepare a CDC report on young ART patients and select at random 6 ART cycles of patients under 35 years of age for a special review. None of the cycles resulted in a live birth. Your manager feels it is impossible to select at random 10 ART cycles that do not result in a live birth. Use the pie chart at the right and your knowledge of statistics to determine whether your manager is correct.

**Results of ART Cycles for Patients Under 35 Using Own Eggs**

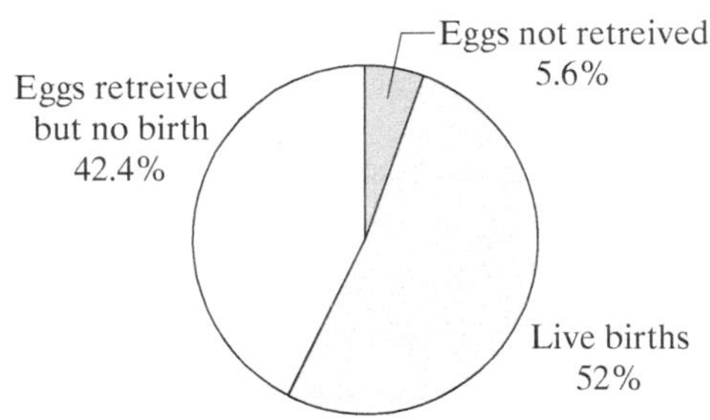


(Source: Centers for Disease Control and Prevention)

## EXERCISES

1. ***How Would You Do It?***
   (a) How would you determine whether your manager is correct, that it is impossible to select at random six ART cycles that do not result in a live birth?
   (b) What probability distribution do you think best describes the situation? Do you think the distribution of the number of live births is discrete or continuous? Explain your reasoning.
2. ***Answering the Question***
   Write an explanation that answers the question, "Is it possible to select at random six ART cycles that do not result in a live birth?" Include in your explanation the appropriate probability distribution and your calculation of the probability of no live births in six ART cycles.
3. ***Suspicious Samples?***
   A lab worker tells you that the samples below were selected at random. Using the graph at the right, which of the samples would you consider suspicious? Would you believe that the samples were selected at random? Explain your reasoning.
   (a) A sample of 8 ART cycles among patients ages 35 through 37, one of which resulted in live birth
   (b) A sample of 10 ART cycles among patients ages 43 and older, two of which resulted in live birth

**Live Birth Rates for ART Cycles Among Patients by Age Group**

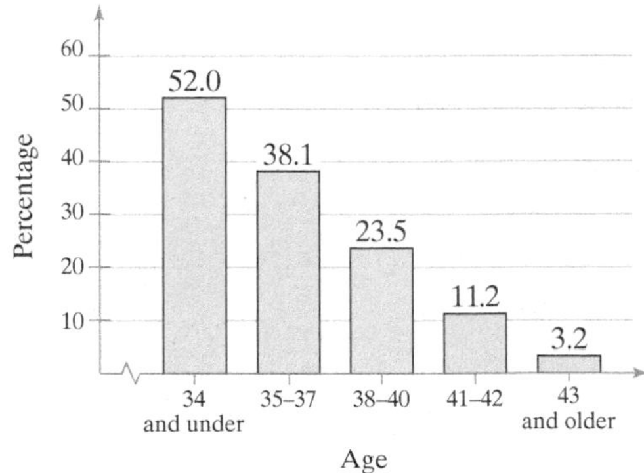


(Source: Centers for Disease Control and Prevention)

# TECHNOLOGY

MINITAB EXCEL TI-84 PLUS

# Using Poisson Distributions as Queuing Models

Queuing means waiting in line to be served. There are many examples of queuing in everyday life: waiting at a traffic light, waiting in line at a grocery checkout counter, waiting for an elevator, holding for a telephone call, and so on.

Poisson distributions are used to model and predict the number of people (calls, computer programs, vehicles) arriving at the line. In the exercises below, you are asked to use Poisson distributions to analyze the queues at a grocery store checkout counter.

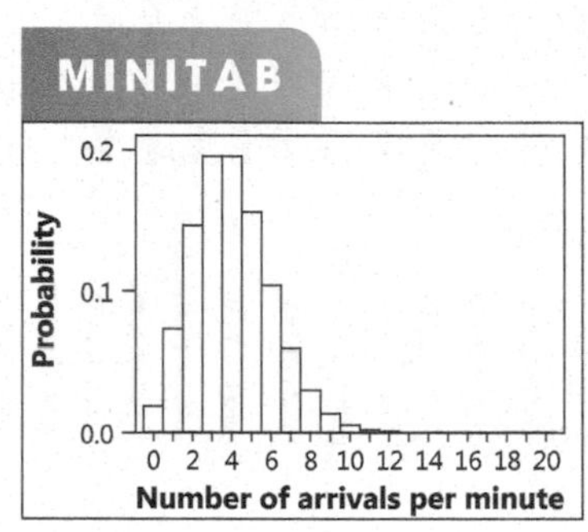


## EXERCISES

*In Exercises 1–7, consider a grocery store that can process a total of four customers at its checkout counters each minute.*

**1.** The mean number of customers who arrive at the checkout counters each minute is 4. Create a Poisson distribution with $\mu = 4$ for $x = 0$ to 20. Compare your results with the histogram shown at the upper right.

**2.** Minitab was used to generate 20 random numbers with a Poisson distribution for $\mu = 4$. Let the random number represent the number of arrivals at the checkout counter each minute for 20 minutes.

3 3 3 3 5 5 6 7 3 6
3 5 6 3 4 6 2 2 4 1

During each of the first four minutes, only three customers arrived. These customers could all be processed, so there were no customers waiting after four minutes.

(a) How many customers were waiting after 5 minutes? 6 minutes? 7 minutes? 8 minutes?

(b) Create a table that shows the number of customers waiting at the end of 1 through 20 minutes.

**3.** Generate a list of 20 random numbers with a Poisson distribution for $\mu = 4$. Create a table that shows the number of customers waiting at the end of 1 through 20 minutes.

**4.** The mean increases to five arrivals per minute, but the store can still process only four per minute. Generate a list of 20 random numbers with a Poisson distribution for $\mu = 5$. Then create a table that shows the number of customers waiting at the end of 20 minutes.

**5.** The mean number of arrivals per minute is five. What is the probability that 10 customers will arrive during the first minute?

**6.** The mean number of arrivals per minute is four. Find the probability that

(a) three, four, or five customers will arrive during the third minute.

(b) more than four customers will arrive during the first minute.

(c) more than four customers will arrive during each of the first four minutes.

**7.** The mean number of arrivals per minute is four. Find the probability that

(a) no customers are waiting in line after one minute.

(b) one customer is waiting in line after one minute.

(c) one customer is waiting in line after one minute and no customers are waiting in line after the second minute.

(d) no customers are waiting in line after two minutes.

Extended solutions are given in the technology manuals that accompany this text. Technical instruction is provided for Minitab, Excel, and the TI-84 Plus.

CHAPTER 5

# Normal Probability Distributions



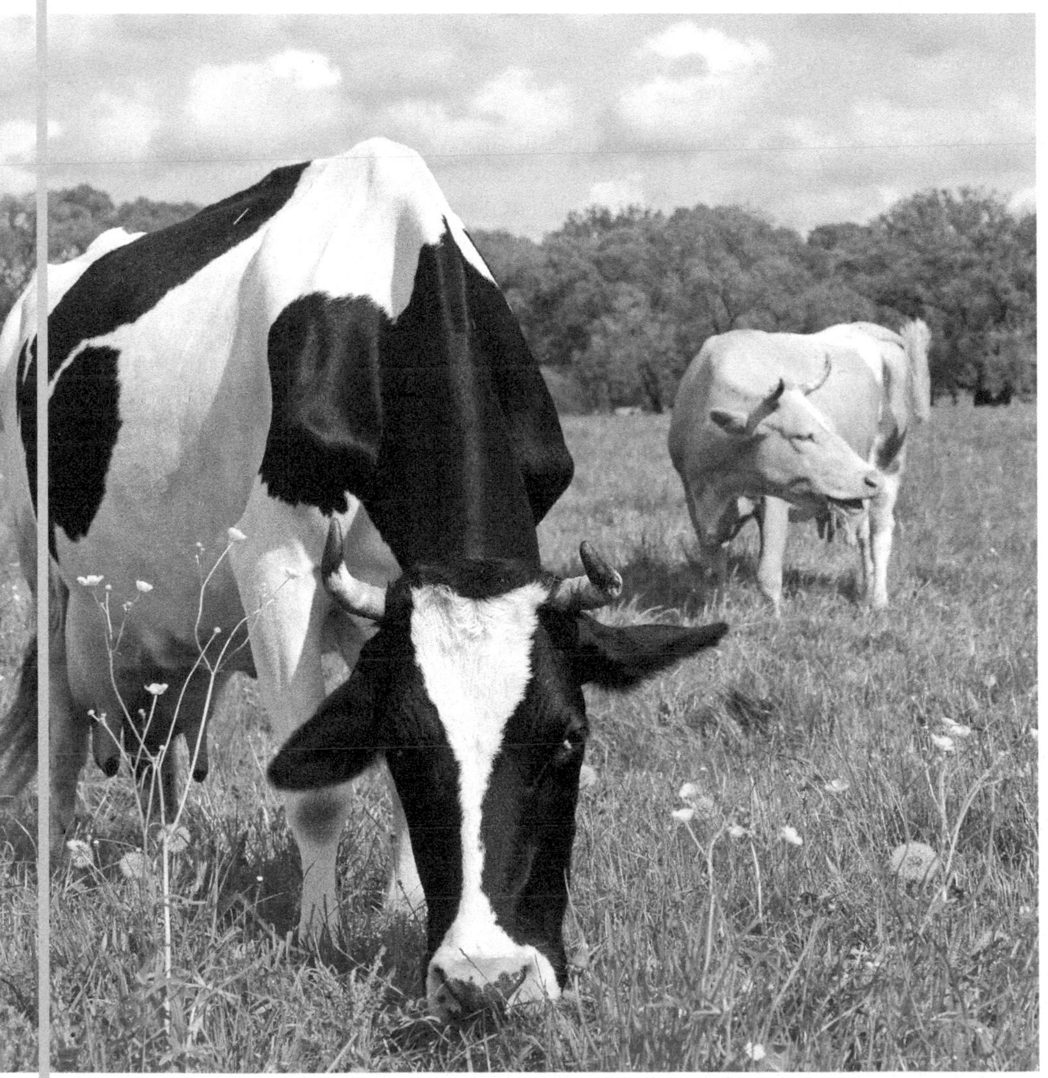

The average dairy cow in the United States produced 23,777 pounds of milk in 2020, more than twice the average from 50 years ago.

## Where You've Been

In Chapters 1 through 4, you learned how to collect and describe data, find the probability of an event, and analyze discrete probability distributions. You also learned that when a sample is used to make inferences about a population, it is critical that the sample not be biased. For instance, how would you organize a study to determine which breed of dairy cow is the most profitable?

When the U.S. Department of Agriculture performs this study, it uses random sampling and then records the measures of various milk production and physical traits such as pounds produced, fat percentage, protein percentage, productive life, somatic cell count, and calving ability. The studies have repeatedly shown Holstein cows to be the most profitable breed of dairy cow. Other top breeds are Jersey, Brown Swiss, and Ayrshire cows.

## Where You're Going

In Chapter 5, you will learn how to recognize normal (bell-shaped) distributions and how to use their properties in real-life applications. Suppose that you are a farmer planning to buy 20 Holstein cows and 10 Jersey cows from a breeder. You want to know the probabilities that the groups of cows will produce certain average daily amounts of milk. You will learn how to calculate this type of probability using a *sampling distribution of sample means* and the *Central Limit Theorem* in Section 5.4. The graphs below show the distributions of sample means of milk produced daily by the two breeds of cows.

The table shows the information given to you by the breeder. Assume that the amounts of milk produced are normally distributed.

| Amount of milk produced per day (in pounds) | | |
|---|---|---|
| **Breed** | **Mean** | **Standard deviation** |
| Holstein | 69.3 | 11.7 |
| Jersey | 49.7 | 10.1 |

You can use this information to make calculations about average amounts of milk produced daily by the cows. For instance, the probability that the 20 Holstein cows will produce an average of at least 65 pounds of milk per day is about 94.95%, and the probability that the 10 Jersey cows will produce an average of between 50 and 60 pounds of milk per day is about 46.35%.

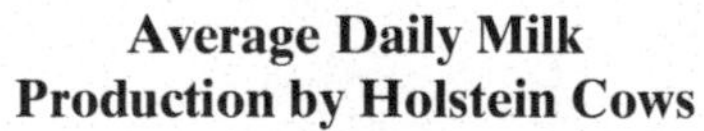

**Average Daily Milk Production by Holstein Cows**

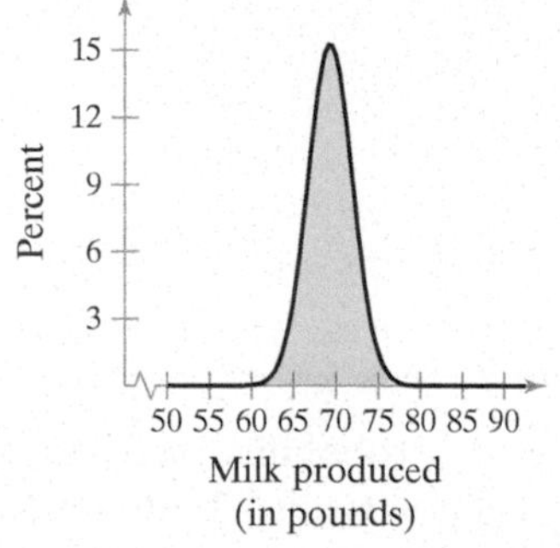


**Average Daily Milk Production by Jersey Cows**

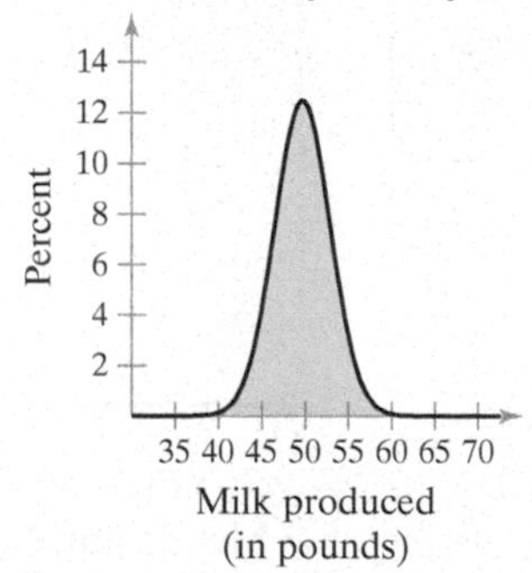

# 5.1 Introduction to Normal Distributions and the Standard Normal Distribution

### What You Should Learn

- How to interpret graphs of normal probability distributions
- How to find areas under the standard normal curve

Properties of a Normal Distribution ■ The Standard Normal Distribution

## Properties of a Normal Distribution

In Section 4.1, you distinguished between discrete and continuous random variables, and learned that a continuous random variable has an infinite number of possible values that can be represented by an interval on a number line. Its probability distribution is called a **continuous probability distribution.** In this chapter, you will study the most important continuous probability distribution in statistics—the **normal distribution.** Normal distributions can be used to model many sets of measurements in nature, industry, and business. For instance, the systolic blood pressures of humans, the lifetimes of smartphones, and housing costs are all normally distributed random variables.

**DEFINITION**

A **normal distribution** is a continuous probability distribution for a random variable $x$. The graph of a normal distribution is called the **normal curve.** A normal distribution has these properties.

1. The mean, median, and mode are equal.
2. The normal curve is bell-shaped and is symmetric about the mean.
3. The total area under the normal curve is equal to 1.
4. The normal curve approaches, but never touches, the $x$-axis as it extends farther and farther away from the mean.
5. Between $\mu - \sigma$ and $\mu + \sigma$ (in the center of the curve), the graph curves downward. The graph curves upward to the left of $\mu - \sigma$ and to the right of $\mu + \sigma$. The points at which the curve changes from curving upward to curving downward are called **inflection points.**

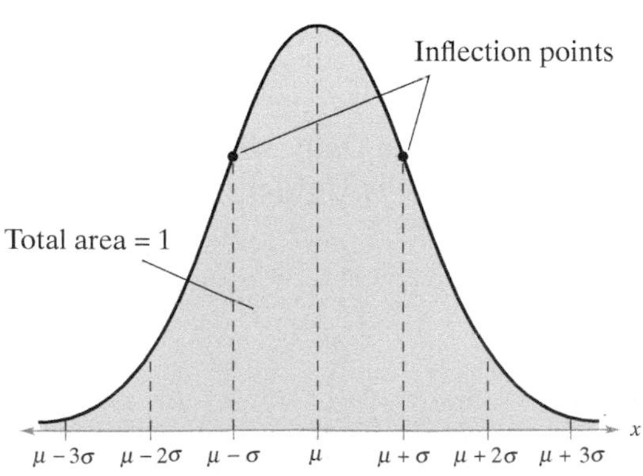

### Study Tip

A normal curve with mean $\mu$ and standard deviation $\sigma$ can be graphed using the normal probability density function

$$y = \frac{1}{\sigma\sqrt{2\pi}} e^{-(x-\mu)^2/(2\sigma^2)}.$$

(This formula will not be used in the text.) Because $e \approx 2.718$ and $\pi \approx 3.14$, a normal curve depends completely on $\mu$ and $\sigma$.

For help with division involving square roots, see *Integrated Review* at

MyLab® Statistics

You have learned that a discrete probability distribution can be graphed with a histogram. For a continuous probability distribution, you can use a **probability density function (pdf).** A probability density function has two requirements: (1) the total area under the curve is equal to 1, and (2) the function can never be negative.

A normal distribution can have any mean and any positive standard deviation. These two parameters, $\mu$ and $\sigma$, determine the shape of the normal curve. The mean gives the location of the line of symmetry, and the standard deviation describes how much the data are spread out.

For instance, in the figures below, curves $A$ and $B$ have the same mean, and curves $B$ and $C$ have the same standard deviation. The total area under each curve is 1. Also, in each graph, one of the inflection points occurs one standard deviation to the left of the mean, and the other occurs one standard deviation to the right of the mean.

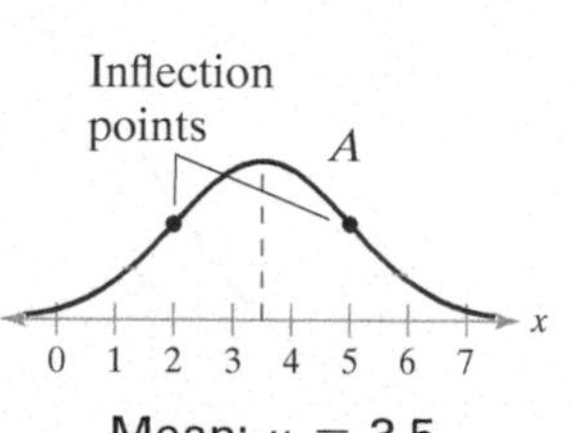


Mean: $\mu = 3.5$
Standard deviation: $\sigma = 1.5$

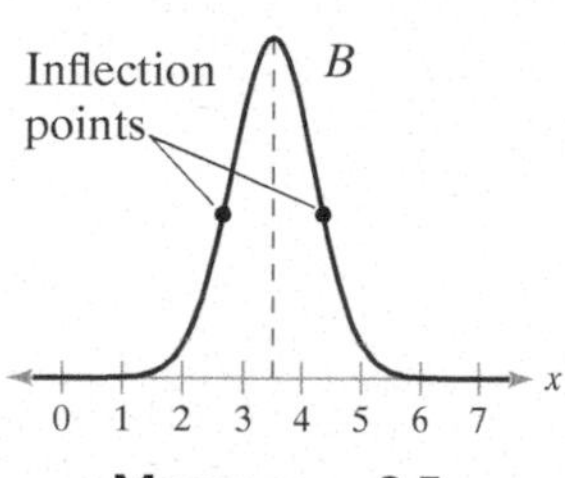


Mean: $\mu = 3.5$
Standard deviation: $\sigma = 0.7$

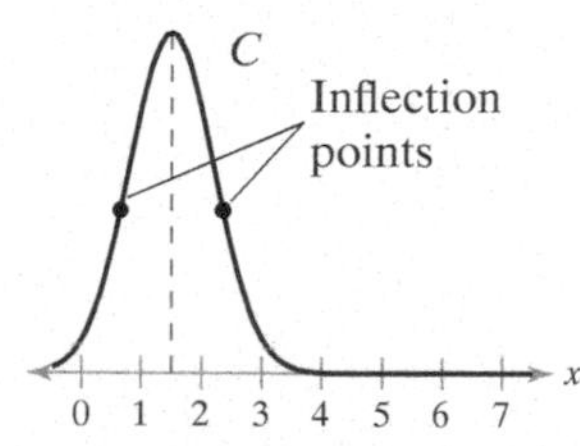


Mean: $\mu = 1.5$
Standard deviation: $\sigma = 0.7$

## Picturing the World

According to the National Center for Health Statistics, the number of births in the United States in a recent year was 3,747,540. The weights of the newborns can be approximated by a normal distribution, as shown in the figure. (Adapted from National Center for Health Statistics)

**Weights of Newborns**

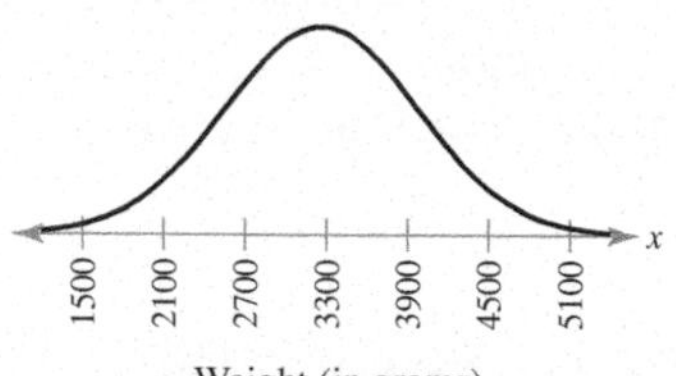


Weight (in grams)

**What is the mean weight of the newborns? Estimate the standard deviation of this normal distribution.**

## EXAMPLE 1

### Understanding Mean and Standard Deviation

1. Which normal curve has a greater mean?
2. Which normal curve has a greater standard deviation?

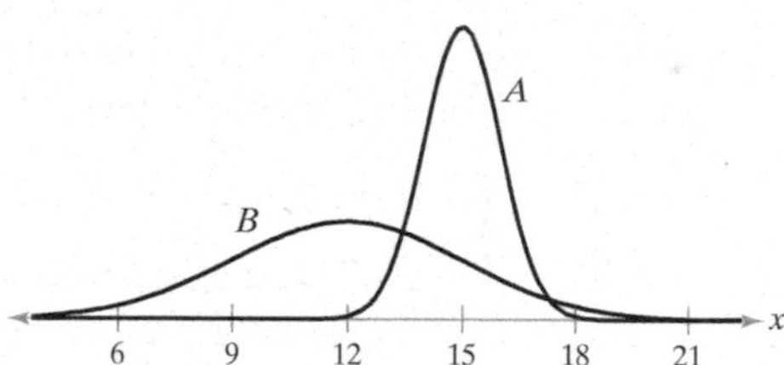


**SOLUTION**

1. The line of symmetry of curve $A$ occurs at $x = 15$. The line of symmetry of curve $B$ occurs at $x = 12$. So, curve $A$ has a greater mean.
2. Curve $B$ is more spread out than curve $A$. So, curve $B$ has a greater standard deviation.

**TRY IT YOURSELF 1**

1. Which normal curve has the greatest mean?
2. Which normal curve has the greatest standard deviation?

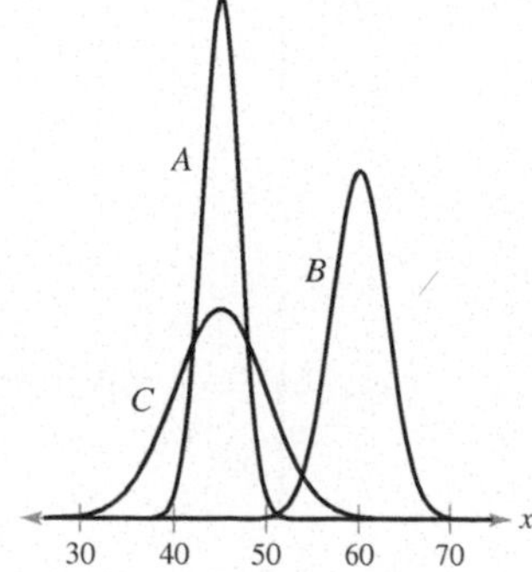


*Answer: Page A39*

## EXAMPLE 2

### Interpreting Graphs of Normal Distributions

The scaled test scores for the New York State Grade 6 Mathematics Operational Test are normally distributed. The normal curve shown below represents this distribution for a recent year. What is the mean test score? Estimate the standard deviation of this normal distribution. *(Adapted from New York State Education Department)*

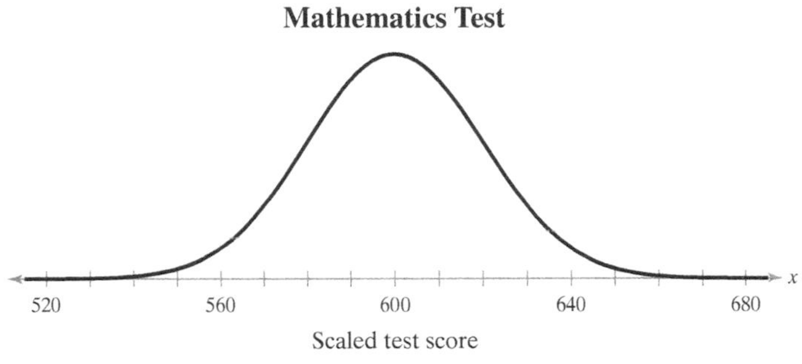


### SOLUTION

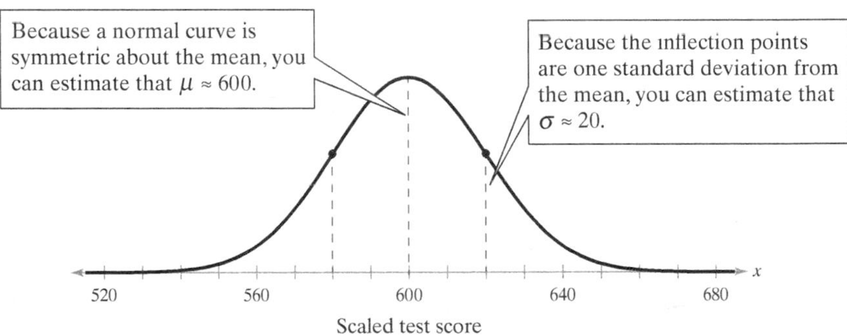


The scaled test scores for the New York State Grade 6 Mathematics Operational Test are normally distributed with a mean of about 600 and a standard deviation of about 20.

***Interpretation*** Using the Empirical Rule (see Section 2.4), you know that about 68% of the scores are between 580 and 620, about 95% of the scores are between 560 and 640, and about 99.7% of the scores are between 540 and 660.

### TRY IT YOURSELF 2

The reading subscores for the New York State Grade 6 English Language Arts Operational Test are normally distributed. The normal curve shown below represents this distribution for a recent year. What is the mean subscore? Estimate the standard deviation of this normal distribution. *(Adapted from New York State Education Department)*

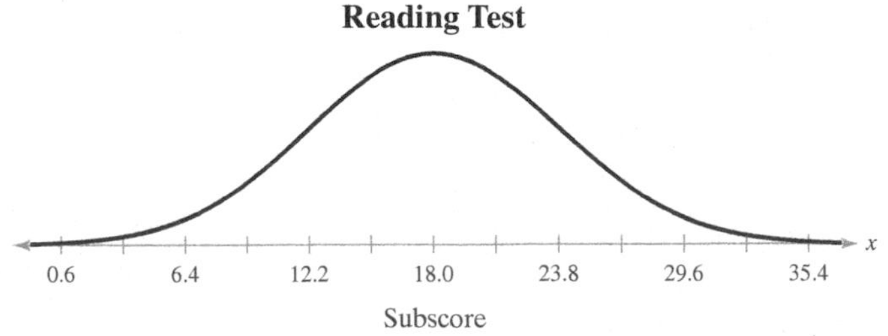


*Answer: Page A39*

**Tech Tip**

You can use technology to graph a normal curve. For instance, you can use a TI-84 Plus to graph the normal curve in Example 2.

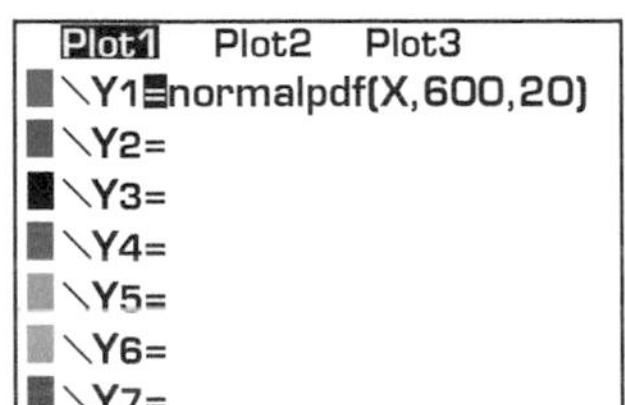


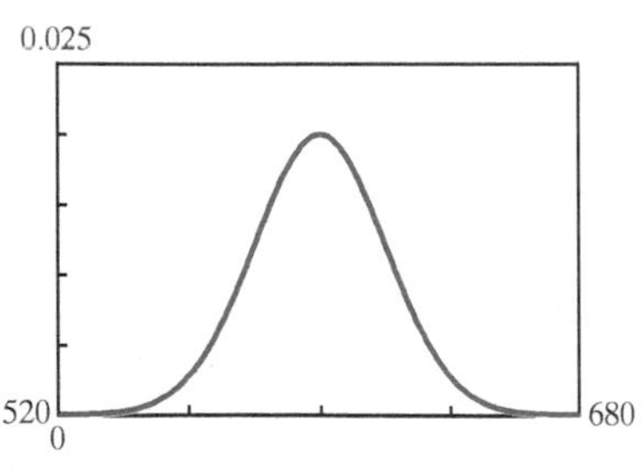

## The Standard Normal Distribution

**Study Tip**

Because every normal distribution can be transformed to the standard normal distribution, you can use $z$-scores and the standard normal curve to find areas (and therefore probabilities) under any normal curve.

There are infinitely many normal distributions, each with its own mean and standard deviation. The normal distribution with a mean of 0 and a standard deviation of 1 is called the **standard normal distribution.** The horizontal scale of the graph of the standard normal distribution corresponds to $z$-scores. In Section 2.5, you learned that a $z$-score is a measure of position that indicates the number of standard deviations a value lies from the mean. Recall that you can transform an $x$-value to a $z$-score using the formula

$$z = \frac{\text{Value} - \text{Mean}}{\text{Standard deviation}}$$

$$= \frac{x - \mu}{\sigma}. \qquad \text{Round to the nearest hundredth.}$$

**DEFINITION**

The **standard normal distribution** is a normal distribution with a mean of 0 and a standard deviation of 1. The total area under its normal curve is 1.

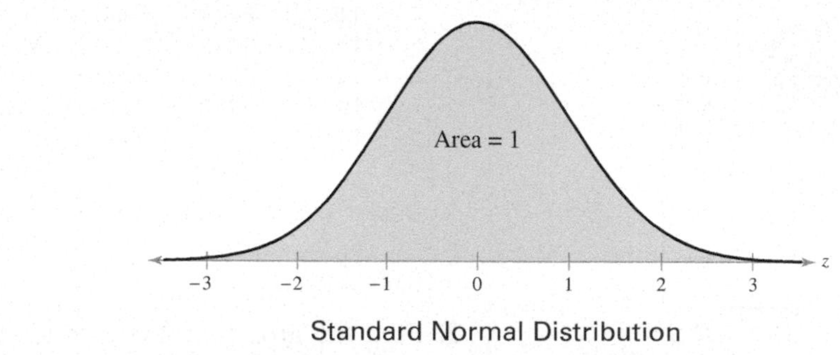


Standard Normal Distribution

**Study Tip**

It is important that you know the difference between $x$ and $z$. The random variable $x$ is sometimes called a raw score and represents values in a nonstandard normal distribution, whereas $z$ represents values in the standard normal distribution.

When each data value of a normally distributed random variable $x$ is transformed into a $z$-score, the result will be the standard normal distribution. After this transformation takes place, the area that falls in the interval under the nonstandard normal curve is the *same* as that under the standard normal curve within the corresponding $z$-boundaries.

In Section 2.4, you learned to use the Empirical Rule to approximate areas under a normal curve when the values of the random variable $x$ corresponded to −3, −2, −1, 0, 1, 2, or 3 standard deviations from the mean. Now, you will learn to calculate areas corresponding to other $x$-values. After you use the formula above to transform an $x$-value to a $z$-score, you can use the Standard Normal Table (Table 4 in Appendix B). The table lists the cumulative area under the standard normal curve to the left of $z$ for $z$-scores from −3.49 to 3.49. As you examine the table, notice the following.

**Properties of the Standard Normal Distribution**

1. The cumulative area is close to 0 for $z$-scores close to $z = -3.49$.
2. The cumulative area increases as the $z$-scores increase.
3. The cumulative area for $z = 0$ is 0.5000.
4. The cumulative area is close to 1 for $z$-scores close to $z = 3.49$.

In addition to using the table, you can use technology to find the cumulative area that corresponds to a $z$-score. For instance, the next example shows how to use the Standard Normal Table and a TI-84 Plus to find the cumulative area that corresponds to a $z$-score.

## EXAMPLE 3

### Using the Standard Normal Table

1. Find the cumulative area that corresponds to a $z$-score of 1.15.

2. Find the cumulative area that corresponds to a $z$-score of $-0.24$.

**SOLUTION**

Area = 0.8749

0 1.15 $z$

1. Find the area that corresponds to $z = 1.15$ by finding 1.1 in the left column and then moving across the row to the column under 0.05. The number in that row and column is 0.8749. So, the area to the left of $z = 1.15$ is 0.8749, as shown in the figure at the left.

| $z$ | .00 | .01 | .02 | .03 | .04 | .05 | .06 |
|---|---|---|---|---|---|---|---|
| **0.0** | .5000 | .5040 | .5080 | .5120 | .5160 | .5199 | .5239 |
| **0.1** | .5398 | .5438 | .5478 | .5517 | .5557 | .5596 | .5636 |
| **0.2** | .5793 | .5832 | .5871 | .5910 | .5948 | .5987 | .6026 |
| **0.9** | .8159 | .8186 | .8212 | .8238 | .8264 | .8289 | .8315 |
| **1.0** | .8413 | .8438 | .8461 | .8485 | .8508 | .8531 | .8554 |
| **1.1** | .8643 | .8665 | .8686 | .8708 | .8729 | .8749 | .8770 |
| **1.2** | .8849 | .8869 | .8888 | .8907 | .8925 | .8944 | .8962 |
| **1.3** | .9032 | .9049 | .9066 | .9082 | .9099 | .9115 | .9131 |
| **1.4** | .9192 | .9207 | .9222 | .9236 | .9251 | .9265 | .9279 |

**TI-84 PLUS**

```
normalcdf(-10000,1.15,0,1)
                0.8749280114
```

You can use technology to find the cumulative area that corresponds to $z = 1.15$, as shown at the left. Note that to specify the lower bound, use $-10,000$.

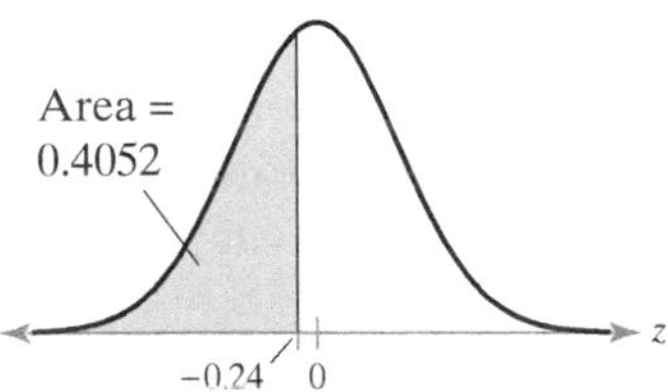


2. Find the area that corresponds to $z = -0.24$ by finding $-0.2$ in the left column and then moving across the row to the column under 0.04. The number in that row and column is 0.4052. So, the area to the left of $z = -0.24$ is 0.4052, as shown in the figure at the left.

| $z$ | .09 | .08 | .07 | .06 | .05 | .04 | .03 |
|---|---|---|---|---|---|---|---|
| **−3.4** | .0002 | .0003 | .0003 | .0003 | .0003 | .0003 | .0003 |
| **−3.3** | .0003 | .0004 | .0004 | .0004 | .0004 | .0004 | .0004 |
| **−3.2** | .0005 | .0005 | .0005 | .0006 | .0006 | .0006 | .0006 |
| **−0.5** | .2776 | .2810 | .2843 | .2877 | .2912 | .2946 | .2981 |
| **−0.4** | .3121 | .3156 | .3192 | .3228 | .3264 | .3300 | .3336 |
| **−0.3** | .3483 | .3520 | .3557 | .3594 | .3632 | .3669 | .3707 |
| **−0.2** | .3859 | .3897 | .3936 | .3974 | .4013 | .4052 | .4090 |
| **−0.1** | .4247 | .4286 | .4325 | .4364 | .4404 | .4443 | .4483 |
| **−0.0** | .4641 | .4681 | .4721 | .4761 | .4801 | .4840 | .4880 |

**TI-84 PLUS**

```
normalcdf(-10000,-.24,0,1)
                0.405165175
```

You can use technology to find the cumulative area that corresponds to $z = -0.24$, as shown at the left. Note that to specify the lower bound, use $-10,000$.

**TRY IT YOURSELF 3**

1. Find the cumulative area that corresponds to a $z$-score of $-2.19$.

2. Find the cumulative area that corresponds to a $z$-score of 2.17.

*Answer: Page A39*

When the $z$-score is not in the table, use the entry closest to it. For a $z$-score that is exactly midway between two $z$-scores, use the area midway between the corresponding areas.

You can use the following guidelines to find various types of areas under the standard normal curve.

## GUIDELINES

**Finding Areas Under the Standard Normal Curve**

1. Sketch the standard normal curve and shade the appropriate area under the curve.
2. Find the area by following the directions for each case shown.
   a. To find the area to the *left* of $z$, find the area that corresponds to $z$ in the Standard Normal Table.

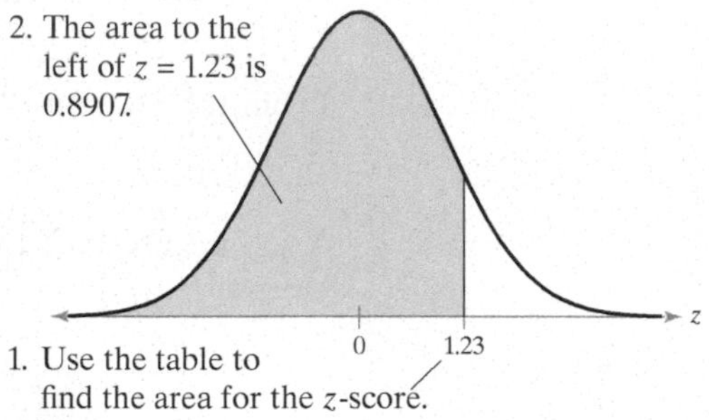
2. The area to the left of z = 1.23 is 0.8907.
0
1.23
z
1. Use the table to find the area for the z-score.

   b. To find the area to the *right* of $z$, use the Standard Normal Table to find the area that corresponds to $z$. Then subtract the area from 1.

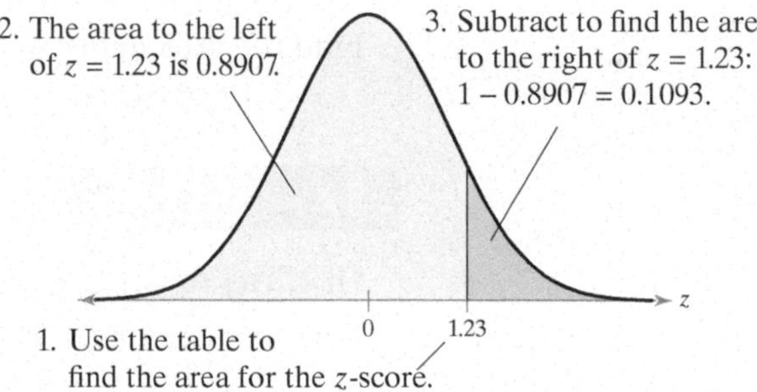
2. The area to the left of z = 1.23 is 0.8907.
3. Subtract to find the area to the right of z = 1.23: 1 − 0.8907 = 0.1093.
0
1.23
z
1. Use the table to find the area for the z-score.

   c. To find the area *between* two $z$-scores, find the area corresponding to each $z$-score in the Standard Normal Table. Then subtract the smaller area from the larger area.

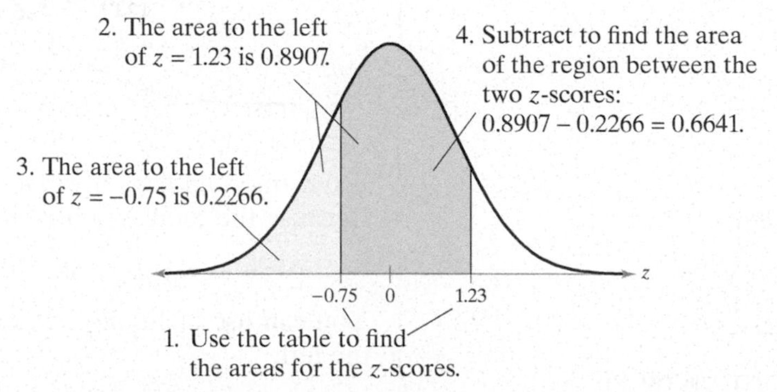
2. The area to the left of z = 1.23 is 0.8907.
4. Subtract to find the area of the region between the two z-scores: 0.8907 − 0.2266 = 0.6641.
3. The area to the left of z = −0.75 is 0.2266.
−0.75
0
1.23
z
1. Use the table to find the areas for the z-scores.

### Tech Tip

You can use technology to find the area under the standard normal curve. For instance, you can use the *ShadeNorm* feature on a TI-84 Plus to graph the area under the standard normal curve between $z = -0.75$ and $z = 1.23$, as shown below. The area between the two $z$-scores is shown below the graph. (Note that when you use technology, your answers may differ slightly from those found using the Standard Normal Table.)

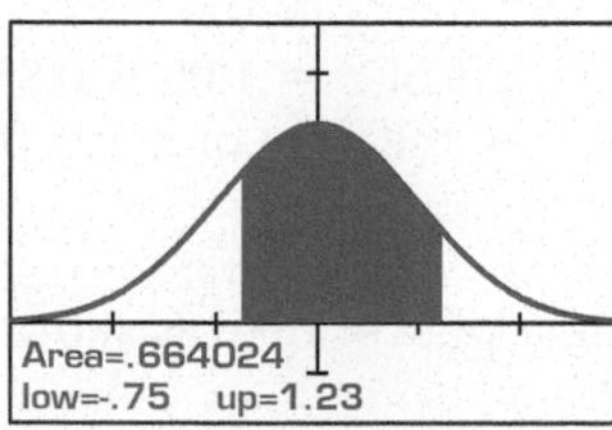
Area=.664024
low=-.75 up=1.23

**EXAMPLE 4**

### Finding Area Under the Standard Normal Curve

Find the area under the standard normal curve to the left of $z = -0.99$.

**SOLUTION**

The area under the standard normal curve to the left of $z = -0.99$ is shown.

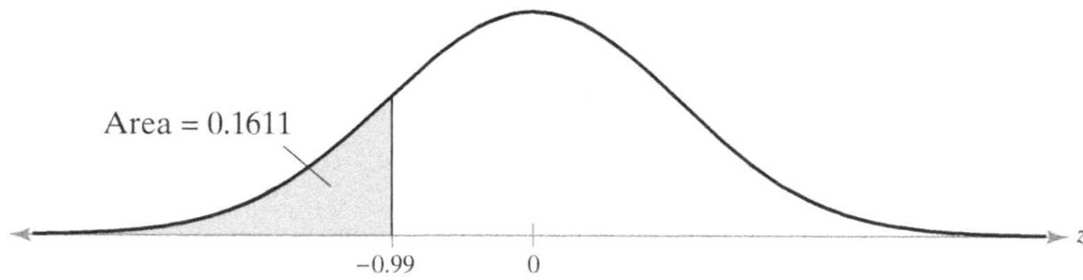


From the Standard Normal Table, this area is equal to

0.1611. Area to the left of $z = -0.99$

You can use technology to find the area to the left of $z = -0.99$, as shown below.

**EXCEL**

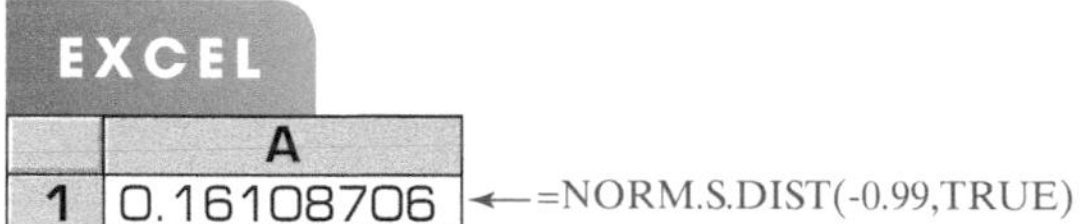

| | A |
|---|---|
| 1 | 0.16108706 |

=NORM.S.DIST(-0.99,TRUE)

**TRY IT YOURSELF 4**

Find the area under the standard normal curve to the left of $z = 2.13$.

*Answer: Page A39*

**EXAMPLE 5**

### Finding Area Under the Standard Normal Curve

Find the area under the standard normal curve to the right of $z = 1.06$.

**SOLUTION**

The area under the standard normal curve to the right of $z = 1.06$ is shown.

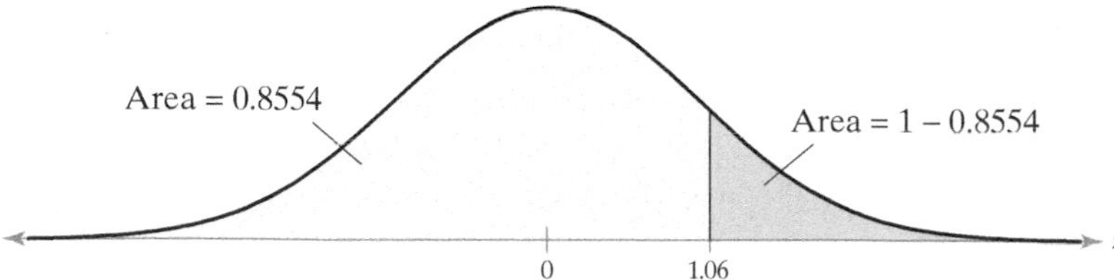


From the Standard Normal Table, the area to the left of $z = 1.06$ is 0.8554. Because the total area under the curve is 1, the area to the right of $z = 1.06$ is

$$\text{Area} = 1 - 0.8554 = 0.1446.$$

You can use technology to find the area to the right of $z = 1.06$, as shown at the left.

**EXCEL**

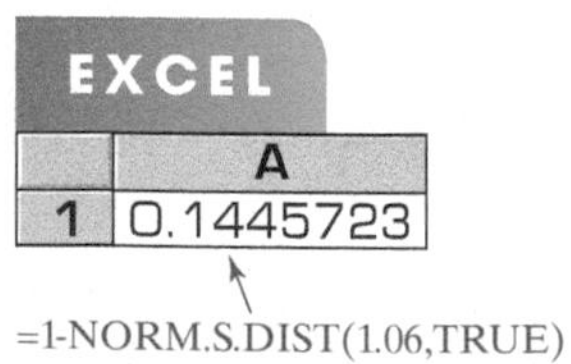

| | A |
|---|---|
| 1 | 0.1445723 |

=1-NORM.S.DIST(1.06,TRUE)

**TRY IT YOURSELF 5**

Find the area under the standard normal curve to the right of $z = -2.16$.

*Answer: Page A39*

## EXAMPLE 6

### Finding Area Under the Standard Normal Curve

Find the area under the standard normal curve between $z = -1.5$ and $z = 1.25$.

**SOLUTION**

The area under the standard normal curve between $z = -1.5$ and $z = 1.25$ is shown.

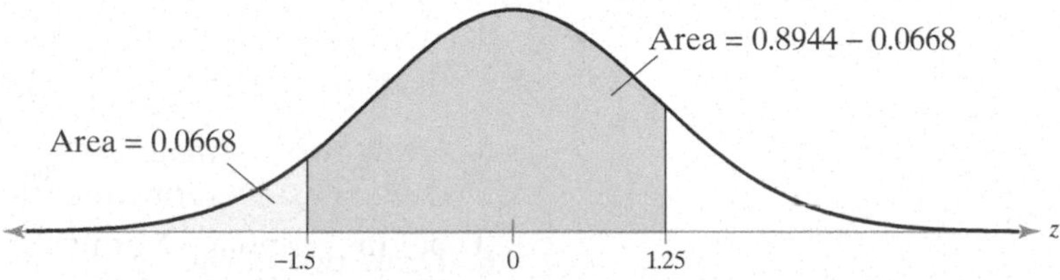


From the Standard Normal Table, the area to the left of $z = 1.25$ is 0.8944 and the area to the left of $z = -1.5$ is 0.0668. So, the area between $z = -1.5$ and $z = 1.25$ is

$$\text{Area} = 0.8944 - 0.0668 = 0.8276.$$

Note that when you use technology, your answers may differ slightly from those found using the Standard Normal Table. For instance, when finding the area on a TI-84 Plus, you get the result shown at the right.

**TI-84 PLUS**

```
normalcdf(-1.5,1.25,0,1)
                0.8275429323
```

***Interpretation*** About 82.76% of the area under the curve falls between $z = -1.5$ and $z = 1.25$.

**TRY IT YOURSELF 6**

Find the area under the standard normal curve between $z = -2.165$ and $z = -1.35$.

*Answer: Page A39*

Because the normal distribution is a continuous probability distribution, the area under the standard normal curve to the left of a $z$-score gives the probability that $z$ is less than that $z$-score. For instance, in Example 4, the area to the left of $z = -0.99$ is 0.1611. So,

$$P(z < -0.99) = 0.1611$$

which is read as "the probability that $z$ is less than $-0.99$ is 0.1611." The table shows the probabilities for Examples 5 and 6. (You will learn more about finding probabilities in the next section.)

| | **Area** | **Probability** |
|---|---|---|
| **Example 5** | To the right of $z = 1.06$: 0.1446 | $P(z > 1.06) = 0.1446$ |
| **Example 6** | Between $z = -1.5$ and $z = 1.25$: 0.8276 | $P(-1.5 < z < 1.25) = 0.8276$ |

Recall from Section 2.4 that values lying more than two standard deviations from the mean are considered unusual. Values lying more than three standard deviations from the mean are considered *very* unusual. So, a $z$-score greater than 2 or less than $-2$ is unusual. A $z$-score greater than 3 or less than $-3$ is *very* unusual.

# 5.1 EXERCISES

For Extra Help: MyLab Statistics

## Building Basic Skills and Vocabulary

1. Given the mean of a normal distribution, how can you find the median?
2. What is the total area under the normal curve?
3. Describe the inflection points on the graph of a normal distribution. At what $x$-values are the inflection points located?
4. Give two real-life examples of a continuous variable. Include one that is likely to be normally distributed. Explain your reasoning.
5. Draw two normal curves that have the same mean but different standard deviations. Describe the similarities and differences.
6. Draw two normal curves that have different means but the same standard deviation. Describe the similarities and differences.
7. What is the mean of the standard normal distribution? What is the standard deviation of the standard normal distribution?
8. Explain how to transform a given $x$-value of a normally distributed variable $x$ into a $z$-score.
9. **Getting at the Concept** Why is it correct to say "a" normal distribution and "the" standard normal distribution?
10. **Getting at the Concept** A $z$-score is 0. Which of these statements must be true? Explain your reasoning.
    (a) The mean is 0.
    (b) The corresponding $x$-value is 0.
    (c) The corresponding $x$-value is equal to the mean.

**Graphical Analysis** *In Exercises 11–16, determine whether the graph could represent a variable with a normal distribution. Explain your reasoning. If the graph appears to represent a normal distribution, estimate the mean and standard deviation.*

**11.**

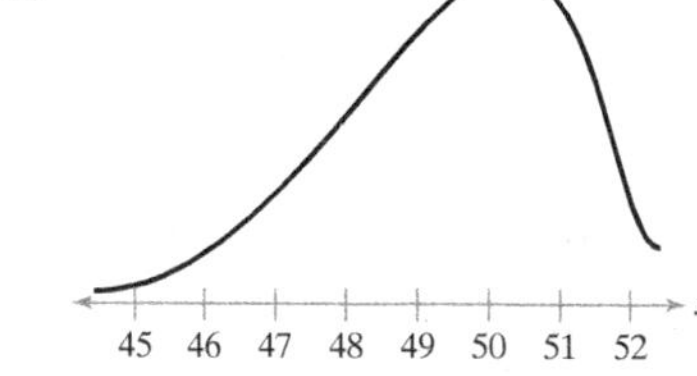


**12.**

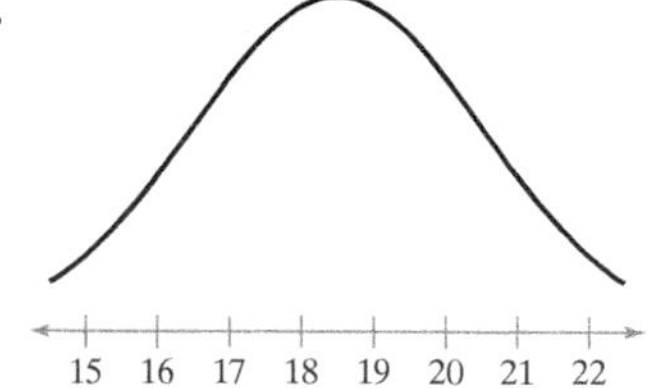


**13.**

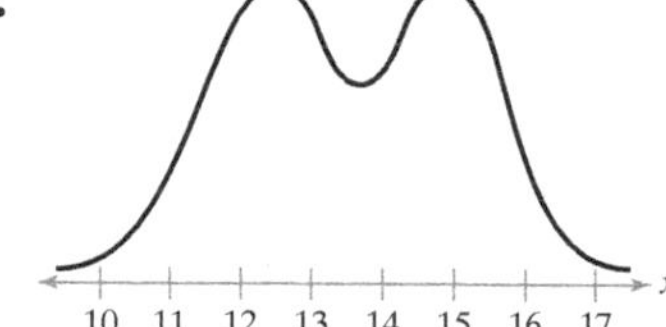


**14.**

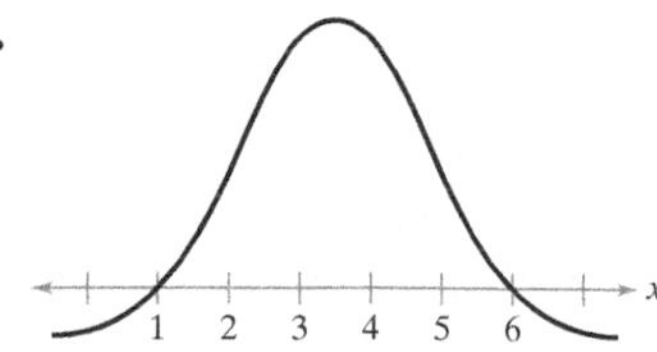


**15.**

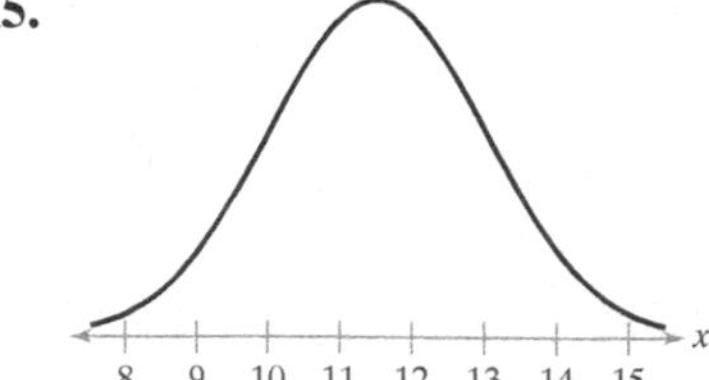


**16.**

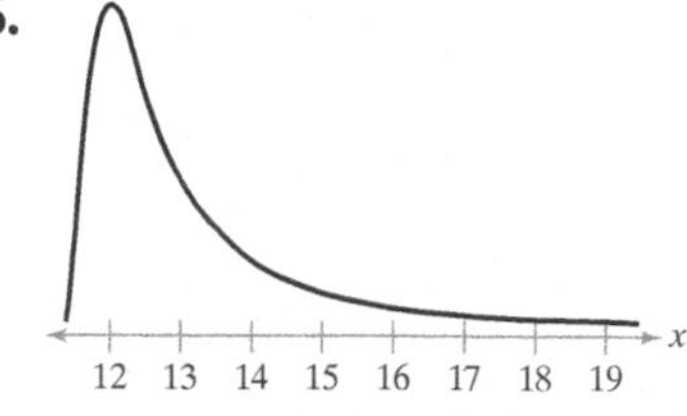

## Using and Interpreting Concepts

**Finding Area** *In Exercises 17–22, find the area of the shaded region under the standard normal curve. If convenient, use technology to find the area.*

**17.**

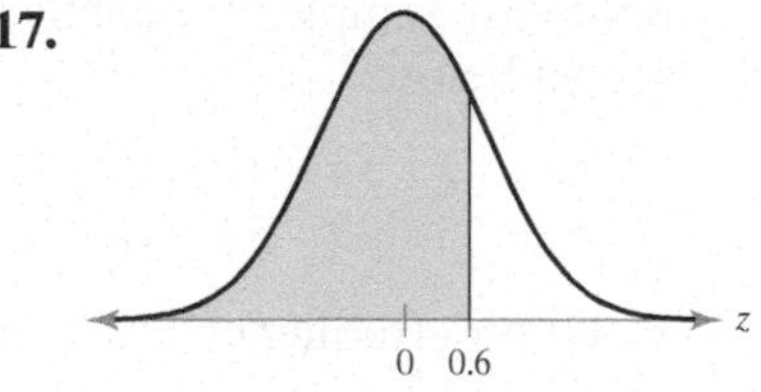


**18.**

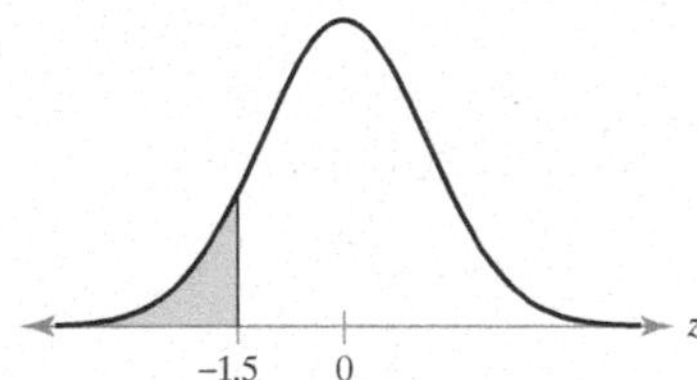


**19.**

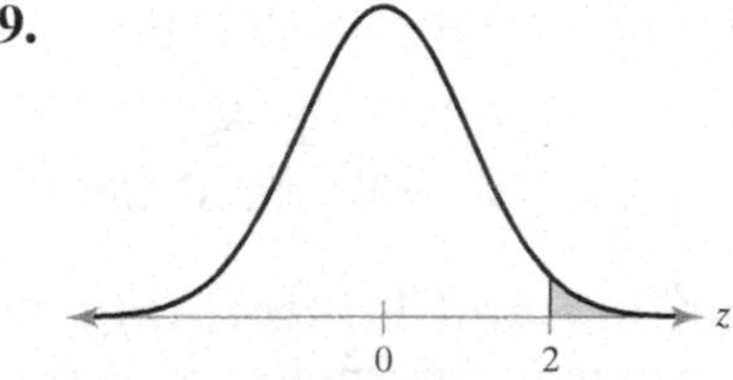


**20.**

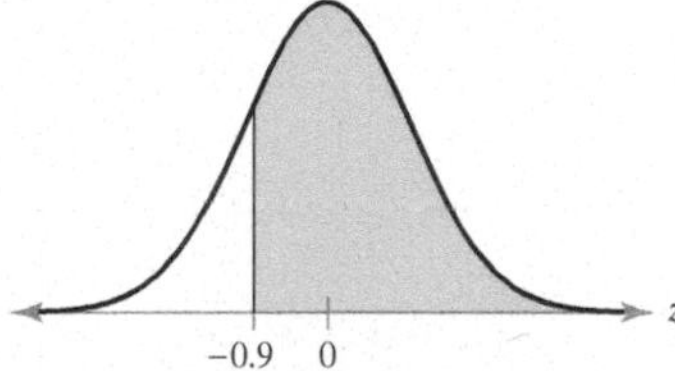


**21.**

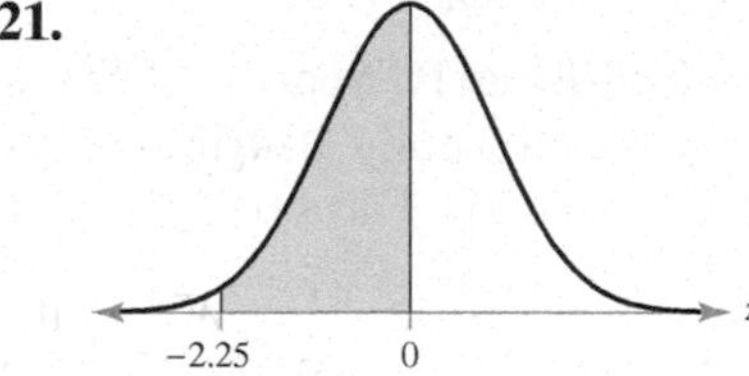


**22.**

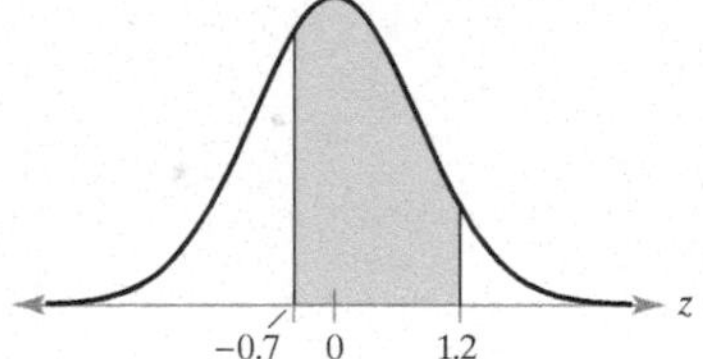


**Finding Area** *In Exercises 23–36, find the indicated area under the standard normal curve. If convenient, use technology to find the area.*

**23.** To the left of $z = 0.33$

**24.** To the left of $z = -3.16$

**25.** To the left of $z = -1.675$

**26.** To the left of $z = 1.365$

**27.** To the right of $z = -0.65$

**28.** To the right of $z = 3.25$

**29.** To the right of $z = -0.355$

**30.** To the right of $z = 2.215$

**31.** Between $z = 0$ and $z = 2.86$

**32.** Between $z = -1.53$ and $z = 0$

**33.** Between $z = -1.55$ and $z = 1.55$

**34.** Between $z = -2.33$ and $z = 2.33$

**35.** To the left of $z = -1.28$ and to the right of $z = 1.28$

**36.** To the left of $z = -1.44$ and to the right of $z = 2.21$

**37. Manufacturer Claims** You work for a consumer watchdog publication and are testing the advertising claims of a tire manufacturer. The manufacturer claims that the life spans of the tires are normally distributed, with a mean of 40,000 miles and a standard deviation of 4000 miles. You test 16 tires and record the life spans shown below.

| | | | | | | | |
|---|---|---|---|---|---|---|---|
| 48,778 | 41,046 | 29,083 | 36,394 | 32,302 | 42,787 | 41,972 | 37,229 |
| 25,314 | 31,920 | 38,030 | 38,445 | 30,750 | 38,886 | 36,770 | 46,049 |

(a) Draw a frequency histogram to display these data. Use five classes. Do the life spans appear to be normally distributed? Explain.

(b) Find the mean and standard deviation of your sample.

(c) Compare the mean and standard deviation of your sample with those in the manufacturer's claim. Discuss the differences.

 **38. Milk Consumption** You are performing a study about weekly per capita milk consumption. A previous study found weekly per capita milk consumption to be normally distributed, with a mean of 48.7 fluid ounces and a standard deviation of 8.6 fluid ounces. You randomly sample 30 people and record the weekly milk consumptions shown below.

| | | | | | | | | | | | | | | |
|---|---|---|---|---|---|---|---|---|---|---|---|---|---|---|
| 40 | 45 | 54 | 41 | 43 | 31 | 47 | 30 | 33 | 37 | 48 | 57 | 52 | 45 | 38 |
| 65 | 25 | 39 | 53 | 51 | 58 | 52 | 40 | 46 | 44 | 48 | 61 | 47 | 49 | 57 |

(a) Draw a frequency histogram to display these data. Use seven classes. Do the consumptions appear to be normally distributed? Explain.

(b) Find the mean and standard deviation of your sample.

(c) Compare the mean and standard deviation of your sample with those of the previous study. Discuss the differences.

**Computing and Interpreting *z*-Scores** *In Exercises 39 and 40, (a) find the z-score that corresponds to each value and (b) determine whether any of the values are unusual.*

**39. Stanford-Binet IQ Scores** The test scores for the Stanford-Binet Intelligence Scale are normally distributed with a mean score of 100 and a standard deviation of 16. The test scores of four students selected at random are 98, 65, 106, and 124. *(Source: StanfordBinetTest.com)*

**40. SAT Scores** The test scores for students who took the SAT (without the essay) are normally distributed with a mean score of 1051 and a standard deviation of 211. The test scores of four students selected at random are 1050, 960, 870, and 1440. *(Source: College Board)*

**Finding Probability** *In Exercises 41–46, find the probability of z occurring in the shaded region of the standard normal distribution. If convenient, use technology to find the probability.*

**41.**

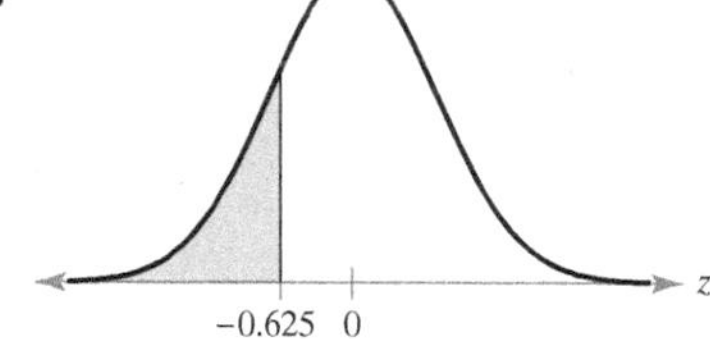


**42.**

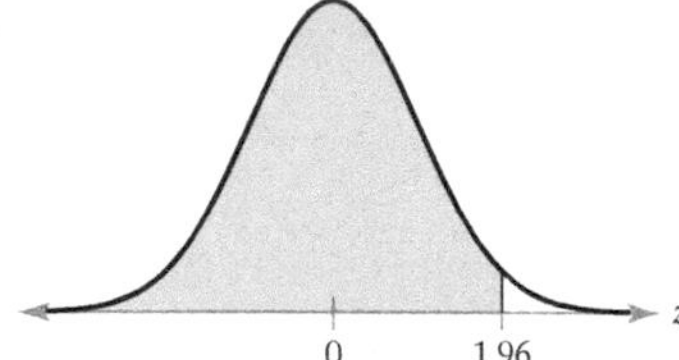


**43.**

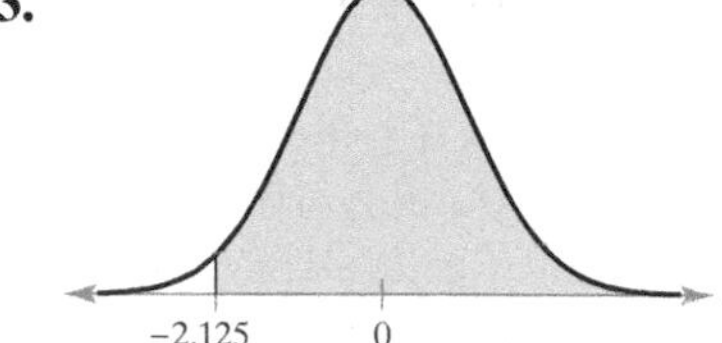


**44.**

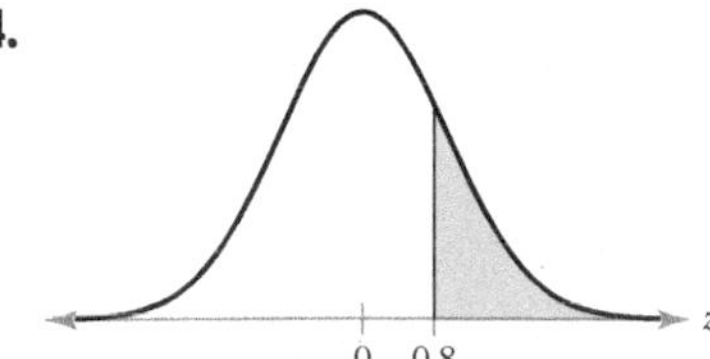


**45.**

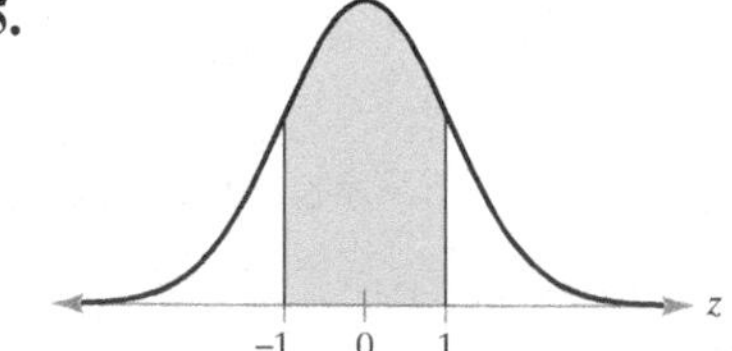


**46.**

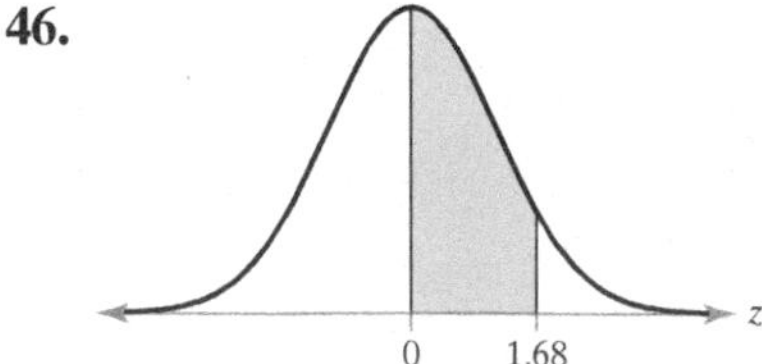

**Finding Probability** *In Exercises 47–56, find the indicated probability using the standard normal distribution. If convenient, use technology to find the probability.*

**47.** $P(z < 0.53)$ **48.** $P(z < -1.11)$ **49.** $P(z > 2.175)$

**50.** $P(z > -1.85)$ **51.** $P(-0.89 < z < 0)$ **52.** $P(0 < z < 0.835)$

**53.** $P(-1.78 < z < 1.78)$ **54.** $P(-1.54 < z < 1.54)$

**55.** $P(z < -2.58 \text{ or } z > 2.58)$ **56.** $P(z < -1.22 \text{ or } z > 1.32)$

## Extending Concepts

**57. Writing** Draw a normal curve with a mean of 60 and a standard deviation of 12. Describe how you constructed the curve and discuss its features.

**58. Writing** Draw a normal curve with a mean of 450 and a standard deviation of 50. Describe how you constructed the curve and discuss its features.

**Uniform Distribution** *A **uniform distribution** is a continuous probability distribution for a random variable x between two values a and b $(a < b)$, where $a \le x \le b$ and all of the values of x are equally likely to occur. The graph of a uniform distribution is shown below.*

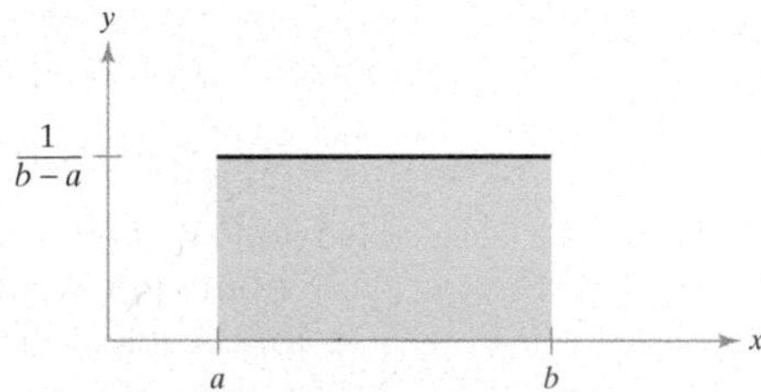


*The probability density function of a uniform distribution is*

$$y = \frac{1}{b - a}$$

*on the interval from $x = a$ to $x = b$. For any value of x less than a or greater than b, $y = 0$. In Exercises 59 and 60, use this information.*

**59.** Show that the probability density function of a uniform distribution satisfies the two conditions for a probability density function.

**60.** For two values $c$ and $d$, where $a \le c < d \le b$, the probability that $x$ lies between $c$ and $d$ is equal to the area under the curve between $c$ and $d$, as shown below.

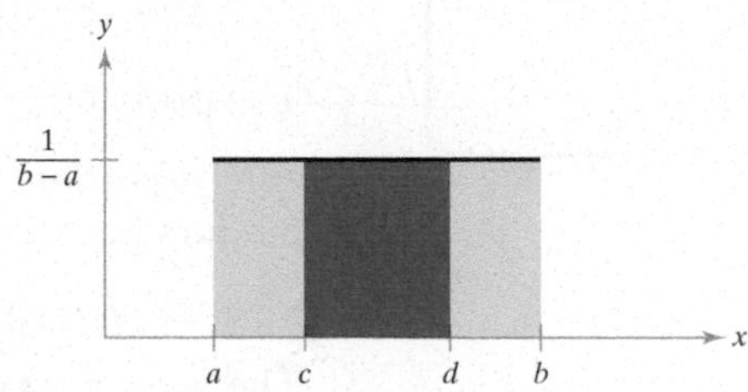


So, the area of the red region equals the probability that $x$ lies between $c$ and $d$. For a uniform distribution from $a = 1$ to $b = 25$, find the probability that

(a) $x$ lies between 2 and 8.

(b) $x$ lies between 4 and 12.

(c) $x$ lies between 5 and 17.

(d) $x$ lies between 8 and 14.

# 5.2 Normal Distributions: Finding Probabilities

### What You Should Learn

- How to find probabilities for normally distributed variables using a table and using technology

Probability and Normal Distributions

## Probability and Normal Distributions

When a random variable $x$ is normally distributed, you can find the probability that $x$ will lie in an interval by calculating the area under the normal curve for the interval. To find the area under any normal curve, first convert the upper and lower bounds of the interval to $z$-scores. Then use the standard normal distribution to find the area. For instance, consider a normal curve with $\mu = 500$ and $\sigma = 100$, as shown at the upper left. The value of $x$ one standard deviation above the mean is $\mu + \sigma = 500 + 100 = 600$. Now consider the standard normal curve shown at the lower left. The value of $z$ one standard deviation above the mean is $\mu + \sigma = 0 + 1 = 1$. Because a $z$-score of 1 corresponds to an $x$-value of 600, and areas are not changed with a transformation to a standard normal curve, the shaded areas in the figures at the left are equal.

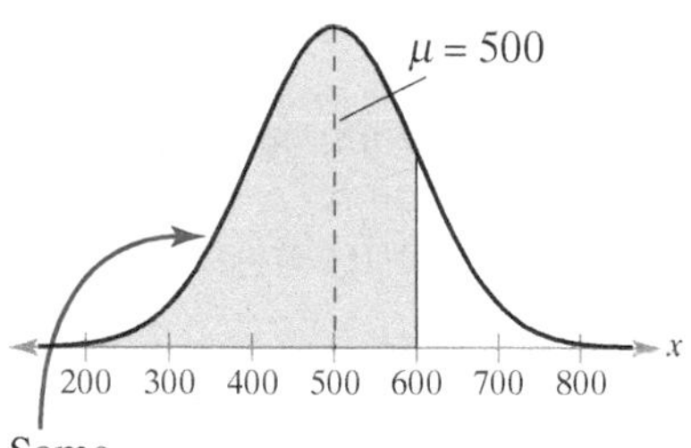


Same area

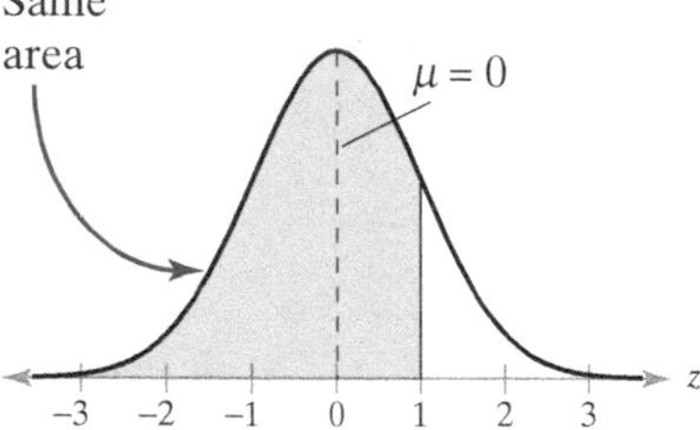


### EXAMPLE 1

### Finding Probabilities for Normal Distributions

A national study found that college students with jobs worked an average of 25 hours per week. The standard deviation is 11 hours. A college student with a job is selected at random. Find the probability that the student works for less than 5 hours per week. Assume that the lengths of time college students work are normally distributed and are represented by the variable $x$. *(Adapted from Statista)*

**SOLUTION**

The figure shows a normal curve with $\mu = 25$, $\sigma = 11$, and the shaded area for $x$ less than 5. The $z$-score that corresponds to 5 hours is

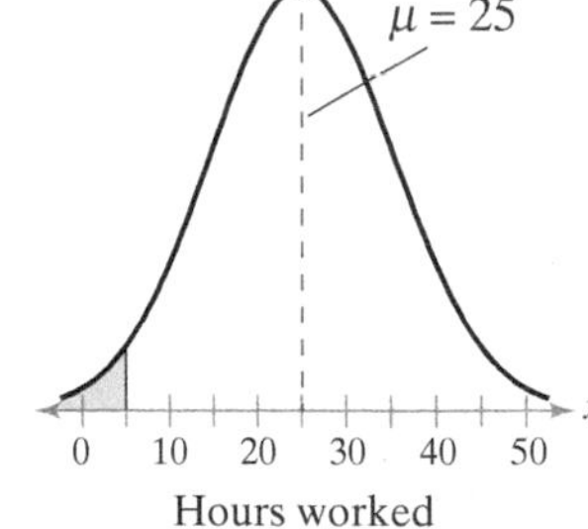


$$z = \frac{x - \mu}{\sigma} = \frac{5 - 25}{11} \approx -1.82.$$

The Standard Normal Table shows that

$$P(z < -1.82) = 0.0344.$$

The probability that the student works for less than 5 hours per week is 0.0344.

***Interpretation*** So, 3.44% of college students with jobs worked for less than 5 hours per week. Because 3.44% is less than 5%, this is an unusual event.

**TRY IT YOURSELF 1**

The average speed of vehicles traveling on a stretch of highway is 67 miles per hour with a standard deviation of 3.5 miles per hour. A vehicle is selected at random. What is the probability that it is violating the speed limit of 70 miles per hour? Assume the speeds are normally distributed and are represented by the variable $x$.

*Answer: Page A39*

### Study Tip

To learn how to determine whether a random sample is taken from a normal distribution, see Appendix C.

In Example 1, because $P(z < -1.82) = P(x < 5)$, another way to write the probability is $P(x < 5) = 0.0344$.

## EXAMPLE 2

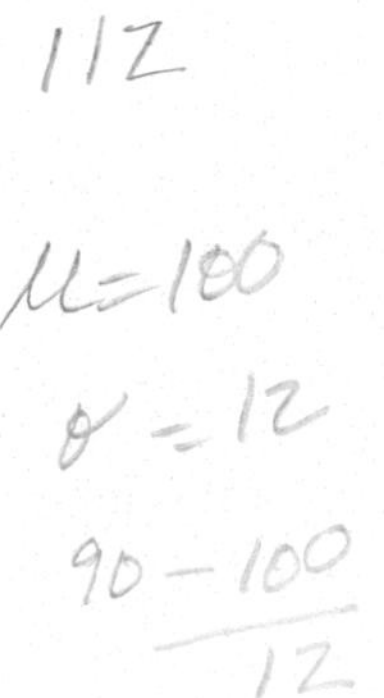

### Finding Probabilities for Normal Distributions

A survey indicates that for each trip to a supermarket, a shopper spends an average of 41 minutes with a standard deviation of 12 minutes in the store. The lengths of time spent in the store are normally distributed and are represented by the variable $x$. A shopper enters the store. (a) Find the probability that the shopper will be in the store for each interval of time listed below. (b) When 200 shoppers enter the store, how many shoppers would you expect to be in the store for each interval of time listed below? *(Adapted from Time Use Institute)*

**1.** Between 20 and 50 minutes

**2.** More than 35 minutes

### SOLUTION

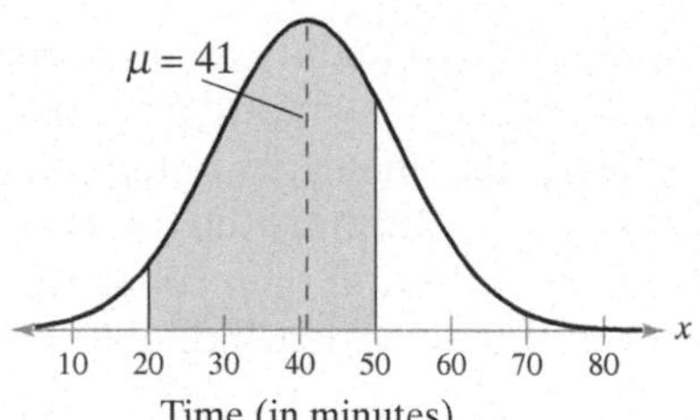


**1.** (a) The figure at the left shows a normal curve with $\mu = 41$ minutes, $\sigma = 12$ minutes, and the shaded area for $x$ between 20 and 50 minutes. The $z$-scores that correspond to 20 minutes and to 50 minutes are

$$z_1 = \frac{20 - 41}{12} = -1.75 \quad \text{and} \quad z_2 = \frac{50 - 41}{12} = 0.75.$$

So, the probability that a shopper will be in the store between 20 and 50 minutes is

$$\begin{aligned} P(20 < x < 50) &= P(-1.75 < z < 0.75) \\ &= P(z < 0.75) - P(z < -1.75) \\ &= 0.7734 - 0.0401 \\ &= 0.7333. \end{aligned}$$

(b) ***Interpretation*** When 200 shoppers enter the store, you would expect about $200(0.7333) = 146.66 \approx 147$ shoppers to be in the store between 20 and 50 minutes.

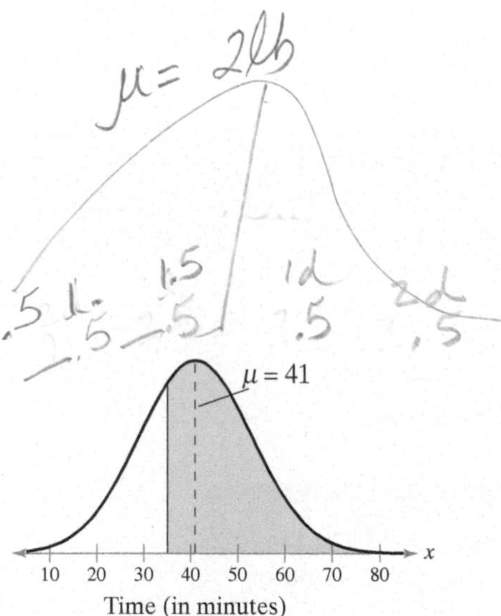


**2.** (a) The figure at the left shows a normal curve with $\mu = 41$ minutes, $\sigma = 12$ minutes, and the shaded area for $x$ greater than 35. The $z$-score that corresponds to 35 minutes is

$$z = \frac{35 - 41}{12} = -0.5.$$

So, the probability that a shopper will be in the store more than 35 minutes is

$$\begin{aligned} P(x > 35) &= P(z > -0.5) \\ &= 1 - P(z < -0.5) \\ &= 1 - 0.3085 \\ &= 0.6915. \end{aligned}$$

(b) ***Interpretation*** When 200 shoppers enter the store, you would expect about $200(0.6915) = 138.3 \approx 138$ shoppers to be in the store more than 35 minutes.

### TRY IT YOURSELF 2

What is the probability that the shopper in Example 2 will be in the supermarket between 29 and 56 minutes? When 200 shoppers enter the store, how many shoppers would you expect to be in the store between 29 and 56 minutes?

*Answer: Page A39*

Another way to find normal probabilities is to use technology. You can find normal probabilities using Minitab, Excel, StatCrunch, and the TI-84 Plus.

## Picturing the World

In baseball, a batting average is the number of hits divided by the number of at bats. The batting averages of all Major League Baseball players in a recent year can be approximated by a normal distribution, as shown in the figure. The mean of the batting averages is 0.245 and the standard deviation is 0.017. (Source: Major League Baseball)

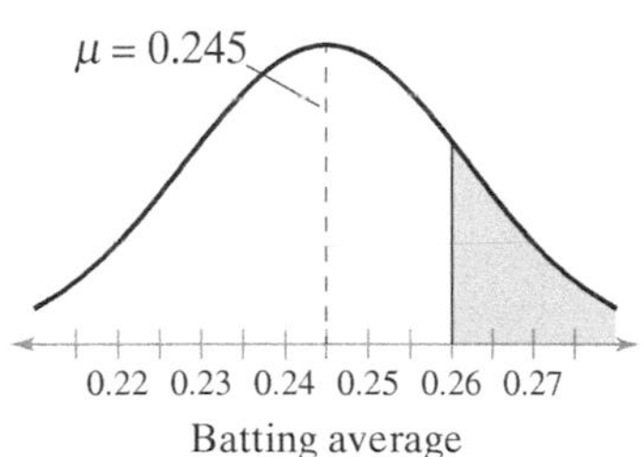


**What percent of the players have a batting average of 0.260 or greater? Out of 40 players on a roster, how many would you expect to have a batting average of 0.260 or greater?**

**EXAMPLE 3**

### Using Technology to Find Normal Probabilities

In the United States, the numbers of physicians involved in patient care per state are normally distributed, with a mean of 280 physicians per 100,000 resident population and a standard deviation of 78 physicians per 100,000 resident population. You randomly select a state. What is the probability that the state has fewer than 300 physicians per 100,000 resident population? Use technology to find the probability. *(Adapted from National Center for Health Statistics)*

**SOLUTION**

Minitab, Excel, StatCrunch, and the TI-84 Plus each have features that allow you to find normal probabilities without first converting to standard $z$-scores. Note that to use these features, you must specify the mean and standard deviation of the population, as well as any $x$-values that determine the interval. You are given that $\mu = 280$ and $\sigma = 78$, and you want to find the probability that the state has fewer than 300 physicians per 100,000 resident population, or $P(x < 300)$.

**MINITAB**

**Cumulative Distribution Function**

Normal with mean = 280 and standard deviation = 78

| x | P(X ≤ x) |
|---|---|
| 300 | 0.601183 |

**EXCEL**

| | A |
|---|---|
| 1 | 0.601182965 |

←=NORM.DIST(300,280,78,TRUE)

**TI-84 PLUS**

normalcdf(-10000, 300, 280, 78)
.6011829115

**STATCRUNCH**

**Normal Calculator**

Mean: 280 Std. Dev.: 78
P(x ≤ 300) = 0.60118297

From the displays, you can see that $P(x < 300) \approx 0.601$.

***Interpretation*** The probability that the state has fewer than 300 physicians per 100,000 resident population is about 0.601, or 60.1%.

**TRY IT YOURSELF 3**

You randomly select a state. Using the data from Example 3, what is the probability that the state has between 300 and 350 physicians per 100,000 resident population? Use technology to find the probability.

*Answer: Page A39*

# 5.2 EXERCISES

For Extra Help: MyLab Statistics

## Building Basic Skills and Vocabulary

**Computing Probabilities for Normal Distributions** *In Exercises 1–6, the random variable x is normally distributed with mean $\mu = 174$ and standard deviation $\sigma = 20$. Find the indicated probability.*

**1.** $P(x < 170)$ **2.** $P(x < 200)$ **3.** $P(x > 182)$

**4.** $P(x > 155)$ **5.** $P(160 < x < 170)$ **6.** $P(172 < x < 192)$

## Using and Interpreting Concepts

**Finding Probabilities for Normal Distributions** *In Exercises 7–12, find the indicated probabilities. If convenient, use technology to find the probabilities.*

**7. Heights of Women** In a survey of 19-year-old U.S. women, their heights were normally distributed, with a mean of 63.9 inches and a standard deviation of 3.3 inches. Find the probability that a randomly selected survey participant has a height that is (a) less than 57 inches, (b) between 60 and 65 inches, and (c) more than 70.5 inches. Identify any unusual events in parts (a)–(c). Explain your reasoning. *(Adapted from National Center for Health Statistics)*

**8. Head Circumference** In a survey of male infants from 3 to 5 months of age, head circumference was found to be normally distributed, with a mean of 42.9 centimeters and a standard deviation of 1.5 centimeters. Find the probability that a randomly selected infant from the survey had a head circumference of (a) less than 41 centimeters, (b) between 41 and 45 centimeters, and (c) more than 45.8 centimeters. Identify any unusual events in parts (a)–(c). Explain your reasoning. *(Adapted from National Center for Health Statistics)*

**9. MCAT Scores** In a recent year, the MCAT total scores were normally distributed, with a mean of 500.9 and a standard deviation of 10.6. Find the probability that a randomly selected medical student who took the MCAT has a total score that is (a) less than 490, (b) between 490 and 510, and (c) more than 515. Identify any unusual events in parts (a)–(c). Explain your reasoning. *(Source: Association of American Medical Colleges)*

**10. MCAT Scores** In a recent year, the MCAT scores for the critical analysis and reasoning skills portion of the test were normally distributed, with a mean of 124.8 and a standard deviation of 2.9. Find the probability that a randomly selected medical student who took the MCAT has a critical analysis and reasoning skills score that is (a) less than 120, (b) between 122 and 127, and (c) more than 131. Identify any unusual events in parts (a)–(c). Explain your reasoning. *(Source: Association of American Medical Colleges)*

**11. Utility Bills** The monthly utility bills in a city are normally distributed, with a mean of \$100 and a standard deviation of \$12. Find the probability that a randomly selected utility bill is (a) less than \$70, (b) between \$90 and \$120, and (c) more than \$140.

**12. Health Club Schedule** The amounts of time per workout an athlete uses a stairclimber are normally distributed, with a mean of 20 minutes and a standard deviation of 5 minutes. Find the probability that a randomly selected athlete uses a stairclimber for (a) less than 17 minutes, (b) between 20 and 28 minutes, and (c) more than 30 minutes.

**Graphical Analysis** *In Exercises 13–16, a member is selected at random from the population represented by the graph. Find the probability that the member selected at random is from the shaded region of the graph. Assume the variable x is normally distributed.*

**13.**

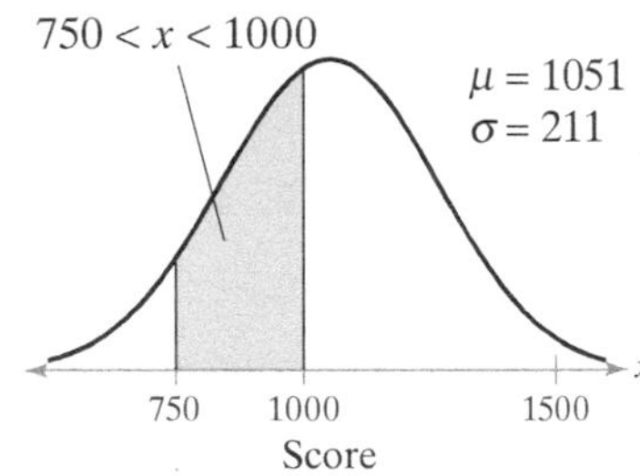


*(Source: College Board)*

**14.**

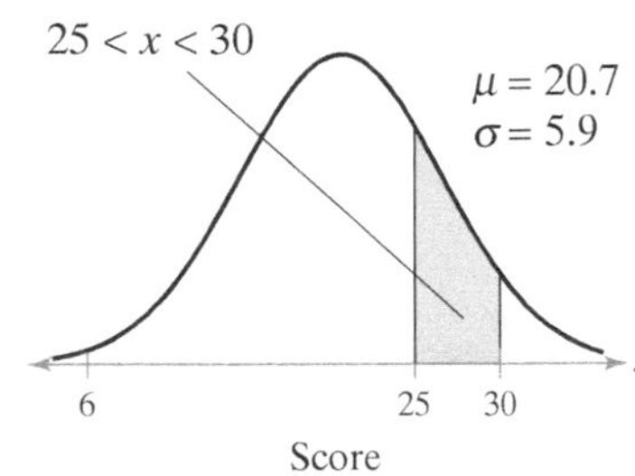


*(Source: ACT, Inc.)*

**15.**

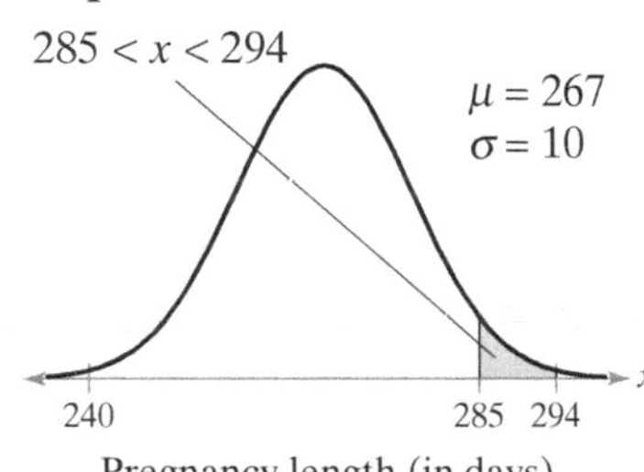


**16.**

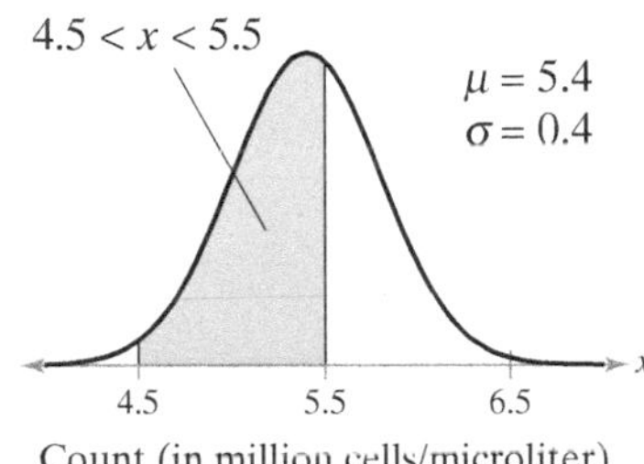


**Using Normal Distributions** *In Exercises 17–20, answer the questions about the specified normal distribution.*

**17. SAT Total Scores** Use the normal distribution in Exercise 13.

(a) What percent of the SAT total scores are less than 1300?

(b) Out of 1000 randomly selected SAT total scores, about how many would you expect to be greater than 1100?

**18. ACT Composite Scores** Use the normal distribution in Exercise 14.

(a) What percent of the ACT composite scores are less than 19?

(b) Out of 1500 randomly selected ACT composite scores, about how many would you expect to be greater than 21?

**19. Pregnancy Length** Use the normal distribution in Exercise 15.

(a) What percent of the new mothers had a pregnancy length of less than 290 days?

(b) What percent of the new mothers had a pregnancy length of between 260 and 300 days?

(c) Out of 250 randomly selected new mothers, about how many would you expect to have had a pregnancy length of greater than 287 days?

**20. Red Blood Cell Count** Use the normal distribution in Exercise 16.

(a) What percent of the adult males have a red blood cell count less than 6 million cells per microliter?

(b) What percent of the adult males have a red blood cell count between 4.7 and 5.3 million cells per microliter?

(c) Out of 200 randomly selected adult males, about how many would you expect to have a red blood cell count greater than 4.8 million cells per microliter?

## Extending Concepts

**Control Charts** ***Statistical process control (SPC)*** *is the use of statistics to monitor and improve the quality of a process, such as manufacturing an engine part. In SPC, information about a process is gathered and used to determine whether a process is meeting all of the specified requirements. One tool used in SPC is a* ***control chart.*** *When individual measurements of a variable x are normally distributed, a control chart can be used to detect processes that are possibly out of statistical control. Three warning signals that a control chart uses to detect a process that may be out of control are listed below.*

*(1) A point lies beyond three standard deviations of the mean.*

*(2) There are nine consecutive points that fall on one side of the mean.*

*(3) At least two of three consecutive points lie more than two standard deviations from the mean.*

*In Exercises 21–24, a control chart is shown. Each chart has horizontal lines drawn at the mean $\mu$, at $\mu \pm 2\sigma$, and at $\mu \pm 3\sigma$. Determine whether the process shown is in control or out of control. Explain.*

**21.** A gear has been designed to have a diameter of 3 inches. The standard deviation of the process is 0.2 inch.

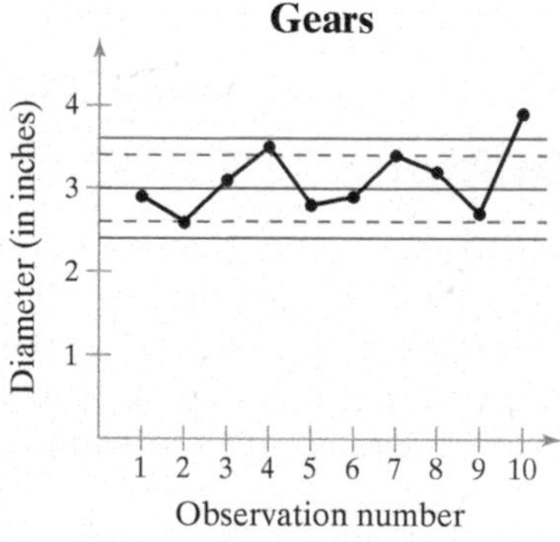


**22.** A nail has been designed to have a length of 4 inches. The standard deviation of the process is 0.12 inch.

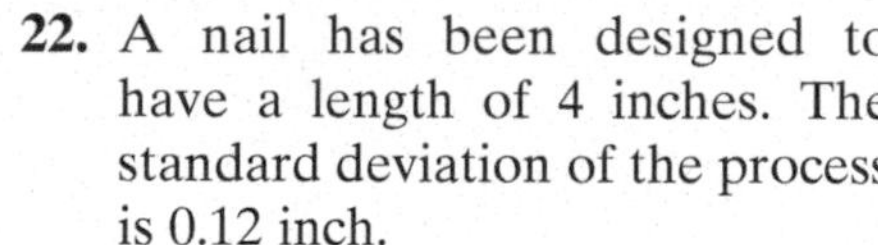

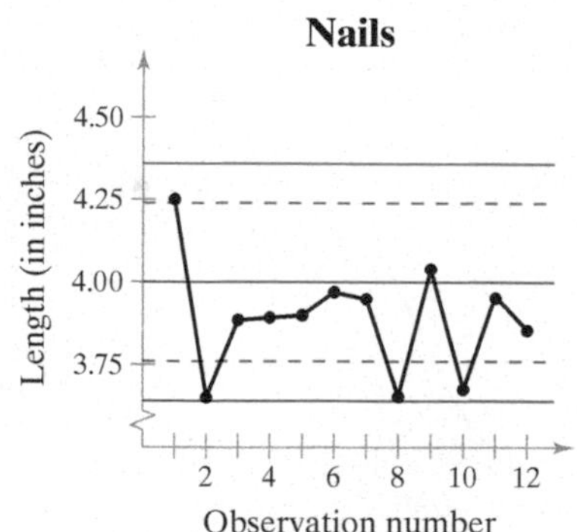


**23.** A liquid-dispensing machine has been designed to fill bottles with 1 liter of liquid. The standard deviation of the process is 0.1 liter.

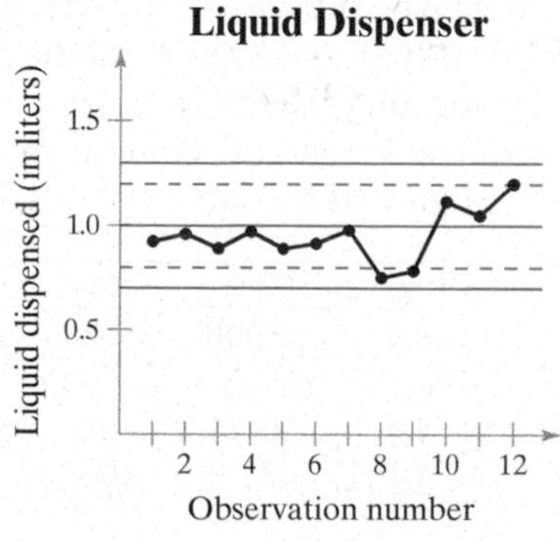


**24.** An engine part has been designed to have a diameter of 55 millimeters. The standard deviation of the process is 0.001 millimeter.

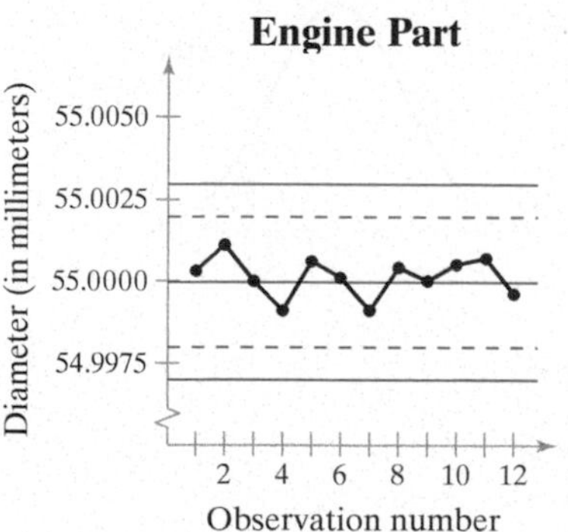

# 5.3 Normal Distributions: Finding Values

### What You Should Learn

- How to find a $z$-score given the area under the normal curve
- How to transform a $z$-score to an $x$-value
- How to find a specific data value of a normal distribution given the probability

Finding $z$-Scores ■ Transforming a $z$-Score to an $x$-Value ■ Finding a Specific Data Value for a Given Probability

## Finding $z$-Scores

In Section 5.2, you were given a normally distributed random variable $x$ and you found the probability that $x$ would lie in an interval by calculating the area under the normal curve for the interval.

But what if you are given a probability and want to find a value? For instance, a university might want to know the lowest test score a student can have on an entrance exam and still be in the top 10%, or a medical researcher might want to know the cutoff values for selecting the middle 90% of patients by age. In this section, you will learn how to find a value given an area under a normal curve (or a probability), as shown in the next example.

**EXAMPLE 1**

### Finding a $z$-Score Given an Area

1. Find the $z$-score that corresponds to a cumulative area of 0.3632.
2. Find the $z$-score that has 10.75% of the distribution's area to its right.

**SOLUTION**

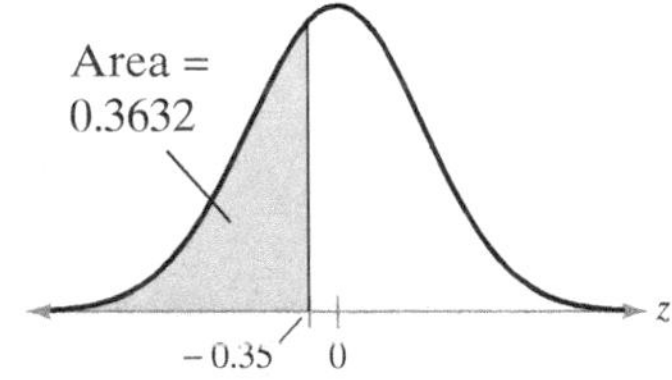


1. Find the $z$-score that corresponds to an area of 0.3632 by locating 0.3632 in the Standard Normal Table. The values at the beginning of the corresponding row and at the top of the corresponding column give the $z$-score. For this area, the row value is −0.3 and the column value is 0.05. So, the $z$-score is −0.35, as shown in the figure at the left.

| z | .09 | .08 | .07 | .06 | .05 | .04 | .03 |
|---|---|---|---|---|---|---|---|
| −3.4 | .0002 | .0003 | .0003 | .0003 | .0003 | .0003 | .0003 |
| −0.5 | .2776 | .2810 | .2843 | .2877 | .2912 | .2946 | .2981 |
| −0.4 | .3121 | .3156 | .3192 | .3228 | .3264 | .3300 | .3336 |
| −0.3 | .3483 | .3520 | .3557 | .3594 | .3632 | .3669 | .3707 |
| −0.2 | .3859 | .3897 | .3936 | .3974 | .4013 | .4052 | .4090 |

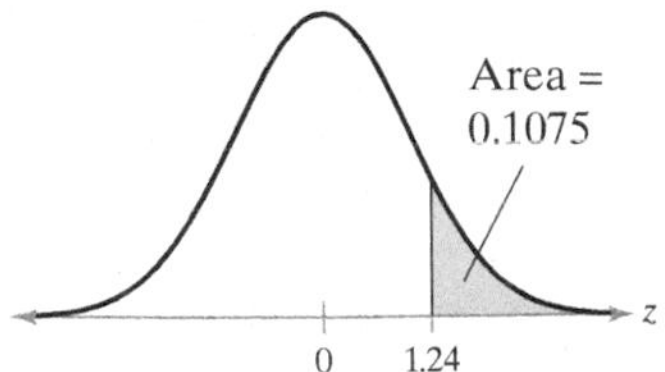


2. Because the area to the right is 0.1075, the cumulative area is $1 - 0.1075 = 0.8925$. Find the $z$-score that corresponds to an area of 0.8925 by locating 0.8925 in the Standard Normal Table. For this area, the row value is 1.2 and the column value is 0.04. So, the $z$-score is 1.24, as shown in the figure at the left.

| z | .00 | .01 | .02 | .03 | .04 | .05 | .06 |
|---|---|---|---|---|---|---|---|
| 0.0 | .5000 | .5040 | .5080 | .5120 | .5160 | .5199 | .5239 |
| 1.0 | .8413 | .8438 | .8461 | .8485 | .8508 | .8531 | .8554 |
| 1.1 | .8643 | .8665 | .8686 | .8708 | .8729 | .8749 | .8770 |
| 1.2 | .8849 | .8869 | .8888 | .8907 | .8925 | .8944 | .8962 |
| 1.3 | .9032 | .9049 | .9066 | .9082 | .9099 | .9115 | .9131 |

**Tech Tip**

You can use technology to find the $z$-scores that correspond to cumulative areas. For instance, you can use a TI-84 Plus to find the $z$-scores in Example 1, as shown below.

```
invNorm(.3632,0,1)
           -0.3499183227
invNorm(.8925,0,1)
            1.239933478
```

**TRY IT YOURSELF 1**

1. Find the $z$-score that has 96.16% of the distribution's area to its right.
2. Find the positive $z$-score for which 95% of the distribution's area lies between $-z$ and $z$.

*Answer: Page A39*

In Example 1, the given areas correspond to entries in the Standard Normal Table. In most cases, the area will not be an entry in the table. In these cases, use the entry closest to it (or use technology, as shown at the left and in Example 2). When the area is halfway between two area entries, use the $z$-score halfway between the corresponding $z$-scores.

In Section 2.5, you learned that percentiles divide a data set into 100 equal parts. To find a $z$-score that corresponds to a percentile, you can use the Standard Normal Table. Recall that if a value $x$ represents the 83rd percentile $P_{83}$, then 83% of the data values are below $x$ and 17% of the data values are above $x$.

**EXAMPLE 2**

### Finding a $z$-Score Given a Percentile

Find the $z$-score that corresponds to each percentile.

**1.** $P_5$ **2.** $P_{50}$ **3.** $P_{90}$

**SOLUTION**

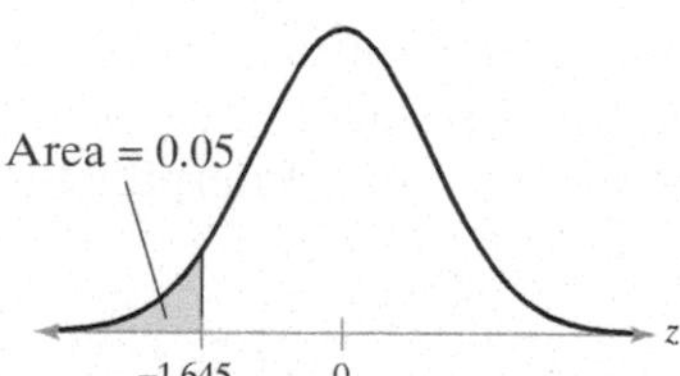


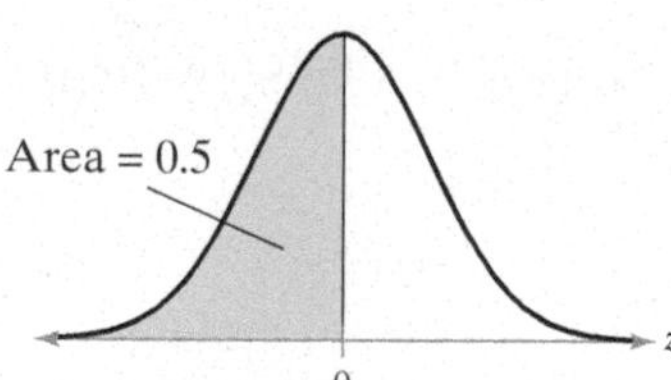


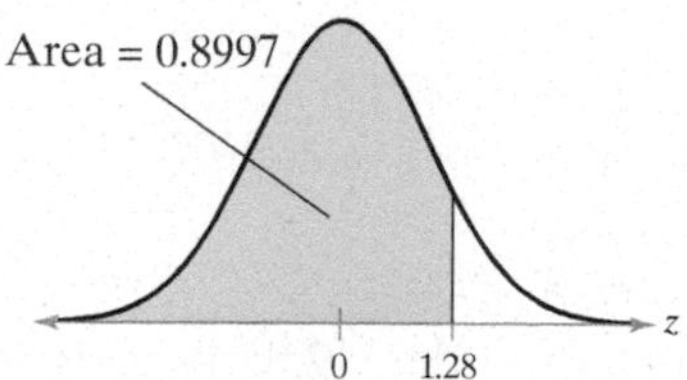


1. To find the $z$-score that corresponds to $P_5$, find the $z$-score that corresponds to an area of 0.05 (see upper figure) by locating 0.05 in the Standard Normal Table. The areas closest to 0.05 in the table are 0.0495 ($z = -1.65$) and 0.0505 ($z = -1.64$). Because 0.05 is halfway between the two areas in the table, use the $z$-score that is halfway between $-1.64$ and $-1.65$. So, the $z$-score that corresponds to an area of 0.05 is $-1.645$.
2. To find the $z$-score that corresponds to $P_{50}$, find the $z$-score that corresponds to an area of 0.5 (see middle figure) by locating 0.5 in the Standard Normal Table. The area closest to 0.5 in the table is 0.5000, so the $z$-score that corresponds to an area of 0.5 is 0.
3. To find the $z$-score that corresponds to $P_{90}$, find the $z$-score that corresponds to an area of 0.9 (see lower figure) by locating 0.9 in the Standard Normal Table. The area closest to 0.9 in the table is 0.8997, so the $z$-score that corresponds to an area of 0.9 is about 1.28.

You can use technology to find the $z$-score that corresponds to each percentile, as shown below. Remember that when you use technology, your answers may differ slightly from those found using the Standard Normal Table.

**EXCEL**

| | A | B | |
|---|---|---|---|
| 1 | 1. | -1.644853627 | ←=NORM.INV(0.05,0,1) |
| 2 | 2. | 0 | ←=NORM.INV(0.5,0,1) |
| 3 | 3. | 1.281551566 | ←=NORM.INV(0.9,0,1) |

**TRY IT YOURSELF 2**

Find the $z$-score that corresponds to each percentile.

**1.** $P_{10}$ **2.** $P_{20}$ **3.** $P_{99}$

*Answer: Page A39*

## Transforming a z-Score to an x-Value

Recall that to transform an $x$-value to a $z$-score, you can use the formula

$$z = \frac{x - \mu}{\sigma}.$$

This formula gives $z$ in terms of $x$. When you solve this formula for $x$, you get a new formula that gives $x$ in terms of $z$.

| | |
|---|---|
| $z = \frac{x - \mu}{\sigma}$ | Formula for $z$ in terms of $x$ |
| $z\sigma = x - \mu$ | Multiply each side by $\sigma$. |
| $\mu + z\sigma = x$ | Add $\mu$ to each side. |
| $x = \mu + z\sigma$ | Interchange sides. |

### Transforming a z-Score to an x-Value

To transform a standard $z$-score to an $x$-value in a given population, use the formula

$$x = \mu + z\sigma.$$

### EXAMPLE 3

### Finding an x-Value Corresponding to a z-Score

A veterinarian records the weights of cats treated at a clinic. The weights are normally distributed, with a mean of 9 pounds and a standard deviation of 2 pounds. Find the weight $x$ corresponding to each $z$-score. Interpret the results.

**1.** $z = 1.96$ **2.** $z = -0.44$ **3.** $z = 0$

**SOLUTION**

The $x$-value that corresponds to each standard $z$-score is calculated using the formula $x = \mu + z\sigma$. Note that $\mu = 9$ and $\sigma = 2$.

**1.** For $z = 1.96$, the corresponding weight $x$ is

$$x = 9 + 1.96(2) = 12.92 \text{ pounds.}$$

**2.** For $z = -0.44$, the corresponding weight $x$ is

$$x = 9 + (-0.44)(2) = 8.12 \text{ pounds.}$$

**3.** For $z = 0$, the corresponding weight $x$ is

$$x = 9 + 0(2) = 9 \text{ pounds.}$$

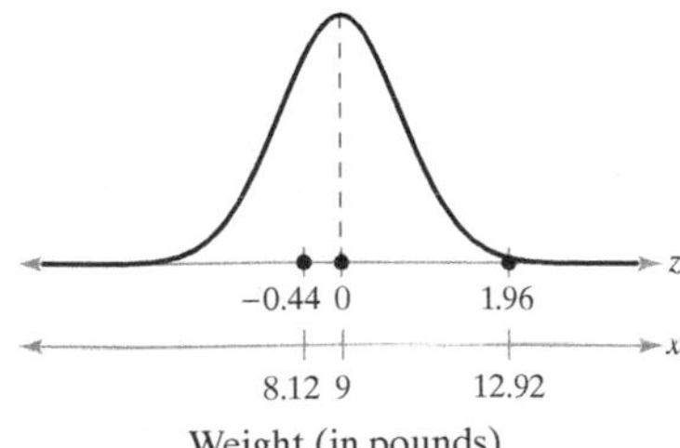


***Interpretation*** From the figure at the left, you can see that 12.92 pounds is to the right of the mean, 8.12 pounds is to the left of the mean, and 9 pounds is equal to the mean.

**TRY IT YOURSELF 3**

A veterinarian records the weights of dogs treated at a clinic. The weights are normally distributed, with a mean of 52 pounds and a standard deviation of 15 pounds. Find the weight $x$ corresponding to each $z$-score. Interpret the results.

**1.** $z = -2.33$ **2.** $z = 3$ **3.** $z = 0.58$

*Answer: Page A39*

## Picturing the World

Many investors choose mutual funds as a way to invest in the stock market. The mean annual rate of return for large growth mutual funds during a recent five-year period was about 21.2% with a standard deviation of 3.5%. (Adapted from Morningstar)

**Annual Rate of Return for Large Growth Mutual Funds**

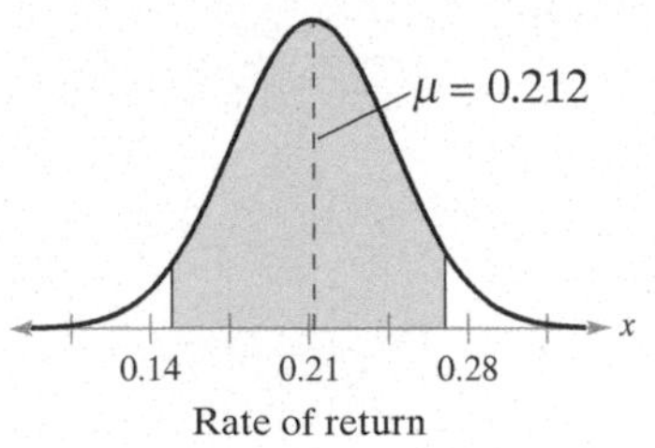


**Between what two values does the middle 90% of the data lie?**

**TI-84 PLUS**

```
invNorm(.9,50,10)
                62.81551567
```

## Finding a Specific Data Value for a Given Probability

You can also use the normal distribution to find a specific data value ($x$-value) for a given probability, as shown in Examples 4 and 5.

**EXAMPLE 4**

### Finding a Specific Data Value

Scores for the California Peace Officer Standards and Training test are normally distributed, with a mean of 50 and a standard deviation of 10. An agency will only hire applicants with scores in the top 10%. What is the lowest score an applicant can earn and still be eligible to be hired by the agency? *(Source: State of California)*

**SOLUTION**

Exam scores in the top 10% correspond to the shaded region shown.

**Scores for the California Peace Officer Standards and Training Test**

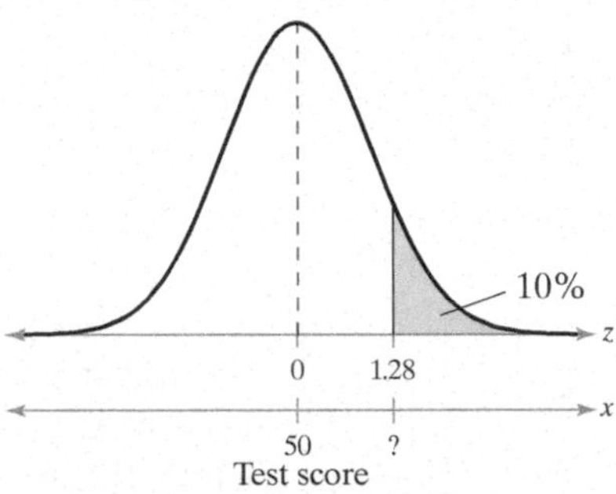


A test score in the top 10% is any score above the 90th percentile. To find the score that represents the 90th percentile, you must first find the $z$-score that corresponds to a cumulative area of 0.9. In the Standard Normal Table, the area closest to 0.9 is 0.8997. So, the $z$-score that corresponds to an area of 0.9 is $z = 1.28$. To find the $x$-value, note that $\mu = 50$ and $\sigma = 10$, and use the formula $x = \mu + z\sigma$, as shown.

$$\begin{aligned} x &= \mu + z\sigma \\ &= 50 + 1.28(10) \\ &= 62.8 \end{aligned}$$

You can check this answer using technology. For instance, you can use a TI-84 Plus to find the $x$-value, as shown at the left.

***Interpretation*** The lowest score an applicant can earn and still be eligible to be hired by the agency is about 63.

**TRY IT YOURSELF 4**

A researcher tests the braking distances of several cars. The braking distance from 60 miles per hour to a complete stop on dry pavement is measured in feet. The braking distances of a sample of cars are normally distributed, with a mean of 132 feet and a standard deviation of 5.18 feet. What is the longest braking distance one of these cars could have and still be in the bottom 1%? *(Adapted from Consumer Reports)*

*Answer: Page A39*

**EXAMPLE 5**

### Finding a Specific Data Value

In a randomly selected sample of U.S. adults ages 20 and over, the mean total cholesterol level is 190 milligrams per deciliter with a standard deviation of 40.9 milligrams per deciliter. Assume the total cholesterol levels are normally distributed. Find the highest total cholesterol level an adult aged 20 or over can have and still be in the bottom 1%. *(Adapted from National Center for Health Statistics)*

**SOLUTION**

Total cholesterol levels in the lowest 1% correspond to the shaded region shown.

**Total Cholesterol Levels in U.S. Adults Ages 20 and Over**

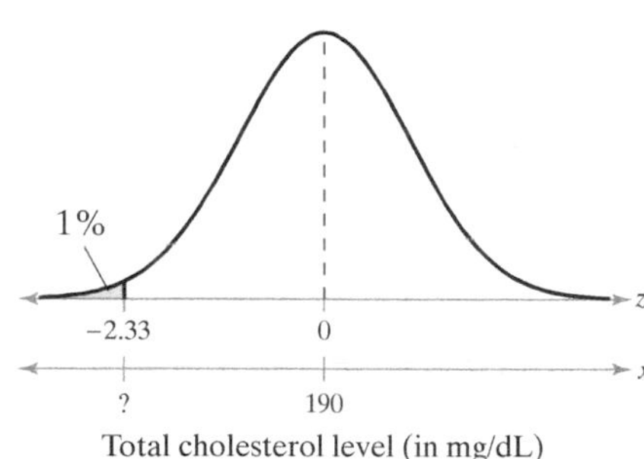


A total cholesterol level in the lowest 1% is any level below the 1st percentile. To find the level that represents the 1st percentile, you must first find the $z$-score that corresponds to a cumulative area of 0.01. In the Standard Normal Table, the area closest to 0.01 is 0.0099. So, the $z$-score that corresponds to an area of 0.01 is $z = -2.33$. To find the $x$-value, note that $\mu = 190$ and $\sigma = 40.9$, and use the formula $x = \mu + z\sigma$, as shown.

$$\begin{aligned} x &= \mu + z\sigma \\ &= 190 + (-2.33)(40.9) \\ &\approx 94.7 \end{aligned}$$

You can check this answer using technology. For instance, you can use Excel to find the $x$-value, as shown below.

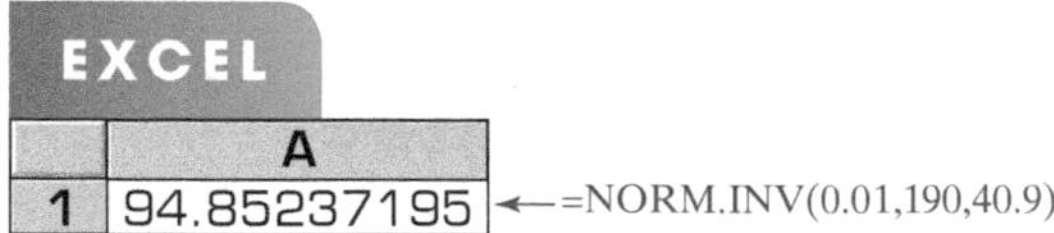


***Interpretation*** The value that separates the lowest 1% of total cholesterol levels for U.S. adults ages 20 and over from the highest 99% is about 95 milligrams per deciliter.

**TRY IT YOURSELF 5**

The lengths of time employees have worked at a corporation are normally distributed, with a mean of 11.2 years and a standard deviation of 2.1 years. In a company cutback, the lowest 10% in seniority are laid off. What is the maximum length of time an employee could have worked and still be laid off?

*Answer: Page A39*

# 5.3 EXERCISES

For Extra Help: MyLab Statistics

## Building Basic Skills and Vocabulary

**Finding a $z$-Score** *In Exercises 1–16, use the Standard Normal Table or technology to find the z-score that corresponds to the cumulative area or percentile.*

**1.** 0.2090 **2.** 0.4364 **3.** 0.6736 **4.** 0.7995

**5.** 0.05 **6.** 0.94 **7.** 0.85 **8.** 0.0093

**9.** $P_{33}$ **10.** $P_{67}$ **11.** $P_{97.5}$ **12.** $P_{1.5}$

**13.** $P_{25}$ **14.** $P_{40}$ **15.** $P_{91}$ **16.** $P_{75}$

**Graphical Analysis** *In Exercises 17–22, find the indicated z-score(s) shown in the graph.*

**17.**

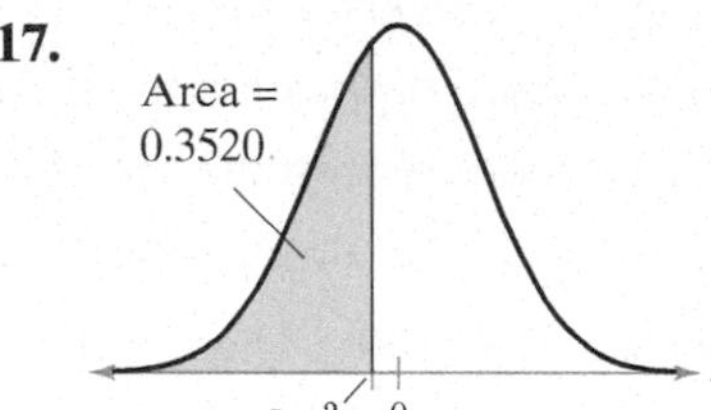


**18.**

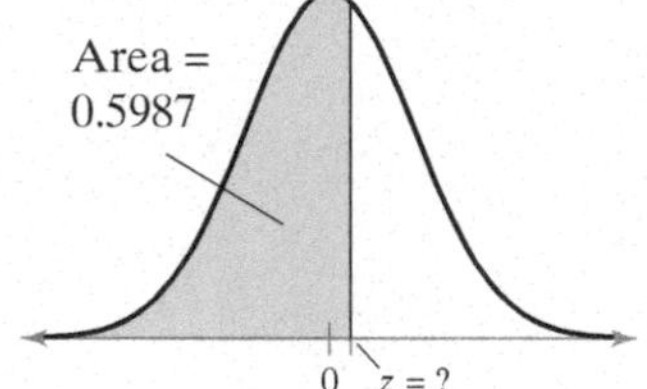


**19.**

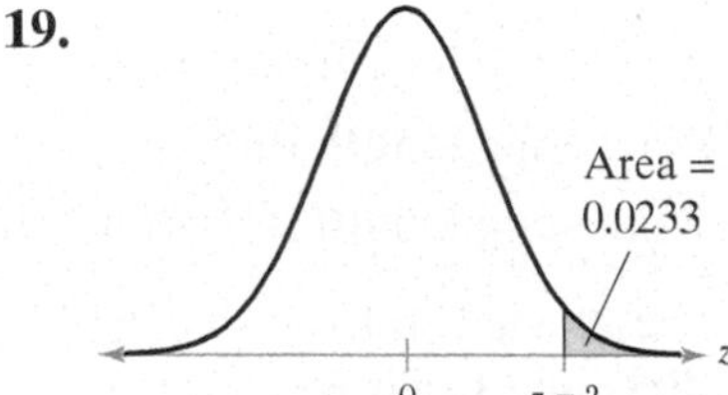


**20.**

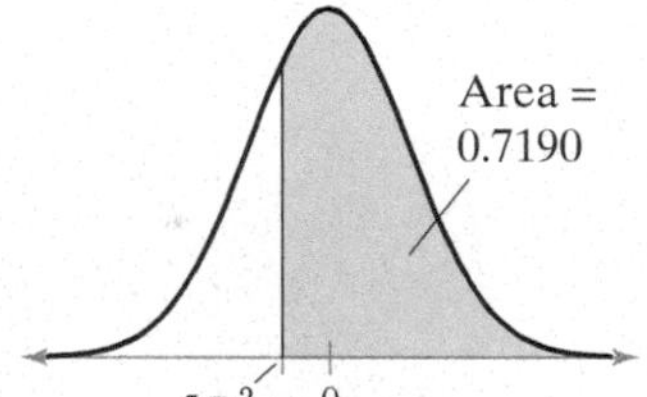


**21.**

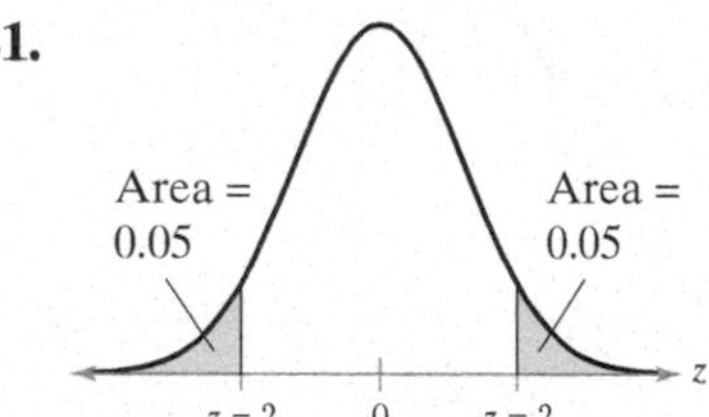


**22.**

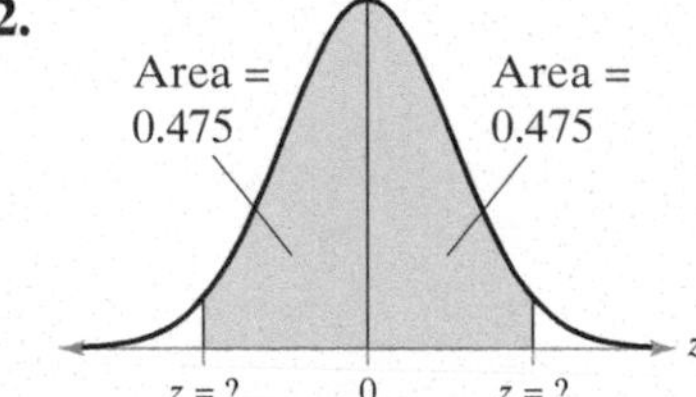


**Finding a $z$-Score Given an Area** *In Exercises 23–30, find the indicated z-score.*

**23.** Find the $z$-score that has 11.9% of the distribution's area to its left.

**24.** Find the $z$-score that has 78.5% of the distribution's area to its left.

**25.** Find the $z$-score that has 63.7% of the distribution's area to its right.

**26.** Find the $z$-score that has 20.9% of the distribution's area to its right.

**27.** Find the $z$-score that has 2.275% of the distribution's area to its left.

**28.** Find the $z$-score that has 84.1345% of the distribution's area to its right.

**29.** Find the positive $z$-score for which 80% of the distribution's area lies between $-z$ and $z$.

**30.** Find the positive $z$-score for which 12% of the distribution's area lies between $-z$ and $z$.

## Using and Interpreting Concepts

**Finding Specified Data Values** *In Exercises 31–38, answer the questions about the specified normal distribution.*

**31. Weights of Teenagers** In a survey of 18-year old males, the mean weight was 166.7 pounds with a standard deviation of 49.3 pounds. *(Adapted from National Center for Health Statistics)*

(a) What weight represents the 95th percentile?

(b) What weight represents the 43rd percentile?

(c) What weight represents the first quartile?

**32. COVID-19 Response** Surveyors asked respondents to rate ten key aspects of their government's response to the COVID-19 pandemic, including preparedness, communication, and material aid. A pandemic response score that ranged from 0 to 100 was calculated. The mean score for U.S. respondents was 50.6 with a standard deviation of 29.0. *(Source: PLOS One)*

(a) What score represents the 88th percentile?

(b) What score represents the 61st percentile?

(c) What score represents the first quartile?

**33. Billboard Hot 100** The length (in seconds) of the 100 most popular songs during the week of May 5, 2021, can be approximated by a normal distribution, as shown in the figure. *(Source: Spotify)*

(a) What song length represents the 5th percentile?

(b) What song length represents the 17th percentile?

(c) What song length represents the third quartile?

**Billboard Hot 100 Song Lengths**

$\mu = 187.9$ s
$\sigma = 32.8$ s

100 150 200 250 $x$

Seconds

FIGURE FOR EXERCISE 33

**Water Footprint of Wheat in the U.S.**

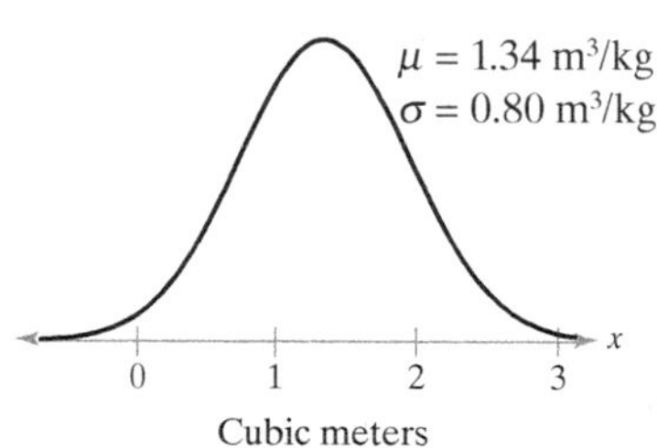


FIGURE FOR EXERCISE 34

**34. Water Footprint** A *water footprint* is a measure of the appropriation of fresh water. The water footprint (in cubic meters) for a kilogram of wheat can be approximated by a normal distribution, as shown in the figure. *(Source: Ecological Indicators)*

(a) What water footprint represents the 80th percentile?

(b) What water footprint represents the 29th percentile?

(c) What water footprint represents the third quartile?

**Advanced Dental Admission Test**

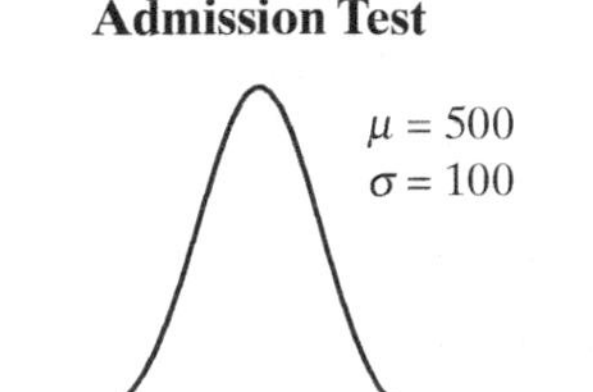


200 400 600 800

Score

FIGURE FOR EXERCISE 35

**35. Advanced Dental Admission Test** The Advanced Dental Admission Test (ADAT) is designed so that the scores fit a normal distribution, as shown in the figure. *(Source: American Dental Association)*

(a) What is the minimum ADAT score that is in the top 5% of scores?

(b) Between what two values does the middle 50% of the ADAT scores lie?

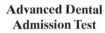

**GRE Analytical Writing Scores**

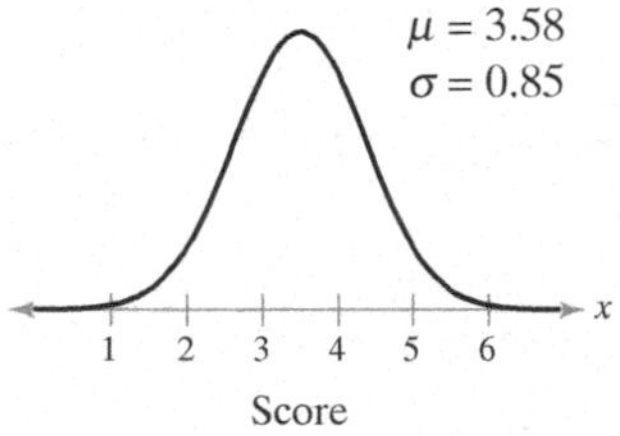


FIGURE FOR EXERCISE 36

**36. GRE Scores** The test scores for the analytical writing section of the Graduate Record Examination (GRE) can be approximated by a normal distribution, as shown in the figure. *(Source: Educational Testing Service)*

(a) What is the maximum score that can be in the bottom 20% of scores?

(b) Between what two values does the middle 80% of the scores lie?

**37. Red Blood Cell Count** The red blood cell counts (in millions of cells per microliter) for a population of adult males can be approximated by a normal distribution, with a mean of 5.4 million cells per microliter and a standard deviation of 0.4 million cells per microliter.

(a) What is the minimum red blood cell count that can be in the top 25% of counts?

(b) What red blood cell counts would be considered unusual?

**38. Pregnancy Length** The pregnancy durations (in days) for a population of new mothers can be approximated by a normal distribution, with a mean of 267 days and a standard deviation of 10 days.

(a) What is the minimum pregnancy durations that can be in the top 10% of pregnancy durations?

(b) What pregnancy durations would be considered unusual?

**39. Bags of Baby Carrots** The weights of bags of baby carrots are normally distributed, with a mean of 32 ounces and a standard deviation of 0.36 ounce. Bags in the upper 4.5% are too heavy and must be repackaged. What is the most a bag of baby carrots can weigh and not need to be repackaged?

**40. Writing a Guarantee** You sell a brand of automobile tire that has a life expectancy that is normally distributed, with a mean life of 30,000 miles and a standard deviation of 2500 miles. You want to give a guarantee for free replacement of tires that do not wear well. You are willing to replace approximately 10% of the tires. How should you word your guarantee?

## Extending Concepts

**41. Vending Machine** A vending machine dispenses coffee into an eight-ounce cup. The amounts of coffee dispensed into the cup are normally distributed, with a standard deviation of 0.03 ounce. You can allow the cup to overflow 1% of the time. What amount should you set as the mean amount of coffee to be dispensed?

**42. History Grades** In a history class, the grades for various assessments are all positive numbers and have different distributions. Determine whether the grades for each assessment could be normally distributed. Explain your reasoning.

(a) a midterm exam with a mean of 67, standard deviation of 15, and 75th percentile score of 77

(b) a final with a mean of 72, standard deviation of 9, and 90th percentile score of 93

(c) a quiz with a mean of 33, a 40th percentile of 30, and a 60th percentile of 39

(d) a homework assignment with a mean of 19, a 10th percentile of 7, and a 90th percentile of 31

(e) an extra credit assignment with a mean of 2.25 and a standard deviation of 2.49

(f) a research paper with a 35th percentile of 120, a 65th percentile of 160, and an 80th percentile of 200

# CASE STUDY Birth Weights in America

The National Center for Health Statistics (NCHS) keeps records of many health-related aspects of people, including the birth weights of all babies born in the United States.

The birth weight of a baby is related to its gestation period (the time between conception and birth). For a given gestation period, the birth weights can be approximated by a normal distribution. The means and standard deviations of the birth weights for various gestation periods are shown in the table below.

One of the many goals of the NCHS is to reduce the percentage of babies born with low birth weights. The figure below shows the percents of preterm births and low birth weights from 2011 to 2019.

| Gestation period | Mean birth weight | Standard deviation |
|---|---|---|
| Under 28 weeks | 1.90 lb | 0.72 lb |
| 28 to 31 weeks | 3.49 lb | 1.01 lb |
| 32 to 33 weeks | 4.62 lb | 0.95 lb |
| 34 to 36 weeks | 5.97 lb | 1.02 lb |
| 37 to 38 weeks | 7.01 lb | 0.92 lb |
| 39 to 40 weeks | 7.59 lb | 0.84 lb |
| 41 weeks | 7.92 lb | 0.87 lb |
| 42 weeks and over | 8.07 lb | 1.01 lb |

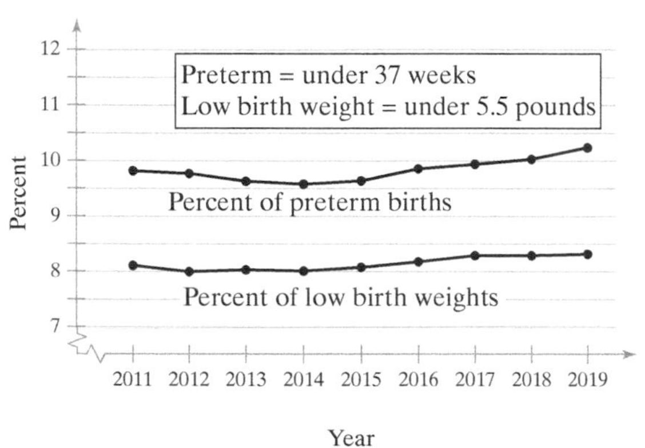


## EXERCISES

1. The distributions of birth weights for three gestation periods are shown. Match each curve with a gestation period. Explain your reasoning.

(a)

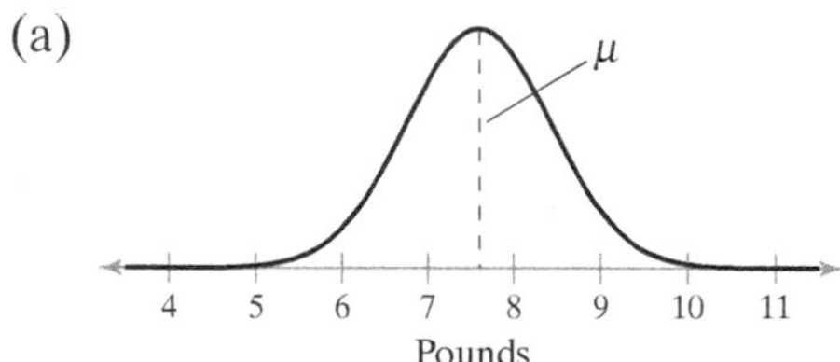


(b)

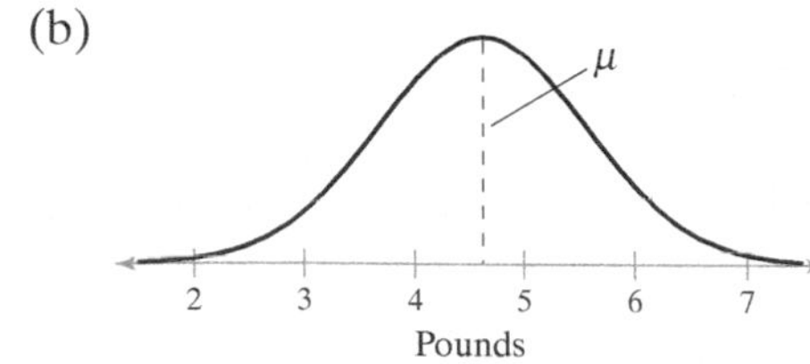


(c)

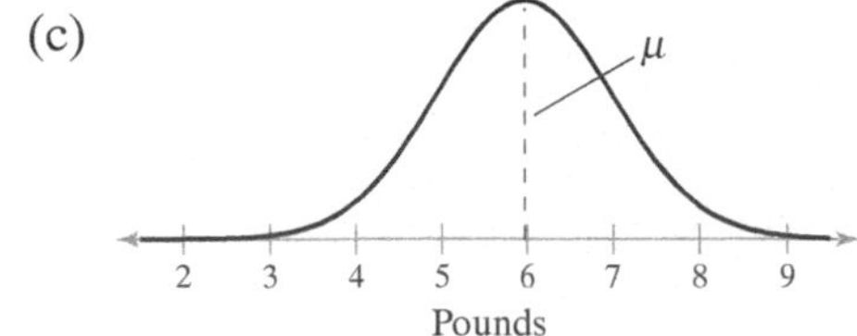


2. What percent of the babies born within each gestation period have a low birth weight (under 5.5 pounds)?
   (a) 28 to 31 weeks (b) 32 to 33 weeks
   (c) 39 to 40 weeks (d) 42 weeks and over

3. Describe the weights of the top 10% of the babies born within each gestation period.
   (a) Under 28 weeks (b) 34 to 36 weeks
   (c) 41 weeks (d) 42 weeks and over

4. For each gestation period, what is the probability that a baby will weigh between 6 and 9 pounds at birth?
   (a) Under 28 weeks (b) 32 to 33 weeks
   (c) 37 to 38 weeks (d) 41 weeks

5. A birth weight of less than 3.25 pounds is classified by the NCHS as a "very low birth weight." What is the probability that a baby has a very low birth weight for each gestation period?
   (a) Under 28 weeks (b) 28 to 31 weeks
   (c) 32 to 33 weeks (d) 39 to 40 weeks

# 5.4 Sampling Distributions and the Central Limit Theorem

## What You Should Learn

- How to find sampling distributions and verify their properties
- How to interpret the Central Limit Theorem
- How to apply the Central Limit Theorem to find the probability of a sample mean

Sampling Distributions ■ The Central Limit Theorem ■ Probability and the Central Limit Theorem

## Sampling Distributions

In previous sections, you studied the relationship between the mean of a population and values of a random variable. In this section, you will study the relationship between a population mean and the means of random samples taken from the population.

**DEFINITION**

A **sampling distribution** is the probability distribution of a sample statistic that is formed when random samples of size $n$ are repeatedly taken from a population. If the sample statistic is the sample mean, then the distribution is the **sampling distribution of sample means.** Every sample statistic has a sampling distribution.

### Study Tip

Sample means can vary from one another and can also vary from the population mean. This type of variation is to be expected and is called *sampling error.* You will learn more about this topic in Section 6.1.

Consider the Venn diagram below. The rectangle represents a large population, and each circle represents a random sample of size $n$. Because the sample entries can differ, the sample means can also differ. The mean of Random Sample 1 is $\overline{x}_1$; the mean of Random Sample 2 is $\overline{x}_2$; and so on. The sampling distribution of the sample means for samples of size $n$ for this population consists of $\overline{x}_1$, $\overline{x}_2$, $\overline{x}_3$, and so on. If the samples are drawn with replacement, then an infinite number of samples can be drawn from the population.

**Population with Mean $\mu$ and Standard Deviation $\sigma$**

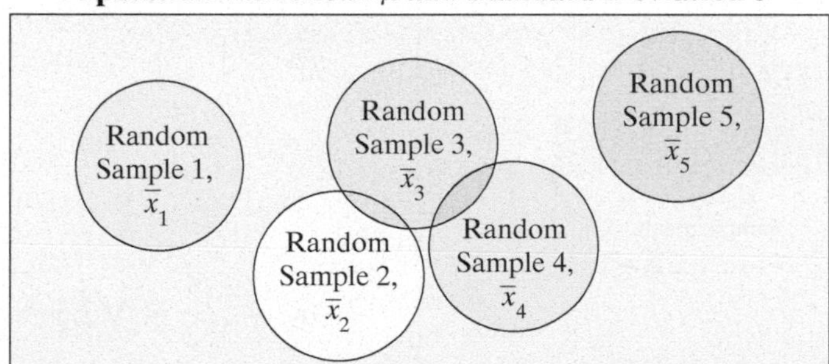


**Properties of Sampling Distributions of Sample Means**

1. The mean of the sample means $\mu_{\overline{x}}$ is equal to the population mean $\mu$.

$$\mu_{\overline{x}} = \mu$$

2. The standard deviation of the sample means $\sigma_{\overline{x}}$ is equal to the population standard deviation $\sigma$ divided by the square root of the sample size $n$.

$$\sigma_{\overline{x}} = \frac{\sigma}{\sqrt{n}}$$

The standard deviation of the sampling distribution of the sample means is called the **standard error of the mean.**

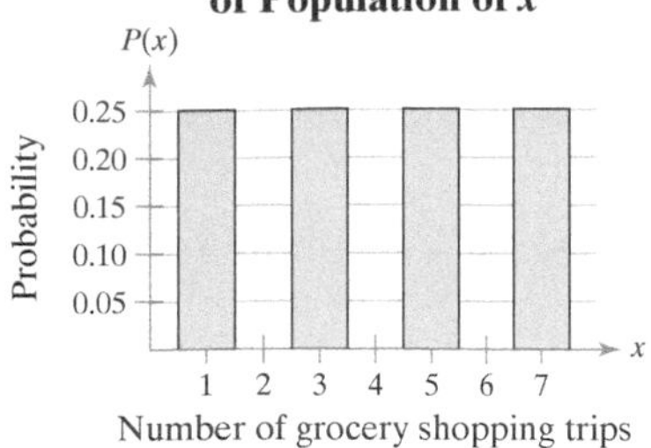


**Probability Distribution of Sample Means**

| $\bar{x}$ | $f$ | Probability |
|---|---|---|
| 1 | 1 | 1/16 |
| 2 | 2 | 2/16 |
| 3 | 3 | 3/16 |
| 4 | 4 | 4/16 |
| 5 | 3 | 3/16 |
| 6 | 2 | 2/16 |
| 7 | 1 | 1/16 |

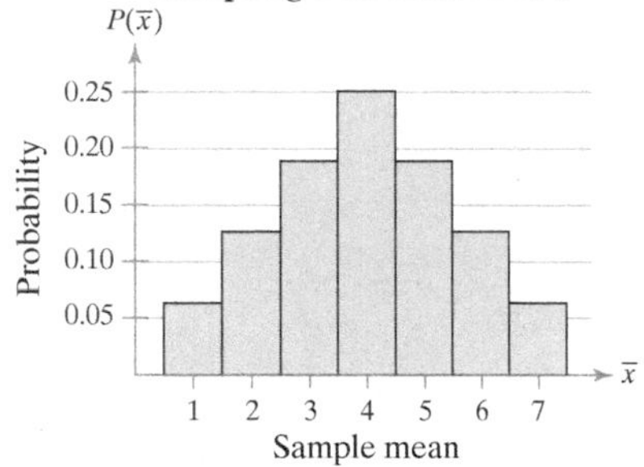


5.4 To explore this topic further, see **Activity 5.4** on page 274.

**Study Tip**

Review Section 4.1 to find the mean and standard deviation of a probability distribution.

## EXAMPLE 1

### A Sampling Distribution of Sample Means

The number of times four people go grocery shopping in a month is given by the population values $\{1, 3, 5, 7\}$. A probability histogram for the data is shown at the left. You randomly choose two of the four people, with replacement. List all possible samples of size $n = 2$ and calculate the mean of each. These means form the sampling distribution of the sample means. Find the mean, variance, and standard deviation of the sample means. Compare your results with the mean $\mu = 4$, variance $\sigma^2 = 5$, and standard deviation $\sigma = \sqrt{5} \approx 2.2$ of the population.

#### SOLUTION

List all 16 samples of size 2 from the population and the mean of each sample.

| Sample | Sample mean, $\bar{x}$ |
|---|---|
| 1, 1 | 1 |
| 1, 3 | 2 |
| 1, 5 | 3 |
| 1, 7 | 4 |
| 3, 1 | 2 |
| 3, 3 | 3 |
| 3, 5 | 4 |
| 3, 7 | 5 |

| Sample | Sample mean, $\bar{x}$ |
|---|---|
| 5, 1 | 3 |
| 5, 3 | 4 |
| 5, 5 | 5 |
| 5, 7 | 6 |
| 7, 1 | 4 |
| 7, 3 | 5 |
| 7, 5 | 6 |
| 7, 7 | 7 |

After constructing a probability distribution of the sample means, you can graph the sampling distribution using a probability histogram as shown at the left. Notice that the shape of the histogram is bell-shaped and symmetric, similar to a normal curve. The mean, variance, and standard deviation of the 16 sample means are

$$\mu_{\bar{x}} = 4$$ Mean of the sample means

$$(\sigma_{\bar{x}})^2 = \frac{5}{2} = 2.5$$ Variance of the sample means

and

$$\sigma_{\bar{x}} = \sqrt{\frac{5}{2}} = \sqrt{2.5} \approx 1.6.$$ Standard deviation of the sample means

These results satisfy the properties of sampling distributions because

$$\mu_{\bar{x}} = \mu = 4$$

and

$$\sigma_{\bar{x}} = \frac{\sigma}{\sqrt{n}} = \frac{\sqrt{5}}{\sqrt{2}} \approx 1.6.$$

#### TRY IT YOURSELF 1

List all possible samples of size $n = 3$, with replacement, from the population $\{1, 3, 5\}$. Calculate the mean of each sample. Find the mean, variance, and standard deviation of the sample means. Compare your results with the mean $\mu = 3$, variance $\sigma^2 = 8/3$, and standard deviation $\sigma = \sqrt{8/3} \approx 1.6$ of the population.

*Answer: Page A39*

## The Central Limit Theorem

The Central Limit Theorem forms the foundation for the inferential branch of statistics. This theorem describes the relationship between the sampling distribution of sample means and the population from which the samples are taken. The Central Limit Theorem is an important tool that provides the information you will need to use sample statistics to make inferences about a population mean.

### The Central Limit Theorem

1. If random samples of size $n$, where $n \geq 30$, are drawn from any population with a mean $\mu$ and a standard deviation $\sigma$, then the sampling distribution of sample means approximates a normal distribution. The greater the sample size, the better the approximation. (See figures for "Any Population Distribution" below.)
2. If random samples of size $n$ are drawn from a population that is normally distributed, then the sampling distribution of sample means is normally distributed for *any* sample size $n$. (See figures for "Normal Population Distribution" below.)

In either case, the sampling distribution of sample means has a mean equal to the population mean.

$$\mu_{\bar{x}} = \mu \qquad \text{Mean of the sample means}$$

The sampling distribution of sample means has a variance equal to $1/n$ times the variance of the population and a standard deviation equal to the population standard deviation divided by the square root of $n$.

$$\sigma_{\bar{x}}^2 = \frac{\sigma^2}{n} \qquad \text{Variance of the sample means}$$

$$\sigma_{\bar{x}} = \frac{\sigma}{\sqrt{n}} \qquad \text{Standard deviation of the sample means}$$

Recall that the standard deviation of the sampling distribution of the sample means, $\sigma_{\bar{x}}$, is also called the standard error of the mean.

**Study Tip**

The distribution of sample means has the same mean as the population. But its standard deviation is less than the standard deviation of the population. This tells you that the distribution of sample means has the same center as the population, but it is not as spread out.

Moreover, the distribution of sample means becomes less and less spread out (tighter concentration about the mean) as the sample size $n$ increases.

**1.** Any Population Distribution

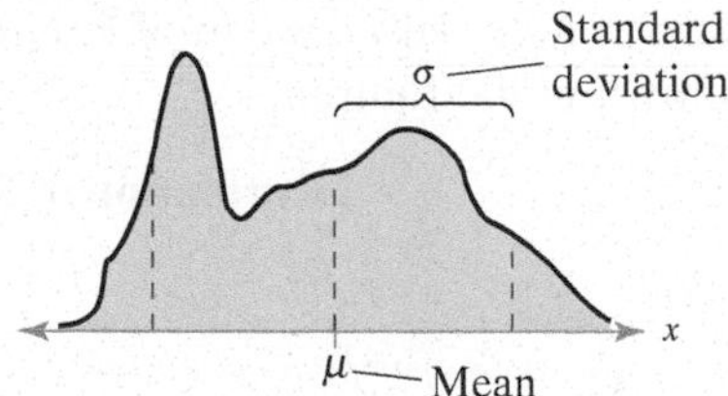

Distribution of Sample Means, $n \geq 30$

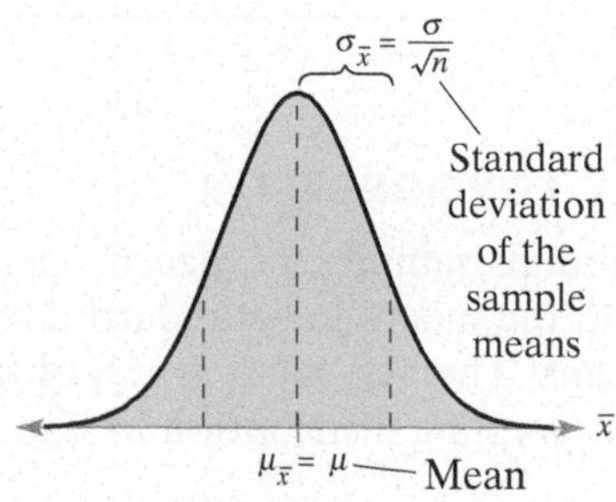


**2.** Normal Population Distribution

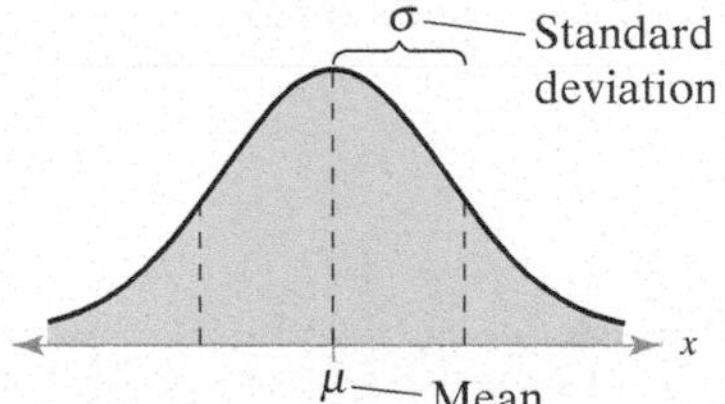


Distribution of Sample Means (any $n$)

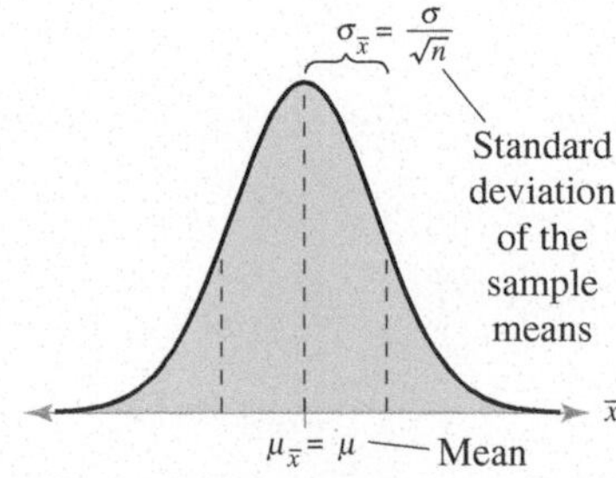

## EXAMPLE 2

### Interpreting the Central Limit Theorem

A study analyzed the sleep habits of college students. The study found that the mean sleep time was 6.9 hours, with a standard deviation of 1.5 hours. Random samples of 100 sleep times are drawn from this population, and the mean of each sample is determined. Find the mean and standard deviation of the sampling distribution of sample means. Then sketch a graph of the sampling distribution. *(Adapted from National Institutes of Health)*

**Distribution for All Sleep Times**

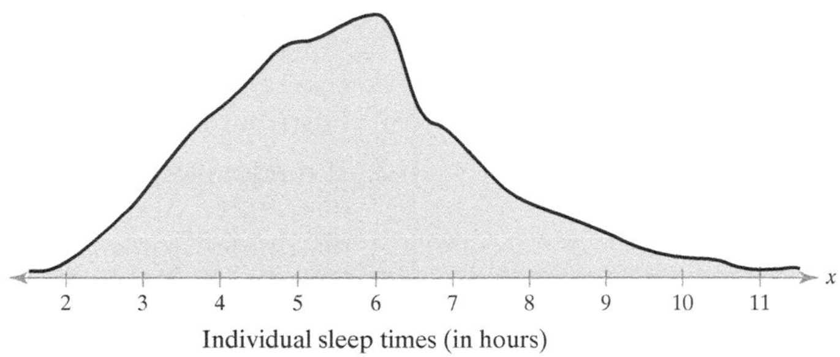


**SOLUTION**

The mean of the sampling distribution is equal to the population mean, and the standard deviation of the sample means is equal to the population standard deviation divided by $\sqrt{n}$. So,

$\mu_{\bar{x}} = \mu = 6.9$ Mean of the sample means

and

$$\sigma_{\bar{x}} = \frac{\sigma}{\sqrt{n}} = \frac{1.5}{\sqrt{100}} = 0.15.$$

Standard deviation of the sample means

***Interpretation*** From the Central Limit Theorem, because the sample size is greater than 30, the sampling distribution can be approximated by a normal distribution with a mean of 6.9 hours and a standard deviation of 0.15 hour, as shown in the figure.

**Distribution of Sample Means with $n$ = 100**

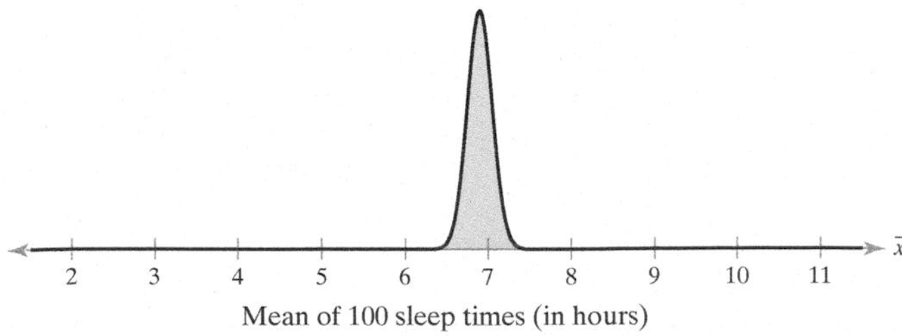


**TRY IT YOURSELF 2**

Random samples of size 64 are drawn from the population in Example 2. Find the mean and standard deviation of the sampling distribution of sample means. Then sketch a graph of the sampling distribution and compare it with the sampling distribution in Example 2.

*Answer: Page A39*

## Picturing the World

In a recent year, there were about 3.8 million parents in the United States who received child support payments. The histogram shows the distribution of children per custodial parent. The mean number of children was about 1.8 and the standard deviation was about 0.9. (Adapted from U.S. Census Bureau)

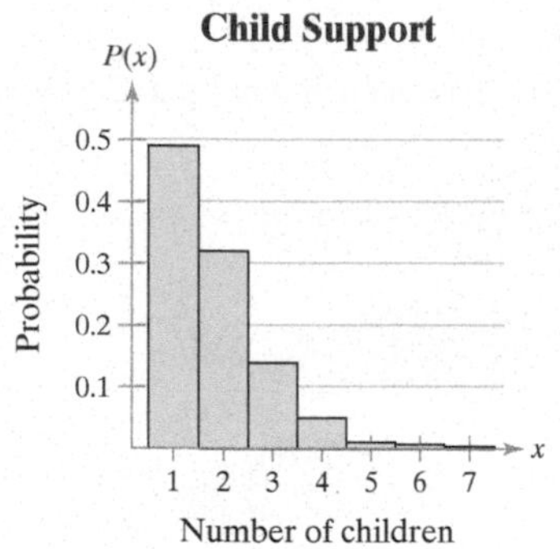


**You randomly select 35 parents who receive child support and ask how many children in their custody are receiving child support payments. What is the probability that the mean of the sample is between 1.5 and 1.9 children?**

## EXAMPLE 3

### Interpreting the Central Limit Theorem

Assume the training heart rates of all 20-year-old athletes are normally distributed, with a mean of 135 beats per minute and a standard deviation of 18 beats per minute, as shown in the figure. Random samples of size 4 are drawn from this population, and the mean of each sample is determined. Find the mean and standard deviation of the sampling distribution of sample means. Then sketch a graph of the sampling distribution.

**Distribution of Population Training Heart Rates**

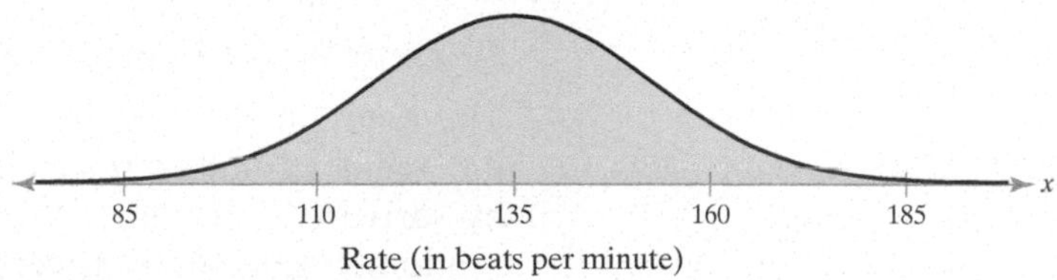


**SOLUTION**

$\mu_{\bar{x}} = \mu = 135$ beats per minute    Mean of the sample means

and

$$\sigma_{\bar{x}} = \frac{\sigma}{\sqrt{n}} = \frac{18}{\sqrt{4}} = 9 \text{ beats per minute}$$

Standard deviation of the sample means

***Interpretation*** From the Central Limit Theorem, because the population is normally distributed, the sampling distribution of the sample means is also normally distributed, as shown in the figure.

**Distribution of Sample Means with $n = 4$**

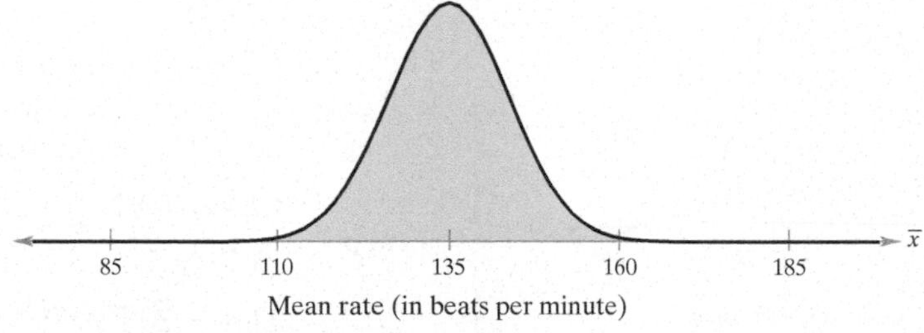


**TRY IT YOURSELF 3**

The diameters of fully grown white oak trees are normally distributed, with a mean of 3.5 feet and a standard deviation of 0.2 foot, as shown in the figure. Random samples of size 16 are drawn from this population, and the mean of each sample is determined. Find the mean and standard deviation of the sampling distribution of sample means. Then sketch a graph of the sampling distribution.

**Distribution of Population Diameters**

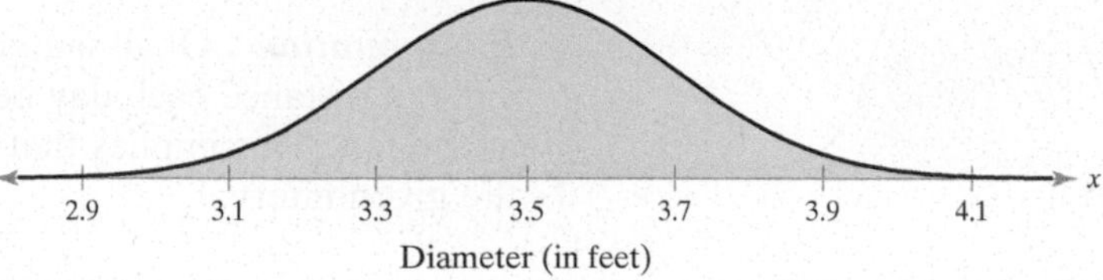


*Answer: Page A39*

## Probability and the Central Limit Theorem

In Section 5.2, you learned how to find the probability that a random variable $x$ will lie in a given interval of population values. In a similar manner, you can find the probability that a sample mean $\bar{x}$ will lie in a given interval of the $\bar{x}$ sampling distribution. To transform $\bar{x}$ to a $z$-score, you can use the formula

$$z = \frac{\text{Value} - \text{Mean}}{\text{Standard error}} = \frac{\bar{x} - \mu_{\bar{x}}}{\sigma_{\bar{x}}} = \frac{\bar{x} - \mu}{\sigma/\sqrt{n}}.$$

### EXAMPLE 4

### Finding Probabilities for Sampling Distributions

The figure at the right shows the mean distances traveled by drivers each day. You randomly select 50 drivers ages 16 to 19. What is the probability that the mean distance traveled each day is between 19.4 and 22.5 miles? Assume $\sigma = 6.5$ miles.

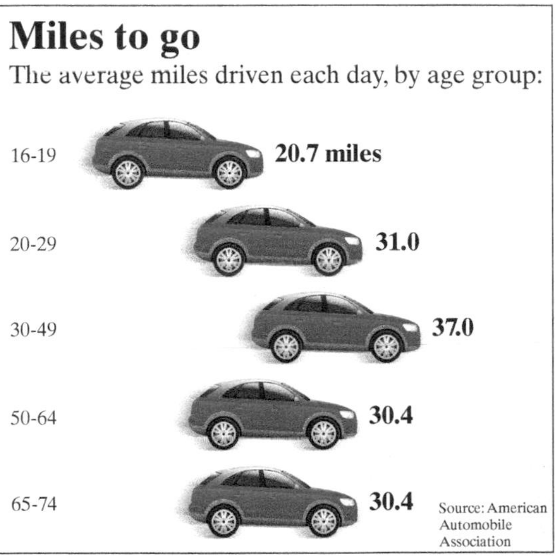


**SOLUTION**

The sample size is greater than 30, so you can use the Central Limit Theorem to conclude that the distribution of sample means is approximately normal, with a mean and a standard deviation of

$$\mu_{\bar{x}} = \mu = 20.7 \text{ miles} \quad \text{and} \quad \sigma_{\bar{x}} = \frac{\sigma}{\sqrt{n}} = \frac{6.5}{\sqrt{50}} \approx 0.9 \text{ mile}.$$

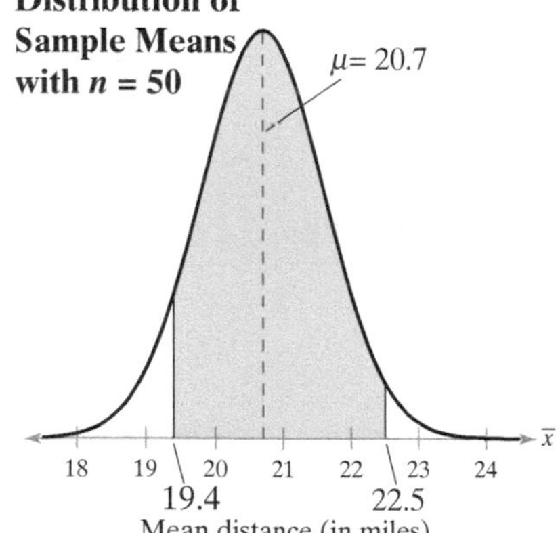


The graph of this distribution is shown at the left with a shaded area between 19.4 and 22.5 miles. The $z$-scores that correspond to sample means of 19.4 and 22.5 miles are found as shown.

$$z_1 = \frac{19.4 - 20.7}{6.5/\sqrt{50}} \approx -1.41 \qquad \text{Convert 19.4 to } z\text{-score}$$

$$z_2 = \frac{22.5 - 20.7}{6.5/\sqrt{50}} \approx 1.96 \qquad \text{Convert 22.5 to } z\text{-score}$$

So, using the Standard Normal Table, the probability that the mean distance driven each day by the sample of 50 people is between 19.4 and 22.5 miles is

$$\begin{aligned} P(19.4 < \bar{x} < 22.5) &= P(-1.41 < z < 1.96) \\ &= P(z < 1.96) - P(z < -1.41) \\ &= 0.9750 - 0.0793 \\ &= 0.8957. \end{aligned}$$

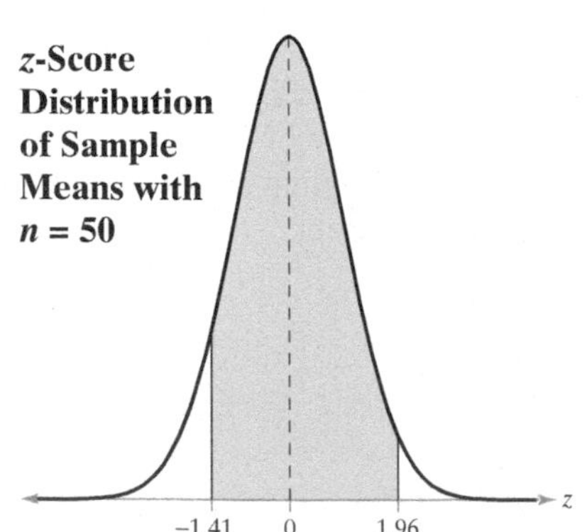


***Interpretation*** Of all samples of 50 drivers ages 16 to 19, about 90% will drive a mean distance each day between 19.4 and 22.5 miles, as shown in the graph at the left. This implies that about 10% of such sample means will lie outside the given interval.

**Study Tip**

Before you find probabilities for intervals of the sample mean $\bar{x}$, use the Central Limit Theorem to determine the mean of the sample means $\mu_{\bar{x}}$ and the standard deviation of the sample means $\sigma_{\bar{x}}$.

### TRY IT YOURSELF 4

You randomly select 100 drivers ages 30 to 49 from Example 4. What is the probability that the mean distance traveled each day is between 36.2 and 37.8 miles? Assume $\sigma = 5.8$ miles.

*Answer: Page A39*

## EXAMPLE 5

### Finding Probabilities for Sampling Distributions

In a recent year, the mean room and board expense at four-year colleges was \$11,806. You randomly select 9 four-year colleges. What is the probability that the mean room and board was less than \$12,250? Assume that the room and board expenses are normally distributed with a standard deviation of \$1650. *(Adapted from National Center for Education Statistics)*

**SOLUTION**

Because the population is normally distributed, you can use the Central Limit Theorem to conclude that the distribution of sample means is normally distributed, with a mean and a standard deviation of

$$\mu_{\bar{x}} = \mu = \$11{,}806 \quad \text{and} \quad \sigma_{\bar{x}} = \frac{\sigma}{\sqrt{n}} = \frac{\$1650}{\sqrt{9}} = \$550.$$

**Distribution of Sample Means with $n = 9$**

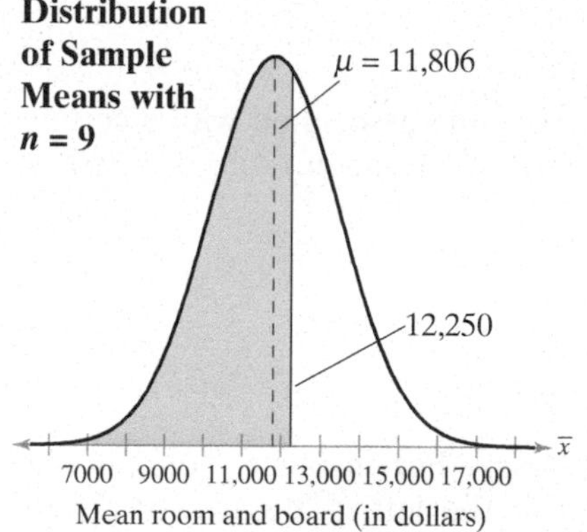


The graph of this distribution is shown at the left. The area to the left of \$12,250 is shaded. The $z$-score that corresponds to \$12,250 is

$$z = \frac{12{,}250 - 11{,}806}{1650/\sqrt{9}} = \frac{444}{550} \approx 0.81.$$

So, using the Standard Normal Table, the probability that the mean room and board expense was less than \$12,250 is

$$P(\bar{x} < 12{,}250) = P(z < 0.81)$$
$$= 0.7910.$$

You can check this answer using technology. For instance, you can use a TI-84 Plus to find the $x$-value, as shown below.

**TI-84 PLUS**

```
normalcdf(-10000,12250,
11806,550)
                0.7902453767
```

***Interpretation*** So, about 79% of such samples with $n = 9$ will have a mean less than \$12,250 and about 21% of these sample means will be greater than \$12,250.

### TRY IT YOURSELF 5

In a recent year, the mean existing home sales price in the United States was \$296,700. You randomly select 12 existing homes. What is the probability that the mean sales price was more than \$275,000? Assume that the sales prices are normally distributed with a standard deviation of \$50,000. *(Adapted from National Association of Realtors)*

*Answer: Page A39*

The Central Limit Theorem can also be used to investigate unusual events. An unusual event is one that occurs with a probability of less than 5%.

**Study Tip**

To find probabilities for individual members of a population with a normally distributed random variable $x$, use the formula

$$z = \frac{x - \mu}{\sigma}.$$

To find probabilities for the mean $\bar{x}$ of a sample of size $n$, use the formula

$$z = \frac{\bar{x} - \mu_{\bar{x}}}{\sigma_{\bar{x}}}.$$

**EXAMPLE 6**

## Finding Probabilities for $x$ and $\bar{x}$

Some college students use credit cards to pay for school-related expenses. For this population, the amount paid is normally distributed, with a mean of \$2172 and a standard deviation of \$740. *(Adapted from Sallie Mae/Ipsos)*

1. What is the probability that a randomly selected college student, who uses a credit card to pay for school-related expenses, paid less than \$1900?
2. You randomly select 25 college students who use credit cards to pay for school-related expenses. What is the probability that their mean amount paid is less than \$1900?
3. Compare the probabilities from parts 1 and 2.

**SOLUTION**

1. In this case, you are asked to find the probability associated with a certain value of the random variable $x$. The $z$-score that corresponds to $x = \$1900$ is

$$z = \frac{x - \mu}{\sigma} = \frac{1900 - 2172}{740} = \frac{-272}{740} \approx -0.37.$$

So, the probability that the student paid less than \$1900 is

$$P(x < 1900) = P(z < -0.37) = 0.3557.$$

You can check this answer using technology. For instance, you can use Excel to find the probability, as shown at the left. (The answer differs slightly due to rounding.)

**EXCEL**

| | A |
|---|---|
| 1 | 0.356597851 |

=NORM.DIST(1900,2172,740,TRUE)

2. Here, you are asked to find the probability associated with a sample mean $\bar{x}$. The $z$-score that corresponds to $\bar{x} = \$1900$ is

$$z = \frac{\bar{x} - \mu_{\bar{x}}}{\sigma_{\bar{x}}} = \frac{\bar{x} - \mu}{\sigma/\sqrt{n}} = \frac{1900 - 2172}{740/\sqrt{25}} = \frac{-272}{148} \approx -1.84.$$

So, the probability that the mean credit card balance of the 25 card holders is less than \$1900 is

$$P(\bar{x} < 1900) = P(z < -1.84) = 0.0329.$$

You can check this answer using technology. For instance, you can use Excel to find the probability, as shown at the left. (The answer differs slightly due to rounding.)

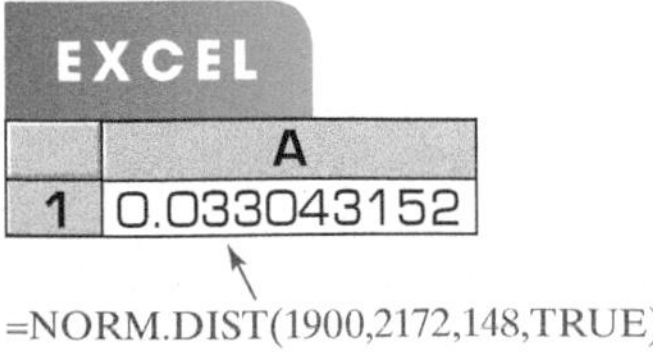

**EXCEL**

| | A |
|---|---|
| 1 | 0.033043152 |

=NORM.DIST(1900,2172,148,TRUE)

3. ***Interpretation*** Although there is about a 36% chance that a college student who uses a credit card to pay for school-related expenses will pay less than \$1900, there is only about a 3% chance that the mean amount a sample of 25 college students will pay is less than \$1900. Because there is only a 3% chance that the mean amount a sample of 25 college students will pay is less than \$1900, this is an unusual event.

**TRY IT YOURSELF 6**

A consumer price analyst claims that prices for computer monitors are normally distributed, with a mean of \$208 and a standard deviation of \$107. What is the probability that a randomly selected monitor costs less than \$200? You randomly select 10 monitors. What is the probability that their mean cost is less than \$200? Compare these two probabilities.

*Answer: Page A39*

# 5.4 EXERCISES

For Extra Help: MyLab Statistics

## Building Basic Skills and Vocabulary

*In Exercises 1–4, a population has a mean $\mu$ and a standard deviation $\sigma$. Find the mean and standard deviation of the sampling distribution of sample means with sample size n.*

**1.** $\mu = 150, \sigma = 25, n = 49$

**2.** $\mu = 45, \sigma = 15, n = 100$

**3.** $\mu = 790, \sigma = 48, n = 250$

**4.** $\mu = 1275, \sigma = 6, n = 1000$

**True or False?** *In Exercises 5–8, determine whether the statement is true or false. If it is false, rewrite it as a true statement.*

**5.** As the sample size increases, the mean of the distribution of sample means increases.

**6.** As the sample size increases, the standard deviation of the distribution of sample means increases.

**7.** A sampling distribution is normal only when the population is normal.

**8.** If the sample size is at least 30, then you can use $z$-scores to determine the probability that a sample mean falls in a given interval of the sampling distribution.

**Graphical Analysis** *In Exercises 9 and 10, the graph of a population distribution is shown with its mean and standard deviation. Random samples of size 100 are drawn from the population. Determine which of the figures labeled (a)–(c) would most closely resemble the sampling distribution of sample means. Explain your reasoning.*

**9.** The waiting time (in seconds) to turn left at an intersection

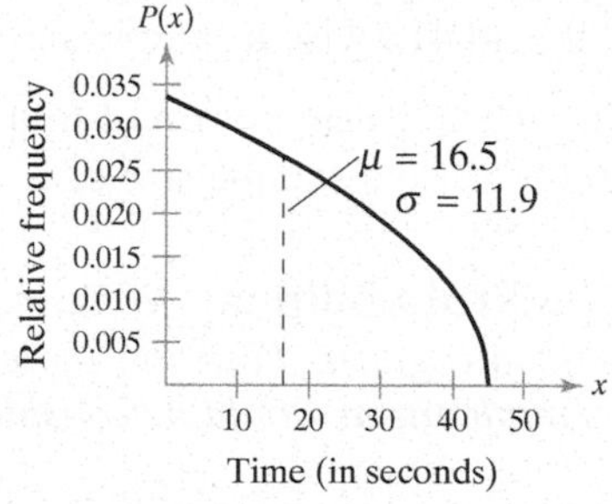


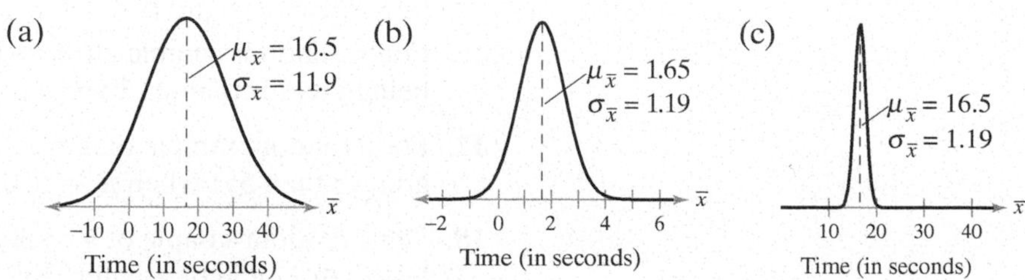

**10.** The annual snowfall (in feet) for a central New York State county

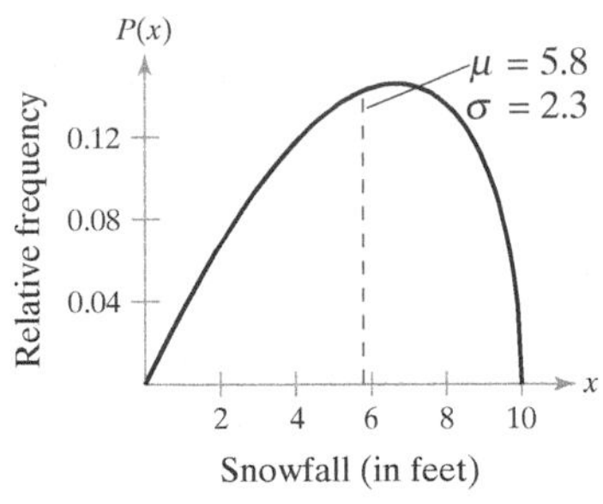


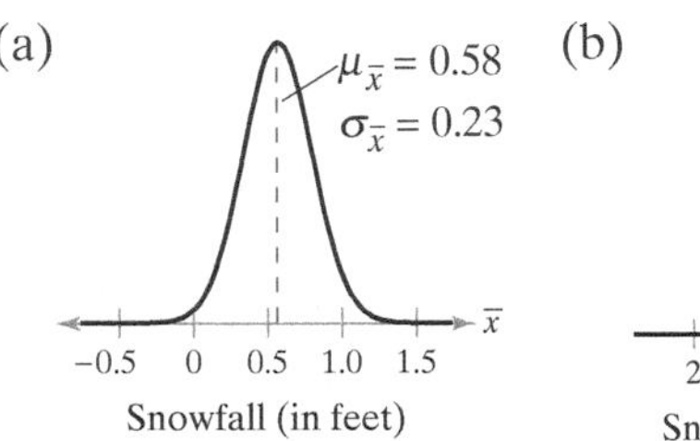


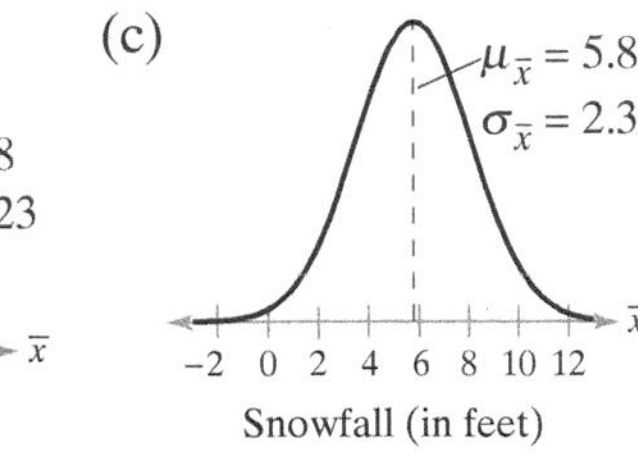

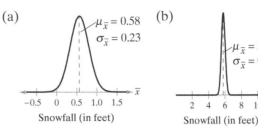


**A Sampling Distribution of Sample Means** *In Exercises 11–14, a population and sample size are given.*

*(a) Find the mean and standard deviation of the population.*

*(b) List all samples (with replacement) of the given size from the population and find the mean of each.*

*(c) Find the mean and standard deviation of the sampling distribution of sample means and compare them with the mean and standard deviation of the population.*

**11.** The load-bearing capacities (in thousands of pounds) of five transmission line insulators are 64, 48, 19, 79, and 56. Use a sample size of 2.

**12.** The diameters (in inches) of four machine parts are 1.000, 1.004, 1.001, and 1.003. Use a sample size of 2.

**13.** The melting points (in degrees Celsius) of three industrial lubricants are 350, 399, and 418. Use a sample size of 3.

**14.** The lifetimes (in hours) of four diamond-tipped cutting tools are 70, 85, 81, and 67. Use a sample size of 3.

**Finding Probabilities** *In Exercises 15–18, the population mean and standard deviation are given. Find the indicated probability and determine whether the given sample mean would be considered unusual.*

**15.** For a random sample of $n = 64$, find the probability of a sample mean being less than 24.3 when $\mu = 24$ and $\sigma = 1.25$.

**16.** For a random sample of $n = 100$, find the probability of a sample mean being greater than 24.3 when $\mu = 24$ and $\sigma = 1.25$.

**17.** For a random sample of $n = 45$, find the probability of a sample mean being greater than 551 when $\mu = 550$ and $\sigma = 3.7$.

**18.** For a random sample of $n = 36$, find the probability of a sample mean being less than 12,750 or greater than 12,753 when $\mu = 12{,}750$ and $\sigma = 1.7$.

## Using and Interpreting Concepts

**Interpreting the Central Limit Theorem** *In Exercises 19–26, find the mean and standard deviation of the indicated sampling distribution of sample means. Then sketch a graph of the sampling distribution.*

**19. Renewable Energy** During a recent period of two years, the day-ahead prices for renewable energy in Germany (in euros per mega-watt hour) have a mean of 31.58 and a standard deviation of 12.293. Random samples of size 75 are drawn from this population, and the mean of each sample is determined. *(Adapted from Multidisciplinary Digital Publishing Institute)*

**20. Renewable Energy** The zloty is the official currency of Poland. During a recent period of two years, the day-ahead prices for renewable energy in Poland (in zlotys per mega-watt hour) have a mean of 158.51 and a standard deviation of 33.424. Random samples of size 100 are drawn from this population, and the mean of each sample is determined. *(Adapted from Multidisciplinary Digital Publishing Institute)*

**21. Female Body Temperature** In a recent study involving 54 women, the mean body temperature of the women was found to be 97.2°F, with a standard deviation of 0.83. Random samples of size 36 are drawn from this population, and the mean of each sample is determined. *(Adapted from PLOS One)*

**22. Male Body Temperature** In a recent study involving 42 men, the mean body temperature of the men was found to be 96.8°F, with a standard deviation of 0.61. Random samples of size 30 are drawn from this population, and the mean of each sample is determined. *(Adapted from PLOS One)*

**23. Salaries** The annual salaries for entry-level marketing analysts are normally distributed, with a mean of about $54,000 and a standard deviation of about $11,000. Random samples of 34 are drawn from this population, and the mean of each sample is determined. *(Adapted from Salary.com)*

**24. Salaries** The annual salaries for web software development managers are normally distributed, with a mean of about $136,000 and a standard deviation of about $11,500. Random samples of 40 are drawn from this population, and the mean of each sample is determined. *(Adapted from Salary.com)*

**25. SAT French Subject Test** The scores on the SAT French Subject Test for the 2018–2020 graduating classes are normally distributed, with a mean of 603 and a standard deviation of 111. Random samples of size 16 are drawn from this population, and the mean of each sample is determined. *(Adapted from College Board)*

**26. SAT Italian Subject Test** The scores on the SAT Italian Subject Test for the 2018–2020 graduating classes are normally distributed, with a mean of 628 and a standard deviation of 110. Random samples of size 25 are drawn from this population, and the mean of each sample is determined. *(Adapted from College Board)*

**27.** Repeat Exercise 25 for samples of size 40 and 60. What happens to the mean and the standard deviation of the distribution of sample means as the sample size increases?

**28.** Repeat Exercise 26 for samples of size 72 and 108. What happens to the mean and the standard deviation of the distribution of sample means as the sample size increases?

**Finding Probabilities for Sampling Distributions** *In Exercises 29–32, find the indicated probability and interpret the results.*

**29. Dow Jones Industrial Average** From 1975 through 2020, the mean annual gain of the Dow Jones Industrial Average was 652. A random sample of 32 years is selected from this population. What is the probability that the mean gain for the sample was between 400 and 700? Assume $\sigma = 1540$.

**30. Standard & Poor's 500** From 1921 through 2020, the mean return of the Standard & Poor's 500 was 12.59%. A random sample of 38 years is selected from this population. What is the probability that the mean return for the sample was between 10.0% and 11.0%? Assume $\sigma = 19.58\%$.

**31. Asthma Prevalence by State** The mean percent of asthma prevalence of the 50 U.S. states is 9.51%. A random sample of 30 states is selected. What is the probability that the mean percent of asthma prevalence for the sample is greater than 10%? Assume $\sigma = 1.17\%$. *(Source: Centers for Disease Control and Prevention)*

**32. Fertility Rates by State** A fertility rate is the number of births per 1000 women aged 15–44. The mean fertility rate of the 50 U.S. states for a recent year was 59.0 with a standard deviation of 5.47. A random sample of 40 states is selected. What is the probability that the mean fertility rate for the sample for the recent year was less than 58? *(Source: Centers for Disease Control and Prevention)*

**33. Which Is More Likely?** Assume that the asthma prevalences in Exercise 31 are normally distributed. Are you more likely to randomly select a state with asthma prevalence less than 10% or to randomly select a sample of 10 states in which the mean of the state asthma prevalences is less than 10%? Explain.

**34. Which Is More Likely?** Assume that the fertility rates in Exercise 32 are normally distributed. Are you more likely to randomly select a state with a fertility rate of less than 65 or to randomly select a sample of 15 states in which the mean of the state fertility rates is less than 65? Explain.

**35. Paint Cans** A machine is set to fill paint cans with a mean of 128 ounces and a standard deviation of 0.2 ounce. A random sample of 40 cans has a mean of 127.9 ounces. The machine needs to be reset when the mean of a random sample is unusual. Does the machine need to be reset? Explain.

**36. Milk Containers** A machine is set to fill milk containers with a mean of 64 ounces and a standard deviation of 0.11 ounce. A random sample of 40 containers has a mean of 64.05 ounces. The machine needs to be reset when the mean of a random sample is unusual. Does the machine need to be reset? Explain.

**37. Lumber Cutter** The lengths of lumber a machine cuts are normally distributed, with a mean of 96 inches and a standard deviation of 0.5 inch.

(a) What is the probability that a randomly selected board cut by the machine has a length greater than 96.25 inches?

(b) You randomly select 40 boards. What is the probability that their mean length is greater than 96.25 inches?

**38. Ice Cream** The weights of ice cream cartons are normally distributed with a mean weight of 10 ounces and a standard deviation of 0.5 ounce.

(a) What is the probability that a randomly selected carton has a weight greater than 10.21 ounces?

(b) You randomly select 25 cartons. What is the probability that their mean weight is greater than 10.21 ounces?

## Extending Concepts

**Finite Correction Factor** *The formula for the standard deviation of the sampling distribution of sample means*

$$\sigma_{\bar{x}} = \frac{\sigma}{\sqrt{n}}$$

*given in the Central Limit Theorem is based on an assumption that the population has infinitely many members. This is the case whenever sampling is done with replacement (each member is put back after it is selected), because the sampling process could be continued indefinitely. The formula is also valid when the sample size is small in comparison with the population. When sampling is done without replacement and the sample size n is more than 5% of the finite population of size N ($n/N > 0.05$), however, there is a finite number of possible samples. A **finite correction factor,***

$$\sqrt{\frac{N-n}{N-1}}$$

*should be used to adjust the standard deviation. The sampling distribution of the sample means will be normal with a mean equal to the population mean, and the standard deviation will be*

$$\sigma_{\bar{x}} = \frac{\sigma}{\sqrt{n}}\sqrt{\frac{N-n}{N-1}}.$$

*In Exercises 39 and 40, determine whether the finite correction factor should be used. If so, use it in your calculations when you find the probability.*

**39. Parking Infractions** In a sample of 1000 fines issued by the City of Toronto for parking infractions in September of 2020, the mean fine was \$49.83 and the standard deviation was \$52.15. A random sample of size 60 is selected from this population. What is the probability that the mean fine is less than \$40? *(Adapted from City of Toronto)*

**40. Old Faithful** In a sample of 100 eruptions of the Old Faithful geyser at Yellowstone National Park, the mean interval between eruptions was 129.58 minutes and the standard deviation was 108.54 minutes. A random sample of size 30 is selected from this population. What is the probability that the mean interval between eruptions is between 120 minutes and 140 minutes? *(Adapted from Geyser Times)*

**Sampling Distribution of Sample Proportions** *For a random sample of size n, the **sample proportion** is the number of individuals in the sample with a specified characteristic divided by the sample size. The **sampling distribution of sample proportions** is the distribution formed when sample proportions of size n are repeatedly taken from a population where the probability of an individual with a specified characteristic is p. The sampling distribution of sample proportions has a mean equal to the population proportion p and a standard deviation equal to $\sqrt{pq/n}$. In Exercises 41 and 42, assume the sampling distribution of sample proportions is a normal distribution.*

**41. Construction** About 63% of the residents in a town are in favor of building a new high school. One hundred five residents are randomly selected. What is the probability that the sample proportion in favor of building a new school is less than 55%? Interpret your result.

**42. Conservation** About 74% of the residents in a town say that they are making an effort to conserve water or electricity. One hundred ten residents are randomly selected. What is the probability that the sample proportion making an effort to conserve water or electricity is greater than 80%? Interpret your result.

# 5.4 ACTIVITY Sampling Distributions

APPLET

You can find the interactive applet for this activity at MyLab Statistics.

The *Sampling distributions* applet allows you to investigate sampling distributions by repeatedly taking random samples from a population. The top plot displays the distribution of a population. Several options are available for the population distribution (Uniform, Bell-shaped, Skewed, Binary, and Custom). Generate random samples of the given size $n$ from the population by clicking **1 time, 5 times,** or **1000 times.** The sample statistics specified in the bottom two plots will be updated for each sample. When the sample size and number of samples are small enough, the display will show, in an animated fashion, the points selected from the population dropping into the second plot and the corresponding summary statistic values dropping into the third and fourth plots. Click **Reset** to stop an animation and clear existing results. Summary statistics for each plot are shown in the panel at the right of the plot.

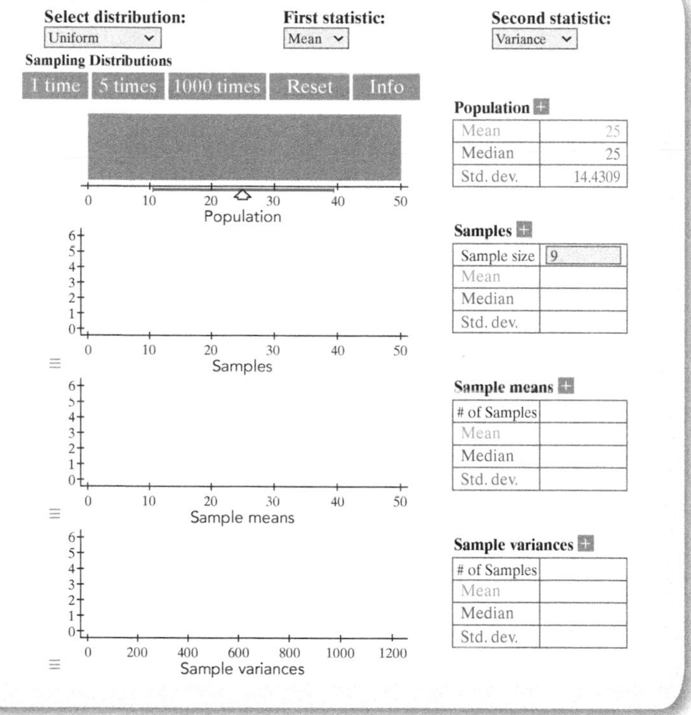


## EXPLORE

**Step 1** Specify a distribution. Specify what summary statistics to display in the bottom two graphs. Specify the sample size $n$.

**Step 2** Click **1 time, 5 times,** or **1000 times** to generate the sampling distributions.

## DRAW CONCLUSIONS

APPLET

1. Run the simulation using $n = 30$ and $N = 10$ for a uniform, a bell-shaped, and a skewed distribution. What is the mean of the sampling distribution of the sample means for each distribution? For each distribution, is this what you would expect?

2. Run the simulation using $n = 50$ and $N = 10$ for a bell-shaped distribution. What is the standard deviation of the distribution of the sample means? Does this agree with the Central Limit Theorem? Is this what you would expect?

# 5.5 Normal Approximations to Binomial Distributions

## What You Should Learn

- How to determine when a normal distribution can approximate a binomial distribution
- How to find the continuity correction
- How to use a normal distribution to approximate binomial probabilities

Approximating a Binomial Distribution ▪ Continuity Correction ▪ Approximating Binomial Probabilities

## Approximating a Binomial Distribution

In Section 4.2, you learned how to find binomial probabilities. For instance, consider a surgical procedure that has an 85% chance of success. When a doctor performs this surgery on 10 patients, you can use the binomial formula to find the probability of exactly two successful surgeries.

But what if the doctor performs the surgical procedure on 150 patients and you want to find the probability of *fewer than 100* successful surgeries? To do this using the techniques described in Section 4.2, you would have to use the binomial formula 100 times and find the sum of the resulting probabilities. This approach is not practical, of course. A better approach is to use a normal distribution to approximate the binomial distribution.

### Normal Approximation to a Binomial Distribution

If $np \geq 5$ and $nq \geq 5$, then the binomial random variable $x$ is approximately normally distributed, with mean

$$\mu = np$$

and standard deviation

$$\sigma = \sqrt{npq}$$

where $n$ is the number of independent trials, $p$ is the probability of success in a single trial, and $q$ is the probability of failure in a single trial.

### Study Tip

Here are some properties of binomial experiments (see Section 4.2).

- $n$ independent trials
- Two possible outcomes: success or failure
- Probability of success is $p$; probability of failure is $q = 1 - p$
- $p$ is the same for each trial

To see why a normal approximation is valid, look at the binomial distributions for $p = 0.25$, $q = 1 - 0.25 = 0.75$, and $n = 4$, $n = 10$, $n = 25$, and $n = 50$ shown below. Notice that as $n$ increases, the shape of the binomial distribution becomes more similar to a normal distribution.

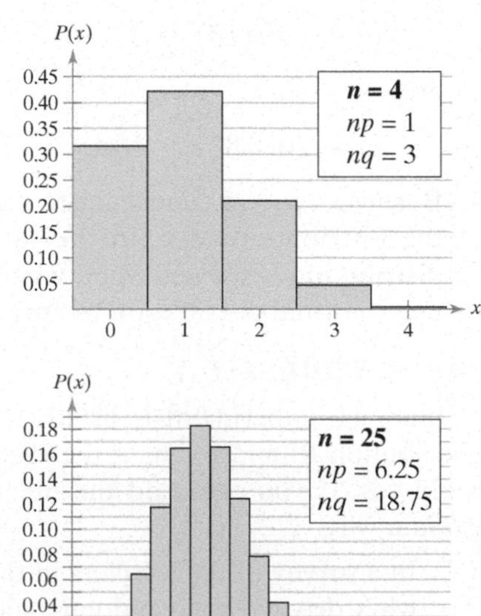


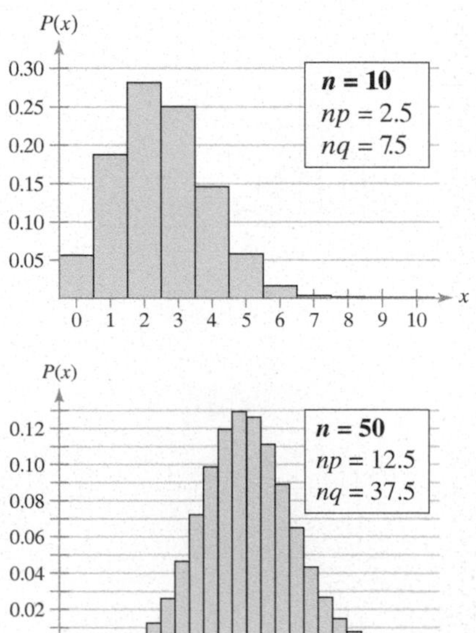

## EXAMPLE 1

### Approximating a Binomial Distribution

Two binomial experiments are listed. Determine whether you can use a normal distribution to approximate the distribution of $x$, the number of people who reply yes. If you can, find the mean and standard deviation. If you cannot, explain why.

1. In a survey of high schools in a certain state, it was reported that 40% of students failed at least one class taken through distance learning. You randomly select 45 students from that state and ask them whether they failed at least one class taken through distance learning. *(Source: Inside Higher Ed)*

2. In a survey of high schools in a certain state, it was reported that 18% of seniors were off track to graduate because of at least one course failure. You randomly select 20 seniors from that state and ask them whether they are off track to graduate because of at least one course failure. *(Source: Inside Higher Ed)*

### SOLUTION

1. In this binomial experiment, $n = 45$, $p = 0.40$, and $q = 0.60$. So,

$$np = 45(0.40) = 18$$

and

$$nq = 45(0.60) = 27.$$

Because $np$ and $nq$ are greater than 5, you can use a normal distribution with

$$\mu = np = 18$$

and

$$\sigma = \sqrt{npq} = \sqrt{45(0.40)(0.60)} \approx 3.29$$

to approximate the distribution of $x$. In the figure at the left, notice that the binomial distribution is approximately bell-shaped, which supports the conclusion that you can use a normal distribution to approximate the distribution of $x$.

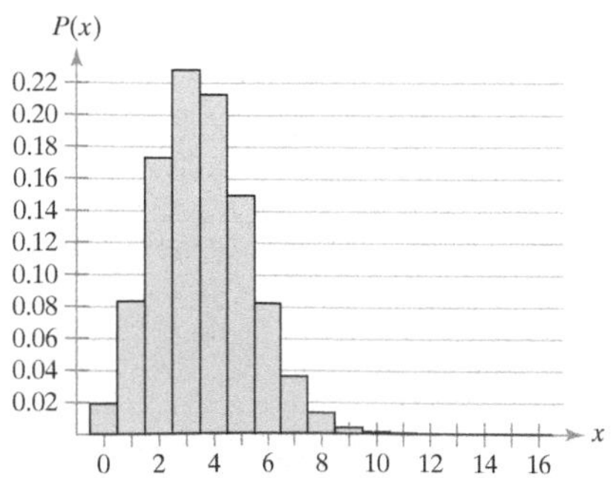


2. In this binomial experiment, $n = 20$, $p = 0.18$, and $q = 0.82$. So,

$$np = 20(0.18) = 3.6$$

and

$$nq = 20(0.82) = 16.4.$$

Because $np < 5$, you cannot use a normal distribution to approximate the distribution of $x$. In the figure at the left, notice that the binomial distribution is skewed right, which supports the conclusion that you cannot use a normal distribution to approximate the distribution of $x$.

### TRY IT YOURSELF 1

A binomial experiment is listed. Determine whether you can use a normal distribution to approximate the distribution of $x$, the number of people who reply yes. If you can, find the mean and standard deviation. If you cannot, explain why.

In a survey of teen drivers in the United States, 35% admit to texting while driving. You randomly select 100 teen drivers in the United States and ask them whether they admit to texting while driving. *(Source: American Automobile Association)*

*Answer: Page A39*

## Continuity Correction

A binomial distribution is discrete and can be represented by a probability histogram. To calculate *exact* binomial probabilities, you can use the binomial formula for each value of $x$ and add the results. Geometrically, this corresponds to adding the areas of bars in the probability histogram (see top figure at the left). Remember that each bar has a width of one unit and $x$ is the midpoint of the interval.

When you use a *continuous* normal distribution to approximate a binomial probability, you need to move 0.5 unit to the left and right of the midpoint to include all possible $x$-values in the interval (see bottom figure at the left). When you do this, you are making a **continuity correction.**

Exact binomial probability

$P(x = c)$

$c$ $x$

Normal approximation

$P(c - 0.5 < x < c + 0.5)$

$c - 0.5$ $c$ $c + 0.5$ $x$

**EXAMPLE 2**

### Using a Continuity Correction

Use a continuity correction to convert each binomial probability to a normal distribution probability.

1. The probability of getting between 270 and 310 successes, inclusive
2. The probability of getting at least 158 successes
3. The probability of getting fewer than 63 successes

**SOLUTION**

1. The discrete midpoint values are 270, 271, . . ., 310. The corresponding interval for the continuous normal distribution is $269.5 < x < 310.5$ and the normal distribution probability is $P(269.5 < x < 310.5)$.
2. The discrete midpoint values are 158, 159, 160, . . .. The corresponding interval for the continuous normal distribution is $x > 157.5$ and the normal distribution probability is $P(x > 157.5)$.
3. The discrete midpoint values are . . ., 60, 61, 62. The corresponding interval for the continuous normal distribution is $x < 62.5$ and the normal distribution probability is $P(x < 62.5)$.

**TRY IT YOURSELF 2**

Use a continuity correction to convert each binomial probability to a normal distribution probability.

1. The probability of getting between 57 and 83 successes, inclusive
2. The probability of getting at most 54 successes

*Answer: Page A39*

### Study Tip

In a discrete distribution, there is a difference between $P(x \geq c)$ and $P(x > c)$. This is true because the probability that $x$ is exactly $c$ is not 0. In a continuous distribution, however, there is no difference between $P(x \geq c)$ and $P(x > c)$ because the probability that $x$ is exactly $c$ is 0.

Shown below are several cases of binomial probabilities involving the number $c$ and how to convert each to a normal distribution probability.

| Binomial | Normal | Notes |
|---|---|---|
| Exactly $c$ | $P(c - 0.5 < x < c + 0.5)$ | Includes $c$ |
| At most $c$ | $P(x < c + 0.5)$ | Includes $c$ |
| Fewer than $c$ | $P(x < c - 0.5)$ | Does not include $c$ |
| At least $c$ | $P(x > c - 0.5)$ | Includes $c$ |
| More than $c$ | $P(x > c + 0.5)$ | Does not include $c$ |

## Picturing the World

In a survey of U.S. adults in a romantic relationship, 60.4% responded that they have hidden purchases from their spouses or partners, as shown in the pie chart. (Adapted from MyBankTracker)

**Have You Ever Hidden Purchases from Your Spouse or Partner?**

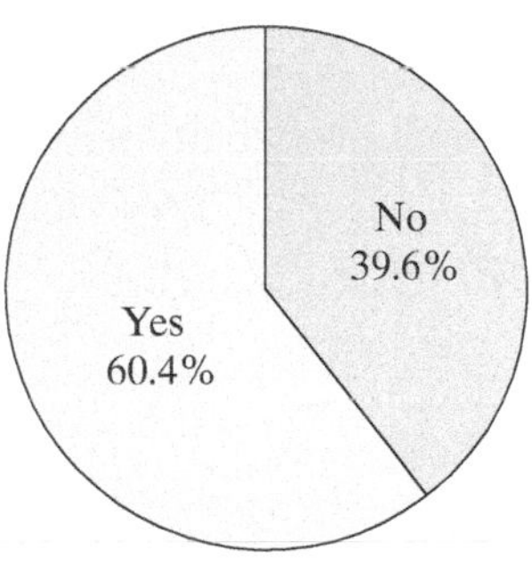


**Assume that this survey is a true indication of the proportion of the population who say they have hidden purchases from their spouses or partners. You sample 50 adults with spouses or partners at random. What is the probability that between 20 and 25, inclusive, would say they have hidden purchases from their spouses or partners?**

## Approximating Binomial Probabilities

### GUIDELINES

**Using a Normal Distribution to Approximate Binomial Probabilities**

| In Words | In Symbols |
|---|---|
| 1. Verify that a binomial distribution applies. | Specify $n$, $p$, and $q$. |
| 2. Determine whether you can use a normal distribution to approximate $x$, the binomial variable. | Is $np \geq 5$? Is $nq \geq 5$? |
| 3. Find the mean $\mu$ and standard deviation $\sigma$ for the distribution. | $\mu = np$ $\sigma = \sqrt{npq}$ |
| 4. Apply the appropriate continuity correction. Shade the corresponding area under the normal curve. | Add 0.5 to (or subtract 0.5 from) the binomial probability. |
| 5. Find the corresponding $z$-score(s). | $z = \dfrac{x - \mu}{\sigma}$ |
| 6. Find the probability. | Use the Standard Normal Table. |

### EXAMPLE 3

#### Approximating a Binomial Probability

In a survey of high schools in a certain state, it was reported that 40% of students failed at least one class taken through distance learning. You randomly select 45 students from that state and ask them whether they failed at least one class taken through distance learning. What is the probability that fewer than 20 of them respond yes? *(Source: Inside Higher Ed)*

**SOLUTION**

From Example 1, you know that you can use a normal distribution with

$$\mu = 18 \quad \text{and} \quad \sigma \approx 3.29$$

to approximate the binomial distribution. To use a normal distribution, note that the probability is "fewer than 20." So, apply the continuity correction by subtracting 0.5 from 20 and write the probability as

$$P(x < 20 - 0.5) = P(x < 19.5).$$

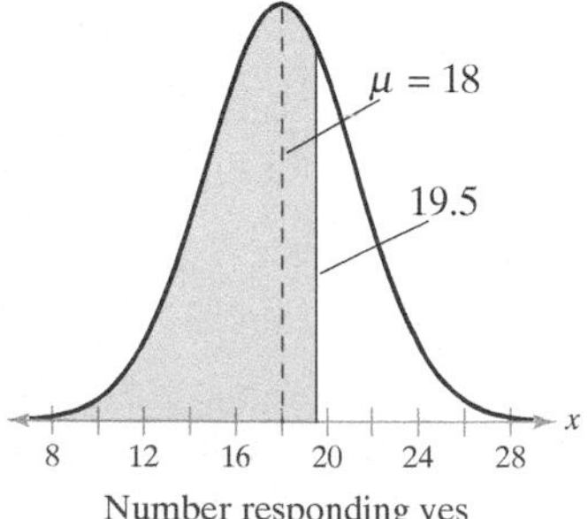


The figure at the left shows a normal curve with $\mu = 18$, $\sigma \approx 3.29$, and the shaded area to the left of 19.5. The $z$-score that corresponds to $x = 19.5$ is

$$z = \frac{x - \mu}{\sigma}$$

$$z \approx \frac{19.5 - 18}{3.29} \approx 0.46.$$

Using the Standard Normal Table,

$$P(z < 0.46) = 0.6772.$$

***Interpretation*** The probability that fewer than twenty students respond yes is approximately 0.6772, or about 67.72%.

**TRY IT YOURSELF 3**

In a survey of teen drivers in the United States, 35% admit to texting while driving. You randomly select 100 teen drivers in the United States and ask them whether they admit to texting while driving. What is the probability that more than 30 respond yes? *(Source: American Automobile Association)*

*Answer: Page A39*

## EXAMPLE 4

### Approximating a Binomial Probability

A study found that 52% of U.S. drivers who use both alcohol and marijuana admit to driving aggressively. You randomly select 200 U.S. drivers who use both alcohol and marijuana and ask them whether they admit to driving aggressively. What is the probability that at least 100 drivers will say yes, they admit to driving aggressively? *(Source: American Automobile Association)*

**SOLUTION**

Because $np = 200(0.52) = 104$ and $nq = 200(0.48) = 96$, the binomial variable $x$ is approximately normally distributed, with

$$\mu = np = 104 \quad \text{and} \quad \sigma = \sqrt{npq} = \sqrt{200(0.52)(0.48)} \approx 7.07.$$

Using the continuity correction, you can rewrite the discrete probability $P(x \geq 100)$ as the continuous probability $P(x > 99.5)$. The figure shows a normal curve with $\mu = 104$, $\sigma = 7.07$, and the shaded area to the right of 99.5.

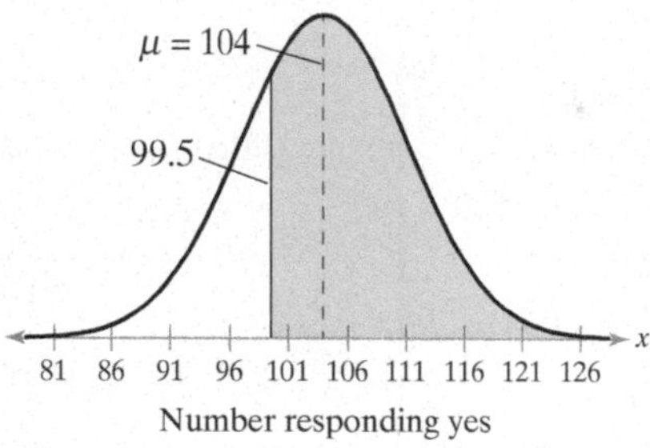


The $z$-score that corresponds to 99.5 is

$$z = \frac{99.5 - 104}{\sqrt{200(0.52)(0.48)}} \approx -0.64.$$

So, the probability that at least 100 drivers will say "yes" is approximately

$$\begin{aligned} P(x > 99.5) &= P(z > -0.64) \\ &= 1 - P(z < -0.64) \\ &= 1 - 0.2611 \\ &= 0.7389. \end{aligned}$$

***Interpretation*** The probability that at least 100 drivers will say "yes" is approximately 0.7389, or about 73.9%.

**TRY IT YOURSELF 4**

In Example 4, what is the probability that at most 90 drivers will say yes, they admit to driving aggressively?

*Answer: Page A39*

**Tech Tip**

Recall that you can use technology to find a normal probability. For instance, in Example 4, you can use a TI-84 Plus to find the probability once the mean, standard deviation, and continuity correction are calculated. (Use 10,000 for the upper bound.)

```
normalcdf(99.5,1000,104,
7.07)
                0.7377722394
```

## EXAMPLE 5

### Approximating a Binomial Probability

A study of former National Football League (NFL) players found that 12.3% have undergone knee joint replacement surgery. You randomly select 100 former NFL players and ask them whether they have undergone knee joint replacement surgery. What is the probability that exactly 15 will say yes? *(Source: BMJ Open Sport & Exercise Medicine)*

**SOLUTION**

Because $np = 100(0.123) = 12.3$ and $nq = 100(0.877) = 87.7$, the binomial variable $x$ is approximately normally distributed, with

$$\mu = np = 12.3 \quad \text{and} \quad \sigma = \sqrt{npq} = \sqrt{100(0.123)(0.877)} \approx 3.28.$$

Using the continuity correction, you can rewrite the discrete probability $P(x = 15)$ as the continuous probability $P(14.5 < x < 15.5)$. The figure shows a normal curve with $\mu = 12.3$, $\sigma \approx 3.28$, and the shaded area under the curve between 14.5 and 15.5.

### Tech Tip

The approximation in Example 5 is comparable to the probability found using the binomial probability feature of a technology tool. For instance, compare the result in Example 5 with the one found on a TI-84 Plus shown below.

```
binompdf(100,.123,15)
           0.0807687299
```

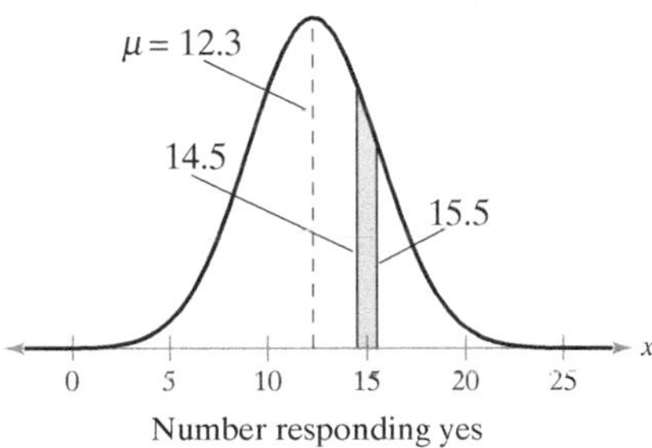


The $z$-score that corresponds to 14.5 is

$$z_1 = \frac{14.5 - 12.3}{\sqrt{100(0.123)(0.877)}} \approx 0.67$$

and the $z$-score that corresponds to 15.5 is

$$z_2 = \frac{15.5 - 12.3}{\sqrt{100(0.123)(0.877)}} \approx 0.97.$$

So, the probability that exactly 15 former NFL players will say they have undergone knee joint replacement surgery is

$$\begin{aligned} P(14.5 < x < 15.5) &= P(0.67 < z < 0.97) \\ &= P(z < 0.97) - P(z < 0.67) \\ &= 0.8340 - 0.7486 \\ &= 0.0854. \end{aligned}$$

***Interpretation*** The probability that exactly 15 former NFL players will say they have undergone knee joint replacement surgery is approximately 0.0854, or about 8.5%.

**TRY IT YOURSELF 5**

The study in Example 5 found that 8.1% of former NFL players have undergone hip joint replacement surgery. You randomly select 100 former NFL players and ask them whether they have undergone hip joint replacement surgery. What is the probability that exactly four will say yes? *(Source: BMJ Open Sport & Exercise Medicine)*

*Answer: Page A39*

# 5.5 EXERCISES

For Extra Help: MyLab Statistics

## Building Basic Skills and Vocabulary

*In Exercises 1–4, the sample size n, probability of success p, and probability of failure q are given for a binomial experiment. Determine whether you can use a normal distribution to approximate the distribution of x.*

**1.** $n = 24, p = 0.85, q = 0.15$

**2.** $n = 15, p = 0.70, q = 0.30$

**3.** $n = 18, p = 0.90, q = 0.10$

**4.** $n = 20, p = 0.65, q = 0.35$

*In Exercises 5–8, match the binomial probability statement with its corresponding normal distribution probability statement (a)–(d) after a continuity correction.*

**5.** $P(x > 109)$

**6.** $P(x \geq 109)$

**7.** $P(x \leq 109)$

**8.** $P(x < 109)$

(a) $P(x > 109.5)$

(b) $P(x < 108.5)$

(c) $P(x < 109.5)$

(d) $P(x > 108.5)$

*In Exercises 9–14, write the binomial probability in words. Then, use a continuity correction to convert the binomial probability to a normal distribution probability.*

**9.** $P(x < 25)$

**10.** $P(x \geq 110)$

**11.** $P(x = 33)$

**12.** $P(x > 65)$

**13.** $P(x \leq 150)$

**14.** $P(55 < x < 60)$

**Graphical Analysis** *In Exercises 15 and 16, write the binomial probability and the normal probability for the shaded region of the graph. Find the value of each probability and compare the results.*

**15.**

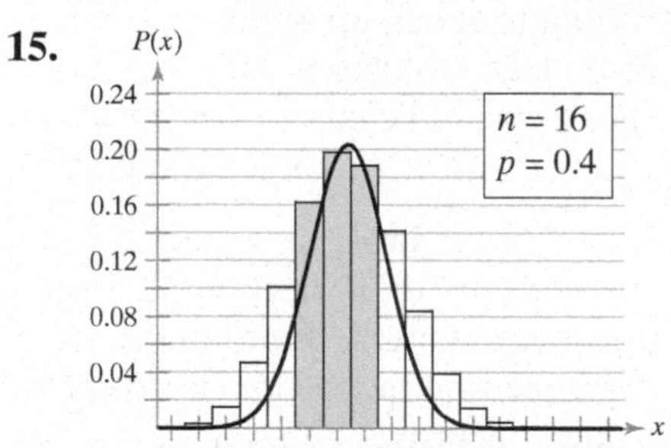


**16.**

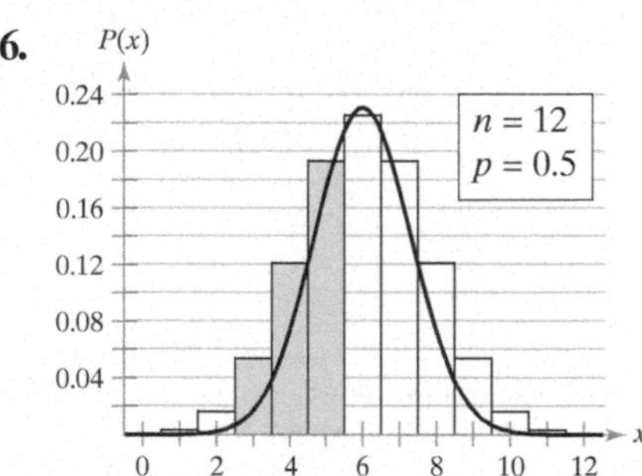


## Using and Interpreting Concepts

**Approximating a Binomial Distribution** *In Exercises 17 and 18, a binomial experiment is given. Determine whether you can use a normal distribution to approximate the binomial distribution. If you can, find the mean and standard deviation. If you cannot, explain why.*

**17. Bachelor's Degrees** Twenty-two percent of adults over 18 years of age have a bachelor's degree. You randomly select 20 adults over 18 years of age and ask whether they have a bachelor's degree. *(Source: U.S. Census Bureau)*

**18. Free Speech** In a survey of U.S. college students, 74% believed that colleges do not have the right to restrict the expression of political views on campus. You randomly select 20 college students and ask them if they believe colleges have the right to restrict the expression of political views on campus. *(Source: Inside Higher Ed)*

**Approximating Binomial Probabilities** *In Exercises 19–26, determine whether you can use a normal distribution to approximate the binomial distribution. If you can, use the normal distribution to approximate the indicated probabilities and sketch their graphs. If you cannot, explain why and use a binomial distribution to find the indicated probabilities. Identify any unusual events. Explain.*

19. **College Programs** In a survey of U.S. college students, 62% said that if their college offers new programs tailored to the new economy, it will make them more likely to re-enroll. You randomly select 40 college students. Find the probability that the number who are more likely to enroll if their college offers new programs tailored to the new economy is (a) exactly 25, (b) at least 30, and (c) at most 24. *(Source: New America)*

20. **Social Media** A survey of Americans found that 55% would be disappointed if Facebook disappeared. You randomly select 500 Americans and ask them whether they would be disappointed if Facebook disappeared. Find the probability that the number who say yes is (a) less than 250, (b) at least 300, and (c) between 240 and 280, inclusive. *(Source: The Verge)*

21. **Gun Legislation** In a survey of U.S. adults, 43% said they would favor allowing people to carry guns in more places. You randomly select 100 U.S. adults. Find the probability that the number who favor allowing people to carry guns in more places is (a) more than 50, (b) at most 50, and (c) between 40 and 45, inclusive. *(Source: Pew Research Center)*

22. **Perception of Police** A survey of U.S. registered voters found that 71% have a favorable opinion of police. You randomly select 150 U.S. registered voters. Find the probability that the number who have a favorable opinion of police is (a) at most 100, (b) more than 120, and (c) between 90 and 110, inclusive. *(Source: Harvard CAPS/Harris Poll)*

23. **Athletes on Social Issues** In a survey of college athletes, 84% said they are willing to speak up and be more active in social issues. You randomly select 25 college athletes. Find the probability that the number who are willing to speak up and be more active in social issues is (a) at least 24, (b) less than 23, and (c) between 18 and 22, inclusive. *(Source: Rise)*

24. **Gun Ownership** In a survey of U.S. registered voters, 36% said that someone in their household owns a gun. You randomly select 20 U.S. registered voters. Find the probability that the number who live with someone who owns a gun is (a) no more than 8, (b) exactly 7, and (c) between 6 and 9 inclusive. *(Source: Harvard CAPS/Harris Poll)*

25. **Clinical Trials** In a survey of U.S. adults, 19% said that they have participated in a clinical trial. You randomly select 200 U.S. adults. Find the probability that the number who have participated in a clinical trial is (a) no fewer than 30, (b) more than 40, and (c) between 35 and 45 inclusive. *(Source: America Speaks!)*

26. **Advancing Research** In a survey of U.S. adults, 77% said are willing to share their personal health information to advance medical research. You randomly select 500 U.S. adults. Find the probability that the number who are willing to share their personal health information to advance medical research is (a) at most 400, (b) more than 360, and (c) between 380 and 390 inclusive. *(Source: America Speaks!)*

**27. Daily Commute** About 83% of U.S. employees drive their own vehicle to work. You randomly select a sample of U.S. employees. Find the probability that more than 100 of the employees drive their own vehicle to work. *(Source: U.S. Bureau of Labor Statistics)*

(a) You select 110 U.S. employees.

(b) You select 125 U.S. employees.

(c) You select 150 U.S. employees.

**28. Employee Wellness** A survey of employed U.S. adults found that only 35% believe their employer cares about their well-being. You randomly select a sample of U.S. employees. Find the probability that fewer than 100 believe their employer cares about their well-being. *(Source: Gallup)*

(a) You select 250 U.S. employees.

(b) You select 300 U.S. employees.

(c) You select 400 U.S. employees.

## Extending Concepts

**Getting Physical** *The figure shows the results of a survey of U.S. adults ages 18 to 29 who were asked whether they participated in a sport. In the survey, 48% of the men and 23% of the women said they participate in sports. The most common sports are shown below. Use this information in Exercises 29 and 30. (Source: NPR)*

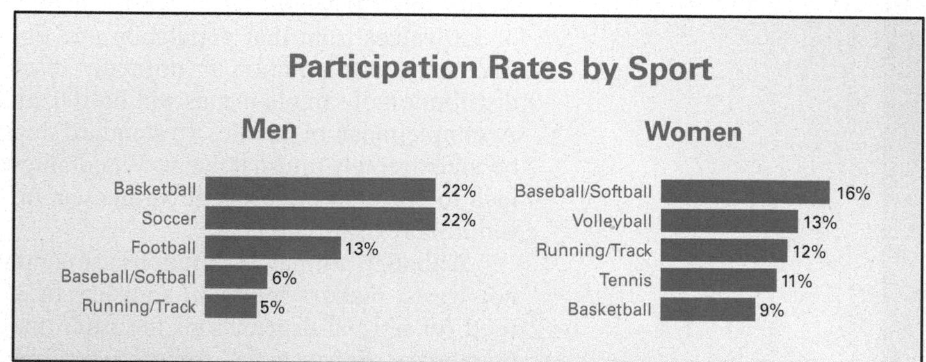


**29.** You randomly select 250 U.S. men ages 18 to 29 and ask them whether they participate in at least one sport. You find that 80% say no. How likely is this result? Do you think this sample is a good one? Explain your reasoning.

**30.** You randomly select 300 U.S. women ages 18 to 29 and ask them whether they participate in at least one sport. Of the 72 who say yes, 50% say they participate in volleyball. How likely is this result? Do you think this sample is a good one? Explain your reasoning.

**Testing a Drug** *A drug manufacturer claims that a drug cures a rare skin disease 75% of the time. The claim is checked by testing the drug on 100 patients. If at least 70 patients are cured, then this claim will be accepted. Use this information in Exercises 31 and 32.*

**31.** Find the probability that the claim will be rejected, assuming that the manufacturer's claim is true.

**32.** Find the probability that the claim will be accepted, assuming that the actual probability that the drug cures the skin disease is 65%.

# USES AND ABUSES Statistics in the Real World

## Uses

Normal distributions can be used to describe many real-life situations and are widely used in the fields of science, business, and psychology. They are the most important probability distributions in statistics and can be used to approximate other distributions, such as discrete binomial distributions.

The most incredible application of the normal distribution lies in the Central Limit Theorem. This theorem states that no matter what type of distribution a population may have, as long as the size of each random sample is at least 30, the distribution of sample means will be approximately normal. When a population is normal, the distribution of sample means is normal for any random sample of size $n$.

The normal distribution is essential to sampling theory. Sampling theory forms the basis of statistical inference, which you will study in the next chapter.

## Abuses

Consider a population that is normally distributed, with a mean of 100 and standard deviation of 15. It would not be unusual for an individual value taken from this population to be 115 or more. In fact, this will happen almost 16% of the time. It *would* be, however, highly unusual to take a random sample of 100 values from that population and obtain a sample mean of 115 or more. Because the population is normally distributed, the mean of the sampling distribution of sample means will be 100, and the standard deviation will be 1.5. A sample mean of 115 lies 10 standard deviations above the mean. This would be an extremely unusual event. When an event this unusual occurs, it is a good idea to question the original parameters or the assumption that the population is normally distributed.

Although normal distributions are common in many populations, you should not try to make *nonnormal* statistics fit a normal distribution. The statistics used for normal distributions are often inappropriate when the distribution is nonnormal. For instance, some economists argue that financial risk managers' reliance on normal distributions to model stock market behavior is a mistake because the normal distributions do not accurately predict unusual events like market crashes.

## EXERCISES

**1.** ***Is It Unusual?*** A population is normally distributed, with a mean of 100 and a standard deviation of 15. Determine whether either event is unusual. Explain your reasoning.

**a.** The mean of a sample of 3 is 112 or more.

**b.** The mean of a sample of 75 is 105 or more.

**2.** ***Find the Error*** The mean age of students at a high school is 16.5, with a standard deviation of 0.7. You use the Standard Normal Table to determine that the probability of selecting one student at random whose age is more than 17.5 years is about 8%. What is the error in this problem?

**3.** Give an example of a distribution that might be nonnormal.

# 5 Chapter Summary

## What Did You Learn?

| What Did You Learn? | Example(s) | Review Exercises |
|---|---|---|
| **Section 5.1** | | |
| ▶ How to interpret graphs of normal probability distributions | 1, 2 | 1–4 |
| ▶ How to find areas under the standard normal curve | 3–6 | 5–26 |
| **Section 5.2** | | |
| ▶ How to find probabilities for normally distributed variables using a table and using technology | 1–3 | 27–36 |
| **Section 5.3** | | |
| ▶ How to find a *z*-score given the area under the normal curve | 1, 2 | 37–44 |
| ▶ How to transform a *z*-score to an *x*-value: $x = \mu + z\sigma$ | 3 | 45, 46 |
| ▶ How to find a specific data value of a normal distribution given the probability | 4, 5 | 47–50 |
| **Section 5.4** | | |
| ▶ How to find sampling distributions and verify their properties | 1 | 51, 52 |
| ▶ How to interpret the Central Limit Theorem | 2, 3 | 53, 54 |
| ▶ How to apply the Central Limit Theorem to find the probability of a sample mean | 4–6 | 55–60 |
| **Section 5.5** | | |
| ▶ How to determine when a normal distribution can approximate a binomial distribution<br>$\mu = np$ Mean $\sigma = \sqrt{npq}$ Standard deviation | 1 | 61, 62 |
| ▶ How to find the continuity correction | 2 | 63–68 |
| ▶ How to use a normal distribution to approximate binomial probabilities | 3–5 | 69, 70 |

## Study Strategies

**Preparing for a Test** Everyone has trouble now and then taking tests. Here are some things you can do to prepare for a test—and some things you should not do.

- Begin studying well before the test.
- Focus on important information in your notes and the textbook. Look for highlighted words and formulas.
- If needed, have a discussion with your professor about where your studying should focus.
- Review each problem type that may appear on the test.
- Try to get a good night's rest the night before the test. *Do not* stay up all night cramming for the test. Eat sensibly before the test.
- *Do not* try to memorize everything in your notes or in the textbook, causing information overload.
- If needed, form a study group, but *do not* use the group for excessive socializing.

For more information, visit Skills for Success in the accompanying MyLab course.

# 5 Review Exercises

## Section 5.1

*In Exercises 1 and 2, use the normal curve to estimate the mean and standard deviation.*

**1.**

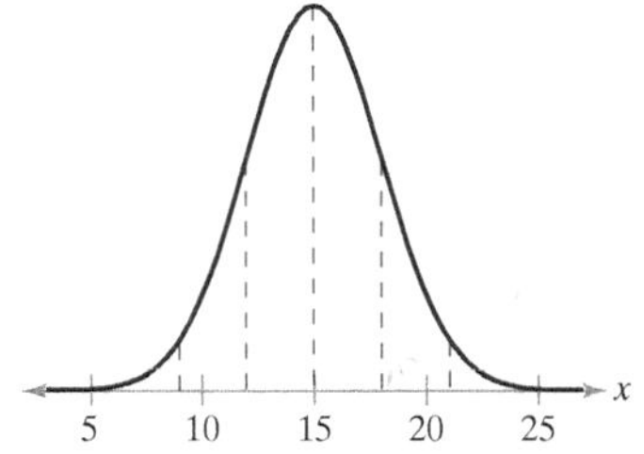


**2.**

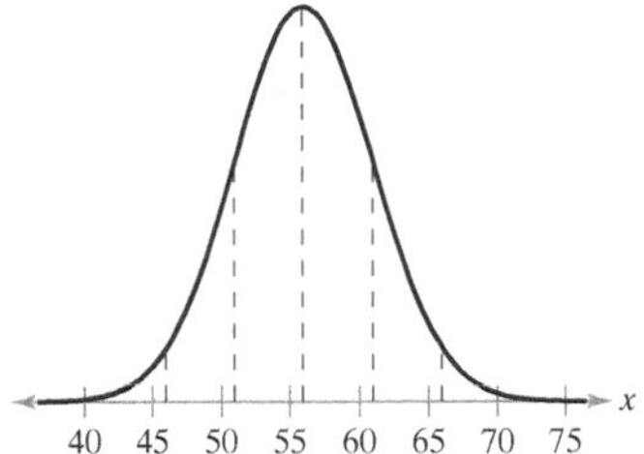


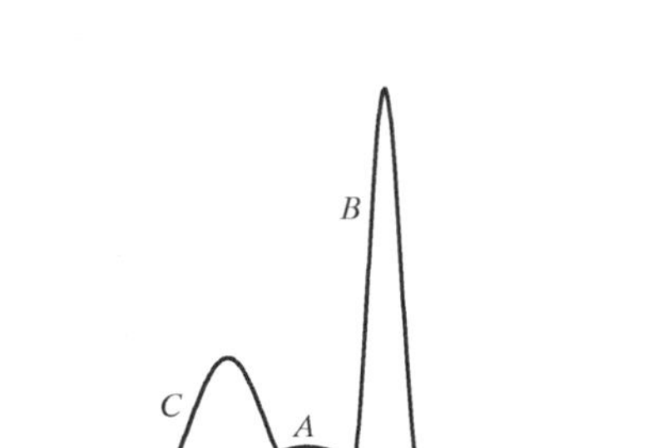


FIGURE FOR EXERCISES 3 AND 4

*In Exercises 3 and 4, use the normal curves shown at the left.*

**3.** Which normal curve has the greatest mean? Explain your reasoning.

**4.** Which normal curve has the greatest standard deviation? Explain your reasoning.

*In Exercises 5 and 6, find the area of the indicated region under the standard normal curve. If convenient, use technology to find the area.*

**5.**

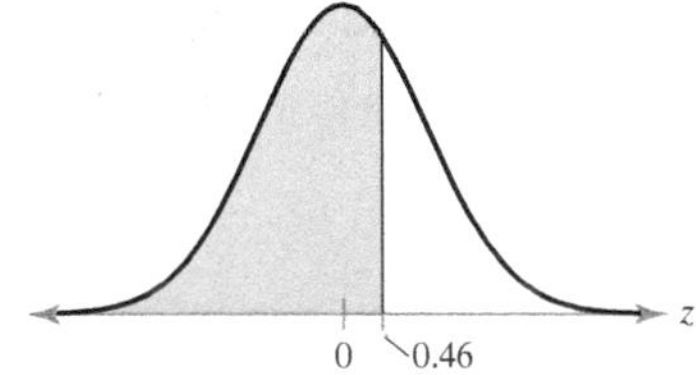


**6.**

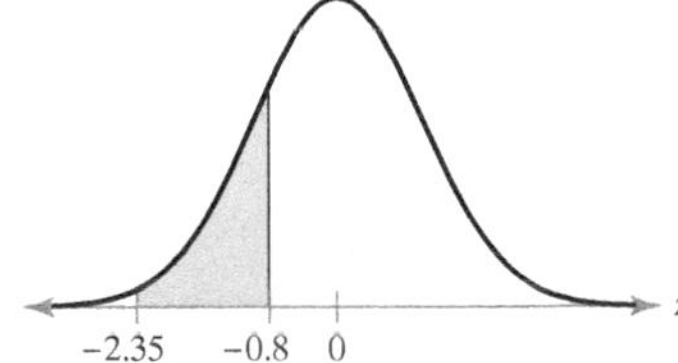


*In Exercises 7–18, find the indicated area under the standard normal curve. If convenient, use technology to find the area.*

**7.** To the left of $z = 0.33$

**8.** To the left of $z = -1.95$

**9.** To the right of $z = -0.57$

**10.** To the right of $z = 3.22$

**11.** To the left of $z = -2.825$

**12.** To the right of $z = 0.015$

**13.** Between $z = -1.64$ and $z = 0$

**14.** Between $z = -1.55$ and $z = 1.04$

**15.** Between $z = 0.05$ and $z = 1.71$

**16.** Between $z = -2.68$ and $z = 2.68$

**17.** To the left of $z = -1.5$ and to the right of $z = 1.5$

**18.** To the left of $z = 0.64$ and to the right of $z = 3.415$

*The scores for the reading portion of the ACT test are normally distributed. In a recent year, the mean test score was 21.2 and the standard deviation was 6.9. The test scores of four students selected at random are 17, 29, 8, and 23. Use this information in Exercises 19 and 20.* (Source: ACT, Inc.)

**19.** Find the $z$-score that corresponds to each value.

**20.** Determine whether any of the values are unusual.

*In Exercises 21–26, find the indicated probability using the standard normal distribution. If convenient, use technology to find the probability.*

**21.** $P(z < 1.28)$

**22.** $P(z > -0.74)$

**23.** $P(-2.15 < z < 1.55)$

**24.** $P(0.42 < z < 3.15)$

**25.** $P(z < -2.50 \text{ or } z > 2.50)$

**26.** $P(z < 0 \text{ or } z > 1.68)$

## Section 5.2

*In Exercises 27–32, the random variable x is normally distributed with mean $\mu = 74$ and standard deviation $\sigma = 8$. Find the indicated probability.*

**27.** $P(x < 84)$

**28.** $P(x < 55)$

**29.** $P(x > 80)$

**30.** $P(x > 71.6)$

**31.** $P(60 < x < 70)$

**32.** $P(72 < x < 82)$

*In Exercises 33 and 34, find the indicated probabilities. If convenient, use technology to find the probabilities.*

**33.** Yearly amounts of greenhouse gases from U.S. energy sources since 1990 are normally distributed, with a mean of 5774 million metric tons carbon dioxide equivalent (MMT $CO_2$ eq.) and a standard deviation of 333 MMT $CO_2$ eq. Find the probability that the amount of greenhouse gases from energy sources for a randomly selected year is

(a) less than 5500 MMT $CO_2$ eq.

(b) between 6000 and 6500 MMT $CO_2$ eq.

(c) greater than 5900 MMT $CO_2$ eq. *(Source: Environmental Protection Agency)*

**34.** The daily surface concentration of carbonyl sulfide on the Indian Ocean is normally distributed, with a mean of 9.1 picomoles per liter and a standard deviation of 3.5 picomoles per liter. Find the probability that on a randomly selected day, the surface concentration of carbonyl sulfide on the Indian Ocean is

(a) between 5.1 and 15.7 picomoles per liter.

(b) between 10.5 and 12.3 picomoles per liter.

(c) more than 11.1 picomoles per liter. *(Source: Atmospheric Chemistry and Physics)*

**35.** Determine whether any of the events in Exercise 33 are unusual. Explain your reasoning.

**36.** Determine whether any of the events in Exercise 34 are unusual. Explain your reasoning.

## Section 5.3

*In Exercises 37–42, use the Standard Normal Table or technology to find the z-score that corresponds to the cumulative area or percentile.*

**37.** 0.4721

**38.** 0.1

**39.** 0.993

**40.** $P_2$

**41.** $P_{85}$

**42.** $P_{46}$

**43.** Find the $z$-score that has 30.5% of the distribution's area to its right.

**44.** Find the positive $z$-score for which 94% of the distribution's area lies between $-z$ and $z$.

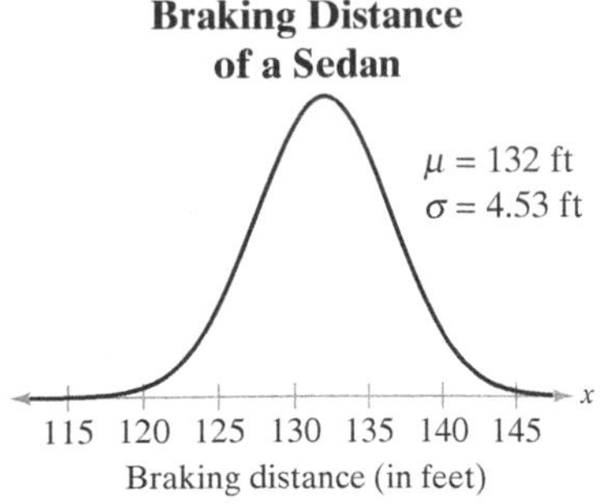


FIGURE FOR EXERCISES 45–50

*On a dry surface, the braking distances (in feet), from 60 miles per hour to a complete stop, of a sedan can be approximated by a normal distribution, as shown in the figure at the left. Use this information in Exercises 45–50.*

**45.** Find the braking distance that corresponds to $z = -2.75$.

**46.** Find the braking distance that corresponds to $z = 1.6$.

**47.** What braking distance represents the 90th percentile?

**48.** What braking distance represents the first quartile?

**49.** What distance is less than 15% of all the braking distances?

**50.** What distance is greater than 20% of all the braking distances?

## Section 5.4

*In Exercises 51 and 52, a population and sample size are given. (a) Find the mean and standard deviation of the population. (b) List all samples (with replacement) of the given size from the population and find the mean of each. (c) Find the mean and standard deviation of the sampling distribution of sample means and compare them with the mean and standard deviation of the population.*

**51.** The goals scored in a season by the four starting defenders on a soccer team are 1, 2, 0, and 3. Use a sample size of 2.

**52.** The minutes of overtime reported by each of the three executives at a corporation are 90, 120, and 210. Use a sample size of 3.

*In Exercises 53 and 54, find the mean and standard deviation of the indicated sampling distribution of sample means. Then sketch a graph of the sampling distribution.*

**53.** The population densities in people per square mile in the 50 U.S. states have a mean of 199.6 and a standard deviation of 265.4. Random samples of size 35 are drawn from this population, and the mean of each sample is determined. *(Source: States101.com)*

**54.** The test scores for the Law School Admission Test (LSAT) in a recent year are normally distributed, with a mean of 151.88 and a standard deviation of 9.95. Random samples of size 40 are drawn from this population, and the mean of each sample is determined. *(Source: Law School Admission Council)*

*In Exercises 55–60, find the indicated probabilities and interpret the results.*

**55.** Refer to Exercise 33. A random sample of 2 years is selected. Find the probability that the mean amount of greenhouse gases for the sample is (a) less than 5500 MMT $CO_2$ eq., (b) between 6000 and 6500 MMT $CO_2$ eq., and (c) greater than 5900 MMT $CO_2$ eq. Compare your answers with those in Exercise 33.

**56.** Refer to Exercise 34. A random sample of six days is selected. Find the probability that the mean surface concentration of carbonyl sulfide for the sample is (a) between 5.1 and 15.7 picomoles per liter, (b) between 10.5 and 12.3 picomoles per liter, and (c) more than 11.1 picomoles per liter. Compare your answers with those in Exercise 34.

**57.** The mean ACT composite score in a recent year is 20.7. A random sample of 36 ACT composite scores is selected. What is the probability that the mean score for the sample is (a) less than 22, (b) greater than 23, and (c) between 20 and 21.5? Assume $\sigma = 5.9$. *(Source: ACT, Inc)*

**58.** The mean MCAT total score in a recent year is 500.9. A random sample of 32 MCAT total scores is selected. What is the probability that the mean score for the sample is (a) less than 503, (b) more than 502, and (c) between 498 and 501? Assume $\sigma = 10.6$. *(Source: Association of American Medical Colleges)*

**59.** The mean annual salary for Level 1 actuaries in the United States is about $72,000. A random sample of 45 Level 1 actuaries is selected. What is the probability that the mean annual salary of the sample is (a) less than $75,000 and (b) more than $68,000? Assume $\sigma = \$11{,}000$. *(Adapted from Salary.com)*

**60.** The mean annual salary for physical therapists in the United States is about $87,000. A random sample of 50 physical therapists is selected. What is the probability that the mean annual salary of the sample is (a) less than $84,000 and (b) more than $85,000? Assume $\sigma = \$10{,}500$. *(Adapted from Salary.com)*

## Section 5.5

*In Exercises 61 and 62, a binomial experiment is given. Determine whether you can use a normal distribution to approximate the binomial distribution. If you can, find the mean and standard deviation. If you cannot, explain why.*

**61.** A survey of U.S. adults ages 33 to 40 earning more than $150,000 per year found that 94% are content with how their lives have turned out so far. You randomly select 20 U.S. adults ages 33 to 40 earning more than $150,000 and ask if they are content with their lives so far. *(Source: The Harris Poll)*

**62.** A survey of U.S. adults found that 69% have a favorable view of farming and agriculture. You randomly select 45 U.S. adults and ask whether they have a favorable view of farming and agriculture. *(Source: Gallup)*

*In Exercises 63–68, write the binomial probability in words. Then, use a continuity correction to convert the binomial probability to a normal distribution probability.*

**63.** $P(x \geq 25)$ **64.** $P(x \leq 36)$ **65.** $P(x = 45)$

**66.** $P(x > 14)$ **67.** $P(x < 60)$ **68.** $P(54 < x < 64)$

*In Exercises 69 and 70, determine whether you can use a normal distribution to approximate the binomial distribution. If you can, use the normal distribution to approximate the indicated probabilities and sketch their graphs. If you cannot, explain why and use a binomial distribution to find the indicated probabilities.*

**69.** A survey of U.S. adults found that 72% used a mobile device to manage their bank account at least once in the previous month. You randomly select 70 U.S. adults and ask whether they used a mobile device to manage their bank account at least once in the previous month. Find the probability that the number who have done so is (a) at most 40, (b) exactly 50, and (c) greater than 60. *(Source: American Bankers Association)*

**70.** Thirty-four percent of U.S. college graduates work in jobs that do not require a college degree. You randomly select 20 U.S. college graduates. Find the probability that the number working in a job that does not require a college degree is (a) exactly 7, (b) at most 6, and (c) between 5 and 10, inclusive. Identify any unusual events. *(Source: Inside Higher Ed)*

# 5 Chapter Quiz

*Take this quiz as you would take a quiz in class. After you are done, check your work against the answers given in the back of the book.*

**1.** Find each probability using the standard normal distribution.

(a) $P(z > -1.68)$

(b) $P(z < 2.23)$

(c) $P(-0.47 < z < 0.47)$

(d) $P(z < -1.992 \text{ or } z > -0.665)$

**2.** The random variable $x$ is normally distributed with the given parameters. Find each probability.

(a) $\mu = 9.2, \sigma \approx 1.62, P(x < 5.97)$

(b) $\mu = 87, \sigma \approx 19, P(x > 40.5)$

(c) $\mu = 5.5, \sigma \approx 0.08, P(5.36 < x < 5.64)$

(d) $\mu = 18.5, \sigma \approx 4.25, P(19.6 < x < 26.1)$

*In a standardized IQ test, scores are normally distributed, with a mean score of 100 and a standardized deviation of 15. Use this information in Exercises 3–10.* (Adapted from 123test)

**3.** Find the probability that a randomly selected person has an IQ score higher than 125. Is this an unusual event? Explain.

**4.** Find the probability that a randomly selected person has an IQ score between 95 and 105. Is this an unusual event? Explain.

**5.** What percent of the IQ scores are greater than 112?

**6.** Out of 2000 randomly selected people, about how many would you expect to have IQ scores less than 90?

**7.** What is the lowest score that would still place a person in the top 5% of the scores?

**8.** What is the highest score that would still place a person in the bottom 10% of the scores?

**9.** A random sample of 60 people is selected from this population. What is the probability that the mean IQ score of the sample is greater than 105? Interpret the result.

**10.** Are you more likely to randomly select one person with an IQ score greater than 105 or are you more likely to randomly select a sample of 15 people with a mean IQ score greater than 105? Explain.

*In a survey of U.S. adults, 81% feel they have little or no control over data collected about them by companies. You randomly select 250 U.S. adults and ask them whether they feel they have control over data collected about them by companies. Use this information in Exercises 11 and 12.* (Source: Pew Research Center)

**11.** Determine whether you can use a normal distribution to approximate the binomial distribution. If you can, find the mean and standard deviation. If you cannot, explain why.

**12.** Find the probability that the number who feel they have little or no control over data collected about them by companies is (a) at most 200, (b) less than 210, and (c) exactly 202. Identify any unusual events. Explain.

# 5 Chapter Test

*Take this test as you would take a test in class.*

**1.** During a recent period of one year, the mean percent increase in value on Wednesdays of the cryptocurrency Dogecoin was 7.46%, with a standard deviation of 53.47%. Random samples of size 50 are drawn from this population and the mean of each sample is determined. *(Source: Crypto Indicators)*

(a) Find the mean and standard deviation of the sampling distribution of sample means.

(b) What is the probability that the mean percent increase for a given sample is more than 25%?

(c) What is the probability that the mean percent increase for a given sample is between −10% and 30%?

*In Exercises 2–4, the random variable x is normally distributed with mean $\mu = 18$ and standard deviation $\sigma = 7.6$.*

**2.** Find each probability.

(a) $P(x > 20)$ (b) $P(0 < x < 5)$ (c) $P(x < 9 \text{ or } x > 27)$

**3.** Find the value of $x$ that has 88.3% of the distribution's area to its left.

**4.** Find the value of $x$ that has 64.8% of the distribution's area to its right.

*In Exercises 5 and 6, determine whether you can use a normal distribution to approximate the binomial distribution. If you can, use the normal distribution to approximate the indicated probabilities and sketch their graphs. If you cannot, explain why and use a binomial distribution to find the indicated probabilities.*

**5.** A survey of U.S. undergraduates found that 37% of those attending in-state colleges would prefer to take a job in a different state after graduation. You randomly select 18 U.S. undergraduates attending in-state colleges. Find the probability that the number who would prefer to take a job in a different state after graduation is (a) exactly 7, (b) less than 5, and (c) at least 10. Identify any unusual events. Explain. *(Source: College Pulse)*

**6.** Fifty-nine percent of information technology (IT) professionals work for companies that rely on human memory to manage passwords. You randomly select 12 IT professionals. Find the probability that the number who work for companies that rely on human memory to manage passwords is (a) exactly 7, (b) more than 8, and (c) less than 4. Identify any unusual events. Explain. *(Source: Yubico)*

*The per capita disposable income for residents of a U.S. city in a recent year is normally distributed, with a mean of about \$44,000 and a standard deviation of about \$2450. Use this information in Exercises 7–10.*

**7.** Find the probability that the disposable income of a resident is more than \$45,000. Is this an unusual event? Explain.

**8.** Out of 800 residents, about how many would you expect to have a disposable income of between \$40,000 and \$42,000?

**9.** Between what two values does the middle 60% of disposable incomes lie?

**10.** Random samples of size 8 are drawn from the population and the mean of each sample is determined. Is the sampling distribution of sample means normally distributed? Explain.

# REAL STATISTICS REAL DECISIONS

# Putting it all together

You work for a pharmaceuticals company as a statistical process analyst. Your job is to analyze processes and make sure they are in statistical control. In one process, a machine is supposed to add 9.8 milligrams of a compound to a mixture in a vial. (Assume this process can be approximated by a normal distribution with a standard deviation of 0.05.) The acceptable range of amounts of the compound added is 9.65 milligrams to 9.95 milligrams, inclusive.

Because of an error with the release valve, the setting on the machine "shifts" from 9.8 milligrams. To check that the machine is adding the correct amount of the compound into the vials, you select at random three samples of five vials and find the mean amount of the compound added for each sample. A coworker asks why you take 3 samples of size 5 and find the mean instead of randomly choosing and measuring the amounts in 15 vials individually to check the machine's settings. (*Note:* Both samples are chosen without replacement.)

## EXERCISES

**1. *Sampling Individuals***

Assume the machine shifts and the distribution of the amount of the compound added now has a mean of 9.96 milligrams and a standard deviation of 0.05 milligram. You select one vial and determine how much of the compound was added.

(a) What is the probability that you select a vial that is within the acceptable range (in other words, you do not detect that the machine has shifted)? (See figure.)

(b) You randomly select 15 vials. What is the probability that you select at least one vial that is within the acceptable range?

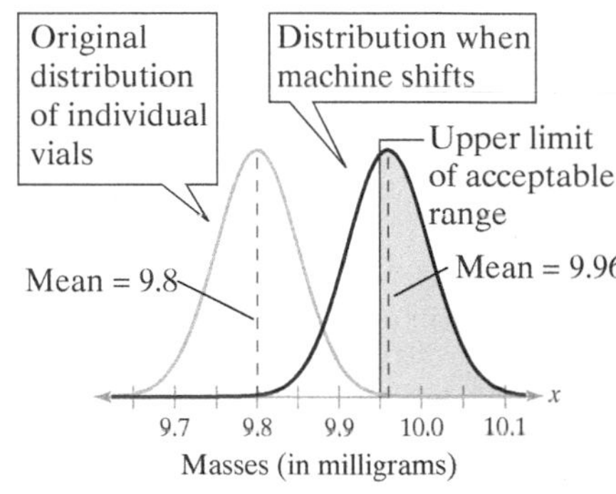


FIGURE FOR EXERCISE 1

**2. *Sampling Groups of Five***

Assume the machine shifts and is filling the vials with a mean amount of 9.96 milligrams and a standard deviation of 0.05 milligram. You select five vials and find the mean amount of compound added.

(a) What is the probability that you select a sample of five vials that has a mean that is within the acceptable range? (See figure.)

(b) You randomly select three samples of five vials. What is the probability that you select at least one sample of five vials that has a mean that is within the acceptable range?

(c) Which is more sensitive to a shift of parameters—an individual random selection or a randomly selected sample mean?

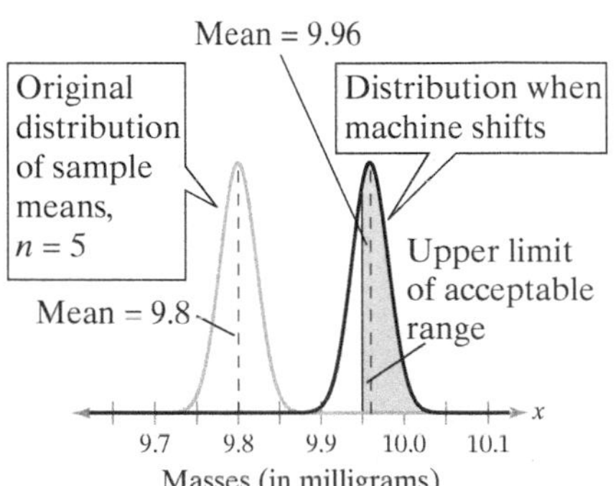


FIGURE FOR EXERCISE 2

**3. *Writing an Explanation***

Write a paragraph to your coworker explaining why you take 3 samples of size 5 and find the mean of each sample instead of randomly choosing and measuring the amounts in 15 vials individually to check the machine's setting.

# TECHNOLOGY

MINITAB | EXCEL | TI-84 PLUS

# Age Distribution in California

One of the jobs of the U.S. Census Bureau is to keep track of the age distribution in the country and in each of the states. The estimated age distribution in California in 2019 is shown in the table and the histogram. *(Adapted from U.S. Census Bureau)*

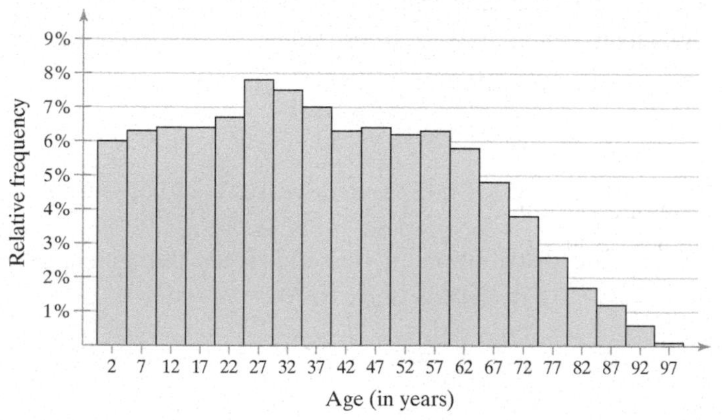


| Class | Class midpoint | Relative frequency |
|---|---|---|
| 0–4 | 2 | 6.0% |
| 5–9 | 7 | 6.3% |
| 10–14 | 12 | 6.4% |
| 15–19 | 17 | 6.4% |
| 20–24 | 22 | 6.7% |
| 25–29 | 27 | 7.8% |
| 30–34 | 32 | 7.5% |
| 35–39 | 37 | 7.0% |
| 40–44 | 42 | 6.3% |
| 45–49 | 47 | 6.4% |
| 50–54 | 52 | 6.2% |
| 55–59 | 57 | 6.3% |
| 60–64 | 62 | 5.8% |
| 65–69 | 67 | 4.8% |
| 70–74 | 72 | 3.8% |
| 75–79 | 77 | 2.6% |
| 80–84 | 82 | 1.7% |
| 85–89 | 87 | 1.2% |
| 90–94 | 92 | 0.6% |
| 95–99 | 97 | 0.1% |

## EXERCISES

 *The means of 36 randomly selected samples generated by technology with $n = 40$ are shown below.*

37.03, 35.43, 39.40, 34.55, 34.88, 41.00
35.30, 34.03, 36.80, 41.90, 39.63, 39.20,
43.50, 38.35, 38.38, 41.85, 38.55, 39.03,
30.50, 33.58, 38.85, 40.88, 41.13, 41.68,
37.75, 34.18, 33.88, 36.28, 41.23, 40.88,
39.93, 36.45, 38.58, 36.63, 38.55, 39.35

1. Use technology and the age distribution to estimate the mean age in California.
2. Use technology to find the mean of the set of 36 sample means. How does it compare with the mean age in California found in Exercise 1? Does this agree with the result predicted by the Central Limit Theorem?
3. Are the ages of people in California normally distributed? Explain your reasoning.
4. Sketch a relative frequency histogram for the 36 sample means. Use nine classes, with interval width 3, starting at 30.5. Is the histogram approximately bell-shaped and symmetric? Does this agree with the result predicted by the Central Limit Theorem?
5. Use technology and the age distribution to find the standard deviation of the ages of people in California.
6. Use technology to find the standard deviation of the set of 36 sample means. How does it compare with the standard deviation of the ages found in Exercise 5? Does this agree with the result predicted by the Central Limit Theorem?

Extended solutions are given in the technology manuals that accompany this text. Technical instruction is provided for Minitab, Excel, and the TI-84 Plus.

# CHAPTERS 3–5 CUMULATIVE REVIEW

**1.** A survey of adults in the United States found that 61% ate at a restaurant at least once in the past week. You randomly select 30 adults and ask them whether they ate at a restaurant at least once in the past week. *(Source: Gallup)*

(a) Verify that a normal distribution can be used to approximate the binomial distribution.

(b) Find the probability that at most 14 adults ate at a restaurant at least once in the past week.

(c) Is it unusual for exactly 14 out of 30 adults to have eaten in a restaurant at least once in the past week? Explain your reasoning.

*In Exercises 2 and 3, find the (a) mean, (b) variance, (c) standard deviation, and (d) expected value of the probability distribution. Interpret the results.*

**2.** The table shows the distribution of household sizes in the United States for a recent year. *(Adapted from U.S. Census Bureau)*

| $x$ | 1 | 2 | 3 | 4 | 5 | 6 | 7 | 8 | 9 |
|---|---|---|---|---|---|---|---|---|---|
| $P(x)$ | 0.282 | 0.348 | 0.151 | 0.127 | 0.058 | 0.023 | 0.007 | 0.003 | 0.002 |

**3.** The table shows the distribution of personal fouls per game for DeMar DeRozan in a recent NBA season. *(Source: National Basketball Association)*

| $x$ | 0 | 1 | 2 | 3 | 4 | 5 | 6 |
|---|---|---|---|---|---|---|---|
| $P(x)$ | 0.044 | 0.162 | 0.221 | 0.368 | 0.103 | 0.088 | 0.015 |

**4.** Use the probability distribution in Exercise 3 to find the probability of randomly selecting a game in which DeMar DeRozan had (a) fewer than four personal fouls, (b) at least three personal fouls, and (c) between two and four personal fouls, inclusive.

**5.** From a pool of 16 candidates, 9 men and 7 women, the offices of president, vice president, secretary, and treasurer will be filled. (a) In how many different ways can the offices be filled? (b) What is the probability that all four of the offices are filled by women?

*In Exercises 6–11, find the indicated area under the standard normal curve. If convenient, use technology to find the area.*

**6.** To the left of $z = 0.72$

**7.** To the left of $z = -3.08$

**8.** To the right of $z = -0.84$

**9.** Between $z = 0$ and $z = 2.95$

**10.** Between $z = -1.22$ and $z = -0.26$

**11.** To the left of $z = 0.12$ or to the right of $z = 1.72$

**12.** Forty-nine percent of U.S. adults think that human activity such as burning fossil fuels contributes a great deal to climate change. You randomly select 25 U.S. adults. Find the probability that the number who think that human activity contributes a great deal to climate change is (a) exactly 12, (b) between 8 and 11, inclusive, and (c) less than two. (d) Are any of these events unusual? Explain your reasoning. *(Source: Pew Research Center)*

**13.** An auto parts seller finds that 1 in every 200 parts sold is defective. Use the geometric distribution to find the probability that (a) the first defective part is the fifth part sold, (b) the first defective part is the first, second, or third part sold, and (c) none of the first 20 parts sold are defective.

**14.** The table shows the results of a survey in which 3,545,286 public and 509,168 private school teachers were asked about their full-time teaching experience. *(Adapted from National Center for Education Statistics)*

| | Public | Private | Total |
|---|---|---|---|
| **Less than 3 years** | 318,274 | 61,809 | 380,083 |
| **3 to 9 years** | 1,003,014 | 151,865 | 1,154,879 |
| **10 to 20 years** | 1,415,824 | 167,400 | 1,583,224 |
| **More than 20 years** | 808,174 | 128,094 | 936,268 |
| **Total** | 3,545,286 | 509,168 | 4,054,454 |

(a) Find the probability that a randomly selected private school teacher has 10 to 20 years of full-time teaching experience.

(b) Find the probability that a randomly selected teacher is at a public school, given that the teacher has 3 to 9 years of full-time experience.

(c) Are the events "being a public school teacher" and "having more than 20 years of full-time teaching experience" independent? Explain.

(d) Find the probability that a randomly selected teacher has 3 to 9 years of full-time teaching experience or is at a private school.

**15.** The initial pressures for bicycle tires when first filled are normally distributed, with a mean of 70 pounds per square inch (psi) and a standard deviation of 1.2 psi.

(a) Random samples of size 40 are drawn from this population, and the mean of each sample is determined. Find the mean and standard deviation of the sampling distribution of sample means. Then sketch a graph of the sampling distribution.

(b) A random sample of 15 tires is drawn from this population. What is the probability that the mean tire pressure of the sample is less than 69 psi?

**16.** The life spans of car batteries are normally distributed, with a mean of 44 months and a standard deviation of 5 months.

(a) Find the probability that the life span of a randomly selected battery is less than 36 months.

(b) Find the probability that the life span of a randomly selected battery is between 42 and 60 months.

(c) What is the shortest life expectancy a car battery can have and still be in the top 5% of life expectancies?

**17.** A florist has 12 different flowers from which floral arrangements can be made. A centerpiece is made using four different flowers. (a) How many different centerpieces can be made? (b) What is the probability that the four flowers in the centerpiece are roses, daisies, hydrangeas, and lilies?

**18.** Sixty-seven percent of dating U.S. adults say their dating lives are not going well. You randomly select 10 dating U.S. adults. (a) Construct a binomial distribution for the random variable $x$, the number who say their dating lives are not going well. (b) Graph the binomial distribution using a histogram and describe its shape. (c) Identify any values of the random variable $x$ that you would consider unusual. Explain. *(Source: Pew Research Center)*

CHAPTER 6

# Confidence Intervals

David Wechsler was one of the most influential psychologists of the 20th century. He is known for developing intelligence tests, such as the Wechsler Adult Intelligence Scale and the Wechsler Intelligence Scale for Children.

## Where You've Been

In Chapters 1 through 5, you studied descriptive statistics (how to collect and describe data) and probability (how to find probabilities and analyze discrete and continuous probability distributions). For instance, psychologists use descriptive statistics to analyze the data collected during experiments and tests.

One of the most commonly administered psychological tests is the Wechsler Adult Intelligence Scale. It is an intelligence quotient (IQ) test that is standardized to have a normal distribution with a mean of 100 and a standard deviation of 15.

## Where You're Going

In this chapter, you will begin your study of inferential statistics—the second major branch of statistics. For instance, a chess club wants to estimate the mean IQ of its members. The mean of a random sample of members is 115. Because this estimate consists of a single number represented by a point on a number line, it is called a *point estimate.* The problem with using a point estimate is that it is rarely equal to the exact parameter (mean, standard deviation, or proportion) of the population.

In this chapter, you will learn how to make a more meaningful estimate by specifying an interval of values on a number line, together with a statement of how confident you are that your interval contains the population parameter. Suppose the club wants to be 90% confident of its estimate for the mean IQ of its members. Here is an overview of how to construct an interval estimate.

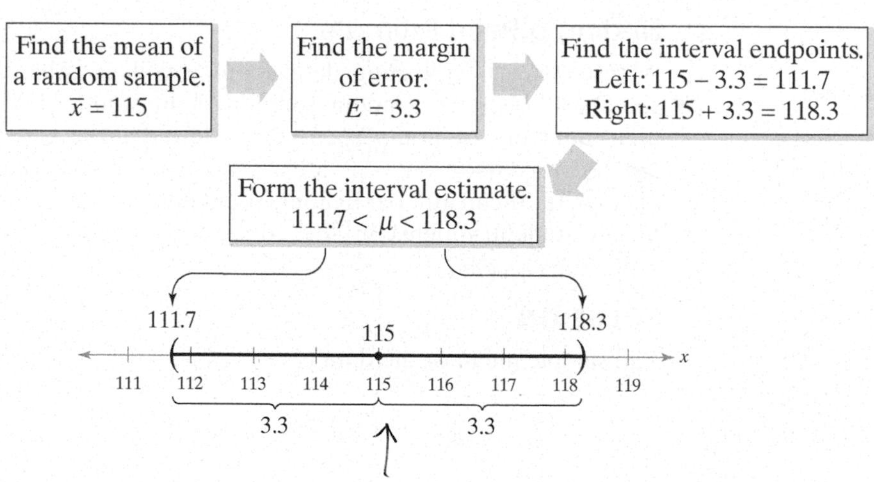


So, the club can be 90% confident that the mean IQ of its members is between 111.7 and 118.3.

# 6.1 Confidence Intervals for the Mean ($\sigma$ Known)

## What You Should Learn

- How to find a point estimate and a margin of error
- How to construct and interpret confidence intervals for a population mean when $\sigma$ is known
- How to determine the minimum sample size required when estimating a population mean

Estimating Population Parameters ■ Confidence Intervals for a Population Mean ■ Sample Size

## Estimating Population Parameters

In this chapter, you will learn an important technique of statistical inference—to use sample statistics to estimate the value of an unknown population parameter. In this section and the next, you will learn how to use sample statistics to make an estimate of the population parameter $\mu$ when the population standard deviation $\sigma$ is known (this section) or when $\sigma$ is unknown (Section 6.2). To make such an inference, begin by finding a **point estimate.**

### DEFINITION

A **point estimate** is a single value estimate for a population parameter. The most unbiased point estimate of the population mean $\mu$ is the sample mean $\bar{x}$.

The validity of an estimation method increases when you use a sample statistic that is unbiased and has low variability. A statistic is unbiased if it does not overestimate or underestimate the population parameter. Recall from Chapter 5 that the mean of all possible sample means of the same size equals the population mean. As a result, $\bar{x}$ is an **unbiased estimator** of $\mu$. When the standard error $\sigma/\sqrt{n}$ of a sample mean decreases by increasing $n$, it becomes less variable.

### EXAMPLE 1

### Finding a Point Estimate

A researcher is collecting data about a college athletic conference and its student-athletes. A random sample of 40 student-athletes is selected and their numbers of hours spent on required athletic activities in one week are recorded (see table at left). Find a point estimate for the population mean $\mu$, the mean number of hours spent per week on required athletic activities by all student-athletes in the conference. *(Adapted from National Collegiate Athletic Association)*

| Number of hours in one week | | | | | | | |
|---|---|---|---|---|---|---|---|
| 19 | 18 | 18 | 15 | 21 | 21 | 23 | 20 |
| 21 | 19 | 16 | 19 | 22 | 15 | 19 | 24 |
| 20 | 24 | 20 | 17 | 18 | 17 | 19 | 20 |
| 20 | 20 | 22 | 24 | 22 | 23 | 23 | 21 |
| 22 | 20 | 17 | 21 | 16 | 18 | 18 | 25 |

**SOLUTION**

The sample mean of the data is

$$\bar{x} = \frac{\Sigma x}{n} = \frac{797}{40} \approx 19.9.$$

So, the point estimate for the mean number of hours spent on required athletic activities by all student-athletes in the conference is about 19.9 hours.

**TRY IT YOURSELF 1**

In Example 1, the researcher selects a second random sample of 40 student-athletes and records their numbers of hours spent on required athletic activities in one day (see table at left). Find a point estimate for the population mean $\mu$, the mean number of hours spent per day on required athletic activities by all student-athletes in the conference. *(Adapted from National Collegiate Athletic Association)*

| Number of hours in one day | | | | | | | |
|---|---|---|---|---|---|---|---|
| 2 | 1 | 1 | 1 | 3 | 1 | 3 | 1 |
| 2 | 4 | 3 | 3 | 1 | 5 | 5 | 3 |
| 3 | 3 | 4 | 5 | 2 | 4 | 3 | 3 |
| 4 | 2 | 2 | 1 | 3 | 5 | 3 | 3 |
| 2 | 4 | 3 | 2 | 3 | 4 | 5 | 2 |

*Answer: Page A40*

In Example 1, the probability that the population mean is exactly 19.9 is virtually zero. So, instead of estimating $\mu$ to be exactly 19.9 using a point estimate, you can estimate that $\mu$ lies in an interval. This is called making an **interval estimate.**

## DEFINITION

An **interval estimate** is an interval, or range of values, used to estimate a population parameter.

Although you can assume that the point estimate in Example 1 is not equal to the actual population mean, it is probably close to it. To form an interval estimate, use the point estimate as the center of the interval, and then add and subtract a margin of error. For instance, if the margin of error is 0.6, then an interval estimate would be given by

$$19.9 \pm 0.6 \quad \text{or} \quad 19.3 < \mu < 20.5.$$

The point estimate and interval estimate are shown in the figure.

For help with intervals on the number line, see *Integrated Review* at

MyLab® Statistics

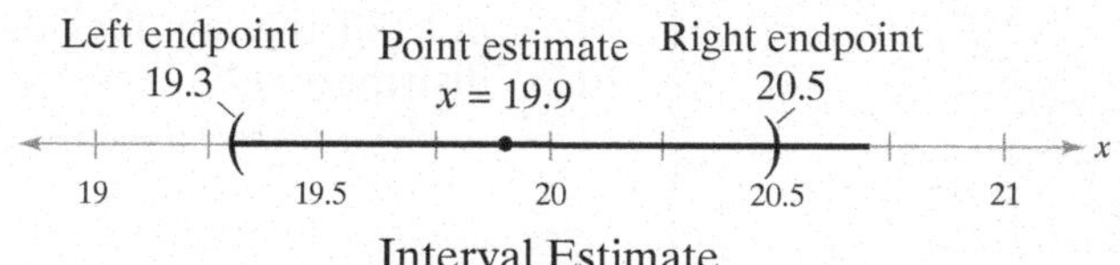


Interval Estimate

Before finding a margin of error for an interval estimate, you should first determine how confident you need to be that your interval estimate contains the population mean $\mu$.

## DEFINITION

The **level of confidence** $c$ is the probability that the interval estimate contains the population parameter, assuming that the estimation process is repeated a large number of times.

### Study Tip

In this text, you will usually use 90%, 95%, and 99% levels of confidence. Here are the z-scores that correspond to these levels of confidence.

| Level of Confidence | $z_c$ |
|---|---|
| 90% | 1.645 |
| 95% | 1.96 |
| 99% | 2.575 |

You know from the Central Limit Theorem that when $n \geq 30$, the sampling distribution of sample means approximates a normal distribution. The level of confidence $c$ is the area under the standard normal curve between the *critical values*, $-z_c$ and $z_c$. **Critical values** are values that separate sample statistics that are probable from sample statistics that are improbable, or unusual. You can see from the figure shown below that $c$ is the percent of the area under the normal curve between $-z_c$ and $z_c$. The area remaining is $1 - c$, so the area in one tail is

$$\tfrac{1}{2}(1 - c). \qquad \text{Area in one tail}$$

For instance, if $c = 90\%$, then 5% of the area lies to the left of $-z_c = -1.645$ and 5% lies to the right of $z_c = 1.645$, as shown in the table.

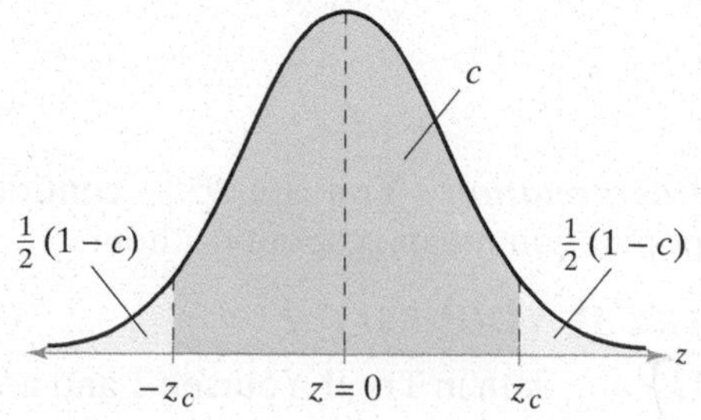


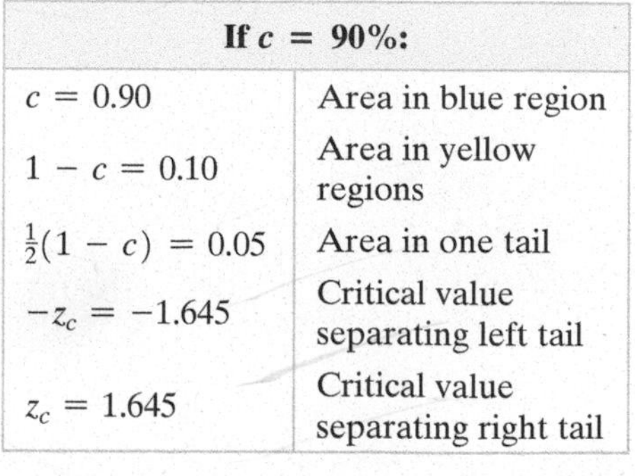

| If $c = 90\%$: | |
|---|---|
| $c = 0.90$ | Area in blue region |
| $1 - c = 0.10$ | Area in yellow regions |
| $\frac{1}{2}(1 - c) = 0.05$ | Area in one tail |
| $-z_c = -1.645$ | Critical value separating left tail |
| $z_c = 1.645$ | Critical value separating right tail |

## Picturing the World

A survey of a random sample of 1000 social media users found that the mean daily time spent on social media was 144 minutes. From previous studies, it is assumed that the population standard deviation is 21.4 minutes. (Adapted from TechJury)

**Daily Time Spent on Social Media**

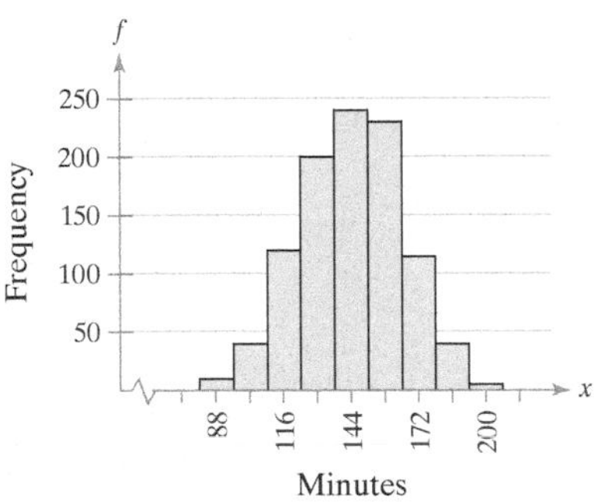


**For a 95% confidence interval, what would be the margin of error for the population mean daily time spent on social media?**

The difference between the point estimate and the actual parameter value is called the **sampling error.** When $\mu$ is estimated, the sampling error is the difference $\bar{x} - \mu$. In most cases, of course, $\mu$ is unknown, and $\bar{x}$ varies from sample to sample. However, you can calculate a maximum value for the error when you know the level of confidence and the sampling distribution.

### DEFINITION

Given a level of confidence $c$, the **margin of error** $E$ (sometimes also called the maximum error of estimate or error tolerance) is the greatest possible distance between the point estimate and the value of the parameter it is estimating. For a population mean $\mu$ where $\sigma$ is known, the margin of error is

$$E = z_c\sigma_{\bar{x}} = z_c\frac{\sigma}{\sqrt{n}}$$ Margin of error for $\mu$ ($\sigma$ known)

when these conditions are met.

1. The sample is random.
2. At least one of the following is true: The population is normally distributed or $n \geq 30$. (Recall from the Central Limit Theorem that when $n \geq 30$, the sampling distribution of sample means approximates a normal distribution.)

### EXAMPLE 2

#### Finding the Margin of Error

Use the data in Example 1 and a 95% confidence level to find the margin of error for the mean number of hours spent per week on required athletic activities by all student-athletes in the conference. Assume the population standard deviation is 2.4 hours.

**SOLUTION**

Because $\sigma$ is known ($\sigma = 2.4$), the sample is random (see Example 1), and $n = 40 \geq 30$, use the formula for $E$ given above. The $z$-score that corresponds to a 95% confidence level is 1.96. This implies that 95% of the area under the standard normal curve falls within 1.96 standard deviations of the mean, as shown in the figure below. (You can approximate the distribution of the sample means with a normal curve by the Central Limit Theorem because $n = 40 \geq 30$.)

Using the values $z_c = 1.96$, $\sigma = 2.4$, and $n = 40$,

$$E = z_c\frac{\sigma}{\sqrt{n}} = 1.96 \cdot \frac{2.4}{\sqrt{40}} \approx 0.7.$$

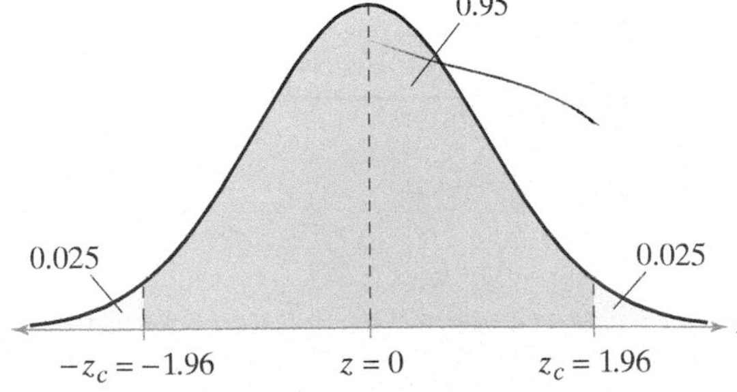


***Interpretation*** You are 95% confident that the margin of error for the population mean is about 0.7 hour.

**TRY IT YOURSELF 2**

Use the data in Try It Yourself 1 and a 95% confidence level to find the margin of error for the mean number of hours spent per day on required athletic activities by all student-athletes in the conference. Assume the population standard deviation is 1.4 hours.

*Answer: Page A40*

## Confidence Intervals for a Population Mean

Using a point estimate and a margin of error, you can construct an interval estimate of a population parameter such as $\mu$. This interval estimate is called a **confidence interval.**

> **Study Tip**
>
> When you construct a confidence interval for a population mean, the general *round-off rule* is to round off to the same number of decimal places as the sample mean.

**DEFINITION**

A **c-confidence interval for a population mean** $\mu$ is

$$\bar{x} - E < \mu < \bar{x} + E.$$

The probability that the confidence interval contains $\mu$ is $c$, assuming that the estimation process is repeated a large number of times.

**GUIDELINES**

**Constructing a Confidence Interval for a Population Mean ($\sigma$ Known)**

| In Words | In Symbols |
|---|---|
| **1.** Verify that $\sigma$ is known, the sample is random, and either the population is normally distributed or $n \geq 30$. | |
| **2.** Find the sample statistics $n$ and $\bar{x}$. | $\bar{x} = \dfrac{\Sigma x}{n}$ |
| **3.** Find the critical value $z_c$ that corresponds to the given level of confidence. | Use Table 4 in Appendix B. |
| **4.** Find the margin of error $E$. | $E = z_c \dfrac{\sigma}{\sqrt{n}}$ |
| **5.** Find the left and right endpoints and form the confidence interval. | Left endpoint: $\bar{x} - E$<br>Right endpoint: $\bar{x} + E$<br>Interval: $\bar{x} - E < \mu < \bar{x} + E$ |

**EXAMPLE 3**

See Minitab steps on page 344.

### Constructing a Confidence Interval

Use the data in Example 1 and the result of Example 2 to construct a 95% confidence interval for the mean number of hours spent per week on required athletic activities by all student-athletes in the conference.

**SOLUTION**

In Examples 1 and 2, you found that $\bar{x} \approx 19.9$ and $E \approx 0.7$. The confidence interval is constructed as shown.

| Left Endpoint | Right Endpoint |
|---|---|
| $\bar{x} - E \approx 19.9 - 0.7$ | $\bar{x} + E \approx 19.9 + 0.7$ |
| $= 19.2$ | $= 20.6$ |

$$19.2 < \mu < 20.6$$

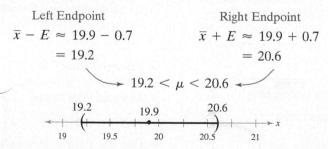

> **Study Tip**
>
> Other ways to represent a confidence interval are $(\bar{x} - E, \bar{x} + E)$ and $\bar{x} \pm E$. For instance, in Example 3, you could write the confidence interval as $(19.2, 20.6)$ or $19.9 \pm 0.7$.

19.2 19.9 20.6

19 19.5 20 20.5 21 $x$

***Interpretation*** With 95% confidence, you can say that the population mean number of hours spent on required athletic activities is between 19.2 and 20.6 hours.

**TRY IT YOURSELF 3**

Use the data in Try It Yourself 1 and the result of Try It Yourself 2 to construct a 95% confidence interval for the mean number of hours spent per day on required athletic activities by all student-athletes in the conference.

*Answer: Page A40*

The width of a confidence interval is $2E$. Examine the formula for $E$ to see why a larger sample size tends to give you a narrower confidence interval for the same level of confidence.

## EXAMPLE 4

### Constructing a Confidence Interval Using Technology

Use the data in Example 1 and technology to construct a 99% confidence interval for the mean number of hours spent per week on required athletic activities by all student-athletes in the conference.

**SOLUTION**

Minitab and StatCrunch each have features that allow you to construct a confidence interval. You can construct a confidence interval by entering the original data or by using the descriptive statistics. The original data were used to construct the confidence intervals shown below. From the displays, a 99% confidence interval for $\mu$ is $(18.9, 20.9)$. Note that this interval is rounded to the same number of decimal places as the sample mean.

**MINITAB**

**One-Sample Z: Hours**

**Descriptive Statistics**

| N | Mean | StDev | SE Mean | 99% CI for μ |
|---|---|---|---|---|
| 40 | 19.925 | 2.556 | 0.379 | (18.948, 20.902) |

*μ: population mean of Hours*
*Known standard deviation: 2.4*

**STATCRUNCH**

**One sample Z confidence interval:**
μ : Mean of variable
Standard deviation = 2.4

**99% confidence interval results:**

| Variable | n | Sample Mean | Std. Err. | L. Limit | U. Limit |
|---|---|---|---|---|---|
| Hours | 40 | 19.925 | 0.37947332 | 18.947542 | 20.902458 |

***Interpretation*** With 99% confidence, you can say that the population mean number of hours spent per week on required athletic activities is between 18.9 and 20.9 hours.

**TRY IT YOURSELF 4**

Use the data in Example 1 and technology to construct 75%, 85%, and 90% confidence intervals for the mean number of hours spent per week on required athletic activities by all student-athletes in the conference. How does the width of the confidence interval change as the level of confidence increases?

*Answer: Page A40*

### Tech Tip

Here are instructions for constructing a confidence interval on a TI-84 Plus. First, either enter the original data into a list or enter the descriptive statistics.

STAT

Choose the TESTS menu.

7: ZInterval...

Select the *Data* input option when you use the original data. Select the *Stats* input option when you use the descriptive statistics. In each case, enter the appropriate values, then select *Calculate*. Your results may differ slightly depending on the method you use. For Example 4, the original data were entered.

ZInterval
(18.948,20.902)
$\bar{x}$=19.925
Sx=2.555913204
n=40

In Examples 3 and 4, and Try It Yourself 4, the same sample data were used to construct confidence intervals with different levels of confidence. Notice that as the level of confidence increases, the width of the confidence interval also increases. In other words, when the same sample data are used, *the greater the level of confidence, the wider the interval.*

For a normally distributed population with $\sigma$ known, you may use the normal sampling distribution for any sample size (even when $n < 30$), as shown in Example 5.

**Tech Tip**

Here are instructions for constructing a confidence interval in Excel. First, click *Formulas* at the top of the screen and click *Insert Function* in the *Function Library* group. Select the category *Statistical* and select the CONFIDENCE.NORM function. In the dialog box, enter the values of alpha, the standard deviation, and the sample size (see below). Then click OK. The value returned is the margin of error, which is used to construct the confidence interval.

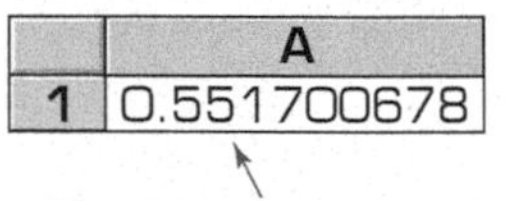

| | A |
|---|---|
| 1 | 0.551700678 |

=CONFIDENCE.NORM(0.1,1.5,20)

Alpha is the *level of significance,* which will be explained in Chapter 7. When using Excel in Chapter 6, you can think of alpha as the complement of the level of confidence. So, for a 90% confidence interval, alpha is equal to $1 - 0.90 = 0.10$.

## EXAMPLE 5

See TI-84 Plus steps on page 345.

### Constructing a Confidence Interval

A college admissions director wishes to estimate the mean age of all students currently enrolled. In a random sample of 20 students, the mean age is found to be 22.9 years. From past studies, the standard deviation is known to be 1.5 years, and the population is normally distributed. Construct a 90% confidence interval for the population mean age.

**SOLUTION**

Because $\sigma$ is known, the sample is random, and the population is normally distributed, use the formula for $E$ given in this section. Using $n = 20$, $\bar{x} = 22.9$, $\sigma = 1.5$, and $z_c = 1.645$, the margin of error at the 90% confidence level is

$$E = z_c \frac{\sigma}{\sqrt{n}} = 1.645 \cdot \frac{1.5}{\sqrt{20}} \approx 0.6.$$

The 90% confidence interval can be written as $\bar{x} \pm E \approx 22.9 \pm 0.6$ or as shown below.

| Left Endpoint | Right Endpoint |
|---|---|
| $\bar{x} - E \approx 22.9 - 0.6$ | $\bar{x} + E \approx 22.9 + 0.6$ |
| $= 22.3$ | $= 23.5$ |

$$22.3 < \mu < 23.5$$

22.3 22.9 23.5

22 22.5 23 23.5 24 $x$

***Interpretation*** With 90% confidence, you can say that the mean age of all the students is between 22.3 and 23.5 years.

**TRY IT YOURSELF 5**

Construct a 90% confidence interval for the population mean age for the college students in Example 5 with the sample size increased to 30 students. Compare your answer with that of Example 5. *Answer: Page A40*

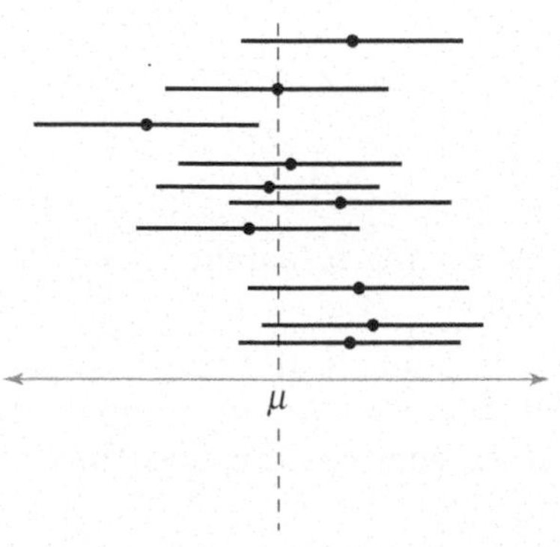


The horizontal segments represent 90% confidence intervals for different samples of the same size. In the long run, 9 of every 10 such intervals will contain $\mu$.

After constructing a confidence interval, it is important that you interpret the results correctly. Consider the 90% confidence interval constructed in Example 5. Because $\mu$ is a fixed value predetermined by the population, it is either in the interval or not. It is *not* correct to say, "There is a 90% probability that the actual mean will be in the interval (22.3, 23.5)." This statement is wrong because it suggests that the value of $\mu$ can vary, which is not true. The correct way to interpret this confidence interval is to say, "With 90% confidence, the mean is in the interval (22.3, 23.5)." This means that when many samples are collected and a confidence interval is created for each sample, approximately 90% of these intervals will contain $\mu$, as shown in the figure at the left. This correct interpretation refers to the success rate of the process being used.

## Sample Size

For the same sample statistics, as the level of confidence increases, the confidence interval widens. As the confidence interval widens, the precision of the estimate decreases. One way to improve the precision of an estimate without decreasing the level of confidence is to increase the sample size. But how large a sample size is needed to guarantee a certain level of confidence for a given margin of error? By using the formula for the margin of error

$$E = z_c \frac{\sigma}{\sqrt{n}}$$

a formula can be derived (see Exercise 59) to find the minimum sample size $n$, as shown in the next definition.

### Finding a Minimum Sample Size to Estimate $\mu$

Given a $c$-confidence level and a margin of error $E$, the minimum sample size $n$ needed to estimate the population mean $\mu$ is

$$n = \left(\frac{z_c \sigma}{E}\right)^2.$$

If $n$ is not a whole number, then round $n$ up to the next whole number (see Example 6). Also, when $\sigma$ is unknown, you can estimate it using $s$, provided you have a preliminary random sample with at least 30 members.

### EXAMPLE 6

#### Determining a Minimum Sample Size

The researcher in Example 1 wants to estimate the mean number of hours spent per week on required athletic activities by all student-athletes in the conference. How many student-athletes must be included in the sample to be 95% confident that the sample mean is within 0.5 hour of the population mean?

**SOLUTION**

Using $c = 0.95$, $z_c = 1.96$, $\sigma = 2.4$ (from Example 2), and $E = 0.5$, you can solve for the minimum sample size $n$.

$$n = \left(\frac{z_c \sigma}{E}\right)^2$$

$$= \left(\frac{1.96 \cdot 2.4}{0.5}\right)^2$$

$$\approx 88.51$$

Because $n$ is not a whole number, round up to 89. So, the researcher needs at least 89 student-athletes in the sample.

***Interpretation*** The researcher already has 40 student-athletes, so the sample needs 49 more members. Note that 89 is the *minimum* number of student-athletes to include in the sample. The researcher could include more, if desired.

**TRY IT YOURSELF 6**

In Example 6, how many student-athletes must the researcher include in the sample to be 95% confident that the sample mean is within 0.75 hour of the population mean? Compare your answer with Example 6.

*Answer: Page A40*

# 6.1 EXERCISES

For Extra Help: MyLab Statistics

## Building Basic Skills and Vocabulary

**1.** When estimating a population mean, are you more likely to be correct when you use a point estimate or an interval estimate? Explain your reasoning.

**2.** Which statistic is the best unbiased estimator for $\mu$?

(a) $s$ (b) $\bar{x}$ (c) the median (d) the mode

**3.** For the same sample statistics, which level of confidence would produce the widest confidence interval? Explain your reasoning.

(a) 90% (b) 95% (c) 98% (d) 99%

**4.** You construct a 95% confidence interval for a population mean using a random sample. The confidence interval is $24.9 < \mu < 31.5$. Is the probability that $\mu$ is in this interval 0.95? Explain.

*In Exercises 5–8, find the critical value $z_c$ necessary to construct a confidence interval at the level of confidence c.*

**5.** $c = 0.80$ **6.** $c = 0.85$ **7.** $c = 0.75$ **8.** $c = 0.97$

**Graphical Analysis** *In Exercises 9–12, use the values on the number line to find the sampling error.*

**9.** $\bar{x} = 3.8$ $\mu = 4.27$ (number line: 3.4 3.6 3.8 4.0 4.2 4.4 4.6 $x$)

**10.** $\mu = 8.76$ $\bar{x} = 9.5$ (number line: 8.6 8.8 9.0 9.2 9.4 9.6 9.8 $x$)

**11.** $\mu = 24.67$ $\bar{x} = 26.43$ (number line: 24 25 26 27 $x$)

**12.** $\bar{x} = 46.56$ $\mu = 48.12$ (number line: 46 47 48 49 $x$)

*In Exercises 13–16, find the margin of error for the values of c, $\sigma$, and n.*

**13.** $c = 0.95, \sigma = 5.2, n = 30$

**14.** $c = 0.90, \sigma = 2.9, n = 50$

**15.** $c = 0.80, \sigma = 1.3, n = 75$

**16.** $c = 0.975, \sigma = 4.6, n = 100$

**Matching** *In Exercises 17–20, match the level of confidence c with the appropriate confidence interval. Assume each confidence interval is constructed for the same sample statistics.*

**17.** $c = 0.88$ **18.** $c = 0.90$ **19.** $c = 0.95$ **20.** $c = 0.98$

(a) 54.9 57.2 59.5 (number line: 54 55 56 57 58 59 60 $x$)

(b) 55.2 57.2 59.2 (number line: 54 55 56 57 58 59 60 $x$)

(c) 55.6 57.2 58.8 (number line: 54 55 56 57 58 59 60 $x$)

(d)

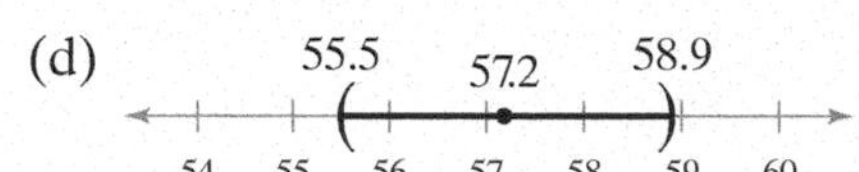


*In Exercises 21–24, construct the indicated confidence interval for the population mean $\mu$.*

**21.** $c = 0.90, \bar{x} = 12.3, \sigma = 1.5, n = 50$

**22.** $c = 0.95, \bar{x} = 31.39, \sigma = 0.80, n = 82$

**23.** $c = 0.99, \bar{x} = 10.50, \sigma = 2.14, n = 45$

**24.** $c = 0.80, \bar{x} = 20.6, \sigma = 4.7, n = 100$

*In Exercises 25–28, use the confidence interval to find the margin of error and the sample mean.*

**25.** (12.0, 14.8)

**26.** (21.61, 30.15)

**27.** (1.71, 2.05)

**28.** (3.144, 3.176)

*In Exercises 29–32, determine the minimum sample size n needed to estimate $\mu$ for the values of c, $\sigma$, and E.*

**29.** $c = 0.90, \sigma = 6.8, E = 1$

**30.** $c = 0.95, \sigma = 2.5, E = 1$

**31.** $c = 0.80, \sigma = 4.1, E = 2$

**32.** $c = 0.98, \sigma = 10.1, E = 2$

## Using and Interpreting Concepts

**Finding the Margin of Error** *In Exercises 33 and 34, use the confidence interval to find the estimated margin of error. Then find the sample mean.*

**33. Commute Times** A government agency reports a confidence interval of (26.2, 30.1) when estimating the mean commute time (in minutes) for the population of workers in a city.

**34. Book Prices** A store manager reports a confidence interval of (244.07, 280.97) when estimating the mean price (in dollars) for the population of textbooks.

**Constructing Confidence Intervals** *In Exercises 35–38, you are given the sample mean and the population standard deviation. Use this information to construct 90% and 95% confidence intervals for the population mean. Interpret the results and compare the widths of the confidence intervals.*

**35. Gold Prices** From a random sample of 48 business days from May 9, 2016, through May 7, 2021, U.S. gold prices had a mean of \$1404.09. Assume the population standard deviation is \$232.09. *(Source: Federal Reserve Bank of St. Louis)*

**36. Stock Prices** From a random sample of 36 business days during the year 2020, the mean closing price of Apple stock was \$97.17. Assume the population standard deviation is \$21.77. *(Source: Nasdaq)*

**37. Video Game Prices** From a random sample of 50 Nintendo Switch games, the mean price for a new game is \$54.97. Assume the population has a standard deviation of \$48.43. *(Source: PriceCharting)*

**38. Tornadoes per Month** From a random sample of 35 months from January 2006 through December 2020, the mean number of tornadoes per month in the United States was about 100. Assume the population standard deviation is 111. *(Source: NOAA)*

**39.** In Exercise 35, would it be unusual for the population mean to be over \$1500? Explain.

**40.** In Exercise 36, would it be unusual for the population mean to be over \$90? Explain.

**41.** In Exercise 37, does it seem likely that the population mean could be greater than \$70? Explain.

**42.** In Exercise 38, does it seem likely that the population mean could be less than 100? Explain.

**43.** When all other quantities remain the same, how does the indicated change affect the width of a confidence interval? Explain.

(a) Increase in the level of confidence

(b) Increase in the sample size

(c) Increase in the population standard deviation

**44.** Describe how you would construct a 90% confidence interval to estimate the population mean age for students at your school.

**Constructing Confidence Intervals** *In Exercises 45 and 46, use the information to construct 90% and 99% confidence intervals for the population mean. Interpret the results and compare the widths of the confidence intervals.*

**45. One-Way Commute Times** Researchers surveyed a random sample of 32 U.S. workers ages 16 years and over who did not work from home and asked how long (in minutes) it takes them to get from home to work. The responses are listed.

| | | | | | | | |
|---|---|---|---|---|---|---|---|
| 30 | 48 | 35 | 46 | 27 | 27 | 25 | 37 |
| 18 | 45 | 18 | 37 | 26 | 38 | 33 | 14 |
| 73 | 16 | 8 | 54 | 27 | 53 | 29 | 72 |
| 40 | 29 | 17 | 42 | 32 | 24 | 62 | 85 |

From past studies, the researchers assume that $\sigma$ is 14.9 minutes. *(Adapted from U.S. Census Bureau)*

**46. Sodium Chloride Concentrations** The sodium chloride concentrations (in grams per liter) for 36 randomly selected seawater samples are listed. Assume that $\sigma$ is 7.61 grams per liter.

| | | | | | |
|---|---|---|---|---|---|
| 30.63 | 33.47 | 26.76 | 15.23 | 13.21 | 10.57 |
| 16.57 | 27.32 | 27.06 | 15.07 | 28.98 | 34.66 |
| 10.22 | 22.43 | 17.33 | 28.40 | 35.70 | 14.09 |
| 11.77 | 33.60 | 27.09 | 26.78 | 22.39 | 30.35 |
| 11.83 | 13.05 | 22.22 | 13.45 | 18.86 | 24.92 |
| 32.86 | 31.10 | 18.84 | 10.86 | 15.69 | 22.35 |

**47. Determining a Minimum Sample Size** Determine the minimum sample size required when you want to be 95% confident that the sample mean is within one unit of the population mean and $\sigma = 4.8$. Assume the population is normally distributed.

**48. Determining a Minimum Sample Size** Determine the minimum sample size required when you want to be 99% confident that the sample mean is within two units of the population mean and $\sigma = 1.4$. Assume the population is normally distributed.

**49. Cholesterol Contents of Cheese** A cheese processing company wants to estimate the mean cholesterol content of all one-ounce servings of a type of cheese. The estimate must be within 0.75 milligram of the population mean.

(a) Determine the minimum sample size required to construct a 95% confidence interval for the population mean. Assume the population standard deviation is 3.10 milligrams.

(b) The sample mean is 29 milligrams. Using the minimum sample size with a 95% level of confidence, does it seem likely that the population mean could be within 3% of the sample mean? within 0.3% of the sample mean? Explain.

50. **Ages of College Students** An admissions director wants to estimate the mean age of all students enrolled at a college. The estimate must be within 1.5 years of the population mean. Assume the population of ages is normally distributed.

 (a) Determine the minimum sample size required to construct a 90% confidence interval for the population mean. Assume the population standard deviation is 1.6 years.

 (b) The sample mean is 20 years of age. Using the minimum sample size with a 90% level of confidence, does it seem likely that the population mean could be within 7% of the sample mean? within 8% of the sample mean? Explain.

Error tolerance = 0.5 oz

Volume = 1 gal (128 oz)

FIGURE FOR EXERCISE 51

51. **Paint Can Volumes** A paint manufacturer uses a machine to fill gallon cans with paint (see figure). The manufacturer wants to estimate the mean volume of paint the machine is putting in the cans within 0.5 ounce. Assume the population of volumes is normally distributed.

 (a) Determine the minimum sample size required to construct a 90% confidence interval for the population mean. Assume the population standard deviation is 0.75 ounce.

 (b) The sample mean is 127.75 ounces. With a sample size of 8, a 90% level of confidence, and a population standard deviation of 0.75 ounce, does it seem likely that the population mean could be exactly 128 ounces? Explain.

Error tolerance = 0.25 fl oz

Volume = 1/2 gal (64 fl oz)

FIGURE FOR EXERCISE 52

52. **Juice Dispensing Machine** A beverage company uses a machine to fill half-gallon bottles with fruit juice (see figure). The company wants to estimate the mean volume of water the machine is putting in the bottles within 0.25 fluid ounce.

 (a) Determine the minimum sample size required to construct a 95% confidence interval for the population mean. Assume the population standard deviation is 1 fluid ounce.

 (b) The sample mean is exactly 64 fluid ounces. With a sample size of 68, a 95% level of confidence, and a population standard deviation of 1 fluid ounce, does it seem likely that the population mean could be greater than 63.85 fluid ounces? Explain.

53. **Soccer Balls** A soccer ball manufacturer wants to estimate the mean circumference of soccer balls within 0.15 inch.

 (a) Determine the minimum sample size required to construct a 99% confidence interval for the population mean. Assume the population standard deviation is 0.5 inch.

 (b) The sample mean is 27.5 inches. With a sample size of 84, a 99% level of confidence, and a population standard deviation of 0.5 inch, does it seem likely that the population mean could be less than 27.6 inches? Explain.

54. **Tennis Balls** A tennis ball manufacturer wants to estimate the mean circumference of tennis balls within 0.05 inch. Assume the population of circumferences is normally distributed.

 (a) Determine the minimum sample size required to construct a 99% confidence interval for the population mean. Assume the population standard deviation is 0.10 inch.

 (b) The sample mean is 8.3 inches. With a sample size of 34, a 99% level of confidence, and a population standard deviation of 0.10 inch, does it seem likely that the population mean could be exactly 8.258 inches? Explain.

**55.** When estimating the population mean, why not construct a 99% confidence interval every time?

**56.** When all other quantities remain the same, how does the indicated change affect the minimum sample size requirement? Explain.

(a) Increase in the level of confidence

(b) Increase in the error tolerance

(c) Increase in the population standard deviation

## Extending Concepts

**Finite Population Correction Factor** *In Exercises 57 and 58, use the information below.*

In this section, you studied the construction of a confidence interval to estimate a population mean. In each case, the underlying assumption was that the sample size $n$ was small in comparison to the population size $N$. When $n \geq 0.05N$, however, the formula that determines the standard error of the mean $\sigma_{\bar{x}}$ needs to be adjusted, as shown below.

$$\sigma_{\bar{x}} = \frac{\sigma}{\sqrt{n}}\sqrt{\frac{N-n}{N-1}}$$

Recall from the Section 5.4 exercises that the expression $\sqrt{(N-n)/(N-1)}$ is called a ***finite population correction factor.*** The margin of error is

$$E = z_c \frac{\sigma}{\sqrt{n}}\sqrt{\frac{N-n}{N-1}}.$$

**57.** Determine the finite population correction factor for each value of $N$ and $n$.

(a) $N = 1000$ and $n = 500$
(b) $N = 1000$ and $n = 100$
(c) $N = 1000$ and $n = 75$
(d) $N = 1000$ and $n = 50$
(e) $N = 100$ and $n = 50$
(f) $N = 400$ and $n = 50$
(g) $N = 700$ and $n = 50$
(h) $N = 1200$ and $n = 50$

What happens to the finite population correction factor as the sample size $n$ decreases but the population size $N$ remains the same? as the population size $N$ increases but the sample size $n$ remains the same?

**58.** Use the finite population correction factor to construct each confidence interval for the population mean.

(a) $c = 0.99, \bar{x} = 8.6, \sigma = 4.9, N = 200, n = 25$

(b) $c = 0.90, \bar{x} = 10.9, \sigma = 2.8, N = 500, n = 50$

(c) $c = 0.95, \bar{x} = 40.3, \sigma = 0.5, N = 300, n = 68$

(d) $c = 0.80, \bar{x} = 56.7, \sigma = 9.8, N = 400, n = 36$

**59. Sample Size** The equation for determining the sample size

$$n = \left(\frac{z_c \sigma}{E}\right)^2$$

can be obtained by solving the equation for the margin of error

$$E = \frac{z_c \sigma}{\sqrt{n}}$$

for $n$. Show that this is true and justify each step.

# 6.2 Confidence Intervals for the Mean ($\sigma$ Unknown)

### What You Should Learn

- How to interpret the $t$-distribution and use a $t$-distribution table
- How to construct and interpret confidence intervals for a population mean when $\sigma$ is not known

The $t$-Distribution ■ Confidence Intervals and $t$-Distributions

## The $t$-Distribution

In many real-life situations, the population standard deviation is unknown. So, how can you construct a confidence interval for a population mean when $\sigma$ is *not* known? For a simple random sample that is drawn from a population that is normally distributed or has a sample size of 30 or more, you can use the sample standard deviation $s$ to estimate the population standard deviation $\sigma$. However, when using $s$, the sampling distribution of $\bar{x}$ does not follow a normal distribution. In this case, the sampling distribution of $\bar{x}$ follows a ***t*-distribution.**

**DEFINITION**

If the distribution of a random variable $x$ is approximately normal, then

$$t = \frac{\bar{x} - \mu}{s/\sqrt{n}}$$

follows a ***t*-distribution.** Critical values of $t$ are denoted by $t_c$. Here are several properties of the $t$-distribution.

1. The mean, median, and mode of the $t$-distribution are equal to 0.
2. The $t$-distribution is bell-shaped and symmetric about the mean.
3. The total area under the $t$-distribution curve is equal to 1.
4. The tails in the $t$-distribution are "thicker" than those in the standard normal distribution.
5. The standard deviation of the $t$-distribution varies with the sample size, but it is greater than 1.
6. The $t$-distribution is a family of curves, each determined by a parameter called the *degrees of freedom.* The **degrees of freedom** (sometimes abbreviated as d.f.) are the number of free choices left after a sample statistic such as $\bar{x}$ is calculated. When you use a $t$-distribution to estimate a population mean, the degrees of freedom are equal to one less than the sample size.

   $$\text{d.f.} = n - 1 \qquad \text{Degrees of freedom}$$

7. As the degrees of freedom increase, the $t$-distribution approaches the standard normal distribution, as shown in the figure. For 30 or more degrees of freedom, the $t$-distribution is close to the standard normal distribution.

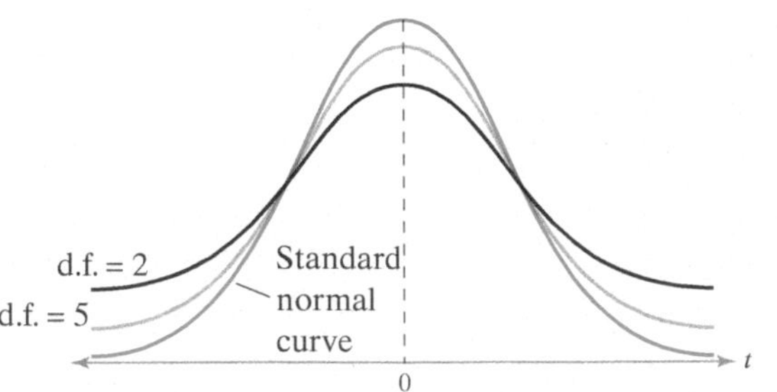

### Study Tip

Here is an example that illustrates the concept of degrees of freedom.

The number of chairs in a classroom equals the number of students: 25 chairs and 25 students. Each of the first 24 students to enter the classroom has a choice on which chair he or she will sit. There is no freedom of choice, however, for the 25th student who enters the room.

Table 5 in Appendix B lists critical values of $t$ for selected confidence intervals and degrees of freedom.

## EXAMPLE 1

### Finding Critical Values of $t$

Find the critical value $t_c$ for a 95% confidence level when the sample size is 15.

**SOLUTION**

Because $n = 15$, the degrees of freedom are d.f. $= n - 1 = 15 - 1 = 14$. A portion of Table 5 is shown. Using d.f. $= 14$ and $c = 0.95$, you can find the critical value $t_c$, as shown by the highlighted areas in the table.

| | **Level of confidence, c** | **0.80** | **0.90** | **0.95** | **0.98** | **0.99** |
|---|---|---|---|---|---|---|
| | **One tail, α** | **0.10** | **0.05** | **0.025** | **0.01** | **0.005** |
| **d.f.** | **Two tails, α** | **0.20** | **0.10** | **0.05** | **0.02** | **0.01** |
| 1 | | 3.078 | 6.314 | 12.706 | 31.821 | 63.657 |
| 2 | | 1.886 | 2.920 | 4.303 | 6.965 | 9.925 |
| 3 | | 1.638 | 2.353 | 3.182 | 4.541 | 5.841 |
| 12 | | 1.356 | 1.782 | 2.179 | 2.681 | 3.055 |
| 13 | | 1.350 | 1.771 | 2.160 | 2.650 | 3.012 |
| 14 | | 1.345 | 1.761 | 2.145 | 2.624 | 2.977 |
| 15 | | 1.341 | 1.753 | 2.131 | 2.602 | 2.947 |
| 16 | | 1.337 | 1.746 | 2.120 | 2.583 | 2.921 |

**Study Tip**

Critical values in the $t$-distribution table for a specific confidence interval can be found in the column headed by $c$ in the appropriate d.f. row. (The symbol $\alpha$ will be explained in Chapter 7.)

From the table, you can see that $t_c = 2.145$. The figure shows the $t$-distribution for 14 degrees of freedom, $c = 0.95$, and $t_c = 2.145$.

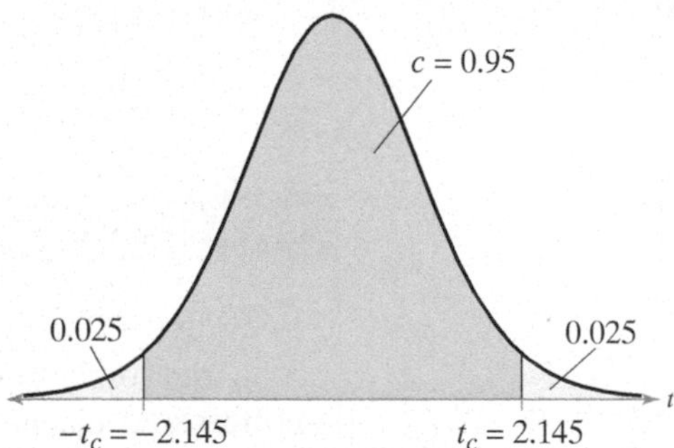


You can use technology to find $t_c$. To use a TI-84 Plus, you need to know the area under the curve to the left of $t_c$, which is

$$0.95 + 0.025 = 0.975. \quad \text{Area to the left of } t_c$$

From the TI-84 Plus display at the left, $t_c \approx 2.145$.

**TI-84 PLUS**

```
invT(.975,14)
                2.144786681
```

***Interpretation*** So, for a $t$-distribution curve with 14 degrees of freedom, 95% of the area under the curve lies between $t = \pm 2.145$.

**TRY IT YOURSELF 1**

Find the critical value $t_c$ for a 90% confidence level when the sample size is 22.

*Answer: Page A40*

When the number of degrees of freedom you need is not in the table, use the closest number in the table that is *less than* the value you need (or use technology, as shown in Example 1). For instance, for d.f. $= 57$, use 50 degrees of freedom. This conservative approach will yield a larger confidence interval with a slightly higher level of confidence $c$.

## Confidence Intervals and *t*-Distributions

Constructing a confidence interval for $\mu$ when $\sigma$ is *not* known using the $t$-distribution is similar to constructing a confidence interval for $\mu$ when $\sigma$ is known using the standard normal distribution—both use a point estimate $\bar{x}$ and a margin of error $E$. When $\sigma$ is not known, the margin of error $E$ is calculated using the sample standard deviation $s$ and the critical value $t_c$. So, the formula for $E$ is

$$E = t_c \frac{s}{\sqrt{n}}. \qquad \text{Margin of error for } \mu \ (\sigma \text{ unknown})$$

Before using this formula, verify that the sample is random, and either the population is normally distributed or $n \geq 30$.

**Study Tip**

Remember that you can calculate the sample standard deviation $s$ using the formula

$$s = \sqrt{\frac{\Sigma(x - \bar{x})^2}{n - 1}}$$

or the alternative formula

$$s = \sqrt{\frac{\Sigma x^2 - (\Sigma x)^2/n}{n - 1}}.$$

However, the most convenient way to find the sample standard deviation is to use technology.

**GUIDELINES**

**Constructing a Confidence Interval for a Population Mean ($\sigma$ Unknown)**

| In Words | In Symbols |
|---|---|
| **1.** Verify that $\sigma$ is not known, the sample is random, and either the population is normally distributed or $n \geq 30$. | |
| **2.** Find the sample statistics $n$, $\bar{x}$, and $s$. | $\bar{x} = \frac{\Sigma x}{n}$, $s = \sqrt{\frac{\Sigma(x - \bar{x})^2}{n - 1}}$ |
| **3.** Identify the degrees of freedom, the level of confidence $c$, and the critical value $t_c$. | d.f. $= n - 1$<br>Use Table 5 in Appendix B. |
| **4.** Find the margin of error $E$. | $E = t_c \frac{s}{\sqrt{n}}$ |
| **5.** Find the left and right endpoints and form the confidence interval. | Left endpoint: $\bar{x} - E$<br>Right endpoint: $\bar{x} + E$<br>Interval: $\bar{x} - E < \mu < \bar{x} + E$ |

**EXAMPLE 2**

See Minitab steps on page 344.

### Constructing a Confidence Interval

You randomly select 16 coffee shops and measure the temperature of the coffee sold at each. The sample mean temperature is 162.0°F with a sample standard deviation of 10.0°F. Construct a 95% confidence interval for the population mean temperature of coffee sold. Assume the temperatures are approximately normally distributed.

**SOLUTION** Because $\sigma$ is unknown, the sample is random, and the temperatures are approximately normally distributed, use the $t$-distribution. Using $n = 16$, $\bar{x} = 162.0$, $s = 10.0$, $c = 0.95$, and d.f. $= 15$, you can use Table 5 to find that $t_c = 2.131$. The margin of error at the 95% confidence level is

$$E = t_c \frac{s}{\sqrt{n}} = 2.131 \cdot \frac{10.0}{\sqrt{16}} \approx 5.3.$$

The confidence interval is shown below and in the figure at the left.

| Left Endpoint | Right Endpoint |
|---|---|
| $\bar{x} - E \approx 162 - 5.3 = 156.7$ | $\bar{x} + E \approx 162 + 5.3 = 167.3$ |

$$156.7 < \mu < 167.3$$

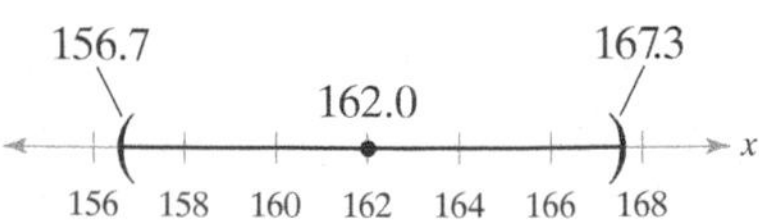


***Interpretation*** With 95% confidence, you can say that the population mean temperature of coffee sold is between 156.7°F and 167.3°F.

**TRY IT YOURSELF 2**

Construct 90% and 99% confidence intervals for the population mean temperature of coffee sold in Example 2.

*Answer: Page 40*

## EXAMPLE 3

See TI-84 Plus steps on page 345.

### Constructing a Confidence Interval

You randomly select 36 cars of the same model that were sold at a car dealership and determine the number of days each car was on the dealership's lot before it was sold. The sample mean is 9.75 days, with a sample standard deviation of 2.39 days. Construct a 99% confidence interval for the population mean number of days the car model is on the dealership's lot.

**SOLUTION**

Because $\sigma$ is unknown, the sample is random, and $n = 36 \geq 30$, use the $t$-distribution. Using $n = 36$, $\bar{x} = 9.75$, $s = 2.39$, $c = 0.99$, and d.f. $= 35$, you can use Table 5 to find that $t_c = 2.724$. The margin of error at the 99% confidence level is

$$E = t_c \frac{s}{\sqrt{n}} = 2.724 \cdot \frac{2.39}{\sqrt{36}} \approx 1.09.$$

The confidence interval is constructed as shown.

| Left Endpoint | Right Endpoint |
|---|---|
| $\bar{x} - E \approx 9.75 - 1.09$ | $\bar{x} + E \approx 9.75 + 1.09$ |
| $= 8.66$ | $= 10.84$ |

$$8.66 < \mu < 10.84$$

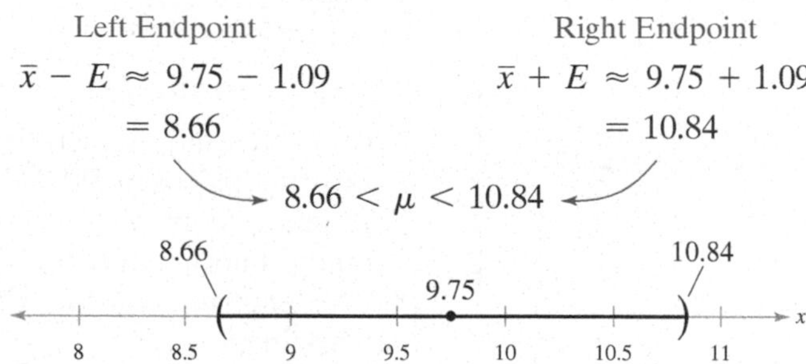


**6.2** To explore this topic further, see **Activity 6.2** on page 318.

**HISTORICAL REFERENCE**

**William S. Gosset** (1876–1937)

Developed the $t$-distribution while employed by the Guinness Brewing Company in Dublin, Ireland. Gosset published his findings using the pseudonym Student. The $t$-distribution is sometimes referred to as Student's $t$-distribution. (See page 35 for others who were important in the history of statistics.)

You can check this answer using technology, as shown below. (When using technology, your answers may differ slightly from those found using Table 5.)

**STATCRUNCH**

**One sample T summary confidence interval:**
μ : Mean of population

**99% confidence interval results:**

| Mean | Sample Mean | Std. Err. | DF | L. Limit | U. Limit |
|---|---|---|---|---|---|
| μ | 9.75 | 0.39833333 | 35 | 8.6650174 | 10.834983 |

***Interpretation*** With 99% confidence, you can say that the population mean number of days the car model is on the dealership's lot is between 8.66 and 10.84.

**TRY IT YOURSELF 3**

Construct 90% and 95% confidence intervals for the population mean number of days the car model is on the dealership's lot in Example 3. Compare the widths of the confidence intervals.

*Answer: Page A40*

## Picturing the World

Two footballs, one filled with air and the other filled with helium, were kicked on a windless day at Ohio State University. The footballs were alternated with each kick. After 10 practice kicks, each football was kicked 29 more times. The distances (in yards) are listed. (Source: The Columbus Dispatch)

**Air Filled**

| Stem | Leaves |
|---|---|
| 1 | 9 |
| 2 | 0 0 2 2 2 |
| 2 | 5 5 5 5 6 6 |
| 2 | 7 7 7 8 8 8 8 8 9 9 9 |
| 3 | 1 1 1 2 |
| 3 | 3 4 |

Key: 1|9 = 19

**Helium Filled**

| Stem | Leaves |
|---|---|
| 1 | 1 2 |
| 1 | 4 |
| 1 | |
| 2 | 2 |
| 2 | 3 4 6 6 6 |
| 2 | 7 8 8 8 9 9 9 9 |
| 3 | 0 0 0 0 1 1 2 2 |
| 3 | 3 4 5 |
| 3 | 9 |

Key: 1|1 = 11

**Assume that the distances are normally distributed for each football. Apply the flowchart at the right to each sample. Construct a 95% confidence interval for the population mean distance each football traveled. Do the confidence intervals overlap? What does this result tell you?**

The flowchart describes when to use the standard normal distribution and when to use the $t$-distribution to construct a confidence interval for a population mean.

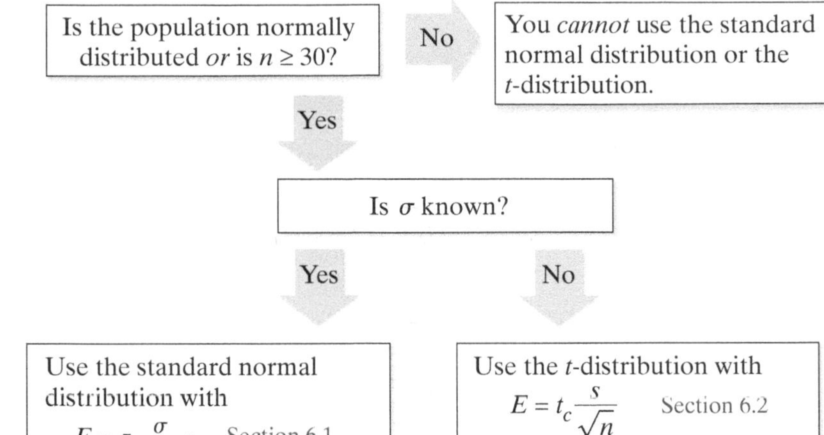


Notice in the flowchart that when both $n < 30$ and the population is *not* normally distributed, you *cannot* use the standard normal distribution or the $t$-distribution.

**EXAMPLE 4**

### Choosing the Standard Normal Distribution or the $t$-Distribution

You randomly select 25 newly constructed houses. The sample mean construction cost is \$299,000 and the population standard deviation is \$46,000. Assuming construction costs are normally distributed, should you use the standard normal distribution, the $t$-distribution, or neither to construct a 95% confidence interval for the population mean construction cost? Explain your reasoning.

**SOLUTION**

*Is the population normally distributed or is $n \geq 30$?*
Yes, the population is normally distributed. Note that even though

$$n = 25 < 30$$

you can still use either the standard normal distribution or the $t$-distribution because the population is normally distributed.

*Is $\sigma$ known?*
Yes.

*Decision:*
Use the standard normal distribution.

**TRY IT YOURSELF 4**

You randomly select 18 adult male athletes and measure the resting heart rate of each. The sample mean heart rate is 64 beats per minute, with a sample standard deviation of 2.5 beats per minute. Assuming the heart rates are normally distributed, should you use the standard normal distribution, the $t$-distribution, or neither to construct a 90% confidence interval for the population mean heart rate? Explain your reasoning.

*Answer: Page A40*

# 6.2 EXERCISES

For Extra Help: MyLab Statistics

## Building Basic Skills and Vocabulary

**1.** List six features that are common to both the standard normal curve and the $t$-distribution curve.

**2.** Describe how the $t$-distribution curve changes as the sample size increases.

**Finding Critical Values of *t*** *In Exercises 3–6, find the critical value $t_c$ for the level of confidence c and sample size n.*

**3.** $c = 0.90, n = 10$

**4.** $c = 0.95, n = 12$

**5.** $c = 0.99, n = 16$

**6.** $c = 0.98, n = 40$

*In Exercises 7 and 8, find the margin of error for the values of c, s, and n.*

**7.** $c = 0.95, s = 5, n = 16$

**8.** $c = 0.99, s = 3, n = 6$

*In Exercises 9–12, construct the indicated confidence interval for the population mean $\mu$ using the t-distribution. Assume the population is normally distributed.*

**9.** $c = 0.90, \bar{x} = 12.5, s = 2.0, n = 6$

**10.** $c = 0.95, \bar{x} = 13.4, s = 0.85, n = 8$

**11.** $c = 0.98, \bar{x} = 4.3, s = 0.34, n = 14$

**12.** $c = 0.99, \bar{x} = 24.7, s = 4.6, n = 50$

*In Exercises 13 and 14, use the confidence interval to find the margin of error and the sample mean.*

**13.** (14.7, 22.1)

**14.** (6.17, 8.53)

*In Exercises 15 and 16, find the t-value for the given values of $\bar{x}$, $\mu$, s, and n.*

**15.** $\bar{x} = 70.3, \mu = 64.8, s = 7.1, n = 16$

**16.** $\bar{x} = 22.9, \mu = 24.5, s = 4.3, n = 40$

## Using and Interpreting Concepts

**Constructing a Confidence Interval** *In Exercises 17–20, you are given the sample mean and the sample standard deviation. Assume the population is normally distributed and use the t-distribution to find the margin of error and construct a 95% confidence interval for the population mean. Interpret the results.*

**17. Commute Time** In a random sample of eight people, the mean commute time to work was 35.5 minutes and the standard deviation was 7.2 minutes.

**18. Driving Distance** In a random sample of five people, the mean driving distance to work was 22.2 miles and the standard deviation was 5.8 miles.

**19. Cell Phone Prices** In a random sample of eight cell phones, the mean full retail price was \$526.50 and the standard deviation was \$184.00.

**20. Mobile Device Repair Costs** In a random sample of 12 mobile devices, the mean repair cost was \$90.42 and the standard deviation was \$33.61.

**21.** You research commute times to work and find that the population standard deviation is 9.3 minutes. Repeat Exercise 17 using the standard normal distribution with the appropriate calculations for a standard deviation that is known. Compare the results.

**22.** You research driving distances to work and find that the population standard deviation is 5.2 miles. Repeat Exercise 18 using the standard normal distribution with the appropriate calculations for a standard deviation that is known. Compare the results.

**23.** You research prices of cell phones and find that the population mean is \$431.61. In Exercise 19, does the $t$-value fall between $-t_{0.95}$ and $t_{0.95}$?

**24.** You research repair costs of mobile devices and find that the population mean is \$89.56. In Exercise 20, does the $t$-value fall between $-t_{0.95}$ and $t_{0.95}$?

**Constructing a Confidence Interval** *In Exercises 25–28, use the data set to (a) find the sample mean, (b) find the sample standard deviation, and (c) construct a 99% confidence interval for the population mean. Assume the population is normally distributed.*

**25. SAT Scores** The SAT scores of 12 randomly selected high school seniors

| | | | | | |
|---|---|---|---|---|---|
| 1130 | 1290 | 1010 | 1320 | 950 | 1250 |
| 1340 | 1100 | 1260 | 1180 | 1470 | 920 |

**26. Grade Point Averages** The grade point averages of 14 randomly selected college students

2.3 3.3 2.6 1.8 3.1 4.0 0.7 2.3 2.0 3.1 3.4 1.3 2.6 2.6

**27. College Football** The weekly time (in hours) spent weight lifting for 16 randomly selected college football players

| | | | | | | | |
|---|---|---|---|---|---|---|---|
| 7.4 | 5.8 | 7.3 | 7.0 | 8.9 | 9.4 | 8.3 | 9.3 |
| 6.9 | 7.5 | 9.0 | 5.8 | 5.5 | 8.6 | 9.3 | 3.8 |

**28. Homework** The weekly time spent (in hours) on homework for 18 randomly selected high school students

| | | | | | | | | |
|---|---|---|---|---|---|---|---|---|
| 12.0 | 11.3 | 13.5 | 11.7 | 12.0 | 13.0 | 15.5 | 10.8 | 12.5 |
| 12.3 | 14.0 | 9.5 | 8.8 | 10.0 | 12.8 | 15.0 | 11.8 | 13.0 |

**29.** In Exercise 25, the population mean SAT score is 1051. Does the $t$-value fall between $-t_{0.99}$ and $t_{0.99}$? *(Source: The College Board)*

**30.** In Exercise 28, the population mean weekly time spent on homework by students is 7.8 hours. Does the $t$-value fall between $-t_{0.99}$ and $t_{0.99}$?

**Constructing a Confidence Interval** *In Exercises 31 and 32, use the data set to (a) find the sample mean, (b) find the sample standard deviation, and (c) construct a 98% confidence interval for the population mean.*

**31. Earnings** The annual earnings (in dollars) of 32 randomly selected intermediate level life insurance underwriters *(Adapted from Salary.com)*

| | | | | | | | |
|---|---|---|---|---|---|---|---|
| 90,198 | 65,357 | 62,108 | 78,201 | 80,882 | 74,759 | 46,382 | 75,196 |
| 56,412 | 74,610 | 65,460 | 68,066 | 53,610 | 92,391 | 57,579 | 99,477 |
| 42,363 | 47,315 | 67,769 | 50,110 | 92,437 | 58,188 | 76,515 | 65,997 |
| 42,713 | 77,745 | 57,928 | 94,066 | 61,748 | 91,868 | 62,445 | 70,359 |

**32. Earnings** The annual earnings (in dollars) of 35 randomly selected senior magnetic resonance imaging (MRI) technologists *(Adapted from Salary.com)*

| | | | | | | |
|---|---|---|---|---|---|---|
| 103,806 | 70,214 | 110,577 | 121,456 | 95,061 | 110,951 | 95,055 |
| 113,446 | 100,863 | 72,326 | 76,846 | 108,294 | 106,126 | 85,180 |
| 88,122 | 81,264 | 109,829 | 83,494 | 108,233 | 86,573 | 99,753 |
| 126,366 | 71,103 | 126,437 | 101,852 | 96,375 | 101,702 | 104,606 |
| 85,439 | 102,420 | 52,090 | 83,010 | 101,074 | 101,895 | 58,667 |

**33.** In Exercise 31, the population mean salary is \$67,319. Does the $t$-value fall between $-t_{0.98}$ and $t_{0.98}$? *(Source: Salary.com)*

**34.** In Exercise 32, the population mean salary is \$93,867. Does the $t$-value fall between $-t_{0.98}$ and $t_{0.98}$? *(Source: Salary.com)*

**Choosing a Distribution** *In Exercises 35–40, use the standard normal distribution or the t-distribution to construct a 95% confidence interval for the population mean. Justify your decision. If neither distribution can be used, explain why. Interpret the results.*

**35. Body Mass Index** In a random sample of 50 people, the mean body mass index (BMI) was 27.7 and the standard deviation was 6.12.

**36. Mortgages** In a random sample of 18 months from January 2011 through December 2020, the mean interest rate for 30-year fixed rate home mortgages was 3.95% and the standard deviation was 0.49%. Assume the interest rates are normally distributed. *(Source: Freddie Mac)*

**37. Toddler Weights** The population standard deviation of the weights of the two-year-old males on a pediatrician's patient list is 2.49 pounds. The mean weight of a sample of 10 of the two-year-old males is 13.68 pounds. Weights are known to be normally distributed.

**38. Data Use** The mean number of gigabytes (GB) of data used in the past month by a sample of 18 college students is 7.9 GB with a standard deviation of 1.7 GB. The distribution is not symmetric due to the various limits on data plans.

**39. Gas Mileage** The gas mileages (in miles per gallon) of 28 randomly selected sports cars are listed. The mileages are not normally distributed.

| | | | | | | | | | | | | | |
|---|---|---|---|---|---|---|---|---|---|---|---|---|---|
| 21 | 30 | 19 | 20 | 21 | 24 | 18 | 24 | 27 | 20 | 22 | 30 | 25 | 26 |
| 22 | 17 | 21 | 24 | 22 | 20 | 24 | 21 | 20 | 18 | 20 | 21 | 20 | 27 |

**40. Yards per Carry** In the 2020–2021 NFL season, the population standard deviation of the yards per carry for all running backs was 1.76. The yards per carry of 13 randomly selected running backs are listed below. Assume the yards per carry are normally distributed. *(Source: National Football League)*

3.3 5.6 5.3 5.1 3.3 5.0 3.9 4.6 4.3 5.3 3.1 4.7 3.6

## Extending Concepts

**41. Tennis Ball Manufacturing** A company manufactures tennis balls. When the balls are dropped onto a concrete surface from a height of 100 inches, the company wants the mean bounce height to be 55.5 inches. This average is maintained by periodically testing random samples of 25 tennis balls. If the $t$-value falls between $-t_{0.99}$ and $t_{0.99}$, then the company will be satisfied that it is manufacturing acceptable tennis balls. For a random sample, the mean bounce height of the sample is 56.0 inches and the standard deviation is 0.25 inch. Assume the bounce heights are approximately normally distributed. Is the company making acceptable tennis balls? Explain.

**42. Light Bulb Manufacturing** A company manufactures light bulbs. The company wants the bulbs to have a mean life span of 1000 hours. This average is maintained by periodically testing random samples of 16 light bulbs. If the $t$-value falls between $-t_{0.99}$ and $t_{0.99}$, then the company will be satisfied that it is manufacturing acceptable light bulbs. For a random sample, the mean life span of the sample is 1015 hours and the standard deviation is 25 hours. Assume the life spans are approximately normally distributed. Is the company making acceptable light bulbs? Explain.

# 6.2 ACTIVITY Confidence Intervals for a Mean

APPLET

You can find the interactive applet for this activity at MyLab Statistics.

The *Comparing confidence intervals for a mean* applet allows you to visually investigate confidence intervals for a population mean. You can specify the **Distribution** (Normal or Right skewed), **Sample size,** population **Mean,** population **Std. Dev.,** and **Interval type** (T or Z). When you click **Update applet,** 100 separate samples of the specified size are selected from a population with these population parameters. For each of the 100 samples, a 95% Z confidence interval (known standard deviation) or a 95% T confidence interval (unknown standard deviation) is displayed in green when it includes the mean, or in red when it does not include the mean. Each time you click **Update applet** you get a new simulation. The level of confidence used for the intervals can be changed within the applet itself by updating the **CI level** input. You can generate additional samples with the given confidence interval by clicking **100 intervals** or **1000 intervals.** The cumulative number of intervals that contain the population mean is also shown. Press **Reset** to clear existing results and start a new simulation.

Distribution: Normal  Sample size: 100  Mean: 50  Std. dev.: 10  Interval type: <

Update Applet

Confidence intervals for a mean: Normal population (μ=50, σ=10)Type=T

Sample size 100  100 intervals  1000 intervals  Reset  Info  Sort graph

| Intervals | CI Level | Containing μ | Total | Prop. contain |
|---|---|---|---|---|
| 74 | 0.95 | 94 | 100 | |
| 75 | | | | |
| 76 | | | | |
| 77 | | | | |
| 78 | | | | |
| 79 | | | | |
| 80 | | | | |
| 81 | | | | |
| 82 | | | | |
| 83 | | | | |
| 84 | | | | |
| 85 | | | | |
| 86 | | | | |
| 87 | | | | |
| 88 | | | | |
| 89 | | | | |
| 90 | | | | |
| 91 | | | | |
| 92 | | | | |
| 93 | | | | |
| 94 | | | | |
| 95 | | | | |

20 30 40 50 60 70
Intervals 1 to 100

## EXPLORE

**Step 1** Specify a **Distribution.**

**Step 2** Specify a **Sample size.**

**Step 3** Specify a value for the **Mean.**

**Step 4** Specify a value for the **Std. Dev.**

**Step 5** Click **Update Applet, 100 intervals,** or **1000 intervals** to generate confidence intervals.

## DRAW CONCLUSIONS

APPLET

1. Set **Distribution** = Normal, **Sample size** = 30, **Mean** = 25, and **Std. Dev.** = 5. At the 95% confidence level, compare the numbers containing $\mu$ for 1000 Z confidence intervals and 1000 T confidence intervals. Is this what you would expect? Explain.

2. In a random sample of 24 high school students, the mean number of hours of sleep per night during the school week was 7.26 hours and the standard deviation was 1.19 hours. Assume the sleep times are normally distributed. Use a sample size of 10 to generate 500 Z confidence intervals and 500 T confidence intervals. At the 95% confidence level, compare the numbers containing $\mu$ for the two distributions. Which type of confidence interval should you use for the mean number of hours of sleep?

# CASE STUDY Marathon Training

A marathon is a foot race with a distance of 26.22 miles. It was one of the original events of the modern Olympics, where it was a men's only event. The women's marathon became an Olympic event in 1984. The Olympic record for the men's marathon was set during the 2008 Olympics by Samuel Kamau Wanjiru of Kenya, with a time of 2 hours, 6 minutes, 32 seconds. The Olympic record for the women's marathon was set during the 2012 Olympics by Tiki Gelana of Ethiopa, with a time of 2 hours, 23 minutes, 7 seconds.

Training for a marathon typically lasts at least 6 months. The training is gradual, with increases in distance about every 2 weeks. About 1 to 3 weeks before the race, the distance run is decreased slightly. The stem-and-leaf plots below show the marathon training times (in minutes) for a random sample of 30 male runners and 30 female runners.

**Training Times (in minutes) of Male Runners**

Key: 15|5 = 155

| Stem | Leaves |
|---|---|
| 15 | 5 8 9 9 9 |
| 16 | 0 0 0 0 1 2 3 4 4 5 8 9 |
| 17 | 0 1 1 3 5 6 6 7 7 9 |
| 18 | 0 1 5 |

**Training Times (in minutes) of Female Runners**

Key: 17|8 = 178

| Stem | Leaves |
|---|---|
| 17 | 8 9 9 |
| 18 | 0 0 0 0 1 2 3 4 6 6 7 9 |
| 19 | 0 0 0 1 3 4 5 5 6 6 |
| 20 | 0 0 1 2 3 |

## EXERCISES

1. Use the sample to find a point estimate for the mean training time of the
   (a) male runners.
   (b) female runners.
2. Find the sample standard deviation of the training times for the
   (a) male runners.
   (b) female runners.
3. Use the sample to construct a 95% confidence interval for the population mean training time of the
   (a) male runners.
   (b) female runners.
4. Interpret the results of Exercise 3.
5. Use the sample to construct a 95% confidence interval for the population mean training time of all runners. How do your results differ from those in Exercise 3? Explain.
6. A trainer wants to estimate the population mean running times for both male and female runners within 2 minutes. Determine the minimum sample size required to construct a 99% confidence interval for the population mean training time of
   (a) male runners. Assume the population standard deviation is 8.9 minutes.
   (b) female runners. Assume the population standard deviation is 8.4 minutes.

# 6.3 Confidence Intervals for Population Proportions

### What You Should Learn

- How to find a point estimate for a population proportion
- How to construct and interpret confidence intervals for a population proportion
- How to determine the minimum sample size required when estimating a population proportion

Point Estimate for a Population Proportion ■ Confidence Intervals for a Population Proportion ■ Finding a Minimum Sample Size

## Point Estimate for a Population Proportion

Recall from Section 4.2 that the probability of success in a single trial of a binomial experiment is $p$. This probability is a **population proportion.** In this section, you will learn how to estimate a population proportion $p$ using a confidence interval. As with confidence intervals for $\mu$, you will start with a point estimate.

**DEFINITION**

The **point estimate for $p$,** the population proportion of successes, is given by the proportion of successes in a sample and is denoted by

$$\hat{p} = \frac{x}{n} \qquad \text{Sample proportion}$$

where $x$ is the number of successes in the sample and $n$ is the sample size. The point estimate for the population proportion of failures is $\hat{q} = 1 - \hat{p}$. The symbols $\hat{p}$ and $\hat{q}$ are read as "$p$ hat" and "$q$ hat."

### Study Tip

In Sections 6.1 and 6.2, estimates were made for quantitative data. In this section, sample proportions are used to make estimates for qualitative data.

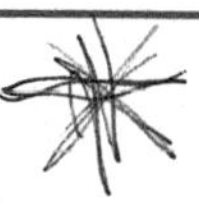

**EXAMPLE 1**

### Finding a Point Estimate for $p$

In a recent survey of 540 U.S. adults, 378 said that they plan on traveling this summer. Find a point estimate for the population proportion of U.S. adults who plan on traveling this summer. *(Adapted from TravelDailyNews International)*

**SOLUTION**

The number of successes is the number of adults who plan on traveling this summer, so $x = 378$. The sample size is $n = 540$. So, the sample proportion is

$$\hat{p} = \frac{x}{n} \qquad \text{Formula for sample proportion}$$

$$= \frac{378}{540} \qquad \text{Substitute 378 for } x \text{ and 540 for } n.$$

$$= 70\%. \qquad \text{Divide and write as a percent.}$$

So, the point estimate for the population proportion of U.S. adults who plan on traveling this summer is 70% or 0.70.

**TRY IT YOURSELF 1**

A poll surveyed 1050 U.S. adults who own smart speakers regarding how concerned they are about how much personal data their smart speakers collect. The results are shown in the table. Find a point estimate for the population proportion of U.S. adults who are very concerned. *(Adapted from Speakergy)*

| How concerned are you? | Number responding yes |
|---|---|
| Very concerned | 147 |
| Somewhat concerned | 420 |
| Not too concerned | 378 |
| Not at all concerned | 105 |

*Answer: Page A40*

## Confidence Intervals for a Population Proportion

Constructing a confidence interval for a population proportion $p$ is similar to constructing a confidence interval for a population mean. You start with a point estimate and calculate a margin of error.

**DEFINITION**

A **$c$-confidence interval for a population proportion $p$** is

$$\hat{p} - E < p < \hat{p} + E$$

where

$$E = z_c\sqrt{\frac{\hat{p}\hat{q}}{n}}. \qquad \text{Margin of error for } p$$

The probability that the confidence interval contains $p$ is $c$, assuming that the estimation process is repeated a large number of times.

In Section 5.5, you learned that a binomial distribution can be approximated by a normal distribution when $np \geq 5$ and $nq \geq 5$. When $n\hat{p} \geq 5$ and $n\hat{q} \geq 5$, the sampling distribution of $\hat{p}$ is approximately normal with a mean of

$$\mu_{\hat{p}} = p \qquad \text{Mean of the sample proportions}$$

and a standard error of

$$\sigma_{\hat{p}} = \sqrt{\frac{pq}{n}}. \qquad \text{Standard error of the sample proportions}$$

$$\left(\text{Notice } \sigma_{\hat{p}} = \frac{\sigma}{n} = \frac{\sqrt{npq}}{n} = \frac{\sqrt{npq}}{\sqrt{n^2}} = \sqrt{\frac{npq}{n^2}} = \sqrt{\frac{pq}{n}}.\right)$$

**GUIDELINES**

**Constructing a Confidence Interval for a Population Proportion**

| In Words | In Symbols |
|---|---|
| **1.** Identify the sample statistics $n$ and $x$. | |
| **2.** Find the point estimate $\hat{p}$. | $\hat{p} = \frac{x}{n}$ |
| **3.** Verify that the sampling distribution of $\hat{p}$ can be approximated by a normal distribution. | $n\hat{p} \geq 5$, $n\hat{q} \geq 5$ |
| **4.** Find the critical value $z_c$ that corresponds to the given level of confidence $c$. | Use Table 4 in Appendix B. |
| **5.** Find the margin of error $E$. | $E = z_c\sqrt{\frac{\hat{p}\hat{q}}{n}}$ |
| **6.** Find the left and right endpoints and form the confidence interval. | Left endpoint: $\hat{p} - E$<br>Right endpoint: $\hat{p} + E$<br>Interval:<br>$\hat{p} - E < p < \hat{p} + E$ |

In Step 4 above, note that the critical value $z_c$ is found the same way it was found in Section 6.1, by either using Table 4 in Appendix B or using technology.

### Picturing the World

A poll surveyed 2140 U.S. adults about the privacy of their personal information. Of those surveyed, 813 said that they think it is possible to go about daily life today without having companies collect data about them. (Adapted from Pew Research Center)

**Do You Think It Is Possible to Go About Daily Life Today Without Having Companies Collect Data About You?**

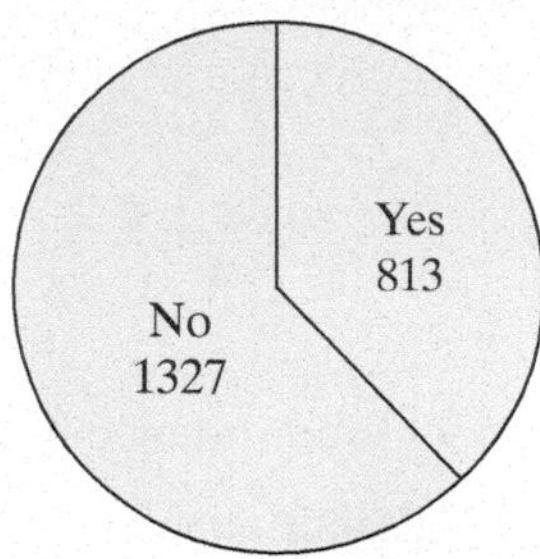


**Find a 90% confidence interval for the population proportion of people who think it is possible to go about daily life today without having companies collect data about them.**

### Tech Tip

Here are instructions for constructing a confidence interval for a population proportion on a TI-84 Plus.

STAT

Choose the TESTS menu.

A: 1–PropZInt . . .

Enter the values of $x$, $n$, and the level of confidence $c$ (C-Level). Then select *Calculate*.

## EXAMPLE 2

Minitab and TI-84 Plus steps are shown on pages 344 and 345.

### Constructing a Confidence Interval for $p$

Use the data in Example 1 to construct a 95% confidence interval for the population proportion of U.S. adults who plan on traveling this summer.

**SOLUTION**

From Example 1, $\hat{p} = 0.70$. So, the point estimate for the population proportion of failures is

$$\hat{q} = 1 - 0.70 = 0.30.$$

Using $n = 540$, you can verify that the sampling distribution of $\hat{p}$ can be approximated by a normal distribution.

$$n\hat{p} = (540)(0.70) = 378 > 5$$

and

$$n\hat{q} = (540)(0.30) = 162 > 5$$

Using $z_c = 1.96$, the margin of error is

$$E = z_c\sqrt{\frac{\hat{p}\hat{q}}{n}} = 1.96\sqrt{\frac{(0.70)(0.30)}{540}} \approx 0.039.$$

Next, find the left and right endpoints and form the 95% confidence interval.

| Left Endpoint | Right Endpoint |
|---|---|
| $\hat{p} - E \approx 0.70 - 0.039 = 0.661$ | $\hat{p} + E \approx 0.70 + 0.039 = 0.739$ |

$$0.661 < p < 0.739$$

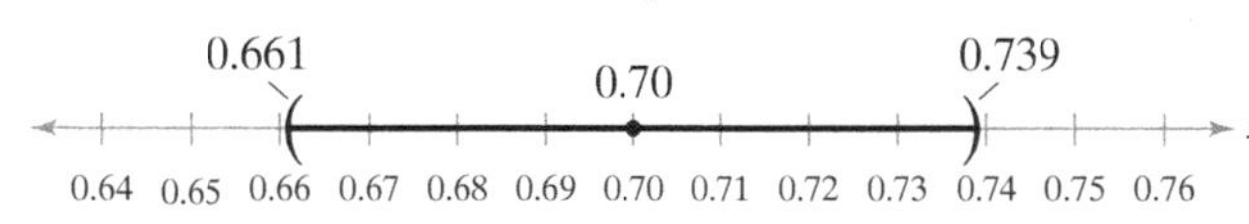


You can check this answer using technology, as shown below. (When using technology, your answers may differ slightly from those found using Table 4.)

**STATCRUNCH**

**95% confidence interval results:**

| Proportion | Count | Total | Sample Prop. | Std. Err. | L. Limit | U. Limit |
|---|---|---|---|---|---|---|
| p | 378 | 540 | 0.7 | 0.019720 | 0.66135 | 0.73865 |

***Interpretation*** With 95% confidence, you can say that the population proportion of U.S. adults who plan on traveling this summer is between 66.1% and 73.9%.

**TRY IT YOURSELF 2**

Use the data in Try It Yourself 1 to construct a 90% confidence interval for the population proportion of U.S. adults who are very concerned about how much personal data their smart speakers collect. *Answer: Page A40*

**Study Tip**

Notice in Example 2 that the confidence interval for the population proportion $p$ is rounded to three decimal places. This *round-off rule* will be used throughout the text.

The confidence level of 95% used in Example 2 is typical of opinion polls. The result, however, is usually not stated as a confidence interval. Instead, the result of Example 2 would be stated as shown.

*A survey found that 70% of U.S. adults plan on traveling this summer. The margin of error for the survey is ±3.9%.*

EXAMPLE 3

## Constructing a Confidence Interval for $p$

The figure below is from a survey of 800 U.S. adults. Construct a 99% confidence interval for the population proportion of U.S. adults who prefer to get their news from television. *(Adapted from Pew Research Center)*

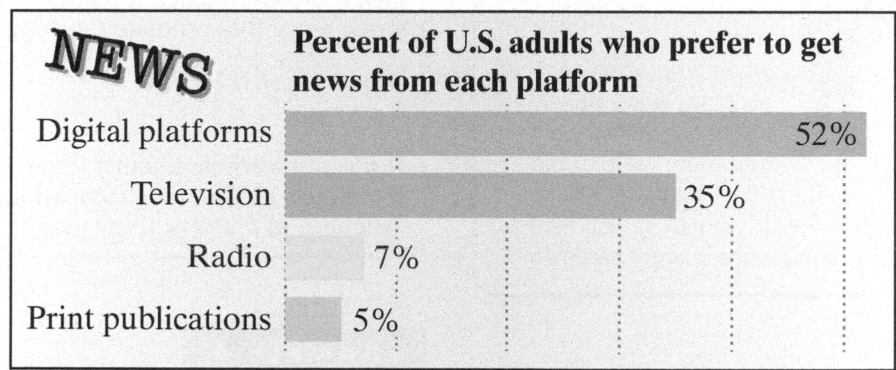


**SOLUTION**

From the figure, $\hat{p} = 0.35$. So, $\hat{q} = 1 - 0.35 = 0.65$. Using $n = 800$, note that

$$n\hat{p} = (800)(0.35) = 280 > 5$$

and

$$n\hat{q} = (800)(0.65) = 520 > 5.$$

So, the sampling distribution of $\hat{p}$ is approximately normal. Using $z_c = 2.575$, the margin of error is

$$E = z_c\sqrt{\frac{\hat{p}\hat{q}}{n}}$$

$$\approx 2.575\sqrt{\frac{(0.35)(0.65)}{800}}$$

Use Table 4 in Appendix B to estimate that $z_c$ is halfway between 2.57 and 2.58.

$$\approx 0.043.$$

6.3 To explore this topic further, see **Activity 6.3** on page 329.

Next, find the left and right endpoints and form the 99% confidence interval.

| Left Endpoint | Right Endpoint |
|---|---|
| $\hat{p} - E \approx 0.35 - 0.043 = 0.307$ | $\hat{p} + E \approx 0.35 + 0.043 = 0.393$ |

$$0.307 < p < 0.393$$

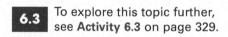

0.307 0.35 0.393

0.29 0.30 0.31 0.32 0.33 0.34 0.35 0.36 0.37 0.38 0.39 0.40 $x$

TI-84 PLUS

1-PropZInt
(.30656,.39344)
p̂=0.35
n=800

You can check this answer using technology, as shown at the left.

***Interpretation*** With 99% confidence, you can say that the population proportion of U.S. adults who prefer to get their news from television is between 30.7% and 39.3%.

**TRY IT YOURSELF 3**

Use the data in Example 3 to construct a 99% confidence interval for the population proportion of U.S. adults who prefer to get their news from digital platforms.

*Answer: Page A40*

## Finding a Minimum Sample Size

One way to increase the precision of a confidence interval without decreasing the level of confidence is to increase the sample size.

**Study Tip**

The reason for using $\hat{p} = 0.5$ and $\hat{q} = 0.5$ when no preliminary estimate is available is that these values yield the maximum value of the product $\hat{p}\hat{q}$. (See Exercise 37.) In other words, without an estimate of $\hat{p}$, you must use a larger sample.

### Finding a Minimum Sample Size to Estimate $p$

Given a $c$-confidence level and a margin of error $E$, the minimum sample size $n$ needed to estimate the population proportion $p$ is

$$n = \hat{p}\hat{q}\left(\frac{z_c}{E}\right)^2.$$

If $n$ is not a whole number, then round $n$ up to the next whole number (see Example 4). Also, note that this formula assumes that you have preliminary estimates of $\hat{p}$ and $\hat{q}$. If not, use $\hat{p} = 0.5$ and $\hat{q} = 0.5$.

**EXAMPLE 4**

### Determining a Minimum Sample Size

You are running a political campaign and wish to estimate, with 95% confidence, the population proportion of registered voters who will vote for your candidate. Your estimate must be accurate within 3% of the population proportion. Find the minimum sample size needed when (1) no preliminary estimate is available and (2) a preliminary estimate gives $\hat{p} = 0.31$. Compare your results.

**SOLUTION**

1. Because you do not have a preliminary estimate of $\hat{p}$, use $\hat{p} = 0.5$ and $\hat{q} = 0.5$. Using $z_c = 1.96$ and $E = 0.03$, you can solve for $n$.

$$n = \hat{p}\hat{q}\left(\frac{z_c}{E}\right)^2 = (0.5)(0.5)\left(\frac{1.96}{0.03}\right)^2 \approx 1067.11$$

Because $n$ is not a whole number, round up to the next whole number, 1068.

2. You have a preliminary estimate of $\hat{p} = 0.31$. So, $\hat{q} = 0.69$. Using $z_c = 1.96$ and $E = 0.03$, you can solve for $n$.

$$n = \hat{p}\hat{q}\left(\frac{z_c}{E}\right)^2 = (0.31)(0.69)\left(\frac{1.96}{0.03}\right)^2 \approx 913.02$$

Because $n$ is not a whole number, round up to the next whole number, 914.

***Interpretation*** With no preliminary estimate, the minimum sample size should be at least 1068 registered voters. With a preliminary estimate of $\hat{p} = 0.31$, the sample size should be at least 914 registered voters. So, you will need a larger sample size when no preliminary estimate is available.

**TRY IT YOURSELF 4**

A researcher is estimating the population proportion of people in the United States who had private health care coverage over a recent 6-month period. The estimate must be accurate within 2% of the population proportion with 90% confidence. Find the minimum sample size needed when (1) no preliminary estimate is available and (2) a previous survey found that 62.2% of people in the United States had private health care coverage over a recent 6-month period. *(Source: National Center for Health Statistics)*

*Answer: Page A40*

# 6.3 EXERCISES

For Extra Help: MyLab Statistics

## Building Basic Skills and Vocabulary

**True or False?** *In Exercises 1 and 2, determine whether the statement is true or false. If it is false, rewrite it as a true statement.*

**1.** The point estimate for the population proportion of failures is $1 - \hat{p}$.

**2.** To find the minimum sample size required for a confidence interval, solve for $n$ in the formula for margin of error and round to the nearest whole number.

**Finding $\hat{p}$ and $\hat{q}$** *In Exercises 3–6, let p be the population proportion for the situation. Find point estimates of p and q.*

**3. Tax Fraud** In a survey of 1040 U.S. adults, 62 have had someone impersonate them to try to claim tax refunds. *(Adapted from Pew Research Center)*

**4. Social Security** In a survey of 351 retired Americans, 200 said that they rely on Social Security as major source of income. *(Adapted from Gallup)*

**5. Social Security** In a survey of 661 non-retired Americans, 218 said that they expect to rely on Social Security as major source of income when they retire. *(Adapted from Gallup)*

**6. Private Internet Browsing** In a survey of 4272 U.S. adults, 1025 knew that private browsing mode only prevents someone using the same computer from seeing one's online activities. *(Adapted from Pew Research Center)*

*In Exercises 7–10, use the confidence interval to find the margin of error and the sample proportion.*

**7.** (0.905, 0.933)

**8.** (0.245, 0.475)

**9.** (0.512, 0.596)

**10.** (0.087, 0.263)

## Using and Interpreting Concepts

**Constructing Confidence Intervals** *In Exercises 11 and 12, construct 90% and 95% confidence intervals for the population proportion. Interpret the results and compare the widths of the confidence intervals.*

**11. New Year's Resolutions** In a survey of 1790 U.S. adults in a recent year, 1325 say they have a New Year's resolution. *(Adapted from Finder)*

**12. New Year's Resolutions** In a survey of 1790 U.S. adults in a recent year, 816 have a New Year's resolution related to their health. *(Adapted from Finder)*

**Constructing Confidence Intervals** *In Exercises 13 and 14, construct a 99% confidence interval for the population proportion. Interpret the results.*

**13. Terrorism** In a survey of 1010 U.S. adults, 364 said that they worry a great deal about the possibility of a future terrorist attack. *(Adapted from Gallup)*

**14. Hunger and Homelessness** In a survey of 1010 U.S. adults, 556 said that they worry a great deal about hunger and homelessness. *(Adapted from Gallup)*

**15. LGBT Identification** In a survey of 15,349 U.S. adults, 860 identify as lesbian, gay, bisexual, or transgender. Construct a 95% confidence interval for the population proportion of U.S. adults who identify as lesbian, gay, bisexual, or transgender. *(Adapted from Gallup)*

**16. Bisexual Idenfitication** In a survey of 692 lesbian, gay, bisexual, or transgender U.S adults, 378 said that they consider themselves bisexual. Construct a 90% confidence interval for the population proportion of lesbian, gay, bisexual, or transgender U.S. adults who consider themselves bisexual. *(Adapted from Gallup)*

**17. Congress** You wish to estimate, with 95% confidence, the population proportion of likely U.S. voters who think Congress is doing a good or excellent job. Your estimate must be accurate within 4% of the population proportion.

(a) No preliminary estimate is available. Find the minimum sample size needed.

(b) Find the minimum sample size needed, using a prior survey that found that 21% of likely U.S. voters think Congress is doing a good or excellent job. *(Source: Rasmussen Reports)*

(c) Compare the results from parts (a) and (b).

**18. Senate Filibuster** You wish to estimate, with 99% confidence, the population proportion of U.S. adults who disapprove of the U.S Senate's use of the filibuster. Your estimate must be accurate within 2% of the population proportion.

(a) No preliminary estimate is available. Find the minimum sample size needed.

(b) Find the minimum sample size needed, using a prior survey that found that 34% of U.S. adults disapprove of the U.S Senate's use of the filibuster. *(Source: Monmouth University)*

(c) Compare the results from parts (a) and (b).

**19. Fast Food** You wish to estimate, with 90% confidence, the population proportion of U.S. families who eat fast food at least once per week. Your estimate must be accurate within 3% of the population proportion.

(a) No preliminary estimate is available. Find the minimum sample size needed.

(b) Find the minimum sample size needed, using a prior study that found that 83% of U.S. families eat fast food at least once per week. *(Source: The Barbecue Lab)*

(c) Compare the results from parts (a) and (b).

**20. Alcohol-Impaired Driving** You wish to estimate, with 95% confidence, the population proportion of motor vehicle fatalities that were caused by alcohol-impaired driving. Your estimate must be accurate within 5% of the population proportion.

(a) No preliminary estimate is available. Find the minimum sample size needed.

(b) Find the minimum sample size needed, using a prior study that found that 28% of motor vehicle fatalities were caused by alcohol-impaired driving. *(Source: National Highway Traffic Safety Administration)*

(c) Compare the results from parts (a) and (b).

**21.** In Exercise 11, would it be unusual for the population proportion to be 72.5%? Explain.

**22.** In Exercise 12, would it be unusual for the population proportion to be 48%? Explain.

**23.** In Exercise 17(b), would a sample size of 400 be acceptable? Explain.

**24.** In Exercise 18(b), would a sample size of 5000 be acceptable? Explain.

**Constructing Confidence Intervals** *In Exercises 25 and 26, use the figure, which shows the results of a survey in which 1051 adults from France, 1042 adults from Germany, 1003 adults from the United Kingdom, and 1000 adults from the United States were asked whether national identity is strongly tied to birthplace.* (*Source: Pew Research Center*)

**National Identity and Birthplace**

People from different countries who believe national identity is strongly tied to birthplace

| | |
|---|---|
| France | 32% |
| Germany | 25% |
| United Kingdom | 31% |
| United States | 35% |

**25. National Identity** Construct a 99% confidence interval for the population proportion of adults who say national identity is strongly tied to birthplace for each country listed.

**26.** In Exercise 25, which two countries are the least likely to have equal population proportions? Explain.

**Constructing Confidence Intervals** *In Exercises 27 and 28, use the figure, which shows the results of a survey in which 1021 U.S. adults were asked whether they see each of the possible threats to the vital interests of the United States as a critical threat in the next 10 years.* (*Source: Gallup*)

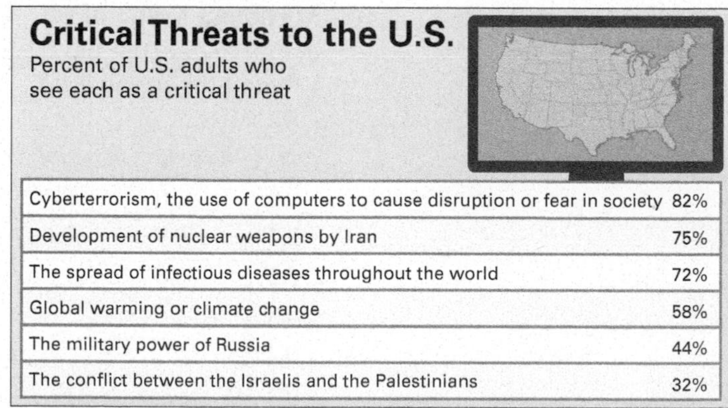

**Critical Threats to the U.S.**

Percent of U.S. adults who see each as a critical threat

| | |
|---|---|
| Cyberterrorism, the use of computers to cause disruption or fear in society | 82% |
| Development of nuclear weapons by Iran | 75% |
| The spread of infectious diseases throughout the world | 72% |
| Global warming or climate change | 58% |
| The military power of Russia | 44% |
| The conflict between the Israelis and the Palestinians | 32% |

**27. Critical Threats** Construct a 95% confidence interval for the population proportion of U.S. adults who gave each response.

**28.** In Exercise 27, which two threats are the most likely to have equal population proportions? Explain.

## Extending Concepts

**Translating Statements** *In Exercises 29–34, translate the statement into a confidence interval. Approximate the level of confidence.*

**29.** In a survey of 1502 U.S. adults, 31% said that they use Pinterest. The survey's margin of error is ±2.9%. *(Source: Pew Research Center)*

**30.** In a survey of 220 U.S. adults ages 18–29, 65% said that they use Snapchat. The survey's margin of error is ±7.9%. *(Source: Pew Research Center)*

**31.** In a survey of 1000 U.S. adults, 71% think teaching is one of the most important jobs in our country today. The survey's margin of error is ±3%. *(Source: Rasmussen Reports)*

**32.** In a survey of 880 unmarried U.S. adults who are living with a partner, 73% say love was a major reason why they decided to move in together. The survey's margin of error is ±4.8%. *(Source: Pew Research Center)*

**33.** In a survey of 2094 U.S. adults who have used an online dating app, 57% said their personal experience with online dating was positive. The survey's margin of error is ±3.6%. *(Source: Pew Research Center)*

**34.** In a survey of 1052 parents of children ages 8–14, 68% say they are willing to get a second or part-time job to pay for their children's college education, and 42% say they lose sleep worrying about college costs. The survey's margin of error is ±3%. *(Source: T. Rowe Price Group, Inc.)*

**35. Why Check It?** Why is it necessary to check that $n\hat{p} \geq 5$ and $n\hat{q} \geq 5$?

**36. Sample Size** The equation for determining the sample size

$$n = \hat{p}\hat{q}\left(\frac{z_c}{E}\right)^2$$

can be obtained by solving the equation for the margin of error

$$E = z_c\sqrt{\frac{\hat{p}\hat{q}}{n}}$$

for $n$. Show that this is true and justify each step.

**37. Maximum Value of $\hat{p}\hat{q}$** Complete the tables for different values of $\hat{p}$ and $\hat{q} = 1 - \hat{p}$. From the tables, which value of $\hat{p}$ appears to give the maximum value of the product $\hat{p}\hat{q}$?

| $\hat{p}$ | $\hat{q} = 1 - \hat{p}$ | $\hat{p}\hat{q}$ |
|---|---|---|
| 0.0 | 1.0 | 0.00 |
| 0.1 | 0.9 | 0.09 |
| 0.2 | 0.8 | |
| 0.3 | | |
| 0.4 | | |
| 0.5 | | |
| 0.6 | | |
| 0.7 | | |
| 0.8 | | |
| 0.9 | | |
| 1.0 | | |

| $\hat{p}$ | $\hat{q} = 1 - \hat{p}$ | $\hat{p}\hat{q}$ |
|---|---|---|
| 0.45 | | |
| 0.46 | | |
| 0.47 | | |
| 0.48 | | |
| 0.49 | | |
| 0.50 | | |
| 0.51 | | |
| 0.52 | | |
| 0.53 | | |
| 0.54 | | |
| 0.55 | | |

# 6.3 ACTIVITY

# Confidence Intervals for a Proportion

APPLET

You can find the interactive applet for this activity at MyLab Statistics.

The *Confidence intervals for a proportion* applet allows you to visually investigate confidence intervals for a population proportion. You can specify the **Sample size** and the population proportion **p.** When you click **Update applet,** 100 separate samples of the specified size are selected from a population with a proportion of successes equal to **p.** For each of the 100 samples, a 95% confidence interval is displayed in green when it includes the mean, or in red when it does not include the mean. Each time you click **Update applet** you get a new simulation. The level of confidence used for the intervals can be changed within the applet itself by updating the **CI level** input. You can generate additional samples with the given confidence interval by clicking **100 intervals** or **1000 intervals.** Each of these intervals is computed using the standard normal approximation. The cumulative number of times intervals that contain the population proportion is also shown. Press **Reset** to clear existing results and start a new simulation.

Sample size: 50 p: 0.5 Update Applet

Confidence intervals for p, p=0.5 Type=Standard-Wald

Sample size 50 100 intervals 1000 intervals Reset Info Sort graph

| CI Level | Containing p | Total | Prop. contain |
|---|---|---|---|
| 0.80 | 82 | 100 | |

Intervals: 79 80 81 82 83 84 85 86 87 88 89 90 91 92 93 94 95 96 97 98 99 100

0 0.2 0.4 0.6 0.8

Intervals 1 to 100

## EXPLORE

**Step 1** Specify a **Sample size.**

**Step 2** Specify a value for **p.**

**Step 3** Click **Update applet, 100 intervals,** or **1000 intervals** to generate confidence intervals.

## DRAW CONCLUSIONS

APPLET

1. At the 95% confidence level, generate 1000 confidence intervals with **p** = 0.6 for each **Sample size:** 10, 20, 40, and 100. Clear your results after each simulation. What proportion of the confidence intervals for each sample size contains the population proportion? What happens as the sample size increases?

2. Generate 1000 confidence intervals for **p** = 0.6 and **Sample size** = 100 at each of several different confidence levels. Describe how the proportion of confidence intervals that contain the population proportion changes as the confidence level increases. Explain your result.

# 6.4 Confidence Intervals for Variance and Standard Deviation

### What You Should Learn

- How to interpret the chi-square distribution and use a chi-square distribution table
- How to construct and interpret confidence intervals for a population variance and standard deviation

The Chi-Square Distribution ■ Confidence Intervals for $\sigma^2$ and $\sigma$

## The Chi-Square Distribution

In manufacturing, it is necessary to control the amount that a process varies. For instance, an automobile part manufacturer must produce thousands of parts to be used in the manufacturing process. It is important that the parts vary little or not at all. How can you measure, and consequently control, the amount of variation in the parts? You can start with a point estimate.

**DEFINITION**

The **point estimate for $\sigma^2$** is $s^2$ and the **point estimate for $\sigma$** is $s$. The most unbiased estimate for $\sigma^2$ is $s^2$.

You can use a **chi-square distribution** to construct a confidence interval for the variance and standard deviation.

### Study Tip

The Greek letter $\chi$ is pronounced "kī," which rhymes with the more familiar Greek letter $\pi$.

**DEFINITION**

If a random variable $x$ has a normal distribution, then the distribution of

$$\chi^2 = \frac{(n-1)s^2}{\sigma^2}$$

forms a **chi-square distribution** for samples of any size $n > 1$. Here are several properties of the chi-square distribution.

1. All values of $\chi^2$ are greater than or equal to 0.
2. The chi-square distribution is a family of curves, each determined by the degrees of freedom. To form a confidence interval for $\sigma^2$, use the chi-square distribution with degrees of freedom equal to one less than the sample size.

   d.f. $= n - 1$ Degrees of freedom
3. The total area under each chi-square distribution curve is equal to 1.
4. The chi-square distribution is positively skewed and therefore the distribution is not symmetric.
5. The chi-square distribution is different for each number of degrees of freedom, as shown in the figure. As the degrees of freedom increase, the chi-square distribution approaches a normal distribution.

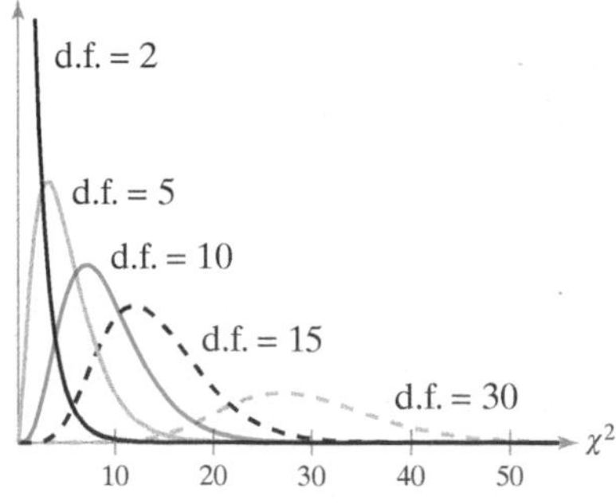


Chi-Square Distribution for Different Degrees of Freedom

**Study Tip**

For chi-square critical values with a *c*-confidence level, the values shown below, $\chi_L^2$ and $\chi_R^2$, are what you look up in Table 6 in Appendix B.

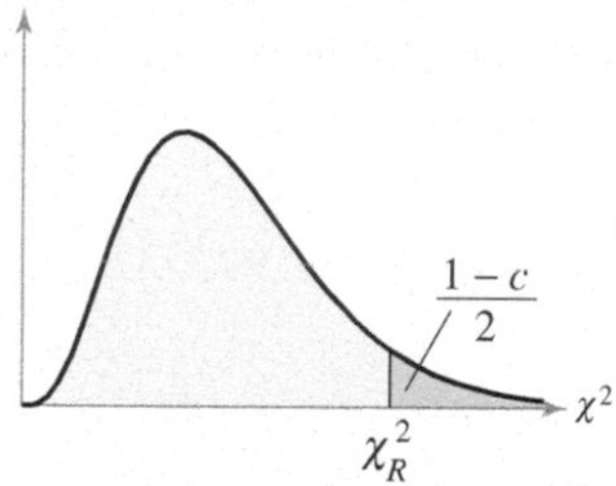


Area to the right of $\chi_R^2$

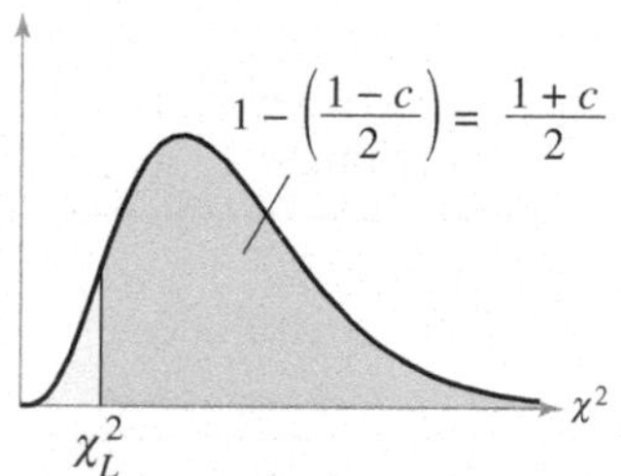


Area to the right of $\chi_L^2$

The result is that you can conclude that the area between the left and right critical values is *c*.

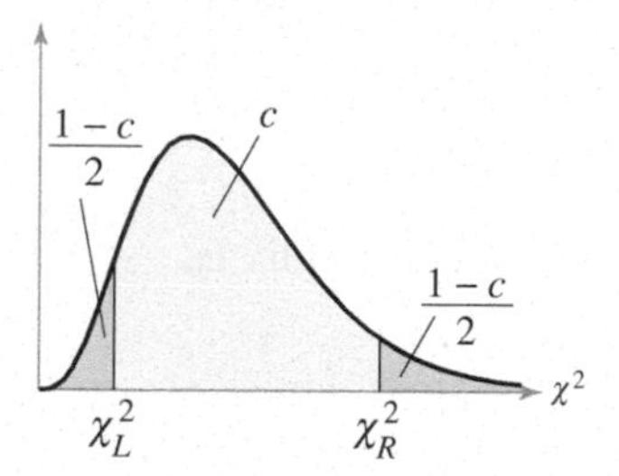


There are two critical values for each level of confidence. The value $\chi_R^2$ represents the right-tail critical value and $\chi_L^2$ represents the left-tail critical value. Table 6 in Appendix B lists critical values of $\chi^2$ for various degrees of freedom and areas. Each area listed in the top row of the table represents the region under the chi-square curve to the *right* of the critical value.

## EXAMPLE 1

### Finding Critical Values for $\chi^2$

Find the critical values $\chi_R^2$ and $\chi_L^2$ for a 95% confidence interval when the sample size is 18.

**SOLUTION**

Because the sample size is 18,

$$\text{d.f.} = n - 1 = 18 - 1 = 17. \qquad \text{Degrees of freedom}$$

The area to the right of $\chi_R^2$ is

$$\text{Area to the right of } \chi_R^2 = \frac{1-c}{2} = \frac{1-0.95}{2} = 0.025$$

and the area to the right of $\chi_L^2$ is

$$\text{Area to the right of } \chi_L^2 = \frac{1+c}{2} = \frac{1+0.95}{2} = 0.975.$$

A portion of Table 6 is shown. Using d.f. = 17 and the areas 0.975 and 0.025, you can find the critical values, as shown by the highlighted areas in the table. (Note that the top row in the table lists areas to the right of the critical value. The entries in the table are critical values.)

Area to the right of $\chi_L^2$ — Area to the right of $\chi_R^2$

| Degrees of freedom | α | | | | | | | |
|---|---|---|---|---|---|---|---|---|
| | 0.995 | 0.99 | 0.975 | 0.95 | 0.90 | 0.10 | 0.05 | 0.025 |
| 1 | — | — | 0.001 | 0.004 | 0.016 | 2.706 | 3.841 | 5.024 |
| 2 | 0.010 | 0.020 | 0.051 | 0.103 | 0.211 | 4.605 | 5.991 | 7.378 |
| 3 | 0.072 | 0.115 | 0.216 | 0.352 | 0.584 | 6.251 | 7.815 | 9.348 |
| 15 | 4.601 | 5.229 | 6.262 | 7.261 | 8.547 | 22.307 | 24.996 | 27.488 |
| 16 | 5.142 | 5.812 | 6.908 | 7.962 | 9.312 | 23.542 | 26.296 | 28.845 |
| 17 | 5.697 | 6.408 | 7.564 | 8.672 | 10.085 | 24.769 | 27.587 | 30.191 |
| 18 | 6.265 | 7.015 | 8.231 | 9.390 | 10.865 | 25.989 | 28.869 | 31.526 |
| 19 | 6.844 | 7.633 | 8.907 | 10.117 | 11.651 | 27.204 | 30.144 | 32.852 |
| 20 | 7.434 | 8.260 | 9.591 | 10.851 | 12.443 | 28.412 | 31.410 | 34.170 |

$\chi_L^2$ — $\chi_R^2$

From the table, you can see that the critical values are

$$\chi_R^2 = 30.191 \quad \text{and} \quad \chi_L^2 = 7.564.$$

***Interpretation*** So, for a chi-square distribution curve with 17 degrees of freedom, 95% of the area under the curve lies between 7.564 and 30.191, as shown in the figure at the left.

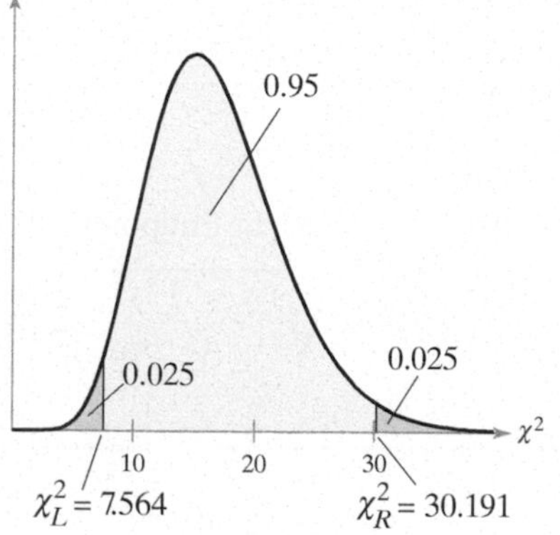


**TRY IT YOURSELF 1**

Find the critical values $\chi_R^2$ and $\chi_L^2$ for a 90% confidence interval when the sample size is 30.

*Answer: Page A40*

## Picturing the World

The Florida panther is an endangered subspecies of *Puma concolor* (also known as puma, cougar, or mountain lion). About 120 to 230 adult panthers are in existence, primarily in southwest Florida. The map below shows occurrence data (yellow circles). Recently, legislation was passed in Florida to improve conservation efforts.

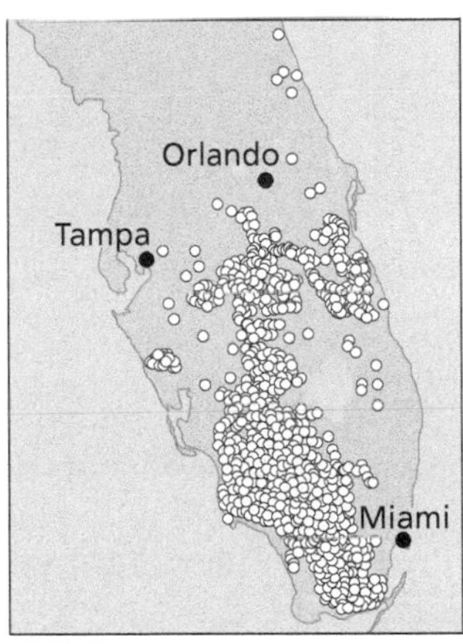


In a study of six Florida panther litters, it was found that the mean litter size was 2.86 kittens, with a standard deviation of 0.82.
(Source: Florida Fish and Wildlife Conservation Commission)

**Construct a 90% confidence interval for the standard deviation of the litter size for Florida panthers. Assume the litter sizes are normally distributed.**

## Confidence Intervals for $\sigma^2$ and $\sigma$

You can use the critical values $\chi_R^2$ and $\chi_L^2$ to construct confidence intervals for a population variance and standard deviation. The best point estimate for the variance is $s^2$ and the best point estimate for the standard deviation is $s$. Because the chi-square distribution is not symmetric, the confidence interval for $\sigma^2$ cannot be written as $s^2 \pm E$. You must perform separate calculations for the endpoints of the confidence interval, as shown in the next definition.

### DEFINITION

The $c$-confidence intervals for the population variance and standard deviation are shown.

**Confidence Interval for $\sigma^2$:**

$$\frac{(n-1)s^2}{\chi_R^2} < \sigma^2 < \frac{(n-1)s^2}{\chi_L^2}$$

**Confidence Interval for $\sigma$:**

$$\sqrt{\frac{(n-1)s^2}{\chi_R^2}} < \sigma < \sqrt{\frac{(n-1)s^2}{\chi_L^2}}$$

The probability that the confidence intervals contain $\sigma^2$ or $\sigma$ is $c$, assuming that the estimation process is repeated a large number of times.

### GUIDELINES

**Constructing a Confidence Interval for a Variance and Standard Deviation**

| In Words | In Symbols |
|---|---|
| **1.** Verify that the population has a normal distribution. | |
| **2.** Identify the sample statistic $n$ and the degrees of freedom. | d.f. $= n - 1$ |
| **3.** Find the point estimate $s^2$. | $s^2 = \dfrac{\Sigma(x-\bar{x})^2}{n-1}$ |
| **4.** Find the critical values $\chi_R^2$ and $\chi_L^2$ that correspond to the given level of confidence $c$ and the degrees of freedom. | Use Table 6 in Appendix B. |
| **5.** Find the left and right endpoints and form the confidence interval for the population variance. | Left Endpoint, Right Endpoint: $\dfrac{(n-1)s^2}{\chi_R^2} < \sigma^2 < \dfrac{(n-1)s^2}{\chi_L^2}$ |
| **6.** Find the confidence interval for the population standard deviation by taking the square root of each endpoint. | Left Endpoint, Right Endpoint: $\sqrt{\dfrac{(n-1)s^2}{\chi_R^2}} < \sigma < \sqrt{\dfrac{(n-1)s^2}{\chi_L^2}}$ |

**EXAMPLE 2**

### Constructing Confidence Intervals

You randomly select and weigh 30 samples of an allergy medicine. The sample standard deviation is 1.20 milligrams. Assuming the weights are normally distributed, construct 99% confidence intervals for the population variance and standard deviation.

**SOLUTION**

The area to the right of $\chi_R^2$ is

$$\text{Area to the right of } \chi_R^2 = \frac{1-c}{2} = \frac{1-0.99}{2} = 0.005$$

and the area to the right of $\chi_L^2$ is

$$\text{Area to the right of } \chi_L^2 = \frac{1+c}{2} = \frac{1+0.99}{2} = 0.995.$$

Using the values $n = 30$, d.f. $= 29$, and $c = 0.99$, the critical values $\chi_R^2$ and $\chi_L^2$ are

$$\chi_R^2 = 52.336 \quad \text{and} \quad \chi_L^2 = 13.121.$$

Using these critical values and $s = 1.20$, the confidence interval for $\sigma^2$ is

Left Endpoint

$$\frac{(n-1)s^2}{\chi_R^2} = \frac{(30-1)(1.20)^2}{52.336} \approx 0.80$$

Right Endpoint

$$\frac{(n-1)s^2}{\chi_L^2} = \frac{(30-1)(1.20)^2}{13.121} \approx 3.18$$

$$0.80 < \sigma^2 < 3.18.$$

The confidence interval for $\sigma$ is

Left Endpoint Right Endpoint

$$\sqrt{\frac{(30-1)(1.20)^2}{52.336}} < \sigma < \sqrt{\frac{(30-1)(1.20)^2}{13.121}}$$

$$0.89 < \sigma < 1.78.$$

You can check your answer using technology, as shown below using Minitab.

**MINITAB**

**Test and CI for One Variance**

| N | StDev | Variance | 99% CI for $\sigma$ using Chi-Square | 99% CI for $\sigma^2$ using Chi-Square |
|---|---|---|---|---|
| 30 | 1.20 | 1.44 | (0.89, 1.78) | (0.80, 3.18) |

***Interpretation*** With 99% confidence, you can say that the population variance is between 0.80 and 3.18, and the population standard deviation is between 0.89 and 1.78 milligrams.

**TRY IT YOURSELF 2**

Construct the 90% and 95% confidence intervals for the population variance and standard deviation of the medicine weights. *Answer: Page A40*

**Study Tip**

When you construct a confidence interval for a population variance or standard deviation, the general *round-off rule* is to round off to the same number of decimal places as the sample variance or standard deviation.

Note in Example 2 that the confidence interval for the population standard deviation *cannot* be written as $s \pm E$ because the confidence interval does not have $s$ as its center. (The same is true for the population variance.)

# 6.4 EXERCISES

For Extra Help: MyLab Statistics

## Building Basic Skills and Vocabulary

1. Does a population have to be normally distributed to use the chi-square distribution?

2. What happens to the shape of the chi-square distribution as the degrees of freedom increase?

**Finding Critical Values for $\chi^2$** *In Exercises 3–8, find the critical values $\chi_R^2$ and $\chi_L^2$ for the level of confidence c and sample size n.*

3. $c = 0.90, n = 8$
4. $c = 0.99, n = 15$
5. $c = 0.95, n = 20$
6. $c = 0.98, n = 26$
7. $c = 0.99, n = 30$
8. $c = 0.80, n = 51$

*In Exercises 9–12, construct the indicated confidence intervals for (a) the population variance $\sigma^2$ and (b) the population standard deviation $\sigma$. Assume the sample is from a normally distributed population.*

9. $c = 0.95, s^2 = 11.56, n = 30$
10. $c = 0.99, s^2 = 0.64, n = 7$
11. $c = 0.90, s = 35, n = 18$
12. $c = 0.98, s = 278.1, n = 41$

## Using and Interpreting Concepts

**Constructing Confidence Intervals** *In Exercises 13–24, assume the sample is from a normally distributed population and construct the indicated confidence intervals for (a) the population variance $\sigma^2$ and (b) the population standard deviation $\sigma$. Interpret the results.*

13. **Bolts** The diameters (in inches) of 18 randomly selected bolts produced by a machine are listed. Use a 95% level of confidence.

4.477 4.425 4.034 4.317 4.003 3.760 3.818 3.749 4.240
3.941 4.131 4.545 3.958 3.741 3.859 3.816 4.448 4.206

14. **Drug Concentration** The times (in minutes) for the drug concentration to peak when the drug epinephrine is injected into 15 randomly selected patients are listed. Use a 90% level of confidence.

4.87 9.67 3.43 8.19 2.92 12.56 19.08 8.70
10.02 9.89 8.37 11.18 6.78 15.55 8.88

15. **Earnings** The annual earnings (in thousands of dollars) of 21 randomly selected level 1 computer hardware engineers are listed. Use a 99% level of confidence. *(Adapted from Salary.com)*

59.4 85.2 86.5 80.2 67.4 79.8 70.8
52.4 69.5 75.4 79.9 65.0 68.8 79.1
61.3 85.4 78.1 72.6 95.5 67.6 76.2

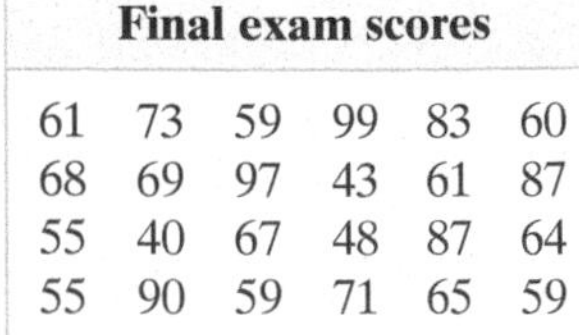

| Final exam scores | | | | | |
|---|---|---|---|---|---|
| 61 | 73 | 59 | 99 | 83 | 60 |
| 68 | 69 | 97 | 43 | 61 | 87 |
| 55 | 40 | 67 | 48 | 87 | 64 |
| 55 | 90 | 59 | 71 | 65 | 59 |

TABLE FOR EXERCISE 16

16. **Final Exam Scores** The final exam scores of 24 randomly selected students in a statistics class are shown in the table at the left. Use a 95% level of confidence.

17. **Space Shuttle Flights** The durations (in days) of 14 randomly selected space shuttle flights have a sample standard deviation of 3.54 days. Use a 99% level of confidence. *(Source: NASA)*

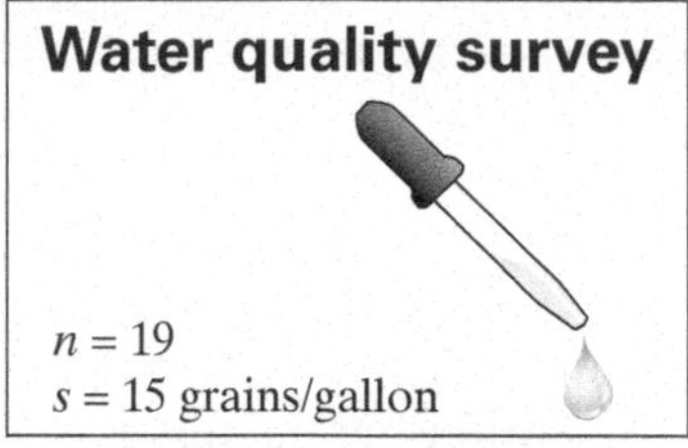


FIGURE FOR EXERCISE 19

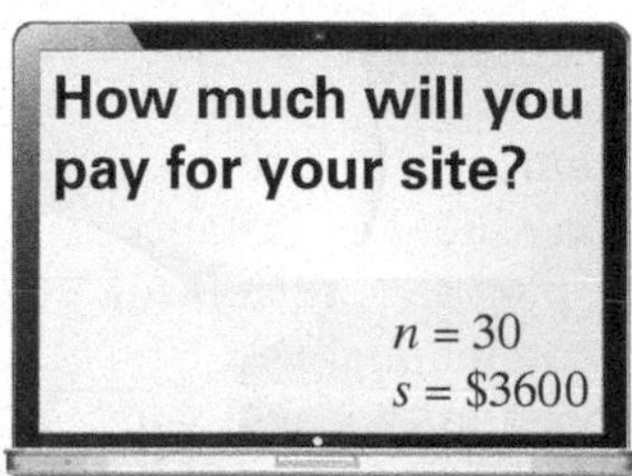


FIGURE FOR EXERCISE 20

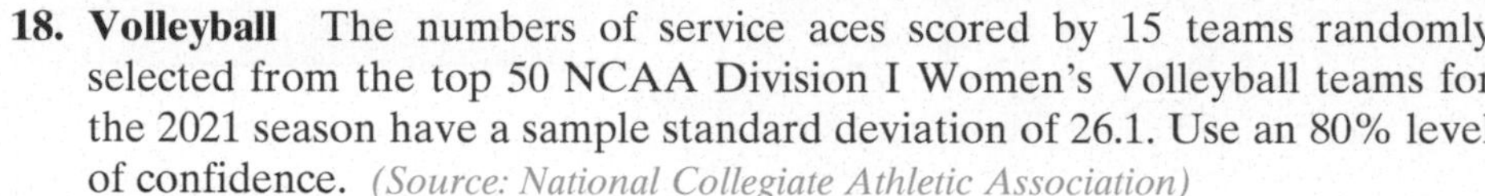

18. **Volleyball** The numbers of service aces scored by 15 teams randomly selected from the top 50 NCAA Division I Women's Volleyball teams for the 2021 season have a sample standard deviation of 26.1. Use an 80% level of confidence. *(Source: National Collegiate Athletic Association)*

19. **Water Quality** As part of a water quality survey, you test the water hardness in several randomly selected streams. The results are shown in the figure at the left. Use a 95% level of confidence.

20. **Website Costs** As part of a survey, you ask a random sample of business owners how much they would be willing to pay for a website for their company. The results are shown in the figure at the left. Use a 90% level of confidence.

21. **Car Batteries** The reserve capacities (in hours) of 18 randomly selected automotive batteries have a sample standard deviation of 0.25 hour. Use an 80% level of confidence.

22. **Annual Precipitation** The annual precipitation amounts (in inches) of a random sample of 61 years for Chicago, Illinois, have a sample standard deviation of 6.46. Use a 98% level of confidence. *(Source: National Oceanic and Atmospheric Administration)*

23. **Drive-Thru Times** The times (in seconds) spent by a random sample of 28 customers in the drive-thru of a fast-food restaurant have a sample standard deviation of 56.1. Use a 98% level of confidence.

24. **Motorcycle Speeds** The times (in seconds) to accelerate from 0 to 60 miles per hour for a random sample of 20 motorcycles have a sample standard deviation of 0.91. Use a 90% level of confidence.

## Extending Concepts

25. **Bolt Diameters** You are analyzing the sample of bolts in Exercise 13. The population standard deviation of the bolts' diameters should be less than 0.5 inch. Does the confidence interval you constructed for $\sigma$ suggest that the variation in the bolts' diameters is at an acceptable level? Explain your reasoning.

26. **Drug Concentration** You are analyzing the times for the drug concentrations to peak in the patients in Exercise 14. The population standard deviation of the times for epinephrine concentrations to peak should be less than 10 minutes. Does the confidence interval you constructed for $\sigma$ suggest that the variation in the times is at an acceptable level? Explain your reasoning.

27. **Battery Reserve Capacities** You are analyzing the sample of car batteries in Exercise 21. The population standard deviation of the batteries' reserve capacities should be less than 0.25 hour. Does the confidence interval you constructed for $\sigma$ suggest that the variation in the batteries' reserve capacities is at an acceptable level? Explain your reasoning.

28. **Drive-Thru Times** You are analyzing the sample of drive-thru times in Exercise 23. The population standard deviation of the drive-thru times should be less than 1 minute. Does the confidence interval you constructed for $\sigma$ suggest that the variation in the drive-thru times is at an acceptable level? Explain your reasoning.

29. In your own words, explain how finding a confidence interval for a population variance is different from finding a confidence interval for a population mean or proportion.

# USES AND ABUSES Statistics in the Real World

## Uses

By now, you know that complete information about population parameters is often not available. The techniques of this chapter can be used to make interval estimates of these parameters so that you can make informed decisions.

From what you learned in this chapter, you know that point estimates (sample statistics) of population parameters are usually close but rarely equal to the actual values of the parameters they are estimating. Remembering this can help you make good decisions in your career and in everyday life. For instance, the results of a survey tell you that 52% of registered voters plan to vote in favor of the rezoning of a portion of a town from residential to commercial use. You know that this is only a point estimate of the actual proportion that will vote in favor of rezoning. If the margin of error is 3%, then the interval estimate is $0.49 < p < 0.55$ and it is possible that the item will not receive a majority vote.

## Abuses

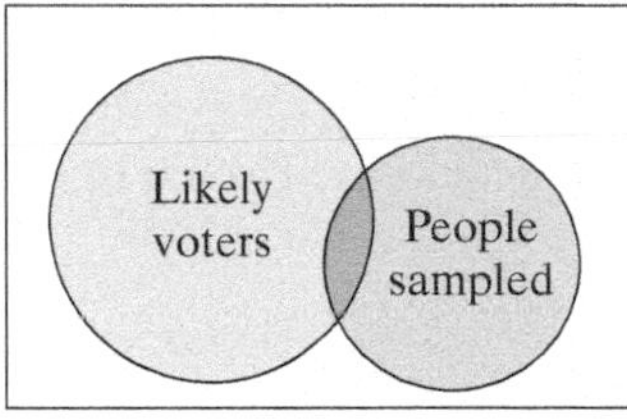


***Unrepresentative Samples*** There are many ways that surveys can result in incorrect predictions. When you read the results of a survey, remember to question the sample size, the sampling technique, and the questions asked. For instance, you want to know the proportion of people who will vote in favor of rezoning. From the diagram at the left, you can see that even when your sample is large enough, it may not consist of people who are likely to vote.

***Biased Survey Questions*** In surveys, it is also important to analyze the wording of the questions. For instance, the question about rezoning might be presented as: "Knowing that rezoning will result in more businesses contributing to school taxes, would you support the rezoning?"

***Misinterpreted Polls*** Some political pundits and voters vowed never to trust polls again after they failed to predict Donald Trump's win over Hillary Clinton in the 2016 U.S. presidential election. However, nationwide polls the week of the election were only off by about 1%—the polls showed Clinton ahead by about 3% and she ended up ahead in votes by about 2%.

Many state polls were inaccurate, most of them in the same direction, with Trump receiving up to 10% more of the vote than expected in some states. This was enough to give him the majority of electoral votes and the presidency. Analysts had a variety of theories why some polls underpredicted Trump's performance in 2016 and to a lesser extent in 2020.

### EXERCISES

1. ***Unrepresentative Samples*** Find an example of a survey that is reported in a newspaper, in a magazine, or on a website. Describe different ways that the sample could have been unrepresentative of the population.

2. ***Biased Survey Questions*** Find an example of a survey that is reported in a newspaper, in a magazine, or on a website. Describe different ways that the survey questions could have been biased.

3. ***Misinterpreted Polls*** Determine whether each state election poll below was misleading. Assume the margin of error is 4% for each poll.
   (a) Michigan poll leader: Clinton by 3.4%; Election winner: Trump by 0.3%
   (b) Wisconsin poll leader: Clinton by 6.5%; Election winner: Trump by 0.7%

# 6 Chapter Summary

| What Did You Learn? | Example(s) | Review Exercises |
|---|---|---|
| **Section 6.1** | | |
| ▶ How to find a point estimate and a margin of error | 1, 2 | 1, 2 |
| ▶ How to construct and interpret confidence intervals for a population mean when $\sigma$ is known | 3–5 | 3–6 |
| ▶ How to determine the minimum sample size required when estimating a population mean | 6 | 7, 8 |
| **Section 6.2** | | |
| ▶ How to interpret the $t$-distribution and use a $t$-distribution table | 1 | 9–12 |
| ▶ How to construct and interpret confidence intervals for a population mean when $\sigma$ is not known | 2–4 | 13–18 |
| **Section 6.3** | | |
| ▶ How to find a point estimate for a population proportion | 1 | 19–24 |
| ▶ How to construct and interpret confidence intervals for a population proportion | 2, 3 | 19–24 |
| ▶ How to determine the minimum sample size required when estimating a population proportion | 4 | 25, 26 |
| **Section 6.4** | | |
| ▶ How to interpret the chi-square distribution and use a chi-square distribution table | 1 | 27–30 |
| ▶ How to construct and interpret confidence intervals for a population variance and standard deviation | 2 | 31, 32 |

## Study Strategies

**Taking a Test** Test taking can be stressful. Here are some things you can do to improve your performance on tests.

- Arrive at the test site early.
- As soon as you receive the test, preview it. Write down things you may have difficulty remembering, such as formulas, on the back of the test.
- Answer problems you know how to solve first.
- Next, attempt the problems that may be a challenge for you. Do not entirely skip them. Receiving partial credit is better than receiving no credit.
- Read the test problems carefully. Pay particular attention to wording in test problems that could cause confusion, such as "at least" or "no more than."
- If the test is multiple choice, decide what the answer should be before reading the choices. Sometimes, you may have to make an educated guess. You may be able to eliminate answers that are obviously wrong or test each answer.
- Check your progress. Try to have more than half of the test completed before half of the allotted time has passed.
- However, take your time. Do not be concerned about being the last student to finish.
- As soon as you complete the test, review it. Correct any mistakes you find.

For more information, visit Skills for Success in the accompanying MyLab course.

# 6 Review Exercises

| Waking times (in minutes past 5:00 A.M.) | | | | | | |
|---|---|---|---|---|---|---|
| 135 | 145 | 95 | 140 | 135 | 95 | 110 |
| 50 | 90 | 165 | 110 | 125 | 80 | 125 |
| 130 | 110 | 25 | 75 | 65 | 100 | 60 |
| 125 | 115 | 135 | 95 | 90 | 140 | 40 |
| 75 | 50 | 130 | 85 | 100 | 160 | 135 |
| 45 | 135 | 115 | 75 | 130 | | |

TABLE FOR EXERCISE 1

| Driving distances to work (in miles) | | | | | |
|---|---|---|---|---|---|
| 12 | 9 | 7 | 2 | 8 | 7 |
| 3 | 27 | 21 | 10 | 13 | 7 |
| 2 | 30 | 7 | 6 | 13 | 6 |
| 4 | 1 | 10 | 3 | 13 | 6 |
| 2 | 9 | 2 | 12 | 16 | 18 |

TABLE FOR EXERCISE 2

## Section 6.1

**1.** The waking times (in minutes past 5:00 A.M.) of 40 people who start work at 8:00 A.M. are shown in the table at the left. Assume the population standard deviation is 45 minutes. Find (a) the point estimate of the population mean $\mu$ and (b) the margin of error for a 90% confidence interval.

**2.** The driving distances (in miles) to work of 30 people are shown in the table at the left. Assume the population standard deviation is 8 miles. Find (a) the point estimate of the population mean $\mu$ and (b) the margin of error for a 95% confidence interval.

**3.** (a) Construct a 90% confidence interval for the population mean in Exercise 1. Interpret the results. (b) Does it seem likely that the population mean could be within 10% of the sample mean? Explain.

**4.** (a) Construct a 95% confidence interval for the population mean in Exercise 2. Interpret the results. (b) Does it seem likely that the population mean could be greater than 12.5 miles? Explain.

*In Exercises 5 and 6, use the confidence interval to find the margin of error and the sample mean.*

**5.** (20.75, 24.10)

**6.** (7.428, 7.562)

**7.** Determine the minimum sample size required to be 95% confident that the sample mean waking time is within 10 minutes of the population mean waking time. Use the population standard deviation from Exercise 1.

**8.** Determine the minimum sample size required to be 99% confident that the sample mean driving distance to work is within 2 miles of the population mean driving distance to work. Use the population standard deviation from Exercise 2.

## Section 6.2

*In Exercises 9–12, find the critical value $t_c$ for the level of confidence c and sample size n.*

**9.** $c = 0.80, n = 10$

**10.** $c = 0.95, n = 24$

**11.** $c = 0.98, n = 15$

**12.** $c = 0.99, n = 30$

*In Exercises 13–16, (a) find the margin of error for the values of c, s, and n, and (b) construct the confidence interval for $\mu$ using the t-distribution. Assume the population is normally distributed.*

**13.** $c = 0.90, s = 25.6, n = 16, \bar{x} = 72.1$

**14.** $c = 0.95, s = 1.1, n = 25, \bar{x} = 3.5$

**15.** $c = 0.98, s = 0.9, n = 12, \bar{x} = 6.8$

**16.** $c = 0.99, s = 16.5, n = 20, \bar{x} = 25.2$

**17.** In a random sample of 36 top-rated roller coasters, the average height is 165 feet and the standard deviation is 67 feet. Construct a 90% confidence interval for $\mu$. Interpret the results. *(Source: POP World Media, LLC)*

**18.** You research the heights of top-rated roller coasters and find that the population mean is 160 feet. In Exercise 17, does the *t*-value fall between $-t_{0.95}$ and $t_{0.95}$?

## Section 6.3

*In Exercises 19–22, let p be the population proportion for the situation. (a) Find point estimates of p and q, (b) construct 90% and 95% confidence intervals for p, and (c) interpret the results of part (b) and compare the widths of the confidence intervals.*

**19.** In a survey of 912 U.S. adults in Generation Z (born after 1996), 383 said they are at least somewhat likely to consider an electric vehicle for their next vehicle purchase. *(Adapted from Pew Research Center)*

**20.** In a survey of 13,749 U.S. adults, 5362 said they are at least somewhat likely to consider an electric vehicle for their next vehicle purchase. *(Adapted from Pew Research Center)*

**21.** In a survey of 73,901 college graduates, 23,991 obtained a postgraduate degree. *(Adapted from Gallup)*

**22.** In a survey of 2223 U.S. adults, 1334 say an occupation as an athlete is prestigious. *(Adapted from The Harris Poll)*

**23.** In Exercise 19, would it be unusual for the population proportion to be 38%? Explain.

**24.** In Exercise 22, would it be unusual for the population proportion to be 58%? Explain.

**25.** You wish to estimate, with 95% confidence, the population proportion of U.S. adults who have taken or planned to take a winter vacation in a recent year. Your estimate must be accurate within 5% of the population proportion.

(a) No preliminary estimate is available. Find the minimum sample size needed.

(b) Find the minimum sample size needed, using a prior study that found that 32% of U.S. adults have taken or planned to take a winter vacation in a recent year. *(Source: Rasmussen Reports)*

(c) Compare the results from parts (a) and (b).

**26.** In Exercise 25(b), would a sample size of 369 be acceptable? Explain.

## Section 6.4

*In Exercises 27–30, find the critical values $\chi^2_R$ and $\chi^2_L$ for the level of confidence c and sample size n.*

**27.** $c = 0.95, n = 13$

**28.** $c = 0.98, n = 25$

**29.** $c = 0.90, n = 16$

**30.** $c = 0.99, n = 10$

*In Exercises 31 and 32, assume the sample is from a normally distributed population and construct the indicated confidence intervals for (a) the population variance $\sigma^2$ and (b) the population standard deviation $\sigma$. Interpret the results.*

**31.** The number of field goals attempted by LeBron James in 13 randomly selected games of a recent NBA basketball season are listed. Use a 95% level of confidence. *(Source: Basketball Reference)*

26 13 25 22 13 15 16 20 15 13 26 23 20

**32.** The average weekly hours worked by service employees in the leisure and hospitality industry during a recent period of 31 months are listed. Use a 98% level of confidence. *(Source: U.S. Bureau of Labor Statistics)*

25.1 24.7 24.8 24.7 24.8 24.9 24.8 24.9 24.8 24.8 24.7
24.8 24.9 24.9 24.7 25.0 24.9 24.9 24.9 25.0 24.9
24.9 24.8 24.8 24.8 24.8 24.9 24.8 24.9 24.7 24.6

# Chapter Quiz

*Take this quiz as you would take a quiz in class. After you are done, check your work against the answers given in the back of the book.*

| Women's Open Division winning times (in hours) | | | | |
|---|---|---|---|---|
| 2.42 | 2.38 | 2.44 | 2.67 | 2.44 |
| 2.57 | 2.39 | 2.49 | 2.39 | 2.41 |
| 2.49 | 2.40 | 2.42 | 2.53 | 2.39 |
| 2.45 | 2.44 | 2.54 | 2.49 | 2.42 |

TABLE FOR EXERCISE 1

**1.** The winning times (in hours) for a sample of 20 randomly selected Boston Marathon Women's Open Division champions from 1980 to 2019 are shown in the table at the left. Assume the population standard deviation is 0.068 hour. *(Source: Boston Athletic Association)*

(a) Find the point estimate of the population mean.

(b) Find the margin of error for a 95% confidence level.

(c) Construct a 95% confidence interval for the population mean. Interpret the results.

(d) Does it seem likely that the population mean could be greater than 2.52 hours? Explain.

**2.** You wish to estimate the mean winning time for Boston Marathon Women's Open Division champions. The estimate must be within 2 minutes of the population mean. Determine the minimum sample size required to construct a 99% confidence interval for the population mean. Use the population standard deviation from Exercise 1.

**3.** The data set represents the amounts of time (in minutes) spent checking email for a random sample of employees at a company.

7.5 2.0 12.1 8.8 9.4 7.3 1.9 2.8 7.0 7.3

(a) Find the sample mean and the sample standard deviation.

(b) Construct a 90% confidence interval for the population mean. Interpret the results. Assume the times are normally distributed.

(c) Repeat part (b), assuming $\sigma = 3.5$ minutes. Compare the results.

**4.** In a random sample of 12 senior-level civil engineers, the mean annual earnings were \$133,326 and the standard deviation was \$36,729. Assume the annual earnings are normally distributed and construct a 95% confidence interval for the population mean annual earnings for senior-level civil engineers. Interpret the results. *(Adapted from Salary.com)*

**5.** You research the salaries of senior-level civil engineers and find that the population mean is \$131,935. In Exercise 4, does the $t$-value fall between $-t_{0.95}$ and $t_{0.95}$?

**6.** In a survey of 1010 U.S. adults, 838 say that the energy situation in the United States is very or fairly serious. *(Adapted from Gallup)*

(a) Find the point estimate for the population proportion.

(b) Construct a 90% confidence interval for the population proportion. Interpret the results.

(c) Would it be unusual for the population proportion to be between 90% and 95% of the point estimate? Explain.

(d) Find the minimum sample size needed to estimate the population proportion at the 99% confidence level to ensure that the estimate is accurate within 4% of the population proportion.

**7.** Refer to the data set in Exercise 3. Assume the population of times spent checking email is normally distributed. Construct a 95% confidence interval for (a) the population variance and (b) the population standard deviation. Interpret the results.

# 6 Chapter Test

*Take this test as you would take a test in class.*

1. In a survey of 2096 U.S. adults, 1740 think football teams of all levels should require players who suffer a head injury to take a set amount of time off from playing to recover. *(Adapted from The Harris Poll)*
   (a) Find the point estimate for the population proportion.
   (b) Construct a 95% confidence interval for the population proportion. Interpret the results.
   (c) Would it be unusual for the population mean to be 80%? Explain.
   (d) Find the minimum sample size needed to estimate the population proportion at the 99% confidence level to ensure that the estimate is accurate within 3% of the population proportion.

2. The data set represents the weights (in pounds) of 10 randomly selected black bears from northeast Pennsylvania. Assume the weights are normally distributed. *(Source: Pennsylvania Game Commission)*

   170 225 183 137 287 191 268 185 211 284

   (a) Find the sample mean and the sample standard deviation.
   (b) Construct a 95% confidence interval for the population mean. Interpret the results.
   (c) Construct a 99% confidence interval for the population standard deviation. Interpret the results.

3. The data set represents the scores of 12 randomly selected students on the SAT Physics Subject Test. Assume the population test scores are normally distributed and the population standard deviation is 108. *(Adapted from The College Board)*

   590 650 730 560 460 400 620 780 510 700 590 670

   (a) Find the point estimate of the population mean.
   (b) Construct a 90% confidence interval for the population mean. Interpret the results.
   (c) Would it be unusual for the population mean to be under 575? Explain.
   (d) Determine the minimum sample size required to be 95% confident that the sample mean test score is within 10 points of the population mean test score.

4. Use the standard normal distribution or the $t$-distribution to construct the indicated confidence interval for the population mean of each data set. Justify your decision. If neither distribution can be used, explain why. Interpret the results.
   (a) In a random sample of 40 patients, the mean waiting time at a dentist's office was 20 minutes and the standard deviation was 7.5 minutes. Construct a 95% confidence interval for the population mean.
   (b) In a random sample of 15 cereal boxes, the mean weight was 11.89 ounces. Assume the weights of the cereal boxes are normally distributed and the population standard deviation is 0.05 ounce. Construct a 90% confidence interval for the population mean.

# REAL STATISTICS REAL DECISIONS

# Putting it all together

The Safe Drinking Water Act, which was passed in 1974, allows the Environmental Protection Agency (EPA) to regulate the levels of contaminants in drinking water. The EPA requires that water utilities give their customers water quality reports annually. These reports include the results of daily water quality monitoring, which is performed to determine whether drinking water is safe for consumption.

A water department tests for contaminants at water treatment plants and at customers' taps. These contaminants include microorganisms, organic chemicals, and inorganic chemicals, such as cyanide. Cyanide's presence in drinking water is the result of discharges from steel, plastics, and fertilizer factories. For drinking water, the maximum contaminant level of cyanide is 0.2 part per million.

As part of your job for your city's water department, you are preparing a report that includes an analysis of the results shown in the figure at the right. The figure shows the point estimates for the population mean concentration and the 95% confidence intervals for $\mu$ for cyanide over a three-year period. The data are based on random water samples taken by the city's three water treatment plants.

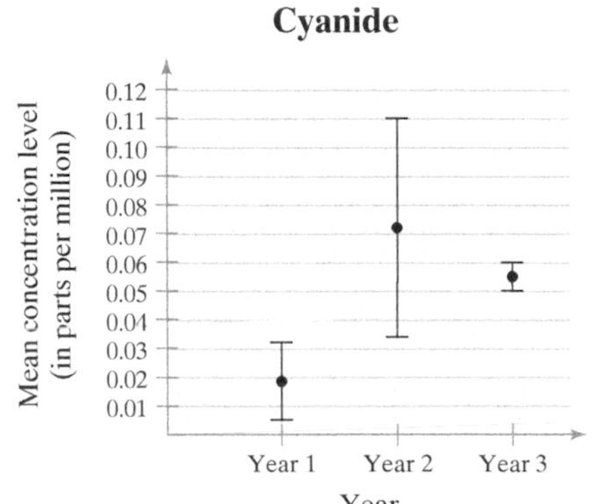


## EXERCISES

1. ***Interpreting the Results***

   Use the figure to determine whether there has been a change in the mean concentration level of cyanide for each time period. Explain your reasoning.

   (a) From Year 1 to Year 2
   (b) From Year 2 to Year 3
   (c) From Year 1 to Year 3

2. ***What Can You Conclude?***

   Using the results of Exercise 1, what can you conclude about the concentrations of cyanide in the drinking water?

3. ***What Do You Think?***

   The confidence interval for Year 2 is much larger than that for the other years. What do you think may have caused this larger confidence level?

4. ***How Can You Improve the Report?***

   What can the water department do to decrease the size of the confidence intervals, regardless of the amount of variance in cyanide levels?

5. ***How Do You Think They Did It?***

   How do you think the water department constructed the 95% confidence intervals for the population mean concentration of cyanide in the water? Include answers to the questions below in your explanation.

   (a) What sampling distribution do you think they used? Why?
   (b) Do you think they used the population standard deviation in calculating the margin of error? Why or why not? If not, what could they have used?

# TECHNOLOGY

MINITAB EXCEL TI-84 PLUS

# United States Foreign Policy Polls

## THE GALLUP ORGANIZATION

www.gallup.com

Since 1935, the Gallup Organization has conducted public opinion polls in the United States and around the world. The table shows the results of Gallup's World Affairs Poll of 2021, in which 1021 U.S. adults were polled. The remaining percentages not shown in the results are adults who were not sure.

| Question | Results |
|---|---|
| Do you view foreign trade as more of an economic *opportunity* or a *threat?* | Opportunity: 63%<br>Threat: 32% |
| In the Israeli-Palestinian conflict, are your sympathies more with the Israelis or the Palestinians? | Israelis: 58%<br>Palestinians: 25% |
| How much of a threat do you feel the economic power of China is to the United States? | Critical or important: 93%<br>Not important: 7% |
| Are you satisfied with the position of the United States in the world today? | Satisfied: 37%<br>Dissatisfied: 62% |

### EXERCISES

**1.** Use technology to find a 95% confidence interval for the population proportion of adults who

(a) view foreign trade as an economic opportunity.

(b) sympathize more with the Israelis than the Palestinians.

(c) feel China's economic power is a critical or an important threat to the United States.

(d) are satisfied with the position of the United States in the world today.

(e) do not sympathize with either the Israelis or the Palestinians more than the other.

**2.** Find the minimum sample size needed to estimate, with 95% confidence, the population proportion of adults who feel that China's economic power is a critical or an important economic threat to the United States. Your estimate must be accurate within 2% of the population proportion.

**3.** Use technology to simulate a poll. Assume that the actual population proportion of adults who view foreign trade as more of an economic opportunity than a threat is 66%. Run the simulation several times using $n = 1527$.

(a) What was the least value you obtained for $\hat{p}$?

(b) What was the greatest value you obtained for $\hat{p}$?

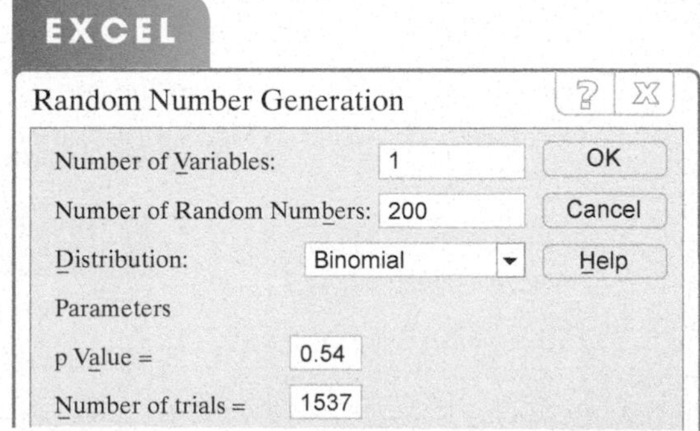


**4.** Is it probable that the population proportion of adults who view foreign trade as more of an economic opportunity than a threat is 66%? Explain your reasoning.

Extended solutions are given in the technology manuals that accompany this text. Technical instruction is provided for Minitab, Excel, and the TI-84 Plus.

# 6 Using Technology to Construct Confidence Intervals

Here are some Minitab and TI-84 Plus printouts for some examples in this chapter. Answers may be slightly different because of rounding.

See Example 3, page 301.

| | | | | | | | | | |
|---|---|---|---|---|---|---|---|---|---|
| 19 | 18 | 18 | 15 | 21 | 21 | 23 | 20 | 21 | 19 |
| 16 | 19 | 22 | 15 | 19 | 24 | 20 | 24 | 20 | 17 |
| 18 | 17 | 19 | 20 | 20 | 20 | 22 | 24 | 22 | 23 |
| 23 | 21 | 22 | 20 | 17 | 21 | 16 | 18 | 18 | 25 |

Display Descriptive Statistics...
Store Descriptive Statistics...
Graphical Summary...

**1-Sample Z...**
1-Sample t...
2-Sample t...
Paired t...

1 Proportion...
2 Proportions...

**MINITAB**

**One-Sample Z: Hours**

**Descriptive Statistics**

| N | Mean | StDev | SE Mean | 95% CI for μ |
|---|---|---|---|---|
| 40 | 19.925 | 2.556 | 0.379 | (19.181, 20.669) |

*μ: population mean of Hours*
*Known standard deviation = 2.4*

See Example 2, page 312.

Display Descriptive Statistics...
Store Descriptive Statistics...
Graphical Summary...

1-Sample Z...
**1-Sample t...**
2-Sample t...
Paired t...

1 Proportion...
2 Proportions...

**MINITAB**

**One-Sample T**

**Descriptive Statistics**

| N | Mean | StDev | SE Mean | 95% CI for μ |
|---|---|---|---|---|
| 16 | 162.00 | 10.00 | 2.50 | (156.67, 167.33) |

*μ: population mean of Sample*

See Example 2, page 322.

Display Descriptive Statistics...
Store Descriptive Statistics...
Graphical Summary...

1-Sample Z...
1-Sample t...
2-Sample t...
Paired t...

**1 Proportion...**
2 Proportions...

**MINITAB**

**Test and CI for One Proportion**

**Method**

p: event proportion
Exact method is used for this analysis.

**Descriptive Statistics**

| N | Event | Sample p | 95% CI for p |
|---|---|---|---|
| 540 | 378 | 0.700000 | (0.661, 0.739) |

See Example 5, page 303.

**TI-84 PLUS**

EDIT CALC **TESTS**
1: Z–Test...
2: T–Test...
3: 2–SampZTest...
4: 2–SampTTest...
5: 1–PropZTest...
6: 2–PropZTest...
**7↓** ZInterval...

**TI-84 PLUS**

**ZInterval**
Inpt:Data **Stats**
$\sigma$:1.5
$\bar{x}$:22.9
n:20
C–Level:.9
Calculate

**TI-84 PLUS**

**ZInterval**
(22.348, 23.452)
$\bar{x}$=22.9
n=20

See Example 3, page 313.

**TI-84 PLUS**

EDIT CALC **TESTS**
2↑ T–Test...
3: 2–SampZTest...
4: 2–SampTTest...
5: 1–PropZTest...
6: 2–PropZTest...
7: ZInterval...
**8↓** TInterval...

**TI-84 PLUS**

**TInterval**
Inpt:Data **Stats**
$\bar{x}$:9.75
Sx:2.39
n:36
C–Level:.99
Calculate

**TI-84 PLUS**

**TInterval**
(8.665, 10.835)
$\bar{x}$=9.75
Sx=2.39
n=36

See Example 2, page 322.

**TI-84 PLUS**

EDIT CALC **TESTS**
5↑ 1–PropZTest...
6: 2–PropZTest...
7: ZInterval...
8: TInterval...
9: 2–SampZInt...
0: 2–SampTInt...
**A↓** 1–PropZInt...

**TI-84 PLUS**

**1-PropZInt**
x:378
n:540
C–Level:.95
Calculate

**TI-84 PLUS**

**1-PropZInt**
(.66135, .73865)
$\hat{p}$=.7
n=540

CHAPTER 7

# Hypothesis Testing with One Sample

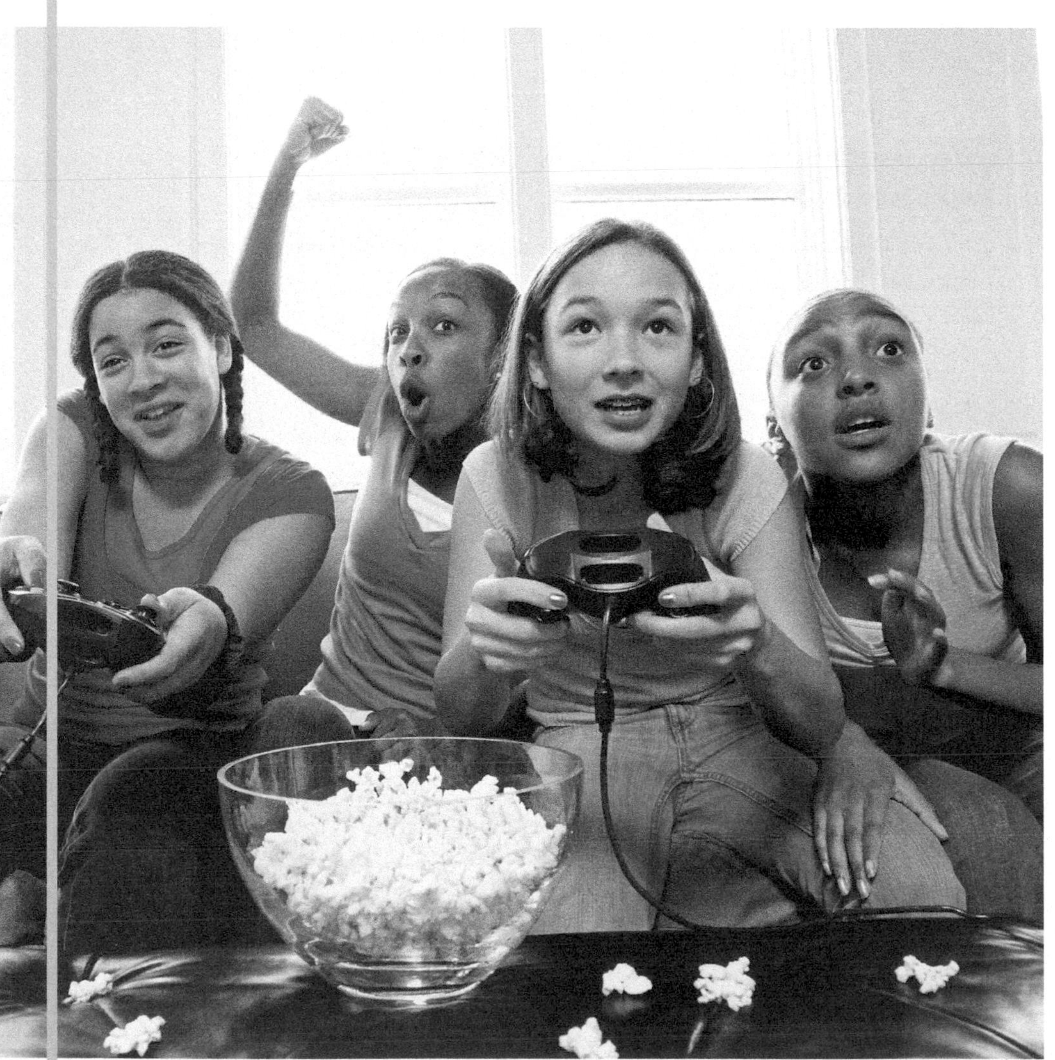

The Entertainment Software Rating Board (ESRB) assigns ratings to video games to indicate the appropriate ages for players. These ratings include E (everyone), E10+ (everyone 10+), T (teen), M (mature), and AO (adults only).

## Where You've Been

In Chapter 6, you began your study of inferential statistics. There, you learned how to form a confidence interval to estimate a population parameter, such as the proportion of people in the United States who agree with a certain statement. For instance, in a nationwide poll conducted by Pew Research Center, 2001 U.S. adults were asked whether they agreed or disagreed with the statement, "People who play violent video games are more likely to be violent themselves." Out of those surveyed, 800 adults agreed with the statement.

You have learned how to use these results to state with 95% confidence that the population proportion of U.S. adults who agree that people who play violent video games are more likely to be violent themselves is between 37.9% and 42.1%.

## Where You're Going

In this chapter, you will continue your study of inferential statistics. But now, instead of making an estimate about a population parameter, you will learn how to test a claim about a parameter.

For instance, suppose that you work for Pew Research Center and are asked to test a claim that the proportion of U.S. adults who agree that people who play violent video games are more likely to be violent themselves is $p = 0.35$. To test the claim, you take a random sample of $n = 2001$ U.S. adults and find that 800 of them think that people who play violent video games are more likely to be violent themselves. Your sample statistic is $\hat{p} \approx 0.400$.

Is your sample statistic different enough from the claim ($p = 0.35$) to decide that the claim is false? The answer lies in the sampling distribution of sample proportions taken from a population in which $p = 0.35$. The figure below shows that your sample statistic is more than 4 standard errors from the claimed value. If the claim is true, then the probability of the sample statistic being 4 standard errors or more from the claimed value is extremely small. Something is wrong! If your sample was truly random, then you can conclude that the actual proportion of the adult population is not 0.35. In other words, you tested the original claim (hypothesis), and you decided to reject it.

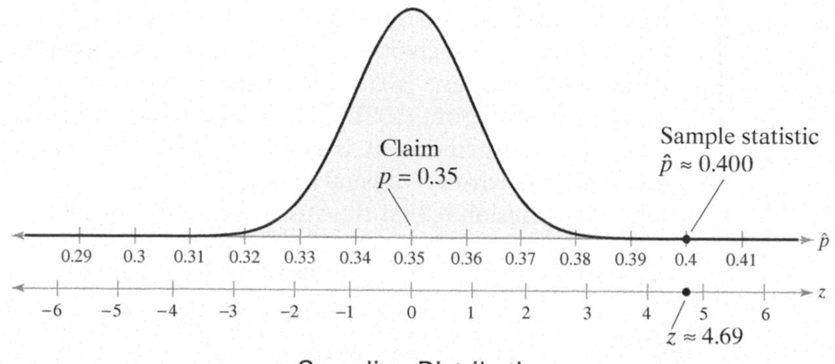

Sampling Distribution

# 7.1 Introduction to Hypothesis Testing

## What You Should Learn

- A practical introduction to hypothesis tests
- How to state a null hypothesis and an alternative hypothesis
- How to identify type I and type II errors and interpret the level of significance
- How to know whether to use a one-tailed or two-tailed statistical test and find a *P*-value
- How to make and interpret a decision based on the results of a statistical test
- How to write a claim for a hypothesis test

Hypothesis Tests ■ Stating a Hypothesis ■ Types of Errors and Level of Significance ■ Statistical Tests and *P*-Values ■ Making a Decision and Interpreting the Decision ■ Strategies for Hypothesis Testing

## Hypothesis Tests

Throughout the remainder of this text, you will study an important technique in inferential statistics called hypothesis testing. A **hypothesis test** is a process that uses sample statistics to test a claim about the value of a population parameter. Researchers in fields such as medicine, psychology, and business rely on hypothesis testing to make informed decisions about new medicines, treatments, and marketing strategies.

For instance, consider a manufacturer that advertises its new hybrid car has a mean gas mileage of 50 miles per gallon. If you suspect that the mean mileage is not 50 miles per gallon, how could you show that the advertisement is false?

Obviously, you cannot test *all* the vehicles, but you can still make a reasonable decision about the mean gas mileage by taking a random sample from the population of vehicles and measuring the mileage of each. If the sample mean differs enough from the advertisement's mean, you can decide that the advertisement is wrong.

For instance, to test that the mean gas mileage of all hybrid vehicles of this type is $\mu = 50$ miles per gallon, you take a random sample of $n = 30$ vehicles and measure the mileage of each. You obtain a sample mean of $\bar{x} = 47$ miles per gallon with a sample standard deviation of $s = 5.5$ miles per gallon. Does this indicate that the manufacturer's advertisement is false?

To decide, you do something unusual—*you assume the advertisement is correct.* That is, you assume that $\mu = 50$. Then, you examine the sampling distribution of sample means (with $n = 30$) taken from a population in which $\mu = 50$ and $\sigma = 5.5$. From the Central Limit Theorem, you know this sampling distribution is normal with a mean of 50 and standard error of

$$\frac{5.5}{\sqrt{30}} \approx 1.$$

In the figure below, notice that the sample mean of $\bar{x} = 47$ miles per gallon is highly unlikely—it is about 3 standard errors ($z \approx -2.99$) from the claimed mean. Using the techniques you studied in Chapter 5, you can determine that if the advertisement is true, then the probability of obtaining a sample mean of 47 or less is about 0.001. This is an unusual event. Your assumption that the company's advertisement is correct has led you to an improbable result. So, either you had a very unusual sample, or the advertisement is probably false. The logical conclusion is that the advertisement is probably false.

### Study Tip

As you study this chapter, do not get confused regarding concepts of certainty and importance. For instance, even if you are very certain that the mean gas mileage of a type of hybrid vehicle is not 50 miles per gallon, the actual mean mileage might be very close to this value and the difference might not be important.

**Sampling Distribution of $\bar{x}$**

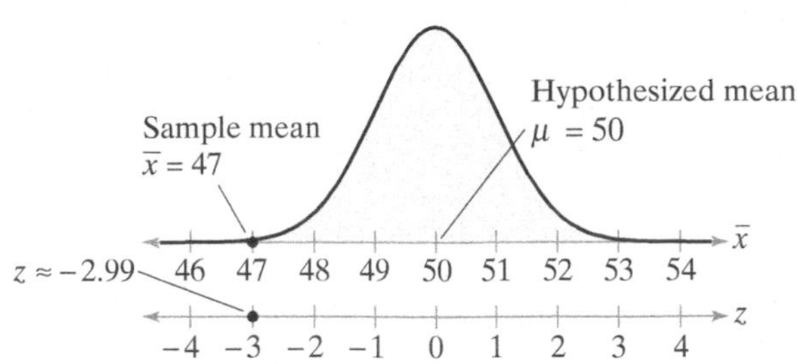

## Stating a Hypothesis

A statement about a population parameter is called a **statistical hypothesis.** To test a population parameter, you should carefully state a pair of hypotheses—one that represents the claim and the other, its complement. When one of these hypotheses is false, the other must be true. Either hypothesis—the **null hypothesis** or the **alternative hypothesis**—may represent the original claim.

### Study Tip

The term *null hypothesis* was introduced by Ronald Fisher (see page 35). If the statement in the null hypothesis is not true, then the alternative hypothesis must be true.

### DEFINITION

1. A **null hypothesis** $H_0$ is a statistical hypothesis that contains a statement of equality, such as $\leq$, $=$, or $\geq$.
2. The **alternative hypothesis** $H_a$ is the complement of the null hypothesis. It is a statement that must be true if $H_0$ is false and it contains a statement of strict inequality, such as $>$, $\neq$, or $<$.

The symbol $H_0$ is read as "H sub-zero" or "H naught" and $H_a$ is read as "H sub-a."

To write the null and alternative hypotheses, translate the claim made about the population parameter from a verbal statement to a mathematical statement. Then, write its complement. For instance, if the claim value is $k$ and the population parameter is $\mu$, then some possible pairs of null and alternative hypotheses are

$$\begin{cases} H_0: \mu \leq k \\ H_a: \mu > k \end{cases}, \quad \begin{cases} H_0: \mu \geq k \\ H_a: \mu < k \end{cases}, \quad \text{and} \quad \begin{cases} H_0: \mu = k \\ H_a: \mu \neq k \end{cases}.$$

### Picturing the World

A study was done on the effect of a drug for the treatment of obesity due to genetic variants. The study used a random sample of 35 patients with severe obesity. At the end of the study, the patients had a mean reduction in baseline body weight of 3.7%. So, it is claimed that the mean reduction in baseline body weight is 3.7% for all patients with severe obesity who take the drug. (Adapted from Rhythm Pharmaceuticals, Inc.)

**Determine a null hypothesis and alternative hypothesis for this claim.**

Regardless of which of the three pairs of hypotheses you use, you always assume $\mu = k$ and examine the sampling distribution on the basis of this assumption. Within this sampling distribution, you will determine whether or not a sample statistic is unusual.

The table shows the relationship between possible verbal statements about the parameter $\mu$ and the corresponding null and alternative hypotheses. Similar statements can be made to test other population parameters, such as $p$, $\sigma$, or $\sigma^2$.

| **Verbal Statement $H_0$** *The mean is . . .* | **Mathematical Statements** | **Verbal Statement $H_a$** *The mean is . . .* |
|---|---|---|
| *. . . greater than or equal to k.*<br>*. . . at least k.*<br>*. . . not less than k.*<br>*. . . not shorter than k.* | $\begin{cases} H_0: \mu \geq k \\ H_a: \mu < k \end{cases}$ | *. . . less than k.*<br>*. . . below k.*<br>*. . . fewer than k.*<br>*. . . shorter than k.* |
| *. . . less than or equal to k.*<br>*. . . at most k.*<br>*. . . not more than k.*<br>*. . . not longer than k.* | $\begin{cases} H_0: \mu \leq k \\ H_a: \mu > k \end{cases}$ | *. . . greater than k.*<br>*. . . above k.*<br>*. . . more than k.*<br>*. . . longer than k.* |
| *. . . equal to k.*<br>*. . . k.*<br>*. . . exactly k.*<br>*. . . the same as k.*<br>*. . . not changed from k.* | $\begin{cases} H_0: \mu = k \\ H_a: \mu \neq k \end{cases}$ | *. . . not equal to k.*<br>*. . . different from k.*<br>*. . . not k.*<br>*. . . different from k.*<br>*. . . changed from k.* |

## EXAMPLE 1

### Stating the Null and Alternative Hypotheses

Write each claim as a mathematical statement. State the null and alternative hypotheses, and identify which represents the claim.

1. A school publicizes that the proportion of its students who are involved in at least one extracurricular activity is 61%.
2. A car dealership announces that the mean time for an oil change is less than 15 minutes.
3. A company advertises that the mean life of its furnaces is more than 18 years.

**SOLUTION**

1. The claim "the proportion . . . is 61%" can be written as $p = 0.61$. Its complement is $p \neq 0.61$, as shown in the figure at the left. Because $p = 0.61$ contains the statement of equality, it becomes the null hypothesis. In this case, the null hypothesis represents the claim. You can write the null and alternative hypotheses as shown.

   $H_0$: $p = 0.61$ (Claim)

   $H_a$: $p \neq 0.61$

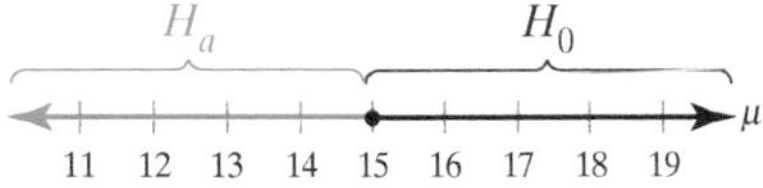

2. The claim "the mean . . . is less than 15 minutes" can be written as $\mu < 15$. Its complement is $\mu \geq 15$, as shown in the figure at the left. Because $\mu \geq 15$ contains the statement of equality, it becomes the null hypothesis. In this case, the alternative hypothesis represents the claim. You can write the null and alternative hypotheses as shown.

   $H_0$: $\mu \geq 15$ minutes

   $H_a$: $\mu < 15$ minutes (Claim)

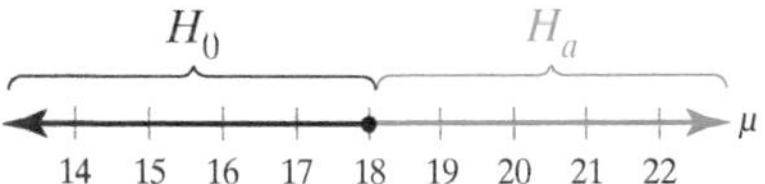

3. The claim "the mean . . . is more than 18 years" can be written as $\mu > 18$. Its complement is $\mu \leq 18$, as shown in the figure at the left. Because $\mu \leq 18$ contains the statement of equality, it becomes the null hypothesis. In this case, the alternative hypothesis represents the claim. You can write the null and alternative hypotheses as shown.

   $H_0$: $\mu \leq 18$ years

   $H_a$: $\mu > 18$ years (Claim)

In the three figures at the left, notice that each point on the number line is in either $H_0$ or $H_a$, but no point is in both.

**TRY IT YOURSELF 1**

Write each claim as a mathematical statement. State the null and alternative hypotheses, and identify which represents the claim.

1. A consumer analyst reports that the mean life of a certain type of automobile battery is not 74 months.
2. An electronics manufacturer publishes that the variance of the life of its home theater systems is less than or equal to 2.7.
3. A realtor publicizes that the proportion of homeowners who feel their house is too small for their family is more than 24%.

*Answer: Page A40*

In Example 1, notice that the claim is represented by either the null hypothesis *or* the alternative hypothesis.

## Types of Errors and Level of Significance

No matter which hypothesis represents the claim, you always begin a hypothesis test by assuming that the equality condition in the null hypothesis is true. So, when you perform a hypothesis test, you make one of two decisions:

**1.** reject the null hypothesis

or

**2.** fail to reject the null hypothesis.

Because your decision is based on a sample rather than the entire population, there is always the possibility you will make the wrong decision.

For instance, you claim that a coin is not fair. To test your claim, you toss the coin 100 times and get 49 heads and 51 tails. You would probably agree that you do not have enough evidence to support your claim. Even so, it is possible that the coin is actually not fair and you had an unusual sample.

But then you toss the coin 100 times and get 21 heads and 79 tails. It would be a rare occurrence to get only 21 heads out of 100 tosses with a fair coin. So, you probably have enough evidence to support your claim that the coin is not fair. However, you cannot be 100% sure. It is possible that the coin is fair and you had an unusual sample.

Letting $p$ represent the proportion of heads, the claim that "the coin is not fair" can be written as the mathematical statement $p \neq 0.5$. Its complement, "the coin is fair," is written as $p = 0.5$, as shown in the figure.

$H_a$ $H_0$ $H_a$

0.48 0.49 0.50 0.51 0.52 $p$

So, the null hypothesis is

$$H_0: p = 0.5$$

and the alternative hypothesis is

$$H_a: p \neq 0.5. \text{ (Claim)}$$

Remember, the only way to be absolutely certain of whether $H_0$ is true or false is to test the entire population. Because your decision—to reject $H_0$ or to fail to reject $H_0$—is based on a sample, you must accept the fact that your decision might be incorrect. You might reject a null hypothesis when it is actually true. Or, you might fail to reject a null hypothesis when it is actually false. These types of errors are summarized in the next definition.

**DEFINITION**

A **type I error** occurs if the null hypothesis is rejected when it is true.

A **type II error** occurs if the null hypothesis is not rejected when it is false.

The table shows the four possible outcomes of a hypothesis test.

| | **Truth of $H_0$** | |
|---|---|---|
| **Decision** | **$H_0$ is true.** | **$H_0$ is false.** |
| **Do not reject $H_0$.** | Correct decision | Type II error |
| **Reject $H_0$.** | Type I error | Correct decision |

Hypothesis testing is sometimes compared to the legal system used in the United States. Under this system, these steps are used.

1. A carefully worded accusation is written.
2. The defendant is assumed innocent ($H_0$) until proven guilty. The burden of proof lies with the prosecution. If the evidence is not strong enough, then there is no conviction. A "not guilty" verdict does not prove that a defendant is innocent.
3. The evidence needs to be conclusive beyond a reasonable doubt. The system assumes that more harm is done by convicting the innocent (type I error) than by not convicting the guilty (type II error).

| | **Truth about defendant** | |
|---|---|---|
| **Verdict** | **Innocent** | **Guilty** |
| **Not guilty** | Justice | Type II error |
| **Guilty** | Type I error | Justice |

The table at the left shows the four possible outcomes.

## EXAMPLE 2

### Identifying Type I and Type II Errors

The USDA limit for salmonella contamination for ground beef is 7.5%. A meat inspector reports that the ground beef produced by a company exceeds the USDA limit. You perform a hypothesis test to determine whether the meat inspector's claim is true. When will a type I or type II error occur? Which error is more serious? *(Source: U.S. Department of Agriculture)*

**SOLUTION**

Let $p$ represent the proportion of the ground beef that is contaminated. The meat inspector's claim is "more than 7.5% is contaminated." You can write the null hypothesis as

$H_0$: $p \leq 0.075$ The proportion is less than or equal to 0.075.

and the alternative hypothesis is

$H_a$: $p > 0.075$. (Claim) The proportion is greater than 0.075.

You can visualize the null and alternative hypotheses using a number line, as shown below.

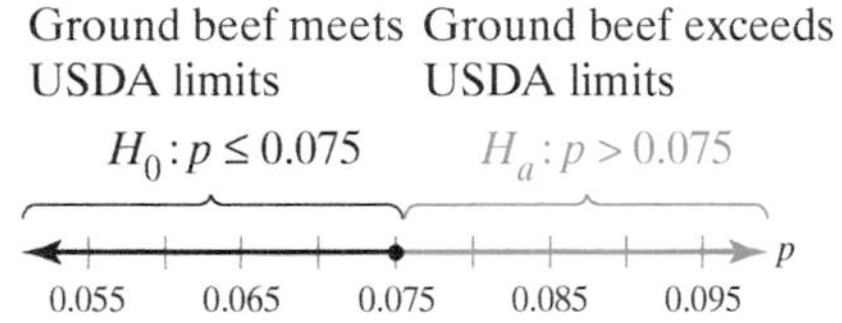


A type I error will occur when the actual proportion of contaminated ground beef is less than or equal to 0.075, but you reject $H_0$. A type II error will occur when the actual proportion of contaminated ground beef is greater than 0.075, but you do not reject $H_0$. With a type I error, you might create a health scare and hurt the sales of ground beef producers who were actually meeting the USDA limits. With a type II error, you could be allowing ground beef that exceeded the USDA contamination limit to be sold to consumers. A type II error is more serious because it could result in sickness or even death.

**TRY IT YOURSELF 2**

A company specializing in parachute assembly states that its main parachute failure rate is not more than 1%. You perform a hypothesis test to determine whether the company's claim is false. When will a type I or type II error occur? Which error is more serious?

*Answer: Page A40*

You will reject the null hypothesis when the sample statistic from the sampling distribution is unusual. You have already identified unusual events to be those that occur with a probability of 0.05 or less. When statistical tests are used, an unusual event is sometimes required to have a probability of 0.10 or less, 0.05 or less, or 0.01 or less. Because there is variation from sample to sample, there is always a possibility that you will reject a null hypothesis when it is actually true. In other words, although the null hypothesis is true, your sample statistic is determined to be an unusual event in the sampling distribution. You can decrease the probability of this happening by lowering the **level of significance.**

**Study Tip**

When you decrease $\alpha$ (the maximum allowable probability of making a type I error), you are likely to be increasing $\beta$. The value $1 - \beta$ is called the *power of the test.* It represents the probability of rejecting the null hypothesis when it is false. The value of the power is difficult (and sometimes impossible) to find in most cases.

**DEFINITION**

In a hypothesis test, the **level of significance** is your maximum allowable probability of making a type I error. It is denoted by $\alpha$, the lowercase Greek letter alpha.

The probability of a type II error is denoted by $\beta$, the lowercase Greek letter beta.

By setting the level of significance at a small value, you are saying that you want the probability of rejecting a true null hypothesis to be small. Three commonly used levels of significance are

$$\alpha = 0.10, \quad \alpha = 0.05, \quad \text{and} \quad \alpha = 0.01.$$

## Statistical Tests and *P*-Values

After stating the null and alternative hypotheses and specifying the level of significance, the next step in a hypothesis test is to obtain a random sample from the population and calculate the sample statistic (such as $\bar{x}$, $\hat{p}$, or $s^2$) corresponding to the parameter in the null hypothesis (such as $\mu$, $p$, or $\sigma^2$). This sample statistic is called the **test statistic.** With the assumption that the null hypothesis is true, the test statistic is then converted to a **standardized test statistic,** such as $z$, $t$, or $\chi^2$. The standardized test statistic is used in making the decision about the null hypothesis.

In this chapter, you will learn about several one-sample statistical tests. The table shows the relationships between population parameters and their corresponding test statistics and standardized test statistics.

| Population parameter | Test statistic | Standardized test statistic |
|---|---|---|
| $\mu$ | $\bar{x}$ | $z$ (Section 7.2, $\sigma$ known), $t$ (Section 7.3, $\sigma$ unknown) |
| $p$ | $\hat{p}$ | $z$ (Section 7.4) |
| $\sigma^2$ | $s^2$ | $\chi^2$ (Section 7.5) |

One way to decide whether to reject the null hypothesis is to determine whether the probability of obtaining the standardized test statistic (or one that is more extreme) is less than the level of significance.

**DEFINITION**

If the null hypothesis is true, then a ***P*-value** (or **probability value**) of a hypothesis test is the probability of obtaining a sample statistic with a value as extreme or more extreme than the one determined from the sample data.

The $P$-value of a hypothesis test depends on the nature of the test. There are three types of hypothesis tests—**left-tailed, right-tailed,** and **two-tailed.** The type of test depends on the location of the region of the sampling distribution that favors a rejection of $H_0$. This region is indicated by the alternative hypothesis.

## DEFINITION

1. If the alternative hypothesis $H_a$ contains the less-than inequality symbol $(<)$, then the hypothesis test is a **left-tailed test.**

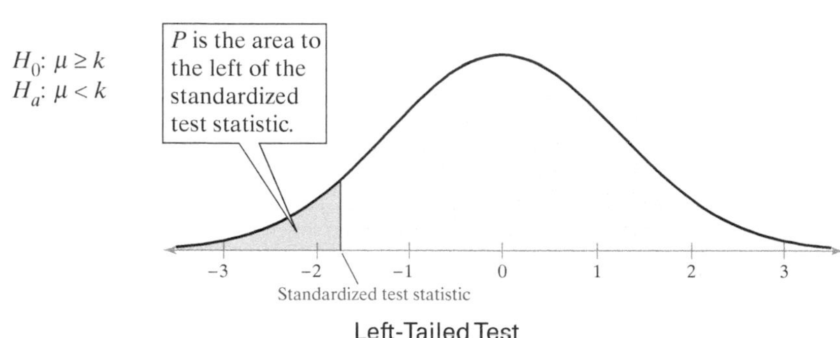
$H_0$: $\mu \geq k$
$H_a$: $\mu < k$
P is the area to the left of the standardized test statistic.
-3
-2
-1
0
1
2
3
Standardized test statistic

Left-Tailed Test

2. If the alternative hypothesis $H_a$ contains the greater-than inequality symbol $(>)$, then the hypothesis test is a **right-tailed test.**

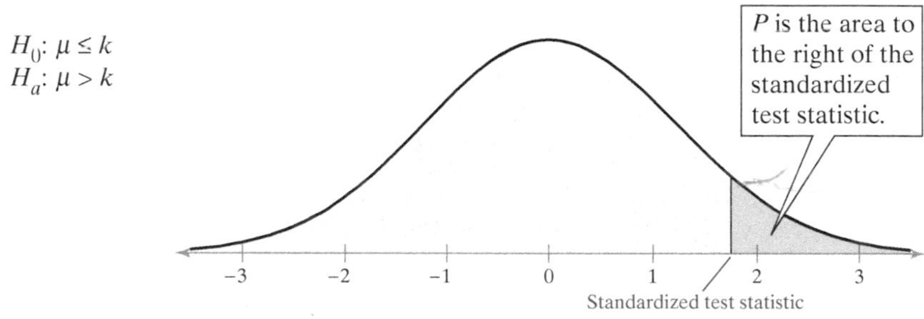
$H_0$: $\mu \leq k$
$H_a$: $\mu > k$
P is the area to the right of the standardized test statistic.
-3
-2
-1
0
1
2
3
Standardized test statistic

Right-Tailed Test

3. If the alternative hypothesis $H_a$ contains the not-equal-to symbol $(\neq)$, then the hypothesis test is a **two-tailed test.** In a two-tailed test, each tail has an area of $\frac{1}{2}P$.

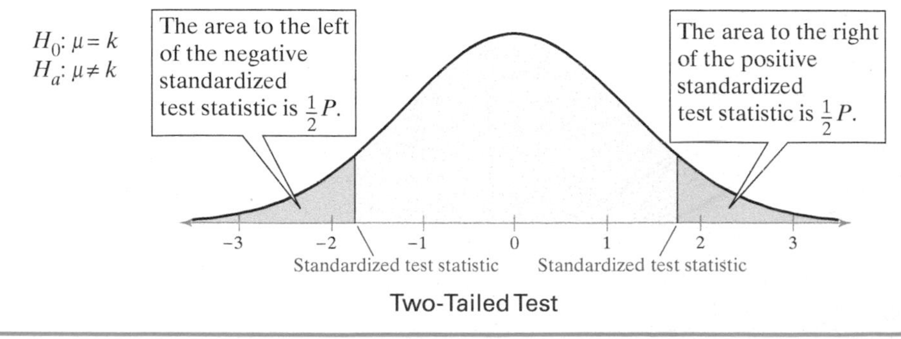
$H_0$: $\mu = k$
$H_a$: $\mu \neq k$
The area to the left of the negative standardized test statistic is $\frac{1}{2}P$.
The area to the right of the positive standardized test statistic is $\frac{1}{2}P$.
-3
-2
-1
0
1
2
3
Standardized test statistic
Standardized test statistic

Two-Tailed Test

**Study Tip**

The third type of test is called a two-tailed test because evidence that would support the alternative hypothesis could lie in either tail of the sampling distribution.

The smaller the $P$-value of the test, the more evidence there is to reject the null hypothesis. A very small $P$-value indicates an unusual event. Remember, however, that even a very low $P$-value does not constitute proof that the null hypothesis is false, only that it is probably false.

## EXAMPLE 3

### Identifying the Nature of a Hypothesis Test

For each claim, state $H_0$ and $H_a$ in symbols and in words. Then determine whether the hypothesis test is a left-tailed test, right-tailed test, or two-tailed test. Sketch a normal sampling distribution and shade the area for the $P$-value.

1. A school publicizes that the proportion of its students who are involved in at least one extracurricular activity is 61%.
2. A car dealership announces that the mean time for an oil change is less than 15 minutes.
3. A company advertises that the mean life of its furnaces is more than 18 years.

**SOLUTION**

| | ***In Symbols*** | ***In Words*** |
|---|---|---|
| **1.** | $H_0$: $p = 0.61$ | The proportion of students who are involved in at least one extracurricular activity is 61%. |
| | $H_a$: $p \neq 0.61$ | The proportion of students who are involved in at least one extracurricular activity is not 61%. |

$\frac{1}{2}$ $P$-value area $\frac{1}{2}$ $P$-value area
0 z
Standardized test statistic

Because $H_a$ contains the $\neq$ symbol, the test is a two-tailed hypothesis test. The figure at the left shows the normal sampling distribution with a shaded area for the $P$-value.

| | ***In Symbols*** | ***In Words*** |
|---|---|---|
| **2.** | $H_0$: $\mu \geq 15$ min | The mean time for an oil change is greater than or equal to 15 minutes. |
| | $H_a$: $\mu < 15$ min | The mean time for an oil change is less than 15 minutes. |

$P$-value area
0 z
Standardized test statistic

Because $H_a$ contains the $<$ symbol, the test is a left-tailed hypothesis test. The figure at the left shows the normal sampling distribution with a shaded area for the $P$-value.

| | ***In Symbols*** | ***In Words*** |
|---|---|---|
| **3.** | $H_0$: $\mu \leq 18$ yr | The mean life of the furnaces is less than or equal to 18 years. |
| | $H_a$: $\mu > 18$ yr | The mean life of the furnaces is more than 18 years. |

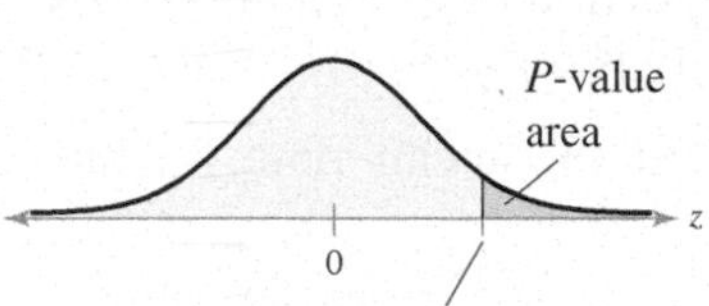


Because $H_a$ contains the $>$ symbol, the test is a right-tailed hypothesis test. The figure at the left shows the normal sampling distribution with a shaded area for the $P$-value.

**TRY IT YOURSELF 3**

For each claim, state $H_0$ and $H_a$ in symbols and in words. Then determine whether the hypothesis test is a left-tailed test, right-tailed test, or two-tailed test. Sketch a normal sampling distribution and shade the area for the $P$-value.

1. A consumer analyst reports that the mean life of a certain type of automobile battery is not 74 months.
2. An electronics manufacturer publishes that the variance of the life of its home theater systems is less than or equal to 2.7.
3. A realtor publicizes that the proportion of homeowners who feel their house is too small for their family is more than 24%.

*Answer: Page A40*

## Making a Decision and Interpreting the Decision

To conclude a hypothesis test, you make a decision and interpret that decision. For any hypothesis test, there are two possible outcomes: (1) reject the null hypothesis or (2) fail to reject the null hypothesis. To decide to reject $H_0$ or fail to reject $H_0$, you can use the following **decision rule.**

**Study Tip**

In this chapter, you will learn that there are two types of decision rules for deciding whether to reject $H_0$ or fail to reject $H_0$. The decision rule described on this page is based on $P$-values. The second type of decision rule is based on rejection regions. When the standardized test statistic falls in the rejection region, the observed probability ($P$-value) of a type I error is less than $\alpha$. You will learn more about rejection regions in the next section.

### Decision Rule Based on $P$-Value

To use a $P$-value to make a decision in a hypothesis test, compare the $P$-value with $\alpha$.

1. If $P \leq \alpha$, then reject $H_0$.
2. If $P > \alpha$, then fail to reject $H_0$.

Failing to reject the null hypothesis does not mean that you have accepted the null hypothesis as true. It simply means that there is not enough evidence to reject the null hypothesis. To support a claim, state it so that it becomes the alternative hypothesis. To reject a claim, state it so that it becomes the null hypothesis. The table will help you interpret your decision.

| | Claim | |
|---|---|---|
| **Decision** | **Claim is $H_0$.** | **Claim is $H_a$.** |
| **Reject $H_0$.** | There is enough evidence to reject the claim. | There is enough evidence to support the claim. |
| **Fail to reject $H_0$.** | There is not enough evidence to reject the claim. | There is not enough evidence to support the claim. |

### EXAMPLE 4

#### Interpreting a Decision

You perform a hypothesis test for each claim. How should you interpret your decision if you reject $H_0$? If you fail to reject $H_0$?

1. $H_0$ (Claim): A school publicizes that the proportion of its students who are involved in at least one extracurricular activity is 61%.
2. $H_a$ (Claim): A car dealership announces that the mean time for an oil change is less than 15 minutes.

**SOLUTION**

1. The claim is represented by $H_0$. If you reject $H_0$, then you should conclude "there is enough evidence to reject the school's claim that the proportion of students who are involved in at least one extracurricular activity is 61%." If you fail to reject $H_0$, then you should conclude "there is not enough evidence to reject the school's claim that the proportion of students who are involved in at least one extracurricular activity is 61%."
2. The claim is represented by $H_a$, so the null hypothesis is "the mean time for an oil change is greater than or equal to 15 minutes." If you reject $H_0$, then you should conclude "there is enough evidence to support the dealership's claim that the mean time for an oil change is less than 15 minutes." If you fail to reject $H_0$, then you should conclude "there is not enough evidence to support the dealership's claim that the mean time for an oil change is less than 15 minutes."

**TRY IT YOURSELF 4**

You perform a hypothesis test for each claim. How should you interpret your decision if you reject $H_0$? If you fail to reject $H_0$?

1. A consumer analyst reports that the mean life of a certain type of automobile battery is not 74 months.
2. $H_a$ (Claim): A realtor publicizes that the proportion of homeowners who feel their house is too small for their family is more than 24%.

*Answer: Page A40*

The general steps for a hypothesis test using $P$-values are summarized below. Note that when performing a hypothesis test, you should always state the null and alternative hypotheses before collecting data. You should not collect the data first and then create a hypothesis based on something unusual in the data.

### Steps for Hypothesis Testing

1. State the claim mathematically and verbally. Identify the null and alternative hypotheses.

   $H_0$: **?** $H_a$: **?**

2. Specify the level of significance.

   $\alpha =$ **?**

3. Determine the standardized sampling distribution and sketch its graph.

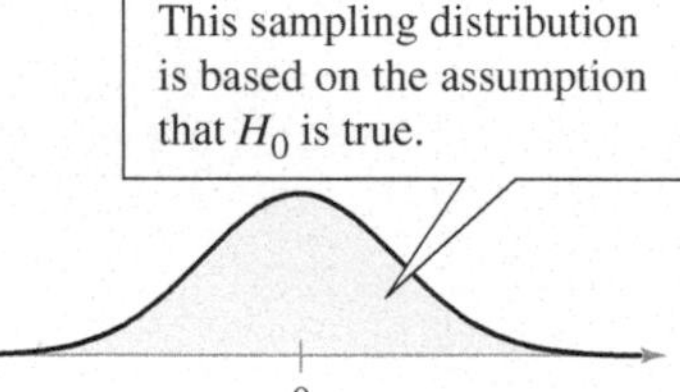
This sampling distribution is based on the assumption that $H_0$ is true.
0

4. Calculate the test statistic and its corresponding standardized test statistic. Add it to your sketch.

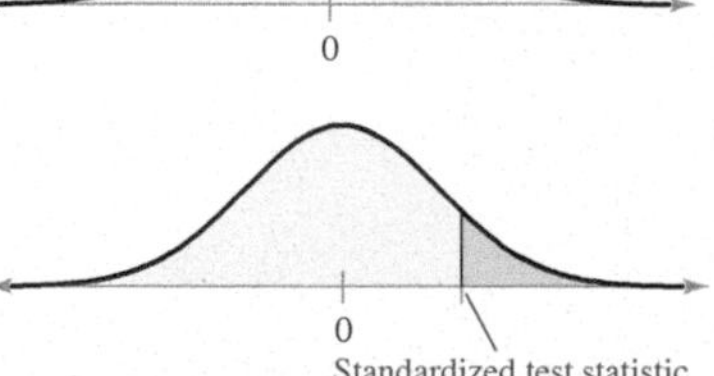
0
Standardized test statistic

5. Find the $P$-value.
6. Use this decision rule.

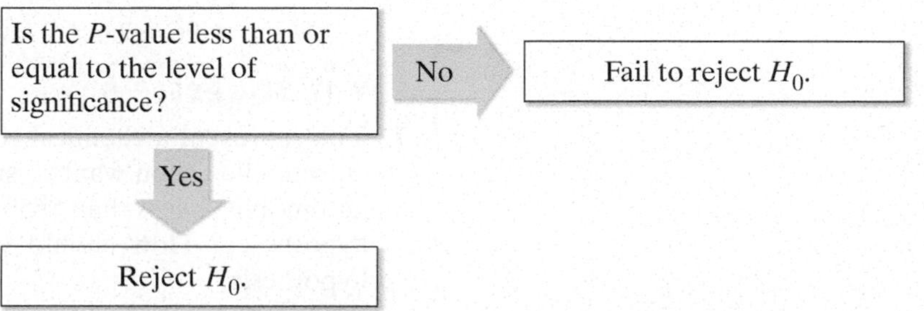
Is the $P$-value less than or equal to the level of significance?
No
Fail to reject $H_0$.
Yes
Reject $H_0$.

7. Write a statement to interpret the decision in the context of the original claim.

In Step 4 above, the figure shows a right-tailed test. However, the same basic steps also apply to left-tailed and two-tailed tests.

## Strategies for Hypothesis Testing

In a courtroom, the strategy used by an attorney depends on whether the attorney is representing the defense or the prosecution. In a similar way, the strategy that you will use in hypothesis testing should depend on whether you are trying to support or reject a claim. Remember that you cannot use a hypothesis test to support your claim when your claim is the null hypothesis. So, as a researcher, to perform a hypothesis test where the possible outcome will support a claim, word the claim so it is the alternative hypothesis. To perform a hypothesis test where the possible outcome will reject a claim, word it so the claim is the null hypothesis.

**EXAMPLE 5**

### Writing the Hypotheses

A medical research team is investigating the benefits of a new surgical treatment. One of the claims is that the mean recovery time for patients after the new treatment is less than 96 hours.

1. How would you write the null and alternative hypotheses when you are on the research team and want to support the claim? How should you interpret a decision that rejects the null hypothesis?
2. How would you write the null and alternative hypotheses when you are on an opposing team and want to reject the claim? How should you interpret a decision that rejects the null hypothesis?

**SOLUTION**

1. To answer the question, first think about the context of the claim. Because you want to support this claim, make the alternative hypothesis state that the mean recovery time for patients is less than 96 hours. So, $H_a$: $\mu < 96$ hours. Its complement, $H_0$: $\mu \geq 96$ hours, would be the null hypothesis. If you reject $H_0$, then you will support the claim that the mean recovery time is less than 96 hours.

   $H_0$: $\mu \geq 96$ and $H_a$: $\mu < 96$ (Claim)

2. First think about the context of the claim. As an opposing researcher, you do not want the recovery time to be less than 96 hours. Because you want to reject this claim, make it the null hypothesis. So, $H_0$: $\mu \leq 96$ hours. Its complement, $H_a$: $\mu > 96$ hours, would be the alternative hypothesis. If you reject $H_0$, then you will reject the claim that the mean recovery time is less than or equal to 96 hours.

   $H_0$: $\mu \leq 96$ (Claim) and $H_a$: $\mu > 96$

**TRY IT YOURSELF 5**

1. You represent a chemical company that is being sued for paint damage to automobiles. You want to support the claim that the mean repair cost per automobile is less than \$650. How would you write the null and alternative hypotheses? How should you interpret a decision that rejects the null hypothesis?
2. You are on a research team that is investigating the mean temperature of adult humans. The commonly accepted claim is that the mean temperature is about 98.6°F. You want to show that this claim is false. How would you write the null and alternative hypotheses? How should you interpret a decision that rejects the null hypothesis?

*Answer: Page A40*

# 7.1 EXERCISES

For Extra Help: MyLab® Statistics

## Building Basic Skills and Vocabulary

**1.** What are the two types of hypotheses used in a hypothesis test? How are they related?

**2.** Describe the two types of errors possible in a hypothesis test decision.

**3.** What are the two decisions that you can make from performing a hypothesis test?

**4.** Does failing to reject the null hypothesis mean that the null hypothesis is true? Explain.

**True or False?** *In Exercises 5–10, determine whether the statement is true or false. If it is false, rewrite it as a true statement.*

**5.** In a hypothesis test, you assume the alternative hypothesis is true.

**6.** A statistical hypothesis is a statement about a sample.

**7.** If you decide to reject the null hypothesis, then you can support the alternative hypothesis.

**8.** The level of significance is the maximum probability you allow for rejecting a null hypothesis when it is actually true.

**9.** A large *P*-value in a test will favor rejection of the null hypothesis.

**10.** To support a claim, state it so that it becomes the null hypothesis.

**Stating Hypotheses** *In Exercises 11–16, the statement represents a claim. Write its complement and state which is $H_0$ and which is $H_a$.*

**11.** $\mu \leq 645$

**12.** $\mu < 128$

**13.** $\sigma \neq 5$

**14.** $\sigma^2 \geq 1.2$

**15.** $p < 0.45$

**16.** $p = 0.21$

**Graphical Analysis** *In Exercises 17–20, match the alternative hypothesis with its graph. Then state the null hypothesis and sketch its graph.*

**17.** $H_a$: $\mu > 3$

(a) 1 2 3 4 $\mu$

**18.** $H_a$: $\mu < 3$

(b) 1 2 3 4 $\mu$

**19.** $H_a$: $\mu \neq 3$

(c) 1 2 3 4 $\mu$

**20.** $H_a$: $\mu > 2$

(d) 1 2 3 4 $\mu$

**Identifying a Test** *In Exercises 21–24, determine whether the hypothesis test is left-tailed, right-tailed, or two-tailed.*

**21.** $H_0$: $\mu \leq 8.0$
$H_a$: $\mu > 8.0$

**22.** $H_0$: $\sigma \geq 5.2$
$H_a$: $\sigma < 5.2$

**23.** $H_0$: $\sigma^2 = 142$
$H_a$: $\sigma^2 \neq 142$

**24.** $H_0$: $p = 0.25$
$H_a$: $p \neq 0.25$

## Using and Interpreting Concepts

**Stating the Null and Alternative Hypotheses** *In Exercises 25–30, write the claim as a mathematical statement. State the null and alternative hypotheses, and identify which represents the claim.*

**25. Tablets** A tablet manufacturer claims that the mean life of the battery for a certain model of tablet is more than 8 hours.

**26. Shipping Errors** As stated by a company's shipping department, the number of shipping errors per million shipments has a standard deviation that is less than 3.

**27. Base Price of an ATV** The standard deviation of the base price of an all-terrain vehicle is no more than \$320.

**28. Attendance** An amusement park claims that the mean daily attendance at the park is at least 20,000 people.

**29. Paying for College** According to a recent survey, 54% of today's college students used student loans to pay for college. *(Source: The Federal Reserve)*

**30. College Debt** According to a recent survey, 14% of adults currently carry student loan debt. *(Source: The Federal Reserve)*

**Identifying Type I and Type II Errors** *In Exercises 31–36, describe type I and type II errors for a hypothesis test of the indicated claim.*

**31. Repeat Customers** A used textbook selling website claims that at least 60% of its new customers will return to buy their next textbook.

**32. Flow Rate** An urban planner claims that the noontime mean traffic flow rate on a busy downtown college campus street is 35 cars per minute.

**33. Chess** A local chess club claims that the length of time to play a game has a standard deviation of more than 12 minutes.

**34. Video Game Systems** A researcher claims that the percentage of U.S. gamers that are women is not 50%.

**35. Security** A campus security department publicizes that at most 25% of applicants become campus security officers.

**36. Phone Repairs** A cell phone repair shop advertises that the mean cost of repairing a phone screen is less than \$120.

**Identifying the Nature of a Hypothesis Test** *In Exercises 37–42, state $H_0$ and $H_a$ in words and in symbols. Then determine whether the hypothesis test is left-tailed, right-tailed, or two-tailed. Explain your reasoning. Sketch a normal sampling distribution and shade the area for the P-value.*

**37. Security Alarms** A security expert claims that at least 14% of all homeowners have a home security alarm.

**38. Clocks** A manufacturer of grandfather clocks claims that the mean time its clocks lose is no more than 0.02 second per day.

**39. Golf** A golf analyst claims that the standard deviation of the 18-hole scores for a golfer is less than 2.1 strokes.

**40. Lung Cancer** A report claims that lung cancer accounts for 25% of all cancer diagnoses. *(Source: American Cancer Society)*

41. **Survey** A polling organization reports that the number of responses to a survey mailed to 100,000 U.S. residents is not 100,000.

42. **High School Graduation Rate** A high school claims that its mean graduation rate is more than 97%.

**Interpreting a Decision** *In Exercises 43–48, determine whether the claim represents the null hypothesis or the alternative hypothesis. If a hypothesis test is performed, how should you interpret a decision that*

(a) *rejects the null hypothesis?*

(b) *fails to reject the null hypothesis?*

43. **Swans** A scientist claims that the mean incubation period for swan eggs is less than 40 days.

44. **Affording Basic Necessities** A report claims that more than 30% of households in a Wisconsin county struggle to afford basic necessities. *(Adapted from Peninsula Pulse)*

45. **Lawn Mowers** A researcher claims that the standard deviation of the life of a brand of lawn mower is at most 2.8 years.

46. **Gas Mileage** An automotive manufacturer claims that the standard deviation for the gas mileage of one of the vehicles it manufactures is 3.9 miles per gallon.

47. **Marketing** A fitness equipment company claims that its competitor's home gym does not have a customer satisfaction rate of 99%.

48. **Rent** A recent study claims that at least 20% of renters are behind on rent payments in New Jersey. *(Source: National Equity Atlas)*

49. **Writing Hypotheses: Medicine** A medical research team is investigating the mean cost of a 30-day supply of a heart medication. A pharmaceutical company thinks that the mean cost is less than $60. You want to support this claim. How would you write the null and alternative hypotheses?

50. **Writing Hypotheses: Transportation Network Company** A transportation network company claims that the mean travel time between two destinations is about 16 minutes. You work for one of the company's competitors and want to reject this claim. How would you write the null and alternative hypotheses?

51. **Writing Hypotheses: Backpack Manufacturer** A backpack manufacturer claims that the mean life of its competitor's backpacks is less than 5 years. You are asked to perform a hypothesis test to test this claim. How would you write the null and alternative hypotheses when
    (a) you represent the manufacturer and want to support the claim?
    (b) you represent the competitor and want to reject the claim?

52. **Writing Hypotheses: Internet Provider** An Internet provider is trying to gain advertising deals and claims that the mean time a customer spends online per day is greater than 28 minutes. You are asked to test this claim. How would you write the null and alternative hypotheses when
    (a) you represent the Internet provider and want to support the claim?
    (b) you represent a competing advertiser and want to reject the claim?

## Extending Concepts

**53. Getting at the Concept** Why can decreasing the probability of a type I error cause an increase in the probability of a type II error?

**54. Getting at the Concept** Explain why a level of significance of $\alpha = 0$ is not used.

**55. Writing** A null hypothesis is rejected with a level of significance of 0.05. Is it also rejected at a level of significance of 0.10? Explain.

**56. Writing** A null hypothesis is rejected with a level of significance of 0.10. Is it also rejected at a level of significance of 0.05? Explain.

**Graphical Analysis** *In Exercises 57–60, you are given a null hypothesis and three confidence intervals that represent three samplings. Determine whether each confidence interval indicates that you should reject $H_0$. Explain your reasoning.*

**57.** $H_0$: $\mu = 70$

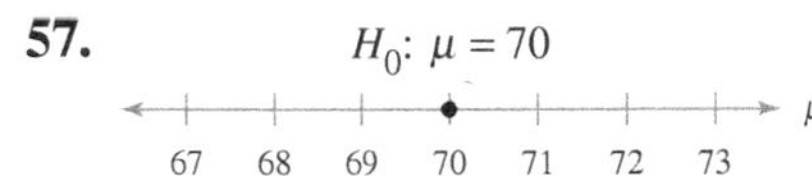


(a) $67 < \mu < 71$

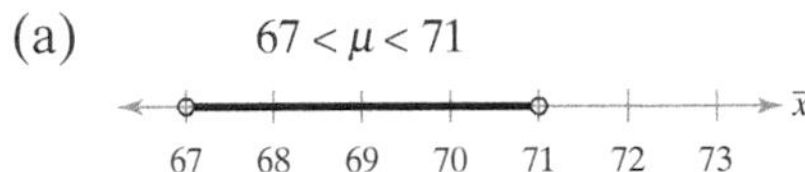


(b) $67 < \mu < 69$

(c) $69.5 < \mu < 72.5$

**58.** $H_0$: $\mu \leq 54$

(a) $53.5 < \mu < 56.5$

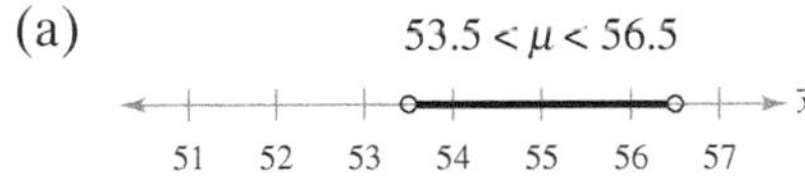


(b) $51.5 < \mu < 54.5$

(c) $54.5 < \mu < 55.5$

**59.** $H_0$: $p \leq 0.20$

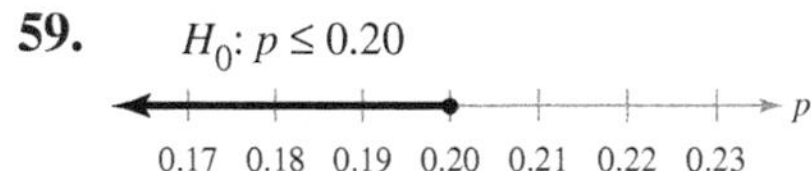


(a) $0.21 < p < 0.23$

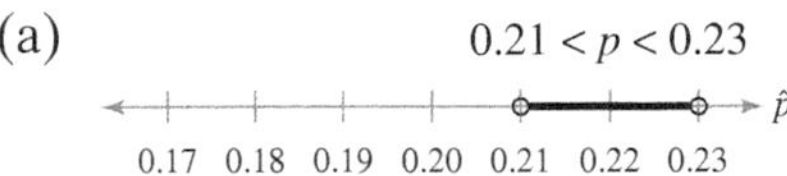


(b) $0.19 < p < 0.23$

(c) $0.175 < p < 0.205$

**60.** $H_0$: $p \geq 0.73$

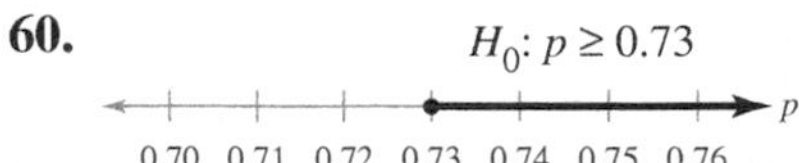


(a) $0.73 < p < 0.75$

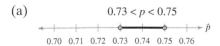

(b) $0.715 < p < 0.725$

(c) $0.695 < p < 0.745$

# 7.2 Hypothesis Testing for the Mean ($\sigma$ Known)

### What You Should Learn

- How to find and interpret *P*-values
- How to use *P*-values for a *z*-test for a mean $\mu$ when $\sigma$ is known
- How to find critical values and rejection regions in the standard normal distribution
- How to use rejection regions for a *z*-test for a mean $\mu$ when $\sigma$ is known

Using *P*-Values to Make Decisions ■ Using *P*-Values for a *z*-Test ■ Rejection Regions and Critical Values ■ Using Rejection Regions for a *z*-Test

## Using *P*-Values to Make Decisions

In Chapter 5, you learned that when the sample size is at least 30, the sampling distribution for $\bar{x}$ (the sample mean) is normal. In Section 7.1, you learned that a way to reach a conclusion in a hypothesis test is to use a *P*-value for the sample statistic, such as $\bar{x}$. Recall that when you assume the null hypothesis is true, a *P*-value (or probability value) of a hypothesis test is the probability of obtaining a sample statistic with a value as extreme as or more extreme than the one determined from the sample data. The decision rule for a hypothesis test based on a *P*-value is repeated below.

### Decision Rule Based on *P*-Value

To use a *P*-value to make a decision in a hypothesis test, compare the *P*-value with $\alpha$.

**1.** If $P \leq \alpha$, then reject $H_0$.

**2.** If $P > \alpha$, then fail to reject $H_0$.

### EXAMPLE 1

#### Interpreting a *P*-Value

The *P*-value for a hypothesis test is $P = 0.0237$. What is your decision when the level of significance is (1) $\alpha = 0.05$ and (2) $\alpha = 0.01$?

**SOLUTION**

**1.** Because $0.0237 < 0.05$, you reject the null hypothesis.

**2.** Because $0.0237 > 0.01$, you fail to reject the null hypothesis.

**TRY IT YOURSELF 1**

The *P*-value for a hypothesis test is $P = 0.0745$. What is your decision when the level of significance is (1) $\alpha = 0.05$ and (2) $\alpha = 0.10$? *Answer: Page A40*

The lower the *P*-value, the more evidence there is in favor of rejecting $H_0$. The *P*-value gives you the lowest level of significance for which the sample statistic allows you to reject the null hypothesis. In Example 1, you would reject $H_0$ at any level of significance greater than or equal to 0.0237.

### Finding the *P*-Value for a Hypothesis Test

After determining the hypothesis test's standardized test statistic and the standardized test statistic's corresponding area, do one of the following to find the *P*-value.

**a.** For a left-tailed test, $P =$ (Area in left tail).

**b.** For a right-tailed test, $P =$ (Area in right tail).

**c.** For a two-tailed test, $P = 2$(Area in tail of standardized test statistic).

**EXAMPLE 2**

## Finding a *P*-Value for a Left-Tailed Test

Find the *P*-value for a left-tailed hypothesis test with a standardized test statistic of $z = -2.23$. Decide whether to reject $H_0$ when the level of significance is $\alpha = 0.01$.

**SOLUTION**

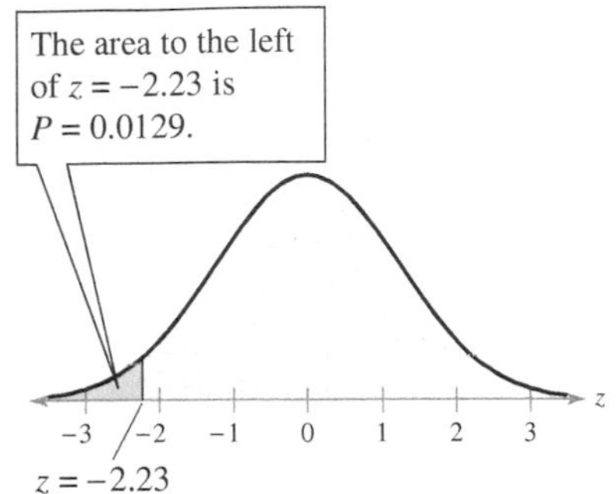


Left-Tailed Test

The figure at the left shows the standard normal curve with a shaded area to the left of $z = -2.23$. For a left-tailed test,

$$P = (\text{Area in left tail}).$$

Using Table 4 in Appendix B, the area corresponding to $z = -2.23$ is 0.0129, which is the area in the left tail. So, the *P*-value for a left-tailed hypothesis test with a standardized test statistic of $z = -2.23$ is $P = 0.0129$. You can check your answer using technology, as shown below.

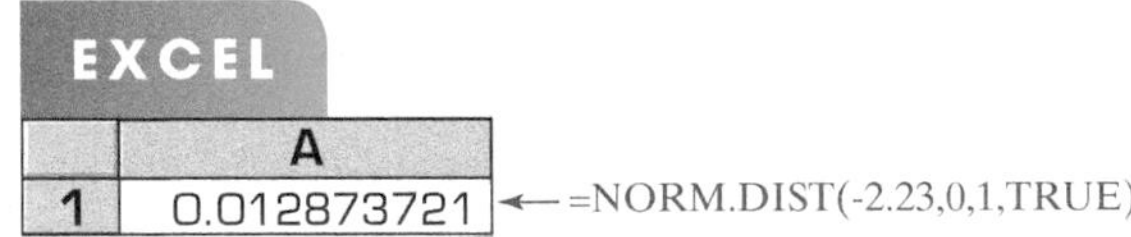

**EXCEL**

| | A | |
|---|---|---|
| 1 | 0.012873721 | ←=NORM.DIST(-2.23,0,1,TRUE) |

***Interpretation*** Because the *P*-value of 0.0129 is greater than 0.01, you fail to reject $H_0$.

**TRY IT YOURSELF 2**

Find the *P*-value for a left-tailed hypothesis test with a standardized test statistic of $z = -1.71$. Decide whether to reject $H_0$ when the level of significance is $\alpha = 0.05$.

*Answer: Page A40*

**EXAMPLE 3**

## Finding a *P*-Value for a Two-Tailed Test

Find the *P*-value for a two-tailed hypothesis test with a standardized test statistic of $z = 2.14$. Decide whether to reject $H_0$ when the level of significance is $\alpha = 0.05$.

**SOLUTION**

The area to the right of $z = 2.14$ is 0.0162, so $P = 2(0.0162) = 0.0324$.

−3 −2 −1 0 1 2 3 z

$z = 2.14$

Two-Tailed Test

The figure at the left shows the standard normal curve with shaded areas to the left of $z = -2.14$ and to the right of $z = 2.14$. For a two-tailed test,

$$P = 2(\text{Area in tail of standardized test statistic}).$$

Using Table 4, the area corresponding to $z = 2.14$ is 0.9838. The area in the right tail is $1 - 0.9838 = 0.0162$. So, the *P*-value for a two-tailed hypothesis test with a standardized test statistic of $z = 2.14$ is

$$P = 2(0.0162) = 0.0324.$$

***Interpretation*** Because the *P*-value of 0.0324 is less than 0.05, you reject $H_0$.

**TRY IT YOURSELF 3**

Find the *P*-value for a two-tailed hypothesis test with a standardized test statistic of $z = 1.64$. Decide whether to reject $H_0$ when the level of significance is $\alpha = 0.10$.

*Answer: Page A40*

## Using *P*-Values for a *z*-Test

You will now learn how to perform a hypothesis test for a mean $\mu$ assuming the standard deviation $\sigma$ is known. When $\sigma$ is known, you can use a $z$-test for the mean. To use the $z$-test, you need to find the standardized value for the test statistic $\bar{x}$. The standardized test statistic takes the form of

$$z = \frac{(\text{Sample mean}) - (\text{Hypothesized mean})}{\text{Standard error}}.$$

### *z*-Test for a Mean $\mu$

The ***z*-test for a mean $\mu$** is a statistical test for a population mean. The **test statistic** is the sample mean $\bar{x}$. The **standardized test statistic** is

$$z = \frac{\bar{x} - \mu}{\sigma/\sqrt{n}} \quad \text{Standardized test statistic for } \mu \ (\sigma \text{ known})$$

when these conditions are met.

1. The sample is random.
2. At least one of the following is true: The population is normally distributed or $n \geq 30$.

Recall that $\sigma/\sqrt{n}$ is the standard error of the mean, $\sigma_{\bar{x}}$.

### GUIDELINES

**Using *P*-Values for a *z*-Test for a Mean $\mu$ ($\sigma$ Known)**

| In Words | In Symbols |
|---|---|
| **1.** Verify that $\sigma$ is known, the sample is random, and either the population is normally distributed or $n \geq 30$. | |
| **2.** State the claim mathematically and verbally. Identify the null and alternative hypotheses. | State $H_0$ and $H_a$. |
| **3.** Specify the level of significance. | Identify $\alpha$. |
| **4.** Find the standardized test statistic. | $z = \dfrac{\bar{x} - \mu}{\sigma/\sqrt{n}}$ |
| **5.** Find the area that corresponds to $z$. | Use Table 4 in Appendix B. |

**6.** Find the *P*-value.

**a.** For a left-tailed test, $P = (\text{Area in left tail})$.

**b.** For a right-tailed test, $P = (\text{Area in right tail})$.

**c.** For a two-tailed test, $P = 2(\text{Area in tail of standardized test statistic})$.

| | |
|---|---|
| **7.** Make a decision to reject or fail to reject the null hypothesis. | If $P \leq \alpha$, then reject $H_0$. Otherwise, fail to reject $H_0$. |
| **8.** Interpret the decision in the context of the original claim. | |

With all hypothesis tests, it is helpful to sketch the sampling distribution. Your sketch should include the standardized test statistic.

EXAMPLE 4

### Hypothesis Testing Using a *P*-Value

In auto racing, a pit stop is where a racing vehicle stops for new tires, fuel, repairs, and other mechanical adjustments. The efficiency of a pit crew that makes these adjustments can affect the outcome of a race. A pit crew claims that its mean pit stop time (for 4 new tires and fuel) is less than 13 seconds. A random sample of 32 pit stop times has a sample mean of 12.9 seconds. Assume the population standard deviation is 0.19 second. Is there enough evidence to support the claim at $\alpha = 0.01$? Use a *P*-value.

**SOLUTION**

Because $\sigma$ is known ($\sigma = 0.19$), the sample is random, and $n = 32 \geq 30$, you can use the $z$-test. The claim is "the mean pit stop time is less than 13 seconds." So, the null and alternative hypotheses are

$$H_0\colon \mu \geq 13 \text{ seconds} \quad \text{and} \quad H_a\colon \mu < 13 \text{ seconds. (Claim)}$$

The level of significance is $\alpha = 0.01$. The standardized test statistic is

$$z = \frac{\bar{x} - \mu}{\sigma / \sqrt{n}} \quad \text{Because } \sigma \text{ is known and } n \geq 30\text{, use the z-test.}$$

$$= \frac{12.9 - 13}{0.19 / \sqrt{32}} \quad \text{Assume } \mu = 13.$$

$$\approx -2.98. \quad \text{Round to two decimal places.}$$

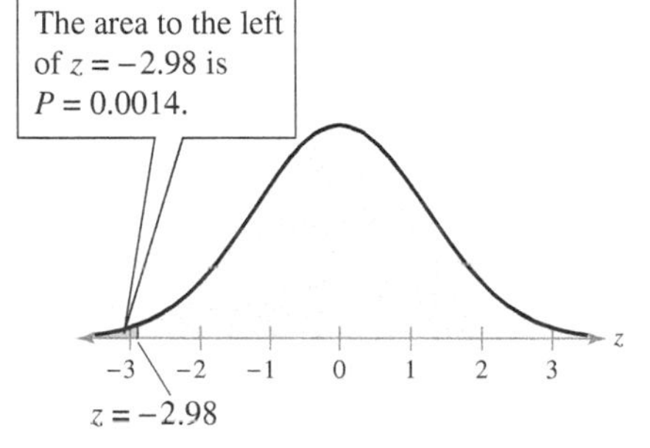

Left-Tailed Test

Using Table 4 in Appendix B, the area corresponding to $z = -2.98$ is 0.0014. Because this test is a left-tailed test, the *P*-value is equal to the area to the left of $z = -2.98$, as shown in the figure at the left. So, $P = 0.0014$. Because the *P*-value is less than $\alpha = 0.01$, you reject the null hypothesis. You can check your answer using technology, as shown below. Note that the *P*-value differs slightly from the one you found due to rounding.

**STATCRUNCH**

**One sample Z summary hypothesis test:**
μ : Mean of population
$H_0$ : μ = 13
$H_A$ : μ < 13
Standard deviation = 0.19

**Hypothesis test results:**

| Mean | n | Sample Mean | Std. Err. | Z-Stat | P-value |
|---|---|---|---|---|---|
| μ | 32 | 12.9 | 0.033587572 | -2.9772917 | 0.0015 |

***Interpretation*** There is enough evidence at the 1% level of significance to support the claim that the mean pit stop time is less than 13 seconds.

**TRY IT YOURSELF 4**

Homeowners claim that the mean speed of automobiles traveling on their street is greater than the speed limit of 35 miles per hour. A random sample of 100 automobiles has a mean speed of 36 miles per hour. Assume the population standard deviation is 4 miles per hour. Is there enough evidence to support the claim at $\alpha = 0.05$? Use a *P*-value.

*Answer: Page A40*

**EXAMPLE 5**

See Minitab steps on page 414.

### Hypothesis Testing Using a *P*-Value

According to a study of U.S. homes that use heating equipment, the mean indoor temperature at night during winter is 68.3°F. You think this information is incorrect. You randomly select 25 U.S. homes that use heating equipment in the winter and find that the mean indoor temperature at night is 67.2°F. From past studies, the population standard deviation is known to be 3.5°F and the population is normally distributed. Is there enough evidence to support your claim at $\alpha = 0.05$? Use a *P*-value. *(Adapted from U.S. Energy Information Administration)*

**SOLUTION**

Because $\sigma$ is known ($\sigma = 3.5$°F), the sample is random, and the population is normally distributed, you can use the $z$-test. The claim is "the mean is different from 68.3°F." So, the null and alternative hypotheses are

$H_0$: $\mu = 68.3$°F and $H_a$: $\mu \neq 68.3$°F. (Claim)

The level of significance is $\alpha = 0.05$. The standardized test statistic is

$$z = \frac{\overline{x} - \mu}{\sigma/\sqrt{n}}$$ Because $\sigma$ is known and the population is normally distributed, use the $z$-test.

$$= \frac{67.2 - 68.3}{3.5/\sqrt{25}}$$ Assume $\mu = 68.3$°F.

$$\approx -1.57.$$ Round to two decimal places.

In Table 4, the area corresponding to $z = -1.57$ is 0.0582. Because the test is a two-tailed test, the *P*-value is equal to twice the area to the left of $z = -1.57$, as shown in the figure.

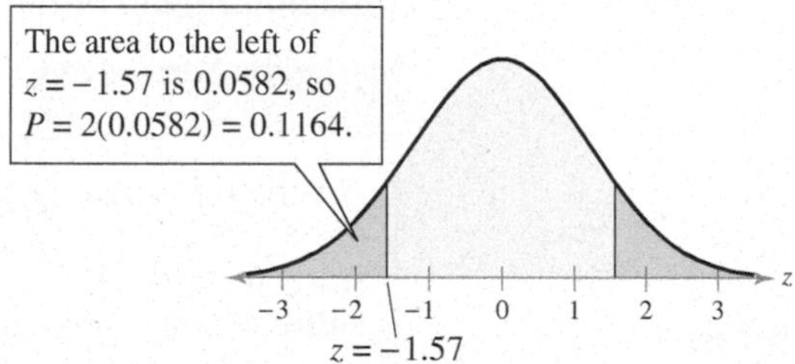
The area to the left of
$z = -1.57$ is 0.0582, so
$P = 2(0.0582) = 0.1164$.
z
−3
−2
−1
0
1
2
3
$z = -1.57$

Two-Tailed Test

So, the *P*-value is $P = 2(0.0582) = 0.1164$. Because the *P*-value is greater than $\alpha = 0.05$, you fail to reject the null hypothesis.

***Interpretation*** There is not enough evidence at the 5% level of significance to support the claim that the mean indoor temperature at night during winter is different from 68.3°F for U.S. homes that use heating equipment.

**TRY IT YOURSELF 5**

According to a study of employed U.S. adults ages 18 and over, the mean number of workdays missed due to illness or injury in the past 12 months is 3.6 days. You think this information is incorrect. You randomly select 25 employed U.S. adults ages 18 and over and find that the mean number of workdays missed is 4 days. Assume the population standard deviation is 1.5 days and the population is normally distributed. Is there enough evidence to support your claim at $\alpha = 0.01$? Use a *P*-value. *(Adapted from U.S. National Center for Health Statistics)*

*Answer: Page A41*

### Tech Tip

Using a TI-84 Plus, you can either enter the original data into a list to find a *P*-value or enter the descriptive statistics.

STAT

Choose the TESTS menu.

1: Z-Test...

Select the *Data* input option when you use the original data. Select the *Stats* input option when you use the descriptive statistics. In each case, enter the appropriate values including the corresponding type of hypothesis test indicated by the alternative hypothesis. Then select *Calculate*.

**EXAMPLE 6**

### Using Technology to Find a *P*-Value

Use the TI-84 Plus displays to make a decision to reject or fail to reject the null hypothesis at a level of significance of $\alpha = 0.05$.

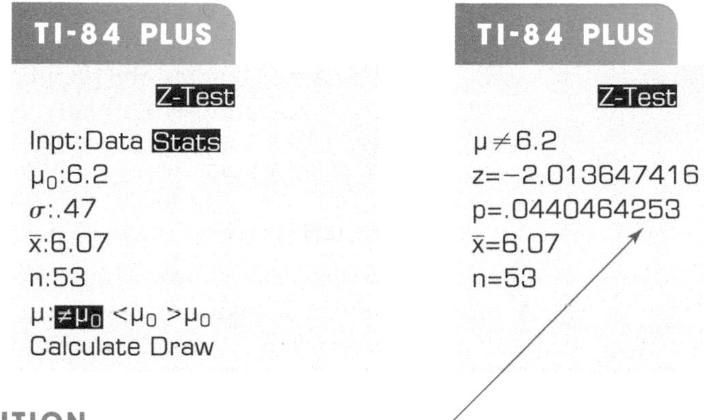


**SOLUTION**

The *P*-value for this test is 0.0440464253. Because the *P*-value is less than $\alpha = 0.05$, you reject the null hypothesis.

**TRY IT YOURSELF 6**

Repeat Example 6 using a level of significance of $\alpha = 0.01$.

*Answer: Page A41*

## Rejection Regions and Critical Values

Another method to decide whether to reject the null hypothesis is to determine whether the standardized test statistic falls within a range of values called the **rejection region** of the sampling distribution.

**DEFINITION**

A **rejection region** (or **critical region**) of the sampling distribution is the range of values for which the null hypothesis is not probable. If a standardized test statistic falls in this region, then the null hypothesis is rejected. A **critical value** $z_0$ separates the rejection region from the nonrejection region.

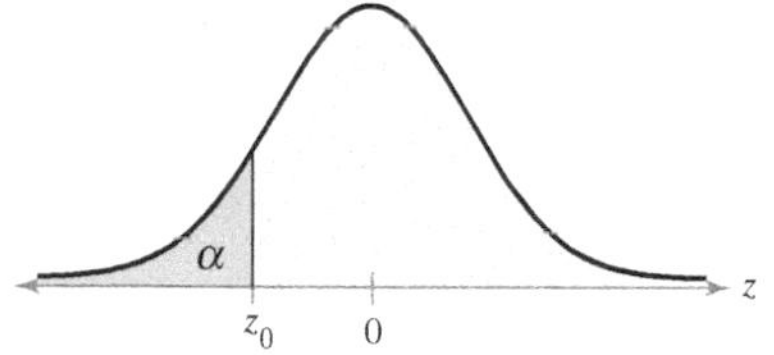

Left-Tailed Test

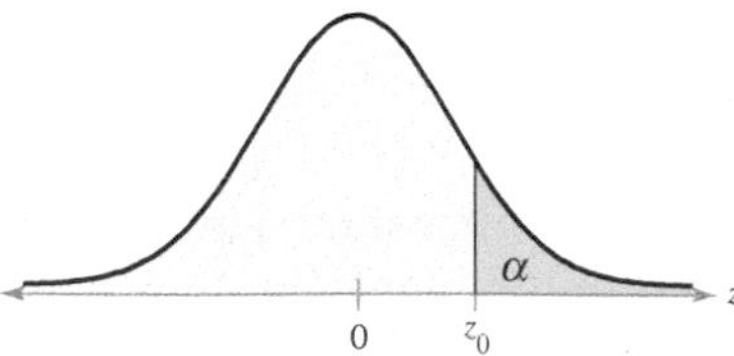

Right-Tailed Test

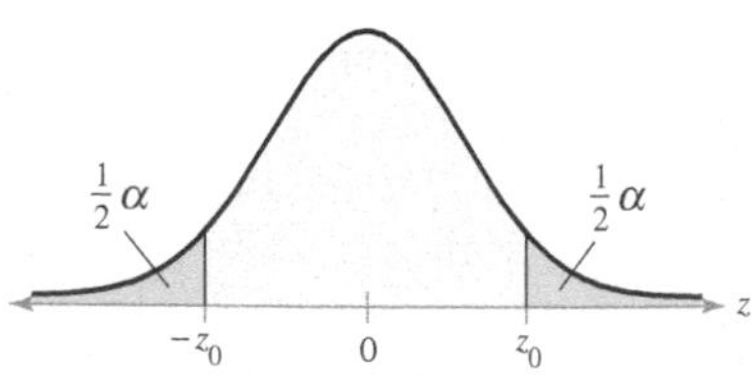

Two-Tailed Test

**GUIDELINES**

**Finding Critical Values in the Standard Normal Distribution**

1. Specify the level of significance $\alpha$.
2. Determine whether the test is left-tailed, right-tailed, or two-tailed.
3. Find the critical value(s) $z_0$. When the hypothesis test is
   - **a.** *left-tailed,* find the $z$-score that corresponds to an area of $\alpha$.
   - **b.** *right-tailed,* find the $z$-score that corresponds to an area of $1 - \alpha$.
   - **c.** *two-tailed,* find the $z$-scores that correspond to $\frac{1}{2}\alpha$ and $1 - \frac{1}{2}\alpha$.
4. Sketch the standard normal distribution. Draw a vertical line at each critical value and shade the rejection region(s). (See the figures at the left.)

Note that a standardized test statistic that falls in a rejection region is considered an unusual event.

When you cannot find the exact area in Table 4, use the area that is closest. For an area that is exactly midway between two areas in the table, use the $z$-score midway between the corresponding $z$-scores.

## EXAMPLE 7

### Finding a Critical Value for a Left-Tailed Test

Find the critical value and rejection region for a left-tailed test with $\alpha = 0.01$.

**SOLUTION**

The figure shows the standard normal curve with a shaded area of 0.01 in the left tail. In Table 4, the $z$-score that is closest to an area of 0.01 is $-2.33$. So, the critical value is

$$z_0 = -2.33.$$

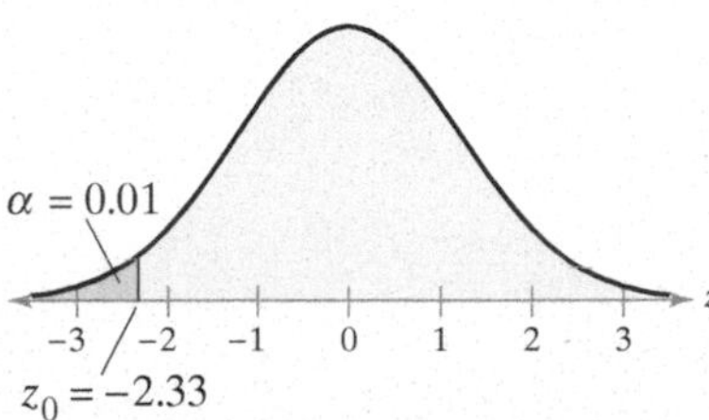


1% Level of Significance

The rejection region is to the left of this critical value. You can check your answer using technology, as shown below.

**EXCEL**

| | A |
|---|---|
| 1 | -2.326347874 |

← =NORM.S.INV(0.01)

**TRY IT YOURSELF 7**

Find the critical value and rejection region for a left-tailed test with $\alpha = 0.10$.

*Answer: Page A41*

Because normal distributions are symmetric, in a two-tailed test the critical values are opposites, as shown in the next example.

## EXAMPLE 8

### Finding Critical Values for a Two-Tailed Test

Find the critical values and rejection regions for a two-tailed test with $\alpha = 0.05$.

**SOLUTION**

The figure shows the standard normal curve with shaded areas of $\frac{1}{2}\alpha = 0.025$ in each tail. The area to the left of $-z_0$ is $\frac{1}{2}\alpha = 0.025$, and the area to the left of $z_0$ is $1 - \frac{1}{2}\alpha = 0.975$. In Table 4, the $z$-scores that correspond to the areas 0.025 and 0.975 are $-1.96$ and 1.96, respectively. So, the critical values are

$$-z_0 = -1.96 \quad \text{and} \quad z_0 = 1.96.$$

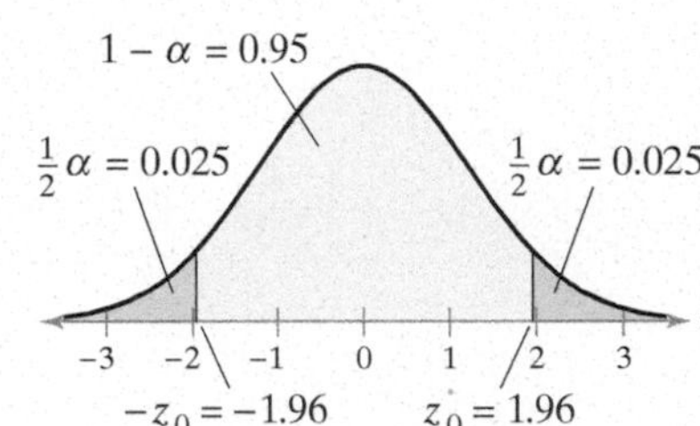


5% Level of Significance

The rejection regions are to the left of $-1.96$ and to the right of 1.96.

**TRY IT YOURSELF 8**

Find the critical values and rejection regions for a two-tailed test with $\alpha = 0.08$.

*Answer: Page A41*

**Study Tip**

The table lists the critical values for commonly used levels of significance.

| Alpha | Tail | $z$ |
|---|---|---|
| 0.10 | Left | −1.28 |
| | Right | 1.28 |
| | Two | ±1.645 |
| 0.05 | Left | −1.645 |
| | Right | 1.645 |
| | Two | ±1.96 |
| 0.01 | Left | −2.33 |
| | Right | 2.33 |
| | Two | ±2.575 |

## Using Rejection Regions for a $z$-Test

To conclude a hypothesis test using rejection region(s), you make a decision and interpret the decision according to the next rule.

### Decision Rule Based on Rejection Region

To use a rejection region to conduct a hypothesis test, calculate the standardized test statistic $z$. If the standardized test statistic

1. is in the rejection region, then reject $H_0$.
2. is *not* in the rejection region, then fail to reject $H_0$.

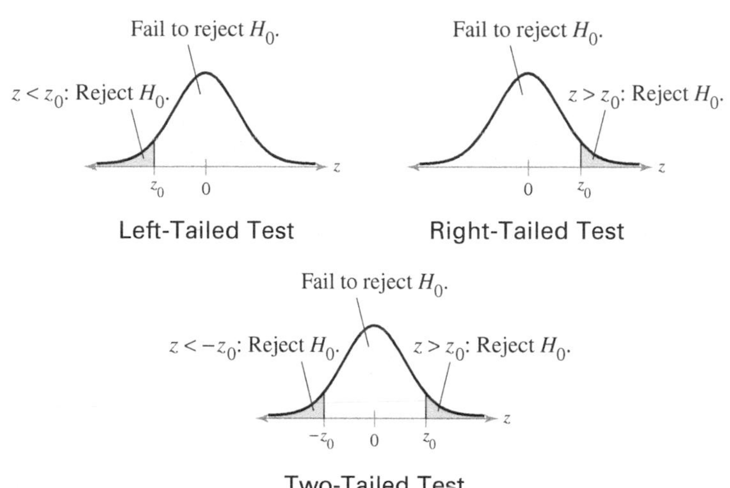


Remember, failing to reject the null hypothesis does not mean that you have accepted the null hypothesis as true. It simply means that there is not enough evidence to reject the null hypothesis.

### GUIDELINES

**Using Rejection Regions for a $z$-Test for a Mean $\mu$ ($\sigma$ Known)**

| In Words | In Symbols |
|---|---|
| **1.** Verify that $\sigma$ is known, the sample is random, and either the population is normally distributed or $n \geq 30$. | |
| **2.** State the claim mathematically and verbally. Identify the null and alternative hypotheses. | State $H_0$ and $H_a$. |
| **3.** Specify the level of significance. | Identify $\alpha$. |
| **4.** Determine the critical value(s). | Use Table 4 in Appendix B. |
| **5.** Determine the rejection region(s). | |
| **6.** Find the standardized test statistic and sketch the sampling distribution. | $z = \dfrac{\bar{x} - \mu}{\sigma/\sqrt{n}}$ |
| **7.** Make a decision to reject or fail to reject the null hypothesis. | If $z$ is in the rejection region, then reject $H_0$. Otherwise, fail to reject $H_0$. |
| **8.** Interpret the decision in the context of the original claim. | |

## Picturing the World

Each year, the Environmental Protection Agency (EPA) publishes reports of gas mileage for all makes and models of passenger vehicles. In a recent year, the subcompact car with the best mileage had a mean combined city/highway mileage of 113 miles per gallon. An auto manufacturer claims its subcompact cars have a combined city/highway mileage that exceeds the population mean of 25.7 miles per gallon. To support its claim, it tests 36 vehicles and obtains a sample mean of 28.5 miles per gallon. Assume the population standard deviation is 14.7 miles per gallon. (Source: U.S. Department of Energy)

**Is the evidence strong enough to support the claim that the subcompact car's combined city/highway mileage exceeds 25.7 miles per gallon? Use a $z$-test with $\alpha = 0.10$.**

**EXAMPLE 9**

See TI-84 Plus steps on page 415.

### Hypothesis Testing Using a Rejection Region

Employees at a construction and mining company claim that the mean salary of the company's mechanical engineers is less than that of one of its competitors, which is \$95,600. A random sample of 20 of the company's mechanical engineers has a mean salary of \$93,300. Assume the population standard deviation is \$9500 and the population is normally distributed. At $\alpha = 0.05$, test the employees' claim.

**SOLUTION**

Because $\sigma$ is known ($\sigma = \$9500$), the sample is random, and the population is normally distributed, you can use the $z$-test. The claim is "the mean salary is less than \$95,600." So, the null and alternative hypotheses can be written as

$H_0$: $\mu \geq \$95{,}600$ and $H_a$: $\mu < \$95{,}600$. (Claim)

Because the test is a left-tailed test and the level of significance is $\alpha = 0.05$, the critical value is $z_0 = -1.645$ and the rejection region is $z < -1.645$. The standardized test statistic is

$$z = \frac{\bar{x} - \mu}{\sigma/\sqrt{n}}$$ Because $\sigma$ is known and the population is normally distributed, use the $z$-test.

$$= \frac{93{,}300 - 95{,}600}{9500/\sqrt{20}}$$ Assume $\mu = \$95{,}600$.

$$\approx -1.08.$$ Round to two decimal places.

The figure shows the location of the rejection region and the standardized test statistic $z$. Because $z$ is not in the rejection region, you fail to reject the null hypothesis.

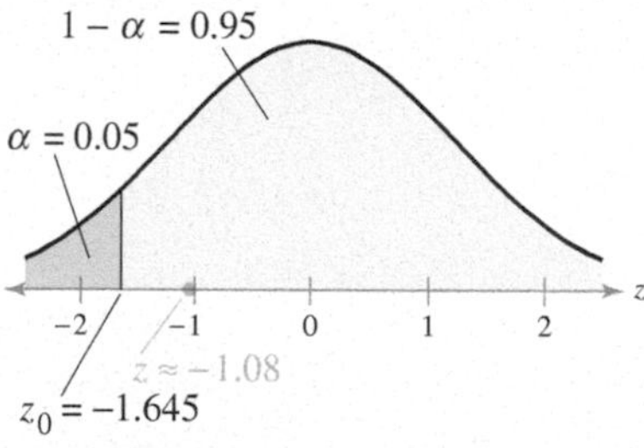


5% Level of Significance

***Interpretation*** There is not enough evidence at the 5% level of significance to support the employees' claim that the mean salary is less than \$95,600.

Be sure you understand the decision made in this example. Even though your sample has a mean of \$93,300, you cannot (at a 5% level of significance) support the claim that the mean of all the mechanical engineers' salaries is less than \$95,600. For instance, the difference between your test statistic ($\bar{x} = \$93{,}300$) and the hypothesized mean ($\mu = \$95{,}600$) could be due to sampling error.

**TRY IT YOURSELF 9**

The CEO of the company in Example 9 claims that the mean workday of the company's mechanical engineers is less than 8.5 hours. A random sample of 25 of the company's mechanical engineers has a mean workday of 8.2 hours. Assume the population standard deviation is 0.5 hour and the population is normally distributed. At $\alpha = 0.01$, test the CEO's claim. *Answer: Page A41*

## EXAMPLE 10

### Hypothesis Testing Using Rejection Regions

A researcher claims that the mean annual cost of raising a child between the ages of 1 and 3 in the U.S. is \$13,350. In a random sample of families in the U.S., the mean annual cost of raising a child between the ages of 1 and 3 is \$13,186. The sample consists of 1000 parents who had a child between the ages of 1 and 3. Assume the population standard deviation is \$2750. At $\alpha = 0.10$, is there enough evidence to reject the claim? *(Adapted from U.S. News & World Report)*

#### SOLUTION

Because $\sigma$ is known ($\sigma = \$2750$), the sample is random, and $n = 1000 \geq 30$, you can use the $z$-test. The claim is "the mean annual cost is \$13,350." So, the null and alternative hypotheses are

$H_0$: $\mu = \$13{,}350$ (Claim) and $H_a$: $\mu \neq \$13{,}350$.

Because the test is a two-tailed test and the level of significance is $\alpha = 0.10$, the critical values are $-z_0 = -1.645$ and $z_0 = 1.645$. The rejection regions are $z < -1.645$ and $z > 1.645$. The standardized test statistic is

$$z = \frac{\bar{x} - \mu}{\sigma/\sqrt{n}}$$ Because $\sigma$ is known and $n \geq 30$, use the $z$-test.

$$= \frac{13{,}186 - 13{,}350}{2750/\sqrt{1000}}$$ Assume $\mu = \$13{,}350$.

$$\approx -1.89.$$ Round to two decimal places.

The figure shows the location of the rejection regions and the standardized test statistic $z$. Because $z$ is in the rejection region, you reject the null hypothesis.

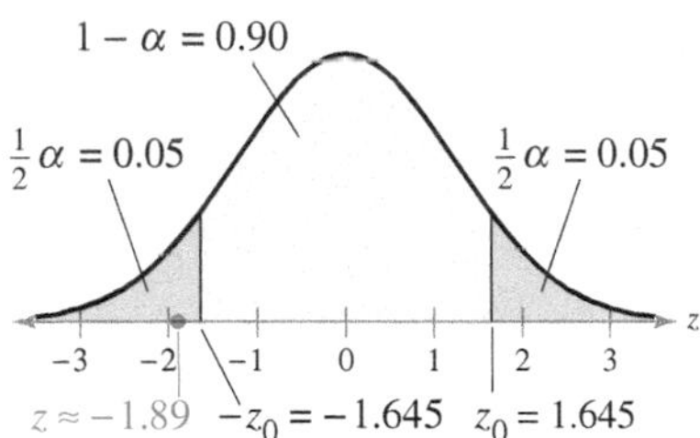


10% Level of Significance

You can check your answer using technology, as shown below.

**MINITAB**

**One-Sample Z**

| N | Mean | SE Mean | 90% CI for μ | Z-Value | P-Value |
|---|---|---|---|---|---|
| 1000 | 13186.0 | 87.0 | (13043.0, 13329.0) | −1.89 | 0.059 |

*μ: population mean of Sample* — *Null hypothesis* H₀: μ = 13350

*Known standard deviation = 2750* — *Alternative hypothesis* H₁: μ ≠ 13350

***Interpretation*** There is enough evidence at the 10% level of significance to reject the claim that the mean annual cost of raising a child between the ages of 1 and 3 in the U.S. is \$13,350.

#### TRY IT YOURSELF 10

In Example 10, at $\alpha = 0.01$, is there enough evidence to reject the claim?

*Answer: Page A41*

# 7.2 EXERCISES

For Extra Help: MyLab Statistics

## Building Basic Skills and Vocabulary

1. Explain the difference between the $z$-test for $\mu$ using a $P$-value and the $z$-test for $\mu$ using rejection region(s).

2. The mean of a random sample of 18 test scores is $\bar{x} = 85$. The standard deviation of the population of all test scores is $\sigma = 6$. Under what condition can you use a $z$-test to decide whether to reject a claim that the population mean is $\mu = 88$?

**Interpreting a *P*-Value** *In Exercises 3–8, the P-value for a hypothesis test is shown. Use the P-value to decide whether to reject $H_0$ when the level of significance is (a) $\alpha = 0.01$, (b) $\alpha = 0.05$, and (c) $\alpha = 0.10$.*

3. $P = 0.0461$
4. $P = 0.0691$
5. $P = 0.1271$
6. $P = 0.0107$
7. $P = 0.0838$
8. $P = 0.0062$

**Graphical Analysis** *In Exercises 9–12, match the P-value or z-statistic with the graph that represents the corresponding area. Explain your reasoning.*

9. $P = 0.0688$
10. $P = 0.2802$

(a)

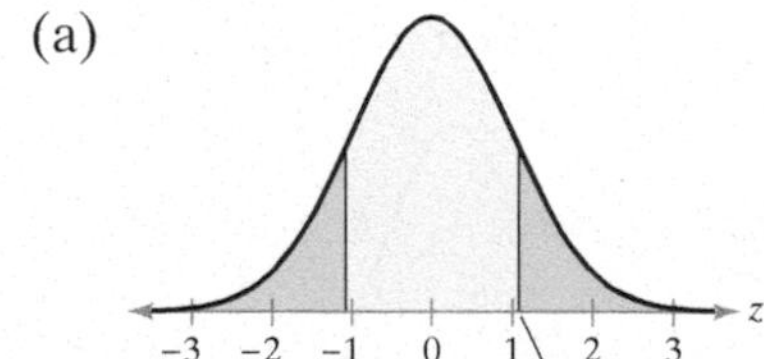


(b)

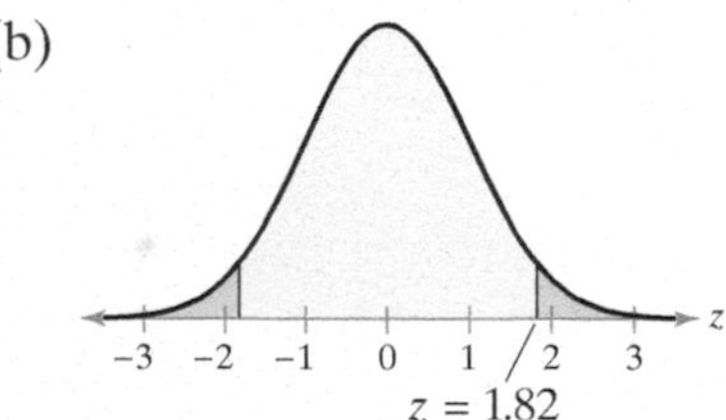


11. $z = -2.37$
12. $z = -0.51$

(a)

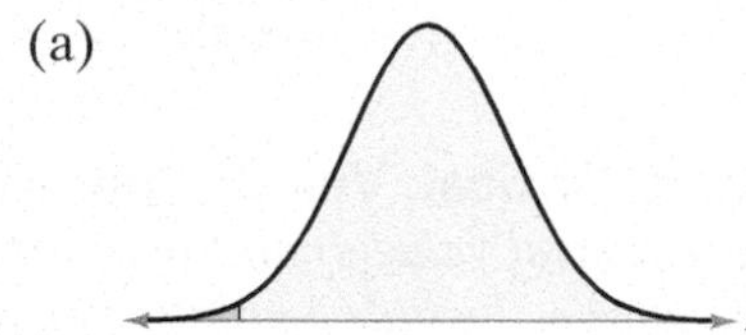


(b)

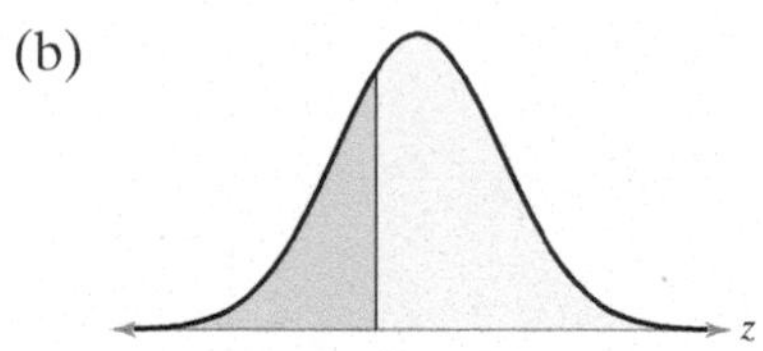


**Finding a *P*-Value** *In Exercises 13–18, find the P-value for the hypothesis test with the standardized test statistic z. Decide whether to reject $H_0$ for the level of significance $\alpha$.*

13. Left-tailed test
$z = -1.32$
$\alpha = 0.10$

14. Left-tailed test
$z = -1.55$
$\alpha = 0.05$

15. Right-tailed test
$z = 2.46$
$\alpha = 0.01$

16. Right-tailed test
$z = 1.23$
$\alpha = 0.10$

17. Two-tailed test
$z = -1.68$
$\alpha = 0.05$

18. Two-tailed test
$z = 1.95$
$\alpha = 0.08$

*In Exercises 19 and 20, use the TI-84 Plus displays to make a decision to reject or fail to reject the null hypothesis at the level of significance.*

**19.** $\alpha = 0.05$

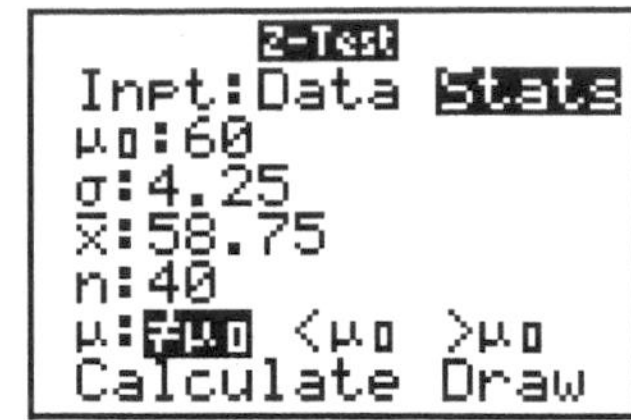


Z-Test
μ≠60
z=-1.86016333
p=.0628622957
x̄=58.75
n=40

**20.** $\alpha = 0.01$

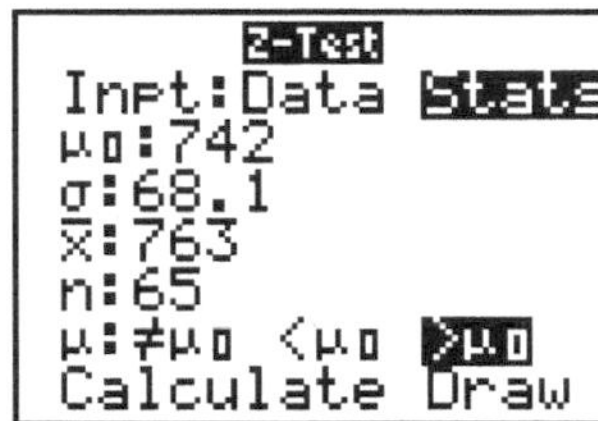


Z-Test
μ>742
z=2.486158777
p=.0064565285
x̄=763
n=65

**Graphical Analysis** *In Exercises 21 and 22, state whether each standardized test statistic z allows you to reject the null hypothesis. Explain your reasoning.*

**21.** (a) $z = -1.301$
(b) $z = 1.203$
(c) $z = 1.280$
(d) $z = 1.286$

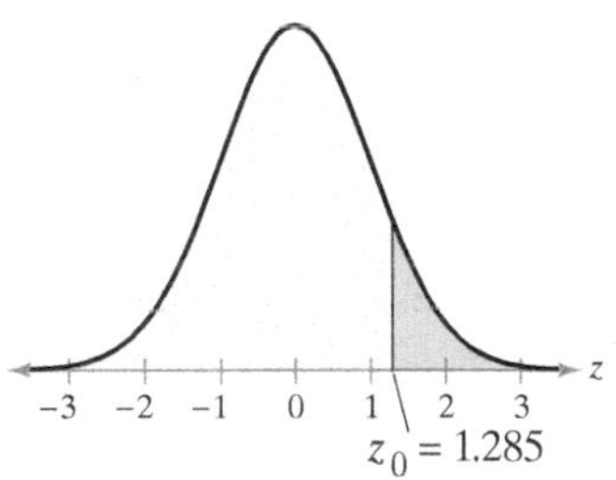


**22.** (a) $z = 1.98$
(b) $z = -1.89$
(c) $z = 1.65$
(d) $z = -1.99$

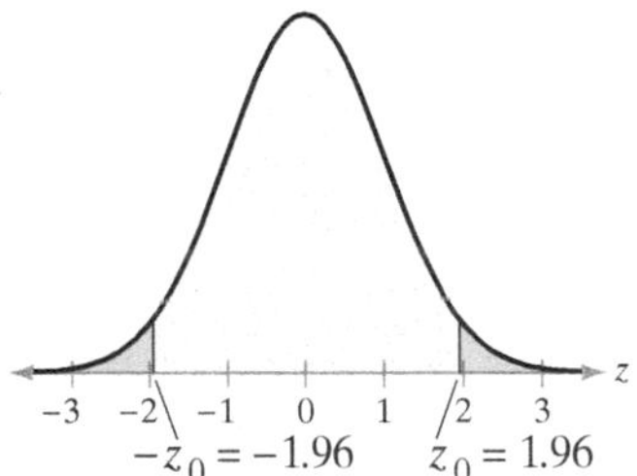


**Finding Critical Values and Rejection Regions** *In Exercises 23–28, find the critical value(s) and rejection region(s) for the type of z-test with level of significance α. Include a graph with your answer.*

**23.** Left-tailed test, $\alpha = 0.03$

**24.** Left-tailed test, $\alpha = 0.09$

**25.** Right-tailed test, $\alpha = 0.05$

**26.** Right-tailed test, $\alpha = 0.08$

**27.** Two-tailed test, $\alpha = 0.02$

**28.** Two-tailed test, $\alpha = 0.12$

*In Exercises 29–32, test the claim about the population mean μ at the level of significance α. Assume the population is normally distributed.*

**29.** Claim: $\mu = 40$; $\alpha = 0.05$; $\sigma = 1.97$
Sample statistics: $\bar{x} = 39.2$, $n = 25$

**30.** Claim: $\mu \geq 1475$; $\alpha = 0.07$; $\sigma = 29$
Sample statistics: $\bar{x} = 1468$, $n = 26$

**31.** Claim: $\mu \neq 5880$; $\alpha = 0.03$; $\sigma = 413$
Sample statistics: $\bar{x} = 5771$, $n = 67$

**32.** Claim: $\mu \leq 22{,}500$; $\alpha = 0.01$; $\sigma = 1200$
Sample statistics: $\bar{x} = 23{,}500$, $n = 45$

## Using and Interpreting Concepts

**Hypothesis Testing Using a *P*-Value** *In Exercises 33–38,*

*(a) identify the claim and state $H_0$ and $H_a$.*

*(b) find the standardized test statistic z.*

*(c) find the corresponding P-value.*

*(d) decide whether to reject or fail to reject the null hypothesis.*

*(e) interpret the decision in the context of the original claim.*

**33. MCAT Scores** A random sample of 100 medical school applicants at a university has a mean total score of 505 on the MCAT. According to a report, the mean total score for the school's applicants is more than 503. Assume the population standard deviation is 10.6. At $\alpha = 0.01$, is there enough evidence to support the report's claim? *(Adapted from Association of American Medical Colleges)*

**34. Sprinkler Systems** A manufacturer of sprinkler systems designed for fire protection claims that the average activating temperature is at least 135°F. To test this claim, you randomly select a sample of 32 systems and find the mean activation temperature to be 133°F. Assume the population standard deviation is 3.3°F. At $\alpha = 0.10$, do you have enough evidence to reject the manufacturer's claim?

**35. Boston Marathon** A sports statistician claims that the mean winning times for Boston Marathon women's open division champions is at least 2.6 hours. The mean winning time of a sample of 30 randomly selected Boston Marathon women's open division champions is 2.52 hours. Assume the population standard deviation is 0.18 hour. At $\alpha = 0.05$, can you reject the claim? *(Adapted from Boston Athletic Association)*

**36. Acceleration Times** A consumer group claims that the mean acceleration time from 0 to 60 miles per hour for all 3-cylinder vehicles is 9.4 seconds. A random sample of 33 3-cylinder vehicles has a mean acceleration time from 0 to 60 miles per hour of 10.2 seconds. Assume the population standard deviation is 2.3 seconds. At $\alpha = 0.05$, can you reject the claim? *(Adapted from Zero to 60 Times)*

**37. Roller Coasters** The vertical drops (in feet) of 36 randomly selected top-rated roller coasters are listed. Assume the population standard deviation is 65.1 feet. At $\alpha = 0.05$, is there enough evidence to reject the claim that the mean vertical drop of top-rated roller coasters is 163 feet? *(Adapted from Coasterpedia )*

| | | | | | | | | |
|---|---|---|---|---|---|---|---|---|
| 100 | 100 | 131 | 116 | 98 | 306 | 180 | 118 | 103 |
| 210 | 215 | 249 | 115 | 104 | 72 | 195 | 135 | 100 |
| 161 | 98 | 89 | 131 | 98 | 151 | 98 | 171 | 154 |
| 151 | 161 | 256 | 98 | 119 | 125 | 131 | 80 | 300 |

**38. Salaries** An analyst claims that the mean annual salary for intermediate level electrical engineers in Baltimore, Maryland, is more than the national mean, \$86,700. The annual salaries (in dollars) for a random sample of 21 intermediate level electrical engineers in Baltimore are listed. Assume the population is normally distributed and the population standard deviation is \$13,600. At $\alpha = 0.09$, is there enough evidence to support the analyst's claim? *(Adapted from Salary.com)*

| | | | | | | |
|---|---|---|---|---|---|---|
| 71,323 | 87,322 | 88,900 | 75,212 | 89,516 | 92,345 | 95,100 |
| 78,444 | 92,634 | 96,117 | 90,309 | 97,818 | 86,437 | 103,345 |
| 97,722 | 93,676 | 89,925 | 90,121 | 92,008 | 91,555 | 86,544 |

**Hypothesis Testing Using Rejection Region(s)** *In Exercises 39–44, (a) identify the claim and state $H_0$ and $H_a$, (b) find the critical value(s) and identify the rejection region(s), (c) find the standardized test statistic z, (d) decide whether to reject or fail to reject the null hypothesis, and (e) interpret the decision in the context of the original claim.*

**39. Caffeine Content** A consumer research organization states that the mean caffeine content per 12-ounce bottle of a population of caffeinated soft drinks is 37.7 milligrams. You want to test this claim. During your tests, you find that a random sample of thirty-six 12-ounce bottles of caffeinated soft drinks has a mean caffeine content of 36.4 milligrams. Assume the population standard deviation is 10.8 milligrams. At $\alpha = 0.01$, can you reject the research organization's claim? *(Source: National Soft Drink Association)*

**40. High School Graduation Rate** An education researcher claims that the mean high school 4-year graduation rate per state in the United States is 83%. You want to test this claim. You find that a random sample of 30 states has a mean high school 4-year graduation rate of 85%. Assume the population standard deviation is 3.9%. At $\alpha = 0.05$, do you have enough evidence to reject the researcher's claim? *(Source: U.S. Department of Education)*

**41. Fast Food** A fast food restaurant estimates that the mean sodium content in one of its breakfast sandwiches is less than 920 milligrams. A random sample of 40 breakfast sandwiches has a mean sodium content of 925 milligrams. Assume the population standard deviation is 18 milligrams. At $\alpha = 0.05$, do you have enough evidence to support the restaurant's claim?

**42. Light Bulbs** A light bulb manufacturer guarantees that the mean life of a certain type of light bulb is at least 750 hours. A random sample of 25 light bulbs has a mean life of 745 hours. Assume the population is normally distributed and the population standard deviation is 60 hours. At $\alpha = 0.02$, do you have enough evidence to reject the manufacturer's claim?

**43. Fluorescent Lamps** A compact fluorescent lamp (CFL) bulb manufacturer guarantees that the mean life of a CFL bulb is at least 10,000 hours. You want to test this guarantee. To do so, you record the lives of a random sample of 32 CFL bulbs. The results (in hours) are listed. Assume the population standard deviation is 1850 hours. At $\alpha = 0.11$, do you have enough evidence to reject the manufacturer's claim?

| | | | | | | | |
|---|---|---|---|---|---|---|---|
| 8,800 | 9,155 | 13,001 | 10,250 | 10,002 | 11,413 | 8,234 | 10,402 |
| 10,016 | 8,015 | 6,110 | 11,005 | 11,555 | 9,254 | 6,991 | 12,006 |
| 10,420 | 8,302 | 8,151 | 10,980 | 10,186 | 10,003 | 8,814 | 11,445 |
| 6,277 | 8,632 | 7,265 | 10,584 | 9,397 | 11,987 | 7,556 | 10,380 |

**44. Gross Domestic Product** A politician estimates that the mean gross domestic product (GDP) per country in a recent year is greater than $400 billion. You want to test this estimate. To do so, you determine the GDPs of 42 randomly selected countries for that year. The results (in billions of dollars) are shown in the table at the left. Assume the population standard deviation is $2099 billion. At $\alpha = 0.06$, can you support the politician's estimate? *(Source: International Monetary Fund)*

| Gross domestic product (in billions of dollars) | | | | | |
|---|---|---|---|---|---|
| 11 | 101 | 59 | 24 | 66 | 1883 |
| 403 | 11 | 18 | 61 | 50 | 3050 |
| 1.7 | 61 | 22 | 25 | 3.4 | 17 |
| 2.5 | 85 | 4.6 | 330 | 7.3 | 19 |
| 482 | 44 | 3.7 | 38 | 4.6 | 66 |
| 127 | 43 | 43 | 17 | 402 | 1618 |
| 151 | 16 | 24 | 14 | 7.8 | 300 |

TABLE FOR EXERCISE 44

## Extending Concepts

**45. Writing** When $P > \alpha$, does the standardized test statistic lie inside or outside of the rejection region(s)? Explain your reasoning.

**46. Writing** In a right-tailed test where $P < \alpha$, does the standardized test statistic lie to the left or the right of the critical value? Explain your reasoning.

# 7.3 Hypothesis Testing for the Mean ($\sigma$ Unknown)

**What You Should Learn**

- How to find critical values in a $t$-distribution
- How to use the $t$-test to test a mean $\mu$ when $\sigma$ is not known
- How to use technology to find $P$-values and use them with a $t$-test to test a mean $\mu$ when $\sigma$ is not known

Critical Values in a $t$-Distribution ■ The $t$-Test for a Mean $\mu$ ■ Using $P$-Values with $t$-Tests

## Critical Values in a $t$-Distribution

In Section 7.2, you learned how to perform a hypothesis test for a population mean when the population standard deviation is known. In many real-life situations, the population standard deviation in *not* known. When either the population has a normal distribution or the sample size is at least 30, you can still test the population mean $\mu$. To do so, you can use the $t$-distribution with $n - 1$ degrees of freedom.

**GUIDELINES**

**Finding Critical Values in a $t$-Distribution**

1. Specify the level of significance $\alpha$.
2. Identify the degrees of freedom, d.f. $= n - 1$.
3. Find the critical value(s) using Table 5 in Appendix B in the row with $n - 1$ degrees of freedom. When the hypothesis test is
   a. *left-tailed,* use the "One Tail, $\alpha$" column with a negative sign.
   b. *right-tailed,* use the "One Tail, $\alpha$" column with a positive sign.
   c. *two-tailed,* use the "Two Tails, $\alpha$" column with a negative and a positive sign.

See the figures below.

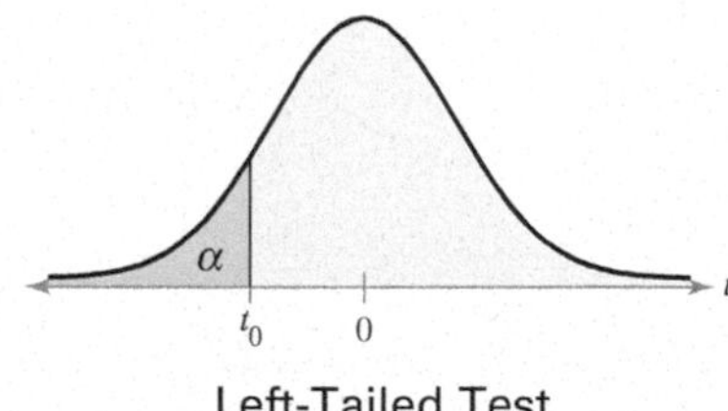

Left-Tailed Test

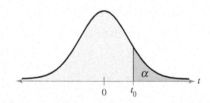

Right-Tailed Test

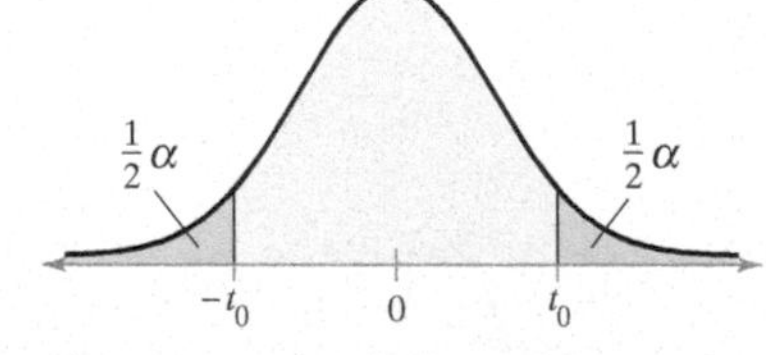

Two-Tailed Test

**EXAMPLE 1**

### Finding a Critical Value for a Left-Tailed Test

Find the critical value $t_0$ for a left-tailed test with $\alpha = 0.05$ and $n = 21$.

**SOLUTION**

The degrees of freedom are

$$\text{d.f.} = n - 1 = 21 - 1 = 20.$$

To find the critical value, use Table 5 in Appendix B with d.f. $= 20$ and $\alpha = 0.05$ in the "One Tail, $\alpha$" column. Because the test is left-tailed, the critical value is negative. So, $t_0 = -1.725$, as shown in the figure at the left.

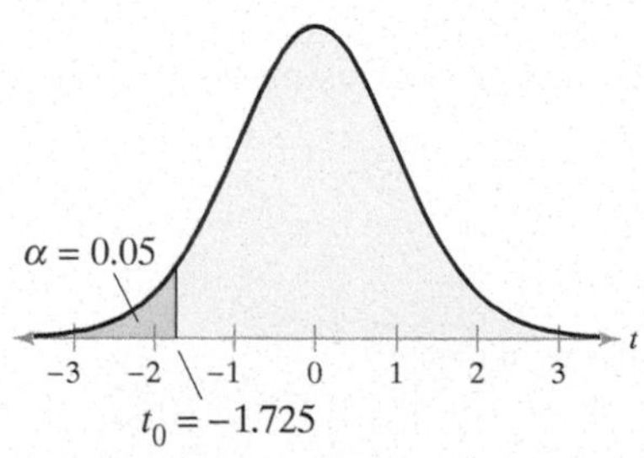

5% Level of Significance

**TRY IT YOURSELF 1**

Find the critical value $t_0$ for a left-tailed test with $\alpha = 0.01$ and $n = 14$.

*Answer: Page A41*

**EXAMPLE 2**

### Finding a Critical Value for a Right-Tailed Test

Find the critical value $t_0$ for a right-tailed test with $\alpha = 0.01$ and $n = 17$.

**SOLUTION**

The degrees of freedom are

$$\begin{aligned} \text{d.f.} &= n - 1 \\ &= 17 - 1 \\ &= 16. \end{aligned}$$

To find the critical value, use Table 5 with d.f. = 16 and $\alpha = 0.01$ in the "One Tail, $\alpha$" column. Because the test is right-tailed, the critical value is positive. So,

$$t_0 = 2.583$$

as shown in the figure.

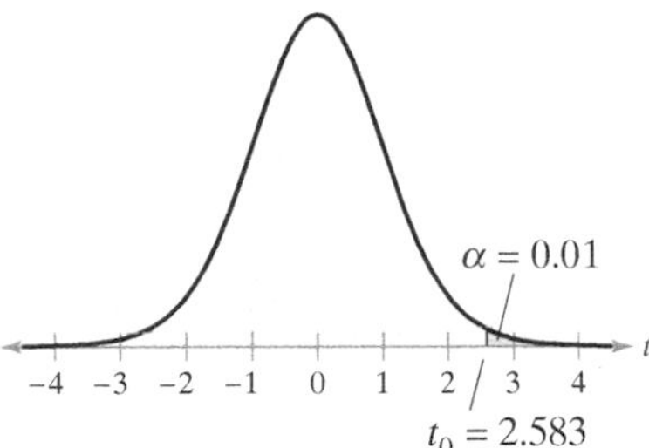


1% Level of Significance

**TRY IT YOURSELF 2**

Find the critical value $t_0$ for a right-tailed test with $\alpha = 0.10$ and $n = 9$.

*Answer: Page A41*

Because $t$-distributions are symmetric, in a two-tailed test the critical values are opposites, as shown in the next example.

**EXAMPLE 3**

### Finding Critical Values for a Two-Tailed Test

Find the critical values $t_0$ and $t_0$ for a two-tailed test with $\alpha = 0.10$ and $n = 26$.

**SOLUTION**

The degrees of freedom are

$$\begin{aligned} \text{d.f.} &= n - 1 \\ &= 26 - 1 \\ &= 25. \end{aligned}$$

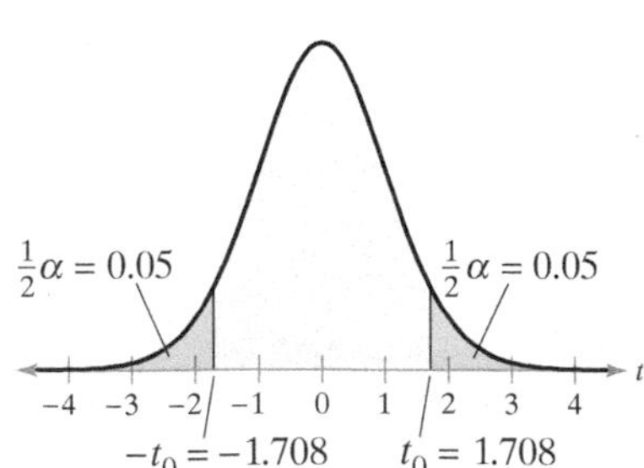


10% Level of Significance

To find the critical values, use Table 5 with d.f. = 25 and $\alpha = 0.10$ in the "Two Tails, $\alpha$" column. Because the test is two-tailed, one critical value is negative and one is positive. So,

$$-t_0 = -1.708 \quad \text{and} \quad t_0 = 1.708$$

as shown in the figure at the left. You can check your answer using technology, as shown below.

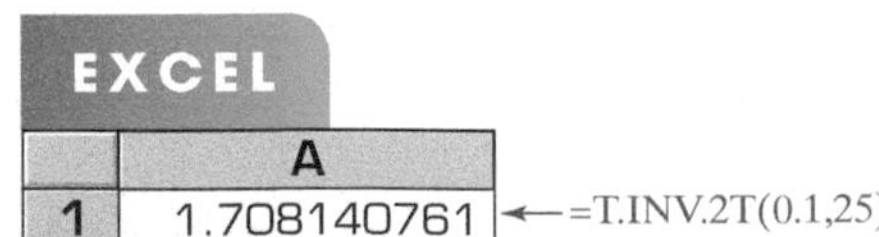


**TRY IT YOURSELF 3**

Find the critical values $-t_0$ and $t_0$ for a two-tailed test with $\alpha = 0.05$ and $n = 16$.

*Answer: Page A41*

## Picturing the World

Exposure to lead may cause red blood cell, kidney, or brain damage. The Environmental Protection Agency established rules that require water systems to monitor drinking water at customer taps. If lead concentrations exceed 0.015 milligram per liter in more than 10% of customer taps sampled, the system must undertake a number of actions, such as source water treatment, public education, and lead service line replacement. On the basis of a *t*-test, a water system makes a decision on whether the mean level of lead in the water exceeds the allowable amount of 0.015 milligram per liter. Assume the null hypothesis is $\mu \leq 0.015$.

(Source: Environmental Protection Agency)

| | $H_0$ is true. | $H_0$ is false. |
|---|---|---|
| **Do not reject $H_0$.** | | |
| **Reject $H_0$.** | | |

**Describe the possible type I and type II errors of this situation.**

## The *t*-Test for a Mean $\mu$

To test a claim about a mean $\mu$ when $\sigma$ is *not* known, you can use a *t*-sampling distribution. The standardized test statistic takes the form of

$$t = \frac{\text{(Sample mean)} - \text{(Hypothesized mean)}}{\text{Standard error}}.$$

Because $\sigma$ is not known, the standardized test statistic is calculated using the sample standard deviation $s$, as shown in the next definition.

### *t*-Test for a Mean $\mu$

The ***t*-test for a mean $\mu$** is a statistical test for a population mean. The **test statistic** is the sample mean $\bar{x}$. The **standardized test statistic** is

$$t = \frac{\bar{x} - \mu}{s/\sqrt{n}} \qquad \text{Standardized test statistic for } \mu \ (\sigma \text{ unknown})$$

when these conditions are met.

1. The sample is random.
2. At least one of the following is true: The population is normally distributed or $n \geq 30$.

The degrees of freedom are d.f. $= n - 1$.

### GUIDELINES

**Using the *t*-Test for a Mean $\mu$ ($\sigma$ Unknown)**

| In Words | In Symbols |
|---|---|
| 1. Verify that $\sigma$ is not known, the sample is random, and either the population is normally distributed or $n \geq 30$. | |
| 2. State the claim mathematically and verbally. Identify the null and alternative hypotheses. | State $H_0$ and $H_a$. |
| 3. Specify the level of significance. | Identify $\alpha$. |
| 4. Identify the degrees of freedom. | d.f. $= n - 1$ |
| 5. Determine the critical value(s). | Use Table 5 in Appendix B. |
| 6. Determine the rejection region(s). | |
| 7. Find the standardized test statistic and sketch the sampling distribution. | $t = \dfrac{\bar{x} - \mu}{s/\sqrt{n}}$ |
| 8. Make a decision to reject or fail to reject the null hypothesis. | If $t$ is in the rejection region, then reject $H_0$. Otherwise, fail to reject $H_0$. |
| 9. Interpret the decision in the context of the original claim. | |

In Step 8 of the guidelines, the decision rule uses rejection regions. You can also test a claim using *P*-values, as shown on page 382. Also, when the number of degrees of freedom you need is not in Table 5, use the closest number in the table that is less than the value you need (or use technology). For instance, for d.f. $= 57$, use 50 degrees of freedom.

**EXAMPLE 4**

See Minitab steps on page 414.

### Hypothesis Testing Using a Rejection Region

A used car dealer says that the mean listing price of all used vehicles sold in the past 12 months is at least \$23,500. You suspect this claim is incorrect and find that a random sample of 14 used vehicles sold in the past 12 months has a mean listing price of \$21,558 and a standard deviation of \$3350. Is there enough evidence to reject the dealer's claim at $\alpha = 0.05$? Assume the population is normally distributed. *(Adapted from Edmunds.com)*

**SOLUTION**

Because $\sigma$ is unknown, the sample is random, and the population is normally distributed, you can use the $t$-test. The claim is "the mean listing price is at least \$23,500." So, the null and alternative hypotheses are

$$H_0: \mu \geq \$23{,}500 \text{ (Claim)}$$

and

$$H_a: \mu < \$23{,}500.$$

The test is a left-tailed test, the level of significance is $\alpha = 0.05$, and the degrees of freedom are

$$\text{d.f.} = 14 - 1 = 13.$$

So, using Table 5, the critical value is $t_0 = -1.771$. The rejection region is $t < -1.771$. The standardized test statistic is

$$t = \frac{\bar{x} - \mu}{s/\sqrt{n}}$$ Because $\sigma$ is unknown and the population is normally distributed, use the $t$-test.

$$= \frac{21{,}558 - 23{,}500}{3350/\sqrt{14}}$$ Assume $\mu = 23{,}500$.

$$\approx -2.169.$$ Round to three decimal places.

7.3 To explore this topic further, see **Activity 7.3** on page 386.

The figure shows the location of the rejection region and the standardized test statistic $t$. Because $t$ is in the rejection region, you reject the null hypothesis.

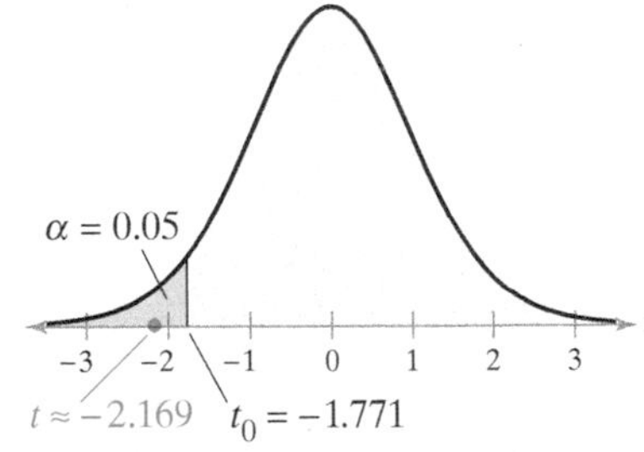

5% Level of Significance

***Interpretation*** There is enough evidence at the 5% level of significance to reject the claim that the mean listing price of all used vehicles sold in the past 12 months is at least \$23,500.

**TRY IT YOURSELF 4**

An industry analyst says that the mean transaction price of all new vehicles sold in the past 12 months is less than \$43,500. A random sample of 25 new vehicles sold in the past 12 months has a mean transaction price of \$40,573 and a standard deviation of \$6250. Is there enough evidence to support the analyst's claim at $\alpha = 0.10$? Assume the population is normally distributed. *(Adapted from Edmunds.com)*

*Answer: Page A41*

Remember that when you make a decision, the possibility of a type I or a type II error exists. For instance, in Example 4, a type I error is possible when you reject $H_0$, because $\mu \geq \$23{,}500$ may be true.

## EXAMPLE 5

See TI-84 Plus steps on page 415.

### Hypothesis Testing Using Rejection Regions

An industrial company claims that the mean pH level of the water in a nearby river is 6.8. You randomly select 39 water samples and measure the pH of each. The sample mean and standard deviation are 6.7 and 0.35, respectively. Is there enough evidence to reject the company's claim at $\alpha = 0.05$?

**SOLUTION**

Because $\sigma$ is unknown, the sample is random, and $n = 39 \geq 30$, you can use the $t$-test. The claim is "the mean pH level is 6.8." So, the null and alternative hypotheses are

$$H_0: \mu = 6.8 \text{ (Claim)} \quad \text{and} \quad H_a: \mu \neq 6.8.$$

The test is a two-tailed test, the level of significance is $\alpha = 0.05$, and the degrees of freedom are d.f. $= 39 - 1 = 38$. So, using Table 5, the critical values are $-t_0 = -2.024$ and $t_0 = 2.024$. The rejection regions are $t < -2.024$ and $t > 2.024$. The standardized test statistic is

$$t = \frac{\bar{x} - \mu}{s/\sqrt{n}}$$ Because $\sigma$ is unknown and $n \geq 30$, use the $t$-test.

$$= \frac{6.7 - 6.8}{0.35/\sqrt{39}}$$ Assume $\mu = 6.8$.

$$\approx -1.784.$$ Round to three decimal places.

The figure shows the location of the rejection regions and the standardized test statistic $t$. Because $t$ is not in the rejection region, you fail to reject the null hypothesis. You can confirm this decision using technology, as shown below.

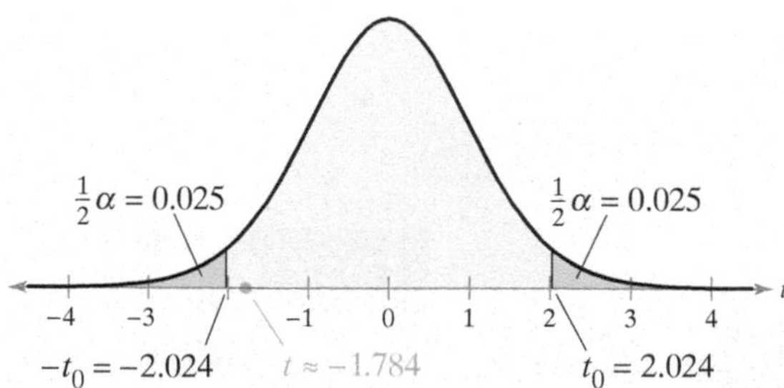


5% Level of Significance

**MINITAB**

**One-Sample T**

| N | Mean | StDev | SE Mean | 95% CI for μ | T-Value | P-Value |
|---|---|---|---|---|---|---|
| 39 | 6.7000 | 0.3500 | 0.0560 | (6.5865, 6.8135) | −1.78 | 0.082 |

*μ: population mean of Sample*

*Null hypothesis* $H_0: \mu = 6.8$

*Alternative hypothesis* $H_1: \mu \neq 6.8$

***Interpretation*** There is not enough evidence at the 5% level of significance to reject the claim that the mean pH level is 6.8.

**TRY IT YOURSELF 5**

The company in Example 5 claims that the mean conductivity of the river is 1890 milligrams per liter. The conductivity of a water sample is a measure of the total dissolved solids in the sample. You randomly select 39 water samples and measure the conductivity of each. The sample mean and standard deviation are 2350 milligrams per liter and 900 milligrams per liter, respectively. Is there enough evidence to reject the company's claim at $\alpha = 0.01$?

*Answer: Page A41*

### Tech Tip

Using a TI-84 Plus, you can either enter the original data into a list to find a *P*-value or enter the descriptive statistics.

STAT

Choose the TESTS menu.

2: T-Test...

Select the *Data* input option when you use the original data. Select the *Stats* input option when you use the descriptive statistics. In each case, enter the appropriate values, including the corresponding type of hypothesis test indicated by the alternative hypothesis. Then select *Calculate*.

## Using *P*-Values With *t*-Tests

You can also use *P*-values for a *t*-test for a mean $\mu$. For instance, consider finding a *P*-value given $t = 1.98$, 15 degrees of freedom, and a right-tailed test. Using Table 5 in Appendix B, you can determine that *P* falls between

$$\alpha = 0.025 \quad \text{and} \quad \alpha = 0.05$$

but you cannot determine an exact value for *P*. In such cases, you can use technology to perform a hypothesis test and find exact *P*-values.

**EXAMPLE 6**

### Using *P*-Values with a *t*-Test

A department of motor vehicles office claims that the mean wait time is less than 14 minutes. A random sample of 10 people has a mean wait time of 13 minutes with a standard deviation of 3.5 minutes. At $\alpha = 0.10$, test the office's claim. Assume the population is normally distributed.

**SOLUTION**

Because $\sigma$ is unknown, the sample is random, and the population is normally distributed, you can use the *t*-test. The claim is "the mean wait time is less than 14 minutes." So, the null and alternative hypotheses are

$$H_0\colon \mu \geq 14 \text{ minutes}$$

and

$$H_a\colon \mu < 14 \text{ minutes.} \qquad \text{(Claim)}$$

The TI-84 Plus display at the far left shows how to set up the hypothesis test. The two displays on the right show the possible results, depending on whether you select *Calculate* or *Draw*.

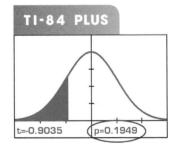

**TI-84 PLUS**

T-Test
Inpt:Data Stats
μ0:14
x̄:13
Sx:3.5
n:10
μ:≠μ0 <μ0 >μ0
Calculate Draw

**TI-84 PLUS**

T-Test
μ<14
t=−.9035079029
p=.1948994027
x̄=13
Sx=3.5
n=10

**TI-84 PLUS**

t=-0.9035 p=0.1949

From the displays, you can see that

$$P \approx 0.1949.$$

Because the *P*-value is greater than $\alpha = 0.10$, you fail to reject the null hypothesis.

***Interpretation*** There is not enough evidence at the 10% level of significance to support the office's claim that the mean wait time is less than 14 minutes.

**TRY IT YOURSELF 6**

Another department of motor vehicles office claims that the mean wait time is at most 18 minutes. A random sample of 12 people has a mean wait time of 15 minutes with a standard deviation of 2.2 minutes. At $\alpha = 0.05$, test the office's claim. Assume the population is normally distributed.

*Answer: Page A41*

# 7.3 EXERCISES

For Extra Help: MyLab Statistics

## Building Basic Skills and Vocabulary

**1.** Explain how to find critical values for a $t$-distribution.

**2.** Explain how to use a $t$-test to test a hypothesized mean $\mu$ when $\sigma$ is unknown. What assumptions are necessary?

*In Exercises 3–8, find the critical value(s) and rejection region(s) for the type of t-test with level of significance $\alpha$ and sample size n.*

**3.** Left-tailed test, $\alpha = 0.10, n = 20$

**4.** Left-tailed test, $\alpha = 0.01, n = 35$

**5.** Right-tailed test, $\alpha = 0.05, n = 23$

**6.** Right-tailed test, $\alpha = 0.01, n = 31$

**7.** Two-tailed test, $\alpha = 0.05, n = 27$

**8.** Two-tailed test, $\alpha = 0.10, n = 38$

**Graphical Analysis** *In Exercises 9–12, state whether each standardized test statistic t allows you to reject the null hypothesis. Explain.*

**9.** (a) $t = 2.091$
(b) $t = 0$
(c) $t = -2.096$

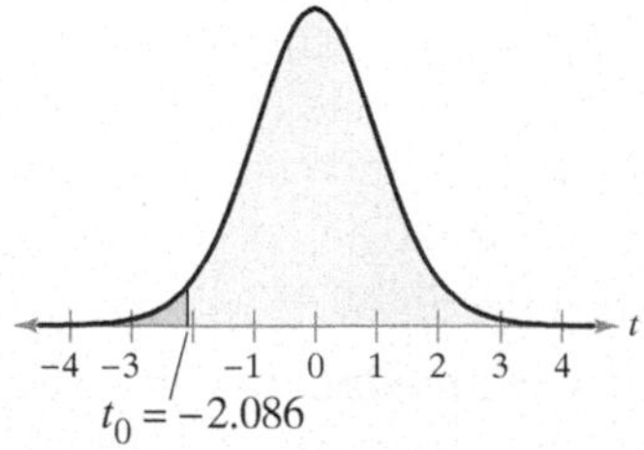


**10.** (a) $t = 1.4$
(b) $t = 1.42$
(c) $t = -1.402$

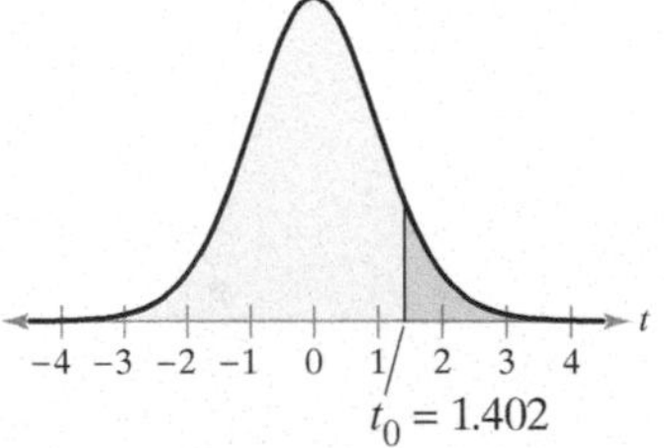


**11.** (a) $t = -1.755$
(b) $t = -1.585$
(c) $t = 1.745$

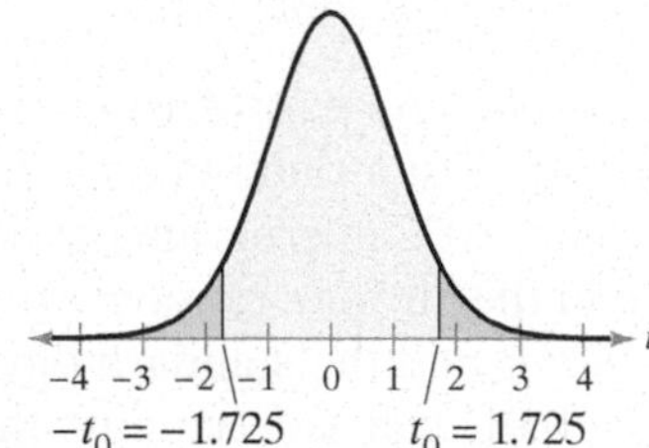


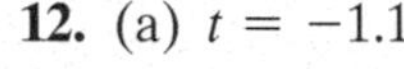

**12.** (a) $t = -1.1$
(b) $t = 1.01$
(c) $t = 1.7$

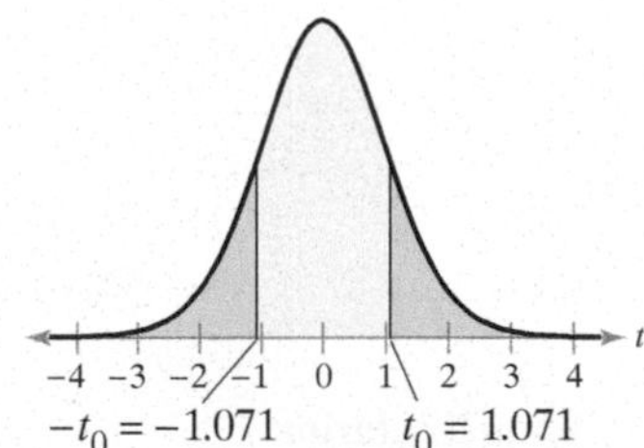


*In Exercises 13–18, test the claim about the population mean $\mu$ at the level of significance $\alpha$. Assume the population is normally distributed.*

**13.** Claim: $\mu = 15$; $\alpha = 0.01$. Sample statistics: $\bar{x} = 13.9, s = 3.23, n = 36$

**14.** Claim: $\mu > 25$; $\alpha = 0.05$. Sample statistics: $\bar{x} = 26.2, s = 2.32, n = 17$

**15.** Claim: $\mu \geq 8000$; $\alpha = 0.01$. Sample statistics: $\bar{x} = 7700, s = 450, n = 25$

**16.** Claim: $\mu \leq 1600$; $\alpha = 0.02$. Sample statistics: $\bar{x} = 1550, s = 165, n = 46$

**17.** Claim: $\mu < 4915$; $\alpha = 0.02$. Sample statistics: $\bar{x} = 5017, s = 5613, n = 51$

**18.** Claim: $\mu \neq 52{,}200$; $\alpha = 0.05$. Sample statistics: $\bar{x} = 53{,}220, s = 2700, n = 34$

## Using and Interpreting Concepts

**Hypothesis Testing Using Rejection Regions** *In Exercises 19–26, (a) identify the claim and state $H_0$ and $H_a$, (b) find the critical value(s) and identify the rejection region(s), (c) find the standardized test statistic t, (d) decide whether to reject or fail to reject the null hypothesis, and (e) interpret the decision in the context of the original claim. Assume the population is normally distributed.*

**19. Listening Time** A product review claims that Apple AirPods have a mean listening time of at least 5.0 hours on a single charge. You suspect this claim is incorrect and find that a random sample of 18 pairs of AirPods has a mean single-charge listening time of 4.69 hours and a standard deviation of 0.57 hour. Is there enough evidence to reject the claim at $\alpha = 0.01$?

**20. DMV Wait Times** A state Department of Transportation claims that the mean wait time for various services at its different locations is at most 6 minutes. A random sample of 34 services at different locations has a mean wait time of 10.3 minutes and a standard deviation of 8.0 minutes. Is there enough evidence to reject the claim at $\alpha = 0.01$?

**21. Credit Card Debt** A credit reporting agency claims that the mean credit card debt in Colorado is greater than \$5540 per borrower. You want to test this claim. You find that a random sample of 30 borrowers has a mean credit card debt of \$5594 per person and a standard deviation of \$597 per person. At $\alpha = 0.05$, can you support the claim? *(Adapted from Experian)*

**22. Used Car Cost** A used car dealer says that the mean price of a three-year-old sport utility vehicle (in good condition) is \$20,000. You suspect this claim is incorrect and find that a random sample of 22 similar vehicles has a mean price of \$20,640 and a standard deviation of \$1990. Is there enough evidence to reject the claim at $\alpha = 0.05$?

**23. Carbon Monoxide Levels** As part of your work for an environmental awareness group, you want to test a claim that the mean amount of carbon monoxide in the air in U.S. cities is less than 1.80 parts per million. You find that the mean amount of carbon monoxide in the air for a random sample of 64 U.S. cities is 1.92 parts per million and the standard deviation is 1.39 parts per million. At $\alpha = 0.10$, can you support the claim? *(Adapted from U.S. Environmental Protection Agency)*

**24. Lead Levels** As part of your work for an environmental awareness group, you want to test a claim that the mean amount of lead in the air in U.S. cities is less than 0.032 microgram per cubic meter. You find that the mean amount of lead in the air for a random sample of 56 U.S. cities is 0.021 microgram per cubic meter and the standard deviation is 0.034 microgram per cubic meter. At $\alpha = 0.01$, can you support the claim? *(Adapted from U.S. Environmental Protection Agency)*

| Annual salaries | | | |
|---|---|---|---|
| 88,050 | 70,505 | 80,450 | 79,000 |
| 84,000 | 62,100 | 63,900 | 70,088 |
| 81,500 | 64,500 | 92,020 | 73,000 |
| 101,200 | 68,970 | 91,400 | 98,350 |

TABLE FOR EXERCISE 25

**25. Annual Salary** An employment information service claims the mean annual salary for mid-level product engineers is \$86,000. The annual salaries (in dollars) for a random sample of 16 mid-level product engineers are shown in the table at the left. At $\alpha = 0.05$, test the claim that the mean salary is \$86,000. *(Adapted from Salary.com)*

| Annual salaries | | | |
|---|---|---|---|
| 126,200 | 136,000 | 129,200 | 109,800 |
| 137,500 | 118,000 | 116,500 | 130,000 |
| 130,400 | 133,500 | 137,000 | 148,300 |

TABLE FOR EXERCISE 26

**26. Annual Salary** An employment information service claims the mean annual salary for senior level statisticians is more than \$124,000. The annual salaries (in dollars) for a random sample of 12 senior level statisticians are shown in the table at the left. At $\alpha = 0.10$, is there enough evidence to support the claim that the mean salary is more than \$124,000? *(Adapted from Salary.com)*

**Using a *P*-Value with a *t*-Test** *In Exercises 27–30, (a) identify the claim and state $H_0$ and $H_a$, (b) use technology to find the P-value, (c) decide whether to reject or fail to reject the null hypothesis, and (d) interpret the decision in the context of the original claim. Assume the population is normally distributed.*

27. **Quarter Mile Times** A consumer group claims that the mean minimum time it takes for a sedan to travel a quarter mile is greater than 15.3 seconds. A random sample of 22 sedans has a mean minimum time to travel a quarter mile of 15.8 seconds and a standard deviation of 2.36 seconds. At $\alpha = 0.10$, do you have enough evidence to support the consumer group's claim? *(Adapted from Zero to 60 Times)*

28. **Dive Duration** An oceanographer claims that the mean dive duration of a North Atlantic right whale is 11.5 minutes. A random sample of 34 dive durations has a mean of 12.2 minutes and a standard deviation of 2.2 minutes. Is there enough evidence to reject the claim at $\alpha = 0.10$? *(Source: Marine Ecology Progress Series)*

| Classroom hours | | | |
|---|---|---|---|
| 11.8 | 8.6 | 12.6 | 7.9 |
| 6.4 | 10.4 | 13.6 | 9.1 |

TABLE FOR EXERCISE 29

29. **Faculty Classroom Hours** The dean of a university estimates that the mean number of classroom hours per week for full-time faculty is 11.0. As a member of the student council, you want to test this claim. A random sample of the number of classroom hours for eight full-time faculty for one week is shown in the table at the left. At $\alpha = 0.01$, can you reject the dean's claim?

| Class sizes | | | | | |
|---|---|---|---|---|---|
| 35 | 28 | 29 | 33 | 32 | 40 |
| 26 | 25 | 29 | 28 | 30 | 36 |
| 33 | 29 | 27 | 30 | 28 | 25 |

TABLE FOR EXERCISE 30

30. **Class Size** You receive a brochure from a large university. The brochure indicates that the mean class size for full-time faculty is fewer than 32 students. You want to test this claim. You randomly select 18 classes taught by full-time faculty and determine the class size of each. The results are shown in the table at the left. At $\alpha = 0.05$, can you support the university's claim?

## Extending Concepts

**Deciding on a Distribution** *In Exercises 31 and 32, decide whether you should use the standard normal sampling distribution or a t-sampling distribution to perform the hypothesis test. Justify your decision. Then use the distribution to test the claim. Write a short paragraph about the results of the test and what you can conclude about the claim.*

31. **Gas Mileage** A car company claims that the mean gas mileage for its luxury sedan is at least 23 miles per gallon. You believe the claim is incorrect and find that a random sample of 5 cars has a mean gas mileage of 22 miles per gallon and a standard deviation of 4 miles per gallon. At $\alpha = 0.05$, test the company's claim. Assume the population is normally distributed.

32. **Tuition and Fees** An education publication claims that the mean in-state tuition and fees at public four-year institutions by state is more than $10,500 per year. A random sample of 30 states has a mean in-state tuition and fees at public four-year institutions of $10,931 per year. Assume the population standard deviation is $2380. At $\alpha = 0.01$, test the publication's claim. *(Adapted from College Board)*

33. **Writing** You are testing a claim and incorrectly use the standard normal sampling distribution instead of the *t*-sampling distribution, mistaking the sample standard deviation for the population standard deviation. Does this make it more or less likely to reject the null hypothesis? Is this result the same no matter whether the test is left-tailed, right-tailed, or two-tailed? Explain your reasoning.

# 7.3 ACTIVITY Hypothesis Tests for a Mean

APPLET

You can find the interactive applet for this activity at MyLab Statistics.

The *Hypothesis tests for a mean* applet generates simulations to investigate hypothesis tests for a mean. Specify the **Sample size,** the shape of the **Distribution** (Normal or Right skewed), the true population mean (**Mean**), the true population standard deviation (**Std. dev.**), the null value for the mean (**Null mean**), and the alternative for the test (**Alternative**). Click **Update applet** to load the applet with the specified parameters. Click **1 test, 5 tests,** or **1000 tests** to generate samples of the specified size with a proportion of successes equal to **True p.** For each sample, a hypothesis test based on the *T*-statistic is performed, and the **T-statistic** or the **P-value** (click one) for the test is plotted. Values colored in red represent tests where the null hypothesis is rejected at the specified level of significance. The default level of 0.05 can be changed by adjusting the **Level.** The table above the graph tracks the cumulative results and shows the **Proportion** of the hypothesis tests where the null hypothesis was rejected. Press **Reset** to clear existing results and start a new simulation.

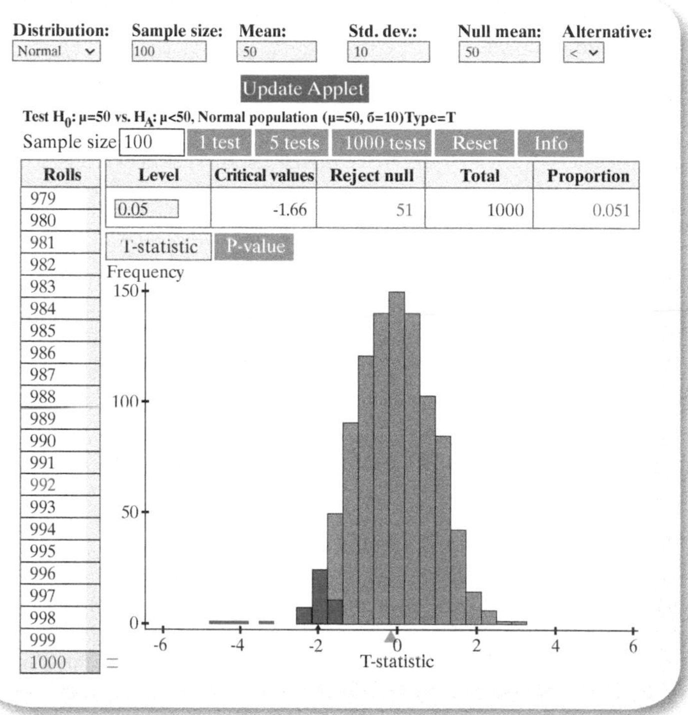


## EXPLORE

**Step 1** Specify values for the **Sample size, Mean, Std. dev., Null mean,** and **Alternative.**

**Step 2** Click **1 test, 5 tests,** or **1000 tests** to generate hypothesis tests.

## DRAW CONCLUSIONS

APPLET

1. Set **Sample size** = 15, **Mean** = 40, **Std. dev.** = 5, and the **Distribution** to "Normal." Test the claim that the mean is equal to 40. What are the null and alternative hypotheses? Run the simulation for at least 1000 hypothesis tests. Compare the proportions of null hypothesis rejections at the 0.05 level and the 0.01 level. Is this what you would expect? Explain.

2. Suppose a null hypothesis is rejected at the 0.01 level. Will it be rejected at the 0.05 level? Explain. Suppose a null hypothesis is rejected at the 0.05 level. Will it be rejected at the 0.01 level? Explain.

3. Set **Sample size** = 25, **Mean** = 25, **Std. dev.** = 3, and the **Distribution** to "Normal." Test the claim that the mean is at least 27. What are the null and alternative hypotheses? Run the simulation for at least 1000 hypothesis tests. Compare the proportions of null hypothesis rejections at the 0.05 level and the 0.01 level. Is this what you would expect? Explain.

# CASE STUDY Human Body Temperature: What's Normal?

In an article in the *Journal of Statistics Education* (vol. 4, no. 2), Allen Shoemaker describes a study that was reported in the *Journal of the American Medical Association (JAMA)*.* It is generally accepted that the mean body temperature of an adult human is 98.6°F. In his article, Shoemaker uses the data from the *JAMA* article to test this hypothesis. Here is a summary of his test.

**Claim:** The body temperature of adults is 98.6°F.

$H_0$: $\mu = 98.6°F$ (Claim) $H_a$: $\mu \neq 98.6°F$

**Sample Size:** $n = 130$

**Population:** Adult human temperatures (Fahrenheit)

**Distribution:** Approximately normal

**Test Statistics:** $\bar{x} \approx 98.25$, $s \approx 0.73$

* Data for the *JAMA* article were collected from healthy men and women, ages 18 to 40, at the University of Maryland Center for Vaccine Development, Baltimore.

**Men's Temperatures (in degrees Fahrenheit)**

| Stem | Leaves |
|---|---|
| 96 | 3 |
| 96 | 7 9 |
| 97 | 0 1 1 1 2 3 4 4 4 4 |
| 97 | 5 5 6 6 6 7 8 8 8 8 9 9 |
| 98 | 0 0 0 0 0 0 1 1 2 2 2 2 3 3 4 4 4 4 |
| 98 | 5 5 6 6 6 6 6 6 7 7 8 8 8 9 |
| 99 | 0 0 0 1 2 3 4 |
| 99 | 5 |
| 100 | |
| 100 | |

Key: 96|3 = 96.3

**Women's Temperatures (in degrees Fahrenheit)**

| Stem | Leaves |
|---|---|
| 96 | 4 |
| 96 | 7 8 |
| 97 | 2 2 4 |
| 97 | 6 7 7 8 8 8 9 9 9 |
| 98 | 0 0 0 0 0 1 2 2 2 2 2 2 3 3 3 4 4 4 4 4 |
| 98 | 5 6 6 6 6 7 7 7 7 7 7 8 8 8 8 8 8 8 9 |
| 99 | 0 0 1 1 2 2 3 4 |
| 99 | 9 |
| 100 | 0 |
| 100 | 8 |

Key: 96|4 = 96.4

## EXERCISES

**1.** Complete the hypothesis test for all adults (men and women) by performing the following steps. Use a level of significance of $\alpha = 0.05$.

(a) Sketch the sampling distribution.

(b) Determine the critical values and add them to your sketch.

(c) Determine the rejection regions and shade them in your sketch.

(d) Find the standardized test statistic. Plot and label it in your sketch.

(e) Make a decision to reject or fail to reject the null hypothesis.

(f) Interpret the decision in the context of the original claim.

**2.** If you lower the level of significance to $\alpha = 0.01$, does your decision change? Explain your reasoning.

**3.** Test the hypothesis that the mean temperature of men is 98.6°F. What can you conclude at a level of significance of $\alpha = 0.01$?

**4.** Test the hypothesis that the mean temperature of women is 98.6°F. What can you conclude at a level of significance of $\alpha = 0.01$?

**5.** Use the sample of 130 temperatures to form a 99% confidence interval for the mean body temperature of adult humans.

**6.** The conventional "normal" body temperature was established by Carl Wunderlich over 100 years ago. What were possible sources of error in Wunderlich's sampling procedure?

# 7.4 Hypothesis Testing for Proportions

**What You Should Learn**

- How to use the $z$-test to test a population proportion $p$

Hypothesis Test for Proportions

## Hypothesis Test for Proportions

In Sections 7.2 and 7.3, you learned how to perform a hypothesis test for a population mean $\mu$. In this section, you will learn how to test a population proportion $p$.

Hypothesis tests for proportions can be used when politicians want to know the proportion of their constituents who favor a certain bill or when quality assurance engineers test the proportion of parts that are defective.

If $np \geq 5$ and $nq \geq 5$ for a binomial distribution, then the sampling distribution for $\hat{p}$ is approximately normal with a mean of $\mu_{\hat{p}} = p$ and a standard error of

$$\sigma_{\hat{p}} = \sqrt{pq/n}.$$

### z-Test for a Proportion p

The **$z$-test for a proportion $p$** is a statistical test for a population proportion. The $z$-test can be used when a binomial distribution is given such that $np \geq 5$ and $nq \geq 5$. The **test statistic** is the sample proportion $\hat{p}$ and the **standardized test statistic** is

$$z = \frac{\hat{p} - \mu_{\hat{p}}}{\sigma_{\hat{p}}} = \frac{\hat{p} - p}{\sqrt{pq/n}}. \qquad \text{Standardized test statistic for } p$$

### GUIDELINES

**Using a $z$-Test for a Proportion $p$**

| In Words | In Symbols |
|---|---|
| **1.** Verify that the sampling distribution of $\hat{p}$ can be approximated by a normal distribution. | $np \geq 5,\ nq \geq 5$ |
| **2.** State the claim mathematically and verbally. Identify the null and alternative hypotheses. | State $H_0$ and $H_a$. |
| **3.** Specify the level of significance. | Identify $\alpha$. |
| **4.** Determine the critical value(s). | Use Table 4 in Appendix B. |
| **5.** Determine the rejection region(s). | |
| **6.** Find the standardized test statistic and sketch the sampling distribution. | $z = \frac{\hat{p} - p}{\sqrt{pq/n}}$. |
| **7.** Make a decision to reject or fail to reject the null hypothesis. | If $z$ is in the rejection region, then reject $H_0$. Otherwise, fail to reject $H_0$. |
| **8.** Interpret the decision in the context of the original claim. | |

In Step 7 of the guidelines, the decision rule uses rejection regions. You can also test a claim using $P$-values, as described in the Study Tip at the left.

**Study Tip**

A hypothesis test for a proportion $p$ can also be performed using $P$-values. Use the guidelines on page 365 for using $P$-values for a $z$-test for a mean $\mu$, but in Step 4 find the standardized test statistic by using the formula

$$z = \frac{\hat{p} - p}{\sqrt{pq/n}}.$$

The other steps in the test are the same.

**7.4** To explore this topic further, see **Activity 7.4** on page 393.

**EXAMPLE 1**

See TI-84 Plus steps on page 415.

## Hypothesis Test for a Proportion

A researcher claims that less than 69% of U.S. adults who use live television streaming platforms have upgraded to advertisement-free service tiers. In a random sample of 100 U.S. adults who use live television streaming platforms, 65% say they have upgraded to advertisement-free service tiers. At $\alpha = 0.01$, is there enough evidence to support the researcher's claim? *(Adapted from The Harris Poll)*

**SOLUTION**

The products

$$np = 100(0.69) = 69 \quad \text{and} \quad nq = 100(0.31) = 31$$

are both greater than 5. So, you can use a $z$-test. The claim is "less than 69% of U.S. adults who use live television streaming platforms have upgraded to advertisement-free service tiers." So, the null and alternative hypotheses are

$$H_0: p \geq 0.69 \quad \text{and} \quad H_a: p < 0.69. \text{ (Claim)}$$

Because the test is a left-tailed test and the level of significance is $\alpha = 0.01$, the critical value is $z_0 = -2.33$ and the rejection region is $z < -2.33$. The standardized test statistic is

$$z = \frac{\hat{p} - p}{\sqrt{pq/n}} \qquad \text{Because } np \geq 5 \text{ and } nq \geq 5, \text{ you can use the } z\text{-test.}$$

$$= \frac{0.65 - 0.69}{\sqrt{(0.69)(0.31)/100}} \qquad \text{Assume } p = 0.69.$$

$$\approx -0.86. \qquad \text{Round to two decimal places.}$$

**Study Tip**

Remember that when you fail to reject $H_0$, a type II error is possible. For instance, in Example 1 the null hypothesis, $p \geq 0.69$, may be false.

The figure shows the location of the rejection region and the standardized test statistic $z$. Because $z$ is not in the rejection region, you fail to reject the null hypothesis.

***Interpretation*** There is not enough evidence at the 1% level of significance to support the claim that less than 69% of U.S. adults who use live television streaming platforms have upgraded to advertisement-free service tiers.

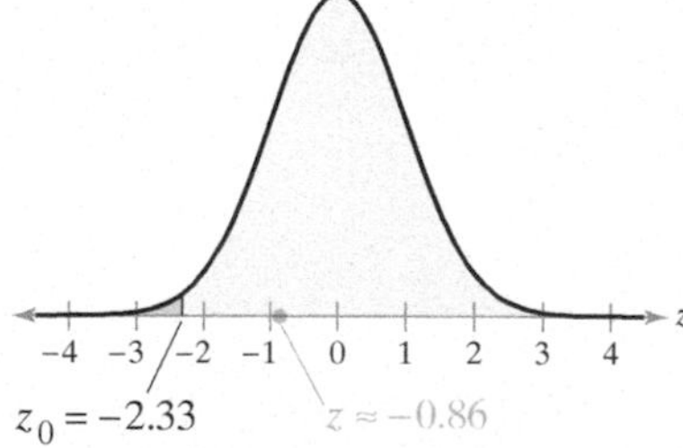


1% Level of Significance

**TRY IT YOURSELF 1**

A researcher claims that more than 36% of U.S. adults would consider buying a product or service directly from an advertisement that is run during streaming programming. In a random sample of 150 adults, 33% say they would consider buying a product or service directly from an advertisement that is run during streaming programming. At $\alpha = 0.01$, is there enough evidence to support the researcher's claim? *(Adapted from The Harris Poll)*

*Answer: Page A41*

**TI-84 PLUS**

1PropZTest
prop<0.69
z=-0.8648775001
p=0.1935529676
$\hat{p}$=0.65
n=100

To use a $P$-value to perform the hypothesis test in Example 1, you can use technology, as shown at the left, or you can use Table 4. Using Table 4, the area corresponding to $z = -0.86$ is 0.1949. Because this is a left-tailed test, the $P$-value is equal to the area to the left of $z = -0.86$. So, $P = 0.1949$. (This value differs from the one found using technology due to rounding.) Because the $P$-value is greater than $\alpha = 0.01$, you fail to reject the null hypothesis. Note that this is the same result obtained in Example 1.

## Picturing the World

According to a survey, 33% of employees working from home say they have encountered at least one type of technical failure. To test this claim, you randomly select 300 employees working from home. In the sample, you find that 93 of them say they have encountered at least one type of technical failure. (Adapted from Deloitte Global)

**At $\alpha = 0.05$, is there enough evidence to reject the claim?**

Recall from Section 6.3 that when the sample proportion is not given, you can find it using the formula

$$\hat{p} = \frac{x}{n} \qquad \text{Sample proportion}$$

where $x$ is the number of successes in the sample and $n$ is the sample size.

### EXAMPLE 2

See Minitab steps on page 414.

#### Hypothesis Test for a Proportion

A researcher claims that 26% of U.S. adults ages 22 to 59 who do not have a parent with a bachelor's degree have completed a bachelor's degree themselves. In a random sample of 7400 adults ages 22 to 59 who do not have a parent with a bachelor's degree, 1984 say they have completed a bachelor's degree themselves. At $\alpha = 0.10$, is there enough evidence to reject the researcher's claim? *(Adapted from Pew Research Center)*

**SOLUTION**

The products $np = 7400(0.26) = 1924$ and $nq = 7400(0.74) = 5476$ are both greater than 5. So, you can use a $z$-test. The claim is "26% of U.S. adults ages 22 to 59 who do not have a parent with a bachelor's degree have completed a bachelor's degree themselves." So, the null and alternative hypotheses are

$$H_0\colon p = 0.26 \text{ (Claim)} \quad \text{and} \quad H_a\colon p \neq 0.26.$$

Because the test is a two-tailed test and the level of significance is $\alpha = 0.10$, the critical values are $-z_0 = -1.645$ and $z_0 = 1.645$. The rejection regions are $z < -1.645$ and $z > 1.645$. Because the number of successes is $x = 1984$ and $n = 7400$, the sample proportion is

$$\hat{p} = \frac{x}{n} = \frac{1984}{7400}.$$

The standardized test statistic is

$$z = \frac{\hat{p} - p}{\sqrt{pq/n}} \qquad \text{Because } np \geq 5 \text{ and } nq \geq 5, \text{ you can use the } z\text{-test.}$$

$$= \frac{(1984/7400) - 0.26}{\sqrt{(0.26)(0.74)/7400}} \qquad \text{Assume } p = 0.26.$$

$$\approx 1.59. \qquad \text{Round to two decimal places.}$$

$-z_0 = -1.645$

$z_0 = 1.645$

$z \approx 1.59$

10% Level of Significance

The figure at the left shows the location of the rejection regions and the standardized test statistic $z$. Because $z$ is not in the rejection region, you fail to reject the null hypothesis.

***Interpretation*** There is not enough evidence at the 10% level of significance to reject the claim that 26% of U.S. adults ages 22 to 59 who do not have a parent with a bachelor's degree have completed a bachelor's degree themselves.

**TRY IT YOURSELF 2**

A researcher claims that 70% of U.S. adults ages 22 to 59 who have at least one parent with a bachelor's degree or beyond have completed a bachelor's degree themselves. In a random sample of 7400 adults ages 22 to 59 who have at least one parent with a bachelor's degree or beyond, 5110 say they have completed a bachelor's degree themselves. At $\alpha = 0.10$, is there enough evidence to reject the researcher's claim? *(Adapted from Pew Research Center)*

*Answer: Page A41*

# 7.4 EXERCISES

For Extra Help: MyLab Statistics

## Building Basic Skills and Vocabulary

1. Explain how to determine whether a normal distribution can be used to approximate a binomial distribution.
2. Explain how to test a population proportion $p$.

*In Exercises 3–6, determine whether a normal sampling distribution can be used. If it can be used, test the claim.*

3. Claim: $p < 0.12$; $\alpha = 0.01$. Sample statistics: $\hat{p} = 0.10$, $n = 40$
4. Claim: $p \geq 0.48$; $\alpha = 0.08$. Sample statistics: $\hat{p} = 0.40$, $n = 90$
5. Claim: $p \neq 0.15$; $\alpha = 0.05$. Sample statistics: $\hat{p} = 0.12$, $n = 500$
6. Claim: $p > 0.70$; $\alpha = 0.04$. Sample statistics: $\hat{p} = 0.64$, $n = 225$

## Using and Interpreting Concepts

**Hypothesis Testing Using Rejection Regions** *In Exercises 7–12, (a) identify the claim and state $H_0$ and $H_a$, (b) find the critical value(s) and identify the rejection region(s), (c) find the standardized test statistic z, (d) decide whether to reject or fail to reject the null hypothesis, and (e) interpret the decision in the context of the original claim.*

7. **School Vaccinations** Prior to COVID-19, a reporter claims that more than 80% of U.S. adults feel children should be vaccinated to attend school. In a random sample of 200 U.S. adults, 84% feel that children should be vaccinated to attend school. At $\alpha = 0.01$, can you support the reporter's claim? *(Adapted from Harvard T.H. Chan School of Public Health)*
8. **Vaccinations** In 2021, a reporter claims that at least 55% of U.S. adults feel that COVID-19 vaccinations should be required for high school students to attend school in the fall. In a random sample of 200 U.S. adults, 56% feel that COVID-19 vaccinations should be required for high school students to attend school in the fall. At $\alpha = 0.10$, is there enough evidence to reject the reporter's claim? *(Adapted from Gallup)*
9. **Tax Refunds** A tax analyst says that at least 60% of tax filers are expecting a tax refund. In a random sample of 2494 U.S. tax filers, 56% are expecting a tax refund. At $\alpha = 0.05$, is there enough evidence to reject the analyst's claim? *(Adapted from CreditCards.com)*
10. **Working Students** An education researcher claims that 65% of full-time college students work year-round. In a random sample of 105 college students, 66 say they work year-round. At $\alpha = 0.10$, is there enough evidence to reject the researcher's claim? *(Adapted from Student Loan Hero)*
11. **Nursing** A patient care manager claims that more than half of all nurses feel they became better professionals during the coronavirus pandemic. In a random sample of 300 nurses, 174 say they became better professionals during the pandemic. At $\alpha = 0.01$, is there enough evidence to support the manager's claim? *(Adapted from University of Phoenix)*
12. **Changing Jobs** A researcher claims that 40% of U.S. adults would consider changing jobs. In a random sample of 50 U.S. adults, 25 say they would consider changing jobs. At $\alpha = 0.10$, is there enough evidence to reject the researcher's claim? *(Adapted from CBS News)*

**Hypothesis Testing Using a *P*-Value** *In Exercises 13–16, (a) identify the claim and state $H_0$ and $H_a$, (b) use technology to find the P-value, (c) decide whether to reject or fail to reject the null hypothesis, and (d) interpret the decision in the context of the original claim.*

**13. Space Travel** A research center claims that 27% of U.S. adults would travel into space on a commercial flight if they could afford it. In a random sample of 1000 U.S. adults, 30% say that they would travel into space on a commercial flight if they could afford it. At $\alpha = 0.05$, is there enough evidence to reject the research center's claim? *(Source: Rasmussen Reports)*

**14. Meat and Poultry** A research center claims that at most 35% of U.S. adults seek to buy naturally raised and fed meat and poultry. In a random sample of 1000 U.S. adults, 38% say they seek to buy naturally raised and fed meat and poultry. At $\alpha = 0.01$, is there enough evidence to reject the center's claim? *(Source: FoodPrint)*

**15. Moral Values** A politician claims that more than 25% of U.S. adults believe moral values in the country are getting better. In a random sample of 50 U.S. adults, 17 say moral values in the country are getting better. At $\alpha = 0.10$, can you support the politician's claim? *(Adapted from Gallup)*

**16. Stray Cats** An animal advocate claims that 25% of U.S. households have taken in a stray cat. In a random sample of 500 U.S. households, 105 say they have taken in a stray cat. At $\alpha = 0.05$, is there enough evidence to reject the advocate's claim? *(Adapted from American Pet Products Association)*

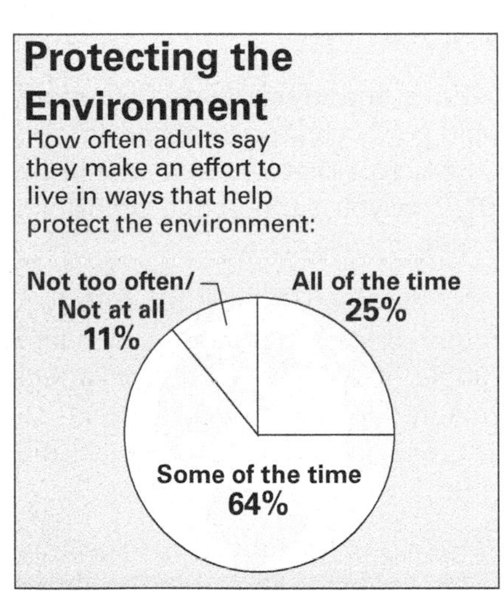


FIGURE FOR EXERCISES 17 AND 18

**Protecting the Environment** *In Exercises 17 and 18, use the figure at the left, which suggests what adults think about protecting the environment. (Adapted from Pew Research Center)*

**17. Are People Concerned About Protecting the Environment?** You interview a random sample of 100 adults. The results of the survey show that 58% of the adults said they live in ways that help protect the environment some of the time. At $\alpha = 0.05$, can you reject the claim that at least 64% of adults make an effort to live in ways that help protect the environment some of the time?

**18. What Are People's Attitudes About Protecting the Environment?** Use your conclusion from Exercise 17 to write a paragraph on people's attitudes about protecting the environment.

## Extending Concepts

**Alternative Formula** *In Exercises 19 and 20, use the information below. When you know the number of successes x, the sample size n, and the population proportion p, it can be easier to use the formula*

$$z = \frac{x - np}{\sqrt{npq}}$$

*to find the standardized test statistic when using a z-test for a population proportion p.*

**19.** Rework Exercise 7 using the alternative formula and verify that the results are the same.

**20.** The alternative formula is derived from the formula

$$z = \frac{\hat{p} - p}{\sqrt{pq/n}} = \frac{(x/n) - p}{\sqrt{pq/n}}.$$

Use this formula to derive the alternative formula. Justify each step.

# 7.4 ACTIVITY Hypothesis Tests for a Proportion

You can find the interactive applet for this activity at MyLab Statistics.

The *Hypothesis tests for a proportion* applet generates simulations to investigate hypothesis tests for a population proportion. Specify the **Sample size**, the population proportion (**True p**), the null value for the proportion (**Null p**), and the alternative for the test (**Alternative**). Click **Update applet** to load the applet with the specified parameters. Click **1 test, 5 tests,** or **1000 tests** to generate samples of the specified size with a proportion of successes equal to **True p.** For each sample, a hypothesis test based on the $Z$-statistic is performed, and the **Z-statistic** or the **P-value** (click one) for the test is plotted. Values colored in red represent tests where the null hypothesis is rejected at the specified level of significance. The default level of 0.05 can be changed by adjusting the **Level.** The table above the graph tracks the cumulative results and shows the **Proportion** of the hypothesis tests where the null hypothesis was rejected. Press **Reset** to clear existing results and start a new simulation.

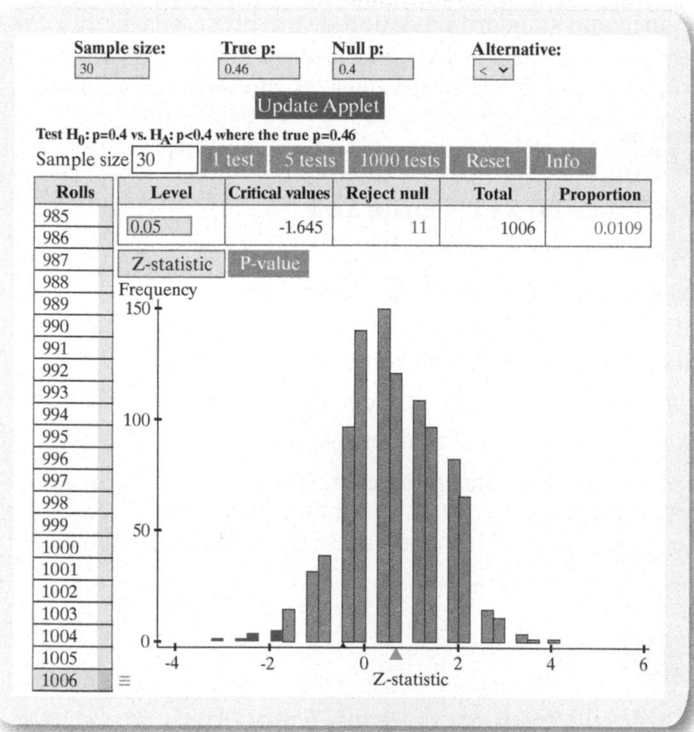


## EXPLORE

**Step 1** Specify values for the **Sample size, True p, Null p,** and **Alternative.**

**Step 2** Click **1 test, 5 tests,** or **1000 tests** to generate hypothesis tests.

## DRAW CONCLUSIONS

1. Set **Sample size** = 25 and **True p** = 0.35. Test the claim that the proportion is equal to 35%. What are the null and alternative hypotheses? Run the simulation for at least 1000 tests. Compare the proportion of null hypothesis rejections for the 0.05 and 0.01 levels. Is this what you would expect? Explain.
2. Set **Sample size** = 50 and **True p** = 0.6. Test the claim that the proportion is at least 40%. What are the null and alternative hypotheses? Run the simulation for at least 1000 tests. Compare the proportion of null hypothesis rejections for the 0.05 and 0.01 levels. Perform a hypothesis test for each level. Use the results of the hypothesis tests to explain the results of the simulation.

# 7.5 Hypothesis Testing for Variance and Standard Deviation

### What You Should Learn

- How to find critical values for a chi-square test
- How to use the chi-square test to test a variance $\sigma^2$ or a standard deviation $\sigma$

Critical Values for a Chi-Square Test ■ The Chi-Square Test

## Critical Values for a Chi-Square Test

In real life, it is important to produce consistent, predictable results. For instance, consider a company that manufactures golf balls. The manufacturer must produce millions of golf balls, each having the same size and the same weight. There is a very low tolerance for variation. For a normally distributed population, you can test the variance and standard deviation of the process using the chi-square distribution with $n - 1$ degrees of freedom. Before learning how to do the test, you must know how to find the critical values, as shown in the guidelines.

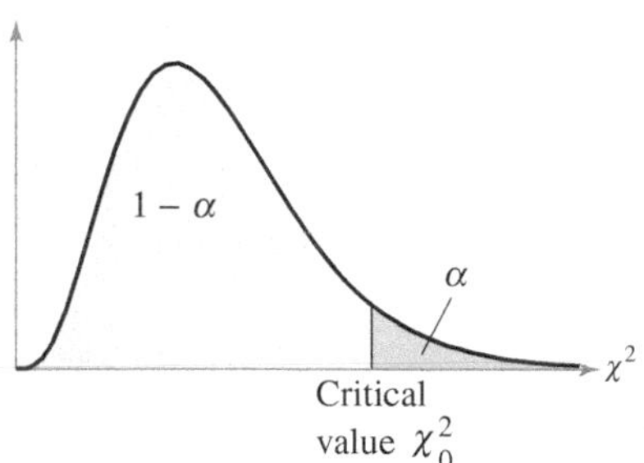

Right-Tailed Test

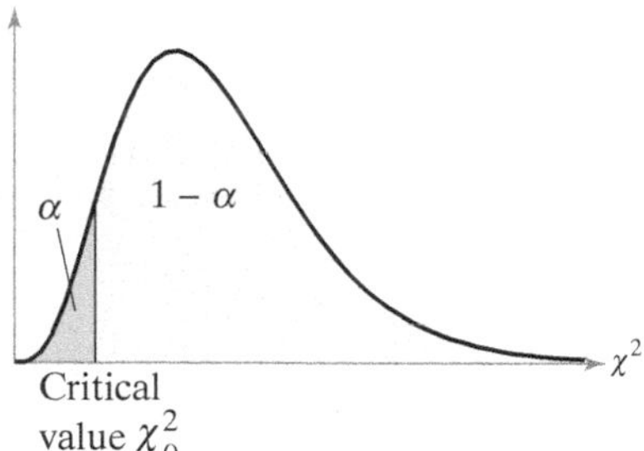

Left-Tailed Test

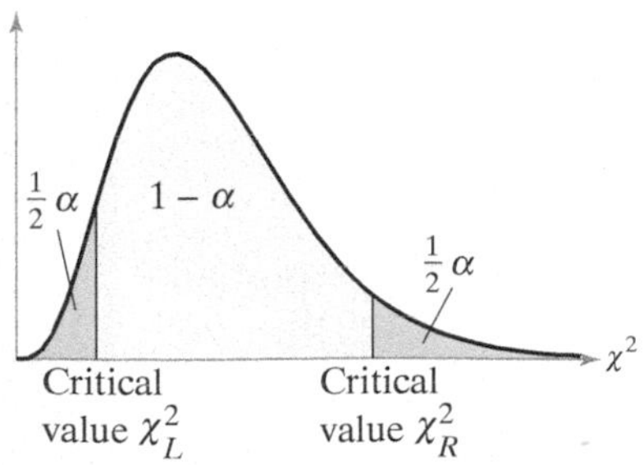

Two-Tailed Test

**GUIDELINES**

**Finding Critical Values for a Chi-Square Test**

1. Specify the level of significance $\alpha$.
2. Identify the degrees of freedom, d.f. $= n - 1$.
3. The critical values for the chi-square distribution are found in Table 6 in Appendix B. To find the critical value(s) for a
   a. *right-tailed test,* use the value that corresponds to d.f. and $\alpha$.
   b. *left-tailed test,* use the value that corresponds to d.f. and $1 - \alpha$.
   c. *two-tailed test,* use the values that correspond to d.f. and $\frac{1}{2}\alpha$, and d.f. and $1 - \frac{1}{2}\alpha$.

See the figures at the left.

**EXAMPLE 1**

### Finding a Critical Value for a Right-Tailed Test

Find the critical value $\chi_0^2$ for a right-tailed test when $n = 26$ and $\alpha = 0.10$.

**SOLUTION**

The degrees of freedom are d.f. $= n - 1 = 26 - 1 = 25$. The figure below shows a chi-square distribution with 25 degrees of freedom and a shaded area of $\alpha = 0.10$ in the right tail. Using Table 6 in Appendix B with d.f. $= 25$ and $\alpha = 0.10$, the critical value is $\chi_0^2 = 34.382$.

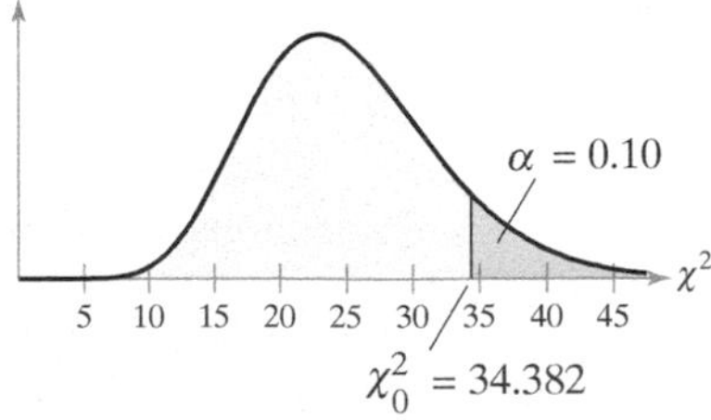


**TRY IT YOURSELF 1**

Find the critical value $\chi_0^2$ for a right-tailed test when $n = 18$ and $\alpha = 0.01$.

*Answer: Page A41*

## EXAMPLE 2

### Finding a Critical Value for a Left-Tailed Test

Find the critical value $\chi_0^2$ for a left-tailed test when $n = 11$ and $\alpha = 0.01$.

**SOLUTION**

The degrees of freedom are

$$\text{d.f.} = n - 1 = 11 - 1 = 10.$$

The figure at the left shows a chi-square distribution with 10 degrees of freedom and a shaded area of $\alpha = 0.01$ in the left tail. The area to the right of the critical value is

$$1 - \alpha = 1 - 0.01 = 0.99.$$

$\alpha = 0.01$

$\chi_0^2 = 2.558$

Using Table 6 with d.f. = 10 and the area 0.99, the critical value is $\chi_0^2 = 2.558$. You can check your answer using technology, as shown below.

**Inverse Cumulative Distribution Function**

Chi-Square with 10 DF

| P ( X ≤ x) | x |
|---|---|
| 0.01 | 2.55821 |

**TRY IT YOURSELF 2**

Find the critical value $\chi_0^2$ for a left-tailed test when $n = 30$ and $\alpha = 0.05$.

*Answer: Page A41*

Note that because chi-square distributions are not symmetric (like normal or $t$-distributions), in a two-tailed test the two critical values are not opposites. Each critical value must be calculated separately, as shown in the next example.

## EXAMPLE 3

### Finding Critical Values for a Two-Tailed Test

Find the critical values $\chi_L^2$ and $\chi_R^2$ for a two-tailed test when $n = 9$ and $\alpha = 0.05$.

**SOLUTION**

The degrees of freedom are

$$\text{d.f.} = n - 1 = 9 - 1 = 8.$$

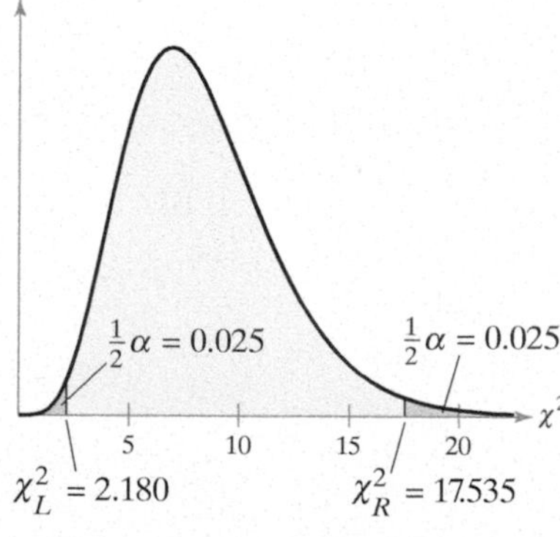


The figure shows a chi-square distribution with 8 degrees of freedom and a shaded area of $\frac{1}{2}\alpha = 0.025$ in each tail. The area to the right of $\chi_R^2$ is $\frac{1}{2}\alpha = 0.025$, and the area to the right of $\chi_L^2$ is $1 - \frac{1}{2}\alpha = 0.975$. Using Table 6 with d.f. = 8 and the areas 0.025 and 0.975, the critical values are $\chi_R^2 = 17.535$ and $\chi_L^2 = 2.180$. You can check you answer using technology, as shown at the left.

**EXCEL**

| | A | |
|---|---|---|
| 1 | 2.179730747 | ←=CHISQ.INV(0.025,8) |
| 2 | 17.53454614 | |

=CHISQ.INV.RT(0.025,8)

**TRY IT YOURSELF 3**

Find the critical values $\chi_L^2$ and $\chi_R^2$ for a two-tailed test when $n = 51$ and $\alpha = 0.01$.

*Answer: Page A41*

## The Chi-Square Test

To test a variance $\sigma^2$ or a standard deviation $\sigma$ of a population that is normally distributed, you can use the chi-square test. The chi-square test for a variance or standard deviation is not as robust as the tests for the population mean $\mu$ or the population proportion $p$. So, it is essential in performing a chi-square test for a variance or standard deviation that the population be normally distributed. The results can be misleading when the population is not normal.

### Chi-Square Test for a Variance $\sigma^2$ or Standard Deviation $\sigma$

The **chi-square test for a variance $\sigma^2$ or standard deviation $\sigma$** is a statistical test for a population variance or standard deviation. The chi-square test can only be used when the population is normal. The **test statistic** is $s^2$ and the **standardized test statistic**

$$\chi^2 = \frac{(n-1)s^2}{\sigma^2} \qquad \text{Standardized test statistic for } \sigma^2 \text{ or } \sigma$$

follows a chi-square distribution with degrees of freedom

d.f. $= n - 1$.

In Step 8 of the guidelines below, the decision rule uses rejection regions. You can also test a claim using $P$-values (see Exercises 31–34).

### GUIDELINES

**Using the Chi-Square Test for a Variance $\sigma^2$ or a Standard Deviation $\sigma$**

| In Words | In Symbols |
|---|---|
| **1.** Verify that the sample is random and the population is normally distributed. | |
| **2.** State the claim mathematically and verbally. Identify the null and alternative hypotheses. | State $H_0$ and $H_a$. |
| **3.** Specify the level of significance. | Identify $\alpha$. |
| **4.** Identify the degrees of freedom. | d.f. $= n - 1$ |
| **5.** Determine the critical value(s). | Use Table 6 in Appendix B. |
| **6.** Determine the rejection region(s). | |
| **7.** Find the standardized test statistic and sketch the sampling distribution. | $\chi^2 = \frac{(n-1)s^2}{\sigma^2}$ |
| **8.** Make a decision to reject or fail to reject the null hypothesis. | If $\chi^2$ is in the rejection region, then reject $H_0$. Otherwise, fail to reject $H_0$. |
| **9.** Interpret the decision in the context of the original claim. | |

For Step 5 of the guidelines, in addition to using Table 6 in Appendix B, you can use technology to find the critical value(s). Also, some technology tools allow you to perform a hypothesis test for a variance (or a standard deviation) using only the descriptive statistics.

## EXAMPLE 4

### Using a Hypothesis Test for the Population Variance

A dairy processing company claims that the variance of the amount of fat in the whole milk processed by the company is no more than 0.25. You suspect this is wrong and find that a random sample of 41 milk containers has a variance of 0.27. At $\alpha = 0.05$, is there enough evidence to reject the company's claim? Assume the population is normally distributed.

**SOLUTION**

Because the sample is random and the population is normally distributed, you can use the chi-square test. The claim is "the variance is no more than 0.25." So, the null and alternative hypotheses are

$$H_0: \sigma^2 \leq 0.25 \text{ (Claim)} \quad \text{and} \quad H_a: \sigma^2 > 0.25.$$

The test is a right-tailed test, the level of significance is $\alpha = 0.05$, and the degrees of freedom are d.f. $= 41 - 1 = 40$. So, using Table 6, the critical value is

$$\chi_0^2 = 55.758.$$

The rejection region is $\chi^2 > 55.758$. The standardized test statistic is

$$\chi^2 = \frac{(n-1)s^2}{\sigma^2} \qquad \text{Use the chi-square test.}$$

$$= \frac{(41-1)(0.27)}{0.25} \qquad \text{Assume } \sigma^2 = 0.25.$$

$$= 43.2.$$

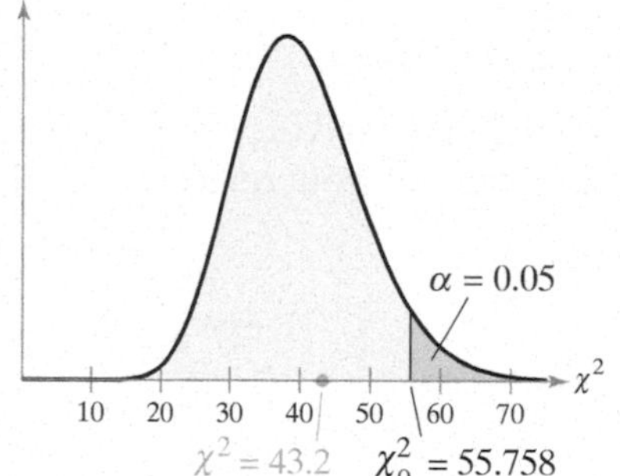


The figure at the left shows the location of the rejection region and the standardized test statistic $\chi^2$. Because $\chi^2$ is not in the rejection region, you fail to reject the null hypothesis. You can check your answer using technology, as shown below. Note that the test statistic, 43.2, is the same as what you found above.

**STATCRUNCH**

**One sample variance summary hypothesis test:**
$\sigma^2$ : Variance of population
$H_0 : \sigma^2 = 0.25$
$H_A : \sigma^2 > 0.25$

**Hypothesis test results:**

| Variance | Sample Var. | DF | Chi-square Stat | P-value |
|---|---|---|---|---|
| $\sigma^2$ | 0.27 | 40 | 43.2 | 0.3362 |

***Interpretation*** There is not enough evidence at the 5% level of significance to reject the company's claim that the variance of the amount of fat in the whole milk is no more than 0.25.

**TRY IT YOURSELF 4**

A bottling company claims that the variance of the amount of sports drink in a 12-ounce bottle is no more than 0.40. A random sample of 31 bottles has a variance of 0.75. At $\alpha = 0.01$, is there enough evidence to reject the company's claim? Assume the population is normally distributed.

*Answer: Page A41*

## EXAMPLE 5

### Using a Hypothesis Test for the Standard Deviation

A company claims that the standard deviation of the lengths of time it takes an incoming telephone call to be transferred to the correct office is less than 1.4 minutes. A random sample of 25 incoming telephone calls has a standard deviation of 1.1 minutes. At $\alpha = 0.10$, is there enough evidence to support the company's claim? Assume the population is normally distributed.

**SOLUTION**

Because the sample is random and the population is normally distributed, you can use the chi-square test. The claim is "the standard deviation is less than 1.4 minutes." So, the null and alternative hypotheses are

$$H_0: \sigma \geq 1.4 \text{ minutes} \quad \text{and} \quad H_a: \sigma < 1.4 \text{ minutes. (Claim)}$$

The test is a left-tailed test, the level of significance is $\alpha = 0.10$, and the degrees of freedom are

$$\text{d.f.} = 25 - 1 = 24.$$

So, using Table 6, the critical value is

$$\chi_0^2 = 15.659.$$

The rejection region is $\chi^2 < 15.659$. The standardized test statistic is

$$\chi^2 = \frac{(n-1)s^2}{\sigma^2} \qquad \text{Use the chi-square test.}$$

$$= \frac{(25-1)(1.1)^2}{(1.4)^2} \qquad \text{Assume } \sigma = 1.4.$$

$$\approx 14.816. \qquad \text{Round to three decimal places.}$$

The figure below shows the location of the rejection region and the standardized test statistic $\chi^2$. Because $\chi^2$ is in the rejection region, you reject the null hypothesis.

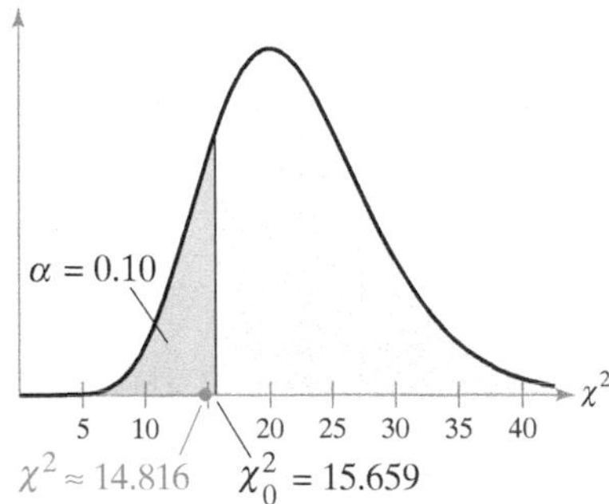


***Interpretation*** There is enough evidence at the 10% level of significance to support the claim that the standard deviation of the lengths of time it takes an incoming telephone call to be transferred to the correct office is less than 1.4 minutes.

**TRY IT YOURSELF 5**

A police chief claims that the standard deviation of the lengths of response times is less than 3.7 minutes. A random sample of 9 response times has a standard deviation of 3.0 minutes. At $\alpha = 0.05$, is there enough evidence to support the police chief's claim? Assume the population is normally distributed.

*Answer: Page A41*

**Study Tip**

Although you are testing a standard deviation in Example 5, the standardized test statistic $\chi^2$ requires variance. Remember to square the standard deviation to calculate the variance.

## Picturing the World

A community center claims that the chlorine level in its pool has a standard deviation of 0.46 parts per million (ppm). A sampling of the pool's chlorine levels at 25 random times during a month yields a standard deviation of 0.61 ppm. (Adapted from American Pool Supply)

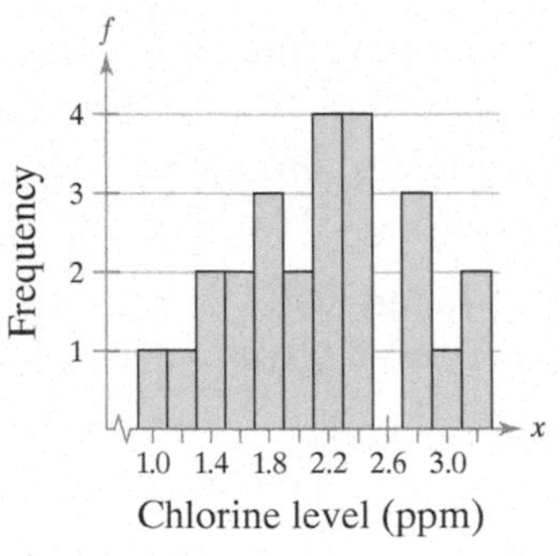


**At 0.05, is there enough evidence to reject the claim?**

**EXAMPLE 6**

### Using a Hypothesis Test for the Population Variance

A sporting goods manufacturer claims that the variance of the strengths of a certain fishing line is 15.9. A random sample of 15 fishing line spools has a variance of 21.8. At $\alpha = 0.05$, is there enough evidence to reject the manufacturer's claim? Assume the population is normally distributed.

**SOLUTION**

Because the sample is random and the population is normally distributed, you can use the chi-square test. The claim is "the variance is 15.9." So, the null and alternative hypotheses are

$$H_0: \sigma^2 = 15.9 \text{ (Claim)} \quad \text{and} \quad H_a: \sigma^2 \neq 15.9.$$

The test is a two-tailed test, the level of significance is $\alpha = 0.05$, and the degrees of freedom are

$$\text{d.f.} = 15 - 1 = 14.$$

Using Table 6, the critical values are $\chi^2_L = 5.629$ and $\chi^2_R = 26.119$. The rejection regions are

$$\chi^2 < 5.629 \quad \text{and} \quad \chi^2 > 26.119.$$

The standardized test statistic is

$$\chi^2 = \frac{(n-1)s^2}{\sigma^2} \qquad \text{Use the chi-square test.}$$

$$= \frac{(15-1)(21.8)}{(15.9)} \qquad \text{Assume } \sigma^2 = 15.9.$$

$$\approx 19.195. \qquad \text{Round to three decimal places.}$$

The figure below shows the location of the rejection regions and the standardized test statistic $\chi^2$. Because $\chi^2$ is not in the rejection regions, you fail to reject the null hypothesis.

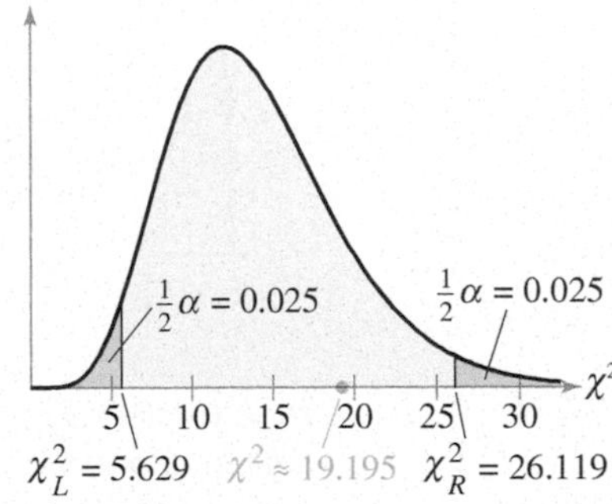


***Interpretation*** There is not enough evidence at the 5% level of significance to reject the claim that the variance of the strengths of the fishing line is 15.9.

**TRY IT YOURSELF 6**

A company that offers dieting products and weight loss services claims that the variance of the weight losses of their users is 25.5. A random sample of 13 users has a variance of 10.8. At $\alpha = 0.10$, is there enough evidence to reject the company's claim? Assume the population is normally distributed.

*Answer: Page A41*

# 7.5 EXERCISES

For Extra Help: MyLab Statistics

## Building Basic Skills and Vocabulary

**1.** Explain how to find critical values in a chi-square distribution.

**2.** Can a critical value for the chi-square test be negative? Explain.

**3.** How do the critical values for a two-tailed test change as $\alpha$ decreases?

**4.** Describe the difference between calculating the standardized test statistic, $\chi^2$, for a chi-square test for variance and a chi-square test for standard deviation.

**5.** How do the requirements for a chi-square test for a variance or standard deviation differ from a $z$-test or a $t$-test for a mean?

**6.** Explain how to test a population variance or a population standard deviation.

*In Exercises 7–12, find the critical value(s) and rejection region(s) for the type of chi-square test with sample size n and level of significance $\alpha$.*

**7.** Right-tailed test, $n = 27, \alpha = 0.05$

**8.** Right-tailed test, $n = 10, \alpha = 0.10$

**9.** Left-tailed test, $n = 7, \alpha = 0.01$

**10.** Left-tailed test, $n = 24, \alpha = 0.05$

**11.** Two-tailed test, $n = 81, \alpha = 0.10$

**12.** Two-tailed test, $n = 61, \alpha = 0.01$

**Graphical Analysis** *In Exercises 13 and 14, state whether each standardized test statistic $\chi^2$ allows you to reject the null hypothesis. Explain.*

**13.** (a) $\chi^2 = 2.091$
(b) $\chi^2 = 0$
(c) $\chi^2 = 6.3471$

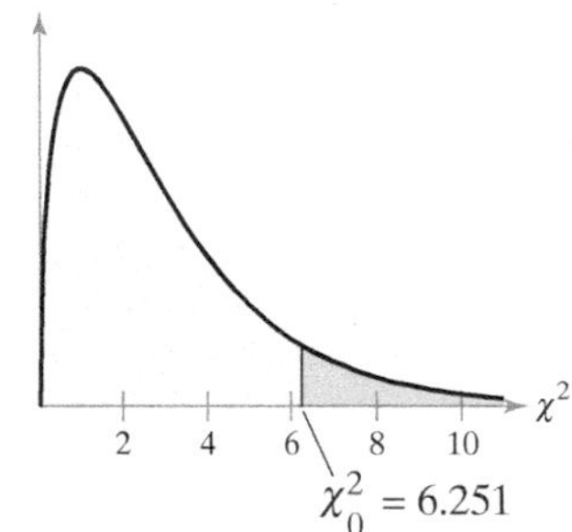


**14.** (a) $\chi^2 = 22.302$
(b) $\chi^2 = 23.309$
(c) $\chi^2 = 8.457$

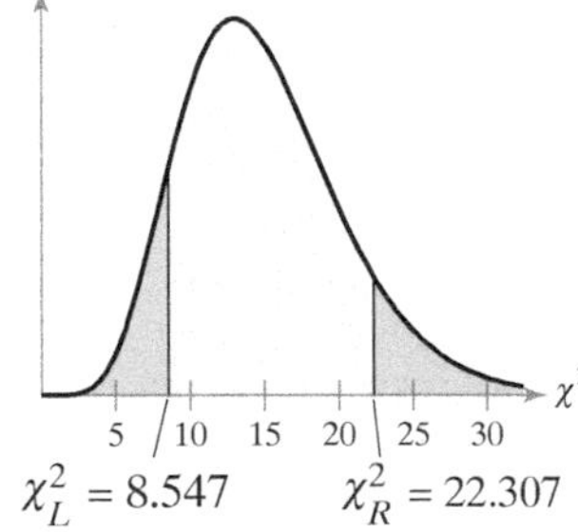


*In Exercises 15–22, test the claim about the population variance $\sigma^2$ or standard deviation $\sigma$ at the level of significance $\alpha$. Assume the population is normally distributed.*

**15.** Claim: $\sigma^2 = 0.52$; $\alpha = 0.05$. Sample statistics: $s^2 = 0.508, n = 18$

**16.** Claim: $\sigma^2 = 63$; $\alpha = 0.01$. Sample statistics: $s^2 = 58, n = 29$

**17.** Claim: $\sigma^2 \geq 8.5$; $\alpha = 0.05$. Sample statistics: $s^2 = 7.45, n = 23$

**18.** Claim: $\sigma \leq 0.92$; $\alpha = 0.01$. Sample statistics: $s = 0.67, n = 41$

**19.** Claim: $\sigma < 40$; $\alpha = 0.01$. Sample statistics: $s = 40.8, n = 12$

**20.** Claim: $\sigma^2 > 19$; $\alpha = 0.1$. Sample statistics: $s^2 = 28, n = 17$

**21.** Claim: $\sigma^2 \neq 32.8$; $\alpha = 0.1$. Sample statistics: $s^2 = 40.9, n = 101$

**22.** Claim: $\sigma \neq 24.9$; $\alpha = 0.10$. Sample statistics: $s = 29.1, n = 51$

## Using and Interpreting Concepts

**Hypothesis Testing Using Rejection Regions** *In Exercises 23–30, (a) identify the claim and state $H_0$ and $H_a$, (b) find the critical value(s) and identify the rejection region(s), (c) find the standardized test statistic $\chi^2$, (d) decide whether to reject or fail to reject the null hypothesis, and (e) interpret the decision in the context of the original claim. Assume the population is normally distributed.*

**23. Tires** A tire manufacturer claims that the variance of the diameters in a tire model is 8.6. A random sample of 10 tires has a variance of 4.3. At $\alpha = 0.01$, is there enough evidence to reject the claim?

**24. Gas Mileage** An auto manufacturer claims that the variance of the gas mileages in a model of hybrid vehicle is 0.16. A random sample of 30 vehicles has a variance of 0.26. At $\alpha = 0.05$, is there enough evidence to reject the claim?

**25. Mathematics Assessment Tests** A school administrator claims that the standard deviation for grade 12 students on a mathematics assessment test is less than 37 points. A random sample of 28 grade 12 test scores has a standard deviation of 34 points. At $\alpha = 0.10$, is there enough evidence to support the claim? *(Adapted from National Center for Educational Statistics)*

**26. Reading Assessment Tests** A school administrator claims that the standard deviation for grade 12 students on a reading assessment test is greater than 41 points. A random sample of 25 grade 12 test scores has a standard deviation of 46 points. At $\alpha = 0.01$, is there enough evidence to support the claim? *(Adapted from National Center for Educational Statistics)*

**27. Waiting Times** A hospital claims that the standard deviation of the waiting times for patients in its emergency department is no more than 0.5 minute. A random sample of 25 waiting times has a standard deviation of 0.7 minute. At $\alpha = 0.10$, is there enough evidence to reject the claim?

**28. Hotel Room Rates** A travel analyst claims that the standard deviation of the room rates for two adults at three-star hotels in Denver is at least \$68. A random sample of 18 three-star hotels has a standard deviation of \$40. At $\alpha = 0.01$, is there enough evidence to reject the claim? *(Adapted from Expedia)*

**29. Salaries** The annual salaries (in dollars) of 15 randomly chosen senior level graphic design specialists are shown in the table at the left. At $\alpha = 0.05$, is there enough evidence to support the claim that the standard deviation of the annual salaries is different from \$13,056? *(Adapted from Salary.com)*

| Annual salaries | | |
|---|---|---|
| 55,060 | 75,140 | 89,050 |
| 73,200 | 67,400 | 86,220 |
| 96,000 | 59,900 | 111,700 |
| 99,750 | 52,250 | 98,100 |
| 74,700 | 56,000 | 77,900 |

TABLE FOR EXERCISE 29

**30. Salaries** The annual salaries (in dollars) of 12 randomly chosen nursing supervisors are shown in the table at the left. At $\alpha = 0.10$, is there enough evidence to reject the claim that the standard deviation of the annual salaries is \$18,630? *(Adapted from Salary.com)*

| Annual salaries | | |
|---|---|---|
| 68,700 | 108,300 | 107,000 |
| 98,900 | 73,900 | 87,800 |
| 83,400 | 116,600 | 94,300 |
| 96,000 | 99,300 | 79,900 |

TABLE FOR EXERCISE 30

## Extending Concepts

**TI-84 PLUS**

```
χ²cdf(0,43.2,40)
                0.6637768667
```

***P*-Values** *You can calculate the P-value for a chi-square test using technology. After calculating the standardized test statistic, use the cumulative distribution function (CDF) to calculate the area under the curve. From Example 4 on page 397, $\chi^2 = 43.2$. Using a TI-84 Plus (choose 8 from the DISTR menu), enter 0 for the lower bound, 43.2 for the upper bound, and 40 for the degrees of freedom, as shown at the left. Because it is a right-tailed test, the P-value is approximately $1 - 0.6638 = 0.3362$. Because $P > \alpha = 0.05$, fail to reject $H_0$. In Exercises 31–34, use the P-value method to perform the hypothesis test for the indicated exercise.*

**31.** Exercise 25 **32.** Exercise 26 **33.** Exercise 27 **34.** Exercise 28

# 7 A Summary of Hypothesis Testing

With hypothesis testing, perhaps more than any other area of statistics, it can be difficult to see the overall picture. So, a summary of what you studied in this chapter is provided below.

### Writing the Hypotheses

- You are given a claim about a population parameter $\mu$, $p$, $\sigma^2$, or $\sigma$.
- Rewrite the claim and its complement using $\underbrace{\leq, \geq, =}_{H_0}$ and $\underbrace{>, <, \neq}_{H_a}$.
- Identify the claim. Is it $H_0$ or $H_a$?

### Specifying a Level of Significance

- Specify $\alpha$, the maximum acceptable probability of rejecting a valid $H_0$ (a type I error).

**Study Tip**

Large sample sizes will usually increase the cost and effort of testing a hypothesis, but they also tend to make your decision more reliable.

### Specifying the Sample Size

- Specify your sample size $n$.

### Choosing the Test

▲ Normally distributed population ● Any population

- **Mean:** $H_0$ describes a hypothesized population mean $\mu$.
  - ▲ Use a ***z*-test** when $\sigma$ is known and the population is normal.
  - ● Use a ***z*-test** for any population when $\sigma$ is known and $n \geq 30$.
  - ▲ Use a ***t*-test** when $\sigma$ is not known and the population is normal.
  - ● Use a ***t*-test** for any population when $\sigma$ is not known and $n \geq 30$.
- **Proportion:** $H_0$ describes a hypothesized population proportion $p$.
  - ● Use a ***z*-test** for any population when $np \geq 5$ and $nq \geq 5$.
- **Variance or Standard Deviation:** $H_0$ describes a hypothesized population variance $\sigma^2$ or standard deviation $\sigma$.
  - ▲ Use a **chi-square test** when the population is normal.

### Sketching the Sampling Distribution

- Use $H_a$ to decide whether the test is left-tailed, right-tailed, or two-tailed.

### Finding the Standardized Test Statistic

- Take a random sample of size $n$ from the population.
- Determine the test statistic $\bar{x}$, $\hat{p}$, or $s^2$.
- Compute the standardized test statistic $z$, $t$, or $\chi^2$.

### Making a Decision

**Option 1.** Decision based on rejection region

- Use $\alpha$ to find the critical value(s) $z_0$, $t_0$, or $\chi^2_0$ and rejection region(s).
- **Decision Rule:**

  Reject $H_0$ when the standardized test statistic is in the rejection region.
  Fail to reject $H_0$ when the standardized test statistic is not in the rejection region.

**Option 2.** Decision based on $P$-value

- Use the standardized test statistic or technology to find the $P$-value.
- **Decision Rule:**

  Reject $H_0$ when $P \leq \alpha$.
  Fail to reject $H_0$ when $P > \alpha$.

### *z*-Test for a Hypothesized Mean $\mu$ ($\sigma$ Known) *(Section 7.2)*

**Test statistic:** $\bar{x}$

**Critical value:** $z_0$ (Use Table 4.)

Sampling distribution of sample means is a normal distribution.

**Standardized test statistic:** $z$

$$z = \frac{\bar{x} - \mu}{\sigma / \sqrt{n}}$$

Sample mean ($\bar{x}$); Hypothesized mean ($\mu$); Population standard deviation ($\sigma$); Sample size ($n$)

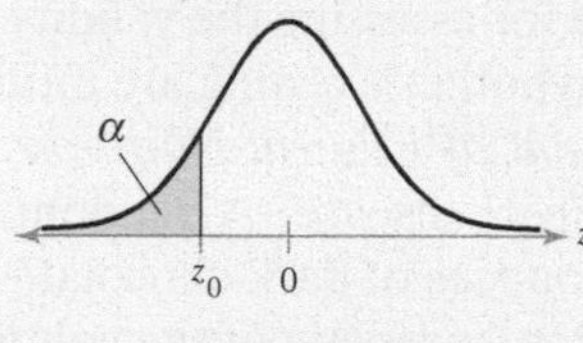


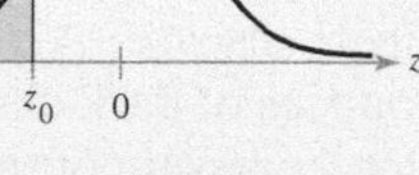

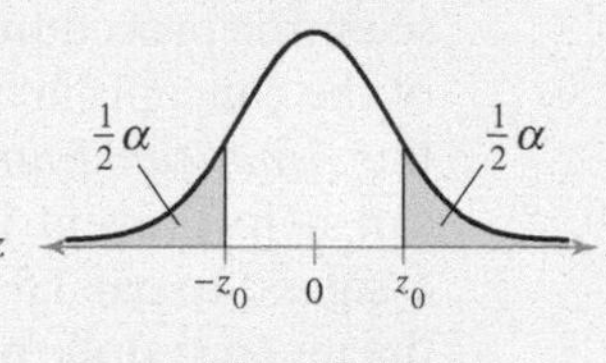


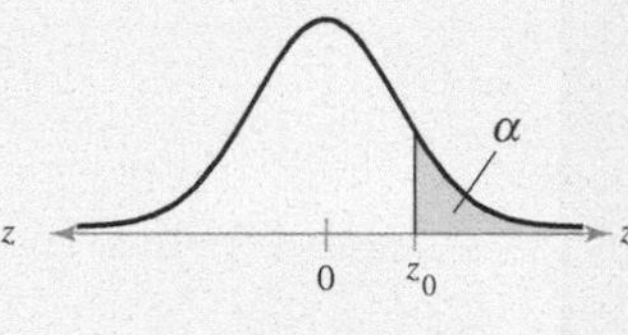


### *z*-Test for a Hypothesized Proportion $p$ *(Section 7.4)*

**Test statistic:** $\hat{p}$

**Critical value:** $z_0$ (Use Table 4.)

Sampling distribution of sample proportions is a normal distribution.

**Standardized test statistic:** $z$

$$z = \frac{\hat{p} - p}{\sqrt{pq/n}}$$

Sample proportion ($\hat{p}$); Hypothesized proportion ($p$); $q = 1 - p$; Sample size ($n$)

**Study Tip**

When your standardized test statistic is $z$ or $t$, remember that these values measure standard deviations from the mean. Values that are outside of $\pm 3$ indicate that $H_0$ is very unlikely. Values that are outside of $\pm 5$ indicate that $H_0$ is almost impossible.

### *t*-Test for a Hypothesized Mean $\mu$ ($\sigma$ Unknown) *(Section 7.3)*

**Test statistic:** $\bar{x}$

**Critical value:** $t_0$ (Use Table 5.)

Sampling distribution of sample means is approximated by a $t$-distribution with d.f. $= n - 1$.

**Standardized test statistic:** $t$

$$t = \frac{\bar{x} - \mu}{s / \sqrt{n}}$$

Sample mean ($\bar{x}$); Hypothesized mean ($\mu$); Sample standard deviation ($s$); Sample size ($n$)

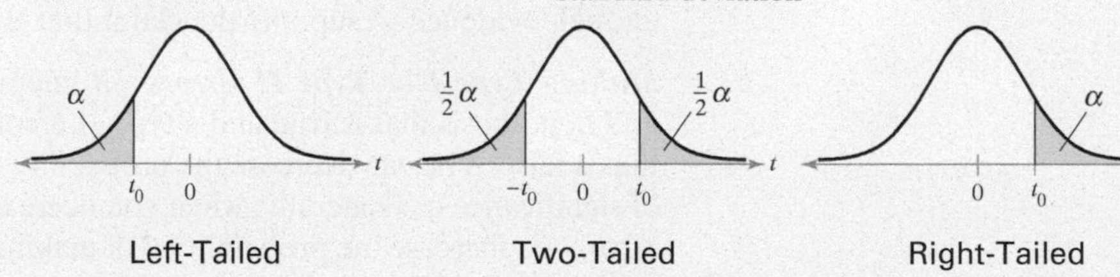


### Chi-Square Test for a Hypothesized Variance $\sigma^2$ or Standard Deviation $\sigma$ *(Section 7.5)*

**Test statistic:** $s^2$

**Critical value:** $\chi^2_0$ (Use Table 6.)

Sampling distribution is approximated by a chi-square distribution with d.f. $= n - 1$.

**Standardized test statistic:** $\chi^2$

$$\chi^2 = \frac{(n-1)s^2}{\sigma^2}$$

Sample size ($n$); Sample variance ($s^2$); Hypothesized variance ($\sigma^2$)

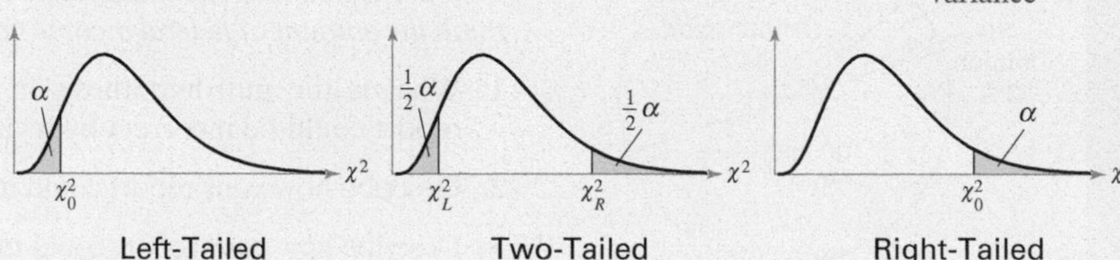

# USES AND ABUSES

# Statistics in the Real World

## Uses

Hypothesis testing is important in many different fields because it gives a scientific procedure for assessing the validity of a claim about a population. Some of the concepts in hypothesis testing are intuitive, but some are not. For instance, the *American Journal of Clinical Nutrition* suggests that eating dark chocolate can help prevent heart disease. A random sample of healthy volunteers were assigned to eat 3.5 ounces of dark chocolate each day for 15 days. After 15 days, the mean systolic blood pressure of the volunteers was 6.4 millimeters of mercury lower. A hypothesis test could show whether this drop in systolic blood pressure is significant or simply due to sampling error.

Careful inferences must be made concerning the results. The study only examined the effects of dark chocolate, so the inference of health benefits cannot be extended to all types of chocolate. You also would not infer that you should eat large quantities of chocolate because the benefits must be weighed against known risks, such as weight gain and acid reflux.

## Abuses

***Not Using a Random Sample*** The entire theory of hypothesis testing is based on the fact that the sample is randomly selected. If the sample is not random, then you cannot use it to infer anything about a population parameter.

***Attempting to Prove the Null Hypothesis*** When the $P$-value for a hypothesis test is greater than the level of significance, you have not proven the null hypothesis is true—only that there is not enough evidence to reject it. For instance, with a $P$-value higher than the level of significance, a researcher could not prove that there is no benefit to eating dark chocolate—only that there is not enough evidence to support the claim that there is a benefit.

***Making Type I or Type II Errors*** Remember that a type I error is rejecting a null hypothesis that is true and a type II error is failing to reject a null hypothesis that is false. You can decrease the probability of a type I error by lowering the level of significance $\alpha$. Generally, when you decrease the probability of making a type I error, you increase the probability $\beta$ of making a type II error. Which error is more serious? It depends on the situation. In a criminal trial, a type I error is considered worse, as explained on page 352. If you are testing a person for a disease and they are assumed to be disease-free $(H_0)$, then a type II error is more serious because you would fail to detect the disease even though the person has it. You can decrease the chance of making both types of errors by increasing the sample size.

**Do You Consider the Amount of Federal Income Tax You Pay as Too High, About Right, or Too Low?**

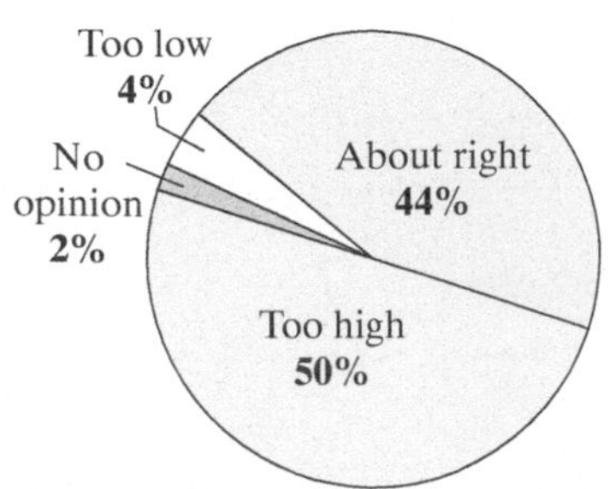


## EXERCISES

*In Exercises 1–3, assume that you work for the Internal Revenue Service. You are asked to write a report about the claim that 50% of U.S. adults think the amount of federal income tax they pay is too high.* (Source: Gallup)

1. What is the null hypothesis in this situation? Describe how your report could be incorrect by trying to prove the null hypothesis.
2. Describe how your report could make a type I error.
3. Describe how your report could make a type II error.

# 7 Chapter Summary

| What Did You Learn? | Example(s) | Review Exercises |
|---|---|---|
| **Section 7.1** | | |
| ▶ How to state a null hypothesis and an alternative hypothesis | 1 | 1–6 |
| ▶ How to identify type I and type II errors | 2 | 7–10 |
| ▶ How to know whether to use a one-tailed or a two-tailed statistical test and find a *P*-value | 3 | 7–10 |
| ▶ How to interpret a decision based on the results of a statistical test | 4 | 7–10 |
| ▶ How to write a claim for a hypothesis test | 5 | 7–10 |
| **Section 7.2** | | |
| ▶ How to find and interpret *P*-values | 1–3 | 11, 12 |
| ▶ How to use *P*-values for a *z*-test for a mean $\mu$ when $\sigma$ is known | 4–6 | 25, 26 |
| ▶ How to find critical values and rejection regions in the standard normal distribution | 7, 8 | 13–16 |
| ▶ How to use rejection regions for a *z*-test for a mean $\mu$ when $\sigma$ is known | 9, 10 | 17–24, 27, 28 |
| **Section 7.3** | | |
| ▶ How to find critical values in a *t*-distribution | 1–3 | 29–34 |
| ▶ How to use the *t*-test to test a mean $\mu$ when $\sigma$ is not known | 4, 5 | 35–42 |
| ▶ How to use technology to find *P*-values and use them with a *t*-test to test a mean $\mu$ when $\sigma$ is not known | 6 | 43, 44 |
| **Section 7.4** | | |
| ▶ How to use the *z*-test to test a population proportion *p* | 1, 2 | 45–50 |
| **Section 7.5** | | |
| ▶ How to find critical values for a chi-square test | 1–3 | 51–54 |
| ▶ How to use the chi-square test to test a variance $\sigma^2$ or a standard deviation $\sigma$ | 4–6 | 55–62 |

## Study Strategies

**Stress Management** Stress is the physical, mental, emotional, or behavioral reaction to perceived threats or demands. Practice stress management to maintain a sense of well-being and balance during your studies.

- Assess your level of stress. Identify and anticipate what is causing your stress (your "stressors").
- Use stress prevention techniques. Some of these include the following.
  - Manage your time wisely. Some tips for time management are given in the Chapter 3 Summary.
  - Treat your body right. Try to include rest, relaxation, exercise, and eating healthy meals in your daily routine. Limit caffeine or alcohol products.
  - Spend time to get a perspective on your life. Use positive and reassuring self-talk.
- Address early warning signs of stress. Do not hesitate to seek help. This could include scheduling tutoring sessions.

For more information, visit Skills for Success in the accompanying MyLab course.

# 7 Review Exercises

## Section 7.1

*In Exercises 1–6, the statement represents a claim. Write its complement and state which is $H_0$ and which is $H_a$.*

**1.** $\mu \leq 375$ **2.** $\mu = 82$ **3.** $p < 0.205$

**4.** $\mu \neq 150{,}020$ **5.** $\sigma > 1.9$ **6.** $p \geq 0.64$

*In Exercises 7–10, (a) state the null and alternative hypotheses and identify which represents the claim, (b) describe type I and type II errors for a hypothesis test of the claim, (c) explain whether the hypothesis test is left-tailed, right-tailed, or two-tailed, (d) explain how you should interpret a decision that rejects the null hypothesis, and (e) explain how you should interpret a decision that fails to reject the null hypothesis.*

**7.** A polling organization reports that the proportion of U.S. adults who believe that Earth's temperature has been increasing over the past 100 years is 81%. *(Source: Resources)*

**8.** An agricultural cooperative guarantees that the mean shelf life of a type of dried fruit is at least 400 days.

**9.** A nonprofit consumer organization says that the standard deviation of the starting prices of its top-rated vehicles for a recent year is no more than \$2900. *(Adapted from U.S. News)*

**10.** An energy bar maker claims that the mean number of grams of carbohydrates in one bar is less than 25.

## Section 7.2

*In Exercises 11 and 12, find the P-value for the hypothesis test with the standardized test statistic z. Decide whether to reject $H_0$ for the level of significance $\alpha$.*

**11.** Left-tailed test, $z = -0.94$, $\alpha = 0.05$

**12.** Two-tailed test, $z = 2.57$, $\alpha = 0.10$

*In Exercises 13–16, find the critical value(s) and rejection region(s) for the type of z-test with level of significance $\alpha$. Include a graph with your answer.*

**13.** Left-tailed test, $\alpha = 0.02$ **14.** Two-tailed test, $\alpha = 0.005$

**15.** Right-tailed test, $\alpha = 0.025$ **16.** Two-tailed test, $\alpha = 0.03$

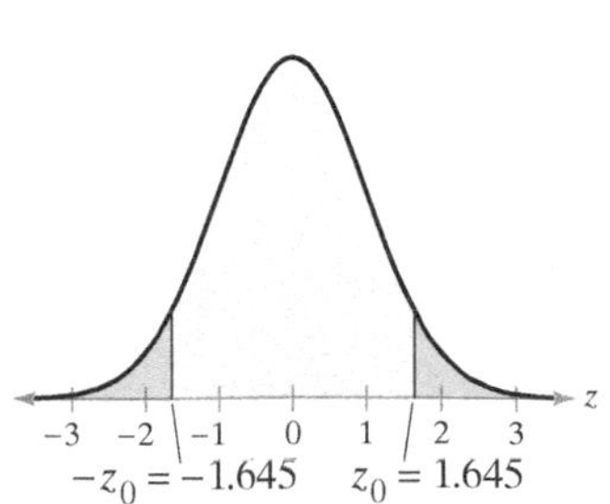


FIGURE FOR EXERCISES 17–20

*In Exercises 17–20, state whether the standardized test statistic z allows you to reject the null hypothesis. Explain your reasoning.*

**17.** $z = 1.631$ **18.** $z = 1.723$ **19.** $z = -1.464$ **20.** $z = -1.655$

*In Exercises 21–24, test the claim about the population mean $\mu$ at the level of significance $\alpha$. Assume the population is normally distributed.*

**21.** Claim: $\mu \leq 45$; $\alpha = 0.05$; $\sigma = 6.7$. Sample statistics: $\bar{x} = 47.2$, $n = 22$

**22.** Claim: $\mu \neq 8.45$; $\alpha = 0.03$; $\sigma = 1.75$. Sample statistics: $\bar{x} = 7.88$, $n = 60$

**23.** Claim: $\mu < 5.500$; $\alpha = 0.01$; $\sigma = 0.011$. Sample statistics: $\bar{x} = 5.497$, $n = 36$

**24.** Claim: $\mu = 7450$; $\alpha = 0.10$; $\sigma = 243$. Sample statistics: $\bar{x} = 7495$, $n = 27$

*In Exercises 25 and 26, (a) identify the claim and state $H_0$ and $H_a$, (b) find the standardized test statistic z, (c) find the corresponding P-value, (d) decide whether to reject or fail to reject the null hypothesis, and (e) interpret the decision in the context of the original claim.*

**25.** A researcher claims that the mean air concentration of nitrogen dioxide in U.S. cities is 9 parts per billion (ppb). In a random sample of 52 U.S. cities, the mean air concentration of nitrogen dioxide is 8.1 ppb. Assume the population standard deviation is 5.65 ppb. At $\alpha = 0.05$, can you reject the claim? *(Source: U.S. Environmental Protection Agency)*

**26.** A researcher claims that the mean air concentration of fine particulate matter (PM 2.5) in U.S. cities is greater than 9 micrograms per cubic meter $(\mu g/m^3)$. In a random sample of 84 U.S. cities, the mean air concentration of PM 2.5 is 8.25 $\mu g/m^3$. Assume the population standard deviation is 2.53 $\mu g/m^3$. At $\alpha = 0.01$, can you support the claim? *(Source: U.S. Environmental Protection Agency)*

*In Exercises 27 and 28, (a) identify the claim and state $H_0$ and $H_a$, (b) find the critical value(s) and identify the rejection region(s), (c) find the standardized test statistic z, (d) decide whether to reject or fail to reject the null hypothesis, and (e) interpret the decision in the context of the original claim.*

**27.** A substance abuse counselor claims that the mean annual drug overdose death rate for the 50 states is at least 25 deaths per 100,000 people. In a random sample of 30 states, the mean annual drug overdose rate is 22.48 per 100,000 people. Assume the population standard deviation is 10.69 deaths per 100,000. At $\alpha = 0.01$, is there enough evidence to reject the claim? *(Source: Centers for Disease Control and Prevention)*

**28.** A travel analyst claims that the mean price of a round trip flight from New York City to Los Angeles is less than \$725. In a random sample of 47 round trip flights from New York City to Los Angeles, the mean price is \$712. Assume the population standard deviation is \$133. At $\alpha = 0.05$, is there enough evidence to support the travel analyst's claim? *(Adapted from Expedia)*

## Section 7.3

*In Exercises 29–34, find the critical value(s) and rejection region(s) for the type of t-test with level of significance $\alpha$ and sample size n.*

**29.** Two-tailed test, $\alpha = 0.05, n = 20$

**30.** Right-tailed test, $\alpha = 0.01, n = 33$

**31.** Right-tailed test, $\alpha = 0.02, n = 63$

**32.** Left-tailed test, $\alpha = 0.05, n = 48$

**33.** Left-tailed test, $\alpha = 0.005, n = 15$

**34.** Two-tailed test, $\alpha = 0.02, n = 12$

*In Exercises 35–40, test the claim about the population mean $\mu$ at the level of significance $\alpha$. Assume the population is normally distributed.*

**35.** Claim: $\mu > 12{,}700$; $\alpha = 0.005$.
Sample statistics: $\bar{x} = 12{,}855, s = 248, n = 21$

**36.** Claim: $\mu \geq 0$; $\alpha = 0.10$. Sample statistics: $\bar{x} = -0.45, s = 2.38, n = 31$

**37.** Claim: $\mu \leq 51$; $\alpha = 0.01$. Sample statistics: $\bar{x} = 52, s = 2.5, n = 40$

**38.** Claim: $\mu < 850$; $\alpha = 0.025$. Sample statistics: $\bar{x} = 875, s = 25, n = 14$

**39.** Claim: $\mu = 195$; $\alpha = 0.10$. Sample statistics: $\bar{x} = 190, s = 36, n = 101$

**40.** Claim: $\mu \neq 333$; $\alpha = 0.05$.
Sample statistics: $\bar{x} = 328, s = 13, n = 35$

*In Exercises 41 and 42, (a) identify the claim and state $H_0$ and $H_a$, (b) find the critical value(s) and identify the rejection region(s), (c) find the standardized test statistic t, (d) decide whether to reject or fail to reject the null hypothesis, and (e) interpret the decision in the context of the original claim. Assume the population is normally distributed.*

**41.** A fitness magazine advertises that the mean monthly cost of joining a health club is \$25. You want to test this claim. You find that a random sample of 18 clubs has a mean monthly cost of \$26.25 and a standard deviation of \$3.23. At $\alpha = 0.10$, do you have enough evidence to reject the advertisement's claim?

**42.** A fitness magazine claims that the mean cost of a yoga session is no more than \$14. You want to test this claim. You find that a random sample of 32 yoga sessions has a mean cost of \$15.59 and a standard deviation of \$2.60. At $\alpha = 0.025$, do you have enough evidence to reject the magazine's claim?

*In Exercises 43 and 44, (a) identify the claim and state $H_0$ and $H_a$, (b) use technology to find the P-value, (c) decide whether to reject or fail to reject the null hypothesis, and (d) interpret the decision in the context of the original claim. Assume the population is normally distributed.*

 **43.** An education publication claims that the mean score for grade 12 students on a science achievement test is more than 145. You want to test this claim. You randomly select 36 grade 12 test scores. The results are listed below. At $\alpha = 0.1$, can you support the publication's claim? *(Adapted from National Center for Education Statistics)*

| | | | | | | | | | | | |
|---|---|---|---|---|---|---|---|---|---|---|---|
| 188 | 80 | 175 | 195 | 201 | 143 | 119 | 81 | 118 | 119 | 165 | 222 |
| 109 | 134 | 200 | 110 | 199 | 181 | 79 | 135 | 124 | 205 | 90 | 120 |
| 216 | 167 | 198 | 183 | 173 | 187 | 143 | 166 | 147 | 219 | 206 | 97 |

 **44.** An education researcher claims that the overall average score of 15-year-old students on an international mathematics literacy test is 489. You want to test this claim. You randomly select the average scores of 30 countries. The results are listed below. At $\alpha = 0.05$, do you have enough evidence to reject the researcher's claim? *(Source: National Center for Education Statistics)*

| | | | | | | | | | |
|---|---|---|---|---|---|---|---|---|---|
| 481 | 507 | 495 | 500 | 499 | 483 | 509 | 515 | 417 | 523 |
| 526 | 487 | 486 | 519 | 451 | 516 | 454 | 527 | 509 | 495 |
| 499 | 481 | 508 | 409 | 502 | 491 | 492 | 481 | 496 | 500 |

## Section 7.4

*In Exercises 45–48, determine whether a normal sampling distribution can be used to approximate the binomial distribution. If it can, test the claim.*

**45.** Claim: $p = 0.15$; $\alpha = 0.05$
Sample statistics: $\hat{p} = 0.09$, $n = 40$

**46.** Claim: $p = 0.65$; $\alpha = 0.03$
Sample statistics: $\hat{p} = 0.76$, $n = 116$

**47.** Claim: $p < 0.70$; $\alpha = 0.01$
Sample statistics: $\hat{p} = 0.50$, $n = 68$

**48.** Claim: $p \geq 0.04$; $\alpha = 0.10$
Sample statistics: $\hat{p} = 0.03$, $n = 30$

*In Exercises 49 and 50, (a) identify the claim and state $H_0$ and $H_a$, (b) find the critical value(s) and identify the rejection region(s), (c) find the standardized test statistic z, (d) decide whether to reject or fail to reject the null hypothesis, and (e) interpret the decision in the context of the original claim.*

**49.** A reporter claims that over 56% of U.S. adults think it is likely that robots and computers will do most jobs 25 years from now. In a random sample of 1000 U.S. adults, 59% say it is likely that most jobs will be done by robots and computers 25 years from now. At $\alpha = 0.01$, is there enough evidence to support the claim? *(Source: Rasmussen Reports)*

**50.** A sports analyst claims that 40% of U.S. adults have a positive view of the sports industry. In a random sample of 550 U.S. adults, 165 say they have a positive view of the sports industry. At $\alpha = 0.05$, is there enough evidence to reject the sports analyst's claim? *(Source: Gallup)*

## Section 7.5

*In Exercises 51–54, find the critical value(s) and rejection region(s) for the type of chi-square test with sample size n and level of significance $\alpha$.*

**51.** Right-tailed test, $n = 20$, $\alpha = 0.05$

**52.** Two-tailed test, $n = 14$, $\alpha = 0.01$

**53.** Two-tailed test, $n = 41$, $\alpha = 0.10$

**54.** Left-tailed test, $n = 6$, $\alpha = 0.05$

*In Exercises 55–58, test the claim about the population variance $\sigma^2$ or standard deviation $\sigma$ at the level of significance $\alpha$. Assume the population is normally distributed.*

**55.** Claim: $\sigma^2 > 2$; $\alpha = 0.10$. Sample statistics: $s^2 = 2.95$, $n = 18$

**56.** Claim: $\sigma^2 \leq 60$; $\alpha = 0.025$. Sample statistics: $s^2 = 72.7$, $n = 15$

**57.** Claim: $\sigma = 1.25$; $\alpha = 0.05$. Sample statistics: $s = 1.03$, $n = 6$

**58.** Claim: $\sigma \neq 0.035$; $\alpha = 0.01$. Sample statistics: $s = 0.026$, $n = 16$

*In Exercises 59 and 60, (a) identify the claim and state $H_0$ and $H_a$, (b) find the critical value(s) and identify the rejection region(s), (c) find the standardized test statistic $\chi^2$, (d) decide whether to reject or fail to reject the null hypothesis, and (e) interpret the decision in the context of the original claim. Assume the population is normally distributed.*

**59.** A bolt manufacturer makes a type of bolt to be used in airtight containers. The manufacturer claims that the variance of the bolt widths is at most 0.01. A random sample of 28 bolts has a variance of 0.064. At $\alpha = 0.005$, is there enough evidence to reject the claim?

**60.** A restaurant claims that the standard deviation of the lengths of serving times is 3 minutes. A random sample of 27 serving times has a standard deviation of 3.9 minutes. At $\alpha = 0.01$, is there enough evidence to reject the claim?

**61.** In Exercise 59, is there enough evidence to reject the claim at the $\alpha = 0.01$ level? Explain.

**62.** In Exercise 60, is there enough evidence to reject the claim at the $\alpha = 0.05$ level? Explain.

# 7 Chapter Quiz

*Take this quiz as you would take a quiz in class. After you are done, check your work against the answers given in the back of the book.*

*For each exercise, perform the steps below.*

*(a) Identify the claim and state $H_0$ and $H_a$.*

*(b) Determine whether the hypothesis test is left-tailed, right-tailed, or two-tailed, and whether to use a z-test, a t-test, or a chi-square test. Explain your reasoning.*

*(c) Choose one of the options.*

*Option 1: Find the critical value(s), identify the rejection region(s), and find the appropriate standardized test statistic.*

*Option 2: Find the appropriate standardized test statistic and the P-value.*

*(d) Decide whether to reject or fail to reject the null hypothesis.*

*(e) Interpret the decision in the context of the original claim.*

**1.** A hat company claims that the mean hat size for a male is at least 7.25. A random sample of 12 hat sizes has a mean of 7.15. At $\alpha = 0.01$, can you reject the company's claim? Assume the population is normally distributed and the population standard deviation is 0.27.

**2.** A travel analyst claims the mean daily base price for renting a full-size or less expensive vehicle in Vancouver, British Columbia, is more than \$86. You want to test this claim. In a random sample of 40 full-size or less expensive vehicles available to rent in Vancouver, British Columbia, the mean daily base price is \$93.23. Assume the population standard deviation is \$28.90. At $\alpha = 0.10$, do you have enough evidence to support the analyst's claim? *(Adapted from Expedia)*

**3.** A government agency reports that the mean amount of earnings for full-time workers ages 18 to 24 with a bachelor's degree in a recent year is \$52,133. In a random sample of 15 full-time workers ages 18 to 24 with a bachelor's degree, the mean amount of earnings is \$48,400 and the standard deviation is \$6679. At $\alpha = 0.05$, is there enough evidence to reject the claim? Assume the population is normally distributed. *(Adapted from U.S. Census Bureau)*

**4.** A weight loss program claims that program participants have a mean weight loss of at least 10.5 pounds after 1 month. The weight losses after 1 month (in pounds) of a random sample of 40 program participants are listed below. At $\alpha = 0.01$, is there enough evidence to reject the program's claim?

| | | | | | | | | | |
|---|---|---|---|---|---|---|---|---|---|
| 4.7 | 6.0 | 7.2 | 8.3 | 9.2 | 10.1 | 14.0 | 11.7 | 12.8 | 10.8 |
| 11.0 | 7.2 | 8.0 | 4.7 | 11.8 | 10.7 | 6.1 | 8.8 | 7.7 | 8.5 |
| 9.5 | 10.2 | 5.6 | 6.9 | 7.9 | 8.6 | 10.5 | 9.6 | 5.7 | 9.6 |
| 12.6 | 12.9 | 6.8 | 12.0 | 5.1 | 14.0 | 9.7 | 10.8 | 9.1 | 12.9 |

**5.** A nonprofit consumer organization says that less than 25% of the televisions the organization rated in a recent year have an overall score of 70 or more. In a random sample of 35 televisions the organization rated in a recent year, 23% have an overall score of 70 or more. At $\alpha = 0.05$, can you support the organization's claim? *(Adapted from Consumer Reports)*

**6.** In Exercise 5, the nonprofit consumer organization says that the standard deviation of the television rating scores is 10.1. A random sample of 35 television rating scores has a standard deviation of 10.9. At $\alpha = 0.10$, is there enough evidence to reject the organization's claim? Assume the population is normally distributed. *(Adapted from Consumer Reports)*

# 7 Chapter Test

*Take this test as you would take a test in class.*

*For each exercise, perform the steps below.*

*(a) Identify the claim and state $H_0$ and $H_a$.*

*(b) Determine whether the hypothesis test is left-tailed, right-tailed, or two-tailed, and whether to use a z-test, a t-test, or a chi-square test. Explain your reasoning.*

*(c) Choose one of the options.*

*Option 1: Find the critical value(s), identify the rejection region(s), and find the appropriate standardized test statistic.*

*Option 2: Find the appropriate standardized test statistic and the P-value.*

*(d) Decide whether to reject or fail to reject the null hypothesis.*

*(e) Interpret the decision in the context of the original claim.*

**1.** A retail grocery chain owner claims that at least 25% of adults have purchased a meal kit in a recent year. In a random sample of 36 adults, 19% have purchased a meal kit in a recent year. At $\alpha = 0.10$, is there enough evidence to reject the owner's claim? *(Adapted from PYMNTS)*

**2.** A travel analyst claims that the mean of the room rates for two adults at three-star hotels in Salt Lake City is \$134. In a random sample of 37 three-star hotels in Salt Lake City, the mean room rate for two adults is \$143. Assume the population standard deviation is \$30. At $\alpha = 0.10$, is there enough evidence to reject the analyst's claim? *(Adapted from Expedia)*

**3.** A travel analyst says that the mean price of a meal for a family of 4 in a resort restaurant is at most \$100. A random sample of 33 meal prices for families of 4 has a mean of \$110 and a standard deviation of \$19. At $\alpha = 0.01$, is there enough evidence to reject the analyst's claim?

**4.** A research center claims that more than 80% of U.S. adults think that mothers should have paid maternity leave. In a random sample of 50 U.S. adults, 82% think that mothers should have paid maternity leave. At $\alpha = 0.05$, is there enough evidence to support the center's claim? *(Adapted from Pew Research Center)*

**5.** A nutrition bar manufacturer claims that the standard deviation of the number of grams of carbohydrates in a bar is 1.11 grams. A random sample of 26 bars has a standard deviation of 1.19 grams. At $\alpha = 0.05$, is there enough evidence to reject the manufacturer's claim? Assume the population is normally distributed.

**6.** A nonprofit consumer organization says that the mean rating of gas grills the organization rated in a recent year is less than 64. In a random sample of 50 gas grills the organization rated in a recent year, the mean rating is 62.9 and the standard deviation is 8.1. At $\alpha = 0.01$, is there enough evidence to support the organization's claim? *(Adapted from Consumer Reports)*

**7.** A researcher claims that the mean age of the residents of a small town is more than 38 years. The ages (in years) of a random sample of 30 residents are listed below. At $\alpha = 0.10$, is there enough evidence to support the researcher's claim? Assume the population standard deviation is 9 years.

41 44 40 30 29 46 42 53 21 29 43 46 39 35 33
42 35 43 35 24 21 29 24 25 85 56 82 87 72 31

# REAL STATISTICS REAL DECISIONS

# Putting it all together

The charts show results of studies on four-year colleges in the United States. You want to portray your college in a positive light for an advertising campaign designed to attract high school students. You decide to use hypothesis tests to show that your college is better than the average in certain aspects.

## EXERCISES

1. ***What Would You Test?***

   What claims could you test if you wanted to convince a student to come to your college? Suppose the student you are trying to convince is mainly concerned with (a) affordability, (b) having a good experience, and (c) graduating and starting a career. List one claim for each case. State the null and alternative hypotheses for each claim.

2. ***Choosing a Random Sample***

   Classmates suggest conducting the following sampling techniques to test various claims. Determine whether the sample will be random. If not, suggest an alternative.

   (a) Survey all the students you have class with and ask about the average time they spend daily on different activities.

   (b) Randomly select former students from a list of recent graduates and ask whether they are employed.

   (c) Randomly select students from a directory, ask how much debt money they borrowed to pay for college this year, and multiply by four.

3. ***Supporting a Claim***

   You want your test to support a positive claim about your college, not just fail to reject one. Should you state your claim so that the null hypothesis contains the claim or the alternate hypothesis contains the claim? Explain.

4. ***Testing a Claim***

   You want to claim that students at your college graduate with an average debt of less than \$25,000. A random sample of 40 recent graduates has a mean amount borrowed of \$23,475 and a standard deviation of \$8000. At $\alpha = 0.05$, is there enough evidence to support your claim?

5. ***Testing a Claim***

   You want to claim that your college has a freshman retention rate of at least 80%. You take a random sample of 60 of last year's freshmen and find that 54 of them still attend your college. At $\alpha = 0.05$, is there enough evidence to reject your claim?

6. ***Conclusion***

   Test one of the claims you listed in Exercise 1 and interpret the results. Discuss any limits of your sampling process.

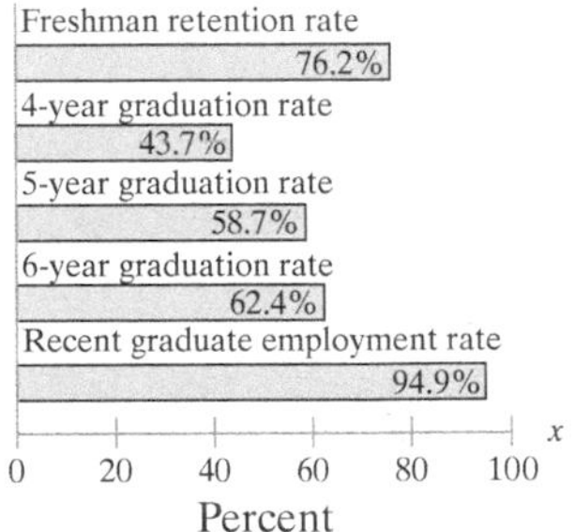


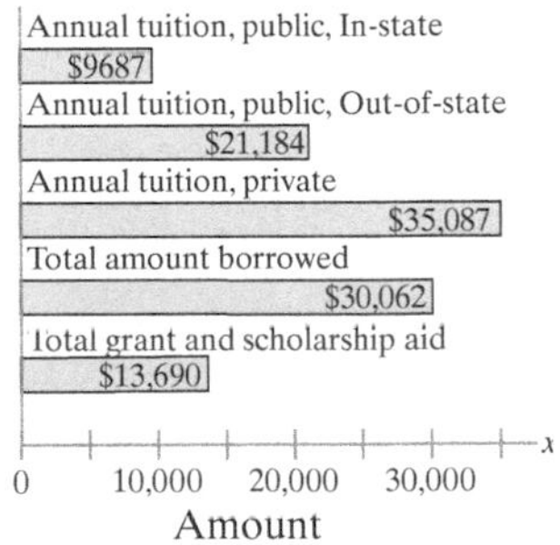


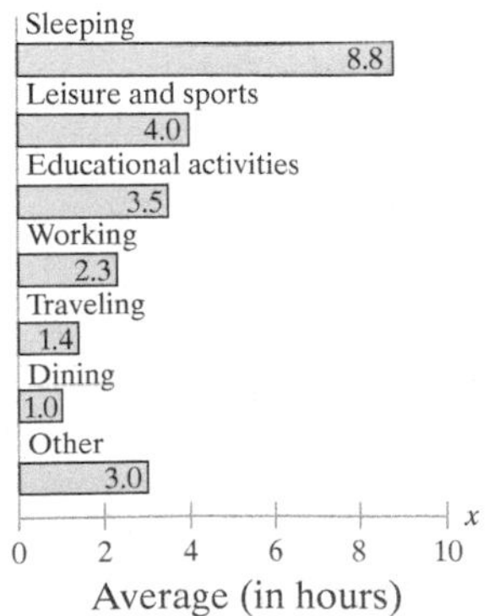

TECHNOLOGY

MINITAB | EXCEL | TI-84 PLUS

# The Case of the Vanishing Women

From 1966 to 1968, Dr. Benjamin Spock and others were tried for conspiracy to violate the Selective Service Act by encouraging resistance to the Vietnam War. By a series of three selections, no women ended up being on the jury. In 1969, Hans Zeisel wrote an article in *The University of Chicago Law Review* using statistics and hypothesis testing to argue that the jury selection was biased. Dr. Spock was a well-known pediatrician and author of books about raising children. Millions of mothers had read his books and followed his advice.

The jury selection process for Dr. Spock's trial, shown at the right, can be used to explore the possibility that the jury selection was biased.

**Stage 1.** The clerk of the Federal District Court selected 350 people "at random" from the Boston City Directory. The directory contained several hundred names, 53% of whom were women. However, only 102 of the 350 people selected were women.

**Stage 2.** The trial judge, Judge Ford, selected 100 people "at random" from the 350 people. This group was called a venire and it contained only nine women.

**Stage 3.** The court clerk assigned numbers to the members of the venire and, one by one, they were interrogated by the attorneys for the prosecution and defense until 12 members of the jury were chosen. At this stage, only one potential female juror was questioned, and she was eliminated by the prosecutor under his quota of peremptory challenges (for which he did not have to give a reason).

## EXERCISES

1. The Minitab display below shows a hypothesis test for a claim that the proportion of women in the city directory is $p = 0.53$. In the test, $n = 350$ and $\hat{p} \approx 0.291$. Should you reject the claim? What is the level of significance? Explain.
2. In Exercise 1, you rejected the claim that $p = 0.53$. But this claim was true. What type of error is this?
3. When you reject a true claim with a level of significance that is virtually zero, what can you infer about the randomness of your sampling process?
4. Describe a hypothesis test for Judge Ford's "random" selection of the venire. Use a claim of

$$p = \frac{102}{350} \approx 0.291.$$

   (a) Write the null and alternative hypotheses.
   (b) Use technology to perform the test.
   (c) Make a decision.
   (d) Interpret the decision in the context of the original claim. Could Judge Ford's selection of 100 venire members have been random?

### MINITAB

**Test and CI for One Proportion**

| N | Event | Sample p | 99% CI for p | Z-Value | P-Value |
|---|---|---|---|---|---|
| 350 | 102 | 0.291429 | (0.228862, 0.353995) | −8.94 | 0.000 |

*p: event proportion* — *Null hypothesis* $H_0$: $p = 0.53$

*Normal approximation used* — *Alternative hypothesis* $H_1$: $p \neq 0.53$

Extended solutions are given in the technology manuals that accompany this text. Technical instruction is provided for Minitab, Excel, and the TI-84 Plus.

# 7 Using Technology to Perform Hypothesis Tests

Here are some Minitab and TI-84 Plus printouts for some of the examples in this chapter.

See Example 5, page 367.

Display Descriptive Statistics...
Store Descriptive Statistics...
Graphical Summary...

**1-Sample Z...**
1-Sample t...
2-Sample t...
Paired t...

1 Proportion...
2 Proportions...

**MINITAB**

**One-Sample Z**

| N | Mean | SE Mean | 95% CI for μ | Z-Value | P-Value |
|---|---|---|---|---|---|
| 25 | 67.200 | 0.700 | (65.828, 68.572) | −1.57 | 0.116 |

*μ: population mean of Sample* — *Null hypothesis* $H_0$: $\mu = 68.3$
*Known standard deviation = 3.5* — *Alternative hypothesis* $H_1$: $\mu \neq 68.3$

See Example 4, page 380.

Display Descriptive Statistics...
Store Descriptive Statistics...
Graphical Summary...

1-Sample Z...
**1-Sample t...**
2-Sample t...
Paired t...

1 Proportion...
2 Proportions...

**MINITAB**

**One-Sample T**

| N | Mean | STDev | SE Mean | 95% Upper Bound for μ | T-Value | P-Value |
|---|---|---|---|---|---|---|
| 14 | 21558 | 3350 | 895 | 23144 | −2.17 | 0.025 |

*μ: population mean of Sample* — *Null hypothesis* $H_0$: $\mu = 23500$
*Alternative hypothesis* $H_1$: $\mu < 23500$

See Example 2, page 390.

Display Descriptive Statistics...
Store Descriptive Statistics...
Graphical Summary...

1-Sample Z...
1-Sample t...
2-Sample t...
Paired t...

**1 Proportion...**
2 Proportions...

**MINITAB**

**Test and CI for One Proportion**

| N | Event | Sample p | 90% CI for p | Z-Value | P-Value |
|---|---|---|---|---|---|
| 7400 | 1984 | 0.268108 | (0.259638, 0.276578) | 1.59 | 0.112 |

*p: event proportion* — *Null hypothesis* $H_0$: $p = 0.26$
*Normal approximation used* — *Alternative hypothesis* $H_1$: $p \neq 0.26$

See Example 9, page 371.

**TI-84 PLUS**

EDIT CALC **TESTS**
**1:** Z–Test...
2: T–Test...
3: 2–SampZTest...
4: 2–SampTTest...
5: 1–PropZTest...
6: 2–PropZTest...
7↓ ZInterval...

**TI-84 PLUS**

**Z-Test**
Inpt:Data **Stats**
$\mu_0$:95600
$\sigma$:9500
$\bar{x}$:93300
n:20
$\mu$:$\neq\mu_0$ **$<\mu_0$** $>\mu_0$
Calculate Draw

**TI-84 PLUS**

**Z-Test**
$\mu$<95600
z=−1.082727652
p=.1394646984
$\bar{x}$=93300
n=20

**TI-84 PLUS**

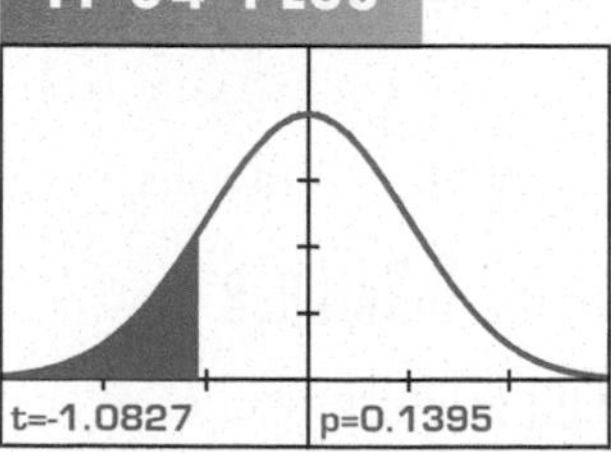


See Example 5, page 381.

**TI-84 PLUS**

EDIT CALC **TESTS**
1: Z–Test...
**2:** T–Test...
3: 2–SampZTest...
4: 2–SampTTest...
5: 1–PropZTest...
6: 2–PropZTest...
7↓ ZInterval...

**TI-84 PLUS**

**T-Test**
Inpt:Data **Stats**
$\mu_0$:6.8
$\bar{x}$:6.7
Sx:.35
n:39
$\mu$:**$\neq\mu_0$** $<\mu_0$ $>\mu_0$
Calculate Draw

**TI-84 PLUS**

**T-Test**
$\mu\neq$6.8
t=−1.784285142
p=.0823638462
$\bar{x}$=6.7
Sx=.35
n=39

**TI-84 PLUS**

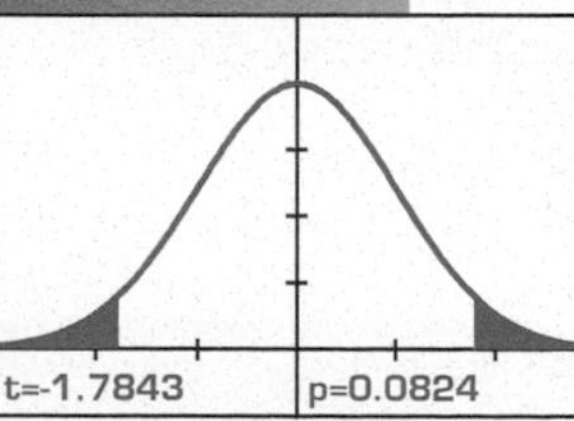


See Example 1, page 389.

**TI-84 PLUS**

EDIT CALC **TESTS**
1: Z–Test...
2: T–Test...
3: 2–SampZTest...
4: 2–SampTTest...
**5:** 1–PropZTest...
6: 2–PropZTest...
7↓ ZInterval...

**TI-84 PLUS**

**1-PropZTest**
$p_0$:.69
x:65
n:100
prop$\neq p_0$ **$<p_0$** $>p_0$
Calculate Draw

**TI-84 PLUS**

**1-PropZTest**
prop<.69
z=−.8648775001
p=.1935529676
$\hat{p}$=.65
n=100

**TI-84 PLUS**

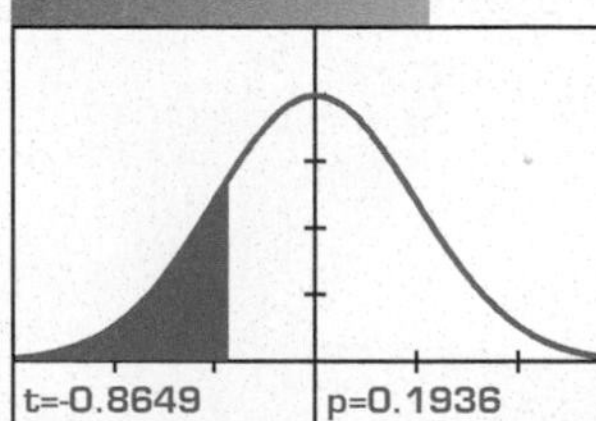

CHAPTER 8

# Hypothesis Testing with Two Samples

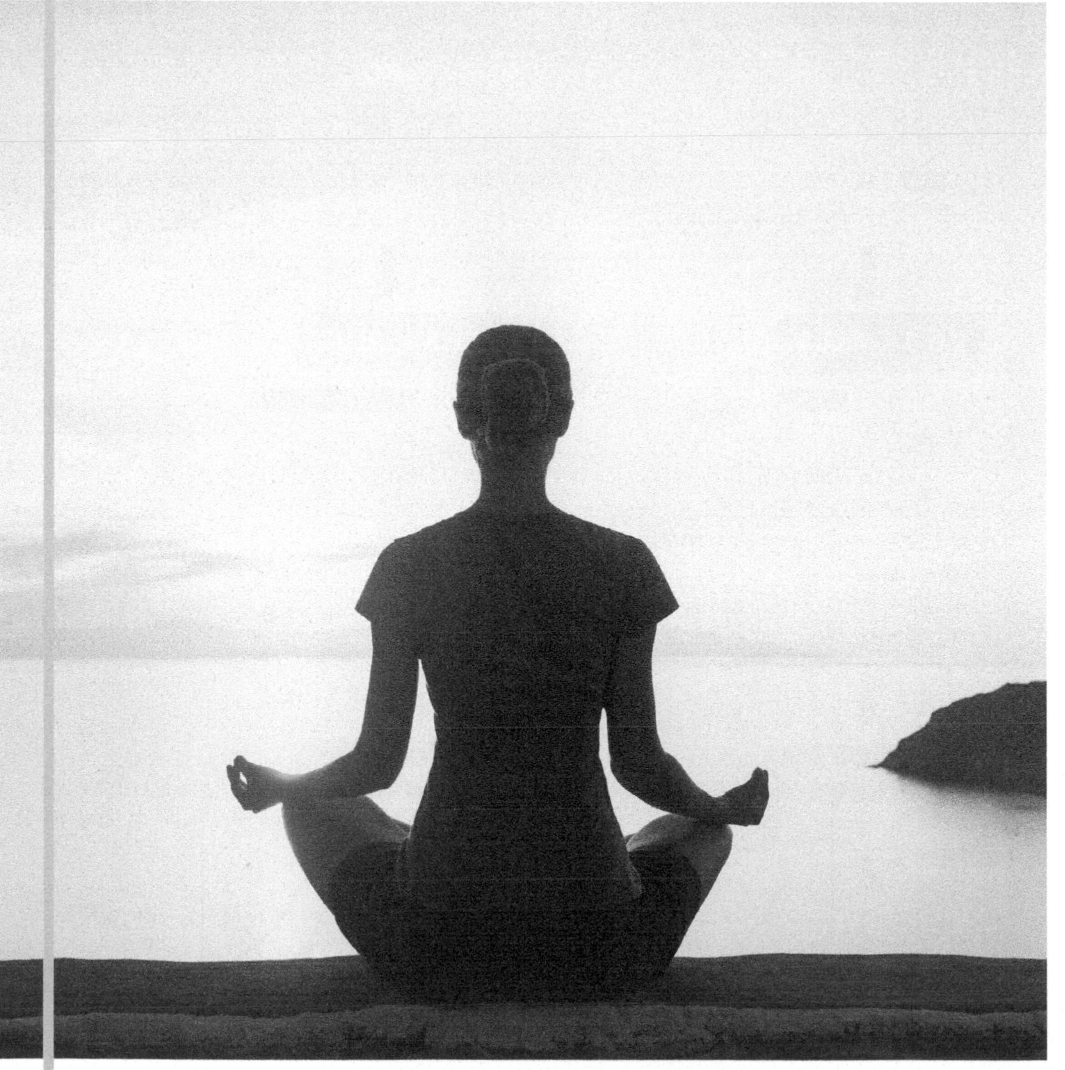

According to a study published in the *Journal of General Internal Medicine,* 50% of people who use yoga are college-educated, while only 23% of people who do not use yoga are college-educated.

## Where You've Been

In Chapter 6, you were introduced to inferential statistics and you learned how to form a confidence interval to estimate a population parameter. Then, in Chapter 7, you learned how to test a claim about a population parameter, basing your decision on sample statistics and their sampling distributions.

Using data from the National Health Interview Survey, a study was conducted to analyze the characteristics of people who use yoga and people who do not use yoga. The study was published in the *Journal of General Internal Medicine.* Some of the results are shown below for a random sample of people who use yoga.

**People Who Use Yoga ($n$ = 1593)**

| Characteristic | Frequency | Proportion |
|---|---|---|
| 40 to 49 years old | 367 | 0.2304 |
| From the western region of the United States | 415 | 0.2605 |
| Non-smoking | 1323 | 0.8305 |

## Where You're Going

In this chapter, you will continue your study of inferential statistics and hypothesis testing. Now, however, instead of testing a hypothesis about a single population, you will learn how to test a hypothesis that compares two populations.

For instance, in the yoga study, a random sample of people who do not use yoga was also surveyed. Here are the study's findings for this second group.

**People Who Do Not Use Yoga ($n$ = 29,948)**

| Characteristic | Frequency | Proportion |
|---|---|---|
| 40 to 49 years old | 6,290 | 0.2100 |
| From the western region of the United States | 5,691 | 0.1900 |
| Non-smoking | 23,360 | 0.7800 |

From these two samples, can you conclude that there is a difference in the proportion of 40- to 49-year-olds, people from the western region of the United States, or non-smokers between people who use yoga and people who do not use yoga? Or, might the differences in the proportions be due to chance?

In this chapter, you will learn to answer these questions by testing the hypothesis that the two proportions are equal. For instance, for non-smokers, you can conclude, at the 1% level of significance, that the proportion of people who use yoga is different from the proportion of people who do not use yoga.

# 8.1 Testing the Difference Between Means (Independent Samples, $\sigma_1$ and $\sigma_2$ Known)

### What You Should Learn

- How to determine whether two samples are independent or dependent
- An introduction to two-sample hypothesis testing for the difference between two population parameters
- How to perform a two-sample $z$-test for the difference between two means $\mu_1$ and $\mu_2$ using independent samples with $\sigma_1$ and $\sigma_2$ known

Independent and Dependent Samples ■ An Overview of Two-Sample Hypothesis Testing ■ Two-Sample $z$-Test for the Difference Between Means

## Independent and Dependent Samples

In Chapter 7, you studied methods for testing a claim about the value of a population parameter. In this chapter, you will learn how to test a claim comparing parameters from two populations. Before learning how to test the difference between two parameters, you need to understand the distinction between **independent samples** and **dependent samples.**

**DEFINITION**

Two samples are **independent** when the sample selected from one population is not related to the sample selected from the second population (see top figure at the left). Two samples are **dependent** when each member of one sample corresponds to a member of the other sample (see bottom figure at the left). Dependent samples are also called **paired samples** or **matched samples.**

**Independent Samples**

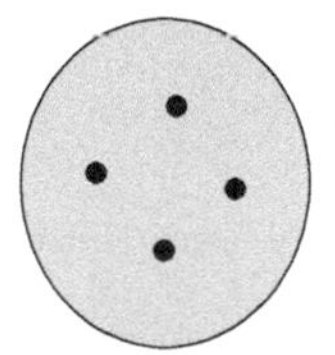

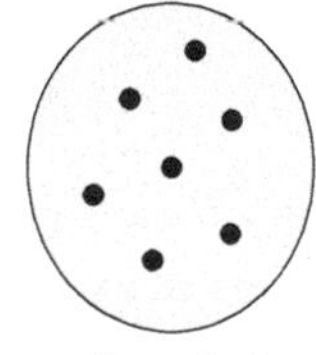

Sample 1 Sample 2

**Dependent Samples**

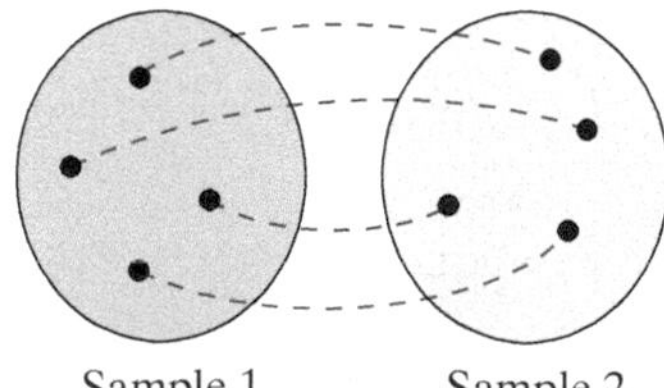

Sample 1 Sample 2

**EXAMPLE 1**

### Independent and Dependent Samples

Classify each pair of samples as independent or dependent.

1. Sample 1: Triglyceride levels of 70 patients
   Sample 2: Triglyceride levels of the same 70 patients after using a triglyceride-lowering drug for 6 months
2. Sample 1: Scores for 38 adult males on a psychological screening test for attention-deficit/hyperactivity disorder
   Sample 2: Scores for 50 adult females on a psychological screening test for attention-deficit/hyperactivity disorder

**SOLUTION**

1. These samples are dependent. Because the triglyceride levels of the same patients are taken, the samples are related. The samples can be paired with respect to each patient.
2. These samples are independent. It is not possible to form a pairing between the members of samples, the sample sizes are different, and the data represent scores for different individuals.

**TRY IT YOURSELF 1**

Classify each pair of samples as independent or dependent.

1. Sample 1: Systolic blood pressures of 30 adult females
   Sample 2: Systolic blood pressures of 30 adult males
2. Sample 1: Midterm exam scores of 14 chemistry students
   Sample 2: Final exam scores of the same 14 chemistry students

*Answer: Page A41*

### Study Tip

Dependent samples often involve before and after results for the same person or object (such as a person's weight before starting a weight-loss program and after 6 weeks), or results of individuals matched for specific characteristics (such as identical twins).

## An Overview of Two-Sample Hypothesis Testing

In this section and the next, you will learn how to test a claim comparing the means of two different populations using independent samples.

For instance, an advertiser is developing a marketing plan and wants to determine whether there is a difference in the amounts of time adults ages 18 to 34 and adults ages 35 to 49 spend on social media each day. The only way to conclude with certainty that there is a difference is to take a census of all adults in both age groups, calculate their mean daily times spent on social media, and find the difference. Of course, it is not practical to take such a census. However, it is possible to determine with some degree of certainty whether such a difference exists.

To determine whether a difference exists, the advertiser begins by assuming that there is no difference in the mean times of the two populations. That is,

$\mu_1 - \mu_2 = 0.$ Assume there is no difference.

Then, by taking a random sample from each population, a two-sample hypothesis test is performed using the test statistic

$\bar{x}_1 - \bar{x}_2 = 0.$ Test statistic

The advertiser obtains the results shown in the next two figures.

**Study Tip**

In the figures at the right, the members in the two samples, adults ages 18 to 34 and adults ages 35 to 49, are not matched or paired, so the samples are independent.

**Adults 18 to 34**

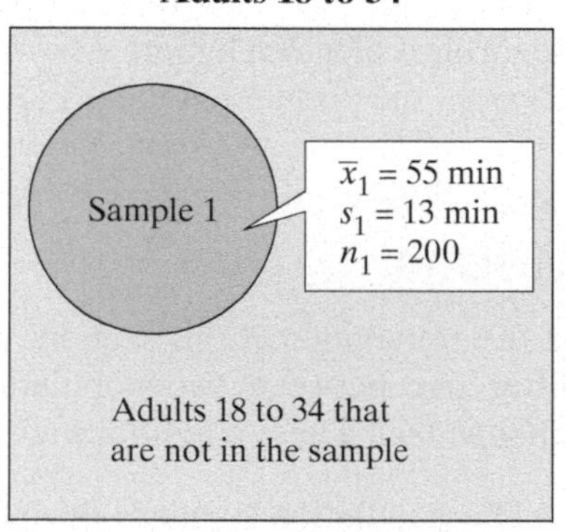


**Adults 35 to 49**

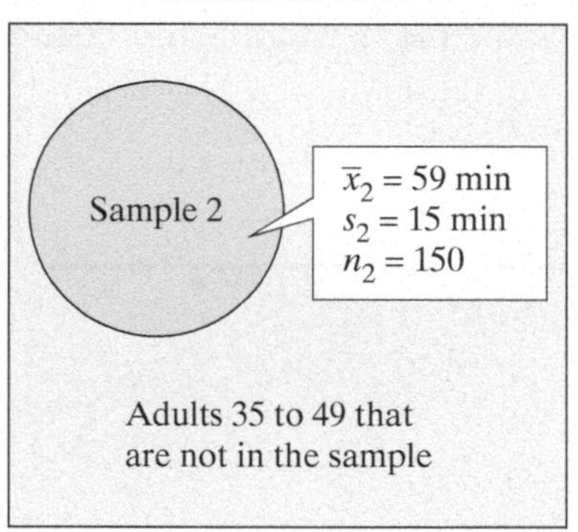


The figure below shows the sampling distribution of $\bar{x}_1 - \bar{x}_2$ for many similar samples taken from two populations for which $\mu_1 - \mu_2 = 0$. The figure also shows the test statistic and the standardized test statistic (assuming that the population variances are not equal).

**Study Tip**

In the figure at the right, the standardized test statistic is from a two-sample *t*-test. You will study this test in the next section.

**Sampling Distribution**

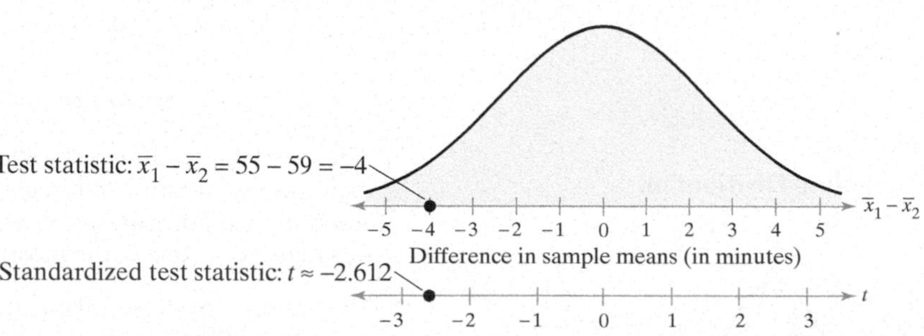


From the figure, you can see that it is quite unlikely to obtain sample means that differ by 4 minutes, assuming the actual difference is 0. The difference of the sample means would be more than 2.5 standard errors from the hypothesized difference of 0. Performing a two-sample hypothesis test using a level of significance of $\alpha = 0.10$, the advertiser can conclude that there is a difference in the amounts of time adults ages 18 to 34 and adults ages 35 to 49 spend on social media each day.

It is important to remember that when you perform a two-sample hypothesis test using independent samples, you are testing a claim concerning the difference between the parameters in two populations, not the values of the parameters themselves.

**DEFINITION**

For a two-sample hypothesis test with independent samples,

1. the **null hypothesis $H_0$** is a statistical hypothesis that usually states there is no difference between the parameters of two populations. The null hypothesis always contains the symbol $\leq$, $=$, or $\geq$.
2. the **alternative hypothesis $H_a$** is a statistical hypothesis that is true when $H_0$ is false. The alternative hypothesis contains the symbol $>$, $\neq$, or $<$.

**Study Tip**

You can also write the null and alternative hypotheses as shown below.

$$\begin{cases} H_0: \mu_1 - \mu_2 = 0 \\ H_a: \mu_1 - \mu_2 \neq 0 \end{cases}$$

$$\begin{cases} H_0: \mu_1 - \mu_2 \leq 0 \\ H_a: \mu_1 - \mu_2 > 0 \end{cases}$$

$$\begin{cases} H_0: \mu_1 - \mu_2 \geq 0 \\ H_a: \mu_1 - \mu_2 < 0 \end{cases}$$

To write the null and alternative hypotheses for a two-sample hypothesis test with independent samples, translate the claim made about the population parameters from a verbal statement to a mathematical statement. Then, write its complementary statement. For instance, for a claim about two population parameters $\mu_1$ and $\mu_2$, some possible pairs of null and alternative hypotheses are

$$\begin{cases} H_0: \mu_1 = \mu_2 \\ H_a: \mu_1 \neq \mu_2 \end{cases}, \quad \begin{cases} H_0: \mu_1 \leq \mu_2 \\ H_a: \mu_1 > \mu_2 \end{cases}, \quad \text{and} \quad \begin{cases} H_0: \mu_1 \geq \mu_2 \\ H_a: \mu_1 < \mu_2 \end{cases}.$$

Regardless of which hypotheses you use, you always assume there is no difference between the population means ($\mu_1 = \mu_2$).

## Two-Sample z-Test for the Difference Between Means

In the remainder of this section, you will learn how to perform a $z$-test for the difference between two population means $\mu_1$ and $\mu_2$ when the samples are *independent*. These conditions are necessary to perform such a test.

1. The population standard deviations are known.
2. The samples are randomly selected.
3. The samples are independent.
4. The populations are normally distributed *or* each sample size is at least 30.

When these conditions are met, the **sampling distribution for $\bar{x}_1 - \bar{x}_2$, the difference of the sample means,** is a normal distribution with mean and standard error as shown in the table below and the figure at the left.

**Sampling Distribution for $\bar{x}_1 - \bar{x}_2$**

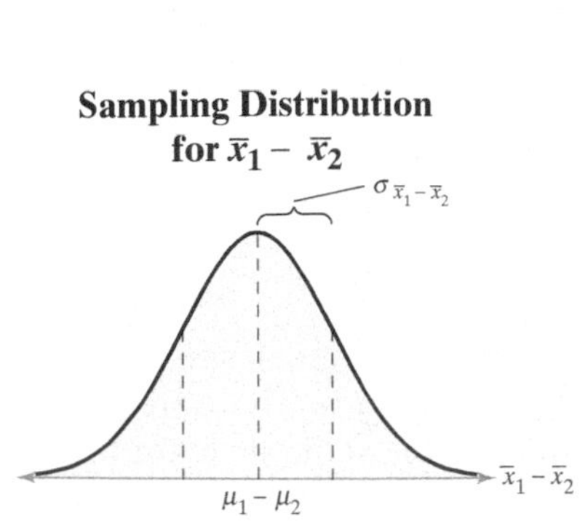


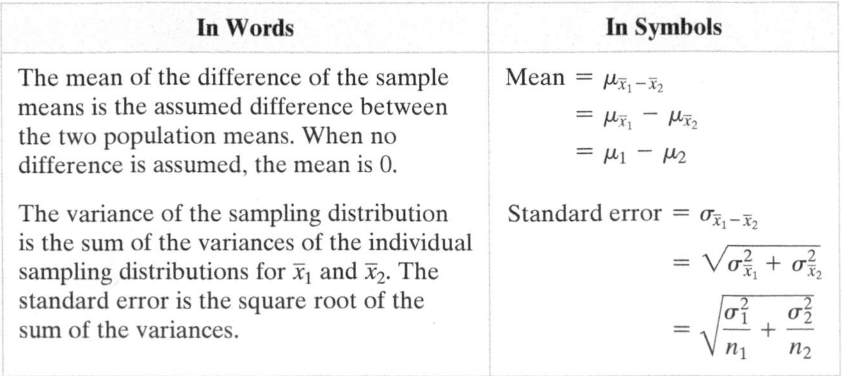

| In Words | In Symbols |
|---|---|
| The mean of the difference of the sample means is the assumed difference between the two population means. When no difference is assumed, the mean is 0. | Mean $= \mu_{\bar{x}_1-\bar{x}_2}$ $= \mu_{\bar{x}_1} - \mu_{\bar{x}_2}$ $= \mu_1 - \mu_2$ |
| The variance of the sampling distribution is the sum of the variances of the individual sampling distributions for $\bar{x}_1$ and $\bar{x}_2$. The standard error is the square root of the sum of the variances. | Standard error $= \sigma_{\bar{x}_1-\bar{x}_2}$ $= \sqrt{\sigma_{\bar{x}_1}^2 + \sigma_{\bar{x}_2}^2}$ $= \sqrt{\frac{\sigma_1^2}{n_1} + \frac{\sigma_2^2}{n_2}}$ |

When the conditions on the preceding page are met and the sampling distribution for $\bar{x}_1 - \bar{x}_2$ is a normal distribution, you can use the $z$-test to test the difference between two population means $\mu_1$ and $\mu_2$. The standardized test statistic takes the form of

$$z = \frac{(\text{Observed difference}) - (\text{Hypothesized difference})}{\text{Standard error}}.$$

As you read the definition and guidelines for a two-sample $z$-test, note that if the null hypothesis states $\mu_1 = \mu_2$, $\mu_1 \leq \mu_2$, or $\mu_1 \geq \mu_2$, then $\mu_1 = \mu_2$ is assumed and the hypothesized difference $\mu_1 - \mu_2$ is equal to 0.

## Two-Sample $z$-Test for the Difference Between Means

A **two-sample $z$-test** can be used to test the difference between two population means $\mu_1$ and $\mu_2$ when these conditions are met.

1. Both $\sigma_1$ and $\sigma_2$ are known.
2. The samples are random.
3. The samples are independent.
4. The populations are normally distributed *or* both $n_1 \geq 30$ and $n_2 \geq 30$.

The **test statistic** is $\bar{x}_1 - \bar{x}_2$. The **standardized test statistic** is

$$z = \frac{(\bar{x}_1 - \bar{x}_2) - (\mu_1 - \mu_2)}{\sigma_{\bar{x}_1 - \bar{x}_2}} \quad \text{where} \quad \sigma_{\bar{x}_1 - \bar{x}_2} = \sqrt{\frac{\sigma_1^2}{n_1} + \frac{\sigma_2^2}{n_2}}.$$

## GUIDELINES

**Using a Two-Sample $z$-Test for the Difference Between Means (Independent Samples, $\sigma_1$ and $\sigma_2$ Known)**

| In Words | In Symbols |
|---|---|
| **1.** Verify that $\sigma_1$ and $\sigma_2$ are known, the samples are random and independent, and either the populations are normally distributed *or* both $n_1 \geq 30$ and $n_2 \geq 30$. | |
| **2.** State the claim mathematically and verbally. Identify the null and alternative hypotheses. | State $H_0$ and $H_a$. |
| **3.** Specify the level of significance. | Identify $\alpha$. |
| **4.** Determine the critical value(s). | Use Table 4 in Appendix B. |
| **5.** Determine the rejection region(s). | |
| **6.** Find the standardized test statistic and sketch the sampling distribution. | $z = \frac{(\bar{x}_1 - \bar{x}_2) - (\mu_1 - \mu_2)}{\sigma_{\bar{x}_1 - \bar{x}_2}}$ |
| **7.** Make a decision to reject or fail to reject the null hypothesis. | If $z$ is in the rejection region, then reject $H_0$. Otherwise, fail to reject $H_0$. |
| **8.** Interpret the decision in the context of the original claim. | |

A hypothesis test for the difference between means can also be performed using $P$-values. Use the guidelines above, skipping Steps 4 and 5. After finding the standardized test statistic, use Table 4 in Appendix B to calculate the $P$-value. Then make a decision to reject or fail to reject the null hypothesis. If $P$ is less than or equal to $\alpha$, then reject $H_0$. Otherwise, fail to reject $H_0$.

### Picturing the World

In a recent year, there were 116,898 public school teachers in Georgia and 113,327 in Ohio. In a survey that year, 200 public school teachers in each of these states were asked to report their salary. The results are shown below. It is claimed that the mean salary in Ohio is greater than the mean salary in Georgia. (Adapted from National Education Association)

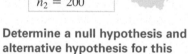

| Georgia |
|---|
| $\bar{x}_1 = \$60{,}578$ <br> $n_1 = 200$ |

| Ohio |
|---|
| $\bar{x}_2 = \$61{,}406$ <br> $n_2 = 200$ |

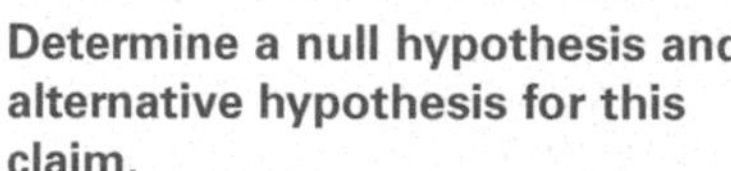

**Determine a null hypothesis and alternative hypothesis for this claim.**

## EXAMPLE 2

See TI-84 Plus steps on page 465.

### A Two-Sample $z$-Test for the Difference Between Means

A credit card watchdog group claims that there is a difference in the mean credit card debts of people in Oklahoma and North Carolina. The results of a random survey of 250 people from each state are shown at the left. The two samples are independent. Assume that $\sigma_1 = \$960$ for Oklahoma and $\sigma_2 = \$845$ for North Carolina. Do the results support the group's claim? Use $\alpha = 0.05$. *(Adapted from Experian)*

**Sample Statistics for Credit Card Debt**

| Oklahoma | North Carolina |
|---|---|
| $\bar{x}_1 = \$5271$<br>$n_1 = 250$ | $\bar{x}_2 = \$5121$<br>$n_2 = 250$ |

**SOLUTION**

Note that $\sigma_1$ and $\sigma_2$ are known, the samples are random and independent, and both $n_1$ and $n_2$ are at least 30. So, you can use the $z$-test. The claim is "there is a difference in the mean credit card debts of people in Oklahoma and North Carolina." So, the null and alternative hypotheses are

$$H_0: \mu_1 = \mu_2 \quad \text{and} \quad H_a: \mu_1 \neq \mu_2. \quad \text{(Claim)}$$

Because the test is a two-tailed test and the level of significance is $\alpha = 0.05$, the critical values are $-z_0 = -1.96$ and $z_0 = 1.96$. The rejection regions are $z < -1.96$ and $z > 1.96$. The standardized test statistic is

$$z = \frac{(\bar{x}_1 - \bar{x}_2) - (\mu_1 - \mu_2)}{\sqrt{\frac{\sigma_1^2}{n_1} + \frac{\sigma_2^2}{n_2}}} \qquad \text{Use the } z\text{-test.}$$

$$= \frac{(5271 - 5121) - 0}{\sqrt{\frac{960^2}{250} + \frac{845^2}{250}}} \qquad \text{Assume } \mu_1 = \mu_2\text{, so } \mu_1 - \mu_2 = 0.$$

$$\approx 1.85. \qquad \text{Round to two decimal places.}$$

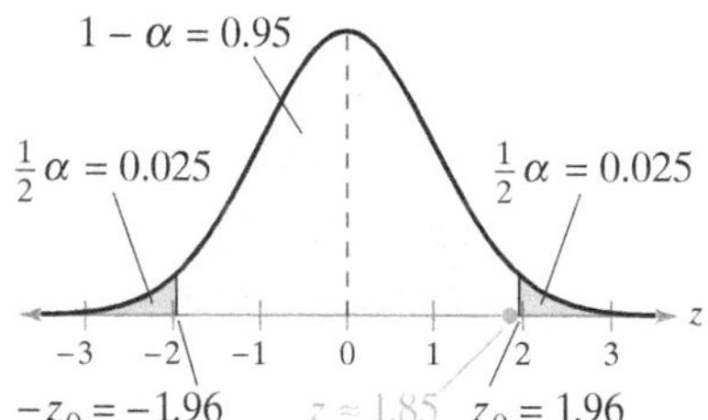


The figure at the left shows the location of the rejection regions and the standardized test statistic $z$. Because $z$ is not in the rejection region, you fail to reject the null hypothesis.

***Interpretation*** There is not enough evidence at the 5% level of significance to support the group's claim that there is a difference in the mean credit card debts of people in Oklahoma and North Carolina.

**TRY IT YOURSELF 2**

A survey indicates that the mean annual wages for forensic science technicians working for local and state governments are \$63,560 and \$62,070, respectively. The survey includes a randomly selected sample of size 100 from each government branch. Assume that the population standard deviations are \$6200 (local) and \$5575 (state). The two samples are independent. At $\alpha = 0.10$, is there enough evidence to conclude that there is a difference in the mean annual wages? *(Adapted from U.S. Bureau of Labor Statistics)*

*Answer: Page A41*

In Example 2, you can also use a $P$-value to perform the hypothesis test. For instance, the test is a two-tailed test, so the $P$-value is equal to twice the area to the right of $z = 1.85$, or

$$P = 2(1 - 0.9678) = 2(0.0322) = 0.0644.$$

Because $0.0644 > 0.05$, you fail to reject $H_0$.

**Sample Statistics for Monthly Rent for a One-Bedroom Apartment**

| Seattle, WA | Washington, DC |
|---|---|
| $\bar{x}_1 = \$2166$<br>$n_1 = 400$ | $\bar{x}_2 = \$2181$<br>$n_2 = 300$ |

## EXAMPLE 3

### Using Technology to Perform a Two-Sample $z$-Test

A rental market researcher claims that the average monthly rent for a one-bedroom apartment in Seattle, WA, is less than the average monthly rent for a one-bedroom apartment in Washington, DC. The table at the left shows the results of a random survey of people who rent apartments in each city. The two samples are independent. Assume that $\sigma_1 = \$190$ for Seattle and $\sigma_2 = \$210$ for Washington, and that both populations are normally distributed. At $\alpha = 0.01$, is there enough evidence to support the claim? *(Adapted from RentPath Holdings, Inc.)*

**SOLUTION**

Note that $\sigma_1$ and $\sigma_2$ are known, the samples are random and independent, and the populations are normally distributed. So, you can use the $z$-test. The claim is "the average monthly rent for a one-bedroom apartment in Seattle, WA, is less than the average monthly rent for a one-bedroom apartment in Washington, DC." So, the null and alternative hypotheses are $H_0$: $\mu_1 \geq \mu_2$ and $H_a$: $\mu_1 < \mu_2$ (claim). The left display shows how to set up the hypothesis test using a TI-84 Plus. The right displays show the results of selecting *Calculate* or *Draw*.

**TI-84 PLUS**

```
2-SampZTest
Inpt:Data Stats
σ1:190
σ2:210
x̄1:2166
n1:400
x̄2:2181
n2:300
μ1:≠μ2 <μ2 >μ2
Calculate Draw
```

**TI-84 PLUS**

```
2-SampZTest
μ1<μ2
z=-.9738412097
p=.1650676893
x̄1=2166
x̄2=2181
n1=400
```

**TI-84 PLUS**

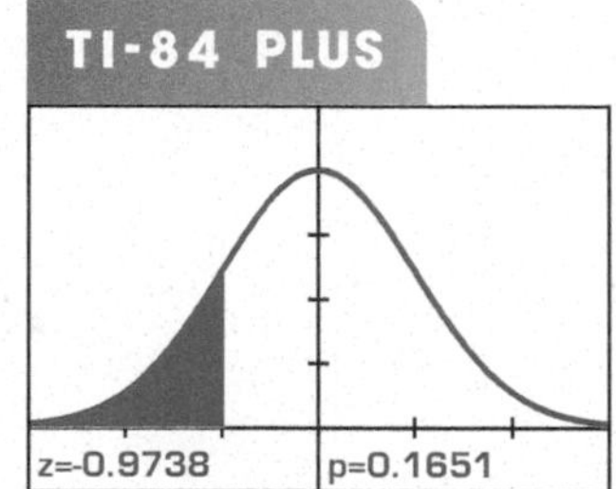


Because the test is a left-tailed test and $\alpha = 0.01$, the rejection region is $z < -2.33$. The standardized test statistic $z \approx -0.97$ is not in the rejection region, so you fail to reject the null hypothesis.

***Interpretation*** There is not enough evidence at the 1% level of significance to support the rental market researcher's claim.

**Tech Tip**

Note that the TI-84 Plus displays $P \approx 0.1651$. Because $P > \alpha$, you fail to reject the null hypothesis.

**TRY IT YOURSELF 3**

A rental market researcher claims that the average monthly rent for a one-bedroom apartment in Atlanta, GA, is greater than the average monthly rent for a one-bedroom apartment in Nashville, TN. The table at the left shows the results of a random survey of people who rent apartments in each city. The two samples are independent. Assume that $\sigma_1 = \$210$ for Atlanta and $\sigma_2 = \$190$ for Nashville, and that both populations are normally distributed. At $\alpha = 0.05$, is there enough evidence to support the claim? *(Adapted from RentPath Holdings, Inc.)*

**Sample Statistics for Monthly Rent for a One-Bedroom Apartment**

| Atlanta, GA | Nashville, TN |
|---|---|
| $\bar{x}_1 = \$1610$<br>$n_1 = 200$ | $\bar{x}_2 = \$1603$<br>$n_2 = 300$ |

*Answer: Page A41*

# 8.1 EXERCISES

For Extra Help: MyLab® Statistics

## Building Basic Skills and Vocabulary

**1.** What is the difference between two samples that are dependent and two samples that are independent? Give an example of each.

**2.** Explain how to perform a two-sample $z$-test for the difference between two population means using independent samples with $\sigma_1$ and $\sigma_2$ known.

**3.** Describe another way you can perform a hypothesis test for the difference between the means of two populations using independent samples with $\sigma_1$ and $\sigma_2$ known that does not use rejection regions.

**4.** What conditions are necessary in order to use the $z$-test to test the difference between two population means?

**Independent and Dependent Samples** *In Exercises 5–8, classify the two samples as independent or dependent and justify your answer.*

**5.** Sample 1: The maximum bench press weights for 53 football players
Sample 2: The maximum bench press weights for the same 53 football players after completing a weight lifting program

**6.** Sample 1: The IQ scores of 60 females
Sample 2: The IQ scores of 60 males

**7.** Sample 1: The average speed of 23 powerboats built using one hull design
Sample 2: The average speed of 14 powerboats built using a different hull design

**8.** Sample 1: The commute times of 10 workers when they use their own vehicles
Sample 2: The commute times of the same 10 workers when they use public transportation

*In Exercises 9 and 10, use the TI-84 Plus display to make a decision to reject or fail to reject the null hypothesis at the level of significance. Make your decision using the standardized test statistic and using the P-value. Assume the sample sizes are equal.*

**9.** $\alpha = 0.05$

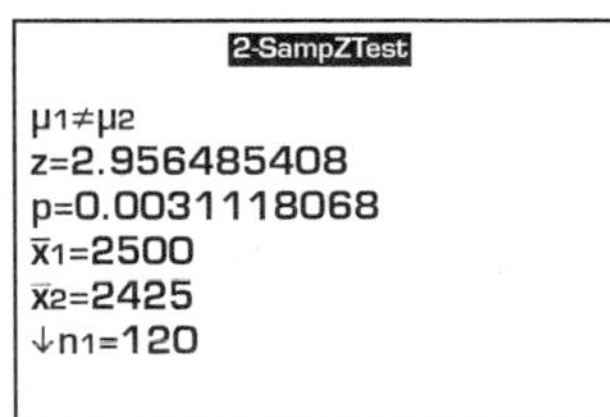


**10.** $\alpha = 0.01$

2-SampZTest
μ1>μ2
z=1.941656065
p=0.0260893059
x̄1=44
x̄2=42
↓n1=50

*In Exercises 11–14, test the claim about the difference between two population means $\mu_1$ and $\mu_2$ at the level of significance $\alpha$. Assume the samples are random and independent, and the populations are normally distributed.*

**11.** Claim: $\mu_1 = \mu_2$; $\alpha = 0.1$
Population statistics: $\sigma_1 = 3.4$ and $\sigma_2 = 1.5$
Sample statistics: $\bar{x}_1 = 16$, $n_1 = 29$ and $\bar{x}_2 = 14$, $n_2 = 28$

**12.** Claim: $\mu_1 > \mu_2$; $\alpha = 0.10$
Population statistics: $\sigma_1 = 40$ and $\sigma_2 = 15$
Sample statistics: $\bar{x}_1 = 500$, $n_1 = 100$ and $\bar{x}_2 = 495$, $n_2 = 75$

**13.** Claim: $\mu_1 < \mu_2$; $\alpha = 0.05$
Population statistics: $\sigma_1 = 75$ and $\sigma_2 = 105$
Sample statistics: $\bar{x}_1 = 2435$, $n_1 = 35$ and $\bar{x}_2 = 2432$, $n_2 = 90$

**14.** Claim: $\mu_1 \leq \mu_2$; $\alpha = 0.03$
Population statistics: $\sigma_1 = 136$ and $\sigma_2 = 215$
Sample statistics: $\bar{x}_1 = 5004$, $n_1 = 144$ and $\bar{x}_2 = 4895$, $n_2 = 156$

## Using and Interpreting Concepts

**Testing the Difference Between Two Means** *In Exercises 15–24, (a) identify the claim and state $H_0$ and $H_a$, (b) find the critical value(s) and identify the rejection region(s), (c) find the standardized test statistic z, (d) decide whether to reject or fail to reject the null hypothesis, and (e) interpret the decision in the context of the original claim. Assume the samples are random and independent, and the populations are normally distributed.*

**15. Braking Distances** To compare the dry braking distances from 60 to 0 miles per hour for two makes of automobiles, a safety engineer conducts braking tests for 16 compact SUVs and 11 midsize SUVs. The mean braking distance for the compact SUVs is 131.8 feet. Assume the population standard deviation is 5.5 feet. The mean braking distance for the midsize SUVs is 132.8 feet. Assume the population standard deviation is 6.7 feet. At $\alpha = 0.10$, can the engineer support the claim that the mean braking distances are different for the two categories of SUVs? *(Adapted from Consumer Reports)*

**16. Bed-in-a-Box** To compare customer satisfaction with mattresses that are delivered compressed in a box and traditional mattresses, a researcher randomly selects 30 ratings of mattresses in boxes and 30 ratings of traditional mattresses. The mean rating of mattresses in boxes is 68.7 out of 100. Assume the population standard deviation is 6.6. The mean rating of traditional mattresses is 70.9 out of 100. Assume the population standard deviation is 5.6. At $\alpha = 0.01$, can the researcher support the claim that the mean rating of traditional mattresses is greater than the mean rating of mattresses in a box? *(Adapted from Consumer Reports)*

**17. Wind Energy** An energy company wants to choose between two regions in a state to install energy-producing wind turbines. A researcher claims that the wind speed in Region A is less than the wind speed in Region B. To test the regions, the average wind speed is calculated for 60 days in each region. The mean wind speed in Region A is 14.0 miles per hour. Assume the population standard deviation is 2.9 miles per hour. The mean wind speed in Region B is 15.1 miles per hour. Assume the population standard deviation is 3.3 miles per hour. At $\alpha = 0.05$, can the company support the researcher's claim?

**18. Repair Costs: Washing Machines** You want to buy a washing machine, and a salesperson tells you that the mean repair costs for Model A and Model B are equal. You research the repair costs. The mean repair cost of 24 Model A washing machines is \$208. Assume the population standard deviation is \$18. The mean repair cost of 26 Model B washing machines is \$221. Assume the population standard deviation is \$22. At $\alpha = 0.01$, can you reject the salesperson's claim?

**19. ACT Mathematics and Science Scores** The mean ACT mathematics score for 60 high school students is 20.2. Assume the population standard deviation is 5.7. The mean ACT science score for 75 high school students is 20.6. Assume the population standard deviation is 5.9. At $\alpha = 0.01$, can you reject the claim that ACT mathematics and science scores are equal? *(Source: ACT, Inc.)*

**20. ACT English and Reading Scores** The mean ACT English score for 120 high school students is 19.9. Assume the population standard deviation is 7.2. The mean ACT reading score for 150 high school students is 21.2. Assume the population standard deviation is 7.1. At $\alpha = 0.10$, can you support the claim that ACT reading scores are higher than ACT English scores? *(Source: ACT, Inc.)*

**21. Home Prices** A real estate agency says that the mean home sales price in Casper, Wyoming, is the same as in Cheyenne, Wyoming. The mean home sales price for 35 homes in Casper is $349,237. Assume the population standard deviation is $158,005. The mean home sales price for 41 homes in Cheyenne is $435,244. Assume the population standard deviation is $154,716. At $\alpha = 0.01$, is there enough evidence to reject the agency's claim? *(Adapted from Realtor.com)*

**22. Home Prices** In Exercise 21, an additional home in Casper sells for $132,000, and another in Cheyenne sells for $495,000. Add these data to the existing samples. At $\alpha = 0.01$, do the adjusted samples lead to a different conclusion? *(Adapted from Realtor.com)*

**23. Precipitation** A climatologist claims that the precipitation in Seattle, Washington, was greater than in Birmingham, Alabama, in a recent year. The daily precipitation amounts (in inches) for 30 days in a recent year in Seattle are shown below. Assume the population standard deviation is 0.25 inch.

| | | | | | | | | | |
|---|---|---|---|---|---|---|---|---|---|
| 0.00 | 0.00 | 0.05 | 0.01 | 0.21 | 0.00 | 0.00 | 0.52 | 0.00 | 0.01 |
| 0.00 | 0.19 | 0.00 | 0.18 | 0.02 | 0.02 | 0.13 | 0.00 | 0.03 | 0.00 |
| 0.04 | 0.00 | 0.41 | 0.23 | 0.00 | 0.80 | 0.15 | 0.00 | 0.00 | 0.79 |

The daily precipitation amounts (in inches) for 30 days in a recent year in Birmingham are shown below. Assume the population standard deviation is 0.52 inch.

| | | | | | | | | | |
|---|---|---|---|---|---|---|---|---|---|
| 0.00 | 0.96 | 0.84 | 0.00 | 0.10 | 0.00 | 0.00 | 0.20 | 0.00 | 0.54 |
| 0.97 | 0.00 | 0.35 | 0.02 | 0.04 | 0.70 | 0.00 | 0.00 | 0.00 | 0.00 |
| 0.03 | 0.01 | 0.15 | 0.27 | 0.00 | 0.00 | 0.93 | 0.00 | 0.89 | 0.01 |

At $\alpha = 0.05$, can you support the climatologist's claim? *(Source: NOAA)*

**24. Temperature** A climatologist claims that the temperature in Seattle, Washington, was lower than in Birmingham, Alabama, in a recent year. The maximum daily temperatures (in degrees Fahrenheit) for 30 days in a recent year in Seattle are shown below. Assume the population standard deviation is 12.0°F.

| | | | | | | | | | | | | | | |
|---|---|---|---|---|---|---|---|---|---|---|---|---|---|---|
| 52 | 45 | 66 | 49 | 62 | 74 | 80 | 75 | 76 | 65 | 67 | 75 | 57 | 50 | 46 |
| 49 | 53 | 57 | 60 | 70 | 85 | 56 | 60 | 44 | 59 | 65 | 70 | 73 | 61 | 61 |

The maximum daily temperatures (in degrees Fahrenheit) for 30 days in a recent year in Birmingham are shown below. Assume the population standard deviation is 13.2°F.

| | | | | | | | | | | | | | | |
|---|---|---|---|---|---|---|---|---|---|---|---|---|---|---|
| 64 | 60 | 91 | 85 | 59 | 93 | 90 | 73 | 87 | 72 | 50 | 58 | 79 | 72 | 85 |
| 57 | 73 | 61 | 89 | 69 | 60 | 93 | 56 | 74 | 94 | 66 | 63 | 91 | 94 | 73 |

At $\alpha = 0.01$, can you support the climatologist's claim? *(Source: NOAA)*

**25. Getting at the Concept** Explain why the null hypothesis $H_0$: $\mu_1 = \mu_2$ is equivalent to the null hypothesis $H_0$: $\mu_1 - \mu_2 = 0$.

**26. Getting at the Concept** Explain why the null hypothesis $H_0$: $\mu_1 \geq \mu_2$ is equivalent to the null hypothesis $H_0$: $\mu_1 - \mu_2 \geq 0$.

## Extending Concepts

**Testing a Difference Other Than Zero** *Sometimes a researcher is interested in testing a difference in means other than zero. In Exercises 27 and 28, you will test the difference between two means using a null hypothesis of $H_0$: $\mu_1 - \mu_2 = k$, $H_0$: $\mu_1 - \mu_2 \geq k$, or $H_0$: $\mu_1 - \mu_2 \leq k$. The standardized test statistic is still*

$$z = \frac{(\bar{x}_1 - \bar{x}_2) - (\mu_1 - \mu_2)}{\sigma_{\bar{x}_1 - \bar{x}_2}} \quad \text{where} \quad \sigma_{\bar{x}_1 - \bar{x}_2} = \sqrt{\frac{\sigma_1^2}{n_1} + \frac{\sigma_2^2}{n_2}}.$$

Entry level software engineers in Santa Clara, CA

$\bar{x}_1 = \$88{,}900$
$n_1 = 42$

Santa Clara

Entry level software engineers in Greenwich, CT

$\bar{x}_2 = \$81{,}600$
$n_2 = 38$

Greenwich

FIGURE FOR EXERCISE 27

**27. Software Engineer Salaries** Is the difference between the mean annual salaries of entry level software engineers in Santa Clara, California, and Greenwich, Connecticut, more than \$4000? To decide, you select a random sample of entry level software engineers from each city. The results of each survey are shown in the figure at the left. Assume the population standard deviations are $\sigma_1 = \$14{,}060$ and $\sigma_2 = \$13{,}050$. At $\alpha = 0.05$, what should you conclude? *(Adapted from Salary.com)*

**28. Architect Salaries** Is the difference between the mean annual salaries of entry level architects in Denver, Colorado, and Lincoln, Nebraska, equal to \$9000? To decide, you select a random sample of entry level architects from each city. The results of each survey are shown in the figure. Assume the population standard deviations are $\sigma_1 = \$6560$ and $\sigma_2 = \$6100$. At $\alpha = 0.01$, what should you conclude? *(Adapted from Salary.com)*

Entry level architects in Denver, CO
$\bar{x}_1 = \$58{,}300$
$n_1 = 32$

Denver

Entry level architects in Lincoln, NE
$\bar{x}_2 = \$54{,}240$
$n_2 = 30$

Lincoln

**Constructing Confidence Intervals for $\mu_1 - \mu_2$** *You can construct a confidence interval for the difference between two population means $\mu_1 - \mu_2$, as shown below, when both population standard deviations are known, and either both populations are normally distributed or both $n_1 \geq 30$ and $n_2 \geq 30$. Also, the samples must be randomly selected and independent.*

$$(\bar{x}_1 - \bar{x}_2) - z_c\sqrt{\frac{\sigma_1^2}{n_1} + \frac{\sigma_2^2}{n_2}} < \mu_1 - \mu_2 < (\bar{x}_1 - \bar{x}_2) + z_c\sqrt{\frac{\sigma_1^2}{n_1} + \frac{\sigma_2^2}{n_2}}$$

*In Exercises 29 and 30, construct the indicated confidence interval for $\mu_1 - \mu_2$.*

**29. Software Engineer Salaries** Construct a 95% confidence interval for the difference between the mean annual salaries of entry level software engineers in Santa Clara, California, and Greenwich, CT, using the data from Exercise 27.

**30. Architect Salaries** Construct a 99% confidence interval for the difference between the mean annual salaries of entry level architects in Denver, Colorado, and Lincoln, Nebraska, using the data from Exercise 28.

# 8.2 Testing the Difference Between Means (Independent Samples, $\sigma_1$ and $\sigma_2$ Unknown)

### What You Should Learn

- How to perform a two-sample $t$-test for the difference between two means $\mu_1$ and $\mu_2$ using independent samples with $\sigma_1$ and $\sigma_2$ unknown

The Two-Sample $t$-Test for the Difference Between Means

## The Two-Sample $t$-Test for the Difference Between Means

In Section 8.1, you learned how to test the difference between means when both population standard deviations are known. Both population standard deviations are *not* known in many real-life situations. In this section, you will learn how to use a $t$-test to test the difference between two population means $\mu_1$ and $\mu_2$ using independent samples from each population when $\sigma_1$ and $\sigma_2$ are unknown. These conditions are necessary to perform such a test: (1) the population standard deviations are unknown, (2) the samples are randomly selected, (3) the samples are independent, and (4) the populations are normally distributed *or* each sample size is at least 30. When these conditions are met, the sampling distribution for the difference between the sample means $\bar{x}_1 - \bar{x}_2$ is approximated by a $t$-distribution with mean $\mu_1 - \mu_2$. So, you can use a two-sample $t$-test to test the difference between the population means $\mu_1$ and $\mu_2$. The standard error and the degrees of freedom of the sampling distribution depend on whether the population variances $\sigma_1^2$ and $\sigma_2^2$ are equal, as shown in the next definition.

### Study Tip

To perform the two-sample $t$-test described at the right, you will need to know whether the variances of two populations are equal. In this chapter, each example and exercise will state whether the variances are equal. You will learn to test for differences between two population variances in Chapter 10.

### Two-Sample $t$-Test for the Difference Between Means

A **two-sample $t$-test** is used to test the difference between two population means $\mu_1$ and $\mu_2$ when (1) $\sigma_1$ and $\sigma_2$ are unknown, (2) the samples are random, (3) the samples are independent, and (4) the populations are normally distributed *or* both $n_1 \geq 30$ and $n_2 \geq 30$. The **test statistic** is $\bar{x}_1 - \bar{x}_2$, and the **standardized test statistic** is

$$t = \frac{(\bar{x}_1 - \bar{x}_2) - (\mu_1 - \mu_2)}{s_{\bar{x}_1 - \bar{x}_2}}.$$

***Variances are equal:*** If the population variances are equal, then information from the two samples is combined to calculate a **pooled estimate of the standard deviation $\hat{\sigma}$.**

$$\hat{\sigma} = \sqrt{\frac{(n_1 - 1)s_1^2 + (n_2 - 1)s_2^2}{n_1 + n_2 - 2}}$$

The standard error for the sampling distribution of $\bar{x}_1 - \bar{x}_2$ is

$$s_{\bar{x}_1 - \bar{x}_2} = \hat{\sigma} \cdot \sqrt{\frac{1}{n_1} + \frac{1}{n_2}} \qquad \text{Variances equal}$$

and d.f. $= n_1 + n_2 - 2$.

***Variances are not equal:*** If the population variances are not equal, then the standard error is

$$s_{\bar{x}_1 - \bar{x}_2} = \sqrt{\frac{s_1^2}{n_1} + \frac{s_2^2}{n_2}} \qquad \text{Variances not equal}$$

and d.f. $=$ smaller of $n_1 - 1$ and $n_2 - 1$.

The requirements for the $z$-test described in Section 8.1 and the $t$-test described in this section are shown in the flowchart below.

**Two-Sample Tests for Independent Samples**

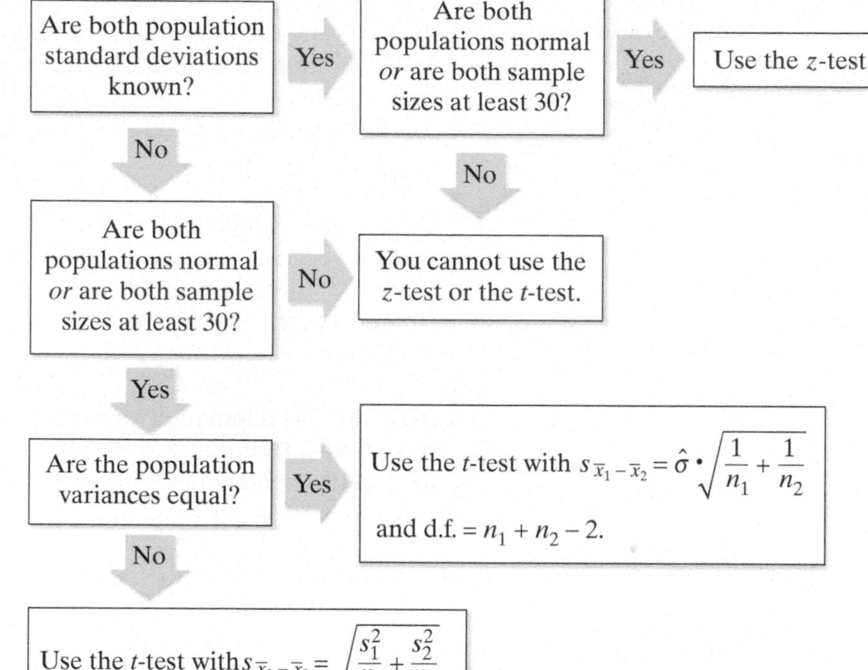


## GUIDELINES

**Using a Two-Sample $t$-Test for the Difference Between Means (Independent Samples, $\sigma_1$ and $\sigma_2$ Unknown)**

| In Words | In Symbols |
|---|---|
| **1.** Verify that $\sigma_1$ and $\sigma_2$ are unknown, the samples are random and independent, and either the populations are normally distributed *or* both $n_1 \geq 30$ and $n_2 \geq 30$. | |
| **2.** State the claim mathematically and verbally. Identify the null and alternative hypotheses. | State $H_0$ and $H_a$. |
| **3.** Specify the level of significance. | Identify $\alpha$. |
| **4.** Determine the degrees of freedom. | d.f. $= n_1 + n_2 - 2$ or d.f. $=$ smaller of $n_1 - 1$ and $n_2 - 1$ |
| **5.** Determine the critical value(s). | Use Table 5 in Appendix B. |
| **6.** Determine the rejection region(s). | |
| **7.** Find the standardized test statistic and sketch the sampling distribution. | $t = \dfrac{(\bar{x}_1 - \bar{x}_2) - (\mu_1 - \mu_2)}{s_{\bar{x}_1-\bar{x}_2}}$ |
| **8.** Make a decision to reject or fail to reject the null hypothesis. | If $t$ is in the rejection region, then reject $H_0$. Otherwise, fail to reject $H_0$. |
| **9.** Interpret the decision in the context of the original claim. | |

## Picturing the World

A study published by the American Psychological Association in the journal *Neuropsychology* reported that children with musical training showed better verbal memory than children with no musical training. The study also showed that the longer the musical training, the better the verbal memory. Suppose you tried to duplicate the results as follows. A verbal memory test with a possible 100 points was administered to 90 children. Half had musical training, while the other half had no training and acted as the control group. The 45 children with training had an average score of 83 with a standard deviation of 5.7. The 45 students in the control group had an average score of 80 with a standard deviation of 6.2. (Adapted from American Psychological Association)

**At $\alpha = 0.05$, is there enough evidence to support the claim that children with musical training have better verbal memory test scores than those without training? Assume the population variances are equal.**

## EXAMPLE 1

See Minitab steps on page 464.

### A Two-Sample $t$-Test for the Difference Between Means

**Sample Statistics for State Mathematics Test Scores**

| Teacher 1 | Teacher 2 |
|---|---|
| $\bar{x}_1 = 473$ | $\bar{x}_2 = 459$ |
| $s_1 = 39.7$ | $s_2 = 24.5$ |
| $n_1 = 8$ | $n_2 = 18$ |

The results of a state mathematics test for random samples of students taught by two different teachers at the same school are shown at the left. Can you conclude that there is a difference in the mean mathematics test scores for the students of the two teachers? Use $\alpha = 0.10$. Assume the populations are normally distributed and the population variances are not equal.

**SOLUTION**

Note that $\sigma_1$ and $\sigma_2$ are unknown, the samples are random and independent, and the populations are normally distributed. So, you can use the $t$-test. The claim is "there is a difference in the mean mathematics test scores for the students of the two teachers." So, the null and alternative hypotheses are

$$H_0: \mu_1 = \mu_2 \quad \text{and} \quad H_a: \mu_1 \neq \mu_2. \text{ (Claim)}$$

Because the population variances are not equal and the smaller sample size is 8, use d.f. $= 8 - 1 = 7$. The test is a two-tailed test with d.f. $= 7$ and $\alpha = 0.10$, so the critical values are $-t_0 = -1.895$ and $t_0 = 1.895$. The rejection regions are $t < -1.895$ and $t > 1.895$. The standardized test statistic is

$$t = \frac{(\bar{x}_1 - \bar{x}_2) - (\mu_1 - \mu_2)}{\sqrt{\frac{s_1^2}{n_1} + \frac{s_2^2}{n_2}}}$$ Use the $t$-test (variances are *not* equal).

$$= \frac{(473 - 459) - 0}{\sqrt{\frac{(39.7)^2}{8} + \frac{(24.5)^2}{18}}}$$ Assume $\mu_1 = \mu_2$, so $\mu_1 - \mu_2 = 0$.

$$\approx 0.922.$$ Round to three decimal places.

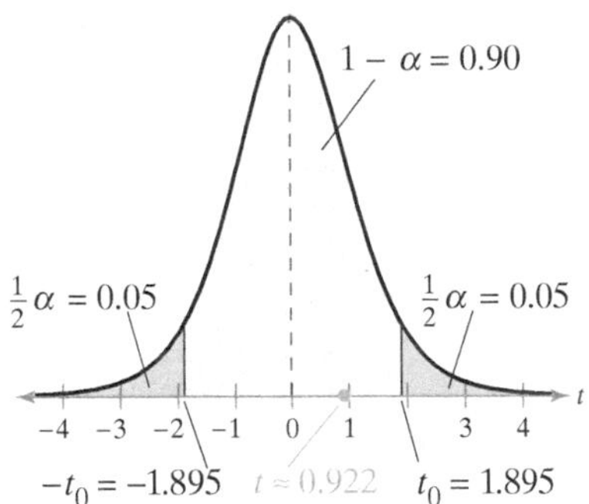


The figure at the left shows the location of the rejection regions and the standardized test statistic $t$. Because $t$ is not in the rejection region, you fail to reject the null hypothesis.

***Interpretation*** There is not enough evidence at the 10% level of significance to support the claim that the mean mathematics test scores for the students of the two teachers are different.

**TRY IT YOURSELF 1**

**Sample Statistics for Annual Earnings**

| High school diploma | Associate's degree |
|---|---|
| $\bar{x}_1 = \$41{,}775$ | $\bar{x}_2 = \$51{,}650$ |
| $s_1 = \$6050$ | $s_2 = \$9580$ |
| $n_1 = 25$ | $n_2 = 16$ |

The results of a survey on the annual earnings of random samples of people with a high school diploma and with an associate's degree are shown at the left. Can you conclude that there is a difference in the mean annual earnings based on level of education? Use $\alpha = 0.05$. Assume the populations are normally distributed and the population variances are not equal. *(Adapted from U.S. Census Bureau)*

*Answer: Page A41*

**TI-84 PLUS**

```
2-SampTTest
μ1≠μ2
t=0.9224141169
p=0.37924039
df=9.458685946
x̄1=473
↓x̄2=459
```

You can also use technology and a $P$-value to perform a hypothesis test for the difference between means. For instance, in Example 1, you can enter the statistics in a TI-84 Plus, as shown at the left, and find $P \approx 0.379$. Because $P > \alpha$, you fail to reject the null hypothesis. Note that when using technology, the number of degrees of freedom for the $t$-test is often determined by the formula

$$\text{d.f.} = \frac{(s_1^2/n_1 + s_2^2/n_2)^2}{(s_1^2/n_1)^2/(n_1 - 1) + (s_2^2/n_2)^2/(n_2 - 1)}.$$

This formula will not be used in the text.

## EXAMPLE 2

See TI-84 Plus steps on page 465.

### A Two-Sample *t*-Test for the Difference Between Means

An automobile manufacturer claims that the mean driving cost per mile of its sedans is less than that of its leading competitor. You conduct a study using 30 randomly selected sedans from the manufacturer and 32 from the leading competitor. The results are shown at the left. At $\alpha = 0.05$, can you support the manufacturer's claim? Assume the population variances are equal. *(Adapted from American Automobile Association)*

**Sample Statistics for Sedan Driving Costs**

| Manufacturer | Competitor |
|---|---|
| $\bar{x}_1 = \$0.52/\text{mi}$ <br> $s_1 = \$0.05/\text{mi}$ <br> $n_1 = 30$ | $\bar{x}_2 = \$0.55/\text{mi}$ <br> $s_2 = \$0.07/\text{mi}$ <br> $n_2 = 32$ |

**SOLUTION**

Note that $\sigma_1$ and $\sigma_2$ are unknown, the samples are random and independent, and both $n_1$ and $n_2$ are at least 30. So, you can use the $t$-test. The claim is "the mean driving cost per mile of the manufacturer's sedans is less than that of its leading competitor." So, the null and alternative hypotheses are

$$H_0: \mu_1 \geq \mu_2 \quad \text{and} \quad H_a: \mu_1 < \mu_2. \quad \text{(Claim)}$$

**Tech Tip**

It is important to note that when using a TI-84 Plus for the two-sample *t*-test, select the *Pooled: Yes* input option when the variances are equal.

The population variances are equal, so d.f. $= n_1 + n_2 - 2 = 30 + 32 - 2 = 60$. Because the test is a left-tailed test with d.f. $= 60$ and $\alpha = 0.05$, the critical value is $t_0 = -1.671$. The rejection region is $t < -1.671$. To make the calculation of the standardized test statistic easier, first find the standard error.

$$s_{\bar{x}_1 - \bar{x}_2} = \sqrt{\frac{(n_1 - 1)s_1^2 + (n_2 - 1)s_2^2}{n_1 + n_2 - 2}} \cdot \sqrt{\frac{1}{n_1} + \frac{1}{n_2}}$$

$$= \sqrt{\frac{(30 - 1)(0.05)^2 + (32 - 1)(0.07)^2}{30 + 32 - 2}} \cdot \sqrt{\frac{1}{30} + \frac{1}{32}}$$

$$\approx 0.0155416$$

The standardized test statistic is

$$t = \frac{(\bar{x}_1 - \bar{x}_2) - (\mu_1 - \mu_2)}{s_{\bar{x}_1 - \bar{x}_2}} \qquad \text{Use the } t\text{-test (variances are equal).}$$

$$\approx \frac{(0.52 - 0.55) - 0}{0.0155416} \qquad \text{Assume } \mu_1 = \mu_2, \text{ so } \mu_1 - \mu_2 = 0.$$

$$\approx -1.930. \qquad \text{Round to three decimal places.}$$

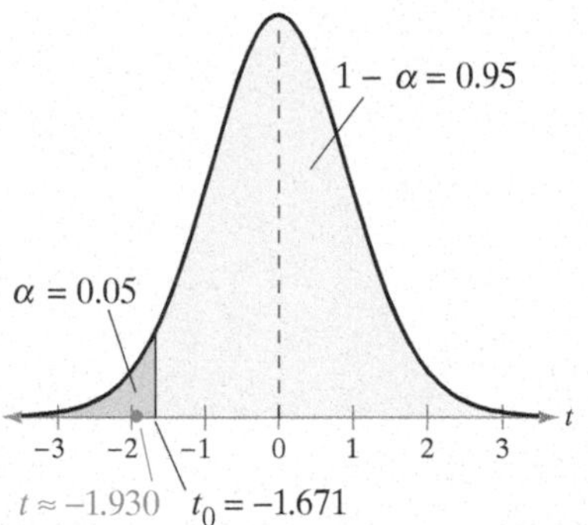


The figure at the left shows the location of the rejection region and the standardized test statistic $t$. Because $t$ is in the rejection region, you reject the null hypothesis.

***Interpretation*** There is enough evidence at the 5% level of significance to support the manufacturer's claim that the mean driving cost per mile of its sedans is less than that of its competitor's.

**TRY IT YOURSELF 2**

An automobile manufacturer claims that the mean driving cost per mile of its minivans is less than that of its leading competitor. You conduct a study using 34 randomly selected minivans from the manufacturer and 38 from the leading competitor. The results are shown at the right. At $\alpha = 0.10$, can you support the manufacturer's claim? Assume the population variances are equal. *(Adapted from American Automobile Association)*

**Sample Statistics for Minivan Driving Costs**

| Manufacturer | Competitor |
|---|---|
| $\bar{x}_1 = \$0.57/\text{mi}$ <br> $s_1 = \$0.09/\text{mi}$ <br> $n_1 = 34$ | $\bar{x}_2 = \$0.59/\text{mi}$ <br> $s_2 = \$0.08/\text{mi}$ <br> $n_2 = 38$ |

*Answer: Page A41*

# 8.2 EXERCISES

For Extra Help: MyLab Statistics

## Building Basic Skills and Vocabulary

**1.** What conditions are necessary to use the $t$-test for testing the difference between two population means?

**2.** Explain how to perform a two-sample $t$-test for the difference between two population means.

*In Exercises 3–8, use Table 5 in Appendix B to find the critical value(s) for the alternative hypothesis, level of significance $\alpha$, and sample sizes $n_1$ and $n_2$. Assume that the samples are random and independent, the populations are normally distributed, and the population variances are (a) equal and (b) not equal.*

**3.** $H_a$: $\mu_1 \neq \mu_2$, $\alpha = 0.10$, $n_1 = 11$, $n_2 = 14$

**4.** $H_a$: $\mu_1 > \mu_2$, $\alpha = 0.01$, $n_1 = 12$, $n_2 = 15$

**5.** $H_a$: $\mu_1 < \mu_2$, $\alpha = 0.05$, $n_1 = 7$, $n_2 = 11$

**6.** $H_a$: $\mu_1 \neq \mu_2$, $\alpha = 0.01$, $n_1 = 19$, $n_2 = 22$

**7.** $H_a$: $\mu_1 > \mu_2$, $\alpha = 0.05$, $n_1 = 13$, $n_2 = 8$

**8.** $H_a$: $\mu_1 < \mu_2$, $\alpha = 0.10$, $n_1 = 30$, $n_2 = 32$

*In Exercises 9–12, test the claim about the difference between two population means $\mu_1$ and $\mu_2$ at the level of significance $\alpha$. Assume the samples are random and independent, and the populations are normally distributed.*

**9.** Claim: $\mu_1 = \mu_2$; $\alpha = 0.01$. Assume $\sigma_1^2 = \sigma_2^2$
Sample statistics: $\bar{x}_1 = 33.7$, $s_1 = 3.5$, $n_1 = 12$ and
$\bar{x}_2 - 35.5$, $s_2 = 2.2$, $n_2 = 17$

**10.** Claim: $\mu_1 < \mu_2$; $\alpha = 0.10$. Assume $\sigma_1^2 = \sigma_2^2$
Sample statistics: $\bar{x}_1 = 0.345$, $s_1 = 0.305$, $n_1 = 11$ and
$\bar{x}_2 = 0.515$, $s_2 = 0.215$, $n_2 = 9$

**11.** Claim: $\mu_1 \leq \mu_2$; $\alpha = 0.05$. Assume $\sigma_1^2 \neq \sigma_2^2$
Sample statistics: $\bar{x}_1 = 2410$, $s_1 = 175$, $n_1 = 13$ and
$\bar{x}_2 = 2305$, $s_2 = 52$, $n_2 = 10$

**12.** Claim: $\mu_1 > \mu_2$; $\alpha = 0.01$. Assume $\sigma_1^2 \neq \sigma_2^2$
Sample statistics: $\bar{x}_1 = 52$, $s_1 = 4.8$, $n_1 = 32$ and
$\bar{x}_2 = 50$, $s_2 = 1.2$, $n_2 = 40$

## Using and Interpreting Concepts

**Testing the Difference Between Two Means** *In Exercises 13–22, (a) identify the claim and state $H_0$ and $H_a$, (b) find the critical value(s) and identify the rejection region(s), (c) find the standardized test statistic t, (d) decide whether to reject or fail to reject the null hypothesis, and (e) interpret the decision in the context of the original claim. Assume the samples are random and independent, and the populations are normally distributed.*

**13. Pet Food** A pet association claims that the mean annual costs of food for dogs and cats are the same. The results for samples of the two types of pets are shown at the left. At $\alpha = 0.10$, can you reject the pet association's claim? Assume the population variances are equal. *(Adapted from American Pet Products Association)*

**Sample Statistics for Annual Costs of Pet Food**

| Dogs | Cats |
|---|---|
| $\bar{x}_1 = \$255$ | $\bar{x}_2 = \$231$ |
| $s_1 = \$30$ | $s_2 = \$28$ |
| $n_1 = 16$ | $n_2 = 18$ |

TABLE FOR EXERCISE 13

**Sample Statistics for Amount Spent by Customers**

| Burger Stop | Fry World |
|---|---|
| $\bar{x}_1 = \$5.46$ | $\bar{x}_2 = \$5.12$ |
| $s_1 = \$0.89$ | $s_2 = \$0.79$ |
| $n_1 = 22$ | $n_2 = 30$ |

TABLE FOR EXERCISE 14

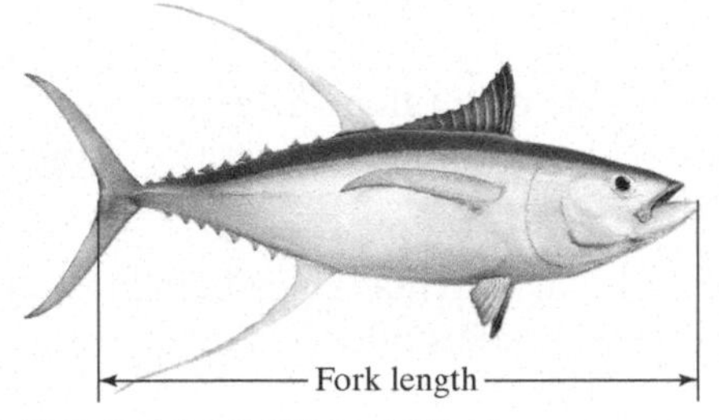

FIGURE FOR EXERCISE 16

**14. Transactions** A magazine claims that the mean amount spent by a customer at Burger Stop is greater than the mean amount spent by a customer at Fry World. The results for samples of customer transactions for the two fast food restaurants are shown at the left. At $\alpha = 0.05$, can you support the magazine's claim? Assume the population variances are equal.

**15. Blue Crabs** A marine researcher claims that the stomachs of blue crabs from one location contain more fish than the stomachs of blue crabs from another location. The stomach contents of a sample of 25 blue crabs from Location A contain a mean of 320 milligrams of fish and a standard deviation of 60 milligrams. The stomach contents of a sample of 15 blue crabs from Location B contain a mean of 280 milligrams of fish and a standard deviation of 80 milligrams. At $\alpha = 0.01$, can you support the marine researcher's claim? Assume the population variances are equal.

**16. Yellowfin Tuna** A marine biologist claims that the mean fork length (see figure at the left) of yellowfin tuna is different in two zones in the eastern tropical Pacific Ocean. A sample of 26 yellowfin tuna collected in Zone A has a mean fork length of 76.2 centimeters and a standard deviation of 16.5 centimeters. A sample of 31 yellowfin tuna collected in Zone B has a mean fork length of 80.8 centimeters and a standard deviation of 23.4 centimeters. At $\alpha = 0.01$, can you support the marine biologist's claim? Assume the population variances are equal. *(Adapted from Fishery Bulletin)*

**17. Annual Income** A politician claims that the mean household income in a recent year is greater in York County, South Carolina, than it is in Elmore County, Alabama. In York County, a sample of 23 residents has a mean household income of \$64,900 and a standard deviation of \$16,000. In Elmore County, a sample of 19 residents has a mean household income of \$59,500 and a standard deviation of \$23,600. At $\alpha = 0.05$, can you support the politician's claim? Assume the population variances are not equal. *(Adapted from U.S. Census Bureau)*

**18. Annual Income** A demographics researcher claims that the mean household income in a recent year is the same in Eagle County, Colorado, and Boulder County, Colorado. In Eagle County, a sample of 18 residents has a mean household income of \$85,400 and a standard deviation of \$26,100. In Boulder County, a sample of 15 residents has a mean household income of \$83,300 and a standard deviation of \$18,200. At $\alpha = 0.10$, can you reject the demographics researcher's claim? Assume the population variances are not equal. *(Adapted from U.S. News)*

**19. Tensile Strength** The tensile strength of a metal is a measure of its ability to resist tearing when it is pulled lengthwise. An experimental method of treatment produced steel bars with the tensile strengths (in newtons per square millimeter) listed below.

Experimental Method:

391 383 333 378 368 401 339 376 366 348

The conventional method produced steel bars with the tensile strengths (in newtons per square millimeter) listed below.

Conventional Method:

362 382 368 398 381 391 400
410 396 411 385 385 395 371

At $\alpha = 0.01$, can you support the claim that the experimental method of treatment makes a difference in the tensile strength of steel bars? Assume the population variances are equal.

**20. Tensile Strength** An engineer wants to compare the tensile strengths of steel bars that are produced using a conventional method and an experimental method. (The tensile strength of a metal is a measure of its ability to resist tearing when pulled lengthwise.) To do so, the engineer randomly selects steel bars that are manufactured using each method and records the tensile strengths (in newtons per square millimeter) listed below.

Experimental Method:

395 389 421 394 407 411 389 402 422
416 402 408 400 386 411 405 389 410

Conventional Method:

362 352 380 382 413 384 400
378 419 379 384 388 372 383

At $\alpha = 0.10$, can the engineer support the claim that the experimental method produces steel with a greater mean tensile strength? Assume the population variances are not equal.

**21. Teaching Methods** A new method of teaching reading is being tested on third grade students. A group of third grade students is taught using the new curriculum. A control group of third grade students is taught using the old curriculum. The reading test scores for the two groups are shown in the back-to-back stem-and-leaf plot.

| Old Curriculum | | New Curriculum |
|---:|:---:|:---|
| 9 | 3 | |
| 9 9 | 4 | 3 |
| 9 8 8 4 3 3 2 1 | 5 | 2 4 |
| 7 6 4 2 2 1 0 0 | 6 | 0 1 1 4 7 7 7 7 7 8 9 9 |
| | 7 | 0 1 1 2 3 3 4 9 |
| | 8 | 2 4 |

Key: 9|4|3 = 49 for old curriculum and 43 for new curriculum

At $\alpha = 0.10$, is there enough evidence to support the claim that the new method of teaching reading produces higher reading test scores than the old method does? Assume the population variances are equal.

**22. Teaching Methods** Two teaching methods and their effects on science test scores are being reviewed. A group of students is taught in traditional lab sessions. A second group of students is taught using interactive simulation software. The science test scores for the two groups are shown in the back-to-back stem-and-leaf plot.

| Traditional Lab | | Interactive Simulation Software |
|---:|:---:|:---|
| 4 | 6 | |
| 9 9 8 8 7 6 6 3 2 1 0 | 7 | 0 4 5 5 7 7 8 |
| 9 8 5 1 1 1 0 0 | 8 | 0 0 3 4 7 8 8 9 9 |
| 2 0 | 9 | 1 3 9 |

Key: 0|9|1 = 90 for traditional and 91 for interactive

At $\alpha = 0.01$, can you support the claim that the mean science test score is lower for students taught using the traditional lab method than it is for students taught using the interactive simulation software? Assume the population variances are equal.

## Extending Concepts

**Constructing Confidence Intervals for $\mu_1 - \mu_2$** *When the sampling distribution for $\bar{x}_1 - \bar{x}_2$ is approximated by a t-distribution and the population variances are not equal, you can construct a confidence interval for $\mu_1 - \mu_2$, as shown below.*

$$(\bar{x}_1 - \bar{x}_2) - t_c\sqrt{\frac{s_1^2}{n_1} + \frac{s_2^2}{n_2}} < \mu_1 - \mu_2 < (\bar{x}_1 - \bar{x}_2) + t_c\sqrt{\frac{s_1^2}{n_1} + \frac{s_2^2}{n_2}}$$

*where d.f. is the smaller of $n_1 - 1$ and $n_2 - 1$*

*In Exercises 23 and 24, construct the indicated confidence interval for $\mu_1 - \mu_2$. Assume the populations are approximately normal with unequal variances.*

**Sample Statistics for Finishing Times of 10K Race Participants**

| Males | Females |
|---|---|
| $\bar{x}_1 = 65.8$ min<br>$s_1 = 34.1$ min<br>$n_1 = 20$ | $\bar{x}_2 = 65.3$ min<br>$s_2 = 17.7$ min<br>$n_2 = 18$ |

TABLE FOR EXERCISE 23

**23. 10K Race** To compare the mean finishing times of male and female participants in a 10K race, you randomly select several finishing times from both sexes. The results are shown at the left. Construct an 80% confidence interval for the difference in mean finishing times of male and female participants in the race. *(Adapted from Great Race)*

**Sample Statistics for Driving Distances**

| Golfer 1 | Golfer 2 |
|---|---|
| $\bar{x}_1 = 267$ yd<br>$s_1 = 6$ yd<br>$n_1 = 9$ | $\bar{x}_2 = 244$ yd<br>$s_2 = 12$ yd<br>$n_2 = 5$ |

TABLE FOR EXERCISE 24

**24. Golf** To compare the mean driving distances for two golfers, you randomly select several drives from each golfer. The results are shown at the left. Construct a 90% confidence interval for the difference in mean driving distances for the two golfers.

**Constructing Confidence Intervals for $\mu_1 - \mu_2$** *When the sampling distribution for $\bar{x}_1 - \bar{x}_2$ is approximated by a t-distribution and the populations have equal variances, you can construct a confidence interval for $\mu_1 - \mu_2$, as shown below.*

$$(\bar{x}_1 - \bar{x}_2) - t_c\hat{\sigma}\cdot\sqrt{\frac{1}{n_1} + \frac{1}{n_2}} < \mu_1 - \mu_2 < (\bar{x}_1 - \bar{x}_2) + t_c\hat{\sigma}\cdot\sqrt{\frac{1}{n_1} + \frac{1}{n_2}}$$

*where* $\hat{\sigma} = \sqrt{\frac{(n_1 - 1)s_1^2 + (n_2 - 1)s_2^2}{n_1 + n_2 - 2}}$ *and* $d.f. = n_1 + n_2 - 2$

*In Exercises 25 and 26, construct the indicated confidence interval for $\mu_1 - \mu_2$. Assume the populations are approximately normal with equal variances.*

**Sample Statistics for Number of Days Waiting for an Appointment with a Family Doctor**

| Miami | Seattle |
|---|---|
| $\bar{x}_1 = 28$ days<br>$s_1 = 39.7$ days<br>$n_1 = 20$ | $\bar{x}_2 = 26$ days<br>$s_2 = 42.4$ days<br>$n_2 = 17$ |

TABLE FOR EXERCISE 25

**25. Family Doctor** To compare the mean number of days spent waiting to see a family doctor for two large cities, you randomly select several people in each city who have had an appointment with a family doctor. The results are shown at the left. Construct a 90% confidence interval for the difference in mean number of days spent waiting to see a family doctor for the two cities. *(Adapted from Merritt Hawkins)*

**26. 10K Race** To compare the mean ages of male and female participants in a 10K race, you randomly select several ages from both sexes. The results are shown below. Construct a 95% confidence interval for the difference in mean ages of male and female participants in the race. *(Adapted from Great Race)*

**Sample Statistics for Ages of 10K Race Participants**

| Males | Females |
|---|---|
| $\bar{x}_1 = 40$ years<br>$s_1 = 12.3$ years<br>$n_1 = 20$ | $\bar{x}_2 = 39$ years<br>$s_2 = 14.5$ years<br>$n_2 = 18$ |

# CASE STUDY

# How Protein Affects Weight Gain in Overeaters

In a study published in the *Journal of the American Medical Association,* three groups of 18- to 35-year-old participants overate for an 8-week period. The groups consumed different levels of protein in their diet. The low protein group's diet was 5% protein, the normal protein group's diet was 15% protein, and the high protein group's diet was 25% protein. The study found that the low protein group gained considerably less weight than the normal protein group or the high protein group.

You are a scientist working at a health research firm. The firm wants you to replicate the experiment. You conduct a similar experiment over an 8-week period. The results of the experiment are shown below.

| | **Low protein group** | **Normal protein group** | **High protein group** |
|---|---|---|---|
| **Weight gain (after 8 weeks)** | $\bar{x}_1 = 6.8$ lb<br>$s_1 = 1.7$ lb<br>$n_1 = 12$ | $\bar{x}_2 = 13.5$ lb<br>$s_2 = 2.5$ lb<br>$n_2 = 16$ | $\bar{x}_3 = 14.2$ lb<br>$s_3 = 2.1$ lb<br>$n_3 = 15$ |

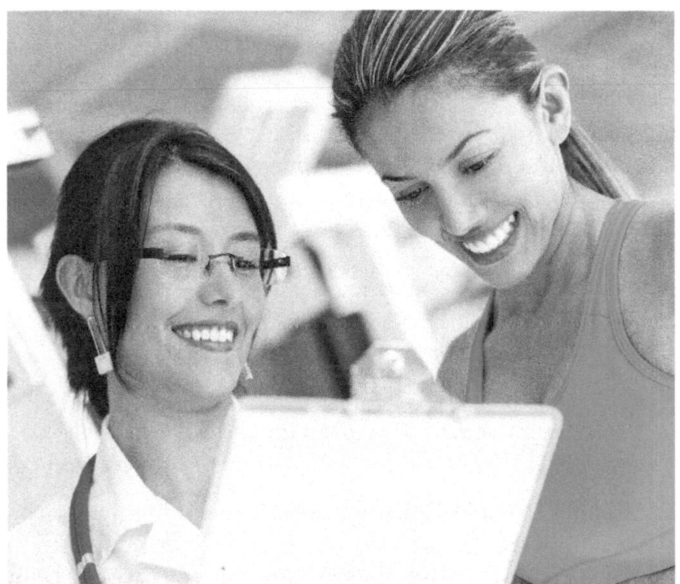

## EXERCISES

*In Exercises 1–3, perform a two-sample t-test to determine whether the mean weight gains of the two indicated studies are different. Assume the populations are normally distributed and the population variances are equal. For each exercise, write your conclusions as a sentence. Use $\alpha = 0.05$.*

**1.** Test the weight gains of the low protein group against those in the normal protein group.

**2.** Test the weight gains of the low protein group against those in the high protein group.

**3.** Test the weight gains of the normal protein group against those in the high protein group.

**4.** In which comparisons in Exercises 1–3 did you find a difference in weight gains? Write a summary of your findings.

**5.** Construct a 95% confidence interval for $\mu_1 - \mu_2$, where $\mu_1$ is the mean weight gain in the normal protein group and $\mu_2$ is the mean weight gain in the high protein group. Assume the populations are normally distributed and the population variances are equal. (See Extending Concepts in Section 8.2 Exercises.)

# 8.3 Testing the Difference Between Means (Dependent Samples)

### What You Should Learn

▶ How to perform a $t$-test to test the mean of the differences for a population of paired data

The $t$-Test for the Difference Between Means

## The $t$-Test for the Difference Between Means

In Sections 8.1 and 8.2, you performed two-sample hypothesis tests with independent samples using the test statistic $\bar{x}_1 - \bar{x}_2$ (the difference between the means of the two samples). To perform a two-sample hypothesis test with dependent samples, you will use a different technique. You will first find the difference $d$ for each data pair.

$d =$ (data entry in first sample) − (corresponding data entry in second sample)

The test statistic is the mean $\bar{d}$ of these differences

$$\bar{d} = \frac{\Sigma d}{n}. \quad \text{Mean of the differences between paired data entries in the dependent samples}$$

These conditions are necessary to conduct the test.

1. The samples are randomly selected.
2. The samples are dependent (paired).
3. The populations are normally distributed *or* the number $n$ of pairs of data is at least 30.

When these conditions are met, the **sampling distribution for $\bar{d}$, the mean of the differences of the paired data entries in the dependent samples,** is approximated by a $t$-distribution with $n - 1$ degrees of freedom, where $n$ is the number of data pairs.

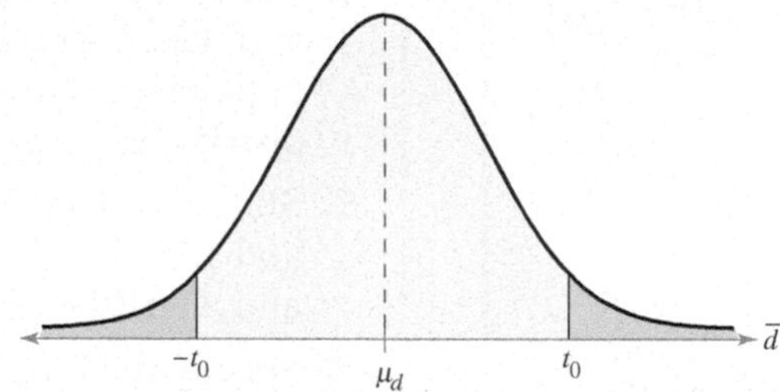

### Study Tip

Recall from Section 8.1 that two samples are dependent when each member of one sample corresponds to a member of the other sample.

The symbols listed in the table are used for the $t$-test for $\mu_d$. Although formulas are given for the mean and standard deviation of differences, you should use technology to calculate these statistics.

| Symbol | Description |
|---|---|
| $n$ | The number of pairs of data |
| $d$ | The difference between entries in a data pair |
| $\mu_d$ | The hypothesized mean of the differences of paired data in the population |
| $\bar{d}$ | The mean of the differences between the paired data entries in the dependent samples $\bar{d} = \frac{\Sigma d}{n}$ |
| $s_d$ | The standard deviation of the differences between the paired data entries in the dependent samples $s_d = \sqrt{\frac{\Sigma(d - \bar{d})^2}{n - 1}}$ |

### Study Tip

You can also calculate the standard deviation of the differences between paired data entries using the alternative formula

$$s_d = \sqrt{\frac{\Sigma d^2 - \left[\frac{(\Sigma d)^2}{n}\right]}{n - 1}}.$$

## Picturing the World

The manufacturer of an appetite suppressant claims that when its product is taken while following a low-fat diet with regular exercise for 4 months, the average weight loss is 20 pounds. To test this claim, you studied 12 randomly selected people taking an appetite suppressant for 4 months. Each person followed a low-fat diet with regular exercise for all 4 months. The results are shown in the table. (Adapted from NetHealth, Inc.)

**Weights (in pounds) of 12 People Taking an Appetite Suppressant**

| | Original weight | Weight after 4th month |
|---|---|---|
| 1 | 185 | 168 |
| 2 | 194 | 177 |
| 3 | 213 | 196 |
| 4 | 198 | 180 |
| 5 | 244 | 229 |
| 6 | 162 | 144 |
| 7 | 211 | 197 |
| 8 | 273 | 252 |
| 9 | 178 | 161 |
| 10 | 192 | 178 |
| 11 | 181 | 161 |
| 12 | 209 | 193 |

**At $\alpha = 0.10$, does your study provide enough evidence to reject the manufacturer's claim? Assume the weights are normally distributed.**

When you use a $t$-distribution to approximate the sampling distribution for $\bar{d}$, the mean of the differences between paired data entries, you can use a $t$-test to test a claim about the mean of the differences for a population of paired data.

### $t$-Test for the Difference Between Means

A $t$-test can be used to test the difference of two population means when these conditions are met.

1. The samples are random.
2. The samples are dependent (paired).
3. The populations are normally distributed *or* $n \geq 30$.

The **test statistic** is

$$\bar{d} = \frac{\Sigma d}{n}$$

and the **standardized test statistic** is

$$t = \frac{\bar{d} - \mu_d}{s_d / \sqrt{n}}.$$

The degrees of freedom are

d.f. $= n - 1$.

### GUIDELINES

**Using the $t$-Test for the Difference Between Means (Dependent Samples)**

| In Words | In Symbols |
|---|---|
| 1. Verify that the samples are random and dependent, and either the populations are normally distributed *or* $n \geq 30$. | |
| 2. State the claim mathematically and verbally. Identify the null and alternative hypotheses. | State $H_0$ and $H_a$. |
| 3. Specify the level of significance. | Identify $\alpha$. |
| 4. Identify the degrees of freedom. | d.f. $= n - 1$ |
| 5. Determine the critical value(s). | Use Table 5 in Appendix B. |
| 6. Determine the rejection region(s). | |
| 7. Calculate $\bar{d}$ and $s_d$. | $\bar{d} = \frac{\Sigma d}{n}$<br>$s_d = \sqrt{\frac{\Sigma(d - \bar{d})^2}{n - 1}}$ |
| 8. Find the standardized test statistic and sketch the sampling distribution. | $t = \frac{\bar{d} - \mu_d}{s_d / \sqrt{n}}$ |
| 9. Make a decision to reject or fail to reject the null hypothesis. | If $t$ is in the rejection region, then reject $H_0$. Otherwise, fail to reject $H_0$. |
| 10. Interpret the decision in the context of the original claim. | |

**Study Tip**

To simplify the calculation of $t$, you can round the values of $\overline{d}$ and $s_d$ to four decimal places, as shown in Examples 1 and 2.

**EXAMPLE 1**

See Minitab steps on page 464.

### The $t$-Test for the Difference Between Means

A golf instruction and club fitting company claims that people who play golf can improve (decrease) their average golf scores by taking lessons from one of their coaches. The average golf scores of eight randomly selected people who play golf are determined before and after taking lessons from one of the company's coaches. The results are shown in the table. At $\alpha = 0.10$, is there enough evidence to support the company's claim? Assume the average golf scores are normally distributed.

| **Person** | 1 | 2 | 3 | 4 | 5 | 6 | 7 | 8 |
|---|---|---|---|---|---|---|---|---|
| **Average golf score (before taking lessons)** | 96 | 95 | 95 | 99 | 87 | 104 | 105 | 94 |
| **Average golf score (after taking lessons)** | 89 | 90 | 95 | 94 | 91 | 100 | 103 | 100 |

**SOLUTION**

Because the samples are random and dependent, and the populations are normally distributed, you can use the $t$-test. The claim is that "people who play golf can improve (decrease) their average golf scores." In other words, the company claims that a person's average golf score before taking the lessons will be greater than the person's average golf score after taking the lessons. Each difference is given by

$$d = (\text{score before lessons}) - (\text{score after lessons}).$$

The null and alternative hypotheses are $H_0$: $\mu_d \leq 0$ and $H_a$: $\mu_d > 0$ (claim). Because the test is a right-tailed test, $\alpha = 0.10$, and d.f. $= 8 - 1 = 7$, the critical value is $t_0 = 1.415$. The rejection region is $t > 1.415$. Using the table at the left, you can calculate $\overline{d}$ and $s_d$ as shown below. Notice that the alternative formula is used to calculate the standard deviation.

| **Before** | **After** | $d$ | $d^2$ |
|---|---|---|---|
| 96 | 89 | 7 | 49 |
| 95 | 90 | 5 | 25 |
| 95 | 95 | 0 | 0 |
| 99 | 94 | 5 | 25 |
| 87 | 91 | −4 | 16 |
| 104 | 100 | 4 | 16 |
| 105 | 103 | 2 | 4 |
| 94 | 100 | −6 | 36 |
| | | $\Sigma = 13$ | $\Sigma = 171$ |

$$\overline{d} = \frac{\Sigma d}{n} = \frac{13}{8} = 1.625$$

$$s_d = \sqrt{\frac{\Sigma d^2 - \left[\frac{(\Sigma d)^2}{n}\right]}{n-1}} = \sqrt{\frac{171 - \frac{(13)^2}{8}}{8-1}} \approx 4.6272$$

The standardized test statistic is

$$t = \frac{\overline{d} - \mu_d}{s_d/\sqrt{n}} \approx \frac{1.625 - 0}{4.6272/\sqrt{8}} \approx 0.9933.$$

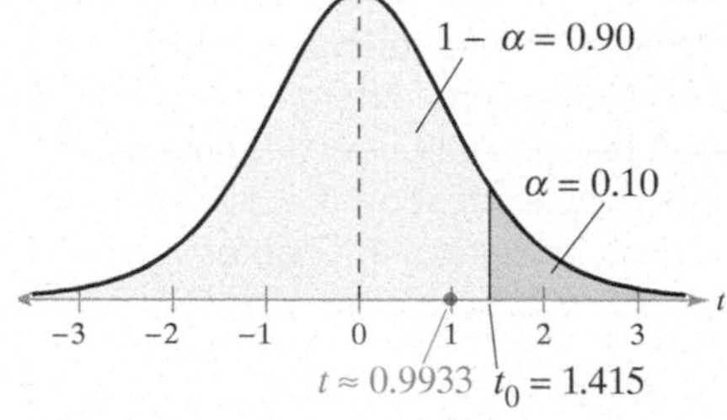


The figure shows the location of the rejection region and the standardized test statistic $t$. Because $t$ is not in the rejection region, you fail to reject the null hypothesis.

***Interpretation*** There is not enough evidence at the 10% level of significance to support the golf instruction and club fitting company's claim that people who play golf can improve (decrease) their average golf scores by taking lessons from one of their coaches.

**Study Tip**

You can also use a $P$-value to perform a hypothesis test for the difference between means. For instance, in Example 1, you can enter the data in Minitab (as shown on page 464) and find $P = 0.177$. Because $P > \alpha$, you fail to reject the null hypothesis.

**TRY IT YOURSELF 1**

A golf instruction and club fitting company claims that people who play golf can improve (decrease) their average golf scores by using the company's newly designed golf clubs. The average golf scores of eight randomly selected people who play golf are determined before and after using the company's newly designed golf clubs. The results are shown in the table. At $\alpha = 0.10$, is there enough evidence to support the company's claim? Assume the average golf scores are normally distributed.

| **Athlete** | 1 | 2 | 3 | 4 | 5 | 6 | 7 | 8 |
|---|---|---|---|---|---|---|---|---|
| **Average golf score (before using newly designed golf clubs)** | 89 | 84 | 96 | 82 | 74 | 92 | 85 | 91 |
| **Average golf score (after using newly designed golf clubs)** | 83 | 83 | 92 | 84 | 76 | 91 | 80 | 91 |

*Answer: Page A41*

Note that many advertisements misuse statistical results. For instance, statistical results could be misused by implying a cause-and-effect relationship that has not been substantiated by testing.

## EXAMPLE 2

### The *t*-Test for the Difference Between Means

The campaign staff for a state legislator wants to determine whether the legislator's performance rating (0–100) has changed from last year to this year. The table below shows the legislator's performance ratings from the same 16 randomly selected voters for last year and this year. At $\alpha = 0.05$, is there enough evidence to conclude that the legislator's performance rating has changed? Assume the performance ratings are normally distributed.

| **Voter** | 1 | 2 | 3 | 4 | 5 | 6 | 7 | 8 |
|---|---|---|---|---|---|---|---|---|
| **Rating (last year)** | 60 | 54 | 78 | 84 | 91 | 25 | 50 | 65 |
| **Rating (this year)** | 54 | 46 | 68 | 58 | 83 | 38 | 38 | 53 |

| **Voter** | 9 | 10 | 11 | 12 | 13 | 14 | 15 | 16 |
|---|---|---|---|---|---|---|---|---|
| **Rating (last year)** | 68 | 81 | 75 | 45 | 62 | 79 | 58 | 63 |
| **Rating (this year)** | 78 | 72 | 76 | 48 | 48 | 83 | 51 | 58 |

**Tech Tip**

One way to use technology to perform a hypothesis test for the difference between means is to enter the data in two columns and form a third column in which you calculate the difference for each pair. You can now perform a one-sample *t*-test on the difference column, as shown in Chapter 7.

**SOLUTION**

Because the samples are random and dependent, and the populations are normally distributed, you can use the *t*-test. If there is a change in the legislator's rating, then there will be a difference between last year's ratings and this year's ratings. Because the legislator wants to determine whether there is a difference, the null and alternative hypotheses are

$$H_0\colon \mu_d = 0 \quad \text{and} \quad H_a\colon \mu_d \neq 0. \ \text{(Claim)}$$

Because the test is a two-tailed test, $\alpha = 0.05$, and d.f. $= 16 - 1 = 15$, the critical values are $-t_0 = -2.131$ and $t_0 = 2.131$. The rejection regions are $t < -2.131$ and $t > 2.131$.

| Before | After | $d$ | $d^2$ |
|---|---|---|---|
| 60 | 54 | 6 | 36 |
| 54 | 46 | 8 | 64 |
| 78 | 68 | 10 | 100 |
| 84 | 58 | 26 | 676 |
| 91 | 83 | 8 | 64 |
| 25 | 38 | −13 | 169 |
| 50 | 38 | 12 | 144 |
| 65 | 53 | 12 | 144 |
| 68 | 78 | −10 | 100 |
| 81 | 72 | 9 | 81 |
| 75 | 76 | −1 | 1 |
| 45 | 48 | −3 | 9 |
| 62 | 48 | 14 | 196 |
| 79 | 83 | −4 | 16 |
| 58 | 51 | 7 | 49 |
| 63 | 58 | 5 | 25 |
| | | $\Sigma = 86$ | $\Sigma = 1874$ |

Using the table at the left, you can calculate $\bar{d}$ and $s_d$ as shown below.

$$\bar{d} = \frac{\Sigma d}{n} = \frac{86}{16} = 5.375$$

$$s_d = \sqrt{\frac{\Sigma d^2 - \left[\frac{(\Sigma d)^2}{n}\right]}{n-1}} = \sqrt{\frac{1874 - \frac{86^2}{16}}{16-1}} \approx 9.7014$$

The standardized test statistic is

$$t = \frac{\bar{d} - \mu_d}{s_d / \sqrt{n}} \quad \text{Use the } t\text{-test.}$$

$$\approx \frac{5.375 - 0}{9.7014/\sqrt{16}} \quad \text{Assume } \mu_d = 0.$$

$$\approx 2.216.$$

You can check this result using technology, as shown below using StatCrunch.

**STATCRUNCH**

**Paired T hypothesis test:**

$\mu_D = \mu_1 - \mu_2$ : Mean of the difference between Last year and This year
$H_0 : \mu_D = 0$
$H_A : \mu_D \neq 0$

**Hypothesis test results:**

| Difference | Mean | Std. Err. | DF | T-Stat | P-value |
|---|---|---|---|---|---|
| Last year–This year | 5.375 | 2.4253436 | 15 | 2.2161808 | 0.0426 |

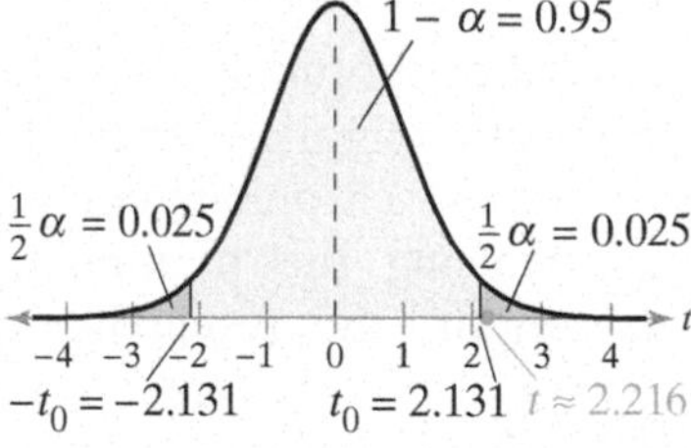


The figure at the left shows the location of the rejection region and the standardized test statistic $t$. Because $t$ is in the rejection region, you reject the null hypothesis.

***Interpretation*** There is enough evidence at the 1% level of significance to conclude that the legislator's performance rating has changed.

**TRY IT YOURSELF 2**

A medical researcher wants to determine whether a drug changes the body's temperature. Seven test subjects are randomly selected, and the body temperature (in degrees Fahrenheit) of each is measured. The subjects are then given the drug and, after 20 minutes, the body temperature of each is measured again. The results are listed below. At $\alpha = 0.05$, is there enough evidence to conclude that the drug changes the body's temperature? Assume the body temperatures are normally distributed.

| Subject | 1 | 2 | 3 | 4 | 5 | 6 | 7 |
|---|---|---|---|---|---|---|---|
| Initial temperature | 101.8 | 98.5 | 98.1 | 99.4 | 98.9 | 100.2 | 97.9 |
| Second temperature | 99.2 | 98.4 | 98.2 | 99.0 | 98.6 | 99.7 | 97.8 |

*Answer: Page A41*

# 8.3 EXERCISES

For Extra Help: MyLab Statistics

## Building Basic Skills and Vocabulary

**1.** What conditions are necessary to use the dependent samples $t$-test for the mean of the differences for a population of paired data?

**2.** Explain what the symbols $\bar{d}$ and $s_d$ represent.

*In Exercises 3–8, test the claim about the mean of the differences for a population of paired data at the level of significance $\alpha$. Assume the samples are random and dependent, and the populations are normally distributed.*

**3.** Claim: $\mu_d < 0$; $\alpha = 0.05$. Sample statistics: $\bar{d} = 1.5$, $s_d = 3.2$, $n = 14$

**4.** Claim: $\mu_d = 0$; $\alpha = 0.01$. Sample statistics: $\bar{d} = 3.2$, $s_d = 8.45$, $n = 8$

**5.** Claim: $\mu_d \leq 0$; $\alpha = 0.10$. Sample statistics: $\bar{d} = 6.5$, $s_d = 9.54$, $n = 16$

**6.** Claim: $\mu_d > 0$; $\alpha = 0.05$. Sample statistics: $\bar{d} = 0.55$, $s_d = 0.99$, $n = 28$

**7.** Claim: $\mu_d \geq 0$; $\alpha = 0.01$. Sample statistics: $\bar{d} = -2.3$, $s_d = 1.2$, $n = 15$

**8.** Claim: $\mu_d \neq 0$; $\alpha = 0.10$. Sample statistics: $\bar{d} = -1$, $s_d = 2.75$, $n = 20$

## Using and Interpreting Concepts

**Testing the Difference Between Two Means** *In Exercises 9–20, (a) identify the claim and state $H_0$ and $H_a$, (b) find the critical value(s) and identify the rejection region(s), (c) calculate $\bar{d}$ and $s_d$, (d) find the standardized test statistic t, (e) decide whether to reject or fail to reject the null hypothesis, and (f) interpret the decision in the context of the original claim. Assume the samples are random and dependent, and the populations are normally distributed.*

**9. Migraines** A researcher claims that injections of onabotulinumtoxinA reduce the number of days per month that chronic migraine sufferers have headaches. The table shows the number of days chronic migraine sufferers suffered migraines before and after using the treatment. At $\alpha = 0.01$, is there enough evidence to support the researcher's claim? *(Adapted from Journal of Headache and Pain)*

| Patient | 1 | 2 | 3 | 4 | 5 | 6 | 7 | 8 | 9 |
|---|---|---|---|---|---|---|---|---|---|
| Days (before) | 20 | 17 | 15 | 27 | 22 | 18 | 25 | 20 | 27 |
| Days (after) | 0 | 15 | 11 | 14 | 5 | 6 | 1 | 4 | 5 |

| Patient | 10 | 11 | 12 | 13 | 14 | 15 | 16 | 17 | 18 |
|---|---|---|---|---|---|---|---|---|---|
| Days (before) | 24 | 22 | 19 | 15 | 31 | 25 | 19 | 15 | 16 |
| Days (after) | 13 | 2 | 12 | 3 | 10 | 7 | 14 | 0 | 15 |

**10. Dow Jones Stocks** A stock market analyst claims that the Dow Jones Industrial Average lost value from the closing prices on the previous day to the current prices. The table shows the prices (in dollars per share) of seven randomly selected stocks. At $\alpha = 0.01$, is there enough evidence to support the analyst's claim? *(Source: Markets Insider)*

| **Stock** | 1 | 2 | 3 | 4 | 5 | 6 | 7 |
|---|---|---|---|---|---|---|---|
| **Previous close** | 199.93 | 323.26 | 220.74 | 136.95 | 243.22 | 411.86 | 279.93 |
| **Current price** | 198.27 | 318.54 | 219.32 | 137.32 | 244.28 | 409.95 | 276.60 |

 **11. SAT Scores** An instructor for a SAT preparation course claims that the course will improve the test scores of students. The table shows the critical reading scores for 10 students the first two times they took the SAT. Before taking the SAT for the second time, the students took the instructor's course to try to improve their critical reading SAT scores. At $\alpha = 0.01$, is there enough evidence to support the instructor's claim?

| **Student** | 1 | 2 | 3 | 4 | 5 | 6 | 7 | 8 | 9 | 10 |
|---|---|---|---|---|---|---|---|---|---|---|
| **Score (first)** | 300 | 450 | 350 | 430 | 300 | 470 | 420 | 370 | 320 | 410 |
| **Score (second)** | 400 | 520 | 400 | 490 | 340 | 580 | 450 | 400 | 390 | 450 |

**12. Interval Training** A researcher claims that sprint interval training improves running performance in trained athletes. The table shows the maximum aerobic speed (MAS), in kilometers per hour, of trained athletes before and after six sessions of sprint interval training. At $\alpha = 0.10$, is there enough evidence to support the researcher's claim? *(Adapted from National Strength and Conditioning Association)*

| **Athlete** | 1 | 2 | 3 | 4 | 5 | 6 | 7 | 8 |
|---|---|---|---|---|---|---|---|---|
| **MAS before training (km/h)** | 18.5 | 17.0 | 12.5 | 16.5 | 16.0 | 13.0 | 17.5 | 15 |
| **MAS after training (km/h)** | 18.5 | 16.5 | 13.0 | 16.5 | 17.5 | 14.0 | 18.0 | 15.5 |

 **13. Batting Averages** A coach claims that a baseball clinic will help players raise their batting averages. The table shows the batting averages of 14 players before participating in the clinic and two months after participating in the clinic. At $\alpha = 0.05$, is there enough evidence to support the coach's claim?

| **Player** | 1 | 2 | 3 | 4 | 5 | 6 | 7 |
|---|---|---|---|---|---|---|---|
| **Batting average (before clinic)** | 0.290 | 0.275 | 0.278 | 0.310 | 0.302 | 0.325 | 0.256 |
| **Batting average (after clinic)** | 0.295 | 0.320 | 0.280 | 0.300 | 0.298 | 0.330 | 0.260 |

| **Player** | 8 | 9 | 10 | 11 | 12 | 13 | 14 |
|---|---|---|---|---|---|---|---|
| **Batting average (before clinic)** | 0.350 | 0.380 | 0.316 | 0.270 | 0.300 | 0.330 | 0.340 |
| **Batting average (after clinic)** | 0.345 | 0.380 | 0.315 | 0.280 | 0.282 | 0.336 | 0.325 |

 **14. Therapeutic Taping** A physical therapist claims that the use of a specific type of therapeutic tape reduces pain in patients with chronic tennis elbow. The table shows the pain levels on a scale of 0 to 10, where 0 is no pain and 10 is the worst pain possible, for 15 patients with chronic tennis elbow when holding a 1 kilogram weight. At $\alpha = 0.05$, is there enough evidence to support the therapist's claim? *(Adapted from BioMed Central, Ltd.)*

| Patient | 1 | 2 | 3 | 4 | 5 | 6 | 7 | 8 |
|---|---|---|---|---|---|---|---|---|
| Pain level (before taping) | 7 | 7 | 4 | 4 | 8 | 5 | 3 | 9 |
| Pain level (after taping) | 6 | 5 | 1 | 1 | 4 | 0 | 0 | 5 |

| Patient | 9 | 10 | 11 | 12 | 13 | 14 | 15 |
|---|---|---|---|---|---|---|---|
| Pain level (before taping) | 3 | 1 | 1 | 3 | 5 | 4 | 2 |
| Pain level (after taping) | 0 | 0 | 3 | 2 | 3 | 1 | 3 |

 **15. Gasoline Prices** A reporter claims that U.S. gasoline prices increased from May to June of 2021. The table shows the prices (in dollars per gallon) of unleaded gasoline at 12 randomly selected U.S. gasoline stations during May and June of 2021. At $\alpha = 0.005$, is there enough evidence to support the reporter's claim? *(Adapted from U.S. Energy Information Administration)*

| Station | 1 | 2 | 3 | 4 | 5 | 6 |
|---|---|---|---|---|---|---|
| Price (May) | 3.19 | 2.92 | 2.95 | 3.02 | 2.90 | 2.90 |
| Price (June) | 3.19 | 2.97 | 2.99 | 3.09 | 2.88 | 2.95 |

| Station | 7 | 8 | 9 | 10 | 11 | 12 |
|---|---|---|---|---|---|---|
| Price (May) | 2.91 | 2.91 | 3.01 | 3.05 | 2.92 | 2.93 |
| Price (June) | 2.90 | 2.96 | 3.05 | 3.09 | 2.91 | 2.98 |

**16. Entry Level Salaries** A career counselor claims that entry level receptionists earn more than entry level customer support representatives in Dallas, Texas. The table shows the salaries (in dollars) paid to entry level customer support representatives and receptionists at seven randomly selected companies in Dallas. At $\alpha = 0.005$, is there enough evidence to support the career counselor's claim? *(Adapted from Salary.com)*

| Company | 1 | 2 | 3 | 4 | 5 | 6 | 7 |
|---|---|---|---|---|---|---|---|
| Customer support salary | 26,000 | 28,750 | 26,260 | 30,130 | 32,200 | 23,200 | 26,675 |
| Receptionist salary | 31,550 | 30,740 | 30,380 | 28,040 | 28,550 | 29,960 | 28,420 |

**17. Product Ratings** A company claims that its consumer product ratings (0–10) have changed from last year to this year. The table shows the company's product ratings from the same eight consumers for last year and this year. At $\alpha = 0.05$, is there enough evidence to support the company's claim?

| Consumer | 1 | 2 | 3 | 4 | 5 | 6 | 7 | 8 |
|---|---|---|---|---|---|---|---|---|
| Rating (last year) | 5 | 7 | 2 | 3 | 9 | 10 | 8 | 7 |
| Rating (this year) | 5 | 9 | 4 | 6 | 9 | 9 | 9 | 8 |

**18. Passing Play Percentages** The passing play percentages of 10 randomly selected NCAA Division 1A college football teams for home and away games in the 2020–2021 season are shown in the table. At $\alpha = 0.20$, is there enough evidence to support the claim that passing play percentage is different for home and away games? *(Source: TeamRankings)*

| College | 1 | 2 | 3 | 4 | 5 | 6 | 7 | 8 | 9 | 10 |
|---|---|---|---|---|---|---|---|---|---|---|
| Home passing play percentage | 54.3 | 48.1 | 44.7 | 40.8 | 45.4 | 46.3 | 53.7 | 37.9 | 73.1 | 40.7 |
| Away passing play percentage | 52.9 | 59.3 | 47.6 | 43.2 | 46.8 | 42.6 | 49.9 | 44.6 | 49.6 | 40.2 |

**19. Cholesterol Levels** A food manufacturer claims that eating its new cereal as part of a daily diet lowers total blood cholesterol levels. The table shows the total blood cholesterol levels (in milligrams per deciliter of blood) of seven patients before eating the cereal and after one year of eating the cereal as part of their diets. At $\alpha = 0.05$, is there enough evidence to support the food manufacturer's claim?

| Patient | 1 | 2 | 3 | 4 | 5 | 6 | 7 |
|---|---|---|---|---|---|---|---|
| Total blood cholesterol level (before) | 210 | 225 | 240 | 250 | 255 | 270 | 235 |
| Total blood cholesterol level (after) | 200 | 220 | 245 | 248 | 252 | 268 | 232 |

**20. Obstacle Course** On a television show, eight contestants try to lose the highest percentage of weight in order to win a cash prize. As part of the show, the contestants are timed as they run an obstacle course. The table shows the times (in seconds) of the contestants at the beginning of the season and at the end of the season. At $\alpha = 0.01$, is there enough evidence to support the claim that the contestants' times have changed?

| Contestant | 1 | 2 | 3 | 4 | 5 | 6 | 7 | 8 |
|---|---|---|---|---|---|---|---|---|
| Time (beginning) | 130.2 | 104.8 | 100.1 | 136.4 | 125.9 | 122.6 | 150.4 | 158.2 |
| Time (end) | 121.5 | 100.7 | 90.2 | 135.0 | 112.1 | 120.5 | 139.8 | 142.9 |

## Extending Concepts

**21.** In Exercise 15, use technology to perform the hypothesis test with a $P$-value. Compare your result with the result obtained using rejection regions. Are they the same?

**22.** In Exercise 18, use technology to perform the hypothesis test with a $P$-value. Compare your result with the result obtained using rejection regions. Are they the same?

**Constructing Confidence Intervals for $\mu_d$** *To construct a confidence interval for $\mu_d$, use the inequality below.*

$$\bar{d} - t_c\frac{s_d}{\sqrt{n}} < \mu_d < \bar{d} + t_c\frac{s_d}{\sqrt{n}}$$

*In Exercises 23 and 24, construct the indicated confidence interval for $\mu_d$. Assume the populations are normally distributed.*

**23. Drug Testing** A sleep disorder specialist wants to test the effectiveness of a new drug that is reported to increase the number of hours of sleep patients get during the night. To do so, the specialist randomly selects 16 patients and records the number of hours of sleep each gets with and without the new drug. The table shows the results of the two-night study. Construct a 90% confidence interval for $\mu_d$.

| **Patient** | 1 | 2 | 3 | 4 | 5 | 6 | 7 | 8 |
|---|---|---|---|---|---|---|---|---|
| **Hours of sleep (without the drug)** | 1.8 | 2.0 | 3.4 | 3.5 | 3.7 | 3.8 | 3.9 | 3.9 |
| **Hours of sleep (using the drug)** | 3.0 | 3.6 | 4.0 | 4.4 | 4.5 | 5.2 | 5.5 | 5.7 |

| **Patient** | 9 | 10 | 11 | 12 | 13 | 14 | 15 | 16 |
|---|---|---|---|---|---|---|---|---|
| **Hours of sleep (without the drug)** | 4.0 | 4.9 | 5.1 | 5.2 | 5.0 | 4.5 | 4.2 | 4.7 |
| **Hours of sleep (using the drug)** | 6.2 | 6.3 | 6.6 | 7.8 | 7.2 | 6.5 | 5.6 | 5.9 |

**24. Herbal Medicine Testing** A sleep disorder specialist wants to test whether herbal medicine increases the number of hours of sleep patients get during the night. To do so, the specialist randomly selects 14 patients and records the number of hours of sleep each gets with and without the medicine. The table shows the results of the two-night study. Construct a 95% confidence interval for $\mu_d$.

| **Patient** | 1 | 2 | 3 | 4 | 5 | 6 | 7 |
|---|---|---|---|---|---|---|---|
| **Hours of sleep (without medicine)** | 1.0 | 1.4 | 3.4 | 3.7 | 5.1 | 5.1 | 5.2 |
| **Hours of sleep (using medicine)** | 2.9 | 3.3 | 3.5 | 4.4 | 5.0 | 5.0 | 5.2 |

| **Patient** | 8 | 9 | 10 | 11 | 12 | 13 | 14 |
|---|---|---|---|---|---|---|---|
| **Hours of sleep (without medicine)** | 5.3 | 5.5 | 5.8 | 4.2 | 4.8 | 2.9 | 4.5 |
| **Hours of sleep (using medicine)** | 5.3 | 6.0 | 6.5 | 4.4 | 4.7 | 3.1 | 4.7 |

# 8.4 Testing the Difference Between Proportions

## What You Should Learn

- How to perform a two-sample $z$-test for the difference between two population proportions $p_1$ and $p_2$

Two-Sample $z$-Test for the Difference Between Proportions

## Two-Sample $z$-Test for the Difference Between Proportions

In this section, you will learn how to use a $z$-test to test the difference between two population proportions $p_1$ and $p_2$ using a sample proportion from each population. If a claim is about two population parameters $p_1$ and $p_2$, then some possible pairs of null and alternative hypotheses are

$$\begin{cases} H_0: p_1 = p_2 \\ H_a: p_1 \neq p_2 \end{cases}, \quad \begin{cases} H_0: p_1 \leq p_2 \\ H_a: p_1 > p_2 \end{cases}, \quad \text{and} \quad \begin{cases} H_0: p_1 \geq p_2 \\ H_a: p_1 < p_2 \end{cases}.$$

Regardless of which hypotheses you use, you always assume there is no difference between the population proportions $(p_1 = p_2)$.

For instance, suppose you want to determine whether the proportion of college students who earn a bachelor of science degree in four years is different from the proportion of college students who earn a bachelor of arts degree in four years. These conditions are necessary to use a $z$-test to test such a difference.

1. The samples are randomly selected.
2. The samples are independent.
3. The samples are large enough to use a normal sampling distribution. That is, $n_1p_1 \geq 5$, $n_1q_1 \geq 5$, $n_2p_2 \geq 5$, and $n_2q_2 \geq 5$.

When these conditions are met, the **sampling distribution for $\hat{p}_1 - \hat{p}_2$, the difference between the sample proportions,** is a normal distribution with mean

$$\mu_{\hat{p}_1 - \hat{p}_2} = p_1 - p_2$$

and standard error

$$\sigma_{\hat{p}_1 - \hat{p}_2} = \sqrt{\frac{p_1q_1}{n_1} + \frac{p_2q_2}{n_2}}.$$

Notice that you need to know the population proportions to calculate the standard error. Because a hypothesis test for $p_1 - p_2$ is based on the assumption that $p_1 = p_2$, you can calculate a weighted estimate of $p_1$ and $p_2$ using

$$\bar{p} = \frac{x_1 + x_2}{n_1 + n_2}$$

where $x_1 = n_1\hat{p}_1$ and $x_2 = n_2\hat{p}_2$. With the weighted estimate $\bar{p}$, the standard error of the sampling distribution for $\hat{p}_1 - \hat{p}_2$ is

$$\sigma_{\hat{p}_1 - \hat{p}_2} = \sqrt{\bar{p}\,\bar{q}\left(\frac{1}{n_1} + \frac{1}{n_2}\right)}$$

where $\bar{q} = 1 - \bar{p}$.

Also, you need to know the population proportions to verify that the samples are large enough to be approximated by the normal distribution. But when determining whether the $z$-test can be used for the difference between proportions for a binomial experiment, you should use $\bar{p}$ in place of $p_1$ and $p_2$ and use $\bar{q}$ in place of $q_1$ and $q_2$.

### Study Tip

You can also write the null and alternative hypotheses as shown below.

$$\begin{cases} H_0: p_1 - p_2 = 0 \\ H_a: p_1 - p_2 \neq 0 \end{cases}$$

$$\begin{cases} H_0: p_1 - p_2 \leq 0 \\ H_a: p_1 - p_2 > 0 \end{cases}$$

$$\begin{cases} H_0: p_1 - p_2 \geq 0 \\ H_a: p_1 - p_2 < 0 \end{cases}$$

### Study Tip

The symbols in the table below are used in the $z$-test for $p_1 - p_2$. See Sections 4.2 and 5.5 to review the binomial distribution.

| Symbol | Description |
|---|---|
| $p_1, p_2$ | Population proportions |
| $x_1, x_2$ | Number of successes in each sample |
| $n_1, n_2$ | Size of each sample |
| $\hat{p}_1, \hat{p}_2$ | Sample proportions of successes |
| $\bar{p}$ | Weighted estimate of $p_1$ and $p_2$ |
| $\bar{q}$ | Weighted estimate of $q_1$ and $q_2$, $\bar{q} = 1 - \bar{p}$ |

## Picturing the World

A medical research team conducted a study to test whether the administration of vitamin D reduces the incidence of acute kidney injury (AKI) after cardiac surgery. In the study, 50 patients received vitamin D and 61 patients received a placebo. The results are shown below. (Source: Cardiorenal Medicine)

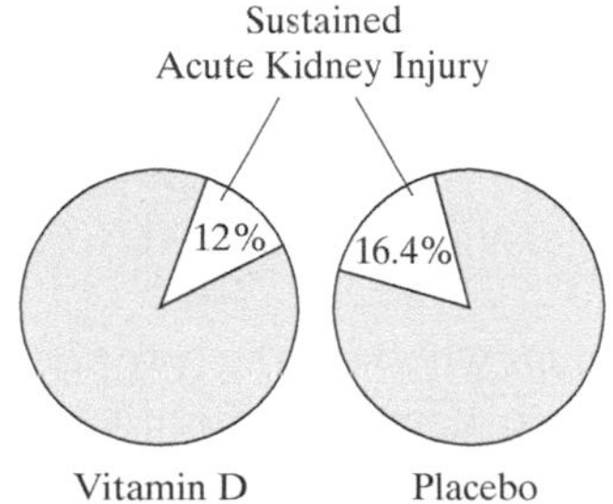


**At $\alpha = 0.05$, can you support the claim that the administration of vitamin D reduces the incidence of AKI after cardiac surgery?**

### Study Tip

To simplify the calculation of $z$, you can round the values of $\overline{p}$, $\overline{q}$, $\hat{p}_1$, and $\hat{p}_2$ to four decimal places, as shown in Examples 1 and 2.

When the sampling distribution for $\hat{p}_1 - \hat{p}_2$ is normal, you can use a two-sample $z$-test to test the difference between two population proportions $p_1$ and $p_2$.

### Two-Sample $z$-Test for the Difference Between Proportions

A two-sample $z$-test is used to test the difference between two population proportions $p_1$ and $p_2$ when these conditions are met.

1. The samples are random.
2. The samples are independent.
3. The quantities $n_1\overline{p}$, $n_1\overline{q}$, $n_2\overline{p}$, and $n_2\overline{q}$ are at least 5.

The **test statistic** is $\hat{p}_1 - \hat{p}_2$. The **standardized test statistic** is

$$z = \frac{(\hat{p}_1 - \hat{p}_2) - (p_1 - p_2)}{\sqrt{\overline{p}\,\overline{q}\left(\frac{1}{n_1} + \frac{1}{n_2}\right)}}$$

where $\overline{p} = \frac{x_1 + x_2}{n_1 + n_2}$ and $\overline{q} = 1 - \overline{p}$.

If the null hypothesis states $p_1 = p_2$, $p_1 \le p_2$, or $p_1 \ge p_2$, then $p_1 = p_2$ is assumed and the expression $p_1 - p_2$ is equal to 0 in the preceding test.

### GUIDELINES

**Using a Two-Sample $z$-Test for the Difference Between Proportions**

| In Words | In Symbols |
|---|---|
| **1.** Verify that the samples are random and independent. | |
| **2.** Find the weighted estimate of $p_1$ and $p_2$. Verify that $n_1\overline{p}$, $n_1\overline{q}$, $n_2\overline{p}$, and $n_2\overline{q}$ are at least 5. | $\overline{p} = \frac{x_1 + x_2}{n_1 + n_2}$, $\overline{q} = 1 - \overline{p}$ |
| **3.** State the claim mathematically and verbally. Identify the null and alternative hypotheses. | State $H_0$ and $H_a$. |
| **4.** Specify the level of significance. | Identify $\alpha$. |
| **5.** Determine the critical value(s). | Use Table 4 in Appendix B. |
| **6.** Determine the rejection region(s). | |
| **7.** Find the standardized test statistic and sketch the sampling distribution. | $z = \frac{(\hat{p}_1 - \hat{p}_2) - (p_1 - p_2)}{\sqrt{\overline{p}\,\overline{q}\left(\frac{1}{n_1} + \frac{1}{n_2}\right)}}$ |
| **8.** Make a decision to reject or fail to reject the null hypothesis. | If $z$ is in the rejection region, then reject $H_0$. Otherwise, fail to reject $H_0$. |
| **9.** Interpret the decision in the context of the original claim. | |

A hypothesis test for the difference between proportions can also be performed using $P$-values. Use the guidelines above, skipping Steps 5 and 6. After finding the standardized test statistic, use Table 4 in Appendix B to calculate the $P$-value. Then make a decision to reject or fail to reject the null hypothesis. If $P$ is less than or equal to $\alpha$, then reject $H_0$. Otherwise, fail to reject $H_0$.

## EXAMPLE 1

See TI-84 Plus steps on page 465.

**Study Tip**

To find $x_1$ and $x_2$, use $x_1 = n_1\hat{p}_1$ and $x_2 = n_2\hat{p}_2$.

### A Two-Sample z-Test for the Difference Between Proportions

A study of 200 randomly selected people driving vehicles in Washington and 250 randomly selected people driving vehicles in Vermont shows that 93.0% of people driving vehicles in Washington and 88.8% of people driving vehicles in Vermont wear seat belts while driving. At $\alpha = 0.10$, can you reject the claim that the proportion of people who wear seat belts while driving is the same for Washington and Vermont? *(Adapted from National Highway Traffic Safety Administration)*

**Sample Statistics for Seat Belt Use**

| Washington | Vermont |
|---|---|
| $n_1 = 200$<br>$\hat{p}_1 = 0.930$<br>$x_1 = 186$ | $n_2 = 250$<br>$\hat{p}_2 = 0.888$<br>$x_2 = 222$ |

**SOLUTION**

The samples are random and independent. Also, the weighted estimate of $p_1$ and $p_2$ is

$$\bar{p} = \frac{x_1 + x_2}{n_1 + n_2} = \frac{186 + 222}{200 + 250} = \frac{408}{450} \approx 0.9067$$

and the value of $\bar{q}$ is

$$\bar{q} = 1 - \bar{p} \approx 1 - 0.9067 = 0.0933.$$

Because $n_1\bar{p} \approx 200(0.9067)$, $n_1\bar{q} \approx 200(0.0933)$, $n_2\bar{p} \approx 250(0.9067)$, and $n_2\bar{q} \approx 250(0.0933)$ are at least 5, you can use a two-sample $z$-test. The claim is "the proportion of people who wear seatbelts while driving is the same for Washington and Vermont." So, the null and alternative hypotheses are

$$H_0\colon p_1 = p_2 \text{ (Claim)} \quad \text{and} \quad H_a\colon p_1 \neq p_2.$$

Because the test is two-tailed and the level of significance is $\alpha = 0.10$, the critical values are $-z_0 = -1.645$ and $z_0 = 1.645$. The rejection regions are $z < -1.645$ and $z > 1.645$. The standardized test statistic is

$$z = \frac{(\hat{p}_1 - \hat{p}_2) - (p_1 - p_2)}{\sqrt{\bar{p}\,\bar{q}\left(\frac{1}{n_1} + \frac{1}{n_2}\right)}} \approx \frac{(0.930 - 0.888) - 0}{\sqrt{(0.9067)(0.0933)\left(\frac{1}{200} + \frac{1}{250}\right)}} \approx 1.52.$$

The figure below shows the location of the rejection regions and the standardized test statistic $z$. Because $z$ is not in the rejection region, you fail to reject the null hypothesis.

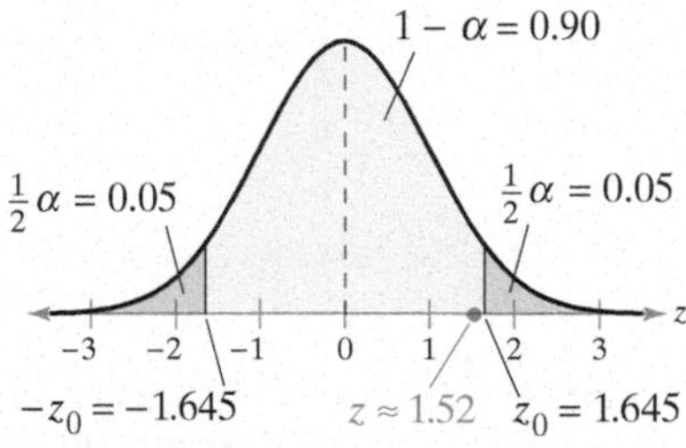


***Interpretation*** There is not enough evidence at the 10% level of significance to reject the claim that the proportion of people who wear seatbelts while driving is the same for Washington and Vermont.

**TRY IT YOURSELF 1**

Consider the results of the study discussed on page 417. At $\alpha = 0.05$, can you support the claim that there is a difference between the proportion of people who use yoga who are 40- to 49-year-olds and the proportion of people who do not use yoga who are 40- to 49-year-olds?

*Answer: Page A41*

**Study Tip**

To find $\hat{p}_1$ and $\hat{p}_2$ use

$\hat{p}_1 = \frac{x_1}{n_1}$ and $\hat{p}_2 = \frac{x_2}{n_2}$.

**Sample Statistics for Post-Traumatic Stress Disorder Treatment Medication**

| Received medication | Received placebo |
|---|---|
| $n_1 = 42$ | $n_2 = 37$ |
| $x_1 = 28$ | $x_2 = 12$ |
| $\hat{p}_1 \approx 0.6667$ | $\hat{p}_2 \approx 0.3243$ |

**EXAMPLE 2**

### A Two-Sample *z*-Test for the Difference Between Proportions

A medical research team conducted a study to test the effect of a medication to treat patients with post-traumatic stress disorder (PTSD). At the end of the study, the researchers found that of the 42 randomly selected subjects who took the medication, 28 no longer met the diagnostic criteria for PTSD. Of the 37 randomly selected subjects who took a placebo, 12 no longer met the diagnostic criteria for PTSD. At $\alpha = 0.01$, can you support the claim that the reduction rate in the diagnostic criteria for PTSD is higher for those who took the medication than for those who took the placebo? *(Source: Nature Medicine)*

**SOLUTION**

The samples are random and independent. Also, the weighted estimate of $p_1$ and $p_2$ is

$$\bar{p} = \frac{x_1 + x_2}{n_1 + n_2} = \frac{28 + 12}{42 + 37} = \frac{40}{79} \approx 0.5063$$

and the value of $\bar{q}$ is

$$\bar{q} = 1 - \bar{p} \approx 1 - 0.5063 = 0.4937.$$

Because $n_1\bar{p} \approx 42(0.5063)$, $n_1\bar{q} \approx 42(0.4937)$, $n_2\bar{p} \approx 37(0.5063)$, and $n_2\bar{q} \approx 37(0.4937)$ are at least 5, you can use a two-sample $z$-test. The claim is "the reduction rate in the diagnostic criteria for PTSD is higher for those who took the medication than for those who took the placebo." So, the null and alternative hypotheses are $H_0: p_1 \le p_2$ and $H_a: p_1 > p_2$ (claim). Because the test is right-tailed and the level of significance is $\alpha = 0.01$, the critical value is $z_0 = 2.33$. The rejection region is $z > 2.33$. The standardized test statistic is

$$z = \frac{(\hat{p}_1 - \hat{p}_2) - (p_1 - p_2)}{\sqrt{\bar{p}\,\bar{q}\left(\frac{1}{n_1} + \frac{1}{n_2}\right)}} \approx \frac{(0.6667 - 0.3243) - 0}{\sqrt{(0.5063)(0.4937)\left(\frac{1}{42} + \frac{1}{37}\right)}} \approx 3.04.$$

The figure below shows the location of the rejection region and the standardized test statistic $z$. Because $z$ is in the rejection region, you reject the null hypothesis.

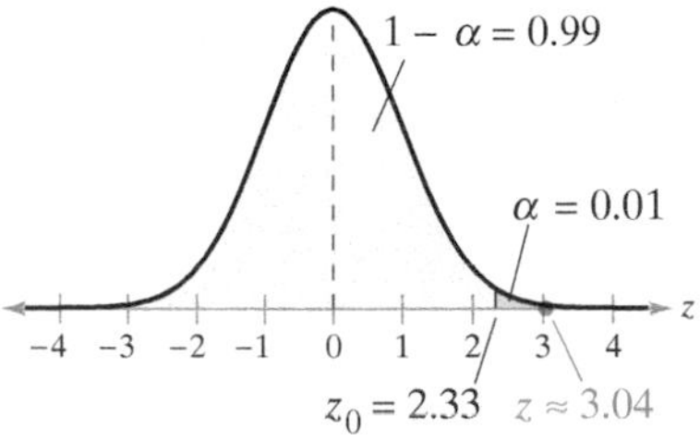


***Interpretation*** There is enough evidence at the 1% level of significance to support the claim that the reduction rate in the diagnostic criteria for PTSD is higher for those who took the medication than for those who took the placebo.

**TRY IT YOURSELF 2**

Consider the results of the study discussed on page 417. At $\alpha = 0.05$, can you reject the claim that the proportion of people who use yoga who are from the western region of the United States is greater than or equal to the proportion of people who do not use yoga who are from the western region of the United States?

*Answer: Page A41*

# 8.4 EXERCISES

For Extra Help: MyLab Statistics

## Building Basic Skills and Vocabulary

1. What conditions are necessary to use the $z$-test for testing the difference between two population proportions?

2. Explain how to perform a two-sample $z$-test for the difference between two population proportions.

*In Exercises 3–6, determine whether a normal sampling distribution can be used. If it can be used, test the claim about the difference between two population proportions $p_1$ and $p_2$ at the level of significance $\alpha$. Assume the samples are random and independent.*

3. Claim: $p_1 \neq p_2$; $\alpha = 0.01$
   Sample statistics: $x_1 = 35, n_1 = 70$ and $x_2 = 36, n_2 = 60$

4. Claim: $p_1 < p_2$; $\alpha = 0.05$
   Sample statistics: $x_1 = 471, n_1 = 785$ and $x_2 = 372, n_2 = 465$

5. Claim: $p_1 = p_2$; $\alpha = 0.10$
   Sample statistics: $x_1 = 42, n_1 = 150$ and $x_2 = 76, n_2 = 200$

6. Claim: $p_1 > p_2$; $\alpha = 0.01$
   Sample statistics: $x_1 = 6, n_1 = 20$ and $x_2 = 4, n_2 = 30$

## Using and Interpreting Concepts

**Testing the Difference Between Two Proportions** *In Exercises 7–12, (a) identify the claim and state $H_0$ and $H_a$, (b) find the critical value(s) and identify the rejection region(s), (c) find the standardized test statistic $z$, (d) decide whether to reject or fail to reject the null hypothesis, and (e) interpret the decision in the context of the original claim. Assume the samples are random and independent.*

**How Many Subjects Had 12-Week Confirmed Disability Progression and How Many Did Not?**

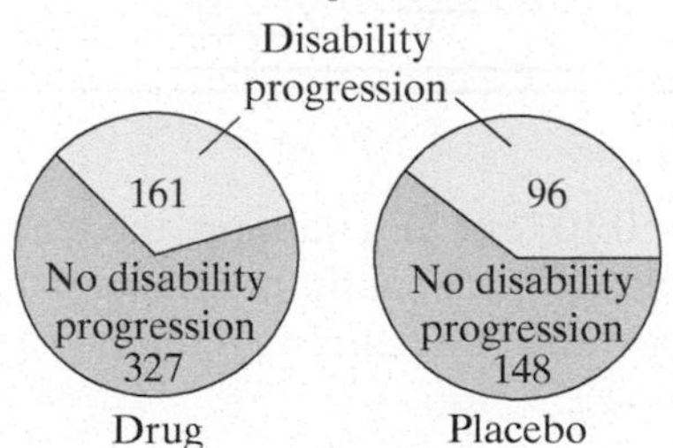


FIGURE FOR EXERCISE 7

**How Many Subjects Survived for 12 Years and How Many Did Not?**

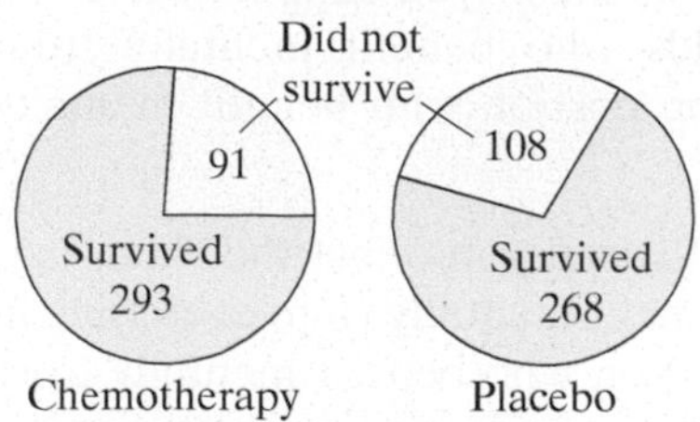


FIGURE FOR EXERCISE 8

7. **Multiple Sclerosis Drug** In a study to determine the effectiveness of using a drug to treat multiple sclerosis, 488 subjects were given the drug and 244 subjects were given a placebo. The numbers of subjects who had 12-week confirmed disability progression were tracked. The results are shown at the left. At $\alpha = 0.01$, can you support the claim that there is a difference in the proportion of subjects who had no 12-week confirmed disability progression? *(Adapted from The New England Journal of Medicine)*

8. **Cancer Drug** In a study, 760 men with recurrent prostate cancer underwent radiation with or without a type of hormone-based chemotherapy. For 24 months, 384 subjects were given the chemotherapy and 376 subjects were given a placebo. The numbers who survived and did not survive after 12 years were tracked. The results are shown at the left. At $\alpha = 0.10$, can you support the claim that the proportion of people who survived for 12 years is greater for subjects who were given the chemotherapy than for subjects who were given the placebo? *(Adapted from The New England Journal of Medicine)*

9. **Young Adults** In a survey of 3500 males ages 20 to 24 whose highest level of education is some college, but no bachelor's degree, 80.2% were employed. In a survey of 2000 males ages 20 to 24 whose highest level of education is a bachelor's degree or higher, 86.4% were employed. At $\alpha = 0.01$, can you support the claim that there is a difference in the proportion of those employed between the two groups? *(Adapted from National Center for Education Statistics)*

**10. Young Adults** In a survey of 1000 males ages 18 to 24, 13.3% were neither in school nor working. In a survey of 1000 females ages 18 to 24, 12.4% were neither in school nor working. At $\alpha = 0.10$, can you support the claim that the proportion of males ages 18 to 24 who were neither in school nor working is greater than the proportion of females ages 18 to 24 who were neither in school nor working? *(Adapted from National Center for Education Statistics)*

**11. Seat Belt Use** In a survey of 1000 drivers from the West, 934 wear a seat belt. In a survey of 1000 drivers from the Northeast, 909 wear a seat belt. At $\alpha = 0.05$, can you support the claim that the proportion of drivers who wear seat belts is greater in the West than in the Northeast? *(Adapted from National Highway Traffic Safety Administration)*

**12. Seat Belt Use** In a survey of 1000 drivers from the Midwest, 855 wear a seat belt. In a survey of 1000 drivers from the South, 909 wear a seat belt. At $\alpha = 0.10$, can you support the claim that the proportion of drivers who wear seat belts in the Midwest is less than the proportion of drivers who wear seat belts in the South? *(Adapted from National Highway Traffic Safety Administration)*

**Parks and Mental Health** *In Exercises 13–18, use the figure, which shows the percentages from a survey of two hundred 18- to 24-year-olds in the United States who say that various park and recreation activities have a positive impact on their mental health. (Adapted from National Recreation and Park Association)*

**13. Exercising and Socializing** At $\alpha = 0.10$, can you reject the claim that the proportion of 18- to 24-year-olds who benefit mentally from exercising in parks is the same as the proportion who benefit mentally from socializing in parks?

**14. Taking Classes and Enjoying Nature** At $\alpha = 0.05$, can you support the claim that the proportion of 18- to 24-year-olds who benefit mentally from taking classes in parks is less than the proportion who benefit mentally from enjoying nature in parks?

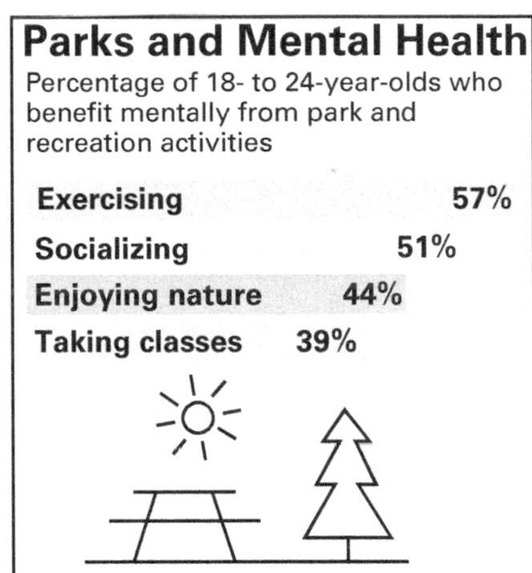

Parks and Mental Health
Percentage of 18- to 24-year-olds who benefit mentally from park and recreation activities
Exercising 57%
Socializing 51%
Enjoying nature 44%
Taking classes 39%


**15. Socializing and Enjoying Nature** At $\alpha = 0.10$, can you support the claim that the proportion of 18- to 24-year-olds who benefit mentally from socializing in parks is greater than the proportion who benefit mentally from enjoying nature in parks?

**16. Socializing and Taking Classes** At $\alpha = 0.05$, can you support the claim that the proportion of 18- to 24-year-olds who benefit mentally from socializing in parks is different from the proportion who benefit mentally from taking classes in parks?

**17. Enjoying Nature and Exercising** At $\alpha = 0.01$, can you support the claim that the proportion of 18- to 24-year-olds who benefit mentally from enjoying nature in parks is less than the proportion who benefit mentally from exercising in parks?

**18. Exercising and Taking Classes** At $\alpha = 0.01$, can you reject the claim that the proportion of 18- to 24-year-olds who benefit mentally from exercising in parks is greater than or equal to the proportion who benefit mentally from taking classes in parks?

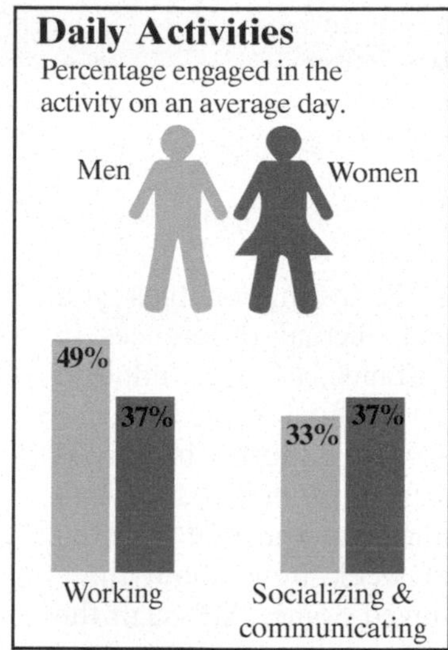


FIGURE FOR EXERCISES 19–22

**Daily Activities** *In Exercises 19–22, the results of a survey of 200 U.S. randomly selected U.S. men and 300 randomly selected U.S. women are shown in the figure at the left, which displays the percentages engaged in working or socializing and communicating on an average day. (Adapted from U.S. Bureau of Labor Statistics)*

**19. Men's Activities** At $\alpha = 0.01$, can you support the claim that the proportion of men who work is greater than the proportion of men who socialize and communicate on an average day?

**20. Women's Activities** At $\alpha = 0.01$, can you reject the claim that the proportion of women who work is the same as the proportion of women who socialize and communicate on an average day?

**21. Working** At $\alpha = 0.01$, can you support the claim that the proportion of women who work is less than the proportion of men who work on an average day?

**22. Communicating** At $\alpha = 0.10$, can you support the claim that the proportion of women who socialize and communicate is greater than the proportion of men who socialize and communicate on an average day?

## Extending Concepts

**Constructing Confidence Intervals for $p_1 - p_2$** *You can construct a confidence interval for the difference between two population proportions $p_1 - p_2$ by using the inequality below.*

$$(\hat{p}_1 - \hat{p}_2) - z_c\sqrt{\frac{\hat{p}_1\hat{q}_1}{n_1} + \frac{\hat{p}_2\hat{q}_2}{n_2}} < p_1 - p_2 < (\hat{p}_1 - \hat{p}_2) + z_c\sqrt{\frac{\hat{p}_1\hat{q}_1}{n_1} + \frac{\hat{p}_2\hat{q}_2}{n_2}}$$

*In Exercises 23–26, construct the indicated confidence interval for $p_1 - p_2$. Assume the samples are random and independent.*

**23. Students Planning to Study Visual and Performing Arts** In a survey of 10,000 students taking the SAT, 7% were planning to study visual and performing arts in college. In another survey of 8000 students taken 10 years before, 8% were planning to study visual and performing arts in college. Construct a 95% confidence interval for $p_1 - p_2$, where $p_1$ is the proportion from the recent survey and $p_2$ is the proportion from the survey taken 10 years ago. *(Adapted from College Board)*

**24. Students Undecided on an Intended College Major** In a survey of 10,000 students taking the SAT, 9% were undecided on an intended college major. In another survey of 8000 students taken 10 years before, 7% were undecided on an intended college major. Construct a 90% confidence interval for $p_1 - p_2$, where $p_1$ is the proportion from the recent survey and $p_2$ is the proportion from the survey taken 10 years ago. *(Adapted from College Board)*

**25. Critical Threats** In Section 6.3, Exercises 27 and 28, let $p_1$ be the proportion of the population of U.S. adults who see cyberterrorism as a critical threat to the country and let $p_2$ be the proportion of the population of U.S. adults who see the spread of infectious diseases as a critical threat to the country. Construct a 95% confidence interval for $p_1 - p_2$. Compare your result with the result in Section 6.3, Exercise 27.

**26. Critical Threats** Repeat Exercise 25 but with a 99% confidence interval. Describe the likelihood that equal proportions of the population see cyberterrorism and the spread of infectious diseases as critical threats in the next 10 years.

# USES AND ABUSES Statistics in the Real World

## Uses

***Hypothesis Testing with Two Samples*** Hypothesis testing enables you to determine whether differences in samples indicate actual differences in populations or are merely due to sampling error. For instance, a study conducted on about 1400 American children in a variety of settings compared the behavior of the children who attended day care with the behavior of those who stayed home. Aggressive behavior such as stealing toys, pushing other children, and starting fights was measured in both groups. The study showed that children who attended day care for more than 30 hours per week were about three times more likely to be aggressive than those who stayed home. Although the aggressive behavior observed in the study was well within the normal range for healthy children, these statistics have been used to persuade parents to keep their children at home until they start school.

## Abuses

***Confounding Variables*** The U.S. study found that the results were the same regardless of quality of the day care center and income of the family. However, the overall quality of care experienced by most of the children studied could be the problem—a survey of American day care centers that measured aspects such as number and expertise of caregivers found that only 10 percent of American day care centers provided high-quality care.

A similar study of preschoolers and aggressive behavior in Norway, where day care centers are subject to strict standards and the ratio of adult caregivers to children is high, found that the link between day care attendance and aggressive behavior was minimal. Another Norwegian study included an additional variable, differences between siblings, and found no relationship between day care attendance and behavior problems. These additional variables that are often out of the researcher's control are known as *confounding variables.*

***Study Funding*** A series of studies was conducted on various methods for reducing the number of cigarettes that smokers smoke. The study compared smokers who were simply told to smoke less and those who tried methods such as nicotine replacement therapy, electronic cigarettes, and using reduced tar, carbon, or nicotine cigarettes. Some methods were shown to be effective in reducing the number of cigarettes smoked.

Some of the studies were funded by the tobacco industry, which could profit from promoting strategies other than quitting as beneficial to smokers' health. When dealing with statistics, it is always good to know who is paying for a study, and whether the researchers are unbiased.

## EXERCISES

1. ***Confounding Variables*** A pharmaceutical company has applied for approval to market a new arthritis medication. The research involved a test group that was given the medication and another test group that was given a placebo. Describe some possible confounding variables that could influence the results of the study.
2. Medical research often involves blind and double-blind testing. Explain what these two terms mean.

# 8 Chapter Summary

| What Did You Learn? | Example(s) | Review Exercises |
|---|---|---|
| **Section 8.1** | | |
| How to determine whether two samples are independent or dependent | 1 | 1–4 |
| How to perform a two-sample $z$-test for the difference between two means $\mu_1$ and $\mu_2$ using independent samples with $\sigma_1$ and $\sigma_2$ known $z = \dfrac{(\bar{x}_1 - \bar{x}_2) - (\mu_1 - \mu_2)}{\sigma_{\bar{x}_1 - \bar{x}_2}}$ | 2, 3 | 5–10 |
| **Section 8.2** | | |
| How to perform a two-sample $t$-test for the difference between two means $\mu_1$ and $\mu_2$ using independent samples with $\sigma_1$ and $\sigma_2$ unknown $t = \dfrac{(\bar{x}_1 - \bar{x}_2) - (\mu_1 - \mu_2)}{s_{\bar{x}_1 - \bar{x}_2}}$ | 1, 2 | 11–18 |
| **Section 8.3** | | |
| How to perform a $t$-test to test the mean of the differences for a population of paired data $t = \dfrac{\bar{d} - \mu_d}{s_d / \sqrt{n}}$ | 1, 2 | 19–24 |
| **Section 8.4** | | |
| How to perform a two-sample $z$-test for the difference between two population proportions $p_1$ and $p_2$ $z = \dfrac{(\hat{p}_1 - \hat{p}_2) - (p_1 - p_2)}{\sqrt{\bar{p}\,\bar{q}\left(\frac{1}{n_1} + \frac{1}{n_2}\right)}}$ | 1, 2 | 25–30 |

## Study Strategies

**Taking Text Notes** Notes can be a vitally important aid to actively learning course material. How you take notes is a personal choice. Three common systems for taking notes include the outline system, the Cornell system, and the concept map system.

- The outline system provides clear structure. Ideas are organized by level of importance. Roman numerals are used to list key ideas to signify that they are more important than the supporting details. The outline system works well for students who think linearly or learn verbally.
- In the Cornell system, a block of notes is structured with a *recall* or *cue* column on the left, a *notes* column on the right, and a *summary* area at the bottom. Such a structure allows you to easily test yourself by covering either the *recall* or the *notes* column.
- The concept map system uses different shapes to help identify levels of importance and connections. Because it uses a visual style to show relationships between ideas, it is highly suited for students who learn visually.

For more information, visit Skills for Success in the accompanying MyLab course.

# 8 Review Exercises

## Section 8.1

*In Exercises 1–4, classify the two samples as independent or dependent and justify your answer.*

**1.** Sample 1: The heights of 37 children
Sample 2: The heights of the same 37 children after 1 year

**2.** Sample 1: The weights of 45 oranges
Sample 2: The weights of 40 grapefruits

**3.** Sample 1: The retail prices of 20 motorcycles
Sample 2: The retail prices of 20 minivans

**4.** Sample 1: The fuel efficiencies of 12 cars
Sample 2: The fuel efficiencies of the same 12 cars using an alternative fuel

*In Exercises 5–8, test the claim about the difference between two population means $\mu_1$ and $\mu_2$ at the level of significance $\alpha$. Assume the samples are random and independent, and the populations are normally distributed.*

**5.** Claim: $\mu_1 \geq \mu_2$; $\alpha = 0.05$
Population statistics: $\sigma_1 = 0.30$ and $\sigma_2 = 0.23$
Sample statistics: $\bar{x}_1 = 1.28$, $n_1 = 96$ and $\bar{x}_2 = 1.34$, $n_2 = 85$

**6.** Claim: $\mu_1 = \mu_2$; $\alpha = 0.01$
Population statistics: $\sigma_1 = 52$ and $\sigma_2 = 68$
Sample statistics: $\bar{x}_1 = 5595$, $n_1 = 156$ and $\bar{x}_2 = 5575$, $n_2 = 216$

**7.** Claim: $\mu_1 < \mu_2$; $\alpha = 0.10$
Population statistics: $\sigma_1 = 0.11$ and $\sigma_2 = 0.10$
Sample statistics: $\bar{x}_1 = 0.28$, $n_1 = 41$ and $\bar{x}_2 = 0.33$, $n_2 = 34$

**8.** Claim: $\mu_1 \neq \mu_2$; $\alpha = 0.05$
Population statistics: $\sigma_1 = 14$ and $\sigma_2 = 15$
Sample statistics: $\bar{x}_1 = 87$, $n_1 = 410$ and $\bar{x}_2 = 85$, $n_2 = 340$

*In Exercises 9 and 10, (a) identify the claim and state $H_0$ and $H_a$, (b) find the critical value(s) and identify the rejection region(s), (c) find the standardized test statistic z, (d) decide whether to reject or fail to reject the null hypothesis, and (e) interpret the decision in the context of the original claim. Assume the samples are random and independent, and the populations are normally distributed.*

**9.** A researcher claims that the mean sodium content of sandwiches at Restaurant A is less than the mean sodium content of sandwiches at Restaurant B. The mean sodium content of 22 randomly selected sandwiches at Restaurant A is 670 milligrams. Assume the population standard deviation is 20 milligrams. The mean sodium content of 28 randomly selected sandwiches at Restaurant B is 690 milligrams. Assume the population standard deviation is 30 milligrams. At $\alpha = 0.05$, is there enough evidence to support the claim?

**10.** A career counselor claims that the mean annual salaries of entry level paralegals in Dayton, Ohio, and Coventry, Rhode Island, are the same. The mean annual salary of 40 randomly selected entry level paralegals in Dayton is \$58,180. Assume the population standard deviation is \$10,990. The mean annual salary of 35 randomly selected entry level paralegals in Coventry is \$61,120. Assume the population standard deviation is \$11,850. At $\alpha = 0.10$, is there enough evidence to reject the counselor's claim? *(Adapted from Salary.com)*

## Section 8.2

*In Exercises 11–16, test the claim about the difference between two population means $\mu_1$ and $\mu_2$ at the level of significance $\alpha$. Assume the samples are random and independent, and the populations are normally distributed.*

**11.** Claim: $\mu_1 = \mu_2$; $\alpha = 0.05$. Assume $\sigma_1^2 = \sigma_2^2$
Sample statistics: $\bar{x}_1 = 228$, $s_1 = 27$, $n_1 = 20$ and
$\bar{x}_2 = 207$, $s_2 = 25$, $n_2 = 13$

**12.** Claim: $\mu_1 < \mu_2$; $\alpha = 0.10$. Assume $\sigma_1^2 \neq \sigma_2^2$
Sample statistics: $\bar{x}_1 = 0.015$, $s_1 = 0.011$, $n_1 = 8$ and
$\bar{x}_2 = 0.019$, $s_2 = 0.004$, $n_2 = 6$

**13.** Claim: $\mu_1 \leq \mu_2$; $\alpha = 0.10$. Assume $\sigma_1^2 \neq \sigma_2^2$
Sample statistics: $\bar{x}_1 = 664.5$, $s_1 = 2.4$, $n_1 = 40$ and
$\bar{x}_2 = 665.5$, $s_2 = 4.1$, $n_2 = 40$

**14.** Claim: $\mu_1 \geq \mu_2$; $\alpha = 0.01$. Assume $\sigma_1^2 = \sigma_2^2$
Sample statistics: $\bar{x}_1 = 44.5$, $s_1 = 5.85$, $n_1 = 17$ and
$\bar{x}_2 = 49.1$, $s_2 = 5.25$, $n_2 = 18$

**15.** Claim: $\mu_1 \neq \mu_2$; $\alpha = 0.01$. Assume $\sigma_1^2 = \sigma_2^2$
Sample statistics: $\bar{x}_1 = 61$, $s_1 = 3.3$, $n_1 = 5$ and
$\bar{x}_2 = 55$, $s_2 = 1.2$, $n_2 = 7$

**16.** Claim: $\mu_1 > \mu_2$; $\alpha = 0.10$. Assume $\sigma_1^2 \neq \sigma_2^2$
Sample statistics: $\bar{x}_1 = 520$, $s_1 = 25$, $n_1 = 7$ and
$\bar{x}_2 = 500$, $s_2 = 55$, $n_2 = 6$

*In Exercises 17 and 18, (a) identify the claim and state $H_0$ and $H_a$, (b) find the critical value(s) and identify the rejection region(s), (c) find the standardized test statistic t, (d) decide whether to reject or fail to reject the null hypothesis, and (e) interpret the decision in the context of the original claim. Assume the samples are random and independent, and the populations are normally distributed.*

**17.** A new method of teaching mathematics is being tested on sixth grade students. A group of sixth grade students is taught using the new curriculum. A control group of sixth grade students is taught using the old curriculum. The mathematics test scores for the two groups are shown in the back-to-back stem-and-leaf plot.

| Old Curriculum | | New Curriculum |
|---:|:---:|:---|
| 4 5 8 | 0 | |
| 0 1 1 5 7 | 1 | |
| 1 6 | 2 | 2 4 5 7 7 |
| 0 1 2 8 | 3 | 4 7 |
| 0 2 6 9 | 4 | 2 5 6 7 |
| 1 3 4 9 | 5 | 1 5 7 |
| 0 7 | 6 | 2 3 5 6 6 7 |
| 3 3 3 4 4 6 8 | 7 | 0 0 2 5 5 6 |
| 1 9 | 8 | 2 3 6 6 9 |
| 4 4 4 | 9 | 0 1 4 6 8 |

Key: 6|2|2 = 26 for old curriculum and
22 for new curriculum

At $\alpha = 0.05$, is there enough evidence to support the claim that the new method of teaching mathematics produces higher mathematics test scores than the old method does? Assume the population variances are equal.

**18.** A real estate agent claims that there is no difference between the mean household incomes of two neighborhoods. The mean income of 12 randomly selected households from the first neighborhood is $52,750 with a standard deviation of $2900. In the second neighborhood, 10 randomly selected households have a mean income of $51,200 with a standard deviation of $2225. At $\alpha = 0.01$, can you reject the real estate agent's claim? Assume the population variances are equal.

## Section 8.3

*In Exercises 19–22, test the claim about the mean of the differences for a population of paired data at the level of significance $\alpha$. Assume the samples are random and dependent, and the populations are normally distributed.*

**19.** Claim: $\mu_d = 0$; $\alpha = 0.01$. Sample statistics: $\bar{d} = 8.5$, $s_d = 10.7$, $n = 16$

**20.** Claim: $\mu_d < 0$; $\alpha = 0.10$. Sample statistics: $\bar{d} = 3.2$, $s_d = 5.68$, $n = 25$

**21.** Claim: $\mu_d \leq 0$; $\alpha = 0.10$. Sample statistics: $\bar{d} = 10.3$, $s_d = 18.19$, $n = 33$

**22.** Claim: $\mu_d \neq 0$; $\alpha = 0.05$. Sample statistics: $\bar{d} = 17.5$, $s_d = 4.05$, $n = 37$

*In Exercises 23 and 24, (a) identify the claim and state $H_0$ and $H_a$, (b) find the critical value(s) and identify the rejection region(s), (c) calculate $\bar{d}$ and $s_d$, (d) find the standardized test statistic t, (e) decide whether to reject or fail to reject the null hypothesis, and (f) interpret the decision in the context of the original claim. Assume the samples are random and dependent, and the populations are normally distributed.*

**23.** A sports statistician claims that the numbers of runs scored in a season by NCAA Division 1 baseball teams changed from 2019 to 2021. The table shows the numbers of runs scored by 10 randomly selected NCAA Division 1 baseball teams in the 2019 and 2021 seasons. At $\alpha = 0.05$, is there enough evidence to support the sports statistician's claim? *(Source: NCAA)*

| **Team** | 1 | 2 | 3 | 4 | 5 |
|---|---|---|---|---|---|
| **Runs (2019)** | 578 | 377 | 312 | 287 | 387 |
| **Runs (2021)** | 454 | 345 | 264 | 260 | 363 |

| **Team** | 6 | 7 | 8 | 9 | 10 |
|---|---|---|---|---|---|
| **Runs (2019)** | 320 | 447 | 334 | 288 | 228 |
| **Runs (2021)** | 370 | 304 | 313 | 354 | 150 |

**24.** A physical fitness instructor claims that a weight loss supplement will help users lose weight after two weeks. The table shows the weights (in pounds) of 9 adults before using the supplement and two weeks after using the supplement. At $\alpha = 0.10$, is there enough evidence to support the physical fitness instructor's claim?

| **User** | 1 | 2 | 3 | 4 | 5 | 6 | 7 | 8 | 9 |
|---|---|---|---|---|---|---|---|---|---|
| **Weight (before)** | 228 | 210 | 245 | 272 | 203 | 198 | 256 | 217 | 240 |
| **Weight (after)** | 225 | 208 | 242 | 270 | 205 | 196 | 250 | 220 | 240 |

## Section 8.4

*In Exercises 25–28, determine whether a normal sampling distribution can be used. If it can be used, test the claim about the difference between two population proportions $p_1$ and $p_2$ at the level of significance $\alpha$. Assume the samples are random and independent.*

**25.** Claim: $p_1 = p_2$; $\alpha = 0.05$
Sample statistics: $x_1 = 425$, $n_1 = 840$ and $x_2 = 410$, $n_2 = 760$

**26.** Claim: $p_1 \leq p_2$; $\alpha = 0.01$
Sample statistics: $x_1 = 36$, $n_1 = 100$ and $x_2 = 46$, $n_2 = 200$

**27.** Claim: $p_1 > p_2$; $\alpha = 0.10$
Sample statistics: $x_1 = 261$, $n_1 = 556$ and $x_2 = 207$, $n_2 = 483$

**28.** Claim: $p_1 < p_2$; $\alpha = 0.05$
Sample statistics: $x_1 = 86$, $n_1 = 900$ and $x_2 = 107$, $n_2 = 1200$

*In Exercises 29 and 30, (a) identify the claim and state $H_0$ and $H_a$, (b) find the critical value(s) and identify the rejection region(s), (c) find the standardized test statistic z, (d) decide whether to reject or fail to reject the null hypothesis, and (e) interpret the decision in the context of the original claim. Assume the samples are random and independent.*

**29.** A medical research team conducted a study to test the effect of a drug used to treat a type of inflammation. In the study, 68 subjects took the drug and 68 subjects took a placebo. The results are shown below. At $\alpha = 0.05$, can you reject the claim that the proportion of subjects who had at least 24 weeks of accrued remission is the same for the two groups? *(Source: The New England Journal of Medicine)*

**Do You Have At Least 24 Weeks of Accrued Remission?**

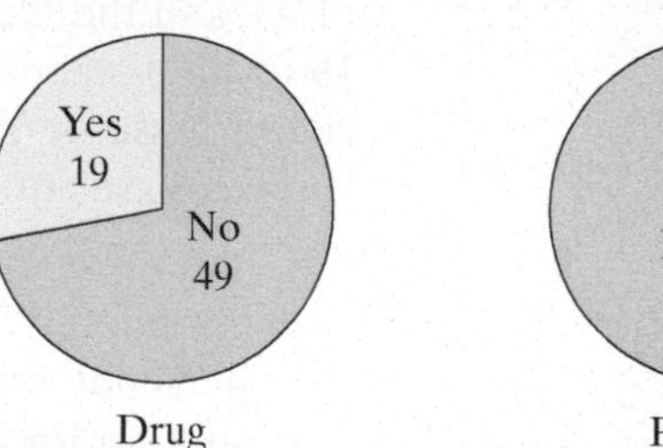


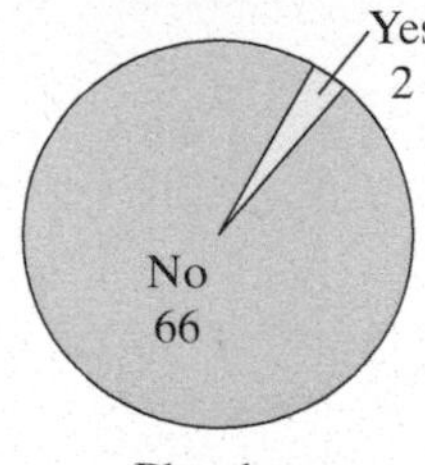


**30.** A traffic safety research team conducted a survey over two years on the use of motorcycle helmets. In the survey, motorcyclists in states where helmet use is required were asked whether they use helmets that are compliant with federal safety regulations. In 2019, 389 motorcyclists were surveyed and in 2020, 338 motorcyclists were surveyed. The results are shown below. At $\alpha = 0.01$, can you support the claim that the proportion of motorcyclists in states where helmet use is required who use such helmets decreased from 2019 to 2020? *(Adapted from National Highway Traffic Safety Administration)*

**Do You Use Helmets That Are Compliant with Federal Safety Regulations?**

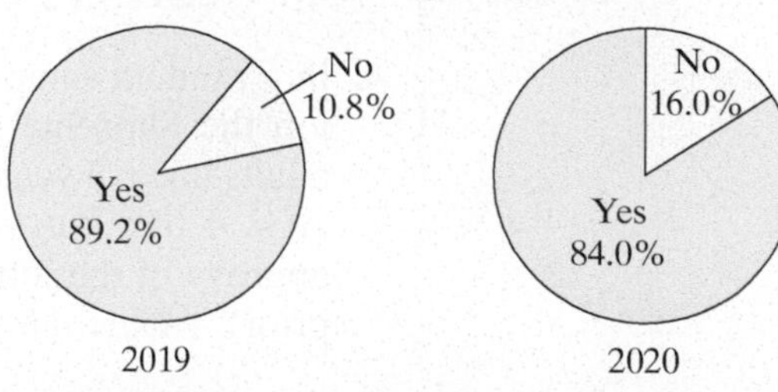

# 8 Chapter Quiz

*Take this quiz as you would take a quiz in class. After you are done, check your work against the answers given in the back of the book.*

*For each exercise, perform the steps below.*

*(a) Identify the claim and state $H_0$ and $H_a$.*

*(b) Determine whether the hypothesis test is left-tailed, right-tailed, or two-tailed, and whether to use a z-test or a t-test. Explain your reasoning.*

*(c) Find the critical value(s) and identify the rejection region(s).*

*(d) Find the appropriate standardized test statistic.*

*(e) Decide whether to reject or fail to reject the null hypothesis.*

*(f) Interpret the decision in the context of the original claim.*

**1.** The mean score on a reading assessment test for 49 randomly selected male high school students was 279. Assume the population standard deviation is 41. The mean score on the same test for 50 randomly selected female high school students was 292. Assume the population standard deviation is 39. At $\alpha = 0.05$, can you support the claim that the mean score on the reading assessment test for male high school students is less than the mean score for female high school students? *(Adapted from National Center for Education Statistics)*

**2.** A music teacher claims that the mean scores on a music assessment test for eighth grade students in public and private schools are equal. The mean score for 13 randomly selected public school students is 146 with a standard deviation of 49, and the mean score for 15 randomly selected private school students is 160 with a standard deviation of 42. At $\alpha = 0.1$, can you reject the teacher's claim? Assume the populations are normally distributed and the population variances are equal. *(Adapted from National Center for Education Statistics)*

**3.** The table shows the credit scores for 12 randomly selected adults who are considered high-risk borrowers before and two years after they attend a personal finance seminar. At $\alpha = 0.01$, is there enough evidence to support the claim that the personal finance seminar helps adults increase their credit scores? Assume the populations are normally distributed.

| **Adult** | 1 | 2 | 3 | 4 | 5 | 6 |
|---|---|---|---|---|---|---|
| **Credit score (before seminar)** | 608 | 620 | 610 | 650 | 640 | 680 |
| **Credit score (after seminar)** | 646 | 692 | 715 | 669 | 725 | 786 |

| **Adult** | 7 | 8 | 9 | 10 | 11 | 12 |
|---|---|---|---|---|---|---|
| **Credit score (before seminar)** | 655 | 602 | 644 | 656 | 632 | 664 |
| **Credit score (after seminar)** | 700 | 650 | 660 | 650 | 680 | 702 |

**4.** In a random sample of 1007 U.S. adults in a recent year, 584 approve of the job the Supreme Court is doing. In another random sample of 1022 U.S. adults taken 3 years prior, 501 approve of the job the Supreme Court is doing. At $\alpha = 0.05$, can you support the claim that the proportion of U.S. adults who approve of the job the Supreme Court is doing is greater than it was 3 years prior? *(Adapted from Gallup)*

# 8 Chapter Test

*Take this test as you would take a test in class.*

*For each exercise, perform the steps below.*

(a) *Identify the claim and state $H_0$ and $H_a$.*

(b) *Determine whether the hypothesis test is left-tailed, right-tailed, or two-tailed, and whether to use a z-test or a t-test. Explain your reasoning.*

(c) *Find the critical value(s) and identify the rejection region(s).*

(d) *Find the appropriate standardized test statistic.*

(e) *Decide whether to reject or fail to reject the null hypothesis.*

(f) *Interpret the decision in the context of the original claim.*

**1.** In a survey of 5000 students taking the SAT, 350 were undecided on an intended college major. In another survey of 12,000 students taken 10 years before, 360 were undecided on an intended college major. At $\alpha = 0.10$, can you reject the claim that the proportion of students taking the SAT who are undecided on an intended college major has not changed? *(Adapted from College Board)*

**2.** A real estate agency says that the mean home sales price in Olathe, Kansas, is greater than in Rolla, Missouri. The mean home sales price for 39 homes in Olathe is $392,453. Assume the population standard deviation is $224,902. The mean home sales price for 38 homes in Rolla is $285,787. Assume the population standard deviation is $330,578. At $\alpha = 0.05$, is there enough evidence to support the agency's claim? *(Adapted from Realtor.com)*

**3.** A physical therapist suggests that soft tissue massage therapy helps to reduce the lengths of time patients suffer from headaches. The table shows the numbers of hours per day 18 patients suffered from headaches before and after 6 weeks of receiving treatment. At $\alpha = 0.05$, is there enough evidence to support the therapist's claim? Assume the populations are normally distributed. *(Adapted from Annals of Musculoskeletal Medicine)*

| **Patient** | 1 | 2 | 3 | 4 | 5 | 6 | 7 | 8 | 9 |
|---|---|---|---|---|---|---|---|---|---|
| **Hours (before)** | 5.2 | 5.1 | 4.9 | 1.6 | 6.1 | 2.3 | 4.6 | 5.2 | 3.1 |
| **Hours (after)** | 3.5 | 3.3 | 3.7 | 2.3 | 2.7 | 2.4 | 2.1 | 2.5 | 2.8 |

| **Patient** | 10 | 11 | 12 | 13 | 14 | 15 | 16 | 17 | 18 |
|---|---|---|---|---|---|---|---|---|---|
| **Hours (before)** | 4.4 | 4.2 | 5.4 | 3.3 | 5.2 | 3.7 | 2.6 | 2.7 | 2.6 |
| **Hours (after)** | 4.1 | 3.0 | 2.4 | 2.4 | 2.7 | 2.6 | 2.4 | 2.7 | 2.4 |

**4.** A demographics researcher claims that the mean household income in a recent year is different for native-born households and foreign-born households. A sample of 18 native-born households has a mean household income of $69,474 and a standard deviation of $21,249. A sample of 21 foreign-born households has a mean household income of $64,900 and a standard deviation of $17,896. At $\alpha = 0.01$, can you support the demographics researcher's claim? Assume the populations are normally distributed and the population variances are not equal. *(Adapted from U.S. Census Bureau)*

# REAL STATISTICS REAL DECISIONS

# Putting it all together

The U.S. Department of Health & Human Services (HHS) is a department of the U.S. federal government with the motto "Improving the health, safety, and well-being of America." The Centers for Medicare & Medicaid Services work within the HHS to help administer Medicare, Medicaid, and other health programs. They also gather information about health expenditure, program utilization, and other data. One area studied is the average amount of time that Medicare patients spend at short-stay hospitals.

You work for the Centers for Medicare & Medicaid Services. You want to test the claim that the mean length of stay for inpatients in 2019 is different than what it was in 2000 from a random sample of inpatient records. The results for several inpatients from 2000 and 2019 are shown in the histograms.

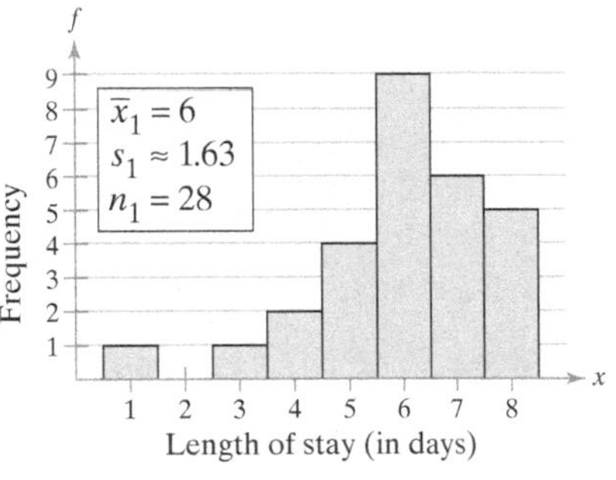


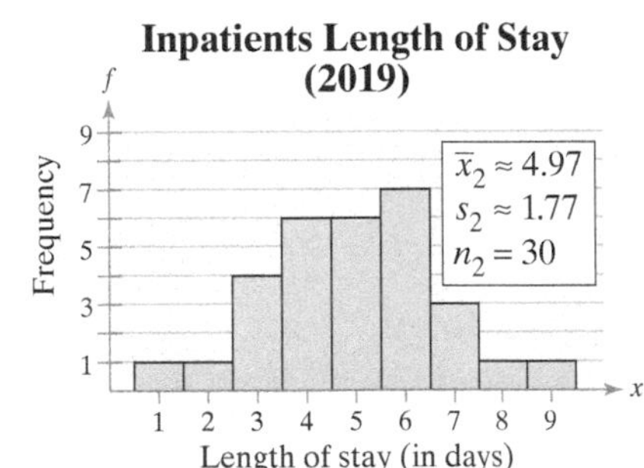


## EXERCISES

1. ***How Could You Do It?***

   Explain how you could use each sampling technique to select the sample for the study.

   (a) stratified sample

   (b) cluster sample

   (c) systematic sample

   (d) simple random sample

2. ***Choosing a Sampling Technique***

   (a) Which sampling technique in Exercise 1 would you choose to implement for the study? Why?

   (b) Identify possible flaws or biases in your study.

3. ***Choosing a Test***

   To test the claim that there is a difference in the mean length of hospital stays, should you use a $z$-test or a $t$-test? Are the samples independent or dependent? Do you need to know what each population's distribution is? Do you need to know anything about the population variances?

4. ***Testing a Mean***

   Test the claim that there is a difference in the mean length of hospital stays for inpatients. Assume the populations are normal and the population variances are equal. Use $\alpha = 0.05$. Interpret the test's decision. Does the decision support the claim?

# TECHNOLOGY

MINITAB | EXCEL | TI-84 PLUS

# Tails over Heads

In the article "Tails over Heads" in the *Washington Post* (Oct. 13, 1996), journalist William Casey describes one of his hobbies—keeping track of every coin he finds on the street! From January 1, 1985, until the article was written, Casey found 11,902 coins.

As each coin is found, Casey records the time, date, location, value, mint location, and whether the coin is lying heads up or tails up. In the article, Casey notes that 6130 coins were found tails up and 5772 were found heads up. Of the 11,902 coins found, 43 were minted in San Francisco, 7133 were minted in Philadelphia, and 4726 were minted in Denver.

A simulation of Casey's experiment can be done in Minitab as shown below. A frequency histogram of one simulation's results is shown at the right.

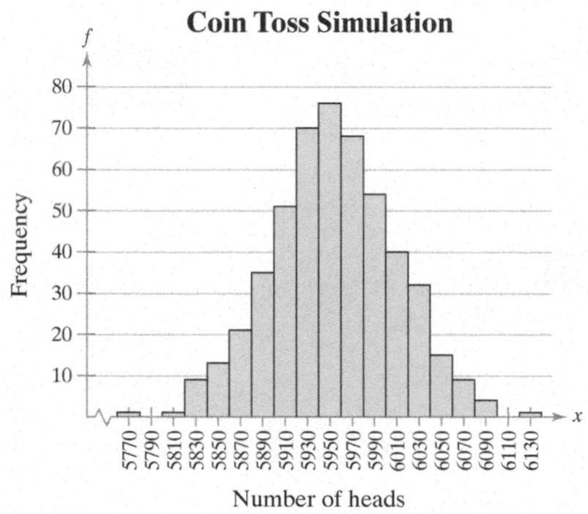


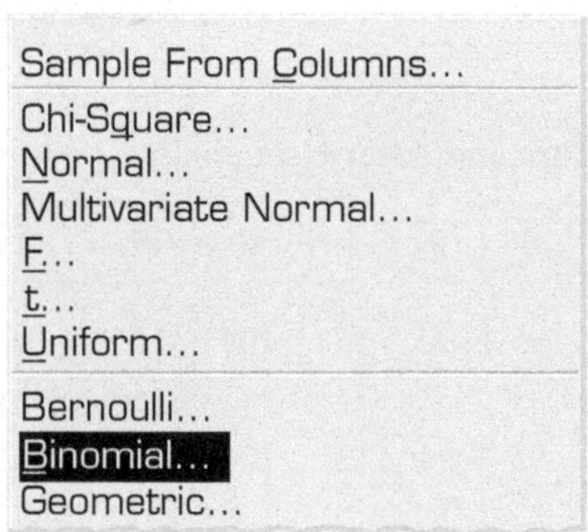


**MINITAB**

Number of rows of data to generate: 500

Store in column(s): C1

Number of trials: 11902

Event probability: .5

## EXERCISES

1. Use technology to perform a one-sample $z$-test to test the hypothesis that the proportion of coins found lying heads up is 0.5. Use $\alpha = 0.01$. Use Casey's data as your sample and write your conclusion as a sentence.
2. Do Casey's data differ significantly from chance? If so, what might be the reason?
3. In the simulation shown above, what percent of the trials had heads less than or equal to the number of heads in Casey's data? Use technology to repeat the simulation. Are your results comparable?

*In Exercises 4 and 5, use technology to perform a two-sample t-test to determine whether there is a difference in the mint dates and in the values of coins found on a street from 1985 through 1996 for the two mint locations. Write your conclusion as a sentence. Use* $\alpha = 0.05$.

4. Mint dates of coins (years)
   Philadelphia: $\bar{x}_1 = 1984.8$ $s_1 = 8.6$
   Denver: $\bar{x}_2 = 1983.4$ $s_2 = 8.4$
   Assume population variances are equal.
5. Value of coins (dollars)
   Philadelphia: $\bar{x}_1 = \$0.034$ $s_1 = \$0.054$
   Denver: $\bar{x}_2 = \$0.033$ $s_2 = \$0.052$
   Assume population variances are not equal.

Extended solutions are given in the technology manuals that accompany this text. Technical instruction is provided for Minitab, Excel, and the TI-84 Plus.

# 8 Using Technology to Perform Two-Sample Hypothesis Tests

Here are some Minitab and TI-84 Plus printouts for several examples in this chapter.

See Example 1, page 430.

Display Descriptive Statistics...
Store Descriptive Statistics...
Graphical Summary...

1-Sample Z...
1-Sample t...
**2-Sample t...**
Paired t...

1 Proportion...
2 Proportions...

**MINITAB**

**Two-Sample T-Test and CI**

```
Sample    N    Mean    StDev    SE Mean
1         8   473.0     39.7         14
2        18   459.0     24.5        5.8

Difference = mu (1) − mu (2)
Estimate for difference: 14.0
90% CI for difference: (−13.8, 41.8)
T-Test of difference = 0 (vs not =): T-Value = 0.92  P-Value = 0.380  DF = 9
```

See Example 1, page 439.

**Vertical Jump Heights, Before and After Using Shoes**

| **Person** | 1 | 2 | 3 | 4 | 5 | 6 | 7 | 8 |
|---|---|---|---|---|---|---|---|---|
| **Average golf score (before taking lessons)** | 96 | 95 | 95 | 99 | 87 | 104 | 105 | 94 |
| **Average golf score (after taking lessons)** | 89 | 90 | 95 | 94 | 91 | 100 | 103 | 100 |

Display Descriptive Statistics...
Store Descriptive Statistics...
Graphical Summary...

1-Sample Z...
1-Sample t...
2-Sample t...
**Paired t...**

1 Proportion...
2 Proportions...

**MINITAB**

**Paired T-Test and CI: Before, After**

```
Paired T for Before − After
              N     Mean    StDev    SE Mean
Before        8    96.88     5.79       2.05
After         8    95.25     5.23       1.85
Difference    8     1.63     4.63       1.64

90% upper bound for mean difference: −0.69
T-Test of mean difference = 0 (vs > 0): T-Value = 0.99  P-Value = 0.177
```

See Example 2, page 422.

**TI-84 PLUS**

EDIT CALC **TESTS**
1: Z–Test...
2: T–Test...
**3:** 2–SampZTest...
4: 2–SampTTest...
5: 1–PropZTest...
6: 2–PropZTest...
7↓ ZInterval...

**TI-84 PLUS**

**2-SampZTest**
Inpt:Data **Stats**
$\sigma$1:960
$\sigma$2:845
$\bar{x}$1:5271
n1:250
$\bar{x}$2:5121
↓n2:250

**TI-84 PLUS**

**2-SampZTest**
↑$\sigma$2:845
$\bar{x}$1:5271
n1:250
$\bar{x}$2:5121
n2:250
μ1:**≠μ2** <μ2 >μ2
Calculate Draw

**TI-84 PLUS**

**2-SampZTest**
$\mu_1 \neq \mu_2$
z=1.854468212
p=.0636720795
$\bar{x}_1$=5271
$\bar{x}_2$=5121
↓$n_1$=250

See Example 2, page 431.

**TI-84 PLUS**

EDIT CALC **TESTS**
1: Z–Test...
2: T–Test...
3: 2–SampZTest...
**4:** 2–SampTTest...
5: 1–PropZTest...
6: 2–PropZTest...
7↓ ZInterval...

**TI-84 PLUS**

**2-SampTTest**
Inpt:Data **Stats**
$\bar{x}$1:.52
Sx1:.05
n1:30
$\bar{x}$2:.55
Sx2:.07
↓n2:32

**TI-84 PLUS**

**2-SampTTest**
↑n1:30
$\bar{x}$2:.55
Sx2:.07
n2:32
μ1:≠μ2 **<μ2** >μ2
Pooled:No **Yes**
Calculate Draw

**TI-84 PLUS**

**2-SampTTest**
$\mu_1 < \mu_2$
t=−1.930301843
p=.0291499618
df=60
$\bar{x}_1$=.52
↓$\bar{x}_2$=.55

See Example 1, page 449.

**TI-84 PLUS**

EDIT CALC **TESTS**
1: Z–Test...
2: T–Test...
3: 2–SampZTest...
4: 2–SampTTest...
5: 1–PropZTest...
**6:** 2–PropZTest...
7↓ ZInterval...

**TI-84 PLUS**

**2-PropZTest**
x1:186
n1:200
x2:222
n2:250
p1:**≠p2** <p2 >p2
Calculate Draw

**TI-84 PLUS**

**2-PropZTest**
$p_1 \neq p_2$
z=1.521898969
p=.12803444
$\hat{p}_1$=.93
$\hat{p}_2$=.888
↓$\hat{p}$=.9066666667

# CHAPTERS 6–8
# CUMULATIVE REVIEW

**1.** In a survey of 4860 U.S. adults, 77% said they would date or have already dated someone whose religion was different from theirs. *(Source: Pew Research Center)*

(a) Construct a 95% confidence interval for the proportion of U.S. adults who say they would date or have already dated someone whose religion was different from theirs.

(b) A researcher claims that more than 75% of U.S. adults say they would date or have already dated someone whose religion was different from theirs. At $\alpha = 0.05$, can you support the researcher's claim? Interpret the decision in the context of the original claim.

**2. Gas Mileage** The table shows the gas mileages (in miles per gallon) of eight cars with and without using a fuel additive. At $\alpha = 0.10$, is there enough evidence to conclude that the additive improved gas mileage? Assume the populations are normally distributed.

| **Car** | 1 | 2 | 3 | 4 | 5 | 6 | 7 | 8 |
|---|---|---|---|---|---|---|---|---|
| **Gas mileage (without fuel additive)** | 23.1 | 25.4 | 21.9 | 24.3 | 19.9 | 21.2 | 25.9 | 24.8 |
| **Gas mileage (with fuel additive)** | 23.6 | 27.7 | 23.6 | 26.8 | 22.1 | 22.4 | 26.3 | 26.6 |

*In Exercises 3–6, construct the indicated confidence interval for the population mean $\mu$. Which distribution did you use to create the confidence interval?*

**3.** $c = 0.95, \bar{x} = 26.97, \sigma = 3.4, n = 42$

**4.** $c = 0.95, \bar{x} = 3.46, s = 1.63, n = 16$

**5.** $c = 0.99, \bar{x} = 12.1, s = 2.64, n = 26$

**6.** $c = 0.90, \bar{x} = 8.21, \sigma = 0.62, n = 8$

*In Exercises 7–10, the statement represents a claim. Write its complement and state which is $H_0$ and which is $H_a$.*

**7.** $\mu < 33$

**8.** $p \geq 0.19$

**9.** $\sigma = 0.63$

**10.** $\mu \neq 2.28$

**11.** A pediatrician claims that the mean birth weight of a single-birth baby is greater than the mean birth weight of a baby that has a twin. The mean birth weight of a random sample of 85 single-birth babies is 3086 grams. Assume the population standard deviation is 563 grams. The mean birth weight of a random sample of 68 babies that have a twin is 2263 grams. Assume the population standard deviation is 624 grams. At $\alpha = 0.10$, can you support the pediatrician's claim? Interpret the decision in the context of the original claim.

**12.** The mean room rate for two adults for a random sample of 26 three-star hotels in Cincinnati has a sample standard deviation of \$31. Assume the population is normally distributed. *(Adapted from Expedia)*

(a) Construct a 99% confidence interval for the population variance.

(b) Construct a 99% confidence interval for the population standard deviation.

(c) A travel analyst claims that the standard deviation of the mean room rate for two adults at three-star hotels in Cincinnati is at most \$30. At $\alpha = 0.01$, can you reject the travel analyst's claim? Interpret the decision in the context of the original claim.

**13.** An education organization claims that the mean SAT scores for male athletes and male non-athletes at a college are different. A random sample of 26 male athletes at the college has a mean SAT score of 1189 and a standard deviation of 218. A random sample of 18 male non-athletes at the college has a mean SAT score of 1376 and a standard deviation of 186. At $\alpha = 0.05$, can you support the organization's claim? Interpret the decision in the context of the original claim. Assume the populations are normally distributed and the population variances are equal.

**14.** The annual earnings (in dollars) for 30 randomly selected locksmiths are shown below. Assume the population is normally distributed. *(Adapted from Salary.com)*

| | | | | | |
|---|---|---|---|---|---|
| 48,694 | 46,856 | 42,912 | 61,672 | 71,112 | 54,861 |
| 69,454 | 71,841 | 59,751 | 69,612 | 54,284 | 52,166 |
| 66,360 | 48,164 | 65,272 | 35,250 | 61,127 | 65,397 |
| 58,925 | 58,916 | 59,017 | 53,070 | 45,199 | 69,941 |
| 69,492 | 57,085 | 53,829 | 52,692 | 68,298 | 53,792 |

(a) Construct a 95% confidence interval for the population mean annual earnings for locksmiths.

(b) A researcher claims that the mean annual earnings for locksmiths is \$55,000. At $\alpha = 0.05$, can you reject the researcher's claim? Interpret the decision in the context of the original claim.

**15.** A medical research team studied the use of a marijuana extract to treat children with an epilepsy disorder. Of the 52 children who were given the extract, the number of convulsive seizures was reduced from 12 to 6 per month. Of the 56 children who were given a placebo, the number of convulsive seizures was reduced from 15 to 14 per month. At $\alpha = 0.10$, can you support the claim that the proportion of monthly convulsive seizure reduction is greater for the group that received the extract than for the group that received the placebo? Interpret the decision in the context of the original claim. *(Adapted from the New England Journal of Medicine)*

**16.** A random sample of 40 ostrich eggs has a mean incubation period of 42 days. Assume the population standard deviation is 1.6 days.

(a) Construct a 95% confidence interval for the population mean incubation period.

(b) A zoologist claims that the mean incubation period for ostriches is at least 45 days. At $\alpha = 0.05$, can you reject the zoologist's claim? Interpret the decision in the context of the original claim.

**17.** A researcher claims that 5% of people who wear eyeglasses purchase their eyeglasses online. Describe type I and type II errors for a hypothesis test of the claim. *(Source: Consumer Reports)*

CHAPTER 9

# Correlation and Regression

In a recent year, the New York Yankees had the highest team salary in Major League Baseball at $228.4 million and the Tampa Bay Rays had the lowest team salary at $56.1 million. In the same year, the Los Angeles Dodgers had the highest average home game attendance at 49,066 and the Miami Marlins had the lowest average home game attendance at 10,016.

# Where You've Been

In Chapters 1–8, you studied descriptive statistics, probability, and inferential statistics. One of the techniques you learned in descriptive statistics was graphing paired data with a scatter plot (see Section 2.2). For instance, the salaries and average home game attendances for the teams in Major League Baseball in a recent year are shown in the scatter plot at the right and in the table below.

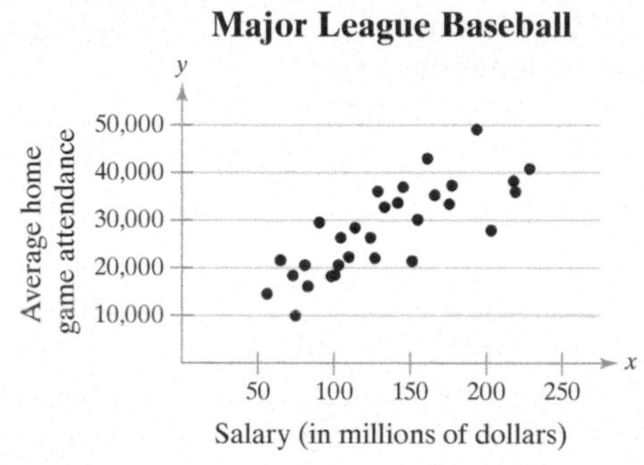


| Salary (in millions of dollars) | 124.0 | 133.2 | 82.7 | 219.0 | 217.8 | 80.8 | 109.7 | 151.3 | 145.3 | 100.6 |
|---|---|---|---|---|---|---|---|---|---|---|
| **Average home game attendance** | 26,364 | 32,777 | 16,146 | 35,994 | 38,208 | 20,622 | 22,334 | 21,465 | 36,954 | 18,536 |

| Salary (in millions of dollars) | 166.0 | 98.2 | 177.3 | 193.6 | 74.7 | 128.8 | 113.8 | 154.8 | 228.4 | 102.9 |
|---|---|---|---|---|---|---|---|---|---|---|
| **Average home game attendance** | 35,276 | 18,267 | 37,321 | 49,066 | 10,016 | 36,091 | 28,436 | 30,155 | 40,795 | 20,626 |

| Salary (in millions of dollars) | 141.8 | 72.9 | 90.3 | 126.9 | 175.6 | 161.1 | 56.1 | 104.4 | 64.7 | 203.0 |
|---|---|---|---|---|---|---|---|---|---|---|
| **Average home game attendance** | 33,672 | 18,413 | 29,585 | 22,112 | 33,429 | 42,968 | 14,552 | 26,333 | 21,607 | 27,899 |

# Where You're Going

In this chapter, you will study how to describe and test the significance of relationships between two variables when data are presented as ordered pairs. For instance, in the scatter plot above, it appears that higher team salaries tend to correspond to higher average attendances and lower team salaries tend to correspond to lower average attendances. This relationship is described by saying that the team salaries are positively correlated to the average attendances. Graphically, the relationship can be described by drawing a line, called a regression line, that fits the points as closely as possible, as shown below. The second scatter plot below shows the salaries and wins for the teams in Major League Baseball in the same year. From the scatter plot, it appears that there is a weak positive correlation between the team salaries and wins.

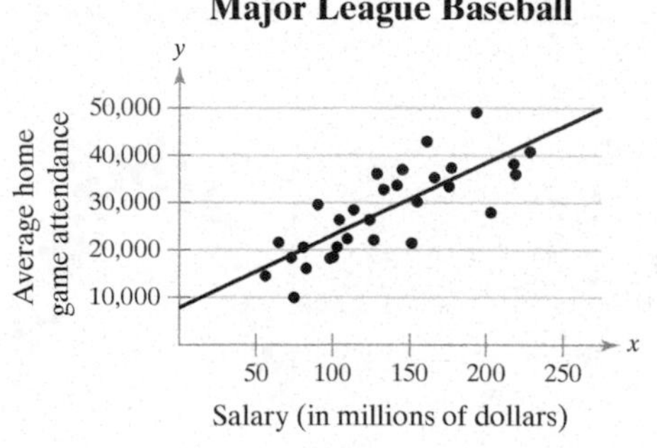


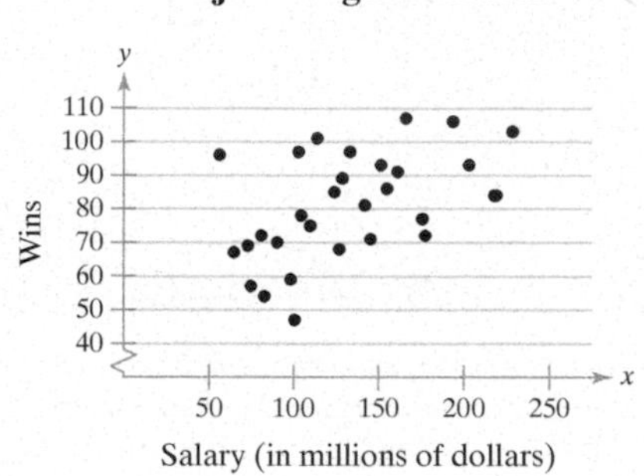

# 9.1 Correlation

**What You Should Learn**

- An introduction to linear correlation, independent and dependent variables, and the types of correlation
- How to find a correlation coefficient
- How to test a population correlation coefficient $\rho$ using a table
- How to perform a hypothesis test for a population correlation coefficient $\rho$
- How to distinguish between correlation and causation

An Overview of Correlation ■ Correlation Coefficient ■ Using a Table to Test a Population Correlation Coefficient $\rho$ ■ Hypothesis Testing for a Population Correlation Coefficient $\rho$ ■ Correlation and Causation

## An Overview of Correlation

Suppose a safety inspector wants to determine whether a relationship exists between the number of hours of training for an employee and the number of accidents involving that employee. Or suppose a psychologist wants to know whether a relationship exists between the number of hours a person sleeps each night and that person's reaction time. How would he or she determine if any relationship exists?

In this section, you will study how to describe what type of relationship, or correlation, exists between two quantitative variables and how to determine whether the correlation is significant.

**DEFINITION**

A **correlation** is a relationship between two variables. The data can be represented by the ordered pairs $(x, y)$, where $x$ is the **independent** (or **explanatory**) **variable** and $y$ is the **dependent** (or **response**) **variable.**

In Section 2.2, you learned that the graph of ordered pairs $(x, y)$ is called a *scatter plot*. In a scatter plot, the ordered pairs $(x, y)$ are graphed as points in a coordinate plane. The independent (explanatory) variable $x$ is measured on the horizontal axis, and the dependent (response) variable $y$ is measured on the vertical axis. A scatter plot can be used to determine whether a linear (straight line) correlation exists between two variables. The scatter plots below show several types of correlation.

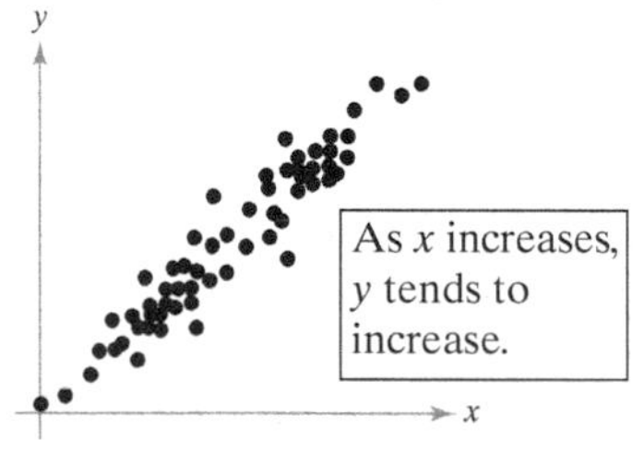


Positive Linear Correlation

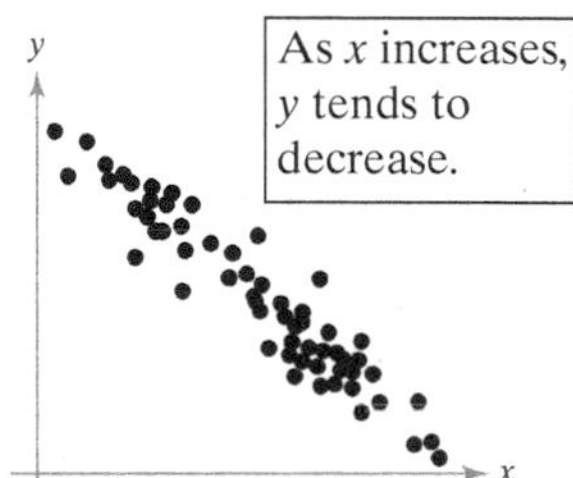


Negative Linear Correlation

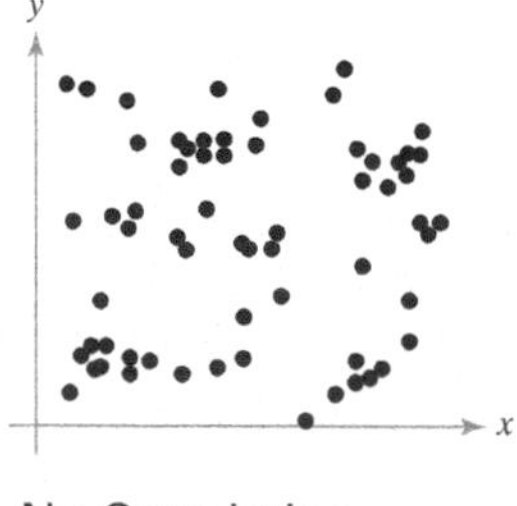


No Correlation

Nonlinear Correlation

## EXAMPLE 1

### Constructing a Scatter Plot

A researcher wants to determine whether there is a linear relationship between a country's gross domestic product (GDP) and carbon dioxide ($CO_2$) emissions. The data for 10 different countries in a recent year are shown in the table at the left. Display the data in a scatter plot and describe the type of correlation. *(Source: U.S. Energy Information Administration)*

| GDP (in trillions of dollars), $x$ | $CO_2$ emissions (in millions of metric tons), $y$ |
|---|---|
| 1.7 | 620.1 |
| 2.4 | 475.2 |
| 3.0 | 457.6 |
| 1.2 | 389.7 |
| 4.1 | 810.8 |
| 2.3 | 352.9 |
| 0.9 | 235.0 |
| 1.8 | 297.8 |
| 2.9 | 413.9 |
| 5.4 | 1216.5 |

**SOLUTION**

The scatter plot is shown below. From the scatter plot, it appears that there is a positive linear correlation between the variables.

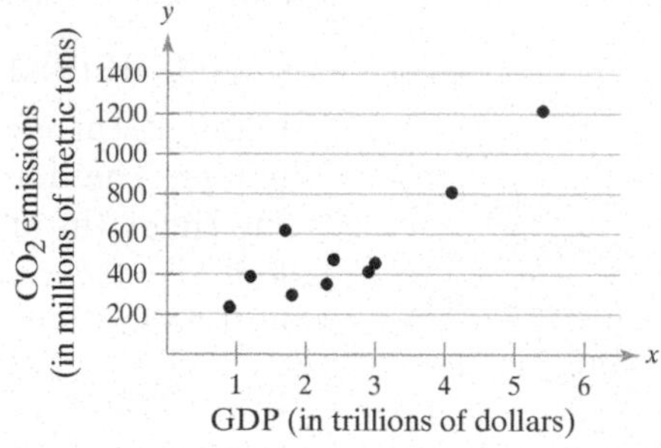


***Interpretation*** As the gross domestic products increase, the carbon dioxide emissions tend to increase.

**TRY IT YOURSELF 1**

A director of alumni affairs at a small college wants to determine whether there is a linear relationship between the number of years alumni have been out of school and their annual contributions (in thousands of dollars). The data are shown in the table below. Display the data in a scatter plot and describe the type of correlation.

| Number of years out of school, $x$ | 1 | 10 | 5 | 15 | 3 | 24 | 30 |
|---|---|---|---|---|---|---|---|
| Annual contribution (in thousands of dollars), $y$ | 12.5 | 8.7 | 14.6 | 5.2 | 9.9 | 3.1 | 2.7 |

*Answer: Page A42*

### Tech Tip

Remember that all data sets containing 20 or more entries are available electronically. Also, some of the data sets in this section are used throughout the chapter, so save any data that you enter. For instance, the data used in Example 1 are also used later in this section and in Sections 9.2 and 9.3.

## EXAMPLE 2

### Constructing a Scatter Plot

A student conducts a study to determine whether there is a linear relationship between the number of hours a student exercises each week and the student's grade point average (GPA). The data are shown in the table below. Display the data in a scatter plot and describe the type of correlation.

| Hours of exercise, $x$ | 12 | 3 | 0 | 6 | 10 | 2 | 18 | 14 | 15 | 5 |
|---|---|---|---|---|---|---|---|---|---|---|
| GPA, $y$ | 3.6 | 4.0 | 3.9 | 2.5 | 2.4 | 2.2 | 3.7 | 3.0 | 1.8 | 3.1 |

**SOLUTION**

The scatter plot is shown at the left. From the scatter plot, it appears that there is no linear correlation between the variables.

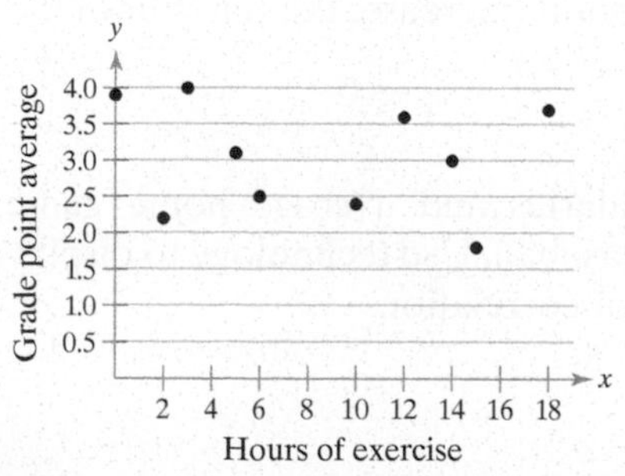


***Interpretation*** The number of hours a student exercises each week does not appear to be related to the student's grade point average.

**TRY IT YOURSELF 2**

A researcher conducts a study to determine whether there is a linear relationship between a person's height (in inches) and pulse rate (in beats per minute). The data are shown in the table below. Display the data in a scatter plot and describe the type of correlation.

| **Height, *x*** | 68 | 72 | 65 | 70 | 62 | 75 | 78 | 64 | 68 |
|---|---|---|---|---|---|---|---|---|---|
| **Pulse rate, *y*** | 90 | 85 | 88 | 100 | 105 | 98 | 70 | 65 | 72 |

*Answer: Page A42*

| Duration, $x$ | Time, $y$ | Duration, $x$ | Time, $y$ |
|---|---|---|---|
| 1.80 | 56 | 3.78 | 79 |
| 1.82 | 58 | 3.83 | 85 |
| 1.90 | 62 | 3.88 | 80 |
| 1.93 | 56 | 4.10 | 89 |
| 1.98 | 57 | 4.27 | 90 |
| 2.05 | 57 | 4.30 | 89 |
| 2.13 | 60 | 4.43 | 89 |
| 2.30 | 57 | 4.47 | 86 |
| 2.37 | 61 | 4.53 | 89 |
| 2.82 | 73 | 4.55 | 86 |
| 3.13 | 76 | 4.60 | 92 |
| 3.27 | 77 | 4.63 | 91 |
| 3.65 | 77 | | |

**EXAMPLE 3**

## Constructing a Scatter Plot Using Technology

Old Faithful, located in Yellowstone National Park, is the world's most famous geyser. The durations (in minutes) of several of Old Faithful's eruptions and the times (in minutes) until the next eruption are shown in the table at the left. Use technology to display the data in a scatter plot. Describe the type of correlation.

**SOLUTION**

MINITAB, Excel, the TI-84 Plus, and StatCrunch each have features for graphing scatter plots. Use such technology to draw the scatter plots shown. From the scatter plots, it appears that the variables have a positive linear correlation.

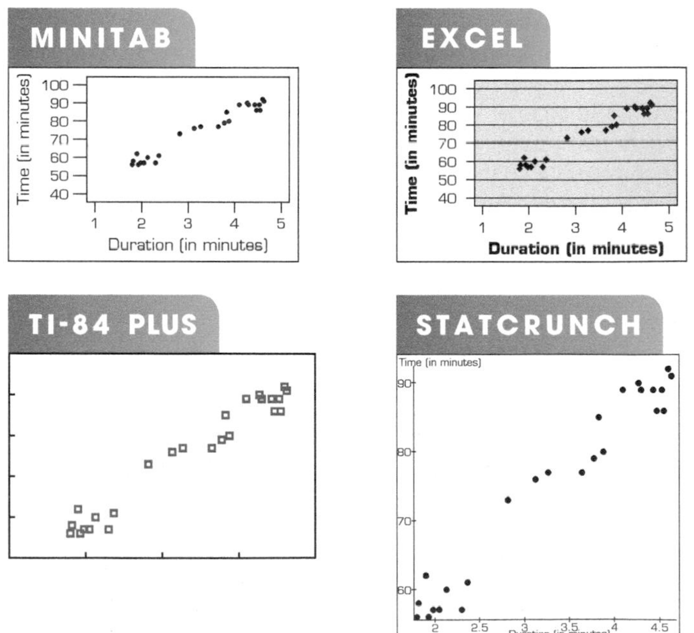


***Interpretation*** As the durations of the eruptions increase, the times until the next eruption tend to increase.

**TRY IT YOURSELF 3**

Consider the data on page 469 on the salaries and average home game attendances for the teams in Major League Baseball. Use technology to display the data in a scatter plot. Describe the type of correlation.

*Answer: Page A42*

## Correlation Coefficient

Interpreting correlation using a scatter plot is subjective. A precise measure of the type and strength of a linear correlation between two variables is to calculate the **correlation coefficient.** A formula for the sample correlation coefficient is given, but it is more convenient to use technology to calculate this value.

**Study Tip**

The formal name for $r$ is the *Pearson product moment correlation coefficient.* It is named after the English statistician Karl Pearson (1857–1936). (See page 35.)

**DEFINITION**

The **correlation coefficient** is a measure of the strength and the direction of a linear relationship between two variables. The symbol $r$ represents the sample correlation coefficient. A formula for $r$ is

$$r = \frac{n\Sigma xy - (\Sigma x)(\Sigma y)}{\sqrt{n\Sigma x^2 - (\Sigma x)^2}\sqrt{n\Sigma y^2 - (\Sigma y)^2}} \quad \text{Sample correlation coefficient}$$

where $n$ is the number of pairs of data. The **population correlation coefficient** is represented by $\rho$ (the lowercase Greek letter rho, pronounced "row").

The range of the correlation coefficient is $-1$ to 1, inclusive. When $x$ and $y$ have a strong positive linear correlation, $r$ is close to 1. When $x$ and $y$ have a strong negative linear correlation, $r$ is close to $-1$. When $x$ and $y$ have perfect positive linear correlation or perfect negative linear correlation, $r$ is equal to 1 or $-1$, respectively. When there is no linear correlation, $r$ is close to 0. It is important to remember that when $r$ is close to 0, it does not mean that there is no relation between $x$ and $y$, just that there is no *linear* relation. Several examples are shown below.

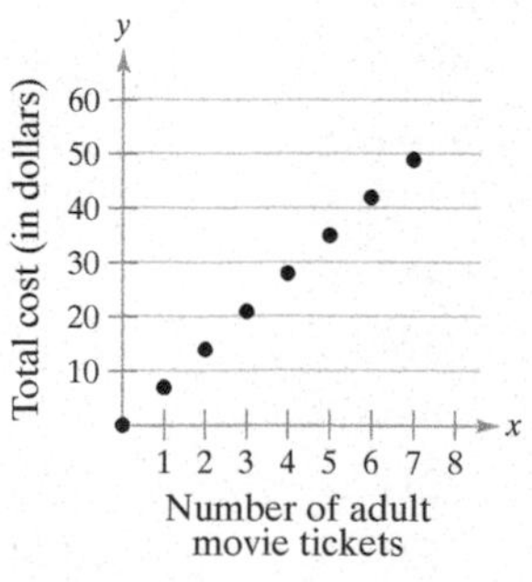


Perfect positive correlation
$r = 1$

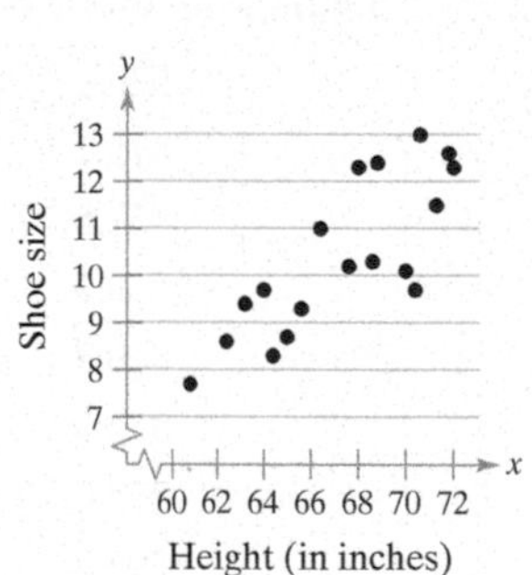


Strong positive correlation
$r = 0.81$

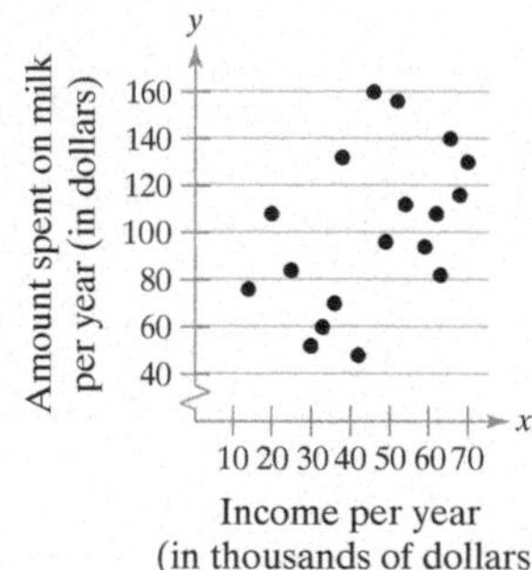


Weak positive correlation
$r = 0.45$

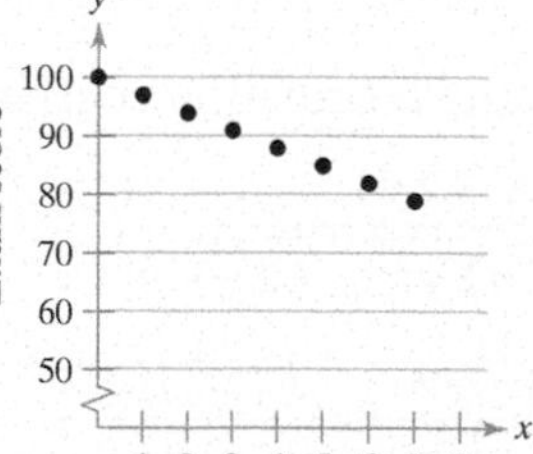


Perfect negative correlation
$r = -1$

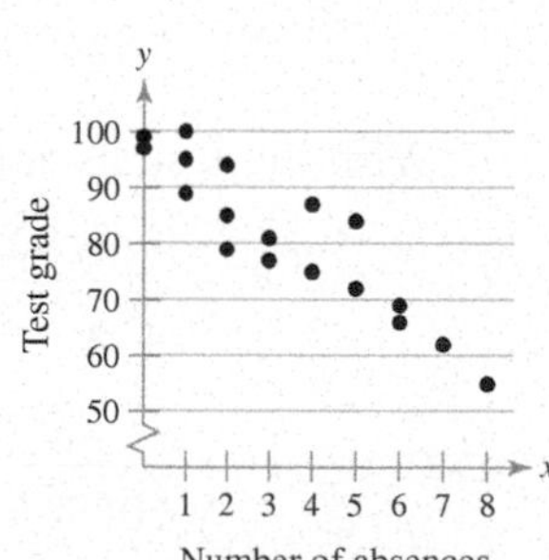


Strong negative correlation
$r = -0.92$

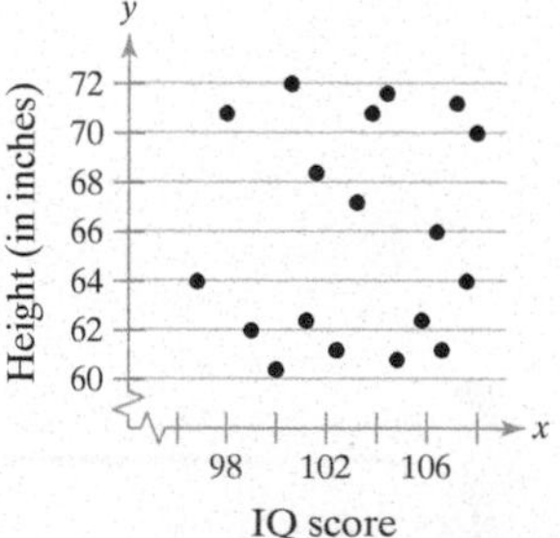


No correlation
$r = 0.04$

To use a correlation coefficient $r$ to make an inference about a population, it is required that (1) the sample paired data $(x, y)$ are random and (2) $x$ and $y$ have a *bivariate normal distribution* (you will learn more about this distribution in Section 9.3). In this text, unless stated otherwise, you can assume that these requirements are met.

**Study Tip**

The symbol $\Sigma x^2$ means square each value and add the squares. The symbol $(\Sigma x)^2$ means add the values and square the sum.

**GUIDELINES**

**Calculating a Correlation Coefficient**

| In Words | In Symbols |
|---|---|
| **1.** Find the sum of the $x$-values. | $\Sigma x$ |
| **2.** Find the sum of the $y$-values. | $\Sigma y$ |
| **3.** Multiply each $x$-value by its corresponding $y$-value and find the sum. | $\Sigma xy$ |
| **4.** Square each $x$-value and find the sum. | $\Sigma x^2$ |
| **5.** Square each $y$-value and find the sum. | $\Sigma y^2$ |
| **6.** Use these five sums to calculate the correlation coefficient. | $r = \dfrac{n\Sigma xy - (\Sigma x)(\Sigma y)}{\sqrt{n\Sigma x^2 - (\Sigma x)^2}\sqrt{n\Sigma y^2 - (\Sigma y)^2}}$ |

**EXAMPLE 4**

## Calculating a Correlation Coefficient

Calculate the correlation coefficient for the gross domestic products and carbon dioxide emissions data in Example 1. Interpret the result in the context of the data.

**SOLUTION** Use a table to help calculate the correlation coefficient.

| GDP (in trillions of dollars), $x$ | $CO_2$ emissions (in millions of metric tons), $y$ | $xy$ | $x^2$ | $y^2$ |
|---|---|---|---|---|
| 1.7 | 620.1 | 1054.17 | 2.89 | 384,524.01 |
| 2.4 | 475.2 | 1140.48 | 5.76 | 225,815.04 |
| 3.0 | 457.6 | 1372.8 | 9 | 209,397.76 |
| 1.2 | 389.7 | 467.64 | 1.44 | 151,866.09 |
| 4.1 | 810.8 | 3324.28 | 16.81 | 657,396.64 |
| 2.3 | 352.9 | 811.67 | 5.29 | 124,538.41 |
| 0.9 | 235.0 | 211.5 | 0.81 | 55,225 |
| 1.8 | 297.8 | 536.04 | 3.24 | 88,684.84 |
| 2.9 | 413.9 | 1200.31 | 8.41 | 171,313.21 |
| 5.4 | 1216.5 | 6569.1 | 29.16 | 1,479,872.25 |
| $\Sigma x = 25.7$ | $\Sigma y = 5269.5$ | $\Sigma xy = 16{,}687.99$ | $\Sigma x^2 = 82.81$ | $\Sigma y^2 = 3{,}548{,}633.25$ |

With these sums and $n = 10$, the correlation coefficient is

$$r = \frac{n\Sigma xy - (\Sigma x)(\Sigma y)}{\sqrt{n\Sigma x^2 - (\Sigma x)^2}\sqrt{n\Sigma y^2 - (\Sigma y)^2}}$$

$$= \frac{10(16{,}687.99) - (25.7)(5269.5)}{\sqrt{10(82.81) - (25.7)^2}\sqrt{10(3{,}548{,}633.25) - (5269.5)^2}}$$

$$= \frac{31{,}453.75}{\sqrt{167.61}\sqrt{7{,}718{,}702.25}}$$

$$\approx 0.874. \qquad \text{Round to three decimal places.}$$

The result $r \approx 0.874$ suggests a strong positive linear correlation.

***Interpretation*** As the gross domestic product increases, the carbon dioxide emissions tend to increase.

**Study Tip**

Notice that the correlation coefficient $r$ in Example 4 is rounded to three decimal places. This *round-off rule* will be used throughout the text.

| Number of years out of school, $x$ | Annual contribution (in thousands of dollars), $y$ |
|---|---|
| 1 | 12.5 |
| 10 | 8.7 |
| 5 | 14.6 |
| 15 | 5.2 |
| 3 | 9.9 |
| 24 | 3.1 |
| 30 | 2.7 |

**9.1** To explore this topic further, see **Activity 9.1** on page 485.

### Tech Tip

Before using the TI-84 Plus to calculate $r$, make sure the *diagnostics* feature is on. To turn on this feature, from the home screen, press 2nd CATALOG and cursor to *DiagnosticOn*. Then press ENTER twice.

**TRY IT YOURSELF 4**

Calculate the correlation coefficient for the number of years out of school and annual contribution data in Try It Yourself 1. Interpret the result in the context of the data.

*Answer: Page A42*

## EXAMPLE 5

### Using Technology to Calculate a Correlation Coefficient

Use technology to calculate the correlation coefficient for the Old Faithful data in Example 3. Interpret the result in the context of the data.

**SOLUTION**

Minitab, Excel, the TI-84 Plus, and StatCrunch each have features that allow you to calculate a correlation coefficient for paired data sets. Use such technology to find $r$. You should obtain results similar to the displays shown.

**MINITAB**

**Method**

| Correlation type | Pearson |
|---|---|
| Number of rows used | 25 |

**Correlations**

| | Duration |
|---|---|
| Time | 0.979 |

**EXCEL**

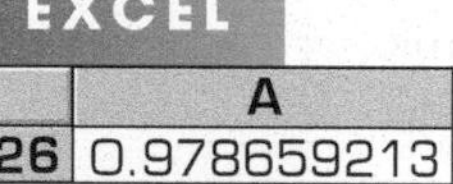

| | A |
|---|---|
| 26 | 0.978659213 |

List the eruption durations in cells A1 through A25 and the times until the next eruption in cells B1 through B25.

← =CORREL(A1:A25,B1:B25)

**TI-84 PLUS**

```
LinReg
y=ax+b
a=12.48094391
b=33.68290034
r²=.9577738551
r=.9786592129
```

**STATCRUNCH**

Correlation between Duration and Time is:
0.97865921

Rounded to three decimal places, the correlation coefficient is

$r \approx 0.979.$ Round to three decimal places.

This value of $r$ suggests a strong positive linear correlation.

***Interpretation*** As the duration of the eruptions increases, the time until the next eruption tends to increase.

**TRY IT YOURSELF 5**

Use technology to calculate the correlation coefficient for the data on page 469 on the salaries and average home game attendances for the teams in Major League Baseball. Interpret the result in the context of the data.

*Answer: Page A42*

## Using a Table to Test a Population Correlation Coefficient $\rho$

**Study Tip**

The level of significance is denoted by $\alpha$, the lowercase Greek letter alpha.

Once you have calculated $r$, the sample correlation coefficient, you will want to determine whether there is enough evidence to decide that the population correlation coefficient $\rho$ is significant. In other words, based on a few pairs of data, can you make an inference about the population of all such data pairs? Remember that you are using sample data to make a decision about population data, so it is always possible that your inference may be wrong. In correlation studies, the small percentage of times when you decide that the correlation is significant when it is really not is called the *level of significance.* It is typically set at $\alpha = 0.01$ or 0.05. When $\alpha = 0.05$, you will probably decide that the population correlation coefficient is significant when it is really not 5% of the time. (Of course, 95% of the time, you will correctly determine that a correlation coefficient is significant.) When $\alpha = 0.01$, you will make this type of error only 1% of the time. When using a lower level of significance, however, you may fail to identify some significant correlations.

**Study Tip**

The symbol $|r|$ represents the absolute value of $r$. Recall that the absolute value of a number is its value, disregarding its sign. For example, $|3| = 3$ and $|-7| = 7$.

For a correlation coefficient to be significant, its absolute value must be close to 1. To determine whether the population correlation coefficient $\rho$ is significant, use the critical values given in Table 11 in Appendix B. A portion of the table is shown below. If $|r|$ is greater than the critical value, then there is enough evidence to decide that the correlation is significant. Otherwise, there is *not* enough evidence to say that the correlation is significant. For instance, to determine whether $\rho$ is significant for five pairs of data ($n = 5$) at a level of significance of $\alpha = 0.01$, you need to compare $|r|$ with a critical value of 0.959, as shown in the table.

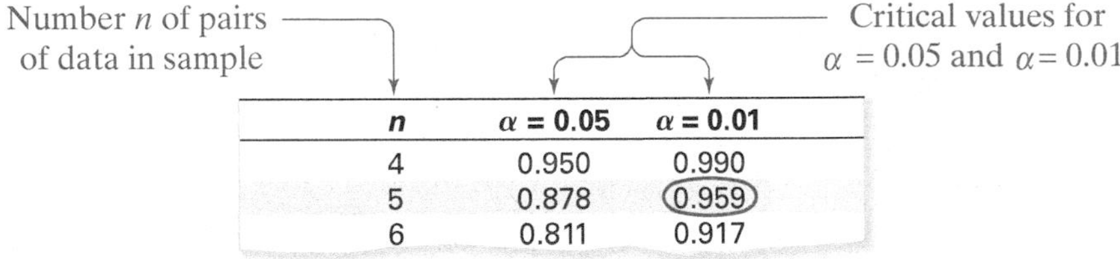


| $n$ | $\alpha = 0.05$ | $\alpha = 0.01$ |
|---|---|---|
| 4 | 0.950 | 0.990 |
| 5 | 0.878 | 0.959 |
| 6 | 0.811 | 0.917 |

If $|r| > 0.959$, then the correlation is significant. Otherwise, there is *not* enough evidence to conclude that the correlation is significant. Here are the guidelines for this process.

**Study Tip**

If you determine that the linear correlation is significant, then you will be able to proceed to write the equation for the line that best describes the data. This line, called the *regression line,* can be used to predict the value of $y$ when given a value of $x$. You will learn how to write this equation in the next section.

**GUIDELINES**

**Using Table 11 for the Correlation Coefficient $\rho$**

| In Words | In Symbols |
|---|---|
| **1.** Determine the number of pairs of data in the sample. | Determine $n$. |
| **2.** Specify the level of significance. | Identify $\alpha$. |
| **3.** Find the critical value. | Use Table 11 in Appendix B. |
| **4.** Decide whether the correlation is significant. | If $|r|$ is greater than the critical value, then the correlation is significant. Otherwise, there is *not* enough evidence to conclude that the correlation is significant. |
| **5.** Interpret the decision in the context of the original claim. | |

To use Table 11 to test a correlation coefficient, note that the requirements for calculating a correlation coefficient given on page 473 also apply to the test. In this text, unless stated otherwise, you can assume that these requirements are met.

## EXAMPLE 6

### Using Table 11 for a Correlation Coefficient

In Example 5, you used 25 pairs of data to find $r \approx 0.979$. Is the correlation coefficient significant? Use $\alpha = 0.05$.

**SOLUTION**

The number of pairs of data is 25, so $n = 25$. The level of significance is $\alpha = 0.05$. Using Table 11, find the critical value in the $\alpha = 0.05$ column that corresponds to the row with $n = 25$. The number in that column and row is 0.396.

Critical values for $\alpha = 0.05$

| $n$ | $\alpha = 0.05$ | $\alpha = 0.01$ |
|---|---|---|
| 4 | 0.950 | 0.990 |
| 5 | 0.878 | 0.959 |
| 6 | 0.811 | 0.917 |
| 7 | 0.754 | 0.875 |
| 8 | 0.707 | 0.834 |
| 9 | 0.666 | 0.798 |
| 10 | 0.632 | 0.765 |
| 11 | 0.602 | 0.735 |
| 12 | 0.576 | 0.708 |
| 13 | 0.553 | 0.684 |
| 14 | 0.532 | 0.661 |
| 15 | 0.514 | 0.641 |
| 16 | 0.497 | 0.623 |
| 17 | 0.482 | 0.606 |
| 18 | 0.468 | 0.590 |
| 19 | 0.456 | 0.575 |
| 20 | 0.444 | 0.561 |
| 21 | 0.433 | 0.549 |
| 22 | 0.423 | 0.537 |
| 23 | 0.413 | 0.526 |
| 24 | 0.404 | 0.515 |
| 25 | 0.396 | 0.505 |
| 26 | 0.388 | 0.496 |
| 27 | 0.381 | 0.487 |
| 28 | 0.374 | 0.479 |
| 29 | 0.367 | 0.471 |

$n = 25$ →

Because $|r| \approx 0.979 > 0.396$, you can decide that the population correlation is significant.

***Interpretation*** There is enough evidence at the 5% level of significance to conclude that there is a significant linear correlation between the duration of Old Faithful's eruptions and the time between eruptions.

**TRY IT YOURSELF 6**

In Try It Yourself 4, you calculated the correlation coefficient of the number of years out of school and annual contribution data to be $r \approx -0.908$. Is the correlation coefficient significant? Use $\alpha = 0.01$.

*Answer: Page A42*

In Table 11, notice that for fewer data pairs (smaller values of $n$), stronger evidence is needed to conclude that the correlation coefficient is significant.

## Hypothesis Testing for a Population Correlation Coefficient $\rho$

You can also use a hypothesis test to determine whether the sample correlation coefficient $r$ provides enough evidence to conclude that the population correlation coefficient $\rho$ is significant. A hypothesis test for $\rho$ can be one-tailed or two-tailed. The null and alternative hypotheses for these tests are listed below.

$$\begin{cases} H_0: \rho \geq 0 \text{ (no significant negative correlation)} \\ H_a: \rho < 0 \text{ (significant negative correlation)} \end{cases}$$ Left-tailed test

$$\begin{cases} H_0: \rho \leq 0 \text{ (no significant positive correlation)} \\ H_a: \rho > 0 \text{ (significant positive correlation)} \end{cases}$$ Right-tailed test

$$\begin{cases} H_0: \rho = 0 \text{ (no significant correlation)} \\ H_a: \rho \neq 0 \text{ (significant correlation)} \end{cases}$$ Two-tailed test

In this text, you will consider only two-tailed hypothesis tests for $\rho$.

### The $t$-Test for the Correlation Coefficient

A **$t$-test** can be used to test whether the correlation between two variables is significant. The **test statistic** is $r$ and the **standardized test statistic**

$$t = \frac{r}{\sigma_r} = \frac{r}{\sqrt{\dfrac{1 - r^2}{n - 2}}}$$

follows a $t$-distribution with $n - 2$ degrees of freedom, where $n$ is the number of pairs of data. (Note that there are $n - 2$ degrees of freedom because one degree of freedom is lost for each variable.)

### GUIDELINES

**Using the $t$-Test for the Correlation Coefficient $\rho$**

| In Words | In Symbols |
|---|---|
| **1.** Identify the null and alternative hypotheses. | State $H_0$ and $H_a$. |
| **2.** Specify the level of significance. | Identify $\alpha$. |
| **3.** Identify the degrees of freedom. | d.f. $= n - 2$ |
| **4.** Determine the critical value(s) and the rejection region(s). | Use Table 5 in Appendix B. |
| **5.** Find the standardized test statistic. | $t = \frac{r}{\sqrt{\frac{1 - r^2}{n - 2}}}$ |
| **6.** Make a decision to reject or fail to reject the null hypothesis. | If $t$ is in the rejection region, then reject $H_0$. Otherwise, fail to reject $H_0$. |
| **7.** Interpret the decision in the context of the original claim. | |

To use the $t$-test for a correlation coefficient, note that the requirements for calculating a correlation coefficient given on page 473 also apply to the test. In this text, unless stated otherwise, you can assume that these requirements are met.

## EXAMPLE 7

### The $t$-Test for a Correlation Coefficient

In Example 4, you used 10 pairs of data to find $r \approx 0.874$. Test the significance of this correlation coefficient. Use $\alpha = 0.05$.

**SOLUTION**

The null and alternative hypotheses are

$$H_0: \rho = 0 \text{ (no correlation)} \quad \text{and} \quad H_a: \rho \neq 0 \text{ (significant correlation)}.$$

Because there are 10 pairs of data in the sample, there are $10 - 2 = 8$ degrees of freedom. Because the test is a two-tailed test, $\alpha = 0.05$, and d.f. = 8, the critical values are $-t_0 = -2.306$ and $t_0 = 2.306$. The rejection regions are $t < -2.306$ and $t > 2.306$. Using the $t$-test, the standardized test statistic is

$$t = \frac{r}{\sqrt{\frac{1 - r^2}{n - 2}}}$$ Use the $t$-test for $\rho$.

$$\approx \frac{0.874}{\sqrt{\frac{1 - (0.874)^2}{10 - 2}}}$$ Substitute 0.874 for $r$ and 10 for $n$.

$$\approx 5.087.$$ Round to three decimal places.

**TI-84 PLUS**

LinRegTTest
y=ax+b
β≠0 and ρ≠0
t=5.099174604
p=9.3079858E-4
df=8
↓a=44.66291987

You can check this result using technology. For instance, using a TI-84 Plus, you can find the standardized test statistic, as shown at the left. (Note that the result differs slightly due to rounding.) The figure below shows the location of the rejection regions and the standardized test statistic.

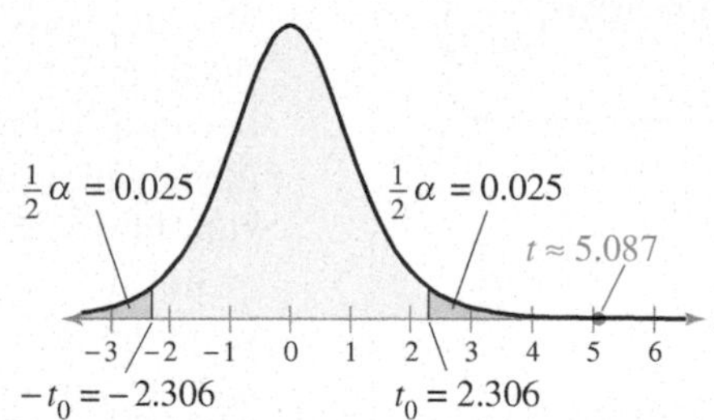


Because $t$ is in the rejection region, you reject the null hypothesis.

***Interpretation*** There is enough evidence at the 5% level of significance to conclude that there is a significant linear correlation between gross domestic products and carbon dioxide emissions.

**Study Tip**

Be sure you see in Example 7 that rejecting the null hypothesis means that there is enough evidence that the correlation is significant.

**TRY IT YOURSELF 7**

In Try It Yourself 5, you calculated the correlation coefficient of the salaries and average home game attendances for the teams in Major League Baseball to be $r \approx 0.792$. Test the significance of this correlation coefficient. Use $\alpha = 0.01$.

*Answer: Page A42*

In Example 7, you can use Table 11 in Appendix B to test the population correlation coefficient $\rho$. Given $n = 10$ and $\alpha = 0.05$, the critical value from Table 11 is 0.632. Because $|r| \approx 0.874 > 0.632$, the correlation is significant. Note that this is the same result you obtained using a $t$-test for the population correlation coefficient $\rho$.

## Picturing the World

The scatter plot shows the results of a survey conducted by students in a high school statistics class. In the survey, 125 high school students were asked their grade point average (GPA) and the number of caffeine drinks they consumed each day.

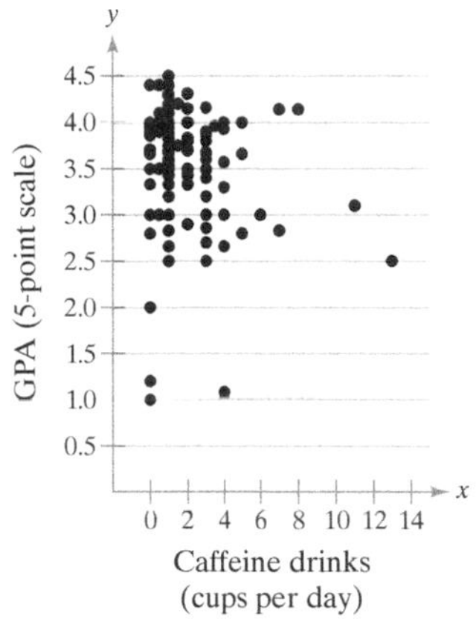


**What type of correlation, if any, does the scatter plot show between caffeine consumption and GPA?**

## Correlation and Causation

*The fact that two variables are strongly correlated does not in itself imply a cause-and-effect relationship between the variables.* More in-depth study is usually needed to determine whether there is a causal relationship between the variables.

When there is a significant correlation between two variables, a researcher should consider these possibilities.

1. **Is there a direct cause-and-effect relationship between the variables?**

   That is, does $x$ cause $y$? For instance, consider the relationship between gross domestic products and carbon dioxide emissions that has been discussed throughout this section. It is reasonable to conclude, from the given data, that countries with higher gross domestic products will have higher carbon dioxide emissions.

2. **Is there a reverse cause-and-effect relationship between the variables?**

   That is, does $y$ cause $x$? For instance, consider the Old Faithful data that have been discussed throughout this section. These variables have a positive linear correlation, and it is possible to conclude that the duration of an eruption affects the time before the next eruption. However, it is also possible that the time between eruptions affects the duration of the next eruption.

3. **Is it possible that the relationship between the variables can be caused by a third variable or perhaps a combination of several other variables?**

   For instance, consider the salaries and average home game attendances for the teams in Major League Baseball listed on page 469. Although these variables have a positive linear correlation, it is doubtful that just because a team's salary decreases, the average attendance per home game will also decrease. The relationship is probably due to other variables, such as the economy, the players on the team, and whether or not the team is winning games. Variables that have an effect on the variables being studied but are not included in the study are called **lurking variables.**

4. **Is it possible that the relationship between two variables may be a coincidence?**

   For instance, although it may be possible to find a significant correlation between the number of animal species living in certain regions and the number of people who own more than two cars in those regions, it is highly unlikely that the variables are directly related. The relationship is probably due to coincidence.

Determining which of the cases above is valid for a data set can be difficult. For instance, consider this example. A person breaks out in a rash after eating shrimp at a certain restaurant. This happens every time the person eats shrimp at the restaurant. The natural conclusion is that the person is allergic to shrimp. However, upon further study by an allergist, it is found that the person is not allergic to shrimp, but to a type of seasoning the chef is putting into the shrimp.

# 9.1 EXERCISES

For Extra Help: MyLab® Statistics

## Building Basic Skills and Vocabulary

1. Two variables have a positive linear correlation. Does the dependent variable increase or decrease as the independent variable increases? What if the variables have a negative linear correlation?

2. Describe the range of values for the correlation coefficient.

3. What does the sample correlation coefficient $r$ measure? Which value indicates a stronger correlation: $r = 0.918$ or $r = -0.932$? Explain your reasoning.

4. Give examples of two variables that have perfect positive linear correlation and two variables that have perfect negative linear correlation.

5. Explain how to determine whether a sample correlation coefficient indicates that the population correlation coefficient is significant.

6. Discuss the difference between $r$ and $\rho$.

7. What are the null and alternate hypotheses for a two-tailed $t$-test for the population correlation coefficient $\rho$? When do you reject the null hypothesis?

8. In your own words, what does it mean to say "correlation does not imply causation"? List a pair of variables that have correlation but no cause-and-effect relationship.

*In Exercises 9 and 10, identify the explanatory variable and the response variable.*

9. A nutritionist wants to determine whether the amounts of water consumed each day by persons of the same weight and on the same diet can be used to predict individual weight loss.

10. An actuary at an insurance company wants to determine whether the number of hours of safety driving classes can be used to predict the number of driving accidents for each driver.

**Graphical Analysis** *In Exercises 11–14, determine whether there is a perfect positive linear correlation, a strong positive linear correlation, a perfect negative linear correlation, a strong negative linear correlation, or no linear correlation between the variables.*

11.
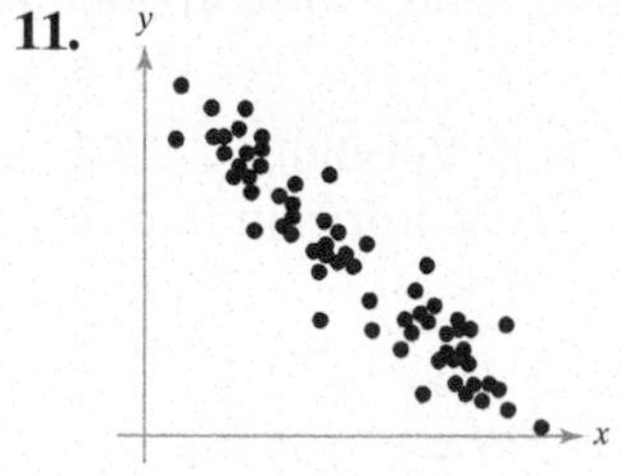


12.
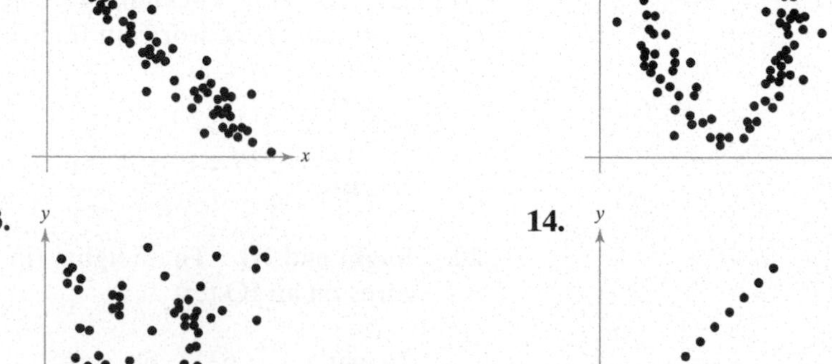


13.

14.
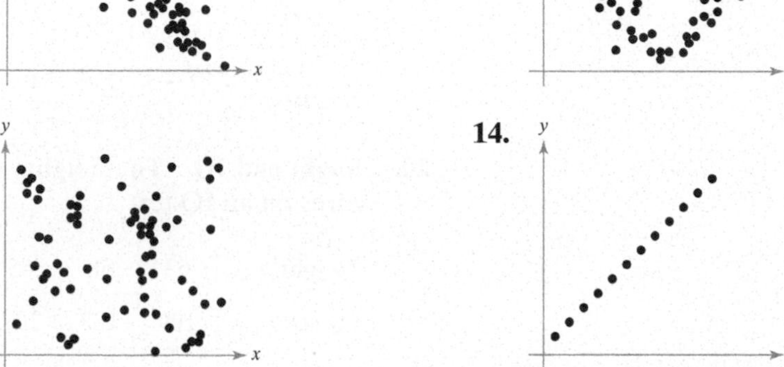

**Graphical Analysis** *In Exercises 15–18, the scatter plots show the results of a survey of 20 randomly selected adults ages 24–35. Using age as the explanatory variable, match each graph with the appropriate description. Explain your reasoning.*

*(a) Age and body temperature* *(b) Age and balance on student loans*

*(c) Age and income* *(d) Age and height*

**15.**

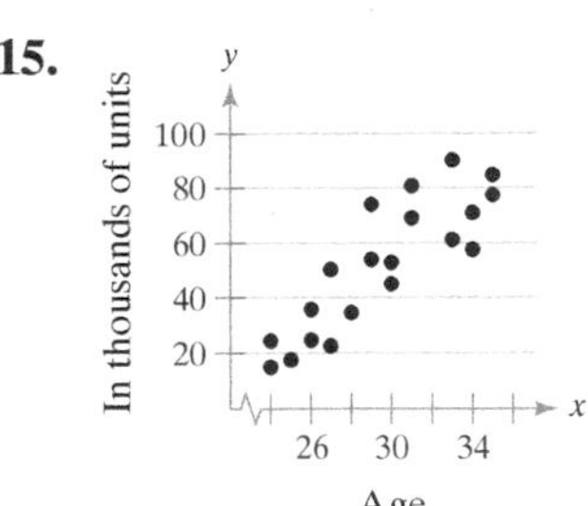


**16.**

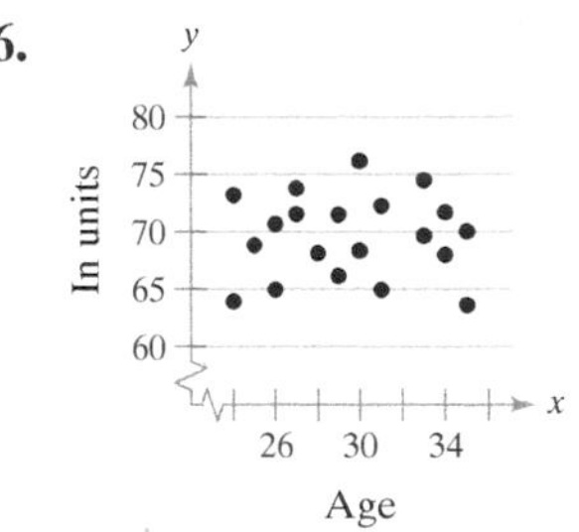


**17.**

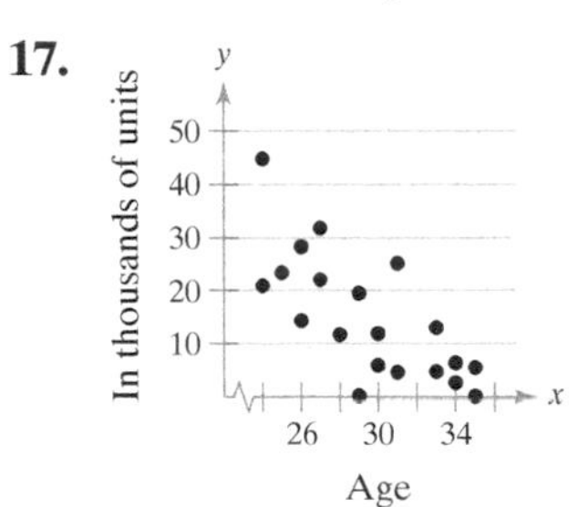


**18.**

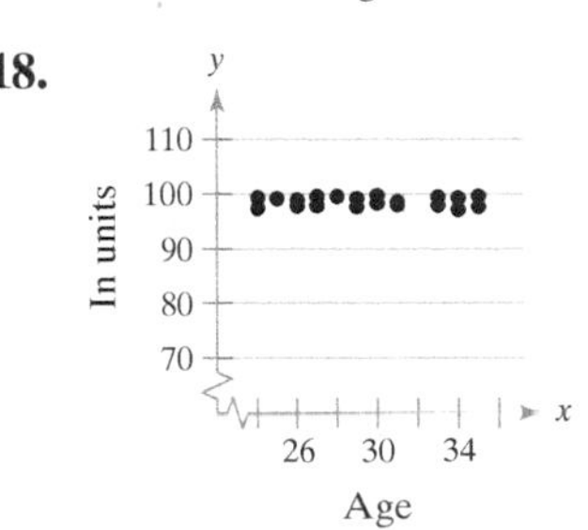


*In Exercises 19–22, two variables are given that have been shown to have correlation but no cause-and-effect relationship. Describe at least one possible reason for the correlation.*

**19.** Value of home and life span

**20.** Alcohol use and tobacco use

**21.** Ice cream sales and homicide rates

**22.** Marriage rate in Kentucky and number of deaths caused by falling out of a fishing boat

## Using and Interpreting Concepts

**Constructing a Scatter Plot and Determining Correlation** *In Exercises 23–28, (a) display the data in a scatter plot, (b) calculate the sample correlation coefficient r, (c) describe the type of correlation, if any, and interpret the correlation in the context of the data, and (d) use Table 11 in Appendix B to make a conclusion about the correlation coefficient. If convenient, use technology. Let* $\alpha = 0.01$*.*

**23. Age and Vocabulary** The ages (in years) of 11 children and the numbers of words in their vocabulary

| **Age, *x*** | 1 | 2 | 3 | 4 | 5 | 6 | 3 | 5 | 2 | 4 | 6 |
|---|---|---|---|---|---|---|---|---|---|---|---|
| **Vocabulary size, *y*** | 3 | 220 | 540 | 1100 | 2100 | 2600 | 730 | 2200 | 260 | 1200 | 2500 |

**24. Height and IQ** The heights (in inches) of 8 high school students and their scores on an IQ test

| **Height, *x*** | 62 | 58 | 65 | 67 | 59 | 64 | 65 | 57 |
|---|---|---|---|---|---|---|---|---|
| **IQ score, *y*** | 109 | 102 | 107 | 114 | 96 | 110 | 116 | 128 |

**25. Maximal Strength and Jump Height** The maximum weights (in kilograms) for which one repetition of a half squat can be performed and the jump heights (in centimeters) for 12 international soccer players *(Adapted from British Journal of Sports Medicine)*

| **Maximum weight, $x$** | 190 | 185 | 155 | 180 | 175 | 170 |
|---|---|---|---|---|---|---|
| **Jump height, $y$** | 60 | 57 | 54 | 60 | 56 | 64 |

| **Maximum weight, $x$** | 150 | 160 | 160 | 180 | 190 | 210 |
|---|---|---|---|---|---|---|
| **Jump height, $y$** | 52 | 51 | 49 | 57 | 59 | 64 |

**26. Maximal Strength and Sprint Performance** The maximum weights (in kilograms) for which one repetition of a half squat can be performed and the times (in seconds) to run a 10-meter sprint for 12 international soccer players *(Adapted from British Journal of Sports Medicine)*

| **Maximum weight, $x$** | 175 | 180 | 155 | 210 | 150 | 190 |
|---|---|---|---|---|---|---|
| **Time, $y$** | 1.80 | 1.77 | 2.05 | 1.42 | 2.04 | 1.61 |

| **Maximum weight, $x$** | 185 | 160 | 190 | 180 | 160 | 170 |
|---|---|---|---|---|---|---|
| **Time, $y$** | 1.70 | 1.91 | 1.60 | 1.63 | 1.98 | 1.90 |

**27. Earnings and Dividends** The earnings per share (in dollars) and the dividends per share (in dollars) for 6 companies in a recent year *(Source: The Value Line Investment Survey)*

| **Earnings per share, $x$** | 3.53 | 1.01 | 3.16 | 5.55 | 2.61 | 8.64 |
|---|---|---|---|---|---|---|
| **Dividends per share, $y$** | 1.18 | 0.88 | 2.64 | 2.16 | 0.90 | 2.68 |

**28. Speed of Sound** Eleven altitudes (in thousands of feet) and the speeds of sound (in feet per second) at these altitudes

| **Altitude, $x$** | 0 | 5 | 10 | 15 | 20 | 25 |
|---|---|---|---|---|---|---|
| **Speed of sound, $y$** | 1116.3 | 1096.9 | 1077.3 | 1057.2 | 1036.8 | 1015.8 |

| **Altitude, $x$** | 30 | 35 | 40 | 45 | 50 |
|---|---|---|---|---|---|
| **Speed of sound, $y$** | 994.5 | 969.0 | 967.7 | 967.7 | 967.7 |

**29.** In Exercise 23, add data for a child who is 6 years old and has a vocabulary of 900 words. Describe how this affects the correlation coefficient $r$.

**30.** In Exercise 24, remove the data for the student who is 57 inches tall and scored 128 on the IQ test. Describe how this affects the correlation coefficient $r$.

**31.** In Exercise 25, remove the data for the international soccer player with a maximum weight of 170 kilograms and a jump height of 64 centimeters. Describe how this affects the correlation coefficient $r$.

**32.** In Exercise 26, add data for an international soccer player who can perform the half squat with a maximum of 210 kilograms and can sprint 10 meters in 2.00 seconds. Describe how this affects the correlation coefficient $r$.

**The *t*-Test for Correlation Coefficients** *In Exercises 33–36, perform a hypothesis test using Table 5 in Appendix B to make a conclusion about the correlation coefficient.*

**33. Braking Distances: Dry Surface** The weights (in pounds) of eight vehicles and the variabilities of their braking distances (in feet) when stopping on a dry surface are shown in the table. At $\alpha = 0.01$, is there enough evidence to conclude that there is a significant linear correlation between vehicle weight and variability in braking distance on a dry surface? *(Adapted from National Highway Traffic Safety Administration)*

| Weight, $x$ | 5940 | 5340 | 6500 | 5100 | 5850 | 4800 | 5600 | 5890 |
|---|---|---|---|---|---|---|---|---|
| Variability, $y$ | 1.78 | 1.93 | 1.91 | 1.59 | 1.66 | 1.50 | 1.61 | 1.70 |

**34. Braking Distances: Wet Surface** The weights (in pounds) of eight vehicles and the variabilities of their braking distances (in feet) when stopping on a wet surface are shown in the table. At $\alpha = 0.05$, is there enough evidence to conclude that there is a significant linear correlation between vehicle weight and variability in braking distance on a wet surface? *(Adapted from National Highway Traffic Safety Administration)*

| Weight, $x$ | 5890 | 5340 | 6500 | 4800 | 5940 | 5600 | 5100 | 5850 |
|---|---|---|---|---|---|---|---|---|
| Variability, $y$ | 2.92 | 2.40 | 4.09 | 1.72 | 2.88 | 2.53 | 2.32 | 2.78 |

**35. Maximal Strength and Jump Height** The table in Exercise 25 shows the maximum weights (in kilograms) for which one repetition of a half squat can be performed and the jump heights (in centimeters) for 12 international soccer players. At $\alpha = 0.05$, is there enough evidence to conclude that there is a significant linear correlation between the data? (Use the value of $r$ found in Exercise 25.)

**36. Maximal Strength and Sprint Performance** The table in Exercise 26 shows the maximum weights (in kilograms) for which one repetition of a half squat can be performed and the times (in seconds) to run a 10-meter sprint for 12 international soccer players. At $\alpha = 0.01$, is there enough evidence to conclude that there is a significant linear correlation between the data? (Use the value of $r$ found in Exercise 26.)

## Extending Concepts

**37. Interchanging $x$ and $y$** In Exercise 26, let the time (in seconds) to sprint 10 meters represent the $x$-values and the maximum weight (in kilograms) for which one repetition of a half squat can be performed represent the $y$-values. Calculate the correlation coefficient $r$. What effect does switching the explanatory and response variables have on the correlation coefficient?

**38. Writing** Use an appropriate research source to find a real-life data set with the indicated cause-and-effect relationship. Write a paragraph describing each variable and explain why you think the variables have the indicated cause-and-effect relationship.

(a) *Direct Cause-and-Effect:* Changes in one variable cause changes in the other variable.
(b) *Other Factors:* The relationship between the variables is caused by a third variable.
(c) *Coincidence:* The relationship between the variables is a coincidence.

# 9.1 ACTIVITY Correlation by Eye

You can find the interactive applet for this activity at MyLab Statistics.

The *Correlation by eye* applet allows you to guess the sample correlation coefficient $r$ for a data set. When the applet loads, a data set consisting of 20 points is displayed. To add a point, click at the desired location or click **Add point** and enter the coordinates. To remove a point, click and drag the point outside the axis area. You can change the **Sample size** by entering a new value. Click **Simulate** to generate a new set of points. Click **Reset** to remove all the points. Enter a **Guess** for $r$ and click **Check** to see if you are within 0.1. Click **Show** to see the value of $r$.

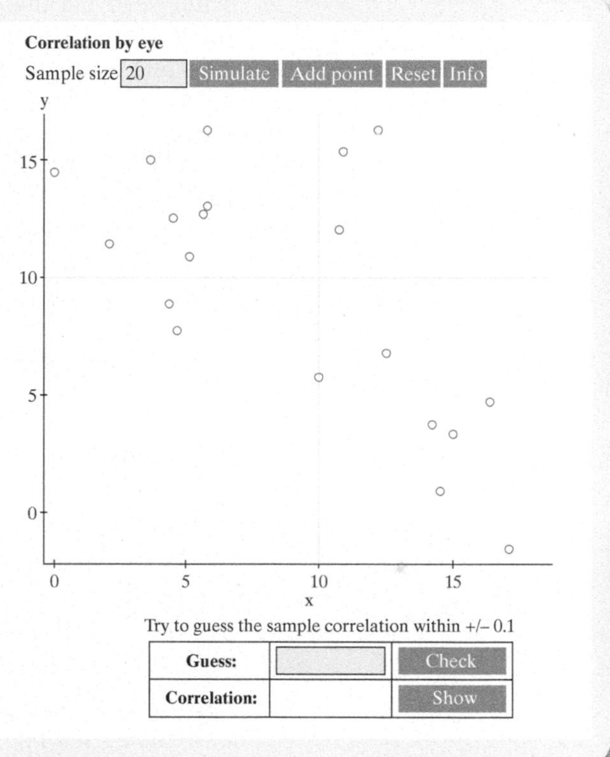


## EXPLORE

**Step 1** Add five points to the plot.
**Step 2** Enter a **Guess** for $r$. Click **Check.**
**Step 3** Click **Show.**
**Step 4** Enter a new **Sample size** and click **Simulate.**
**Step 5** Remove five points from the plot.
**Step 6** Repeatedly enter a **Guess** for $r$ and **Check** its value until you are within 0.1. Then **Show** the value of $r$.

## DRAW CONCLUSIONS

1. Generate a new data set. Using your knowledge of correlation, try to guess the value of $r$ for the data set. Repeat this 10 times. How many times were you correct? Describe how you chose each $r$ value.
2. Describe how to create a data set with a value of $r$ that is approximately 1.
3. Describe how to create a data set with a value of $r$ that is approximately 0.
4. Try to create a data set with a value of $r$ that is approximately $-0.9$. Then try to create a data set with a value of $r$ that is approximately 0.9. What did you do differently to create the two data sets?

# 9.2 Linear Regression

### What You Should Learn

- How to find the equation of a regression line
- How to predict $y$-values using a regression equation

Regression Lines ■ Applications of Regression Lines

## Regression Lines

After verifying that the linear correlation between two variables is significant, the next step is to determine the equation of the line that best models the data. This line is called a **regression line,** and its equation can be used to predict the value of $y$ for a given value of $x$. Although many lines can be drawn through a set of points, a regression line is determined by specific criteria.

Consider the scatter plot and the line shown below. For each data point, $d_i$ represents the difference between the observed $y$-value and the predicted $y$-value for a given $x$-value. These differences are called **residuals** and can be positive, negative, or zero. When the point is above the line, $d_i$ is positive. When the point is below the line, $d_i$ is negative. When the observed $y$-value equals the predicted $y$-value, $d_i = 0$. Of all possible lines that can be drawn through a set of points, the regression line is the line for which the sum of the squares of all the residuals

$\Sigma d_i^2$ Sum of the squares of the residuals

is a minimum.

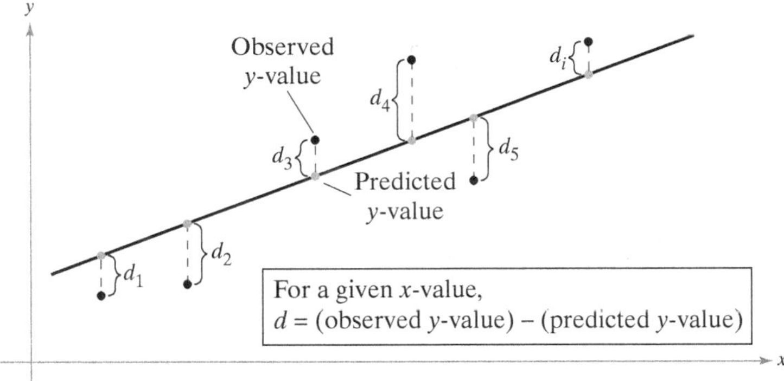


For help with slope-intercept form of the equation of a line, see *Integrated Review* at

MyLab Statistics

> **DEFINITION**
>
> A **regression line,** also called a **line of best fit,** is the line for which the sum of the squares of the residuals is a minimum.

> **Study Tip**
>
> When determining the equation of a regression line, it is helpful to construct a scatter plot of the data to check for outliers, which can greatly influence a regression line. You should also check for gaps and clusters in the data.

In algebra, you learned that you can write an equation of a line by finding its slope $m$ and $y$-intercept $b$. The equation has the form

$$y = mx + b.$$

Recall that the slope of a line is the ratio of its rise over its run and the $y$-intercept is the $y$-value of the point at which the line crosses the $y$-axis. It is the $y$-value when $x = 0$. For instance, the graph of $y = 2x + 1$ is shown in the figure at the right. The slope of the line is 2 and the $y$-intercept is 1.

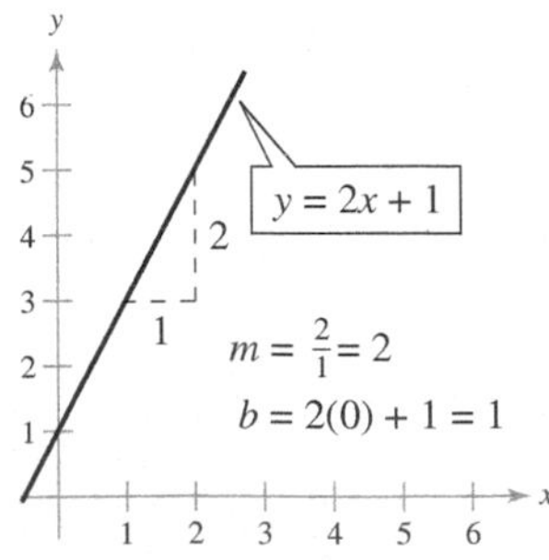


In algebra, you used two points to determine the equation of a line. In statistics, you will use every point in the data set to determine the equation of the regression line.

The equation of a regression line allows you to use the independent (explanatory) variable $x$ to make predictions for the dependent (response) variable $y$.

### Tech Tip

Although formulas for the slope and $y$-intercept are given, it is more convenient to use technology to calculate the equation of a regression line (see Example 2).

## The Equation of a Regression Line

The equation of a regression line for an independent variable $x$ and a dependent variable $y$ is

$$\hat{y} = mx + b$$

where $\hat{y}$ is the predicted $y$-value for a given $x$-value. The slope $m$ and $y$-intercept $b$ are given by

$$m = \frac{n\Sigma xy - (\Sigma x)(\Sigma y)}{n\Sigma x^2 - (\Sigma x)^2} \quad \text{and} \quad b = \bar{y} - m\bar{x} = \frac{\Sigma y}{n} - m\frac{\Sigma x}{n}$$

where $\bar{y}$ is the mean of the $y$-values in the data set, $\bar{x}$ is the mean of the $x$-values, and $n$ is the number of pairs of data. The regression line always passes through the point $(\bar{x}, \bar{y})$.

## EXAMPLE 1

### Finding the Equation of a Regression Line

Find the equation of the regression line for the gross domestic products and carbon dioxide emissions data used in Section 9.1. (See table at the left.)

| GDP (in trillions of dollars), $x$ | $CO_2$ emissions (in millions of metric tons), $y$ |
|---|---|
| 1.7 | 620.1 |
| 2.4 | 475.2 |
| 3.0 | 457.6 |
| 1.2 | 389.7 |
| 4.1 | 810.8 |
| 2.3 | 352.9 |
| 0.9 | 235.0 |
| 1.8 | 297.8 |
| 2.9 | 413.9 |
| 5.4 | 1216.5 |

**SOLUTION**

Recall from Example 7 of Section 9.1 that there is a significant linear correlation between gross domestic products and carbon dioxide emissions. Also, in Example 4 of Section 9.1, you found that $n = 10$, $\Sigma x = 25.7$, $\Sigma y = 5269.5$, $\Sigma xy = 16{,}687.99$, and $\Sigma x^2 = 82.81$. You can use these values to calculate the slope $m$ of the regression line

$$m = \frac{n\Sigma xy - (\Sigma x)(\Sigma y)}{n\Sigma x^2 - (\Sigma x)^2} = \frac{10(16{,}687.99) - (25.7)(5269.5)}{10(82.81) - (25.7)^2} \approx 187.660343$$

and its $y$-intercept $b$.

$$\begin{aligned} b &= \bar{y} - m\bar{x} \\ &\approx \frac{5269.5}{10} - (187.660343)\left(\frac{25.7}{10}\right) \\ &\approx 44.663 \end{aligned}$$

So, the equation of the regression line is

$$\hat{y} = 187.660x + 44.663.$$

### Study Tip

In Example 1, when writing the equation of a regression line, the slope $m$ and the $y$-intercept $b$ are rounded to three decimal places. This *round-off rule* will be used throughout the text.

To sketch the regression line, first choose two $x$-values between the least and greatest $x$-values in the data set. Next, calculate the corresponding $y$-values using the regression equation. Then draw a line through the two points. The regression line and scatter plot of the data are shown at the right. Notice that the line passes through the point $(\bar{x}, \bar{y}) = (2.57, 526.95)$.

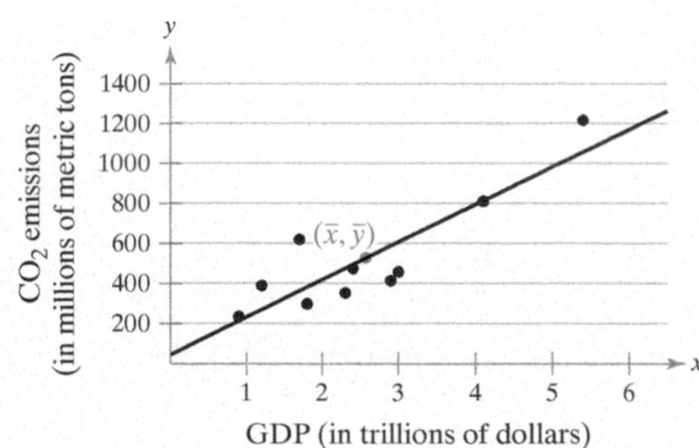

**TRY IT YOURSELF 1**

Find the equation of the regression line for the number of years out of school and annual contribution data used in Try It Yourself 4 in Section 9.1.

*Answer: Page A42*

| Duration, $x$ | Time, $y$ | Duration, $x$ | Time, $y$ |
|---|---|---|---|
| 1.80 | 56 | 3.78 | 79 |
| 1.82 | 58 | 3.83 | 85 |
| 1.90 | 62 | 3.88 | 80 |
| 1.93 | 56 | 4.10 | 89 |
| 1.98 | 57 | 4.27 | 90 |
| 2.05 | 57 | 4.30 | 89 |
| 2.13 | 60 | 4.43 | 89 |
| 2.30 | 57 | 4.47 | 86 |
| 2.37 | 61 | 4.53 | 89 |
| 2.82 | 73 | 4.55 | 86 |
| 3.13 | 76 | 4.60 | 92 |
| 3.27 | 77 | 4.63 | 91 |
| 3.65 | 77 | | |

**9.2** To explore this topic further, see **Activity 9.2** on page 496.

**EXAMPLE 2**

## Using Technology to Find a Regression Equation

Use technology to find the equation of the regression line for the Old Faithful data used in Section 9.1. (See table at the left.)

**SOLUTION**

Recall from Example 6 of Section 9.1 that there is a significant linear correlation between the duration of Old Faithful's eruptions and the time between eruptions. Minitab, Excel, and the TI-84 Plus each have features that calculate a regression equation. Use such technology to find the regression equation. You should obtain results similar to the displays shown below.

**MINITAB**

**Regression Analysis: Time versus Duration**

Regression Equation

Time = 33.68 + 12.481 Duration

Coefficients

| Term | Coef | SE Coef | T-Value | P-Value |
|---|---|---|---|---|
| Constant | 33.68 | 1.89 | 17.79 | 0.000 |
| Duration | 12.481 | 0.546 | 22.84 | 0.000 |

**EXCEL**

| | A |
|---|---|
| 26 | Slope: |
| 27 | 12.48094 |
| 28 | Y-intercept: |
| 29 | 33.6829 |

List the eruption durations in cells A1 through A25 and the times until the next eruption in cells B1 through B25.

Row 27: =SLOPE(B1:B25, A1:A25)

Row 29: =INTERCEPT(B1:B25, A1:A25)

**TI-84 PLUS**

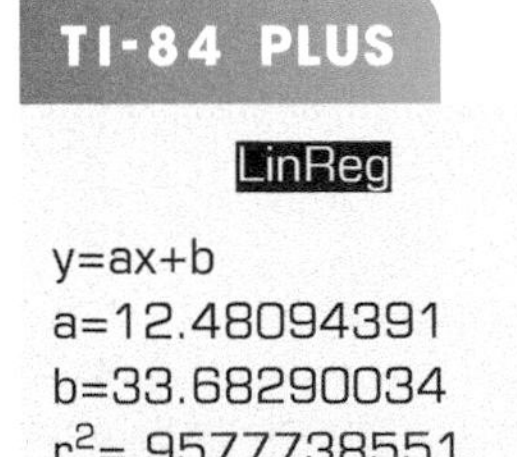


From the displays, you can see that the regression equation is

$$\hat{y} = 12.481x + 33.683.$$

The TI-84 Plus display at the right shows the regression line and a scatter plot of the data in the same viewing window. To do this, use the *Stat Plot* feature to construct the scatter plot and enter the regression equation as $y_1$.

**TI-84 PLUS**

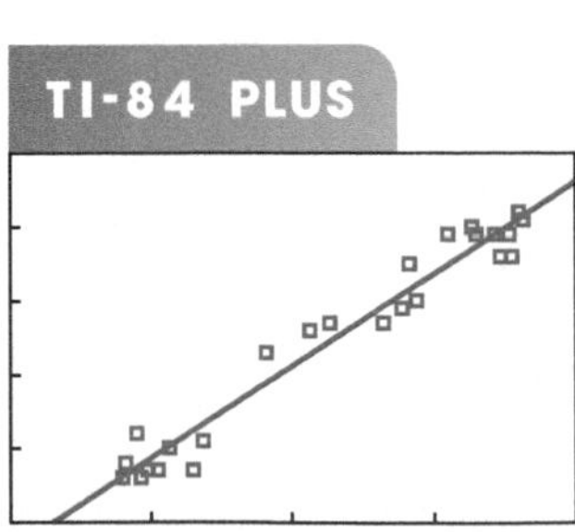

**TRY IT YOURSELF 2**

Use technology to find the equation of the regression line for the salaries and average home game attendances for the teams in Major League Baseball listed on page 469.

*Answer: Page A42*

## Applications of Regression Lines

When the correlation between $x$ and $y$ is *significant* (see Section 9.1), the equation of a regression line can be used to predict $y$-values for certain $x$-values. Prediction values are meaningful only for $x$-values in (or close to) the range of the observed $x$-values in the data. For instance, in Example 1 the observed $x$-values in the data range from \$0.9 trillion to \$5.4 trillion. So, it would not be appropriate to use the regression equation found in Example 1 to predict carbon dioxide emissions for gross domestic products such as \$0.2 trillion or \$14.5 trillion.

To predict $y$-values, substitute an $x$-value into the regression equation, then calculate $\hat{y}$, the predicted $y$-value. This process is shown in the next example.

### Picturing the World

The scatter plot shows the relationship between the number of farms (in thousands) in a state and the total net income of the farms (in millions of dollars) in that state. (Source: U.S. Department of Agriculture)

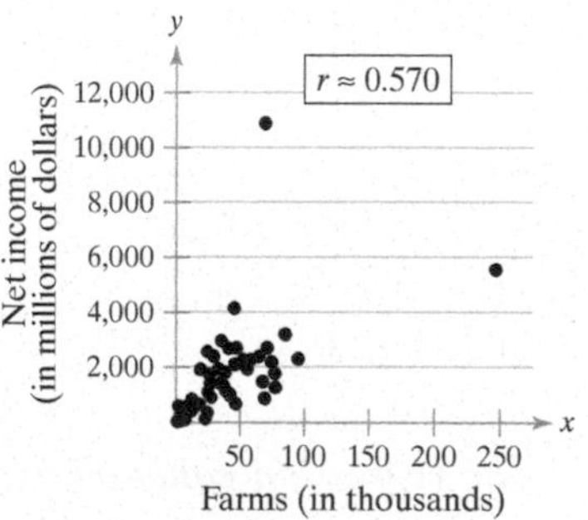


**Describe the correlation between these two variables. Use the scatter plot to predict the total net income in a state that has 150,000 farms ($x = 150$). The regression line for this scatter plot is $\hat{y} = 25.696x + 622.707$. Use this equation to predict the total net income in a state that has 150,000 farms. (Per the methods of Section 9.1, $x$ and $y$ have a significant linear correlation.) How does your algebraic prediction compare with your graphical one?**

### EXAMPLE 3

### Predicting $y$-Values Using Regression Equations

The regression equation for the gross domestic products (in trillions of dollars) and carbon dioxide emissions (in millions of metric tons) data is

$$\hat{y} = 187.660x + 44.663.$$ See Example 1.

Use this equation to predict the *expected* carbon dioxide emissions for each gross domestic product.

**1.** \$1.2 trillion

**2.** \$2.0 trillion

**3.** \$2.6 trillion

#### SOLUTION

Recall from Section 9.1, Example 7, that $x$ and $y$ have a significant linear correlation. So, you can use the regression equation to predict $y$-values. Note that the given gross domestic products are in the range (\$0.9 trillion to \$5.4 trillion) of the observed $x$-values. To predict the expected carbon dioxide emissions, substitute each gross domestic product for $x$ in the regression equation. Then calculate $\hat{y}$.

**1.** $\hat{y} = 187.660x + 44.663$
$= 187.660(1.2) + 44.663$
$= 269.855$

***Interpretation*** When the gross domestic product is \$1.2 trillion, the predicted $CO_2$ emissions are 269.855 million metric tons.

**2.** $\hat{y} = 187.660x + 44.663$
$= 187.660(2.0) + 44.663$
$= 419.983$

***Interpretation*** When the gross domestic product is \$2.0 trillion, the predicted $CO_2$ emissions are 419.983 million metric tons.

**3.** $\hat{y} = 187.660x + 44.663$
$= 187.660(2.6) + 44.663$
$= 532.579$

***Interpretation*** When the gross domestic product is \$2.6 trillion, the predicted $CO_2$ emissions are 532.579 million metric tons.

#### TRY IT YOURSELF 3

The regression equation for the Old Faithful data is $\hat{y} = 12.481x + 33.683$. Use this to predict the time until the next eruption for each eruption duration. (Recall from Section 9.1, Example 6, that $x$ and $y$ have a significant linear correlation.)

**1.** 2 minutes

**2.** 3.32 minutes

*Answer: Page A42*

When the correlation between $x$ and $y$ is *not* significant, the best predicted $y$-value is $\bar{y}$, the mean of the $y$-values in the data.

# 9.2 EXERCISES

For Extra Help: MyLab Statistics

## Building Basic Skills and Vocabulary

1. What is a residual? Explain when a residual is positive, negative, and zero.
2. Two variables have a positive linear correlation. Is the slope of the regression line for the variables positive or negative?
3. Explain how to predict $y$-values using the equation of a regression line.
4. For a set of data and a corresponding regression line, describe all values of $x$ that provide meaningful predictions for $y$.
5. To predict $y$-values using the equation of a regression line, what must be true about the correlation coefficient of the variables?
6. Why is it not appropriate to use a regression line to predict $y$-values for $x$-values that are not in (or close to) the range of $x$-values found in the data?

*In Exercises 7–12, match the description in the left column with its symbol(s) in the right column.*

7. The $y$-value of a data point corresponding to $x_i$
8. The $y$-value for a point on the regression line corresponding to $x_i$
9. Slope
10. $y$-intercept
11. The mean of the $y$-values
12. The point a regression line always passes through

a. $\hat{y}_i$
b. $y_i$
c. $b$
d. $(\bar{x}, \bar{y})$
e. $m$
f. $\bar{y}$

**Graphical Analysis** *In Exercises 13–16, match the regression equation with the appropriate graph.*

13. $\hat{y} = -1.361x + 21.952$
14. $\hat{y} = 2.115x + 21.958$
15. $\hat{y} = 2.125x + 9.588$
16. $\hat{y} = -0.705x + 27.214$

a.

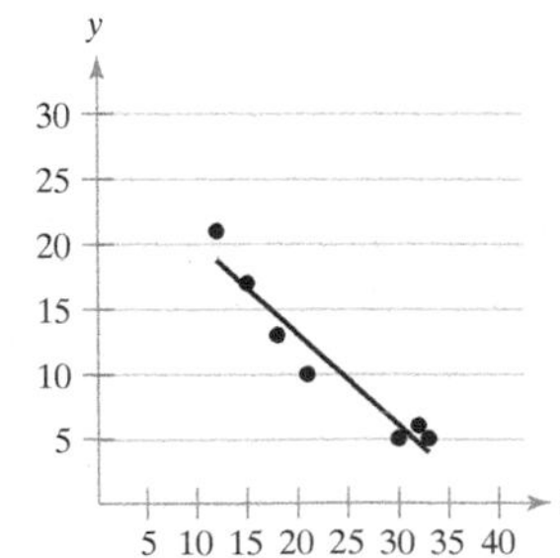


b.

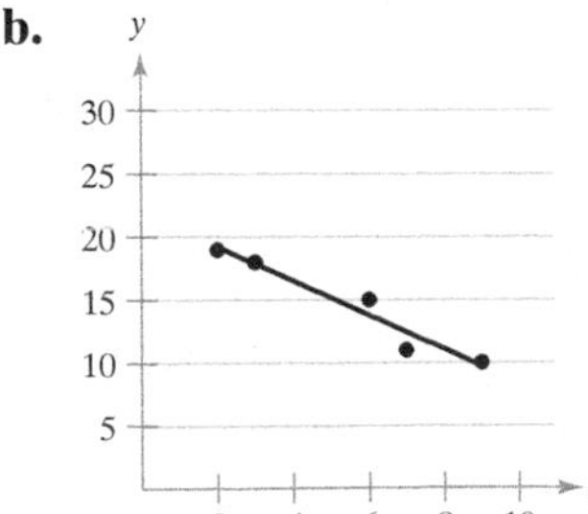


c.

d.

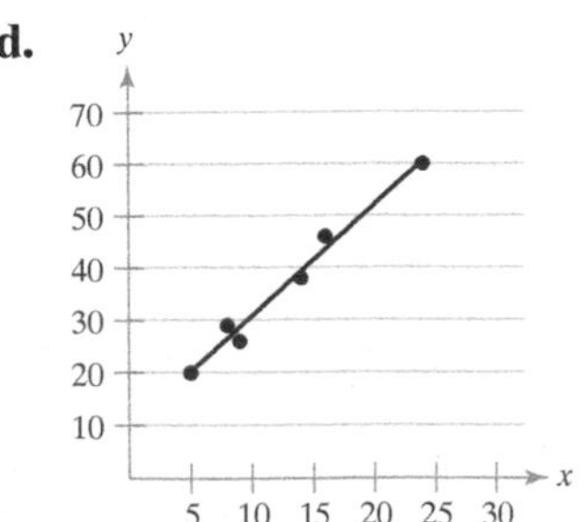

## Using and Interpreting Concepts

**Finding the Equation of a Regression Line** *In Exercises 17–26, find the equation of the regression line for the data. Then construct a scatter plot of the data and draw the regression line. (Each pair of variables has a significant correlation.) Then use the regression equation to predict the value of y for each of the x-values, if meaningful. If the x-value is not meaningful to predict the value of y, explain why not. If convenient, use technology.*

| Square footage, $x$ | Sale price, $y$ |
|---|---|
| 1438 | 120.0 |
| 1280 | 109.5 |
| 1680 | 289.0 |
| 5627 | 915.0 |
| 1040 | 49.9 |
| 1180 | 79.9 |
| 876 | 59.9 |
| 1552 | 94.9 |
| 2180 | 199.9 |

TABLE FOR EXERCISE 18

**17. Height and Number of Stories** The heights (in feet) and the numbers of stories of the nine tallest buildings in Houston, Texas *(Source: Emporis Corporation)*

| Height, $x$ | 1002 | 992 | 901 | 780 | 762 | 756 | 752 | 741 | 735 |
|---|---|---|---|---|---|---|---|---|---|
| Stories, $y$ | 75 | 71 | 64 | 56 | 53 | 55 | 48 | 47 | 47 |

(a) $x = 950$ feet (b) $x = 850$ feet
(c) $x = 800$ feet (d) $x = 650$ feet

**18. Square Footage and Home Sale Price** The square footages and sale prices (in thousands of dollars) of nine homes in Akron, Ohio, are shown in the table at the left. *(Source: Howard Hanna)*

(a) $x = 1100$ square feet (b) $x = 725$ square feet
(c) $x = 2575$ square feet (d) $x = 950$ square feet

**19. Hours Studying and Test Scores** The number of hours 9 students spent studying for a test and their scores on that test

| Hours spent studying, $x$ | 0 | 2 | 4 | 5 | 5 | 5 | 6 | 7 | 8 |
|---|---|---|---|---|---|---|---|---|---|
| Test scores, $y$ | 40 | 51 | 64 | 69 | 73 | 75 | 93 | 90 | 95 |

(a) $x = 3$ hours (b) $x = 6.5$ hours
(c) $x = 13$ hours (d) $x = 4.5$ hours

**20. Goal Differential and Wins** The goal differential (goals scored minus goals conceded) and the number of wins for the top 10 teams in the 2020–2021 English Premier League season *(Source: Premier League)*

| Goal differential, $x$ | 51 | 29 | 26 | 22 | 18 | 15 | 23 | 16 | 8 | −1 |
|---|---|---|---|---|---|---|---|---|---|---|
| Wins, $y$ | 27 | 21 | 20 | 19 | 20 | 19 | 18 | 18 | 18 | 17 |

(a) $x = 0$ goals (b) $x = 20$ goals
(c) $x = 40$ goals (d) $x = 60$ goals

**Electrocardiogram**

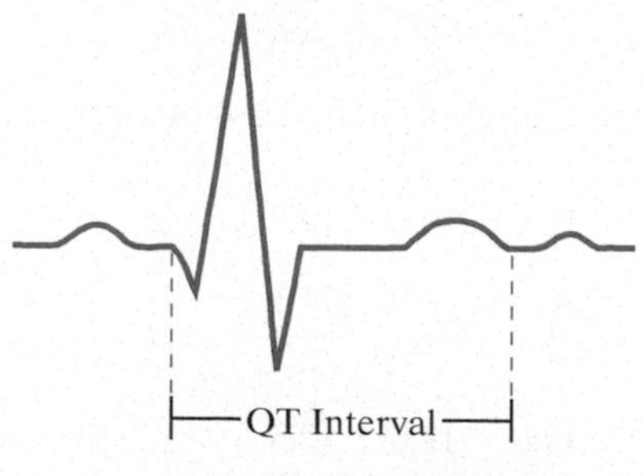


The QT interval is a measure of electrical waves of the heart. A lengthened QT interval can indicate heart health problems.

FIGURE FOR EXERCISE 21

**21. Heart Rate and QT Interval** The heart rates (in beats per minute) and QT intervals (in milliseconds) for 13 males (The figure at the left shows the QT interval of a heartbeat in an electrocardiogram.) *(Adapted from Chest)*

| Heart rate, $x$ | 60 | 75 | 62 | 68 | 84 | 97 | 66 |
|---|---|---|---|---|---|---|---|
| QT interval, $y$ | 403 | 363 | 381 | 367 | 341 | 317 | 401 |

| Heart rate, $x$ | 65 | 86 | 78 | 93 | 75 | 88 |
|---|---|---|---|---|---|---|
| QT interval, $y$ | 384 | 342 | 377 | 329 | 377 | 349 |

(a) $x = 120$ beats per minute (b) $x = 67$ beats per minute
(c) $x = 90$ beats per minute (d) $x = 83$ beats per minute

**22. Length and Girth of Harbor Seals** The lengths (in centimeters) and girths (in centimeters) of 12 harbor seals *(Adapted from Moss Landing Marine Laboratories)*

| **Length, $x$** | 137 | 168 | 152 | 145 | 159 | 159 |
|---|---|---|---|---|---|---|
| **Girth, $y$** | 106 | 130 | 116 | 106 | 125 | 119 |

| **Length, $x$** | 124 | 137 | 155 | 148 | 147 | 146 |
|---|---|---|---|---|---|---|
| **Girth, $y$** | 103 | 104 | 120 | 110 | 107 | 109 |

(a) $x = 140$ centimeters (b) $x = 172$ centimeters
(c) $x = 164$ centimeters (d) $x = 158$ centimeters

**23. Hot Dogs: Caloric and Sodium Content** The caloric contents and the sodium contents (in milligrams) of 12 brands of beef hot dogs *(Source: Walmart)*

| **Calories, $x$** | 180 | 220 | 230 | 90 | 160 | 190 |
|---|---|---|---|---|---|---|
| **Sodium, $y$** | 510 | 740 | 740 | 280 | 530 | 580 |

| **Calories, $x$** | 150 | 110 | 110 | 160 | 140 | 150 |
|---|---|---|---|---|---|---|
| **Sodium, $y$** | 490 | 480 | 330 | 640 | 480 | 460 |

(a) $x = 170$ calories (b) $x = 100$ calories
(c) $x = 260$ calories (d) $x = 210$ calories

**24. Employees and Revenue** The number of employees and the 2020 revenue (in millions of dollars) of 14 hotel and gaming companies *(Adapted from Value Line)*

| **Employees, $x$** | 9000 | 42,000 | 18,000 | 19,700 | 7600 | 7300 | 30,200 |
|---|---|---|---|---|---|---|---|
| **Revenue, $y$** | 1300 | 5162 | 2886 | 1728 | 1182 | 1964 | 2096 |

| **Employees, $x$** | 14,300 | 7000 | 46,000 | 800 | 2600 | 141,000 | 15,500 |
|---|---|---|---|---|---|---|---|
| **Revenue, $y$** | 2179 | 1054 | 3612 | 316 | 615 | 10,571 | 2160 |

(a) $x = 32{,}500$ employees (b) $x = 6000$ employees
(c) $x = 1350$ employees (d) $x = 100{,}000$ employees

**25. Shoe Size and Height** The shoe sizes and heights (in inches) of 14 men

| **Shoe size, $x$** | 8.5 | 9.0 | 9.0 | 9.5 | 10.0 | 10.0 | 10.5 |
|---|---|---|---|---|---|---|---|
| **Height, $y$** | 66.0 | 68.5 | 67.5 | 70.0 | 70.0 | 72.0 | 71.5 |

| **Shoe size, $x$** | 10.5 | 11.0 | 11.0 | 11.0 | 12.0 | 12.0 | 12.5 |
|---|---|---|---|---|---|---|---|
| **Height, $y$** | 69.5 | 71.5 | 72.0 | 73.0 | 73.5 | 74.0 | 74.0 |

(a) $x =$ size 11.5 (b) $x =$ size 8.0
(c) $x =$ size 15.5 (d) $x =$ size 10.0

 **26. Age and Hours Slept** The ages (in years) of 10 infants and the numbers of hours each slept in a day

| Age, $x$ | 0.1 | 0.2 | 0.4 | 0.7 | 0.6 | 0.9 |
|---|---|---|---|---|---|---|
| Hours slept, $y$ | 14.5 | 14.3 | 14.1 | 13.9 | 13.9 | 13.7 |

| Age, $x$ | 0.1 | 0.2 | 0.4 | 0.9 |
|---|---|---|---|---|
| Hours slept, $y$ | 14.3 | 14.2 | 14.0 | 13.8 |

(a) $x = 0.3$ year (b) $x = 3.9$ years
(c) $x = 0.6$ year (d) $x = 0.8$ year

 **Registered Nurse Salaries** *In Exercises 27–30, use the table, which shows the years of experience of 14 registered nurses and their annual salaries (in thousands of dollars).* (Adapted from Payscale, Inc.)

| Years of experience, $x$ | 0.5 | 2 | 4 | 5 | 7 | 9 | 10 |
|---|---|---|---|---|---|---|---|
| Annual salary (in thousands of dollars), $y$ | 48.3 | 53.4 | 58.5 | 63.4 | 65.7 | 67.3 | 70.6 |

| Years of experience, $x$ | 12.5 | 13 | 16 | 18 | 20 | 22 | 25 |
|---|---|---|---|---|---|---|---|
| Annual salary (in thousands of dollars), $y$ | 71.8 | 69.8 | 73.2 | 75.5 | 74.3 | 78.9 | 76.6 |

**27. Correlation** Using the scatter plot of the registered nurse salary data shown below, what type of correlation, if any, do you think the data have? Explain.

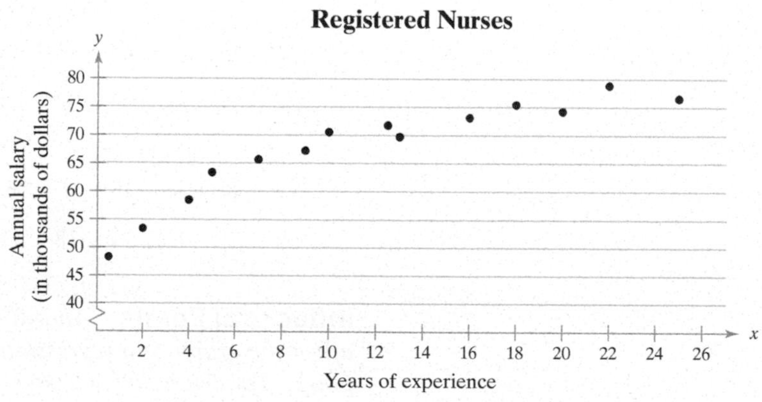


**28. Regression Line** Find an equation of the regression line for the data. Sketch a scatter plot of the data and draw the regression line.

**29. Using the Regression Line** An analyst used the regression line you found in Exercise 28 to predict the annual salary for a registered nurse with 28 years of experience. Is this a valid prediction? Explain your reasoning.

**30. Significant Correlation?** A salary analyst claims that the population has a significant correlation for $\alpha = 0.01$. Test this claim.

## Extending Concepts

**Interchanging *x* and *y*** *In Exercises 31 and 32, perform the steps below.*

*(a) Find the equation of the regression line for the data, letting Row 1 represent the x-values and Row 2 the y-values. Sketch a scatter plot of the data and draw the regression line.*

*(b) Find the equation of the regression line for the data, letting Row 2 represent the x-values and Row 1 the y-values. Sketch a scatter plot of the data and draw the regression line.*

*(c) Describe the effect of switching the explanatory and response variables on the regression line.*

**31.**

| **Row 1** | 0 | 1 | 2 | 3 | 3 | 5 | 5 | 5 | 6 | 7 |
|---|---|---|---|---|---|---|---|---|---|---|
| **Row 2** | 96 | 85 | 82 | 74 | 95 | 68 | 76 | 84 | 58 | 65 |

**32.**

| **Row 1** | 16 | 25 | 39 | 45 | 49 | 64 | 70 |
|---|---|---|---|---|---|---|---|
| **Row 2** | 109 | 122 | 143 | 132 | 199 | 185 | 199 |

**Residual Plots** *A* ***residual plot*** *allows you to assess correlation data and check for possible problems with a regression model. To construct a residual plot, make a scatter plot of* $(x, y - \hat{y})$, *where* $y - \hat{y}$ *is the residual of each y-value. If the resulting plot shows any type of pattern, then the regression line is not a good representation of the relationship between the two variables. If it does not show a pattern—that is, if the residuals fluctuate about 0—then the regression line is a good representation. Be aware that if a point on the residual plot appears to be outside the pattern of the other points, then it may be an outlier.*

*In Exercises 33 and 34, (a) find the equation of the regression line, (b) construct a scatter plot of the data and draw the regression line, (c) construct a residual plot, and (d) determine whether there are any patterns in the residual plot and explain what they suggest about the relationship between the variables.*

**33.**

| $x$ | 38 | 34 | 40 | 46 | 43 | 48 | 60 | 55 | 52 |
|---|---|---|---|---|---|---|---|---|---|
| $y$ | 24 | 22 | 27 | 32 | 30 | 31 | 27 | 26 | 28 |

**34.**

| $x$ | 8 | 4 | 15 | 7 | 6 | 3 | 12 | 10 | 5 |
|---|---|---|---|---|---|---|---|---|---|
| $y$ | 18 | 11 | 29 | 18 | 14 | 8 | 25 | 20 | 12 |

**Influential Points** *An* ***influential point*** *is a point in a data set that can greatly affect the graph of a regression line. An outlier may or may not be an influential point. To determine whether a point is influential, find two regression lines: one including all the points in the data set, and the other excluding the possible influential point. If the slope or y-intercept of the regression line shows significant changes, then the point can be considered influential. An influential point can be removed from a data set only when there is proper justification.*

*In Exercises 35 and 36, (a) construct a scatter plot of the data, (b) identify any possible outliers, and (c) determine whether the point is influential. Explain your reasoning.*

**35.**

| $x$ | 5 | 6 | 9 | 10 | 14 | 17 | 19 | 44 |
|---|---|---|---|---|---|---|---|---|
| $y$ | 32 | 33 | 28 | 26 | 25 | 23 | 23 | 8 |

**36.**

| $x$ | 1 | 3 | 6 | 8 | 12 | 14 |
|---|---|---|---|---|---|---|
| $y$ | 4 | 7 | 10 | 9 | 15 | 3 |

**Transformations to Achieve Linearity** *When a linear model is not appropriate for representing data, other models can be used. In some cases, the values of x or y must be transformed to find an appropriate model. In a* ***logarithmic transformation,*** *the logarithms of the variables are used instead of the original variables when creating a scatter plot and calculating the regression line.*

| Number of hours, $x$ | Number of bacteria, $y$ |
|---|---|
| 1 | 165 |
| 2 | 280 |
| 3 | 468 |
| 4 | 780 |
| 5 | 1310 |
| 6 | 1920 |
| 7 | 4900 |

TABLE FOR EXERCISES 37–40

*In Exercises 37–40, use the data shown in the table at the left, which shows the number of bacteria present after a certain number of hours.*

**37.** Find the equation of the regression line for the data. Then construct a scatter plot of $(x, y)$ and sketch the regression line with it.

**38.** Replace each $y$-value in the table with its logarithm, $\log y$. Find the equation of the regression line for the transformed data. Then construct a scatter plot of $(x, \log y)$ and sketch the regression line with it. What do you notice?

**39.** An **exponential equation** is a nonlinear regression equation of the form $y = ab^x$. Use technology to find and graph the exponential equation for the original data. Include the original data in your graph. Note that you can also find this model by solving the equation $\log y = mx + b$ from Exercise 38 for $y$.

**40.** Compare your results in Exercise 39 with the equation of the regression line and its graph in Exercise 37. Which equation is a better model for the data? Explain.

| $x$ | $y$ |
|---|---|
| 1 | 695 |
| 2 | 410 |
| 3 | 256 |
| 4 | 110 |
| 5 | 80 |
| 6 | 75 |
| 7 | 68 |
| 8 | 74 |

TABLE FOR EXERCISES 41–44

*In Exercises 41–44, use the data shown in the table at the left.*

**41.** Find the equation of the regression line for the data. Then construct a scatter plot of $(x, y)$ and sketch the regression line with it.

**42.** Replace each $x$-value and $y$-value in the table with its logarithm. Find the equation of the regression line for the transformed data. Then construct a scatter plot of $(\log x, \log y)$ and sketch the regression line with it. What do you notice?

**43.** A **power equation** is a nonlinear regression equation of the form $y = ax^b$. Use technology to find and graph the power equation for the original data. Include a scatter plot in your graph. Note that you can also find this model by solving the equation $\log y = m(\log x) + b$ from Exercise 42 for $y$.

**44.** Compare your results in Exercise 43 with the equation of the regression line and its graph in Exercise 41. Which equation is a better model for the data? Explain.

**Logarithmic Equation** *The* ***logarithmic equation*** *is a nonlinear regression equation of the form $y = a + b \ln x$. In Exercises 45–48, use this information and technology.*

**45.** Find and graph the logarithmic equation for the data in Exercise 25.

**46.** Find and graph the logarithmic equation for the data in Exercise 26.

**47.** Compare your results in Exercise 45 with the equation of the regression line and its graph. Which equation is a better model for the data? Explain.

**48.** Compare your results in Exercise 46 with the equation of the regression line and its graph. Which equation is a better model for the data? Explain.

# 9.2 ACTIVITY Regression by Eye

You can find the interactive applet for this activity at MyLab Statistics.

The *Regression by eye* applet allows you to interactively estimate the regression line for a data set. When the applet loads, a data set consisting of 20 points is displayed. To add a point, click at the desired location or click **Add point** and enter the coordinates. To remove a point, click and drag it outside the axis area. All of the points on the plot can be removed by clicking **Reset.** You can move the green line on the plot by clicking and dragging the endpoints. Without looking at the intercept and slope of the regression line, move the line to try to minimize the sum of the squares of the residuals, also known as the sum of square error (SSE). Note that the regression line minimizes the SSE. The intercept, slope, and SSE for the green line and for the regression line are shown below the plot. Click **Simulate** to generate a new data set.

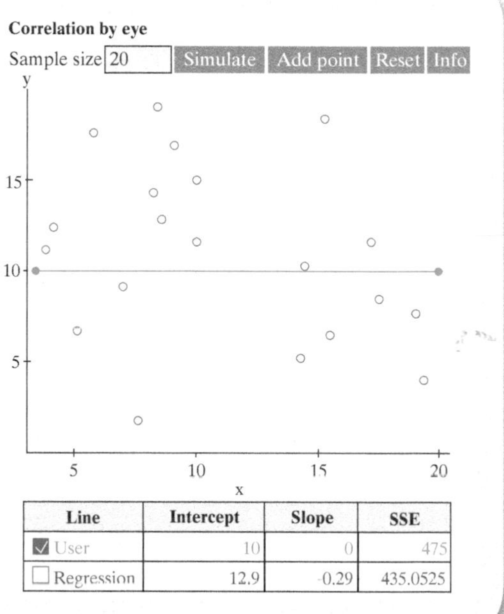


## EXPLORE

**Step 1** Move the endpoints of the green line to try to approximate the regression line.

**Step 2** Click **Regression** to show the line.

## DRAW CONCLUSIONS

1. Click **Simulate** to generate a new data set. Move the green line to try to approximate the regression line. Then click **Regression** to show the line. Repeat this five times. Describe your process for approximating the regression line.
2. On a blank plot, place 10 points so that they have a strong positive correlation. Record the equation of the regression line. Then, add a point in the upper-left corner of the plot and record the equation of the regression line. How does the regression line change?
3. Remove the point from the upper-left corner of the plot. Add 10 more points so that there is still a strong positive correlation. Record the equation of the regression line. Add a point in the upper-left corner of the plot and record the equation of the regression line. How does the regression line change?
4. Use the results of Exercises 2 and 3 to describe what happens to the slope of the regression line when an outlier is added as the sample size increases.

CASE STUDY

# Correlation of Body Measurements

In a study published in *Medicine and Science in Sports and Exercise* (volume 17, no. 2, page 189), the measurements of 252 men (ages 22–81) were taken. Of the 14 measurements taken of each man, some have significant correlations and others do not. For instance, the scatter plot at the right shows that the hip and abdomen circumferences of the men have a strong linear correlation ($r \approx 0.874$). The partial table shown here lists only the first nine rows of the data.

**Hip and Abdomen Circumferences**

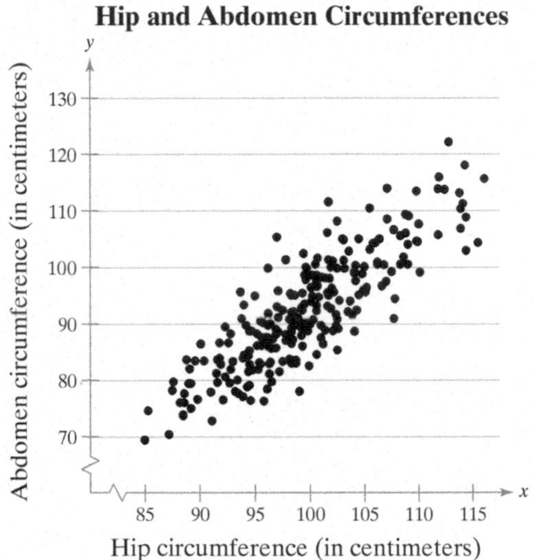


| Age (yr) | Weight (lb) | Height (in.) | Neck (cm) | Chest (cm) | Abdom. (cm) | Hip (cm) | Thigh (cm) | Knee (cm) | Ankle (cm) | Bicep (cm) | Forearm (cm) | Wrist (cm) | Body fat % |
|---|---|---|---|---|---|---|---|---|---|---|---|---|---|
| 22 | 173.25 | 72.25 | 38.5 | 93.6 | 83.0 | 98.7 | 58.7 | 37.3 | 23.4 | 30.5 | 28.9 | 18.2 | 6.1 |
| 22 | 154.00 | 66.25 | 34.0 | 95.8 | 87.9 | 99.2 | 59.6 | 38.9 | 24.0 | 28.8 | 25.2 | 16.6 | 25.3 |
| 23 | 154.25 | 67.75 | 36.2 | 93.1 | 85.2 | 94.5 | 59.0 | 37.3 | 21.9 | 32.0 | 27.4 | 17.1 | 12.3 |
| 23 | 198.25 | 73.50 | 42.1 | 99.6 | 88.6 | 104.1 | 63.1 | 41.7 | 25.0 | 35.6 | 30.0 | 19.2 | 11.7 |
| 23 | 159.75 | 72.25 | 35.5 | 92.1 | 77.1 | 93.9 | 56.1 | 36.1 | 22.7 | 30.5 | 27.2 | 18.2 | 9.4 |
| 23 | 188.15 | 77.50 | 38.0 | 96.6 | 85.3 | 102.5 | 59.1 | 37.6 | 23.2 | 31.8 | 29.7 | 18.3 | 10.3 |
| 24 | 184.25 | 71.25 | 34.4 | 97.3 | 100.0 | 101.9 | 63.2 | 42.2 | 24.0 | 32.2 | 27.7 | 17.7 | 28.7 |
| 24 | 210.25 | 74.75 | 39.0 | 104.5 | 94.4 | 107.8 | 66.0 | 42.0 | 25.6 | 35.7 | 30.6 | 18.8 | 20.9 |
| 24 | 156.00 | 70.75 | 35.7 | 92.7 | 81.9 | 95.3 | 56.4 | 36.5 | 22.0 | 33.5 | 28.3 | 17.3 | 14.2 |

Source: "Generalized Body Composition Prediction Equation for Men Using Simple Measurement Techniques" by K.W. Penrose et al. (1985). MEDICINE AND SCIENCE IN SPORTS AND EXERCISE, vol. 17, no.2, p. 189.

## EXERCISES

**1.** Using your intuition, classify each $(x, y)$ pair as having a weak correlation $(0 < r < 0.5)$, a moderate correlation $(0.5 < r < 0.8)$, or a strong correlation $(0.8 < r < 1.0)$.

(a) (weight, neck)
(b) (weight, height)
(c) (age, body fat)
(d) (chest, hip)
(e) (age, wrist)
(f) (ankle, wrist)
(g) (forearm, height)
(h) (bicep, forearm)
(i) (weight, body fat)
(j) (knee, thigh)
(k) (hip, abdomen)
(l) (abdomen, hip)

**2.** Use technology to find the correlation coefficient for each pair in Exercise 1. Compare your results with those obtained by intuition.

**3.** Use technology to find the regression line for each pair in Exercise 1 that has a strong correlation.

**4.** Use the results of Exercise 3 to predict the following.

(a) The hip circumference of a man whose chest circumference is 95 centimeters
(b) The height of a man whose forearm circumference is 28 centimeters

**5.** Are there pairs of measurements that have stronger correlation coefficients than 0.85? Use technology and intuition to reach a conclusion.

# 9.3 Measures of Regression and Prediction Intervals

## What You Should Learn

- How to interpret the three types of variation about a regression line
- How to find and interpret the coefficient of determination
- How to find and interpret the standard error of estimate for a regression line
- How to construct and interpret a prediction interval for $y$

Variation About a Regression Line ■ The Coefficient of Determination ■ The Standard Error of Estimate ■ Prediction Intervals

## Variation About a Regression Line

In this section, you will study two measures used in correlation and regression studies—the coefficient of determination and the standard error of estimate. You will also learn how to construct a prediction interval for $y$ using a regression equation and a given value of $x$. Before studying these concepts, you need to understand the three types of variation about a regression line.

To find the total variation, the explained variation, and the unexplained variation about a regression line, you must first calculate the **total deviation,** the **explained deviation,** and the **unexplained deviation** for each ordered pair $(x_i, y_i)$ in a data set. These deviations are shown in the figure.

Total deviation $= y_i - \bar{y}$

Explained deviation $= \hat{y}_i - \bar{y}$

Unexplained deviation $= y_i - \hat{y}_i$

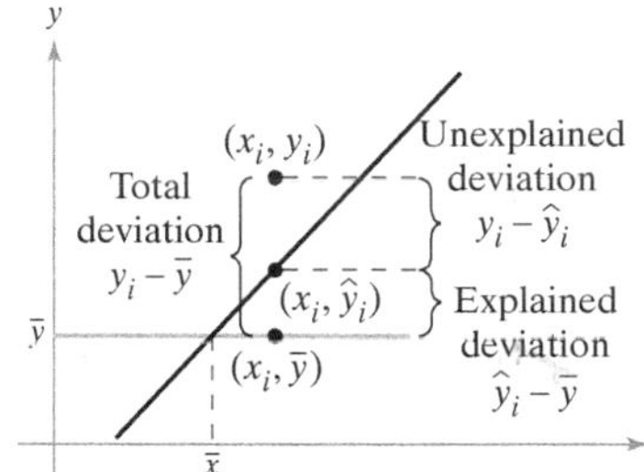


After calculating the deviations for each data point $(x_i, y_i)$, you can find the **total variation,** the **explained variation,** and the **unexplained variation.**

### DEFINITION

The **total variation** about a regression line is the sum of the squares of the differences between the $y$-value of each ordered pair and the mean of $y$.

$$\text{Total variation} = \Sigma(y_i - \bar{y})^2$$

The **explained variation** is the sum of the squares of the differences between each predicted $y$-value and the mean of $y$.

$$\text{Explained variation} = \Sigma(\hat{y}_i - \bar{y})^2$$

The **unexplained variation** is the sum of the squares of the differences between the $y$-value of each ordered pair and each corresponding predicted $y$-value.

$$\text{Unexplained variation} = \Sigma(y_i - \hat{y}_i)^2$$

The sum of the explained and unexplained variations is equal to the total variation.

$$\text{Total variation} = \text{Explained variation} + \text{Unexplained variation}$$

As its name implies, the *explained variation* can be explained by the relationship between $x$ and $y$. The *unexplained variation* cannot be explained by the relationship between $x$ and $y$ and is due to other factors, such as sampling error, coincidence, or lurking variables. (Recall from Section 9.1 that lurking variables are variables that have an effect on the variables being studied but are not included in the study.)

## Picturing the World

Professor Emeritus Janette Benson (Department of Psychology, University of Denver) performed a study relating the mean age at which infants begin to crawl (in weeks after birth) with the average monthly ambient temperature six months after birth. Her results are based on a sample of 414 infants. Benson believes that the reason for the correlation of temperature and crawling age is that parents tend to bundle infants in more restrictive clothing and blankets during cold months. This bundling does not allow the infant as much opportunity to move and experiment with crawling.

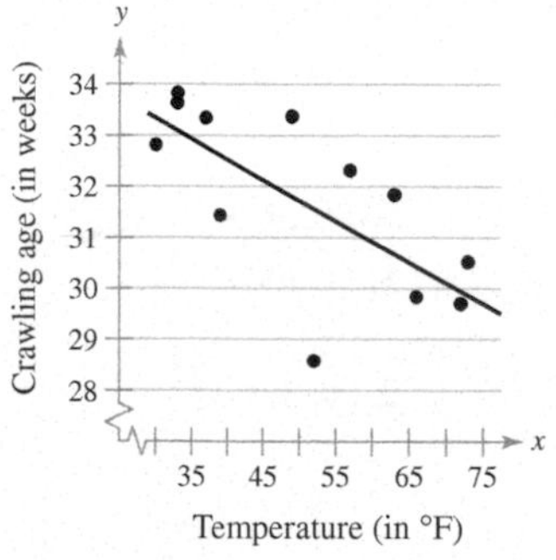


**The correlation coefficient is $r \approx -0.700$. What percent of the variation in the data can be explained? What percent is due to other factors, such as sampling error, coincidence, or lurking variables?**

## The Coefficient of Determination

You already know how to calculate the correlation coefficient $r$. The square of this coefficient is called the **coefficient of determination.** It can be shown that the coefficient of determination is equal to the ratio of the explained variation to the total variation.

### DEFINITION

The **coefficient of determination $r^2$** is the ratio of the explained variation to the total variation. That is,

$$r^2 = \frac{\text{Explained variation}}{\text{Total variation}}.$$

It is important that you interpret the coefficient of determination correctly. For instance, if the correlation coefficient is $r = 0.900$, then the coefficient of determination is

$$r^2 = (0.900)^2$$
$$= 0.810.$$

This means that 81% of the variation in $y$ can be explained by the relationship between $x$ and $y$. The remaining 19% of the variation is unexplained and is due to other factors, such as sampling error, coincidence, or lurking variables.

### EXAMPLE 1

### Finding the Coefficient of Determination

The correlation coefficient for the gross domestic products and carbon dioxide emissions data is

$r \approx 0.874$. See Example 4 in Section 9.1.

Find the coefficient of determination. What does this tell you about the explained variation of the data about the regression line? about the unexplained variation?

**SOLUTION**

The coefficient of determination is

$$r^2 \approx (0.874)^2$$
$$\approx 0.764. \quad \text{Round to three decimal places.}$$

***Interpretation*** About 76.4% of the variation in the carbon dioxide emissions can be explained by the relationship between the gross domestic products and carbon dioxide emissions. About 23.6% of the variation is unexplained and is due to other factors, such as sampling error, coincidence, or lurking variables.

**TRY IT YOURSELF 1**

The correlation coefficient for the Old Faithful data is

$r \approx 0.979$. See Example 5 in Section 9.1.

Find the coefficient of determination. What does this tell you about the explained variation of the data about the regression line? about the unexplained variation?

*Answer: Page A42*

## The Standard Error of Estimate

When a $\hat{y}$-value is predicted from an $x$-value, the prediction is a point estimate. You can construct an interval estimate for $\hat{y}$, but first you need to calculate the **standard error of estimate.**

### DEFINITION

The **standard error of estimate $s_e$** is the standard deviation of the observed $y_i$-values about the predicted $\hat{y}$-value for a given $x_i$-value. It is given by

$$s_e = \sqrt{\frac{\Sigma(y_i - \hat{y}_i)^2}{n - 2}}$$

where $n$ is the number of pairs of data.

From this formula, you can see that the standard error of estimate is the square root of the unexplained variation divided by the square root of $n - 2$. So, the closer the observed $y$-values are to the predicted $\hat{y}$-values, the smaller the standard error of estimate will be.

### GUIDELINES

**Finding the Standard Error of Estimate $s_e$**

| In Words | In Symbols |
|---|---|
| **1.** Make a table that includes the five column headings shown at the right. | $x_i, y_i, \hat{y}_i, (y_i - \hat{y}_i), (y_i - \hat{y}_i)^2$ |
| **2.** Use the regression equation to calculate the predicted $y$-values. | $\hat{y}_i = mx_i + b$ |
| **3.** Calculate the sum of the squares of the differences between each observed $y$-value and the corresponding predicted $y$-value. | $\Sigma(y_i - \hat{y}_i)^2$ |
| **4.** Find the standard error of estimate. | $s_e = \sqrt{\frac{\Sigma(y_i - \hat{y}_i)^2}{n - 2}}$ |

Instead of the formula used in Step 4, you can also find the standard error of estimate using the alternative formula

$$s_e = \sqrt{\frac{\Sigma y^2 - b\Sigma y - m\Sigma xy}{n - 2}}.$$

You can use this formula when you have already calculated the slope $m$, the $y$-intercept $b$, and several of the sums. For instance, consider the gross domestic products and carbon dioxide emissions data (see Example 4 in Section 9.1 and Example 1 in Section 9.2). To use the alternative formula, note that the regression equation for these data is $\hat{y} = 187.660x + 44.663$ and the values of the sums are $\Sigma y^2 = 3{,}548{,}633.25$, $\Sigma y = 5269.5$, and $\Sigma xy = 16{,}687.99$. So, using the alternative formula, the standard error of estimate is

$$\begin{aligned} s_e &= \sqrt{\frac{\Sigma y^2 - b\Sigma y - m\Sigma xy}{n - 2}} \\ &= \sqrt{\frac{3{,}548{,}633.25 - (44.663)(5269.5) - (187.660)(16{,}687.99)}{10 - 2}} \\ &\approx 150.671. \end{aligned}$$

## EXAMPLE 2

### Finding the Standard Error of Estimate

The regression equation for the gross domestic products and carbon dioxide emissions data is

$\hat{y} = 187.660x + 44.663.$ See Example 1 in Section 9.2.

Find the standard error of estimate.

**SOLUTION**

Use a table to calculate the sum of the squared differences of each observed $y$-value and the corresponding predicted $y$-value.

| $x_i$ | $y_i$ | $\hat{y}_i$ | $y_i - \hat{y}_i$ | $(y_i - \hat{y}_i)^2$ |
|---|---|---|---|---|
| 1.7 | 620.1 | 363.685 | 256.415 | 65,748.65223 |
| 2.4 | 475.2 | 495.047 | −19.847 | 393.903409 |
| 3.0 | 457.6 | 607.643 | −150.043 | 22,512.90185 |
| 1.2 | 389.7 | 269.855 | 119.845 | 14,362.82403 |
| 4.1 | 810.8 | 814.069 | −3.269 | 10.686361 |
| 2.3 | 352.9 | 476.281 | −123.381 | 15,222.87116 |
| 0.9 | 235.0 | 213.557 | 21.443 | 459.802249 |
| 1.8 | 297.8 | 382.451 | −84.651 | 7165.791801 |
| 2.9 | 413.9 | 588.877 | −174.977 | 30,616.95053 |
| 5.4 | 1216.5 | 1058.027 | 158.473 | 25,113.69173 |
| | | | | $\Sigma = 181{,}608.0754$ |

Unexplained variation

Because $n = 10$ and $\Sigma(y_i - \hat{y}_i)^2 = 181{,}608.0754$ are used, the standard error of estimate is

$$s_e = \sqrt{\frac{\Sigma(y_i - \hat{y}_i)^2}{n - 2}}$$

$$= \sqrt{\frac{181{,}608.0754}{10 - 2}}$$

$$\approx 150.669.$$

***Interpretation*** The standard error of estimate of the carbon dioxide emissions for a specific gross domestic product is about 150.669 million metric tons.

**TRY IT YOURSELF 2**

A researcher collects the data shown below and concludes that there is a significant relationship between the amount of radio advertising time (in minutes per week) and the weekly sales of a product (in hundreds of dollars).

| Radio ad time, $x$ | 15 | 20 | 20 | 30 | 40 | 45 | 50 | 60 |
|---|---|---|---|---|---|---|---|---|
| **Weekly sales, $y$** | 26 | 32 | 38 | 56 | 54 | 78 | 80 | 88 |

Find the standard error of estimate. Use the regression equation

$\hat{y} = 1.405x + 7.311.$

*Answer: Page A42*

## Prediction Intervals

Recall from Section 9.1 that one of the requirements for calculating a correlation coefficient is that the two variables $x$ and $y$ have a bivariate normal distribution. Two variables have a **bivariate normal distribution** when for any fixed values of $x$ the corresponding values of $y$ are normally distributed, and for any fixed values of $y$ the corresponding values of $x$ are normally distributed.

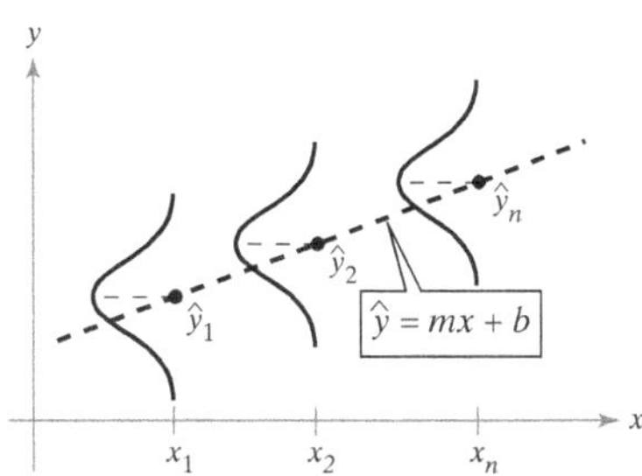


Bivariate Normal Distribution

Because regression equations are determined using random samples of paired data and because $x$ and $y$ are assumed to have a bivariate normal distribution, you can construct a **prediction interval** for the true value of $y$. To construct the prediction interval, use a $t$-distribution with $n - 2$ degrees of freedom.

### DEFINITION

Given a linear regression equation $\hat{y} = mx + b$ and $x_0$, a specific value of $x$, a **$c$-prediction interval** for $y$ is $\hat{y} - E < y < \hat{y} + E$ where

$$E = t_c s_e \sqrt{1 + \frac{1}{n} + \frac{n(x_0 - \bar{x})^2}{n\Sigma x^2 - (\Sigma x)^2}}.$$

The point estimate is $\hat{y}$ and the margin of error is $E$. The probability that the prediction interval contains $y$ is $c$ (the level of confidence), assuming that the estimation process is repeated a large number of times.

**Study Tip**

The formulas for $s_e$ and $E$ use the quantities $\Sigma(y_i - \hat{y}_i)^2$, $(\Sigma x)^2$, and $\Sigma x^2$. Use a table to calculate these quantities.

### GUIDELINES

**Constructing a Prediction Interval for $y$ for a Specific Value of $x$**

| In Words | In Symbols |
|---|---|
| **1.** Identify the number $n$ of pairs of data and the degrees of freedom. | d.f. $= n - 2$ |
| **2.** Use the regression equation and the given $x$-value to find the point estimate $\hat{y}$. | $\hat{y}_i = mx_i + b$ |
| **3.** Find the critical value $t_c$ that corresponds to the given level of confidence $c$. | Use Table 5 in Appendix B. |
| **4.** Find the standard error of estimate $s_e$. | $s_e = \sqrt{\frac{\Sigma(y_i - \hat{y}_i)^2}{n - 2}}$ |
| **5.** Find the margin of error $E$. | $E = t_c s_e \sqrt{1 + \frac{1}{n} + \frac{n(x_0 - \bar{x})^2}{n\Sigma x^2 - (\Sigma x)^2}}$ |
| **6.** Find the left and right endpoints and form the prediction interval. | Left endpoint: $\hat{y} - E$<br>Right endpoint: $\hat{y} + E$<br>Interval: $\hat{y} - E < y < \hat{y} + E$ |

## EXAMPLE 3

### Constructing a Prediction Interval

Using the results of Example 2, construct a 90% prediction interval for the carbon dioxide emissions when the gross domestic product is \$2.8 trillion. What can you conclude?

**SOLUTION**

Because $n = 10$, there are d.f. $= 10 - 2 = 8$ degrees of freedom. Using the regression equation

$$\hat{y} = 187.660x + 44.663$$

and

$$x = 2.8$$

the point estimate is

$$\begin{aligned}\hat{y} &= 187.660x + 44.663\\ &= 187.660(2.8) + 44.663\\ &= 570.111.\end{aligned}$$

From Table 5, the critical value is $t_c = 1.860$ and from Example 2, $s_e \approx 150.669$. From Example 4 in Section 9.1, you found that $\Sigma x = 25.7$ and $\Sigma x^2 = 82.81$. Also, $\bar{x} = 2.57$. Using these values, the margin of error is

$$\begin{aligned}E &= t_c s_e\sqrt{1 + \frac{1}{n} + \frac{n(x_0 - \bar{x})^2}{n\Sigma x^2 - (\Sigma x)^2}}\\ &\approx (1.860)(150.669)\sqrt{1 + \frac{1}{10} + \frac{10(2.8 - 2.57)^2}{10(82.81) - (25.7)^2}}\\ &\approx 294.344.\end{aligned}$$

Using $\hat{y} = 570.111$ and $E \approx 294.344$, the prediction interval is constructed as shown.

| Left Endpoint | Right Endpoint |
|---|---|
| $\hat{y} - E \approx 570.111 - 294.344$ | $\hat{y} + E \approx 570.111 + 294.344$ |
| $= 275.767$ | $= 864.455$ |

$$275.767 < y < 864.455$$

***Interpretation*** You can be 90% confident that when the gross domestic product is \$2.8 trillion, the carbon dioxide emissions will be between 275.767 and 864.455 million metric tons.

**TRY IT YOURSELF 3**

Using the results of Example 2, construct a 95% prediction interval for the carbon dioxide emissions when the gross domestic product is \$4 trillion. What can you conclude?

*Answer: Page A42*

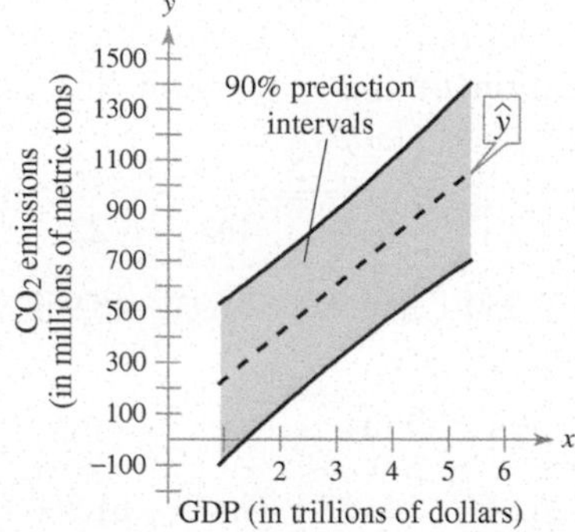


For $x$-values near $\bar{x}$, the prediction interval for $y$ becomes narrower. For $x$-values further from $\bar{x}$, the prediction interval for $y$ becomes wider. (This is one reason why the regression equation should not be used to predict $y$-values for $x$-values outside the range of the observed $x$-values in the data.) For instance, consider the 90% prediction intervals for $y$ in Example 3 shown at the left. The range of the $x$-values is $0.9 \le x \le 5.4$. Notice how the confidence interval bands curve away from the regression line as $x$ gets closer to 0.9 or to 5.4.

# 9.3 EXERCISES

For Extra Help: MyLab Statistics

## Building Basic Skills and Vocabulary

**Graphical Analysis** *In Exercises 1–3, use the figure.*

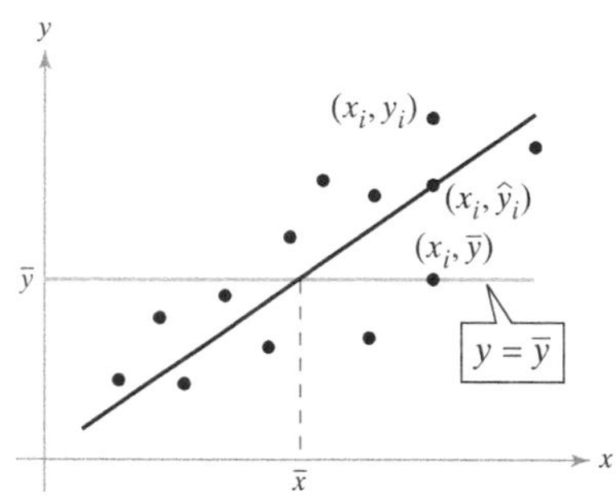


**1.** Describe the total variation about a regression line in words and in symbols.

**2.** Describe the explained variation about a regression line in words and in symbols.

**3.** Describe the unexplained variation about a regression line in words and in symbols.

**4.** The coefficient of determination $r^2$ is the ratio of which two types of variations? What does $r^2$ measure? What does $1 - r^2$ measure?

**5.** What is the coefficient of determination for two variables that have perfect positive linear correlation or perfect negative linear correlation? Interpret your answer.

**6.** Two variables have a bivariate normal distribution. Explain what this means.

*In Exercises 7–10, use the value of the correlation coefficient r to calculate the coefficient of determination $r^2$. What does this tell you about the explained variation of the data about the regression line? about the unexplained variation?*

**7.** $r = 0.465$

**8.** $r = -0.328$

**9.** $r = -0.957$

**10.** $r = 0.881$

## Using and Interpreting Concepts

**Finding the Coefficient of Determination and the Standard Error of Estimate** *In Exercises 11–20, use the data to (a) find the coefficient of determination $r^2$ and interpret the result, and (b) find the standard error of estimate $s_e$ and interpret the result.*

 **11. Stock Offerings** The numbers of initial public offerings of stock issued and the total proceeds of these offerings (in millions of dollars) for 12 years are shown in the table. The equation of the regression line is $\hat{y} = 222.346x + 5001.340$. *(Source: University of Florida)*

| Number of offerings, *x* | 42 | 101 | 82 | 104 | 162 | 225 |
|---|---|---|---|---|---|---|
| **Proceeds, *y*** | 13,307 | 30,742 | 27,750 | 32,065 | 39,093 | 46,967 |

| Number of offerings, *x* | 125 | 79 | 118 | 143 | 115 | 165 |
|---|---|---|---|---|---|---|
| **Proceeds, *y*** | 22,296 | 13,234 | 24,044 | 34,027 | 39,479 | 61,860 |

**12. Median and Mean Hourly Wages** The table shows the median and mean hourly wages (in dollars) in 10 states in a recent year. The equation of the regression line is $\hat{y} = 1.208x + 1.495$. *(Source: U.S. Census Bureau)*

| Median hourly wage, $x$ | 17.43 | 22.52 | 18.07 | 18.56 | 18.59 |
|---|---|---|---|---|---|
| Mean hourly wage, $y$ | 22.52 | 29.25 | 24.05 | 23.39 | 23.37 |

| Median hourly wage, $x$ | 22.41 | 18.63 | 20.08 | 18.98 | 19.79 |
|---|---|---|---|---|---|
| Mean hourly wage, $y$ | 28.23 | 24.52 | 25.94 | 24.73 | 24.64 |

**13. Goals Allowed and Points Earned** The table shows the number of goals allowed and the total points earned by the 15 North and West Division teams in the 2020–2021 National Hockey League season. The equation of the regression line is $\hat{y} = -0.552x + 152.584$. *(Source: ESPN)*

| Goals allowed, $x$ | 190 | 188 | 168 | 161 | 154 | 148 | 154 |
|---|---|---|---|---|---|---|---|
| Points earned, $y$ | 51 | 50 | 59 | 55 | 63 | 77 | 72 |

| Goals allowed, $x$ | 179 | 199 | 170 | 176 | 170 | 160 | 133 | 124 |
|---|---|---|---|---|---|---|---|---|
| Points earned, $y$ | 43 | 49 | 49 | 54 | 63 | 75 | 82 | 82 |

**14. Trees** The table shows the heights (in feet) and trunk diameters (in inches) of eight trees. The equation of the regression line is $\hat{y} = 0.479x - 24.086$.

| Height, $x$ | 70 | 72 | 75 | 76 |
|---|---|---|---|---|
| Trunk diameter, $y$ | 8.3 | 10.5 | 11.0 | 11.4 |

| Height, $x$ | 85 | 78 | 77 | 82 |
|---|---|---|---|---|
| Trunk diameter, $y$ | 14.9 | 14.0 | 16.3 | 15.8 |

**15. STEM Employment and Mean Wage** The table shows the percentage of employment in STEM (science, technology, engineering, and math) occupations and mean annual wage (in thousands of dollars) for 14 industries in a recent year. The equation of the regression line is $\hat{y} = 1.224x + 81.643$. *(Source: U.S. Bureau of Labor Statistics)*

| Percentage of employment in STEM occupations, $x$ | 15.4 | 1.7 | 11.6 | 8.0 | 1.2 | 27.0 | 18.7 |
|---|---|---|---|---|---|---|---|
| Mean annual wage, $y$ | 102.5 | 82.7 | 98.5 | 95.5 | 89.3 | 110.3 | 107.8 |

| Percentage of employment in STEM occupations, $x$ | 3.9 | 4.8 | 1.1 | 0.8 | 0.1 | 1.8 | 8.6 |
|---|---|---|---|---|---|---|---|
| Mean annual wage, $y$ | 88.9 | 82.5 | 86.4 | 81.0 | 72.8 | 84.3 | 88.7 |

**16. Voter Turnout** The U.S. voting age populations (in millions) and the number of ballots cast (in millions) for the highest office in federal elections for ten nonpresidential election years are shown in the table. The equation of the regression line is $\hat{y} = 0.429x - 10.763$. *(Source: United States Elections Project)*

| **Voting age population, *x*** | 166.0 | 177.9 | 186.2 | 195.3 | 205.3 |
|---|---|---|---|---|---|
| **Ballots cast in federal elections, *y*** | 67.6 | 65.0 | 67.9 | 75.1 | 72.5 |

| **Voting age population, *x*** | 215.5 | 225.5 | 236.0 | 245.7 | 255.8 |
|---|---|---|---|---|---|
| **Ballots cast in federal elections, *y*** | 78.4 | 83.8 | 89.1 | 81.7 | 117.1 |

**17. Natural Gas** The table shows the marketed productions of natural gas (in billions of cubic feet) in the United States and the exports of natural gas (in billions of cubic feet) from the United States for seven years. The equation of the regression line is $\hat{y} = 0.355x - 7960.686$. *(Source: U.S. Energy Information Administration)*

| **Marketed production, *x*** | 27,498 | 28,772 | 28,400 | 29,238 | 33,009 | 36,515 | 36,173 |
|---|---|---|---|---|---|---|---|
| **Export, *y*** | 1514 | 1784 | 2335 | 3154 | 3608 | 4656 | 5284 |

 **18. Fund Assets** The table shows the total assets (in billions of dollars) of individual retirement accounts (IRAs) and federal defined benefit (DB) plans for ten years. The equation of the regression line is $\hat{y} = 0.122x + 558.880$. *(Source: Investment Company Institute)*

| **IRAs, *x*** | 5550 | 6123 | 6961 | 7400 | 7610 |
|---|---|---|---|---|---|
| **Federal DB plans, *y*** | 1220 | 1288 | 1364 | 1425 | 1504 |

| **IRAs, *x*** | 8415 | 9395 | 9925 | 9365 | 12,555 |
|---|---|---|---|---|---|
| **Federal DB plans, *y*** | 1589 | 1679 | 1781 | 1895 | 2006 |

 **19. New Vehicle Sales** The table shows the numbers of new vehicle sales (in thousands) in the United States for Ford and General Motors for 11 years. The equation of the regression line is $\hat{y} = 0.937x + 637.674$. *(Source: NADA Industry Analysis Division)*

| **New vehicle sales (Ford), *x*** | 1942 | 1656 | 1905 | 2111 | 2206 | 2435 |
|---|---|---|---|---|---|---|
| **New vehicle sales (General Motors), *y*** | 2956 | 2072 | 2211 | 2504 | 2596 | 2786 |

| **New vehicle sales (Ford), *x*** | 2418 | 2549 | 2542 | 2513 | 1968 |
|---|---|---|---|---|---|
| **New vehicle sales (General Motors), *y*** | 2935 | 3082 | 3042 | 3000 | 2536 |

**20. New Vehicle Sales** The table shows the numbers of new vehicle sales (in thousands) in the United States for Toyota and Honda for 11 years. The equation of the regression line is $\hat{y} = 0.584x + 169.227$. *(Source: NADA Industry Analysis Division)*

| New vehicle sales (Toyota), $x$ | 2218 | 1770 | 1764 | 1645 | 2083 | 2236 |
|---|---|---|---|---|---|---|
| **New vehicle sales (Honda), $y$** | 1429 | 1151 | 1231 | 1147 | 1423 | 1525 |

| New vehicle sales (Toyota), $x$ | 2374 | 2499 | 2500 | 2435 | 2113 |
|---|---|---|---|---|---|
| **New vehicle sales (Honda), $y$** | 1541 | 1587 | 1638 | 1641 | 1347 |

**Constructing and Interpreting a Prediction Interval** *In Exercises 21–30, construct the indicated prediction interval and interpret the results.*

**21. Proceeds** Construct a 95% prediction interval for the proceeds from initial public offerings in Exercise 11 when the number of offerings is 200.

**22. Mean Hourly Wage** Construct a 95% prediction interval for the mean hourly wage in Exercise 12 when the median hourly wage is \$21.50.

**23. Points Earned** Construct a 90% prediction interval for total points earned in Exercise 13 when the number of goals allowed by the team is 140.

**24. Trees** Construct a 90% prediction interval for the trunk diameter of a tree in Exercise 14 when the height is 80 feet.

**25. Mean Wage** Construct a 99% prediction interval for the mean annual wage in Exercise 15 when the percentage of employment in STEM occupations is 13% in the industry.

**26. Voter Turnout** Construct a 99% prediction interval for number of ballots cast in Exercise 16 when the voting age population is 210 million.

**27. Natural Gas** Construct a 95% prediction interval for the export of natural gas from the United States in Exercise 17 when the marketed production of natural gas in the United States is 31 trillion cubic feet.

**28. Total Assets** Construct a 90% prediction interval for the total assets in federal defined benefit plans in Exercise 18 when the total assets in IRAs are \$6400 billion.

**29. New Vehicle Sales** Construct a 95% prediction interval for new vehicle sales for General Motors in Exercise 19 when the number of new vehicles sold by Ford is 2028 thousand.

**30. New Vehicle Sales** Construct a 99% prediction interval for new vehicle sales for Honda in Exercise 20 when the number of new vehicles sold by Toyota is 2159 thousand.

**Old Vehicles** *In Exercises 31–34, use the figure shown at the left.*

**31. Scatter Plot** Construct a scatter plot of the data. Show $\bar{y}$ and $\bar{x}$ on the graph.

**32. Regression Line** Find and draw the regression line.

**33. Coefficient of Determination** Find the coefficient of determination $r^2$ and interpret the results.

**34. Error of Estimate** Find the standard error of estimate $s_e$ and interpret the results.

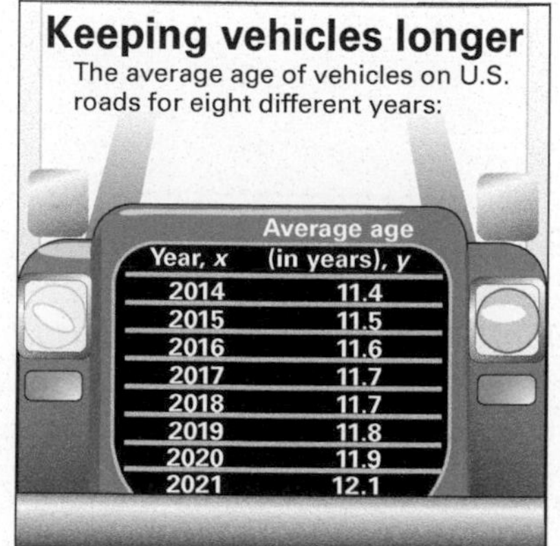
Keeping vehicles longer
The average age of vehicles on U.S. roads for eight different years:

| Year, $x$ | Average age (in years), $y$ |
|---|---|
| 2014 | 11.4 |
| 2015 | 11.5 |
| 2016 | 11.6 |
| 2017 | 11.7 |
| 2018 | 11.7 |
| 2019 | 11.8 |
| 2020 | 11.9 |
| 2021 | 12.1 |

(Sources: Bureau of Transportation Statistics, IHS Markit)

FIGURE FOR EXERCISES 31–34

## Extending Concepts

**Hypothesis Testing for Slope** *When testing the slope M of the regression line for the population, you usually test that the slope is 0, or* $H_0$: $M = 0$. *A slope of 0 indicates that there is no linear relationship between x and y. To perform the t-test for the slope M, use the standardized test statistic*

$$t = \frac{m}{s_e}\sqrt{\Sigma x^2 - \frac{(\Sigma x)^2}{n}}$$

*with* $n - 2$ *degrees of freedom. Then, using the critical values found in Table 5 in Appendix B, make a decision whether to reject or fail to reject the null hypothesis. You can also use the LinRegTTest feature on a TI-84 Plus to calculate the standardized test statistic as well as the corresponding P-value. If* $P \le \alpha$, *then reject the null hypothesis. If* $P > \alpha$, *then do not reject* $H_0$.

*In Exercises 35 and 36, test the claim and interpret the results in the context of the problem. If convenient, use technology.*

**35.** The table shows the weights (in pounds) and the numbers of hours slept in a day by a random sample of infants. Test the claim that $M \neq 0$. Use $\alpha = 0.01$.

| **Weight, x** | 8.1 | 10.2 | 9.9 | 7.2 | 6.9 | 11.2 | 11 | 15 |
|---|---|---|---|---|---|---|---|---|
| **Hours slept, y** | 14.8 | 14.6 | 14.1 | 14.2 | 13.8 | 13.2 | 13.9 | 12.5 |

 **36.** The table shows the ages (in years) and salaries (in thousands of dollars) of a random sample of employees at a company. Test the claim that $M \neq 0$. Use $\alpha = 0.05$.

| **Age, x** | 25 | 34 | 29 | 30 | 42 | 38 | 49 | 52 | 35 | 40 |
|---|---|---|---|---|---|---|---|---|---|---|
| **Salary, y** | 57.5 | 61.2 | 59.9 | 58.7 | 87.5 | 67.4 | 89.2 | 85.3 | 69.5 | 75.1 |

**Confidence Intervals for *y*-Intercept and Slope** *You can construct confidence intervals for the y-intercept B and slope M of the regression line* $y = Mx + B$ *for the population by using the inequalities below.*

***y*-intercept *B*:** $b - E < B < b + E$

*where* $E = t_c s_e \sqrt{\frac{1}{n} + \frac{\bar{x}^2}{\Sigma x^2 - \frac{(\Sigma x)^2}{n}}}$ *and*

***slope M*:** $m - E < M < m + E$

*where* $E = \dfrac{t_c s_e}{\sqrt{\Sigma x^2 - \frac{(\Sigma x)^2}{n}}}$

*The values of m and b are obtained from the sample data, and the critical value* $t_c$ *is found using Table 5 in Appendix B with* $n - 2$ *degrees of freedom.*

*In Exercises 37 and 38, construct the indicated confidence intervals for B and M using the gross domestic products and carbon dioxide emissions data found in Example 2.*

**37.** 95% confidence interval

**38.** 99% confidence interval

# 9.4 Multiple Regression

### What You Should Learn

- How to use technology to find and interpret a multiple regression equation, the standard error of estimate, and the coefficient of determination
- How to use a multiple regression equation to predict $y$-values

Finding a Multiple Regression Equation ■ Predicting $y$-Values

## Finding a Multiple Regression Equation

In many instances, a better prediction model can be found for a dependent (response) variable by using more than one independent (explanatory) variable. For instance, a more accurate prediction for the carbon dioxide emissions discussed in previous sections might be made by considering the number of cars as well as the gross domestic product. Models that contain more than one independent variable are called *multiple regression models.*

**DEFINITION**

A **multiple regression equation** for independent variables $x_1, x_2, x_3, \ldots, x_k$ and a dependent variable $y$ has the form

$$\hat{y} = b + m_1x_1 + m_2x_2 + m_3x_3 + \cdots + m_kx_k$$

where $\hat{y}$ is the predicted $y$-value for given $x_i$ values and $b$ is the $y$-intercept. The $y$-intercept $b$ is the value of $\hat{y}$ when all $x_i$ are 0. Each coefficient $m_i$ is the amount of change in $\hat{y}$ when the independent variable $x_i$ is changed by one unit and all other independent variables are held constant.

**Tech Tip**

Detailed instructions for using Minitab and Excel to find a multiple regression equation are shown in the technology manuals that accompany this text.

Because the mathematics associated with multiple regression is complicated, this section focuses on how to use technology to find a multiple regression equation and how to interpret the results.

**EXAMPLE 1**

### Finding a Multiple Regression Equation

A researcher wants to determine how employee salaries at a company are related to the length of employment, previous experience, and education. The researcher selects eight employees from the company and obtains the data shown in the table.

| Employee | Salary (in dollars), $y$ | Employment (in years), $x_1$ | Experience (in years), $x_2$ | Education (in years), $x_3$ |
|---|---|---|---|---|
| A | 57,310 | 10 | 2 | 16 |
| B | 57,380 | 5 | 6 | 16 |
| C | 54,135 | 3 | 1 | 12 |
| D | 56,985 | 6 | 5 | 14 |
| E | 58,715 | 8 | 8 | 16 |
| F | 60,620 | 20 | 0 | 12 |
| G | 59,200 | 8 | 4 | 18 |
| H | 60,320 | 14 | 6 | 17 |

Use Minitab to find a multiple regression equation that models the data.

**SOLUTION**

Enter the $y$-values in C1 and the $x_1$-, $x_2$-, and $x_3$-values in C2, C3, and C4, respectively. From the *Stat* menu, select "Regression▶Regression▶Fit Regression Model." Using the salaries as the response variable and the remaining data as the continuous predictors, you should obtain results similar to the display shown.

**Study Tip**

In Example 1, it is important that you interpret the coefficients $m_1$, $m_2$, and $m_3$ correctly. For instance, if $x_2$ and $x_3$ are held constant and $x_1$ increases by 1, then $y$ increases by \$364. Similarly, if $x_1$ and $x_3$ are held constant and $x_2$ increases by 1, then $y$ increases by \$228. If $x_1$ and $x_2$ are held constant and $x_3$ increases by 1, then $y$ increases by \$267.

**MINITAB**

**Regression Analysis: Salary, y versus x1, x2, x3**

Regression Equation

Salary, y = 49764 + 364.4 x1 + 228 x2 + 267 x3

Coefficients

| Term | Coef | SE Coef | T-Value | P-Value |
|---|---|---|---|---|
| Constant | 49764 ← $b$ | 1981 | 25.12 | 0.000 |
| x1 | 364.4 ← $m_1$ | 48.3 | 7.54 | 0.002 |
| x2 | 228 ← $m_2$ | 124 | 1.84 | 0.140 |
| x3 | 267 ← $m_3$ | 147 | 1.81 | 0.144 |

Model Summary

| S | R-sq | R-sq(adj) | R-sq(pred) |
|---|---|---|---|
| 659.490 | 94.38% | 90.17% | 48.98% |

The regression equation is $\hat{y} = 49{,}764 + 364x_1 + 228x_2 + 267x_3$.

**TRY IT YOURSELF 1**

A statistics professor wants to determine how students' final grades are related to the midterm exam grades and number of classes missed. The professor selects 10 students and obtains the data shown in the table.

| Student | Final grade, $y$ | Midterm exam, $x_1$ | Classes missed, $x_2$ |
|---|---|---|---|
| 1 | 81 | 75 | 1 |
| 2 | 90 | 80 | 0 |
| 3 | 86 | 91 | 2 |
| 4 | 76 | 80 | 3 |
| 5 | 51 | 62 | 6 |
| 6 | 75 | 90 | 4 |
| 7 | 44 | 60 | 7 |
| 8 | 81 | 82 | 2 |
| 9 | 94 | 88 | 0 |
| 10 | 93 | 96 | 1 |

Use technology to find a multiple regression equation that models the data.

*Answer: Page A42*

Minitab displays much more than the regression equation and the coefficients of the independent variables. For instance, it also displays the standard error of estimate, denoted by $S$, and the coefficient of determination, denoted by *R-Sq*. In Example 1, $S = 659.490$ and $R\text{-}Sq = 94.38\%$. So, the standard error of estimate is \$659.49. The coefficient of determination tells you that 94.38% of the variation in $y$ can be explained by the multiple regression model. The remaining 5.62% is unexplained and is due to other factors, such as sampling error, coincidence, or lurking variables.

## Picturing the World

In a lake in Finland, 159 fish of 7 species were caught and measured for weight $G$ (in grams), length $L$ (in centimeters), height $H$, and width $W$ ($H$ and $W$ are percents of $L$). The regression equation for $G$ and $L$ is

$$G = -491 + 28.5L,$$
$$r \approx 0.925,\ r^2 \approx 0.855.$$

When all four variables are used, the regression equation is

$$G = -712 + 28.3L + 1.46H + 13.3W,$$
$$r \approx 0.930,\ r^2 \approx 0.865.$$

(Source: Journal of Statistics Education)

**Predict the weight of a fish with the following measurements: $L = 40$, $H = 17$, and $W = 11$. How do your predictions vary when you use a single variable versus many variables? Which do you think is more accurate?**

## Predicting $y$-Values

After finding the equation of the multiple regression line, you can use the equation to predict $y$-values over the range of the data. To predict $y$-values, substitute the given value for each independent variable into the equation, then calculate $\hat{y}$.

### EXAMPLE 2

### Predicting $y$-Values Using Multiple Regression Equations

Use the regression equation

$$\hat{y} = 49{,}764 + 364x_1 + 228x_2 + 267x_3$$

found in Example 1 to predict an employee's salary for each set of conditions.

1. 12 years of current employment
   5 years of previous experience
   16 years of education
2. 4 years of current employment
   2 years of previous experience
   12 years of education
3. 8 years of current employment
   7 years of previous experience
   17 years of education

**SOLUTION**

To predict each employee's salary, substitute the values for $x_1$, $x_2$, and $x_3$ into the regression equation. Then calculate $\hat{y}$.

1. $$\begin{aligned}\hat{y} &= 49{,}764 + 364x_1 + 228x_2 + 267x_3\\ &= 49{,}764 + 364(12) + 228(5) + 267(16)\\ &= 59{,}544\end{aligned}$$

   The employee's predicted salary is \$59,544.

2. $$\begin{aligned}\hat{y} &= 49{,}764 + 364x_1 + 228x_2 + 267x_3\\ &= 49{,}764 + 364(4) + 228(2) + 267(12)\\ &= 54{,}880\end{aligned}$$

   The employee's predicted salary is \$54,880.

3. $$\begin{aligned}\hat{y} &= 49{,}764 + 364x_1 + 228x_2 + 267x_3\\ &= 49{,}764 + 364(8) + 228(7) + 267(17)\\ &= 58{,}811\end{aligned}$$

   The employee's predicted salary is \$58,811.

**TRY IT YOURSELF 2**

Use the regression equation found in Try It Yourself 1 to predict a student's final grade for each set of conditions.

1. A student has a midterm exam score of 89 and misses 1 class.
2. A student has a midterm exam score of 78 and misses 3 classes.
3. A student has a midterm exam score of 83 and misses 2 classes.

*Answer: Page A42*

# 9.4 EXERCISES

For Extra Help: MyLab Statistics

## Building Basic Skills and Vocabulary

**1.** Interpret the meaning of the coefficient −8.2 in the multiple regression equation $\hat{y} = 112.1 + 0.43x_1 - 8.2x_2 + 29.5x_3$.

**2.** Compare the numbers of dependent and independent variables in a multiple regression equation and a single regression equation.

**Predicting *y*-Values** *In Exercises 3–6, use the multiple regression equation to predict the y-values for the values of the independent variables.*

**3. Cauliflower Yield** The equation used to predict the annual cauliflower yield (in pounds per acre) is

$$\hat{y} = 24{,}791 + 4.508x_1 - 4.723x_2$$

where $x_1$ is the number of acres planted and $x_2$ is the number of acres harvested. *(Adapted from United States Department of Agriculture)*

(a) $x_1 = 36{,}500, x_2 = 36{,}100$
(b) $x_1 = 38{,}100, x_2 = 37{,}800$
(c) $x_1 = 39{,}000, x_2 = 38{,}800$
(d) $x_1 = 42{,}200, x_2 = 42{,}100$

**4. Sorghum Yield** The equation used to predict the annual sorghum yield (in bushels per acre) is

$$\hat{y} = 80.1 - 20.2x_1 + 21.2x_2$$

where $x_1$ is the number of acres planted (in millions) and $x_2$ is the number of acres harvested (in millions). *(Adapted from United States Department of Agriculture)*

(a) $x_1 = 5.5, x_2 = 3.9$
(b) $x_1 = 8.3, x_2 = 7.3$
(c) $x_1 = 6.5, x_2 = 5.7$
(d) $x_1 = 9.4, x_2 = 7.8$

**5. Black Cherry Tree Volume** The volume (in cubic feet) of a black cherry tree can be modeled by the equation

$$\hat{y} = -52.2 + 0.3x_1 + 4.5x_2$$

where $x_1$ is the tree's height (in feet) and $x_2$ is the tree's diameter (in inches). *(Source: Journal of the Royal Statistical Society)*

(a) $x_1 = 70, x_2 = 8.6$
(b) $x_1 = 65, x_2 = 11.0$
(c) $x_1 = 83, x_2 = 17.6$
(d) $x_1 = 87, x_2 = 19.6$

**6. Elephant Weight** The equation used to predict the weight of an elephant (in kilograms) is

$$\hat{y} = -4016 + 11.5x_1 + 7.55x_2 + 12.5x_3$$

where $x_1$ represents the girth of the elephant (in centimeters), $x_2$ represents the length of the elephant (in centimeters), and $x_3$ represents the circumference of a footpad (in centimeters). *(Source: Field Trip Earth)*

(a) $x_1 = 421, x_2 = 224, x_3 = 144$
(b) $x_1 = 311, x_2 = 171, x_3 = 102$
(c) $x_1 = 376, x_2 = 226, x_3 = 124$
(d) $x_1 = 231, x_2 = 135, x_3 = 86$

## Using and Interpreting Concepts

**Finding a Multiple Regression Equation** *In Exercises 7 and 8, use technology to find (a) the multiple regression equation for the data shown in the table, (b) the standard error of estimate, and (c) the coefficient of determination. Interpret the results.*

**7. Used Cars** The table shows the prices (in dollars), age (in years), and mileage (in thousands of miles) of nine pre-owned Honda Civic sedans.

| Price, $y$ | Age, $x_1$ | Mileage, $x_2$ |
|---|---|---|
| \$20,368 | 2 | 11.0 |
| \$16,889 | 3 | 83.7 |
| \$11,300 | 5 | 83.0 |
| \$19,430 | 3 | 27.0 |
| \$9777 | 7 | 94.9 |
| \$9899 | 6 | 88.0 |
| \$14,600 | 6 | 27.8 |
| \$19,930 | 4 | 23.1 |
| \$19,000 | 5 | 46.5 |

**8. Nutrition** The table shows the calories, fat (in grams), carbohydrates (in grams), and protein (in grams) per serving size of eight common foods.

| Food | Calories, $y$ | Fat (g), $x_1$ | Carbs (g), $x_2$ | Protein (g), $x_3$ |
|---|---|---|---|---|
| Eggs | 80 | 5 | 0 | 7 |
| Broccoli | 31 | 0 | 6 | 3 |
| Potato chips | 160 | 10 | 15 | 2 |
| Sirloin steak | 240 | 16 | 0 | 22 |
| Avocado | 240 | 22 | 13 | 3 |
| Shredded cheddar | 110 | 9 | 2 | 7 |
| Snickers bar | 250 | 12 | 32 | 4 |
| Wheat bread | 70 | 1 | 13 | 3 |

## Extending Concepts

**Adjusted $r^2$** *The calculation of the coefficient of determination $r^2$ depends on the number of data pairs and the number of independent variables. An adjusted value of $r^2$ based on the number of degrees of freedom is calculated using the formula*

$$r^2_{adj} = 1 - \left[\frac{(1 - r^2)(n - 1)}{n - k - 1}\right]$$

*where n is the number of data pairs and k is the number of independent variables.*

*In Exercises 9 and 10, calculate $r^2_{adj}$ and determine the percentage of the variation in y that can be explained by the relationships between variables according to $r^2_{adj}$. Compare this result with the one obtained using $r^2$.*

**9.** Calculate $r^2_{\text{adj}}$ for the data in Exercise 7.

**10.** Calculate $r^2_{\text{adj}}$ for the data in Exercise 8.

# USES AND ABUSES Statistics in the Real World

## Uses

***Correlation and Regression*** Correlation and regression analysis can be used to determine whether there is a significant relationship between two variables. When there is, you can use one of the variables to predict the value of the other variable. For instance, educators have used correlation and regression analysis to determine that there is a significant correlation between a student's SAT score and the grade point average from a student's freshman year at college. Consequently, many colleges and universities use SAT scores of high school applicants as a predictor of the applicant's initial success at college.

## Abuses

***Confusing Correlation and Causation*** The most common abuse of correlation in studies is to confuse the concepts of correlation with those of causation (see page 480). Good SAT scores do not cause good college grades. Rather, there are other variables, such as good study habits and motivation, that contribute to both. When a strong correlation is found between two variables, look for other variables that are correlated with both.

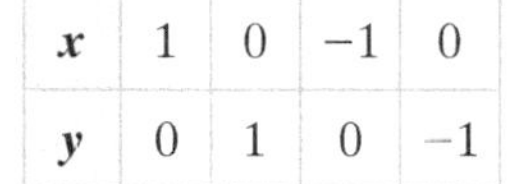

| $x$ | 1 | 0 | −1 | 0 |
|---|---|---|---|---|
| $y$ | 0 | 1 | 0 | −1 |

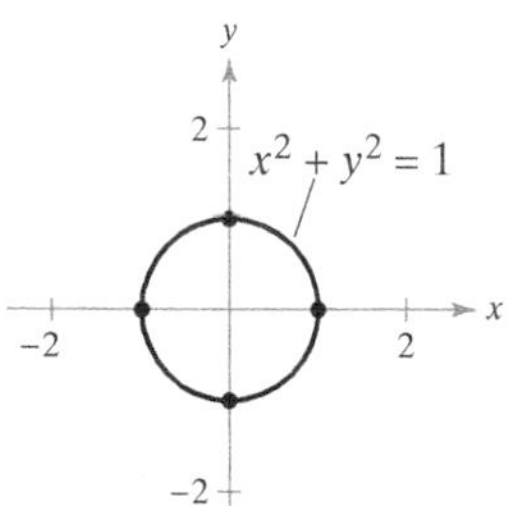


***Considering Only Linear Correlation*** The correlation studied in this chapter is linear correlation. When the correlation coefficient is close to 1 or close to −1, the data points can be modeled by a straight line. It is possible that a correlation coefficient is close to 0 but there is still a strong correlation of a different type. Consider the data listed in the table at the left. The value of the correlation coefficient is 0. However, the data are perfectly correlated with the equation $x^2 + y^2 = 1$, as shown in the figure at the left.

## Ethics

When data are collected, all of the data should be used when calculating statistics. In this chapter, you learned that before finding the equation of a regression line, it is helpful to construct a scatter plot of the data to check for outliers, gaps, and clusters in the data. Researchers must not choose to use only those data points that fit their hypotheses or those that show a significant correlation. Although eliminating outliers may help a data set coincide with predicted patterns or fit a regression line, it is unethical to amend data in such a way. An outlier or any other point that influences a regression model can be removed only when it is properly justified.

In most cases, the best and sometimes safest approach for presenting statistical measurements is with and without an outlier being included. By doing this, the decision of whether or not to recognize the outlier is left to the reader.

### EXERCISES

1. ***Confusing Correlation and Causation*** Find an example of an article that confuses correlation and causation. Discuss other variables that could contribute to the relationship between the variables.

2. ***Considering Only Linear Correlation*** Find an example of two real-life variables that have a nonlinear correlation.

# 9 Chapter Summary

| What Did You Learn? | Example(s) | Review Exercises |
|---|---|---|
| **Section 9.1** | | |
| How to construct a scatter plot and how to find a correlation coefficient $r = \dfrac{n\Sigma xy - (\Sigma x)(\Sigma y)}{\sqrt{n\Sigma x^2 - (\Sigma x)^2}\sqrt{n\Sigma y^2 - (\Sigma y)^2}}$ | 1–5 | 1–4 |
| How to test a population correlation coefficient $\rho$ using a table and how to perform a hypothesis test for a population correlation coefficient $\rho$ | 6, 7 | 5–8 |
| **Section 9.2** | | |
| How to find the equation of a regression line and how to predict $y$-values using a regression equation $\hat{y} = mx + b$, where $m = \dfrac{n\Sigma xy - (\Sigma x)(\Sigma y)}{n\Sigma x^2 - (\Sigma x)^2}$ and $b = \bar{y} - m\bar{x} = \dfrac{\Sigma y}{n} - m\dfrac{\Sigma x}{n}$ | 1–3 | 9–12 |
| **Section 9.3** | | |
| How to find and interpret the coefficient of determination | 1 | 13–18 |
| How to find and interpret the standard error of estimate for a regression line | 2 | 17, 18 |
| How to construct and interpret a prediction interval for $y$ $\hat{y} - E < y < \hat{y} + E$, where $E = t_c s_e\sqrt{1 + \dfrac{1}{n} + \dfrac{n(x_0 - \bar{x})^2}{n\Sigma x^2 - (\Sigma x)^2}}$ | 3 | 19–24 |
| **Section 9.4** | | |
| How to use technology to find and interpret a multiple regression equation, the standard error of estimate, and the coefficient of determination | 1 | 25, 26 |
| How to use a multiple regression equation to predict $y$-values | 2 | 27, 28 |

## Study Strategies

**Using Text Notes to Build Critical Thinking Skills** Instructors expect you to use critical thinking skills. To use text notes to build critical thinking skills, you can follow the steps outlined by educational psychologist Dr. Benjamin Bloom (listed below). This process will help you learn more effectively, enabling you to truly master a body of knowledge.

- Take notes to build knowledge about main concepts and terms in your reading. (Taking text notes is discussed in the Chapter 8 Summary.)
- Research a passage to find examples so you can apply your knowledge.
- Analyze what information is similar or different between your class notes and your reading notes and analyze what is most important to learn.
- Synthesize by combining your class and reading notes.
- Evaluate what you fully understand and what is still unclear.

For more information, visit Skills for Success in the accompanying MyLab course.

# Review Exercises

## Section 9.1

*In Exercises 1–4, (a) display the data in a scatter plot, (b) calculate the sample correlation coefficient r, and (c) describe the type of correlation and interpret the correlation in the context of the data.*

**1.** The numbers of pass attempts and passing yards for seven professional quarterbacks for a recent regular season *(Source: National Football League)*

| **Pass attempts, $x$** | 626 | 595 | 608 | 492 | 390 | 443 | 368 |
|---|---|---|---|---|---|---|---|
| **Passing yards, $y$** | 4581 | 4336 | 3803 | 3733 | 2942 | 2933 | 2657 |

**2.** The numbers of wildland fires (in thousands) and wildland acres burned (in millions) in the United States for eight years *(Source: National Interagency Fire Center)*

| **Fires, $x$** | 47.6 | 63.3 | 68.2 | 67.7 | 71.5 | 58.1 | 50.5 | 59.0 |
|---|---|---|---|---|---|---|---|---|
| **Acres, $y$** | 4.3 | 3.6 | 10.1 | 5.5 | 10.0 | 8.8 | 4.7 | 10.1 |

**3.** The intelligence quotient (IQ) scores and brain sizes (in grams) for nine adults *(Source: Cerebral Cortex)*

| **IQ score, $x$** | 89 | 95 | 107 | 120 | 73 | 108 | 92 | 80 | 127 |
|---|---|---|---|---|---|---|---|---|---|
| **Brain size, $y$** | 1400 | 1485 | 1570 | 1550 | 1446 | 1210 | 1620 | 1710 | 1570 |

**4.** The annual per capita sugar consumptions (in kilograms) and the average numbers of cavities of 11- and 12-year-old children in seven countries

| **Sugar consumption, $x$** | 2.1 | 5.0 | 6.3 | 6.5 | 7.7 | 8.7 | 11.6 |
|---|---|---|---|---|---|---|---|
| **Cavities, $y$** | 0.59 | 1.51 | 1.55 | 1.70 | 2.18 | 2.10 | 2.73 |

*In Exercises 5–8, use Table 11 in Appendix B, or perform a hypothesis test using Table 5 in Appendix B to make a conclusion about the correlation coefficient.*

**5.** Refer to the data in Exercise 1. At $\alpha = 0.05$, is there enough evidence to conclude that there is a significant linear correlation between the data? (Use the value of $r$ found in Exercise 1.)

**6.** Refer to the data in Exercise 2. At $\alpha = 0.05$, is there enough evidence to conclude that there is a significant linear correlation between the data? (Use the value of $r$ found in Exercise 2.)

**7.** Refer to the data in Exercise 3. At $\alpha = 0.01$, is there enough evidence to conclude that there is a significant linear correlation between the data? (Use the value of $r$ found in Exercise 3.)

**8.** Refer to the data in Exercise 4. At $\alpha = 0.01$, is there enough evidence to conclude that there is a significant linear correlation between the data? (Use the value of $r$ found in Exercise 4.)

## Section 9.2

*In Exercises 9–12, find the equation of the regression line for the data. Then construct a scatter plot of the data and draw the regression line. (Each pair of variables has a significant correlation.) Then use the regression equation to predict the value of y for each of the x-values, if meaningful. If the x-value is not meaningful to predict the value of y, explain why not. If convenient, use technology.*

**9.** The average numbers (in thousands) of milk cows and the amounts (in billions of pounds) of milk produced in the United States for eight years *(Source: U.S. Department of Agriculture)*

| **Milk cows, $x$** | 9224 | 9261 | 9320 | 9334 |
|---|---|---|---|---|
| **Milk produced, $y$** | 201.3 | 206.0 | 208.5 | 212.5 |

| **Milk cows, $x$** | 9406 | 9398 | 9337 | 9388 |
|---|---|---|---|---|
| **Milk produced, $y$** | 215.5 | 217.6 | 218.4 | 223.2 |

(a) $x = 9080$ cows (b) $x = 9230$ cows
(c) $x = 9340$ cows (d) $x = 9400$ cows

**10.** The average times (in hours) per day spent watching television for adults ages 25 to 34 and adults ages 35 to 44 for 10 years *(Source: U.S. Bureau of Labor Statistics)*

| **Adults ages 25 to 34, $x$** | 2.18 | 2.09 | 2.32 | 2.14 | 2.06 |
|---|---|---|---|---|---|
| **Adults ages 35 to 44, $y$** | 2.23 | 2.22 | 2.3 | 2.24 | 2.16 |

| **Adults ages 25 to 34, $x$** | 2.15 | 1.95 | 2.01 | 2.03 | 1.99 |
|---|---|---|---|---|---|
| **Adults ages 35 to 44, $y$** | 2.09 | 2.07 | 2.09 | 2.12 | 2.03 |

(a) $x = 1.97$ hours (b) $x = 2.21$ hours
(c) $x = 2.27$ hours (d) $x = 2.43$ hours

**11.** The ages (in years) and the numbers of hours of sleep in one night for seven adults

| **Age, $x$** | 35 | 20 | 59 | 42 | 68 | 38 | 75 |
|---|---|---|---|---|---|---|---|
| **Hours of sleep, $y$** | 7 | 9 | 5 | 6 | 5 | 8 | 4 |

(a) $x = 16$ years (b) $x = 25$ years
(c) $x = 85$ years (d) $x = 50$ years

**12.** The engine displacements (in cubic inches) and the fuel efficiencies (in miles per gallon) of seven automobiles

| **Displacement, $x$** | 170 | 134 | 220 | 305 | 109 | 256 | 322 |
|---|---|---|---|---|---|---|---|
| **Fuel efficiency, $y$** | 29.5 | 34.5 | 23.0 | 17.0 | 33.5 | 23.0 | 15.5 |

(a) $x = 86$ cubic inches (b) $x = 198$ cubic inches
(c) $x = 289$ cubic inches (d) $x = 407$ cubic inches

## Section 9.3

*In Exercises 13–16, use the value of the correlation coefficient r to calculate the coefficient of determination $r^2$. What does this tell you about the explained variation of the data about the regression line? about the unexplained variation?*

**13.** $r = -0.450$

**14.** $r = -0.937$

**15.** $r = 0.642$

**16.** $r = 0.795$

*In Exercises 17 and 18, use the data to (a) find the coefficient of determination $r^2$ and interpret the result, and (b) find the standard error of estimate $s_e$ and interpret the result.*

**17.** The table shows the times (in seconds) to accelerate from 0 to 60 miles per hour and the top speeds (in miles per hour) for eight electric cars. The regression equation is $\hat{y} = -14.399x + 196.996$. *(Source: Car and Driver)*

| Time to accelerate from 0 to 60 miles per hour, $x$ | 6.4 | 6.7 | 5.1 | 5.1 | 4.3 | 5.1 | 2.4 | 2.4 |
|---|---|---|---|---|---|---|---|---|
| **Top speed, $y$** | 110 | 93 | 114 | 125 | 128 | 141 | 163 | 162 |

 **18.** The table shows the cooking areas (in square inches) of 18 gas grills and their prices (in dollars). The regression equation is $\hat{y} = 1.501x - 341.501$. *(Source: Lowe's)*

| Area, $x$ | 645 | 529 | 650 | 450 | 844 | 395 | 669 | 725 | 620 |
|---|---|---|---|---|---|---|---|---|---|
| **Price, $y$** | 249 | 519 | 299 | 469 | 1199 | 229 | 829 | 549 | 599 |

| Area, $x$ | 445 | 575 | 454 | 529 | 710 | 935 | 710 | 320 | 673 |
|---|---|---|---|---|---|---|---|---|---|
| **Price, $y$** | 349 | 449 | 149 | 649 | 799 | 1149 | 849 | 325 | 518 |

*In Exercises 19–24, construct the indicated prediction interval and interpret the results.*

**19.** Construct a 90% prediction interval for the amount of milk produced in Exercise 9 when there are an average of 9275 thousand milk cows.

**20.** Construct a 90% prediction interval for the average time adults ages 35 to 44 spend per day watching television in Exercise 10 when the average time adults ages 25 to 34 spend per day watching television is 2.25 hours.

**21.** Construct a 95% prediction interval for the number of hours of sleep for an adult in Exercise 11 who is 45 years old.

**22.** Construct a 95% prediction interval for the fuel efficiency of an automobile in Exercise 12 that has an engine displacement of 265 cubic inches.

**23.** Construct a 99% prediction interval for the top speed of an electric car in Exercise 17 that takes 5.9 seconds to accelerate from 0 to 60 miles per hour.

**24.** Construct a 99% prediction interval for the price of a gas grill in Exercise 18 with a usable cooking area of 900 square inches.

## Section 9.4

*In Exercises 25 and 26, use technology to find (a) the multiple regression equation for the data shown in the table, (b) the standard error of estimate, and (c) the coefficient of determination. Interpret the results.*

 **25.** The table shows the carbon monoxide, tar, and nicotine contents, all in milligrams, of ten brands of cigarettes. *(Source: Scientific Reports)*

| Carbon monoxide, $y$ | Tar, $x_1$ | Nicotine, $x_2$ |
|---|---|---|
| 12 | 9.4 | 0.73 |
| 7 | 6.0 | 0.50 |
| 7 | 6.0 | 0.50 |
| 7 | 7.0 | 0.60 |
| 10 | 10.0 | 0.80 |
| 1 | 1.0 | 0.10 |
| 10 | 10.0 | 0.80 |
| 10 | 10.0 | 0.80 |
| 10 | 10.0 | 0.80 |
| 10 | 10.0 | 0.80 |

**26.** The table shows the numbers of acres planted, the numbers of acres harvested, and the annual yields (in pounds per acre) of potatoes for five years. *(Source: United States Department of Agriculture)*

| Yield, $y$ | Acres planted, $x_1$ | Acres harvested, $x_2$ |
|---|---|---|
| 43,400 | 1,056,700 | 1,037,700 |
| 43,200 | 1,052,600 | 1,044,500 |
| 44,300 | 1,026,500 | 1,014,800 |
| 45,300 | 963,300 | 937,300 |
| 45,300 | 921,000 | 914,100 |

*In Exercises 27 and 28, use the multiple regression equation to predict the y-values for the values of the independent variables.*

**27.** An equation that can be used to predict fuel economy (in miles per gallon) for automobiles is

$$\hat{y} = 41.3 - 0.004x_1 - 0.0049x_2$$

where $x_1$ is the engine displacement (in cubic inches) and $x_2$ is the vehicle weight (in pounds).

(a) $x_1 = 305, x_2 = 3750$

(b) $x_1 = 225, x_2 = 3100$

(c) $x_1 = 105, x_2 = 2200$

(d) $x_1 = 185, x_2 = 3000$

**28.** Use the regression equation found in Exercise 25.

(a) $x_1 = 9.0, x_2 = 0.70$

(b) $x_1 = 3.0, x_2 = 0.25$

(c) $x_1 = 8.0, x_2 = 0.60$

(d) $x_1 = 5.2, x_2 = 0.46$

# 9 Chapter Quiz

*Take this quiz as you would take a quiz in class. After you are done, check your work against the answers given in the back of the book.*

*For Exercises 1–8, use the data in the table, which shows the average annual salaries (both in thousands of dollars) for secondary and elementary school teachers, excluding special and vocational education teachers, in the United States for 11 years.* (Source: U.S. Bureau of Labor Statistics)

| Secondary school teachers, $x$ | Elementary school teachers, $y$ |
|---|---|
| 56.0 | 54.3 |
| 56.8 | 55.3 |
| 57.8 | 56.1 |
| 58.3 | 56.3 |
| 59.3 | 56.8 |
| 60.4 | 57.7 |
| 61.4 | 59.0 |
| 62.9 | 60.8 |
| 64.3 | 62.2 |
| 65.9 | 63.9 |
| 67.3 | 65.4 |

**1.** Construct a scatter plot for the data. Do the data appear to have a positive linear correlation, a negative linear correlation, or no linear correlation? Explain.

**2.** Calculate the correlation coefficient $r$ and interpret the result.

**3.** Test the significance of the correlation coefficient $r$ that you found in Exercise 2. Use $\alpha = 0.05$.

**4.** Find the equation of the regression line for the data. Draw the regression line on the scatter plot that you constructed in Exercise 1.

**5.** Use the regression equation that you found in Exercise 4 to predict the average annual salary of elementary school teachers when the average annual salary of secondary school teachers is $63,500.

**6.** Find the coefficient of determination $r^2$ and interpret the result.

**7.** Find the standard error of estimate $s_e$ and interpret the result.

**8.** Construct a 95% prediction interval for the average annual salary of elementary school teachers when the average annual salary of secondary school teachers is $63,500. Interpret the results.

**9. Stock Price** The equation used to predict the stock price (in dollars) at the end of the year for a restaurant chain is

$$\hat{y} = -86 + 7.46x_1 - 1.61x_2$$

where $x_1$ is the total revenue (in billions of dollars) and $x_2$ is the shareholders' equity (in billions of dollars). Use the multiple regression equation to predict the $y$-values for the values of the independent variables.

(a) $x_1 = 27.6, x_2 = 15.3$

(b) $x_1 = 24.1, x_2 = 14.6$

(c) $x_1 = 23.5, x_2 = 13.4$

(d) $x_1 = 22.8, x_2 = 15.3$

# 9 Chapter Test

*Take this test as you would take a test in class.*

1. **Net Sales** The equation used to predict the net sales (in millions of dollars) for a fiscal year for a clothing retailer is

$$\hat{y} = 23{,}769 + 9.18x_1 - 8.41x_2$$

where $x_1$ is the number of stores open at the end of the fiscal year and $x_2$ is the average square footage per store. Use the multiple regression equation to predict the $y$-values for the values of the independent variables.

(a) $x_1 = 1057, x_2 = 3698$

(b) $x_1 = 1012, x_2 = 3659$

(c) $x_1 = 952, x_2 = 3601$

(d) $x_1 = 914, x_2 = 3594$

*For Exercises 2–9, use the data in the table, which shows the average annual salaries (both in thousands of dollars) for librarians and postsecondary library science teachers in the United States for 12 years.* (Source: U.S. Bureau of Labor Statistics)

| Librarians, $x$ | Library science teachers, $y$ |
|---|---|
| 55.7 | 64.3 |
| 56.4 | 67.0 |
| 57.0 | 70.0 |
| 57.2 | 70.8 |
| 57.6 | 73.3 |
| 58.1 | 72.4 |
| 58.9 | 73.0 |
| 59.9 | 72.3 |
| 60.8 | 73.7 |
| 61.5 | 75.5 |
| 61.9 | 77.2 |
| 63.6 | 77.6 |

2. Construct a scatter plot for the data. Do the data appear to have a positive linear correlation, a negative linear correlation, or no linear correlation? Explain.
3. Calculate the correlation coefficient $r$ and interpret the result.
4. Test the significance of the correlation coefficient $r$ that you found in Exercise 3. Use $\alpha = 0.01$.
5. Find the equation of the regression line for the data. Draw the regression line on the scatter plot that you constructed in Exercise 2.
6. Use the regression equation that you found in Exercise 5 to predict the average annual salary of postsecondary library science teachers when the average annual salary of librarians is \$61,000.
7. Find the coefficient of determination $r^2$ and interpret the result.
8. Find the standard error of estimate $s_e$ and interpret the result.
9. Construct a 99% prediction interval for the average annual salary of postsecondary library science teachers when the average annual salary of librarians is \$61,000. Interpret the results.

# REAL STATISTICS REAL DECISIONS

# Putting it all together

Acid rain affects the environment by increasing the acidity of lakes and streams to dangerous levels, damaging trees and soil, accelerating the decay of building materials and paint, and destroying national monuments. The goal of the Environmental Protection Agency's (EPA) Acid Rain Program is to achieve environmental health benefits by reducing the emissions of the primary causes of acid rain: sulfur dioxide and nitrogen oxides.

You work for the EPA and you want to determine whether there is a significant correlation between the average concentrations of sulfur dioxide and nitrogen dioxide.

## EXERCISES

1. ***Analyzing the Data***

(a) The data in the table are the annual averages of the daily maximum concentrations of sulfur dioxide (in parts per billion) and nitrogen dioxide (in parts per billion) for 17 years. Construct a scatter plot of the data and make a conclusion about the type of correlation between the average concentrations of sulfur dioxide and nitrogen dioxide.

(b) Calculate the correlation coefficient $r$ and verify your conclusion in part (a).

(c) Test the significance of the correlation coefficient found in part (b). Use $\alpha = 0.05$.

(d) Find the equation of the regression line for the average concentrations of sulfur dioxide and nitrogen dioxide. Add the graph of the regression line to your scatter plot in part (a). Does the regression line appear to be a good fit?

(e) Can you use the equation of the regression line to predict the average concentration of nitrogen dioxide given the average concentration of sulfur dioxide? Why or why not?

(f) Find the coefficient of determination $r^2$ and the standard error of estimate $s_e$. Interpret your results.

2. ***Making Predictions***

Construct a 95% prediction interval for the average concentration of nitrogen dioxide when the average concentration of sulfur dioxide is 28 parts per billion. Interpret the results.

| Average sulfur dioxide concentration, $x$ | Average nitrogen dioxide concentration, $y$ |
|---|---|
| 72.5 | 57.8 |
| 74.5 | 56.3 |
| 67.0 | 55.6 |
| 62.1 | 54.9 |
| 53.3 | 53.9 |
| 47.1 | 49.4 |
| 40.9 | 48.3 |
| 33.7 | 48.1 |
| 31.1 | 45.2 |
| 27.2 | 46.0 |
| 27.1 | 47.9 |
| 23.3 | 44.9 |
| 15.8 | 43.6 |
| 14.8 | 43.9 |
| 14.6 | 43.6 |
| 12.8 | 42.1 |
| 10.3 | 40.5 |

(Source: Environmental Protection Agency)

TECHNOLOGY

MINITAB | EXCEL | TI-84 PLUS

# Nutrients in Breakfast Cereals

The U.S. Food and Drug Administration (FDA) requires nutrition labeling for most foods. Under FDA regulations, manufacturers are required to list the amounts of certain nutrients in their foods, such as calories, sugar, fat, and carbohydrates. This nutritional information is displayed in the "Nutrition Facts" panel on the food's package.

The table shows the nutritional content below for one cup of each of 21 different breakfast cereals.

$C$ = calories

$S$ = sugar in grams

$F$ = fat in grams

$R$ = carbohydrates in grams

| $C$ | $S$ | $F$ | $R$ |
|---|---|---|---|
| 100 | 12 | 0.5 | 25 |
| 130 | 11 | 1.5 | 29 |
| 100 | 1 | 2 | 20 |
| 130 | 15 | 2 | 31 |
| 130 | 13 | 1.5 | 29 |
| 120 | 3 | 0.5 | 26 |
| 100 | 2 | 0 | 24 |
| 120 | 10 | 0 | 29 |
| 150 | 16 | 1.5 | 31 |
| 110 | 4 | 0 | 25 |
| 110 | 12 | 1 | 25 |
| 150 | 15 | 0 | 36 |
| 160 | 15 | 1.5 | 35 |
| 150 | 12 | 2 | 29 |
| 150 | 15 | 1.5 | 29 |
| 110 | 6 | 1 | 23 |
| 190 | 19 | 1.5 | 45 |
| 100 | 3 | 0 | 23 |
| 120 | 4 | 0.5 | 23 |
| 120 | 11 | 1.5 | 28 |
| 130 | 5 | 0.5 | 29 |

## EXERCISES

**1.** Use technology to draw a scatter plot of the $(x, y)$ pairs in each data set.

(a) (calories, sugar)

(b) (calories, fat)

(c) (calories, carbohydrates)

(d) (sugar, fat)

(e) (sugar, carbohydrates)

(f) (fat, carbohydrates)

**2.** From the scatter plots in Exercise 1, which pairs of variables appear to have a strong linear correlation?

**3.** Use technology to find the correlation coefficient for each pair of variables in Exercise 1. Which has the strongest linear correlation?

**4.** Use technology to find an equation of a regression line for each pair of variables.

(a) (calories, sugar)

(b) (calories, carbohydrates)

**5.** Use the results of Exercise 4 to predict each value.

(a) The sugar content of one cup of cereal that has 120 calories

(b) The carbohydrate content of one cup of cereal that has 120 calories

**6.** Use technology to find the multiple regression equations of each form.

(a) $C = b + m_1S + m_2F + m_3R$

(b) $C = b + m_1S + m_2R$

**7.** Use the equations from Exercise 6 to predict the calories in 1 cup of cereal that has 7 grams of sugar, 0.5 gram of fat, and 31 grams of carbohydrates.

Extended solutions are given in the technology manuals that accompany this text. Technical instruction is provided for Minitab, Excel, and the TI-84 Plus.

CHAPTER 10

# Chi-Square Tests and the *F*-Distribution

Crash tests performed by the Insurance Institute for Highway Safety demonstrate how a vehicle will react when in a realistic collision. Tests are performed on the front, side, rear, and roof of the vehicles. Results of these tests are classified using the ratings *good*, *acceptable*, *marginal*, and *poor*.

## Where You've Been

In Chapter 8, you learned how to test a hypothesis that compares two populations by basing your decisions on sample statistics and their distributions. For instance, the Insurance Institute for Highway Safety buys new vehicles each year and crashes them into a barrier at 40 miles per hour to compare how different vehicles protect drivers in a frontal offset crash. In this test, 40% of the total width of the vehicle strikes the barrier on the driver side. The forces and impacts that occur during a crash test are measured by equipping dummies with special instruments and placing them in the car. The crash test results include data on head, chest, and leg injuries. For a low crash test number, the injury potential is low. If the crash test number is high, then the injury potential is high. Using the techniques of Chapter 8, you can determine whether the mean chest injury potential is the same for midsize SUVs and large pickups. (Assume the populations are normally distributed and the population variances are equal.) The table shows the sample statistics. *(Adapted from Insurance Institute for Highway Safety)*

| Vehicle | Number | Mean chest injury | Standard deviation |
|---|---|---|---|
| Large Pickups | $n_1 = 12$ | $\bar{x}_1 = 23.0$ | $s_1 = 2.09$ |
| Midsize SUVs | $n_2 = 19$ | $\bar{x}_2 = 22.4$ | $s_2 = 4.26$ |

For the means of chest injury, the *P*-value for the hypothesis that $\mu_1 = \mu_2$ is about 0.6655. At $\alpha = 0.01$, you fail to reject the null hypothesis. So, you do not have enough evidence to conclude that there is a significant difference in the means of the chest injury potential in a frontal offset crash at 40 miles per hour for large pickups and midsize SUVs.

## Where You're Going

In this chapter, you will learn how to test a hypothesis that compares three or more populations.

For instance, in addition to the crash tests for large pickups and midsize SUVs, a third group of vehicles was also tested. The table shows the results for all three types of vehicles.

| Vehicle | Number | Mean chest injury | Standard deviation |
|---|---|---|---|
| Large Pickups | $n_1 = 12$ | $\bar{x}_1 = 23.0$ | $s_1 = 2.09$ |
| Midsize SUVs | $n_2 = 19$ | $\bar{x}_2 = 22.4$ | $s_2 = 4.26$ |
| Large Cars | $n_3 = 10$ | $\bar{x}_3 = 27.2$ | $s_3 = 6.65$ |

From these three samples, is there evidence of a difference in chest injury potential among large pickups, midsize SUVs, and large cars in a frontal offset crash at 40 miles per hour?

You can answer this question by testing the hypothesis that the three means are equal. For the means of chest injury, the *P*-value for the hypothesis that $\mu_1 = \mu_2 = \mu_3$ is about 0.0283. At $\alpha = 0.01$, you fail to reject the null hypothesis. So, there is not enough evidence at the 1% level of significance to conclude that at least one of the means is different from the others.

# 10.1 Goodness-of-Fit Test

## What You Should Learn

- How to use the chi-square distribution to test whether a frequency distribution fits an expected distribution

The Chi-Square Goodness-of-Fit Test

## The Chi-Square Goodness-of-Fit Test

A tax preparation company wants to determine the proportions of people who used different methods to prepare their taxes. To determine these proportions, the company can perform a multinomial experiment. A **multinomial experiment** is a probability experiment consisting of a fixed number of independent trials in which there are more than two possible outcomes for each trial. The probability of each outcome is fixed, and each outcome is classified into **categories.** (Remember from Section 4.2 that a binomial experiment has only two possible outcomes.)

The company wants to test a retail trade association's claim concerning the expected distribution of proportions of people who used different methods to prepare their taxes. To do so, the company could compare the distribution of proportions obtained in the multinomial experiment with the association's expected distribution. To compare the distributions, the company can perform a **chi-square goodness-of-fit test.**

**DEFINITION**

A **chi-square goodness-of-fit test** is used to test whether a frequency distribution fits an expected distribution.

**Study Tip**

The hypothesis tests described in Sections 10.1 and 10.2 can be used for qualitative data.

To begin a goodness-of-fit test, you must first state a null and an alternative hypothesis. Generally, the null hypothesis states that the frequency distribution fits an expected distribution and the alternative hypothesis states that the frequency distribution does not fit the expected distribution.

For instance, the association claims that the expected distribution of people who used different methods to prepare their taxes is as shown below.

| Distribution of tax preparation methods | |
|---|---|
| Accountant | 24% |
| By hand | 20% |
| Computer software | 35% |
| Friend or family | 6% |
| Tax preparation service | 15% |

To test the association's claim, the company can perform a chi-square goodness-of-fit test using these null and alternative hypotheses.

$H_0$: The expected distribution of tax preparation methods is 24% by accountant, 20% by hand, 35% by computer software, 6% by friend or family, and 15% by tax preparation service. (Claim)

$H_a$: The distribution of tax preparation methods differs from the expected distribution.

## Picturing the World

The pie chart shows the distribution of health care visits to doctor offices, emergency departments, and home visits in a recent year. (Source: National Center for Health Statistics)

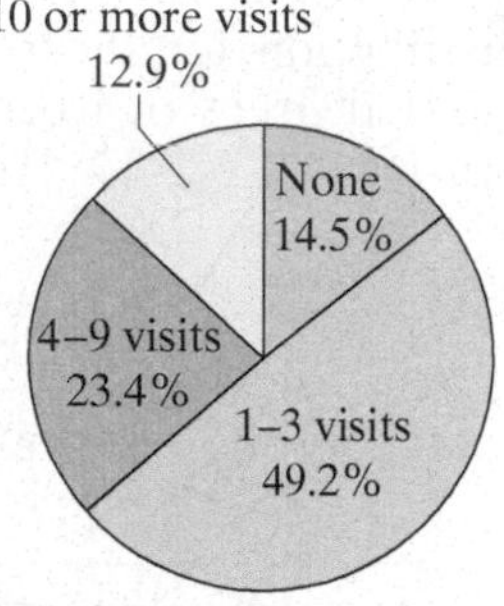


**A researcher randomly selects 200 people and asks them how many visits they make to the doctor in a year: 1–3, 4–9, 10 or more, or none. What is the expected frequency for each response?**

To calculate the test statistic for the chi-square goodness-of-fit test, you can use **observed frequencies** and **expected frequencies.** To calculate the expected frequencies, you must assume the null hypothesis is true.

### DEFINITION

The **observed frequency** $O$ of a category is the frequency for the category observed in the sample data.

The **expected frequency** $E$ of a category is the *calculated* frequency for the category. Expected frequencies are found by using the expected (or hypothesized) distribution and the sample size. The expected frequency for the $i$th category is

$$E_i = np_i$$

where $n$ is the number of trials (the sample size) and $p_i$ is the assumed probability of the $i$th category.

### EXAMPLE 1

### Finding Observed Frequencies and Expected Frequencies

A tax preparation company randomly selects 300 adults and asks them how they prepare their taxes. The results are shown at the right. Find the observed frequency and the expected frequency (using the distribution on the preceding page) for each tax preparation method. *(Adapted from National Retail Federation)*

| Survey results ($n$ = 300) | |
|---|---|
| Accountant | 60 |
| By hand | 43 |
| Computer software | 117 |
| Friend or family | 29 |
| Tax preparation service | 51 |

**SOLUTION**

The observed frequency for each tax preparation method is the number of adults in the survey naming a particular tax preparation method. The expected frequency for each tax preparation method is the product of the number of adults in the survey and the assumed probability that an adult will name a particular tax preparation method. The observed frequencies and expected frequencies are shown in the table below.

| Tax preparation method | % of people | Observed frequency | Expected frequency |
|---|---|---|---|
| Accountant | 24% | 60 | 300(0.24) = 72 |
| By hand | 20% | 43 | 300(0.20) = 60 |
| Computer software | 35% | 117 | 300(0.35) = 105 |
| Friend or family | 6% | 29 | 300(0.06) = 18 |
| Tax preparation service | 15% | 51 | 300(0.15) = 45 |

**TRY IT YOURSELF 1**

The tax preparation company in Example 1 decides it wants a larger sample size, so it randomly selects 500 adults. Find the expected frequency for each tax preparation method for $n$ = 500.

*Answer: Page A42*

The sum of the expected frequencies always equals the sum of the observed frequencies. For instance, in Example 1 the sum of the observed frequencies and the sum of the expected frequencies are both 300.

Before performing a chi-square goodness-of-fit test, you must verify that (1) the observed frequencies were obtained from a random sample and (2) each expected frequency is at least 5. Note that when the expected frequency of a category is less than 5, it may be possible to combine the category with another one to meet the second requirement.

### Study Tip

Remember that a chi-square distribution is positively skewed and its shape is determined by the degrees of freedom. Its graph is not symmetric, but it appears to become more symmetric as the degrees of freedom increase, as shown in Section 6.4.

## The Chi-Square Goodness-of-Fit Test

To perform a chi-square goodness-of-fit test, these conditions must be met.

1. The observed frequencies must be obtained using a random sample.
2. Each expected frequency must be greater than or equal to 5.

If these conditions are met, then the sampling distribution for the test is approximated by a chi-square distribution with $k - 1$ degrees of freedom, where $k$ is the number of categories. The **test statistic** is

$$\chi^2 = \Sigma\frac{(O - E)^2}{E}$$

where $O$ represents the observed frequency of each category and $E$ represents the expected frequency of each category.

When the observed frequencies closely match the expected frequencies, the differences between $O$ and $E$ will be small and the chi-square test statistic will be close to 0. As such, the null hypothesis is unlikely to be rejected. However, when there are large discrepancies between the observed frequencies and the expected frequencies, the differences between $O$ and $E$ will be large, resulting in a large chi-square test statistic. A large chi-square test statistic is evidence for rejecting the null hypothesis. So, the chi-square goodness-of-fit test is always a right-tailed test.

## GUIDELINES

**Performing a Chi-Square Goodness-of-Fit Test**

| In Words | In Symbols |
|---|---|
| **1.** Verify that the observed frequencies were obtained from a random sample and each expected frequency is at least 5. | $E_i = np_i \geq 5$ |
| **2.** Identify the claim. State the null and alternative hypotheses. | State $H_0$ and $H_a$. |
| **3.** Specify the level of significance. | Identify $\alpha$. |
| **4.** Identify the degrees of freedom. | d.f. $= k - 1$ |
| **5.** Determine the critical value. | Use Table 6 in Appendix B. |
| **6.** Determine the rejection region. | |
| **7.** Find the test statistic and sketch the sampling distribution. | $\chi^2 = \Sigma\frac{(O - E)^2}{E}$ |
| **8.** Make a decision to reject or fail to reject the null hypothesis. | If $\chi^2$ is in the rejection region, then reject $H_0$. Otherwise, fail to reject $H_0$. |
| **9.** Interpret the decision in the context of the original claim. | |

## EXAMPLE 2

### Performing a Chi-Square Goodness-of-Fit Test

A retail trade association claims that the tax preparation methods of adults are distributed as shown in the table at the left below. A tax preparation company randomly selects 300 adults and asks them how they prepare their taxes. The results are shown in the table at the right below. At $\alpha = 0.01$, test the association's claim. *(Adapted from National Retail Federation)*

| Distribution of tax preparation methods | |
|---|---|
| Accountant | 24% |
| By hand | 20% |
| Computer software | 35% |
| Friend or family | 6% |
| Tax preparation service | 15% |

| Survey results ($n = 300$) | |
|---|---|
| Accountant | 60 |
| By hand | 43 |
| Computer software | 117 |
| Friend or family | 29 |
| Tax preparation service | 51 |

**SOLUTION**

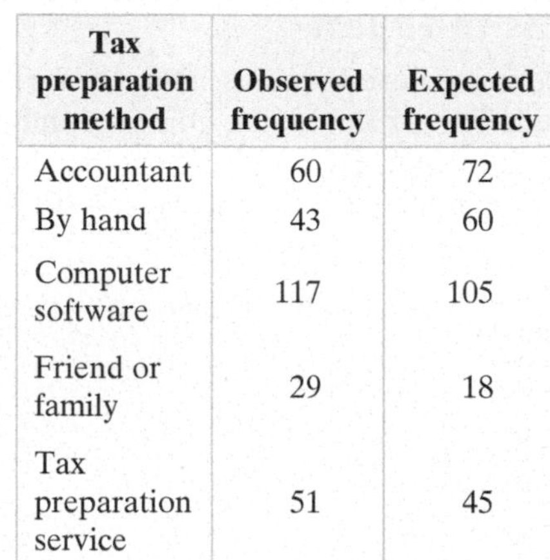

| Tax preparation method | Observed frequency | Expected frequency |
|---|---|---|
| Accountant | 60 | 72 |
| By hand | 43 | 60 |
| Computer software | 117 | 105 |
| Friend or family | 29 | 18 |
| Tax preparation service | 51 | 45 |

The observed and expected frequencies are shown in the table at the left. The expected frequencies were calculated in Example 1. Because the observed frequencies were obtained using a random sample and each expected frequency is at least 5, you can use the chi-square goodness-of-fit test to test the proposed distribution. Here are the null and alternative hypotheses.

$H_0$: The expected distribution of tax preparation methods is 24% by accountant, 20% by hand, 35% by computer software, 6% by friend or family, and 15% by tax preparation service. (Claim)

$H_a$: The distribution of tax preparation methods differs from the expected distribution.

Because there are 5 categories, the chi-square distribution has

$$\text{d.f.} = k - 1 = 5 - 1 = 4$$

degrees of freedom. With d.f. = 4 and $\alpha = 0.01$, the critical value is $\chi_0^2 = 13.277$. The rejection region is

$\chi^2 > 13.277.$ Rejection region

With the observed and expected frequencies, the chi-square test statistic is

$$\begin{aligned}\chi^2 &= \Sigma\frac{(O - E)^2}{E} \\ &= \frac{(60 - 72)^2}{72} + \frac{(43 - 60)^2}{60} + \frac{(117 - 105)^2}{105} \\ &\quad + \frac{(29 - 18)^2}{18} + \frac{(51 - 45)^2}{45} \\ &\approx 15.710.\end{aligned}$$

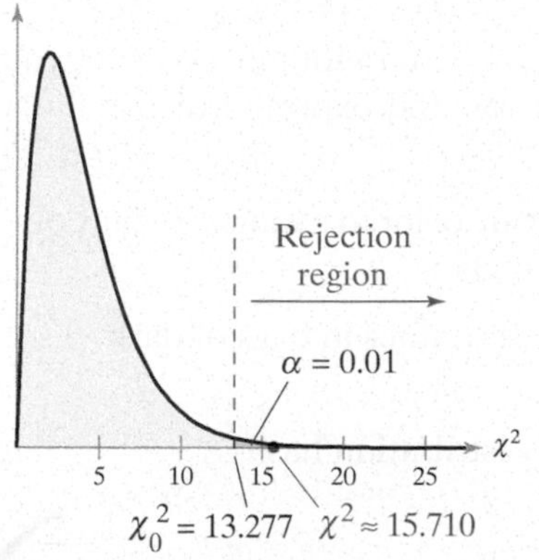


The figure at the left shows the location of the rejection region and the chi-square test statistic. Because $\chi^2$ is in the rejection region, you reject the null hypothesis.

***Interpretation*** There is enough evidence at the 1% level of significance to reject the claim that the distribution of tax preparation methods and the association's expected distribution are the same.

| Ages | Previous age distribution | Survey results |
|---|---|---|
| 0–9 | 16% | 76 |
| 10–19 | 20% | 84 |
| 20–29 | 8% | 30 |
| 30–39 | 14% | 60 |
| 40–49 | 15% | 54 |
| 50–59 | 12% | 40 |
| 60–69 | 10% | 42 |
| 70+ | 5% | 14 |

**TRY IT YOURSELF 2**

A sociologist claims that the age distribution for the residents of a city is different from the distribution 10 years ago. The distribution of ages 10 years ago is shown in the table at the left. You randomly select 400 residents and record the age of each. The survey results are shown in the table. At $\alpha = 0.05$, perform a chi-square goodness-of-fit test to test whether the distribution has changed.

*Answer: Page A42*

The chi-square goodness-of-fit test is often used to determine whether a distribution is uniform. For such tests, the expected frequencies of the categories are equal. When testing a uniform distribution, you can find the expected frequency of each category by dividing the sample size by the number of categories. For instance, suppose a company believes that the number of sales made by its sales force is uniform throughout a five-day workweek. If the sample consists of 1000 sales, then the expected value of the sales for each day will be $1000/5 = 200$.

## EXAMPLE 3

### Performing a Chi-Square Goodness-of-Fit Test

A researcher claims that the number of different-colored candies in bags of dark chocolate M&M's® is uniformly distributed. To test this claim, you randomly select a bag that contains 500 dark chocolate M&M's® and determine the frequency of each color. The results are shown in the table below. At $\alpha = 0.10$, test the researcher's claim. *(Adapted from Mars, Incorporated)*

| Color | Frequency, $f$ |
|---|---|
| Brown | 80 |
| Yellow | 95 |
| Red | 88 |
| Blue | 83 |
| Orange | 76 |
| Green | 78 |

**SOLUTION**

The claim is that the distribution is uniform, so the expected frequencies of the colors are equal. To find each expected frequency, divide the sample size by the number of colors. So, for each color, $E = 500/6 \approx 83.333$. Because each expected frequency is at least 5 and the M&M's® were randomly selected, you can use the chi-square goodness-of-fit test to test the expected distribution. Here are the null and alternative hypotheses.

$H_0$: The expected distribution of the different-colored candies in bags of dark chocolate M&M's® is uniform. (Claim)

$H_a$: The distribution of the different-colored candies in bags of dark chocolate M&M's® is not uniform.

Because there are 6 categories, the chi-square distribution has

$$\text{d.f.} = k - 1 = 6 - 1 = 5$$

degrees of freedom. Using d.f. = 5 and $\alpha = 0.10$, the critical value is $\chi_0^2 = 9.236$. The rejection region is $\chi^2 > 9.236$. To find the chi-square test statistic using a table, use the observed and expected frequencies, as shown on the next page.

| $O$ | $E$ | $O - E$ | $(O - E)^2$ | $\frac{(O - E)^2}{E}$ |
|---|---|---|---|---|
| 80 | 83.333 | −3.333 | 11.108889 | 0.133307201 |
| 95 | 83.333 | 11.667 | 136.118889 | 1.633433202 |
| 88 | 83.333 | 4.667 | 21.780889 | 0.261371713 |
| 83 | 83.333 | −0.333 | 0.110889 | 0.001330673 |
| 76 | 83.333 | −7.333 | 53.772889 | 0.645277249 |
| 78 | 83.333 | −5.333 | 28.440889 | 0.341292033 |
| | | | | $\chi^2 = \Sigma \frac{(O - E)^2}{E} \approx 3.016$ |

The figure shows the location of the rejection region and the chi-square test statistic. Because $\chi^2$ is not in the rejection region, you fail to reject the null hypothesis.

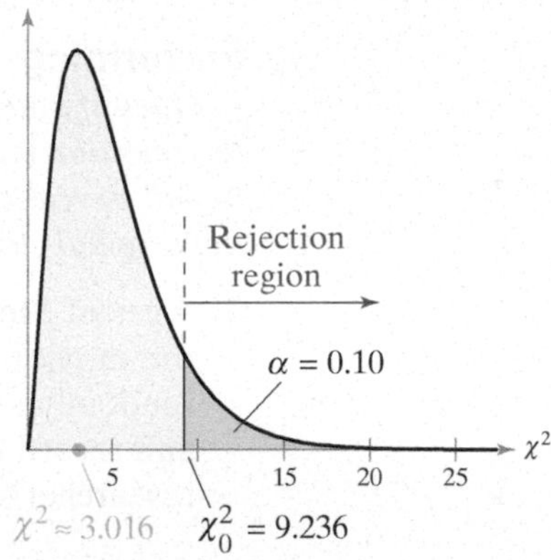


***Interpretation*** There is not enough evidence at the 10% level of significance to reject the claim that the distribution of the different-colored candies in bags of dark chocolate M&M's® is uniform.

**TRY IT YOURSELF 3**

A researcher claims that the number of different-colored candies in bags of peanut M&M's® is uniformly distributed. To test this claim, you randomly select a bag that contains 180 peanut M&M's® and determine the frequency of each color. The results are shown in the table below. Using $\alpha = 0.05$, test the researcher's claim. *(Adapted from Mars, Incorporated)*

| Color | Frequency, $f$ |
|---|---|
| Brown | 22 |
| Yellow | 27 |
| Red | 22 |
| Blue | 41 |
| Orange | 41 |
| Green | 27 |

*Answer: Page A42*

**TI-84 PLUS**

```
χ²GOF-Test
χ²=3.016012072
p=0.6975171071
df=5
CNTRB={0.133307...
```

You can use technology and a $P$-value to perform a chi-square goodness-of-fit test. For instance, using a TI-84 Plus and the data in Example 3, you obtain $P = 0.6975171071$, as shown at the left. Because $P > \alpha$, you fail to reject the null hypothesis.

# 10.1 EXERCISES

For Extra Help: MyLab® Statistics

## Building Basic Skills and Vocabulary

**1.** What is a multinomial experiment?

**2.** What conditions are necessary to use the chi-square goodness-of-fit test?

**Finding Expected Frequencies** *In Exercises 3–6, find the expected frequency for the values of n and $p_i$.*

**3.** $n = 150, p_i = 0.3$

**4.** $n = 500, p_i = 0.9$

**5.** $n = 230, p_i = 0.25$

**6.** $n = 415, p_i = 0.08$

## Using and Interpreting Concepts

**Performing a Chi-Square Goodness-of-Fit Test** *In Exercises 7–16, (a) identify the claim and state $H_0$ and $H_a$, (b) find the critical value and identify the rejection region, (c) find the chi-square test statistic, (d) decide whether to reject or fail to reject the null hypothesis, and (e) interpret the decision in the context of the original claim.*

**7. Ages of Moviegoers** A researcher claims that the ages of people who go to the movies at least once a year are distributed as shown in the figure. You randomly select 1000 people who went to the movies at least once in 2020 and record the age of each. The table shows the results. At $\alpha = 0.10$, test the researcher's claim. *(Adapted from Motion Picture Association of America)*

| Survey results | |
|---|---|
| **Age** | **Frequency, *f*** |
| 2–11 | 146 |
| 12–17 | 116 |
| 18–24 | 131 |
| 25–39 | 232 |
| 40–49 | 117 |
| 50+ | 258 |

**8. Coffee** A researcher claims that the numbers of cups of coffee U.S. adults drink per day are distributed as shown in the figure. You randomly select 1600 U.S. adults and ask them how many cups of coffee they drink per day. The table shows the results. At $\alpha = 0.05$, test the researcher's claim. *(Adapted from Gallup)*

| Survey results | |
|---|---|
| **Response** | **Frequency, *f*** |
| 0 cups | 570 |
| 1 cup | 432 |
| 2 cups | 282 |
| 3 cups | 152 |
| 4 or more cups | 164 |

**9. Ordering Pizza** A research firm claims that the distribution of the days of the week that people are most likely to order pizza (including delivery, takeout, and sitting at restaurants) is different from the distribution shown in the figure. You randomly select 500 people and record which day of the week each is most likely to order pizza. The table shows the results. At $\alpha = 0.01$, test the research firm's claim. *(Adapted from Womply)*

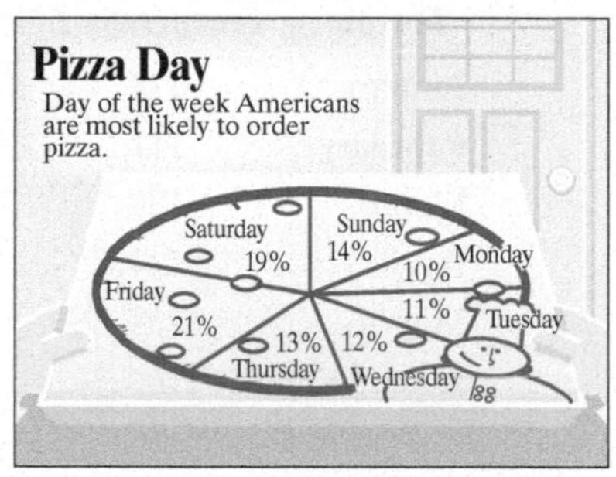


| Survey results | |
|---|---|
| **Day** | **Frequency, $f$** |
| Sunday | 54 |
| Monday | 32 |
| Tuesday | 44 |
| Wednesday | 75 |
| Thursday | 59 |
| Friday | 114 |
| Saturday | 122 |

**10. Ways to Pay** A financial analyst claims that the distribution of people's preferences on how to pay for goods is different from the distribution shown in the figure. You randomly select 600 people and record their preferences on how to pay for goods. The table shows the results. At $\alpha = 0.01$, test the financial analyst's claim. *(Adapted from Travis Credit Union )*

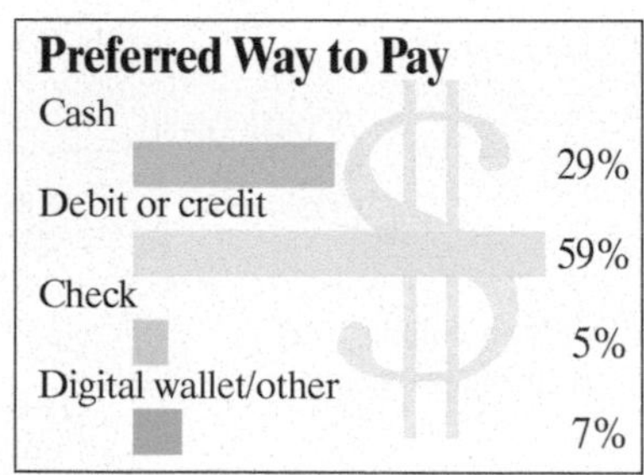


| Survey results | |
|---|---|
| **Response** | **Frequency, $f$** |
| Cash | 194 |
| Debit or credit | 338 |
| Check | 21 |
| Digital wallet/other | 47 |

**11. Homicides by County** A researcher claims that the number of homicide crimes in California by county is uniformly distributed. To test this claim, you randomly select 1000 homicides from a recent year and record the county in which each happened. The table shows the results. At $\alpha = 0.01$, test the researcher's claim. *(Adapted from California Department of Justice)*

| County | Frequency, $f$ |
|---|---|
| Alameda | 58 |
| Contra Costa | 44 |
| Fresno | 53 |
| Kern | 79 |
| Los Angeles | 151 |
| Monterey | 34 |
| Orange | 40 |
| Riverside | 86 |

| County | Frequency, $f$ |
|---|---|
| Sacramento | 62 |
| San Bernardino | 98 |
| San Diego | 69 |
| San Francisco | 38 |
| San Joaquin | 55 |
| Santa Clara | 49 |
| Stanislaus | 45 |
| Tulare | 39 |

12. **Homicides by Month** A researcher claims that the number of homicide crimes in California by month is uniformly distributed. To test this claim, you randomly select 2000 homicides from a recent year and record the month when each happened. The table shows the results. At $\alpha = 0.10$, test the researcher's claim. *(Adapted from California Department of Justice)*

| Month | Frequency, $f$ | Month | Frequency, $f$ |
|---|---|---|---|
| January | 134 | July | 184 |
| February | 111 | August | 181 |
| March | 133 | September | 205 |
| April | 134 | October | 215 |
| May | 158 | November | 184 |
| June | 161 | December | 200 |

13. **College Education** The pie chart shows the results of a survey in which Republican U.S. parents were asked what path they would prefer their child take after high school. A political scientist claims that the distribution of opinions of Democrat U.S. parents is different from the distribution for Republicans. To test this claim, you randomly select 200 Democrat U.S. parents and ask each what path they would prefer their child take after high school. The table shows the results. At $\alpha = 0.05$, test the political scientist's claim. *(Adapted from Gallup)*

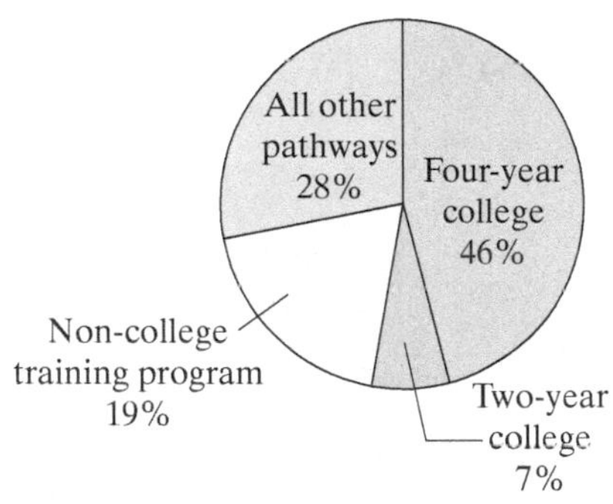


| Survey results | |
|---|---|
| **Response** | **Frequency, $f$** |
| Four-year college | 140 |
| Two-year college | 22 |
| Non-college training program | 14 |
| All other pathways | 24 |

14. **Money Management** The pie chart shows the results of a survey in which married U.S. male adults were asked how much they trust their spouses to manage their finances. A financial services company claims that the distribution of how much married U.S. female adults trust their spouses to manage their finances is the same as the distribution given for married U.S. male adults. To test this claim, you randomly select 400 married U.S. female adults and ask each how much she trusts her spouse to manage their finances. The table shows the results. At $\alpha = 0.10$, test the company's claim. *(Adapted from Country Financial)*

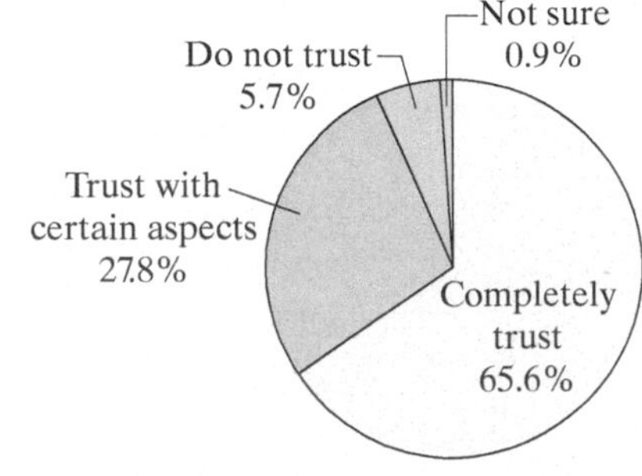


| Survey results | |
|---|---|
| **Response** | **Frequency, $f$** |
| Completely trust | 243 |
| Trust with certain aspects | 108 |
| Do not trust | 36 |
| Not sure | 13 |

| Response | Frequency, $f$ |
|---|---|
| Larger | 285 |
| Same size | 224 |
| Smaller | 291 |

TABLE FOR EXERCISE 15

**15. Home Sizes** An organization claims that the number of prospective home buyers who want their next house to be larger, smaller, or the same size as their current house is not uniformly distributed. To test this claim, you randomly select 800 prospective home buyers and ask them what size they want their next house to be. The table at the left shows the results. At $\alpha = 0.05$, test the organization's claim. *(Adapted from Better Homes and Gardens)*

**16. Births by Day of the Week** A doctor claims that the number of births by day of the week is uniformly distributed. To test this claim, you randomly select 700 births from a recent year and record the day of the week on which each takes place. The table shows the results. At $\alpha = 0.10$, test the doctor's claim. *(Adapted from National Center for Health Statistics)*

| Day | Frequency, $f$ |
|---|---|
| Sunday | 69 |
| Monday | 106 |
| Tuesday | 113 |
| Wednesday | 111 |
| Thursday | 112 |
| Friday | 111 |
| Saturday | 78 |

## Extending Concepts

**Testing for Normality** *Using a chi-square goodness-of-fit test, you can decide, with some degree of certainty, whether a variable is normally distributed. In all chi-square tests for normality, the null and alternative hypotheses are as listed below.*

$H_0$: *The variable has a normal distribution.*

$H_a$: *The variable does not have a normal distribution.*

*To determine the expected frequencies when performing a chi-square test for normality, first estimate the mean and standard deviation of the frequency distribution. Then, use the mean and standard deviation to compute the z-score for each class boundary. Then, use the z-scores to calculate the area under the standard normal curve for each class. Multiplying the resulting class areas by the sample size yields the expected frequency for each class.*

*In Exercises 17 and 18, (a) find the expected frequencies, (b) find the critical value and identify the rejection region, (c) find the chi-square test statistic, (d) decide whether to reject or fail to reject the null hypothesis, and (e) interpret the decision in the context of the original claim.*

**17. Test Scores** At $\alpha = 0.01$, test the claim that the 200 test scores shown in the frequency distribution are normally distributed.

| Class boundaries | 49.5–58.5 | 58.5–67.5 | 67.5–76.5 | 76.5–85.5 | 85.5–94.5 |
|---|---|---|---|---|---|
| Frequency, $f$ | 19 | 61 | 82 | 34 | 4 |

**18. Test Scores** At $\alpha = 0.05$, test the claim that the 400 test scores shown in the frequency distribution are normally distributed.

| Class boundaries | 50.5–60.5 | 60.5–70.5 | 70.5–80.5 | 80.5–90.5 | 90.5–100.5 |
|---|---|---|---|---|---|
| Frequency, $f$ | 46 | 88 | 151 | 97 | 18 |

# 10.2 Independence

## What You Should Learn

- How to use a contingency table to find expected frequencies
- How to use a chi-square distribution to test whether two variables are independent

Contingency Tables ■ The Chi-Square Independence Test

## Contingency Tables

Recall from Section 3.2 that two events are *independent* when the occurrence of one event does not affect the probability of the occurrence of the other event. For instance, the outcomes of a roll of a die and a toss of a coin are independent. But, suppose a medical researcher wants to determine whether there is a relationship between caffeine consumption and heart attack risk. Are these variables independent or are they dependent? In this section, you will learn how to use the chi-square test for independence to answer such a question. Performing this test involves using sample data that are organized in a **contingency table.**

### DEFINITION

An $r \times c$ **contingency table** shows the observed frequencies for two variables. The observed frequencies are arranged in $r$ rows and $c$ columns. The intersection of a row and a column is called a **cell.**

**Study Tip**

Note that "2 × 5" is read as "two-by-five."

A 2 × 5 contingency table is shown below. It has two rows and five columns and shows the results of a random sample of 1984 undergraduate students classified by two variables, *student's living arrangement* and *family college experience.* From the table, you can see that of the students who live on campus, 97 are the first in their family and 428 are the second generation in their family to experience college.

| | **Student's living arrangement** | | | | |
|---|---|---|---|---|---|
| **Family college experience** | **With parents, rent free** | **With parents, pay rent** | **On campus** | **Off campus, w/others** | **Off campus, alone** |
| First in family | 190 | 39 | 97 | 43 | 17 |
| 2nd generation | 651 | 109 | 428 | 349 | 61 |

*(Adapted from Sallie Mae/Ipsos)*

Assuming two variables are independent, you can use a contingency table to find the expected frequency for each cell, as shown in the next definition.

**Study Tip**

In a contingency table, the notation $E_{r,c}$ represents the expected frequency for the cell in row $r$, column $c$. For instance, in the table above, $E_{1,4}$ represents the expected frequency for the cell in row 1, column 4.

### Finding the Expected Frequency for Contingency Table Cells

The expected frequency for a cell $E_{r,c}$ in a contingency table is

$$\text{Expected frequency } E_{r,c} = \frac{(\text{Sum of row } r)\cdot(\text{Sum of column } c)}{\text{Sample size}}.$$

When you find the sum of each row and column in a contingency table, you are calculating the **marginal frequencies.** A marginal frequency is the frequency that an entire category of one of the variables occurs. For instance, in the table above, the marginal frequency for students who live with their parents and pay rent is 39 + 109 = 148. The observed frequencies in the interior of a contingency table are called **joint frequencies.**

## EXAMPLE 1

### Finding Expected Frequencies

Find the expected frequency for each cell in the contingency table on the preceding page. Assume that the variables *student's living arrangement* and *family college experience* are independent.

**SOLUTION**

The marginal frequencies are shown in the table below.

| | **Student's living arrangement** | | | | | |
|---|---|---|---|---|---|---|
| **Family college experience** | **With parents, rent free** | **With parents, pay rent** | **On campus** | **Off campus, w/others** | **Off campus, alone** | **Total** |
| First in family | 190 | 39 | 97 | 43 | 17 | 386 |
| 2nd generation | 651 | 109 | 428 | 349 | 61 | 1598 |
| Total | 841 | 148 | 525 | 392 | 78 | 1984 |

To find each expected frequency, use the formula

$$\text{Expected frequency } E_{r,c} = \frac{(\text{Sum of row } r) \cdot (\text{Sum of column } c)}{\text{Sample size}}.$$

The expected frequencies for the first row are

$$E_{1,1} = \frac{386 \cdot 841}{1984} \approx 163.622 \qquad E_{1,2} = \frac{386 \cdot 148}{1984} \approx 28.794$$

$$E_{1,3} = \frac{386 \cdot 525}{1984} \approx 102.142 \qquad E_{1,4} = \frac{386 \cdot 392}{1984} \approx 76.266$$

$$E_{1,5} = \frac{386 \cdot 78}{1984} \approx 15.175$$

and the expected frequencies for the second row are

$$E_{2,1} = \frac{1598 \cdot 841}{1984} \approx 677.378 \qquad E_{2,2} = \frac{1598 \cdot 148}{1984} \approx 119.206$$

$$E_{2,3} = \frac{1598 \cdot 525}{1984} \approx 422.858 \qquad E_{2,4} = \frac{1598 \cdot 392}{1984} \approx 315.734$$

$$E_{2,5} = \frac{1598 \cdot 78}{1984} \approx 62.825.$$

**Study Tip**

In Example 1, after finding $E_{1,1} \approx 163.622$, you can find $E_{2,1}$ by subtracting 163.622 from the first column's total, 841. So, $E_{2,1} \approx 841 - 163.622 = 677.378$. In general, you can find the expected value for the last cell in a column by subtracting the expected values for the other cells in that column from the column's total. Similarly, you can do this for the last cell in a row using the row's total.

**TRY IT YOURSELF 1**

The contingency table shows the results of a random sample of 1996 undergraduate students classified by their living arrangement and whether they borrowed money to pay for college. Find the expected frequency for each cell. Assume that the variables *student's living arrangement* and *borrowing status* are independent. *(Adapted from Sallie Mae/Ipsos)*

| | **Student's living arrangement** | | | | |
|---|---|---|---|---|---|
| **Borrowing status** | **With parents, rent free** | **With parents, pay rent** | **On campus** | **Off campus, w/others** | **Off campus, alone** |
| Borrowed | 364 | 92 | 303 | 203 | 42 |
| Did not borrow | 484 | 58 | 236 | 186 | 28 |

*Answer: Page A42*

## The Chi-Square Independence Test

After finding the expected frequencies, you can test whether the variables are independent using a **chi-square independence test.**

**DEFINITION**

A **chi-square independence test** is used to test the independence of two variables. Using this test, you can determine whether the occurrence of one variable affects the probability of the occurrence of the other variable.

Before performing a chi-square independence test, you must verify that (1) the observed frequencies were obtained from a random sample and (2) each expected frequency is at least 5.

### Picturing the World

A researcher wants to determine whether a relationship exists between where people work (workplace or home) and their educational attainment. The results of a random sample of 275 employed persons are shown in the contingency table. (Adapted from U.S. Bureau of Labor Statistics)

| | Where they work | |
|---|---|---|
| **Educational attainment** | **Workplace** | **Home** |
| Less than high school | 16 | 2 |
| High school diploma | 56 | 10 |
| Some college | 49 | 11 |
| BA degree or higher | 87 | 44 |

**Can the researcher use this sample to test for independence using a chi-square independence test? Why or why not?**

**The Chi-Square Independence Test**

To perform a chi-square independence test, these conditions must be met.

1. The observed frequencies must be obtained using a random sample.
2. Each expected frequency must be greater than or equal to 5.

If these conditions are met, then the sampling distribution for the test is approximated by a chi-square distribution with

$$\text{d.f.} = (r - 1)(c - 1)$$

degrees of freedom, where $r$ and $c$ are the number of rows and columns, respectively, of a contingency table. The **test statistic** is

$$\chi^2 = \Sigma\frac{(O - E)^2}{E}$$

where $O$ represents the observed frequencies and $E$ represents the expected frequencies.

To begin the independence test, you must first state a null hypothesis and an alternative hypothesis. For a chi-square independence test, the null and alternative hypotheses are always some variation of these statements.

$H_0$: The variables are independent.

$H_a$: The variables are dependent.

The expected frequencies are calculated on the assumption that the two variables are independent. If the variables are independent, then you can expect little difference between the observed frequencies and the expected frequencies. When the observed frequencies closely match the expected frequencies, the differences between $O$ and $E$ will be small and the chi-square test statistic will be close to 0. As such, the null hypothesis is unlikely to be rejected.

For dependent variables, however, there will be large discrepancies between the observed frequencies and the expected frequencies. When the differences between $O$ and $E$ are large, the chi-square test statistic is also large. A large chi-square test statistic is evidence for rejecting the null hypothesis. So, the chi-square independence test is always a right-tailed test.

GUIDELINES

**Performing a Chi-Square Independence Test**

| In Words | In Symbols |
|---|---|
| **1.** Verify that the observed frequencies were obtained from a random sample and each expected frequency is at least 5. | |
| **2.** Identify the claim. State the null and alternative hypotheses. | State $H_0$ and $H_a$. |
| **3.** Specify the level of significance. | Identify $\alpha$. |
| **4.** Determine the degrees of freedom. | d.f. $= (r - 1)(c - 1)$ |
| **5.** Determine the critical value. | Use Table 6 in Appendix B. |
| **6.** Determine the rejection region. | |
| **7.** Find the test statistic and sketch the sampling distribution. | $\chi^2 = \Sigma\frac{(O - E)^2}{E}$ |
| **8.** Make a decision to reject or fail to reject the null hypothesis. | If $\chi^2$ is in the rejection region, then reject $H_0$. Otherwise, fail to reject $H_0$. |
| **9.** Interpret the decision in the context of the original claim. | |

**Study Tip**

For instance, a contingency table with three rows and four columns will have

$(3 - 1)(4 - 1) = (2)(3)$
$= 6$ d.f.

EXAMPLE 2

## Performing a Chi-Square Independence Test

The contingency table shows the results of a random sample of 1984 undergraduate students classified by the student's living arrangement and family college experience. The expected frequencies, calculated in Example 1, are displayed in parentheses. At $\alpha = 0.01$, can you conclude that the variables *student's living arrangement* and *family college experience* are related?

| | **Student's living arrangement** | | | | | |
|---|---|---|---|---|---|---|
| **Family college experience** | **With parents, rent free** | **With parents, pay rent** | **On campus** | **Off campus, w/others** | **Off campus, alone** | **Total** |
| First in family | 190 (163.622) | 39 (28.794) | 97 (102.142) | 43 (76.266) | 17 (15.175) | 386 |
| 2nd generation | 651 (677.378) | 109 (119.206) | 428 (422.858) | 349 (315.734) | 61 (62.825) | 1598 |
| Total | 841 | 148 | 525 | 392 | 78 | 1984 |

SOLUTION

Because each expected frequency is at least 5 and the adults were randomly selected, you can use the chi-square independence test to determine whether the variables are independent. Here are the null and alternative hypotheses.

$H_0$: The *student's living arrangement* is independent of *family college experience.*

$H_a$: The *student's living arrangement* depends on *family college experience.* (Claim)

The contingency table has two rows and five columns, so the chi-square distribution has

$$\text{d.f.} = (r - 1)(c - 1) = (2 - 1)(5 - 1) = 4$$

degrees of freedom. Because d.f. = 4 and $\alpha = 0.01$, the critical value is $\chi_0^2 = 13.277$. The rejection region is $\chi^2 > 13.277$. You can use a table to find the chi-square test statistic, as shown below.

| $O$ | $E$ | $O - E$ | $(O - E)^2$ | $\dfrac{(O - E)^2}{E}$ |
|---|---|---|---|---|
| 190 | 163.622 | 26.378 | 695.798884 | 4.252477564 |
| 39 | 28.794 | 10.206 | 104.162436 | 3.617504897 |
| 97 | 102.142 | −5.142 | 26.440164 | 0.258856925 |
| 43 | 76.266 | −33.266 | 1106.626756 | 14.510093043 |
| 17 | 15.175 | 1.825 | 3.330625 | 0.219481054 |
| 651 | 677.378 | −26.378 | 695.798884 | 1.027194394 |
| 109 | 119.206 | −10.206 | 104.162436 | 0.873801956 |
| 428 | 422.858 | 5.142 | 26.440164 | 0.062527288 |
| 349 | 315.734 | 33.266 | 1106.626756 | 3.504933761 |
| 61 | 62.825 | −1.825 | 3.330625 | 0.053014326 |
| | | | | $\chi^2 = \Sigma\dfrac{(O - E)^2}{E} \approx 28.380$ |

The figure at the right shows the location of the rejection region and the chi-square test statistic. Because

$$\chi^2 \approx 28.380$$

is in the rejection region, you reject the null hypothesis.

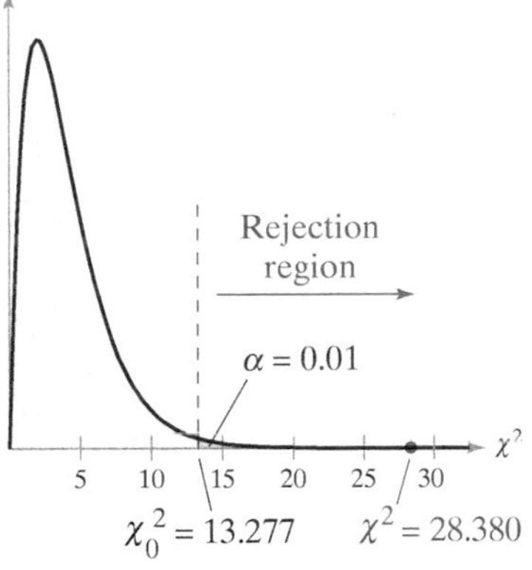


***Interpretation*** There is enough evidence at the 1% level of significance to conclude that the *student's living arrangement* depends on *family college experience.*

**TRY IT YOURSELF 2**

The contingency table shows the results of a random sample of 1996 undergraduate students classified by their living arrangement and whether they borrowed money to pay for college. At $\alpha = 0.01$, can you conclude that the variables *student's living arrangement* and *borrowing status* are related? (The expected frequencies are displayed in parentheses.)

| | **Student's living arrangement** | | | | | |
|---|---|---|---|---|---|---|
| **Borrowing status** | **With parents, rent free** | **With parents, pay rent** | **On campus** | **Off campus, w/others** | **Off campus, alone** | **Total** |
| Borrowed | 364 (426.549) | 92 (75.451) | 303 (271.120) | 203 (195.669) | 42 (35.210) | 1004 |
| Did not borrow | 484 (421.451) | 58 (74.549) | 236 (267.880) | 186 (193.331) | 28 (34.790) | 992 |
| Total | 848 | 150 | 539 | 389 | 70 | 1996 |

*Answer: Page A42*

## EXAMPLE 3

### Using Technology for a Chi-Square Independence Test

A health club manager wants to determine whether the number of days per week that adults exercise is related to demographic cohort, specifically generation. A random sample of 275 adults is selected and the results are classified as shown in the table. At $\alpha = 0.05$, is there enough evidence to conclude that the *number of days an adult exercises per week* is related to *generation?*

| | Number of days of exercise per week | | | | |
|---|---|---|---|---|---|
| **Generation** | **0–1** | **2–3** | **4–5** | **6–7** | **Total** |
| Gen Z (ages 18–24) | 40 | 53 | 26 | 6 | 125 |
| Millennial (ages 25–40) | 34 | 68 | 37 | 11 | 150 |
| Total | 74 | 121 | 63 | 17 | 275 |

**SOLUTION** Here are the null and alternative hypotheses.

$H_0$: The *number of days of exercise per week* is independent of *generation.*

$H_a$: The *number of days of exercise per week* depends on *generation.* (Claim)

Because d.f. = 3 and $\alpha = 0.05$, the critical value is $\chi_0^2 = 7.815$. So, the rejection region is $\chi^2 > 7.815$. Using Minitab (see below), the test statistic is $\chi^2 \approx 3.493$. Because $\chi^2 \approx 3.493$ is not in the rejection region, you fail to reject the null hypothesis.

**MINITAB**

**Chi-Square Test for Association: Generation, Number of days of exercise**

Rows: Generation Columns: Number of days of exercise

| | 0 to 1 | 2 to 3 | 4 to 5 | 6 to 7 | All |
|---|---|---|---|---|---|
| Gen Z | 40 | 53 | 26 | 6 | 125 |
| Millennial | 34 | 68 | 37 | 11 | 150 |
| All | 74 | 121 | 63 | 17 | 275 |

| *Cell Contents* | | **Chi-Square** | **DF** | **P-Value** |
|---|---|---|---|---|
| *Count* | Pearson | 3.493 | 3 | 0.322 |

**Study Tip**

You can also use a *P*-value to perform a chi-square independence test. For instance, in Example 3, note that Minitab displays $P = 0.322$. Because $P > \alpha$, you fail to reject the null hypothesis.

***Interpretation*** There is not enough evidence to conclude that the number of days a student exercises per week is related to generation.

**TRY IT YOURSELF 3**

A researcher wants to determine whether age is related to whether or not a tax credit would influence an adult to make a charitable donation. A random sample of 1250 adults is selected and the results are classified as shown in the table. At $\alpha = 0.01$, is there enough evidence to conclude that *age* is related to the *response?*

| | Age | | | |
|---|---|---|---|---|
| **Response** | **18–34** | **35–54** | **55 and older** | **Total** |
| Yes | 257 | 189 | 143 | 589 |
| No | 218 | 261 | 182 | 661 |
| Total | 475 | 450 | 325 | 1250 |

*Answer: Page A42*

# 10.2 EXERCISES

For Extra Help: MyLab Statistics

## Building Basic Skills and Vocabulary

1. Explain how to find the expected frequency for a cell in a contingency table.

2. Explain the difference between marginal frequencies and joint frequencies in a contingency table.

3. Explain how the chi-square independence test and the chi-square goodness-of-fit test are similar. How are they different?

4. Explain why the chi-square independence test is always a right-tailed test.

**True or False?** *In Exercises 5 and 6, determine whether the statement is true or false. If it is false, rewrite it as a true statement.*

5. If the two variables in a chi-square independence test are dependent, then you can expect little difference between the observed frequencies and the expected frequencies.

6. When the test statistic for the chi-square independence test is large, you will, in most cases, reject the null hypothesis.

**Finding Expected Frequencies** *In Exercises 7–12, (a) calculate the marginal frequencies and (b) find the expected frequency for each cell in the contingency table. Assume that the variables are independent.*

7.

| | Athlete has | |
|---|---|---|
| **Result** | **Stretched** | **Not stretched** |
| Injury | 18 | 22 |
| No injury | 211 | 189 |

8.

| | Treatment | |
|---|---|---|
| **Result** | **Drug** | **Placebo** |
| Nausea | 36 | 13 |
| No nausea | 254 | 262 |

9.

| | Preference | | |
|---|---|---|---|
| **Bank employee** | **New procedure** | **Old procedure** | **No preference** |
| Teller | 92 | 351 | 50 |
| Customer service representative | 76 | 42 | 8 |

10.

| | Rating | | |
|---|---|---|---|
| **Size of restaurant** | **Excellent** | **Fair** | **Poor** |
| Seats 100 or fewer | 182 | 203 | 165 |
| Seats over 100 | 180 | 311 | 159 |

11.

| | Type of car | | | |
|---|---|---|---|---|
| **Gender** | **Compact** | **Full-size** | **SUV** | **Truck/van** |
| Male | 28 | 39 | 21 | 22 |
| Female | 24 | 32 | 20 | 14 |

**12.**

| | Age | | | | |
|---|---|---|---|---|---|
| **Type of movie rented** | **18–24** | **25–34** | **35–44** | **45–64** | **65 and older** |
| Comedy | 38 | 30 | 24 | 10 | 8 |
| Action | 15 | 17 | 16 | 9 | 5 |
| Drama | 12 | 11 | 19 | 25 | 13 |

## Using and Interpreting Concepts

**Performing a Chi-Square Independence Test** *In Exercises 13–28, perform the indicated chi-square independence test by performing the steps below.*

*(a) Identify the claim and state $H_0$ and $H_a$.*

*(b) Determine the degrees of freedom, find the critical value, and identify the rejection region.*

*(c) Find the chi-square test statistic.*

*(d) Decide whether to reject or fail to reject the null hypothesis.*

*(e) Interpret the decision in the context of the original claim.*

**13.** Use the contingency table and expected frequencies from Exercise 7. At $\alpha = 0.01$, test the hypothesis that the variables are independent.

**14.** Use the contingency table and expected frequencies from Exercise 8. At $\alpha = 0.05$, test the hypothesis that the variables are dependent.

**15. Musculoskeletal Injury** The contingency table shows the results of a random sample of patients with pain from musculoskeletal injuries treated with acetaminophen or ibuprofen. At $\alpha = 0.10$, can you conclude that the treatment is related to the result? *(Adapted from American Academy of Pediatrics)*

| | Treatment | |
|---|---|---|
| **Result** | **Acetaminophen** | **Ibuprofen** |
| Significant improvement | 58 | 81 |
| Slight improvement | 42 | 19 |

**16. Attitudes About Safety** The contingency table shows the results of a random sample of students by type of school and their attitudes on safety steps taken by the school staff. At $\alpha = 0.01$, can you conclude that attitudes about the safety steps taken by the school staff are related to the type of school? *(Adapted from Horatio Alger Association)*

| | School staff has | |
|---|---|---|
| **Type of school** | **Taken all steps necessary for student safety** | **Taken some steps toward student safety** |
| Public | 40 | 51 |
| Private | 64 | 34 |

**17. Trying to Quit Smoking** The contingency table shows the results of a random sample of former smokers by their gender and the number of times they tried to quit smoking before they were habit-free. At $\alpha = 0.05$, can you conclude that the number of times they tried to quit before they were habit-free is related to gender? *(Adapted from Porter Novelli HealthStyles for the American Lung Association)*

| | Number of times tried to quit before habit-free | | |
|---|---|---|---|
| **Gender** | **1** | **2–3** | **4 or more** |
| Male | 271 | 257 | 149 |
| Female | 146 | 139 | 80 |

**18. Achievement and School Location** The contingency table shows the results of a random sample of students by the location of school and the number of those students achieving basic skill levels in three subjects. At $\alpha = 0.01$, test the hypothesis that the variables are independent. *(Adapted from HUD State of the Cities Report)*

| | Subject | | |
|---|---|---|---|
| **Location of school** | **Reading** | **Math** | **Science** |
| Urban | 43 | 42 | 38 |
| Suburban | 63 | 66 | 65 |

**19. Continuing Education** You work for a college's continuing education department and want to determine whether the reasons given by workers for continuing their education are related to job type. In your study, you randomly collect the data shown in the contingency table. At $\alpha = 0.01$, can you conclude that the reason and the type of worker are dependent? *(Adapted from Market Research Institute for George Mason University)*

| | Reason for continuing education | | |
|---|---|---|---|
| **Type of worker** | **Professional** | **Personal** | **Professional and personal** |
| Technical | 30 | 36 | 41 |
| Other | 47 | 25 | 30 |

**20. Ages and Goals** You are investigating the relationship between the ages of U.S. adults and what aspect of career development they consider to be the most important. You randomly collect the data shown in the contingency table. At $\alpha = 0.10$, is there enough evidence to conclude that age is related to which aspect of career development is considered to be most important? *(Adapted from The Harris Poll)*

| | Career development aspect | | |
|---|---|---|---|
| **Age** | **Learning new skills** | **Pay increases** | **Career path** |
| 18–26 years | 31 | 22 | 21 |
| 27–41 years | 27 | 31 | 33 |
| 42–61 years | 19 | 14 | 8 |

21. **College Visits** The contingency table shows the results of a survey asking 1858 parents and students of different incomes whether they visited their college before enrolling. At $\alpha = 0.01$, can you conclude that family income is related to college visits? *(Adapted from Sallie Mae)*

| | College visit before enrolling | | | |
|---|---|---|---|---|
| **Family income** | **In person** | **Virtual tour** | **Both** | **Neither** |
| Less than $35,000 | 155 | 60 | 88 | 53 |
| $35,000–$100,000 | 461 | 136 | 171 | 85 |
| Greater than $100,000 | 415 | 52 | 130 | 52 |

22. **Choosing a College** The contingency table shows the results of a survey asking 1858 parents and students of different incomes what their deciding factor was in choosing a college. At $\alpha = 0.01$, can you conclude that the deciding factor in choosing a college is related to the income of the family? *(Adapted from Sallie Mae)*

| | Deciding factor in choosing a college | | | |
|---|---|---|---|---|
| **Family income** | **Finances** | **Academics** | **Personal factors** | **Not sure** |
| Less than $35,000 | 138 | 121 | 78 | 14 |
| $35,000–$100,000 | 290 | 298 | 239 | 26 |
| Greater than $100,000 | 168 | 298 | 175 | 13 |

23. **Vehicles and Crashes** You are studying the relationship between types of vehicles and their points of initial impact in crashes with occupant fatalities. As part of your study, you randomly select 3000 vehicle crashes with occupant fatalities and organize the resulting data as shown in the contingency table. At $\alpha = 0.05$, can you conclude that the types of vehicles and the points of initial impact of crashes with occupant fatalities are dependent? *(Adapted from Insurance Institute for Highway Safety)*

| | Point of initial impact | | |
|---|---|---|---|
| **Vehicle type** | **Front** | **Side** | **Rear** |
| Cars | 1435 | 697 | 161 |
| Pickup trucks | 523 | 150 | 34 |

24. **Alcohol-Related Accidents** The contingency table shows the results of a random sample of fatally injured passenger vehicle drivers (with blood alcohol concentrations greater than or equal to 0.08) by age and gender. At $\alpha = 0.05$, can you conclude that age is related to gender in such alcohol-related accidents? *(Adapted from Insurance Institute for Highway Safety)*

| | Age | | | | | |
|---|---|---|---|---|---|---|
| **Gender** | **16–20** | **21–30** | **31–40** | **41–50** | **51–60** | **61 and older** |
| Male | 27 | 148 | 107 | 71 | 66 | 54 |
| Female | 9 | 45 | 26 | 17 | 16 | 14 |

**25.** Use the contingency table and expected frequencies from Exercise 9. At $\alpha = 0.05$, test the hypothesis that the variables are dependent.

**26.** Use the contingency table and expected frequencies from Exercise 10. At $\alpha = 0.01$, test the hypothesis that the variables are dependent.

**27.** Use the contingency table and expected frequencies from Exercise 11. At $\alpha = 0.10$, test the hypothesis that the variables are independent.

**28.** Use the contingency table and expected frequencies from Exercise 12. At $\alpha = 0.10$, test the hypothesis that the variables are dependent.

## Extending Concepts

**Homogeneity of Proportions Test** *In Exercises 29–32, use this information about the homogeneity of proportions test. Another chi-square test that involves a contingency table is the* ***homogeneity of proportions test.*** *This test is used to determine whether several proportions are equal when samples are taken from different populations. Before the populations are sampled and the contingency table is made, the sample sizes are determined. After randomly sampling different populations, you can test whether the proportion of elements in a category is the same for each population using the same guidelines as the chi-square independence test. The null and alternative hypotheses are always some variation of these statements.*

$H_0$: *The proportions are equal.*

$H_a$: *At least one of the proportions is different from the others.*

*Performing a homogeneity of proportions test requires that the observed frequencies be obtained using a random sample, and each expected frequency must be greater than or equal to 5.*

**29. Motor Vehicle Crash Deaths** The contingency table shows the results of a random sample of motor vehicle crash deaths by age and gender. At $\alpha = 0.05$, perform a homogeneity of proportions test on the claim that the proportions of motor vehicle crash deaths involving males or females are the same for each age group. *(Adapted from Insurance Institute for Highway Safety)*

| | Age | | | |
|---|---|---|---|---|
| **Gender** | **16–24** | **25–34** | **35–44** | **45–54** |
| Male | 80 | 97 | 76 | 73 |
| Female | 33 | 35 | 26 | 27 |

| | Age | | | |
|---|---|---|---|---|
| **Gender** | **55–64** | **65–74** | **75–84** | **85 and older** |
| Male | 81 | 51 | 30 | 12 |
| Female | 26 | 23 | 19 | 9 |

**30. Obsessive-Compulsive Disorder** The contingency table at the left shows the results of a random sample of patients with obsessive-compulsive disorder after being treated with a drug or with a placebo. At $\alpha = 0.10$, perform a homogeneity of proportions test on the claim that the proportions of the results for drug and placebo treatments are the same. *(Adapted from The Journal of the American Medical Association)*

| | Treatment | |
|---|---|---|
| **Result** | **Drug** | **Placebo** |
| Improvement | 39 | 25 |
| No change | 54 | 70 |

TABLE FOR EXERCISE 30

**31.** Is the chi-square homogeneity of proportions test a left-tailed, right-tailed, or two-tailed test?

**32.** Explain how the chi-square independence test is different from the chi-square homogeneity of proportions test.

**Contingency Tables and Relative Frequencies** *In Exercises 33–36, use the information below.*

The frequencies in a contingency table can be written as relative frequencies by dividing each frequency by the sample size. The contingency table below shows the number of U.S. adults (in millions) ages 25 and over by employment status and educational attainment. *(Adapted from U.S. Census Bureau)*

| | Educational attainment | | | |
|---|---|---|---|---|
| **Status** | **Not a high school graduate** | **High school graduate** | **Some college, no degree** | **Associate's, bachelor's, or advanced degree** |
| Employed | 8.3 | 32.9 | 19.7 | 74.6 |
| Unemployed | 0.8 | 2.0 | 1.1 | 2.4 |
| Not in civilian labor force | 11.1 | 26.6 | 13.2 | 30.3 |

**33.** Rewrite the contingency table using relative frequencies.

**34.** Explain why you cannot perform the chi-square independence test on these data.

**35.** What percent of U.S. adults ages 25 and over (a) have a degree and are unemployed and (b) have some college education, but no degree, and are not in the civilian labor force?

**36.** What percent of U.S. adults ages 25 and over (a) are employed and are only high school graduates, (b) are not in the civilian labor force, and (c) are not high school graduates?

**Conditional Relative Frequencies** *In Exercises 37–42, use the contingency table from Exercises 33–36, and the information below.*

Relative frequencies can also be calculated based on the row totals (by dividing each row entry by the row's total) or the column totals (by dividing each column entry by the column's total). These frequencies are **conditional relative frequencies** and can be used to determine whether an association exists between two categories in a contingency table.

**37.** Calculate the conditional relative frequencies in the contingency table based on the row totals.

**38.** What percent of U.S. adults ages 25 and over who are employed have a degree?

**39.** What percent of U.S. adults ages 25 and over who are not in the civilian labor force have some college education, but no degree?

**40.** Calculate the conditional relative frequencies in the contingency table based on the column totals.

**41.** What percent of U.S. adults ages 25 and over who have a degree are not in the civilian labor force?

**42.** What percent of U.S. adults ages 25 and over who are not high school graduates are unemployed?

CASE STUDY

# Living On Mars

How would you like to live on Mars? YouGov polled 1312 U.S. adults and asked them the question below.

*Imagine that you had the opportunity to travel to Mars safely and become one of the first humans to live on the planet in a colony for the remainder of your life. Would you want to live on Mars in a colony?*

The pie chart shows the responses to the question. You conduct a survey using the same question. The contingency table shows the results of your survey classified by age group.

**Would You Want to Live on Mars in a Colony?**

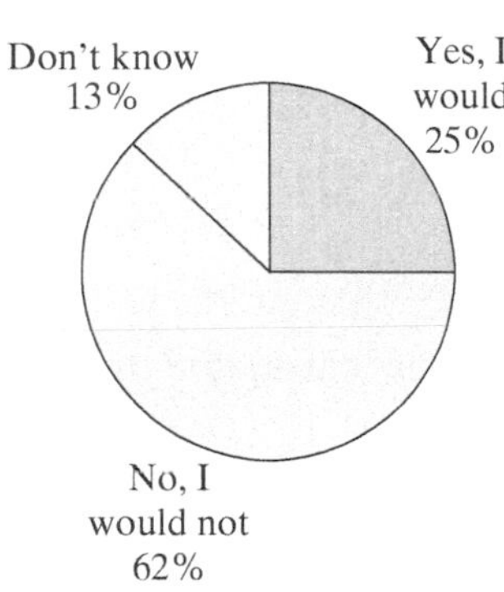


| | Age | | |
|---|---|---|---|
| **Response** | **18–34** | **35–54** | **55+** |
| Yes, I would | 87 | 33 | 10 |
| No, I would not | 80 | 78 | 70 |
| Don't know | 27 | 26 | 8 |

## EXERCISES

1. Assuming the variables *age* and *response* are independent, did the number of respondents in the age groups 18–34, 35–54, or 55+ exceed the expected number of "Yes, I would" responses?

2. Assuming the variables *age* and *response* are independent, did the number of respondents in the age groups 18–34, 35–54, or 55+ exceed the expected number of "No, I would not" responses?

3. At $\alpha = 0.01$, perform a chi-square independence test to determine whether the variables *response* and *age* are independent. What can you conclude?

*In Exercises 4 and 5, perform a chi-square goodness-of-fit test to compare the distribution of responses shown in the pie chart with the distribution of your survey results for each age group. Use the distribution shown in the pie chart as the expected distribution. Use* $\alpha = 0.05$.

4. Compare the distribution of responses by 18- to 34-year-olds with the expected distribution. What can you conclude?

5. Compare the distribution of responses by 35- to 54-year-olds with the expected distribution. What can you conclude?

6. In addition to the variables used in the Case Study, what other variables may be of interest to consider when studying the distribution of U.S. adults' feelings about living on Mars in a colony?

# 10.3 Comparing Two Variances

**What You Should Learn**

- How to interpret the *F*-distribution and use an *F*-table to find critical values
- How to perform a two-sample *F*-test to compare two variances

The *F*-Distribution ■ The Two-Sample *F*-Test for Variances

## The *F*-Distribution

In Chapter 8, you learned how to perform hypothesis tests to compare population means and population proportions. Recall from Section 8.2 that the *t*-test for the difference between two population means depends on whether the population variances are equal. To determine whether the population variances are equal, you can perform a two-sample *F*-test.

In this section, you will learn about the ***F*-distribution** and how it can be used to compare two variances. As you read the next definition, recall that the sample variance $s^2$ is the square of the sample standard deviation $s$.

**DEFINITION**

Let $s_1^2$ and $s_2^2$ represent the sample variances of two different populations. If both populations are normal and the population variances $\sigma_1^2$ and $\sigma_2^2$ are equal, then the sampling distribution of

$$F = \frac{s_1^2}{s_2^2}$$

is an ***F*-distribution.** Here are several properties of the *F*-distribution.

1. The *F*-distribution is a family of curves, each of which is determined by two types of degrees of freedom: the degrees of freedom corresponding to the variance in the numerator, denoted by $\mathbf{d.f._N}$, and the degrees of freedom corresponding to the variance in the denominator, denoted by $\mathbf{d.f._D}$.
2. The *F*-distribution is positively skewed and therefore the distribution is not symmetric (see figure below).
3. The total area under each *F*-distribution curve is equal to 1.
4. All values of *F* are greater than or equal to 0.
5. For all *F*-distributions, the mean value of *F* is approximately equal to 1.

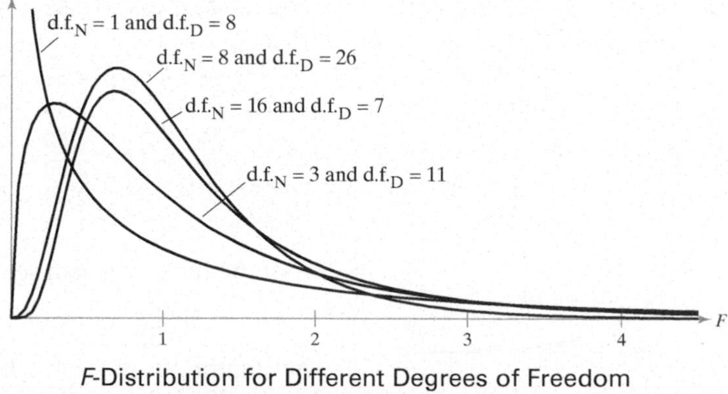


*F*-Distribution for Different Degrees of Freedom

For unequal variances, designate the greater sample variance as $s_1^2$. So, in the sampling distribution of $F = s_1^2/s_2^2$, the variance in the numerator is greater than or equal to the variance in the denominator. This means that *F* is always greater than or equal to 1. As such, all one-tailed tests are right-tailed tests, and for all two-tailed tests, you need only to find the right-tailed critical value.

Table 7 in Appendix B lists the critical values for the $F$-distribution for selected levels of significance $\alpha$ and degrees of freedom $d.f._N$ and $d.f._D$.

## GUIDELINES

**Finding Critical Values for the $F$-Distribution**

1. Specify the level of significance $\alpha$.
2. Determine the degrees of freedom for the numerator $d.f._N$.
3. Determine the degrees of freedom for the denominator $d.f._D$.
4. Use Table 7 in Appendix B to find the critical value. When the hypothesis test is

   **a.** one-tailed, use the $\alpha$ $F$-table.

   **b.** two-tailed, use the $\frac{1}{2}\alpha$ $F$-table.

   Note that because $F$ is always greater than or equal to 1, all one-tailed tests are right-tailed tests. For two-tailed tests, you need only to find the right-tailed critical value.

In Examples 1 and 2, the values of $d.f._N$ and $d.f._D$ are given. You will learn how to determine these values on page 552.

## EXAMPLE 1

### Finding a Critical $F$-Value for a Right-Tailed Test

Find the critical $F$-value for a right-tailed test when $\alpha = 0.10$, $d.f._N = 5$, and $d.f._D = 28$.

**SOLUTION**

A portion of Table 7 is shown below. Using the $\alpha = 0.10$ $F$-table with $d.f._N = 5$ and $d.f._D = 28$, you can find the critical value, as shown by the highlighted areas in the table.

| $d.f._D$: Degrees of freedom, denominator | $\alpha = 0.10$ $d.f._N$: Degrees of freedom, numerator | | | | | | | |
|---|---|---|---|---|---|---|---|---|
| | 1 | 2 | 3 | 4 | 5 | 6 | 7 | 8 |
| 1 | 39.86 | 49.50 | 53.59 | 55.83 | 57.24 | 58.20 | 58.91 | 59.44 |
| 2 | 8.53 | 9.00 | 9.16 | 9.24 | 9.29 | 9.33 | 9.35 | 9.37 |
| 26 | 2.91 | 2.52 | 2.31 | 2.17 | 2.08 | 2.01 | 1.96 | 1.92 |
| 27 | 2.90 | 2.51 | 2.30 | 2.17 | 2.07 | 2.00 | 1.95 | 1.91 |
| 28 | 2.89 | 2.50 | 2.29 | 2.16 | 2.06 | 2.00 | 1.94 | 1.90 |
| 29 | 2.89 | 2.50 | 2.28 | 2.15 | 2.06 | 1.99 | 1.93 | 1.89 |
| 30 | 2.88 | 2.49 | 2.28 | 2.14 | 2.05 | 1.98 | 1.93 | 1.88 |

From the table, you can see that the critical value is

$F_0 = 2.06$. Critical value

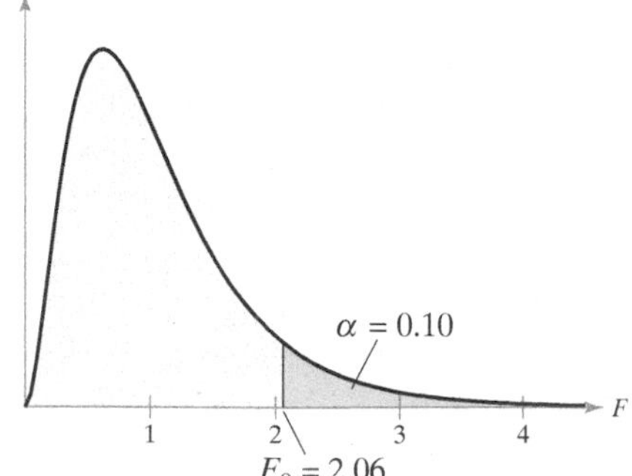


The figure at the left shows the $F$-distribution for $\alpha = 0.10$, $d.f._N = 5$, $d.f._D = 28$, and $F_0 = 2.06$.

**TRY IT YOURSELF 1**

Find the critical $F$-value for a right-tailed test when $\alpha = 0.05$, $d.f._N = 8$, and $d.f._D = 20$.

*Answer: Page A43*

**Study Tip**

When using Table 7 in Appendix B to find a critical value, you will notice that some of the values for d.f.$_N$ or d.f.$_D$ are not included in the table. If the number you need for d.f.$_N$ or d.f.$_D$ is exactly midway between two values in the table, then use the critical value midway between the corresponding critical values. In some cases, though, it is easier to use technology to calculate the *P*-value, compare it to the level of significance, and then decide whether to reject the null hypothesis.

When performing a two-tailed hypothesis test using the *F*-distribution, you need only to find the right-tailed critical value. You must, however, remember to use the $\frac{1}{2}\alpha$ *F*-table.

**EXAMPLE 2**

### Finding a Critical *F*-Value for a Two-Tailed Test

Find the critical *F*-value for a two-tailed test when $\alpha = 0.05$, d.f.$_N = 4$, and d.f.$_D = 8$.

**SOLUTION**

A portion of Table 7 is shown below. Using the

$$\frac{1}{2}\alpha = \frac{1}{2}(0.05) = 0.025$$

*F*-table with d.f.$_N = 4$ and d.f.$_D = 8$, you can find the critical value, as shown by the highlighted areas in the table.

| d.f.$_D$: Degrees of freedom, denominator | $\alpha = 0.025$ | | | | | | | |
|---|---|---|---|---|---|---|---|---|
| | d.f.$_N$: Degrees of freedom, numerator | | | | | | | |
| | 1 | 2 | 3 | 4 | 5 | 6 | 7 | 8 |
| 1 | 647.8 | 799.5 | 864.2 | 899.6 | 921.8 | 937.1 | 948.2 | 956.7 |
| 2 | 38.51 | 39.00 | 39.17 | 39.25 | 39.30 | 39.33 | 39.36 | 39.37 |
| 3 | 17.44 | 16.04 | 15.44 | 15.10 | 14.88 | 14.73 | 14.62 | 14.54 |
| 4 | 12.22 | 10.65 | 9.98 | 9.60 | 9.36 | 9.20 | 9.07 | 8.98 |
| 5 | 10.01 | 8.43 | 7.76 | 7.39 | 7.15 | 6.98 | 6.85 | 6.76 |
| 6 | 8.81 | 7.26 | 6.60 | 6.23 | 5.99 | 5.82 | 5.70 | 5.60 |
| 7 | 8.07 | 6.54 | 5.89 | 5.52 | 5.29 | 5.12 | 4.99 | 4.90 |
| 8 | 7.57 | 6.06 | 5.42 | 5.05 | 4.82 | 4.65 | 4.53 | 4.43 |
| 9 | 7.21 | 5.71 | 5.08 | 4.72 | 4.48 | 4.32 | 4.20 | 4.10 |

From the table, the critical value is

$F_0 = 5.05$. Critical value

The figure shows the *F*-distribution for $\frac{1}{2}\alpha = 0.025$, d.f.$_N = 4$, d.f.$_D = 8$, and $F_0 = 5.05$.

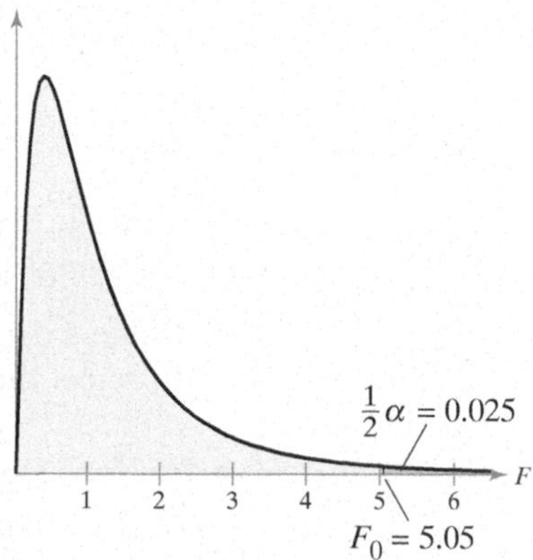


**TRY IT YOURSELF 2**

Find the critical *F*-value for a two-tailed test when $\alpha = 0.01$, d.f.$_N = 2$, and d.f.$_D = 5$.

*Answer: Page A43*

## The Two-Sample *F*-Test for Variances

In the remainder of this section, you will learn how to perform a two-sample *F*-test for comparing two population variances using a sample from each population.

### Two-Sample *F*-Test for Variances

A **two-sample *F*-test** is used to compare two population variances $\sigma_1^2$ and $\sigma_2^2$. To perform this test, these conditions must be met.

1. The samples must be random.
2. The samples must be independent.
3. Each population must have a normal distribution.

The **test statistic** is

$$F = \frac{s_1^2}{s_2^2}$$

where $s_1^2$ and $s_2^2$ represent the sample variances with $s_1^2 \geq s_2^2$. The numerator has $\text{d.f.}_N = n_1 - 1$ degrees of freedom and the denominator has $\text{d.f.}_D = n_2 - 1$ degrees of freedom, where $n_1$ is the size of the sample having variance $s_1^2$ and $n_2$ is the size of the sample having variance $s_2^2$.

### GUIDELINES

**Using a Two-Sample *F*-Test to Compare $\sigma_1^2$ and $\sigma_2^2$**

| In Words | In Symbols |
|---|---|
| **1.** Verify that the samples are random and independent, and the populations have normal distributions. | |
| **2.** Identify the claim. State the null and alternative hypotheses. | State $H_0$ and $H_a$. |
| **3.** Specify the level of significance. | Identify $\alpha$. |
| **4.** Identify the degrees of freedom for the numerator and the denominator. | $\text{d.f.}_N = n_1 - 1$<br>$\text{d.f.}_D = n_2 - 1$ |
| **5.** Determine the critical value. | Use Table 7 in Appendix B. |
| **6.** Determine the rejection region. | |
| **7.** Find the test statistic and sketch the sampling distribution. | $F = \frac{s_1^2}{s_2^2}$ |
| **8.** Make a decision to reject or fail to reject the null hypothesis. | If $F$ is in the rejection region, then reject $H_0$. Otherwise, fail to reject $H_0$. |
| **9.** Interpret the decision in the context of the original claim. | |

In some cases, you will be given the sample standard deviations $s_1$ and $s_2$. Remember to square both standard deviations to calculate the sample variances $s_1^2$ and $s_2^2$ before using a two-sample *F*-test to compare variances.

## Picturing the World

Does location have an effect on the variance of real estate selling prices? A random sample of selling prices (in thousands of dollars) of existing homes sold in the California counties of Los Angeles and San Diego is shown in the table. (Adapted from National Association of Realtors and Move, Inc.)

| Los Angeles | San Diego |
|---|---|
| 443 | 639 |
| 347 | 369 |
| 495 | 649 |
| 595 | 665 |
| 595 | 699 |
| 649 | 779 |
| 250 | 425 |
| 449 | 595 |
| 580 | 649 |
| 369 | 549 |

**Assuming each population of selling prices is normally distributed, is it possible to use a two-sample *F*-test to compare the population variances?**

## EXAMPLE 3

### Performing a Two-Sample *F*-Test

A restaurant manager is designing a system that is intended to decrease the variance of the time customers wait before their meals are served. Under the old system, a random sample of 10 customers had a variance of 400. Under the new system, a random sample of 21 customers had a variance of 256. At $\alpha = 0.10$, is there enough evidence to convince the manager to switch to the new system? Assume both populations are normally distributed.

### SOLUTION

Because $400 > 256$, $s_1^2 = 400$ and $s_2^2 = 256$. Therefore, $s_1^2$ and $\sigma_1^2$ represent the sample and population variances for the old system, respectively. With the claim "the variance of the waiting times under the new system is less than the variance of the waiting times under the old system," the null and alternative hypotheses are

$$H_0\colon \sigma_1^2 \le \sigma_2^2 \quad \text{and} \quad H_a\colon \sigma_1^2 > \sigma_2^2. \quad \text{(Claim)}$$

Note that the test is a right-tailed test with $\alpha = 0.10$, and the degrees of freedom are

$$\text{d.f.}_N = n_1 - 1 = 10 - 1 = 9$$

and

$$\text{d.f.}_D = n_2 - 1 = 21 - 1 = 20.$$

So, the critical value is $F_0 = 1.96$ and the rejection region is $F > 1.96$. The test statistic is

$$F = \frac{s_1^2}{s_2^2} = \frac{400}{256} \approx 1.56.$$

The figure shows the location of the rejection region and the test statistic $F$. Because $F$ is not in the rejection region, you fail to reject the null hypothesis.

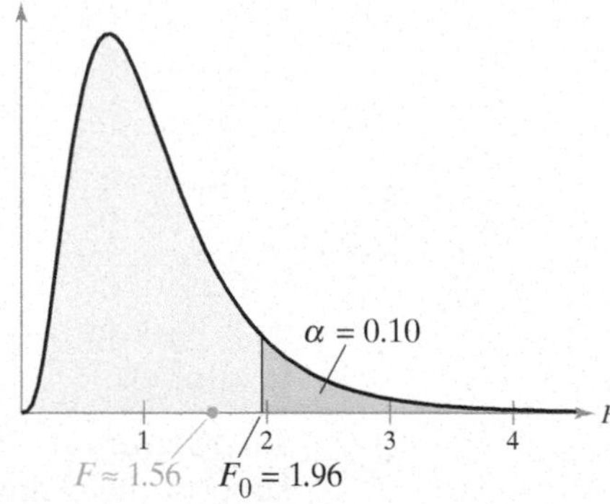


***Interpretation*** There is not enough evidence at the 10% level of significance to convince the manager to switch to the new system.

### TRY IT YOURSELF 3

A medical researcher claims that a specially treated intravenous solution decreases the variance of the time required for nutrients to enter the bloodstream. Independent samples from each type of solution are randomly selected, and the results are shown in the table at the left. At $\alpha = 0.01$, is there enough evidence to support the researcher's claim? Assume the populations are normally distributed.

| Normal solution | Treated solution |
|---|---|
| $n = 25$<br>$s^2 = 180$ | $n = 20$<br>$s^2 = 56$ |

*Answer: Page A43*

## EXAMPLE 4

### Using Technology for a Two-Sample F-Test

| Stock A | Stock B |
|---|---|
| $n_2 = 30$<br>$s_2 = 3.5$ | $n_1 = 31$<br>$s_1 = 5.7$ |

You want to purchase stock in a company and are deciding between two different stocks. Because a stock's risk can be associated with the standard deviation of its daily closing prices, you randomly select samples of the daily closing prices for each stock to obtain the results shown at the left. At $\alpha = 0.05$, can you conclude that one of the two stocks is a riskier investment? Assume the stock closing prices are normally distributed.

**SOLUTION**

Because $5.7^2 > 3.5^2$, $s_1^2 = 5.7^2$ and $s_2^2 = 3.5^2$. Therefore, $s_1^2$ and $\sigma_1^2$ represent the sample and population variances for Stock B, respectively. With the claim "one of the two stocks is a riskier investment," the null and alternative hypotheses are

$$H_0: \sigma_1^2 = \sigma_2^2 \quad \text{and} \quad H_a: \sigma_1^2 \neq \sigma_2^2. \text{ (Claim)}$$

Note that the test is a two-tailed test with $\frac{1}{2}\alpha = \frac{1}{2}(0.05) = 0.025$, and the degrees of freedom are $\text{d.f.}_N = n_1 - 1 = 31 - 1 = 30$ and $\text{d.f.}_D = n_2 - 1 = 30 - 1 = 29$. So, the critical value is $F_0 = 2.09$ and the rejection region is $F > 2.09$.

To perform a two-sample F-test using a TI-84 Plus, begin with the STAT keystroke. Choose the TESTS menu and select *E:2–SampFTest.* Then set up the two-sample F-test as shown in the first screen below. Because you are entering the descriptive statistics, select the *Stats* input option. When entering the original data, select the *Data* input option. The other displays below show the results of selecting *Calculate* or *Draw*.

**TI-84 PLUS**

```
2-SampFTest
Inpt: Data Stats
Sx1:5.7
n1:31
Sx2:3.5
n2:30
σ1:≠σ2 <σ2 >σ2
Calculate Draw
```

**TI-84 PLUS**

```
2-SampFTest
σ1≠σ2
F=2.652244898
p=.0102172459
Sx1=5.7
Sx2=3.5
↓n1=31
```

**TI-84 PLUS**

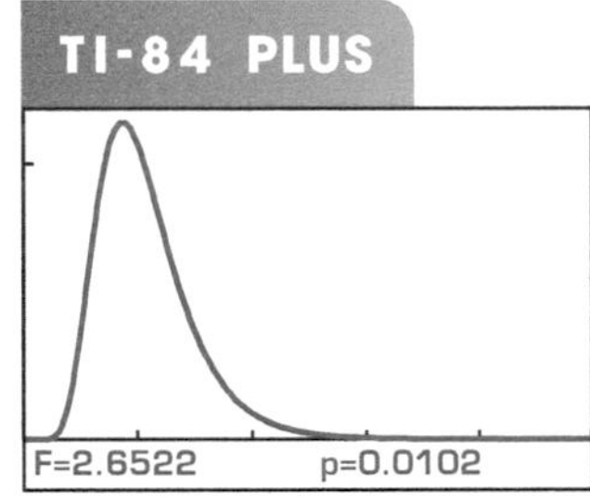


The test statistic $F \approx 2.65$ is in the rejection region, so you reject the null hypothesis.

***Interpretation*** There is enough evidence at the 5% level of significance to support the claim that one of the two stocks is a riskier investment.

**TRY IT YOURSELF 4**

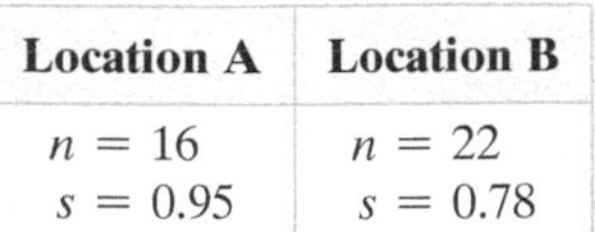

| Location A | Location B |
|---|---|
| $n = 16$<br>$s = 0.95$ | $n = 22$<br>$s = 0.78$ |

A biologist claims that the pH levels of the soil in two geographic locations have equal standard deviations. Independent samples from each location are randomly selected, and the results are shown at the left. At $\alpha = 0.01$, is there enough evidence to reject the biologist's claim? Assume the pH levels are normally distributed.

*Answer: Page A43*

You can also use a P-value to perform a two-sample F-test. For instance, in Example 4, note that the TI-84 Plus displays $P = .0102172459$. Because $P < \alpha$, you reject the null hypothesis.

# 10.3 EXERCISES

For Extra Help: MyLab Statistics

## Building Basic Skills and Vocabulary

1. Explain how to find the critical value for an $F$-test.
2. List five properties of the $F$-distribution.
3. List the three conditions that must be met in order to use a two-sample $F$-test.
4. Explain how to determine the values of $d.f._N$ and $d.f._D$ when performing a two-sample $F$-test.

**Finding a Critical $F$-Value for a Right-Tailed Test** *In Exercises 5–8, find the critical F-value for a right-tailed test using the level of significance $\alpha$ and degrees of freedom $d.f._N$ and $d.f._D$.*

5. $\alpha = 0.05$, $d.f._N = 9$, $d.f._D = 16$
6. $\alpha = 0.01$, $d.f._N = 2$, $d.f._D = 11$
7. $\alpha = 0.10$, $d.f._N = 10$, $d.f._D = 15$
8. $\alpha = 0.025$, $d.f._N = 7$, $d.f._D = 3$

**Finding a Critical $F$-Value for a Two-Tailed Test** *In Exercises 9–12, find the critical F-value for a two-tailed test using the level of significance $\alpha$ and degrees of freedom $d.f._N$ and $d.f._D$.*

9. $\alpha = 0.01$, $d.f._N = 6$, $d.f._D = 7$
10. $\alpha = 0.10$, $d.f._N = 24$, $d.f._D = 28$
11. $\alpha = 0.05$, $d.f._N = 60$, $d.f._D = 40$
12. $\alpha = 0.05$, $d.f._N = 27$, $d.f._D = 19$

*In Exercises 13–18, test the claim about the difference between two population variances $\sigma_1^2$ and $\sigma_2^2$ at the level of significance $\alpha$. Assume the samples are random and independent, and the populations are normally distributed.*

13. Claim: $\sigma_1^2 > \sigma_2^2$; $\alpha = 0.10$.
    Sample statistics: $s_1^2 = 773$,
    $n_1 = 5$ and $s_2^2 = 765$, $n_2 = 6$
14. Claim: $\sigma_1^2 = \sigma_2^2$; $\alpha = 0.05$.
    Sample statistics: $s_1^2 = 310$,
    $n_1 = 7$ and $s_2^2 = 297$, $n_2 = 8$
15. Claim: $\sigma_1^2 \leq \sigma_2^2$; $\alpha = 0.01$.
    Sample statistics: $s_1^2 = 842$,
    $n_1 = 11$ and $s_2^2 = 836$, $n_2 = 10$
16. Claim: $\sigma_1^2 \neq \sigma_2^2$; $\alpha = 0.05$.
    Sample statistics: $s_1^2 = 245$,
    $n_1 = 31$ and $s_2^2 = 112$, $n_2 = 28$
17. Claim: $\sigma_1^2 = \sigma_2^2$; $\alpha = 0.01$.
    Sample statistics: $s_1^2 = 9.8$,
    $n_1 = 13$ and $s_2^2 = 2.5$, $n_2 = 20$
18. Claim: $\sigma_1^2 > \sigma_2^2$; $\alpha = 0.05$.
    Sample statistics: $s_1^2 = 44.6$,
    $n_1 = 16$ and $s_2^2 = 39.3$, $n_2 = 12$

## Using and Interpreting Concepts

**Performing a Two-Sample $F$-Test** *In Exercises 19–26, (a) identify the claim and state $H_0$ and $H_a$, (b) find the critical value and identify the rejection region, (c) find the test statistic F, (d) decide whether to reject or fail to reject the null hypothesis, and (e) interpret the decision in the context of the original claim. Assume the samples are random and independent, and the populations are normally distributed.*

19. **Life of Appliances** Company A claims that the variance of the lives of its appliances is less than the variance of the lives of Company B's appliances. A sample of the lives of 20 of Company A's appliances has a variance of 1.8. A sample of the lives of 25 of Company B's appliances has a variance of 3.9. At $\alpha = 0.025$, can you support Company A's claim?

**20. Carbon Monoxide Emissions** An automobile manufacturer claims that the variance of the carbon monoxide emissions for a make and model of one of its vehicles is less than the variance of the carbon monoxide emissions for a top competitor's equivalent vehicle. A sample of the carbon monoxide emissions of 19 of the manufacturer's specified vehicles has a variance of 0.008. A sample of the carbon monoxide emissions of 21 of its competitor's equivalent vehicles has a variance of 0.045. At $\alpha = 0.10$, can you support the manufacturer's claim? *(Adapted from U.S. Environmental Protection Agency)*

| Golfer 1 | | | Golfer 2 | | |
|---|---|---|---|---|---|
| 227 | 234 | 235 | 262 | 257 | 258 |
| 246 | 223 | 268 | 269 | 253 | 262 |
| 231 | 235 | 245 | 258 | 265 | 255 |
| 248 | | | 262 | | |

TABLE FOR EXERCISE 21

**21. Golf** The table at the left shows a sample of the driving distances (in yards) for two golfers. At $\alpha = 0.10$, can you conclude that the variances of the driving distances differ between the two golfers?

| 18–34 | | 35–49 | | |
|---|---|---|---|---|
| 384 | 326 | 434 | 415 | 413 |
| 318 | 385 | 420 | 408 | 428 |
| 371 | 327 | 454 | 392 | 385 |

TABLE FOR EXERCISE 22

**22. Heart Transplant Waiting Times** The table at the left shows a sample of the waiting times (in days) for a heart transplant for two age groups. At $\alpha = 0.05$, can you conclude that the variances of the waiting times differ between the two age groups? *(Adapted from Organ Procurement and Transplantation Network)*

**23. Science Assessment Tests** A state school administrator claims that the standard deviations of science assessment test scores for eighth-grade students are the same in Districts 1 and 2. A sample of 12 test scores from District 1 has a standard deviation of 36.8 points, and a sample of 14 test scores from District 2 has a standard deviation of 32.5 points. At $\alpha = 0.10$, can you reject the administrator's claim? *(Adapted from National Center for Education Statistics)*

**24. U.S. History Assessment Tests** A state school administrator claims that the standard deviations of U.S. history assessment test scores for eighth-grade students are the same in Districts 1 and 2. A sample of 10 test scores from District 1 has a standard deviation of 30.9 points, and a sample of 13 test scores from District 2 has a standard deviation of 27.2 points. At $\alpha = 0.01$, can you reject the administrator's claim? *(Adapted from National Center for Education Statistics)*

**25. Annual Salaries** An employment information service claims that the standard deviation of the annual salaries for actuaries is less in California than in New York. You select a sample of actuaries from each state. The results of each survey are shown in the figure. At $\alpha = 0.05$, can you support the service's claim? *(Adapted from America's Career InfoNet)*

Actuaries in New York
$s_1 = \$42{,}800$
$n_1 = 41$

Actuaries in California
$s_2 = \$28{,}600$
$n_2 = 61$

FIGURE FOR EXERCISE 25

Public relations managers in Louisiana
$s_1 = \$27{,}200$
$n_1 = 24$

Public relations managers in Florida
$s_2 = \$39{,}100$
$n_2 = 28$

FIGURE FOR EXERCISE 26

**26. Annual Salaries** An employment information service claims that the standard deviation of the annual salaries for public relations managers is less in Louisiana than in Florida. You select a sample of public relations managers from each state. The results of each survey are shown in the figure. At $\alpha = 0.05$, can you support the service's claim? *(Adapted from America's Career InfoNet)*

## Extending Concepts

**Finding Left-Tailed Critical *F*-Values** *In this section, you only needed to calculate the right-tailed critical F-value for a two-tailed test. For other applications of the F-distribution, you will need to calculate the left-tailed critical F-value. To calculate the left-tailed critical F-value, perform the steps below.*

*(1) Interchange the values for* $d.f._N$ *and* $d.f._D$.

*(2) Find the corresponding F-value in Table 7.*

*(3) Calculate the reciprocal of the F-value to obtain the left-tailed critical F-value.*

*In Exercises 27 and 28, find the right- and left-tailed critical F-values for a two-tailed test using the level of significance* $\alpha$ *and degrees of freedom* $d.f._N$ *and* $d.f._D$.

**27.** $\alpha = 0.05$, $\text{d.f.}_N = 6$, $\text{d.f.}_D = 3$

**28.** $\alpha = 0.10$, $\text{d.f.}_N = 20$, $\text{d.f.}_D = 15$

**Confidence Interval for $\sigma_1^2/\sigma_2^2$** *When* $s_1^2$ *and* $s_2^2$ *are the variances of randomly selected, independent samples from normally distributed populations, then a confidence interval for* $\sigma_1^2/\sigma_2^2$ *is*

$$\frac{s_1^2}{s_2^2} \cdot \frac{1}{F_R} < \frac{\sigma_1^2}{\sigma_2^2} < \frac{s_1^2}{s_2^2} \cdot \frac{1}{F_L}$$

*where* $F_R$ *is the right-tailed critical F-value and* $F_L$ *is the left-tailed critical F-value.*

*In Exercises 29 and 30, construct the confidence interval for* $\sigma_1^2/\sigma_2^2$. *Assume the samples are random and independent, and the populations are normally distributed.*

**29. Cholesterol Contents** In a recent study of the cholesterol contents of grilled chicken sandwiches served at fast food restaurants, a nutritionist found that random samples of sandwiches from Restaurant A and from Restaurant B had the sample statistics shown in the table. Construct a 95% confidence interval for $\sigma_1^2/\sigma_2^2$, where $\sigma_1^2$ and $\sigma_2^2$ are the variances of the cholesterol contents of grilled chicken sandwiches from Restaurant A and Restaurant B, respectively.

| **Cholesterol contents of grilled chicken sandwiches** | |
|---|---|
| Restaurant A | Restaurant B |
| $s_1^2 = 10.89$ | $s_2^2 = 9.61$ |
| $n_1 = 16$ | $n_2 = 12$ |

**30. Carbohydrate Contents** In a recent study of the carbohydrate contents of grilled chicken sandwiches served at fast food restaurants, a nutritionist found that random samples of sandwiches from Restaurant A and from Restaurant B had the sample statistics shown in the table. Construct a 95% confidence interval for $\sigma_1^2/\sigma_2^2$, where $\sigma_1^2$ and $\sigma_2^2$ are the variances of the carbohydrate contents of grilled chicken sandwiches from Restaurant A and Restaurant B, respectively.

| **Carbohydrate contents of grilled chicken sandwiches** | |
|---|---|
| Restaurant A | Restaurant B |
| $s_1^2 = 5.29$ | $s_2^2 = 3.61$ |
| $n_1 = 16$ | $n_2 = 12$ |

# 10.4 Analysis of Variance

## What You Should Learn

- How to use one-way analysis of variance to test claims involving three or more means
- An introduction to two-way analysis of variance

One-Way ANOVA ■ Two-Way ANOVA

## One-Way ANOVA

Suppose a medical researcher is analyzing the effectiveness of three types of pain relievers and wants to determine whether there is a difference in the mean lengths of time it takes the three medications to provide relief. To determine whether such a difference exists, the researcher can use the *F*-distribution together with a technique called **analysis of variance.** Because one independent variable is being studied, the process is called **one-way analysis of variance.**

**DEFINITION**

**One-way analysis of variance** is a hypothesis-testing technique that is used to compare the means of three or more populations. Analysis of variance is usually abbreviated as **ANOVA.**

To begin a one-way analysis of variance test, you should first state the null and alternative hypotheses. For a one-way ANOVA test, the null and alternative hypotheses are always similar to these statements.

$H_0$: $\mu_1 = \mu_2 = \mu_3 = \cdots = \mu_k$ (All population means are equal.)

$H_a$: At least one mean is different from the others.

When you reject the null hypothesis in a one-way ANOVA test, you can conclude that at least one of the means is different from the others. Without performing more statistical tests, however, you cannot determine which of the means is different.

Before performing a one-way ANOVA test, you must check that these conditions are satisfied.

1. Each sample must be randomly selected from a normal, or approximately normal, population.
2. The samples must be independent of each other.
3. Each population must have the same variance.

The test statistic for a one-way ANOVA test is the ratio of two variances: the variance between samples and the variance within samples.

$$\text{Test statistic} = \frac{\text{Variance between samples}}{\text{Variancc within samples}}$$

1. The variance between samples measures the differences related to the treatment given to each sample. This variance, sometimes called the **mean square between,** is denoted by $MS_B$.
2. The variance within samples measures the differences related to entries within the same sample and is usually due to sampling error. This variance, sometimes called the **mean square within,** is denoted by $MS_W$.

## One-Way Analysis of Variance Test

To perform a one-way ANOVA test, these conditions must be met.

1. Each of the $k$ samples, $k \geq 3$, must be randomly selected from a normal, or approximately normal, population.
2. The samples must be independent of each other.
3. Each population must have the same variance.

If these conditions are met, then the sampling distribution for the test is approximated by the $F$-distribution. The **test statistic** is

$$F = \frac{MS_B}{MS_W}.$$

The degrees of freedom are

$\text{d.f.}_N = k - 1$ Degrees of freedom for numerator

and

$\text{d.f.}_D = N - k$ Degrees of freedom for denominator

where $k$ is the number of samples and $N$ is the sum of the sample sizes.

If there is little or no difference between the means, then $MS_B$ will be approximately equal to $MS_W$ and the test statistic will be approximately 1. Values of $F$ close to 1 suggest that you should fail to reject the null hypothesis. However, if one of the means differs significantly from the others, then $MS_B$ will be greater than $MS_W$ and the test statistic will be greater than 1. Values of $F$ significantly greater than 1 suggest that you should reject the null hypothesis. So, all one-way ANOVA tests are right-tailed tests. That is, if the test statistic is greater than the critical value, then $H_0$ will be rejected.

### Study Tip

The notations $n_i$, $\bar{x}_i$, and $s_i^2$ represent the sample size, mean, and variance of the *i*th sample, respectively. Also, note that $\bar{\bar{x}}$ is sometimes called the *grand mean*.

## GUIDELINES

**Finding the Test Statistic for a One-Way ANOVA Test**

| In Words | In Symbols |
|---|---|
| **1.** Find the mean and variance of each sample. | $\bar{x}_i = \frac{\Sigma x}{n}, \quad s_i^2 = \frac{\Sigma(x - \bar{x}_i)^2}{n - 1}$ |
| **2.** Find the mean of all entries in all samples. | $\bar{\bar{x}} = \frac{\Sigma x}{N}$ |
| **3.** Find the sum of squares between the samples. | $SS_B = \Sigma n_i(\bar{x}_i - \bar{\bar{x}})^2$ |
| **4.** Find the sum of squares within the samples. | $SS_W = \Sigma(n_i - 1)s_i^2$ |
| **5.** Find the variance between the samples. | $MS_B = \frac{SS_B}{\text{d.f.}_N} = \frac{\Sigma n_i(\bar{x}_i - \bar{\bar{x}})^2}{k - 1}$ |
| **6.** Find the variance within the samples. | $MS_W = \frac{SS_W}{\text{d.f.}_D} = \frac{\Sigma(n_i - 1)s_i^2}{N - k}$ |
| **7.** Find the test statistic. | $F = \frac{MS_B}{MS_W}$ |

Note that in Step 1 of the guidelines above, you are summing the values from just one sample. In Step 2, you are summing the values from all of the samples. The sums $SS_B$ and $SS_W$ are explained on the next page.

In the guidelines for finding the test statistic for a one-way ANOVA test, the notation $SS_B$ represents the sum of squares between the samples.

$$SS_B = n_1(\bar{x}_1 - \bar{\bar{x}})^2 + n_2(\bar{x}_2 - \bar{\bar{x}})^2 + \cdots + n_k(\bar{x}_k - \bar{\bar{x}})^2$$
$$= \Sigma n_i(\bar{x}_i - \bar{\bar{x}})^2$$

Also, the notation $SS_W$ represents the sum of squares within the samples.

$$SS_W = (n_1 - 1)s_i^2 + (n_2 - 1)s_2^2 + \cdots + (n_k - 1)s_k^2$$
$$= \Sigma(n_i - 1)s_i^2$$

## GUIDELINES

### Performing a One-Way Analysis of Variance Test

| In Words | In Symbols |
|---|---|
| **1.** Verify that the samples are random and independent, the populations have normal distributions, and the population variances are equal. | |
| **2.** Identify the claim. State the null and alternative hypotheses. | State $H_0$ and $H_a$. |
| **3.** Specify the level of significance. | Identify $\alpha$. |
| **4.** Determine the degrees of freedom for the numerator and the denominator. | $\text{d.f.}_N = k - 1$<br>$\text{d.f.}_D = N - k$ |
| **5.** Determine the critical value. | Use Table 7 in Appendix B. |
| **6.** Determine the rejection region. | |
| **7.** Find the test statistic and sketch the sampling distribution. | $F = \dfrac{MS_B}{MS_W}$ |
| **8.** Make a decision to reject or fail to reject the null hypothesis. | If $F$ is in the rejection region, then reject $H_0$. Otherwise, fail to reject $H_0$. |
| **9.** Interpret the decision in the context of the original claim. | |

Tables are a convenient way to summarize the results of a one-way analysis of variance test. ANOVA summary tables are set up as shown below.

**ANOVA Summary Table**

| Variation | Sum of squares | Degrees of freedom | Mean squares | F |
|---|---|---|---|---|
| **Between** | $SS_B$ | $\text{d.f.}_N = k - 1$ | $MS_B = \dfrac{SS_B}{\text{d.f.}_N}$ | $\dfrac{MS_B}{MS_W}$ |
| **Within** | $SS_W$ | $\text{d.f.}_D = N - k$ | $MS_W = \dfrac{SS_W}{\text{d.f.}_D}$ | |

**EXAMPLE 1**

### Performing a One-Way ANOVA Test

A medical researcher wants to determine whether there is a difference in the mean lengths of time it takes three types of pain relievers to provide relief from headache pain. Several headache sufferers are randomly selected and given one of the three medications. Each headache sufferer records the time (in minutes) it takes the medication to begin working. The results are shown in the table. At $\alpha = 0.01$, can you conclude that at least one mean time is different from the others? Assume that each population of relief times is normally distributed and that the population variances are equal.

| Medication 1 | Medication 2 | Medication 3 |
|---|---|---|
| 12 | 16 | 14 |
| 15 | 14 | 17 |
| 17 | 21 | 20 |
| 12 | 15 | 15 |
| | 19 | |
| $n_1 = 4$ | $n_2 = 5$ | $n_3 = 4$ |
| $\bar{x}_1 = \frac{56}{4} = 14$ | $\bar{x}_2 = \frac{85}{5} = 17$ | $\bar{x}_3 = \frac{66}{4} = 16.5$ |
| $s_1^2 = 6$ | $s_2^2 = 8.5$ | $s_3^2 = 7$ |

**SOLUTION**

The null and alternative hypotheses are as follows.

$H_0$: $\mu_1 = \mu_2 = \mu_3$

$H_a$: At least one mean is different from the others. (Claim)

Because there are $k = 3$ samples, $\text{d.f.}_\text{N} = k - 1 = 3 - 1 = 2$. The sum of the sample sizes is $N = n_1 + n_2 + n_3 = 4 + 5 + 4 = 13$. So,

$$\text{d.f.}_\text{D} = N - k = 13 - 3 = 10.$$

Using $\text{d.f.}_\text{N} = 2$, $\text{d.f.}_\text{D} = 10$, and $\alpha = 0.01$, the critical value is $F_0 = 7.56$. The rejection region is $F > 7.56$. To find the test statistic, first calculate $\bar{\bar{x}}$, $MS_B$, and $MS_W$.

$$\bar{\bar{x}} = \frac{\Sigma x}{N} = \frac{56 + 85 + 66}{13} \approx 15.92$$

$$\begin{aligned} MS_B = \frac{SS_B}{\text{d.f.}_\text{N}} &= \frac{\Sigma n_i(\bar{x}_i - \bar{\bar{x}})^2}{k - 1} \\ &\approx \frac{4(14 - 15.92)^2 + 5(17 - 15.92)^2 + 4(16.5 - 15.92)^2}{3 - 1} \\ &= \frac{21.9232}{2} \\ &= 10.9616 \end{aligned}$$

$$\begin{aligned} MS_W = \frac{SS_W}{\text{d.f.}_\text{D}} &= \frac{\Sigma(n_i - 1)s_i^2}{N - k} \\ &= \frac{(4 - 1)(6) + (5 - 1)(8.5) + (4 - 1)(7)}{13 - 3} \\ &= \frac{73}{10} \\ &= 7.3 \end{aligned}$$

## Picturing the World

A researcher wants to determine whether there is a difference in the mean lengths of time wasted at work for people in California, Georgia, and Pennsylvania. Several people from each state who work 8-hour days are randomly selected and they are asked to estimate how much time (in hours) they waste at work each day. The results are shown in the table. (Adapted from Salary.com)

| CA | GA | PA |
|---|---|---|
| 2 | 2 | 1.75 |
| 1.75 | 2.5 | 3 |
| 2.5 | 1.25 | 2.75 |
| 3 | 2.25 | 2 |
| 2.75 | 1.5 | 3 |
| 3.25 | 3 | 2.5 |
| 1.25 | 2.75 | 2.75 |
| 2 | 2.25 | 3.25 |
| 2.5 | 2 | 3 |
| 1.75 | 1 | 2.75 |
| 1.5 | | 2.25 |
| 2.25 | | |

**At $\alpha = 0.10$, can the researcher conclude that there is a difference in the mean lengths of time wasted at work among the states? Assume that each population is normally distributed and that the population variances are equal.**

Using $MS_B \approx 10.9616$ and $MS_W = 7.3$, the test statistic is

$$F = \frac{MS_B}{MS_W} \approx \frac{10.9616}{7.3} \approx 1.50.$$

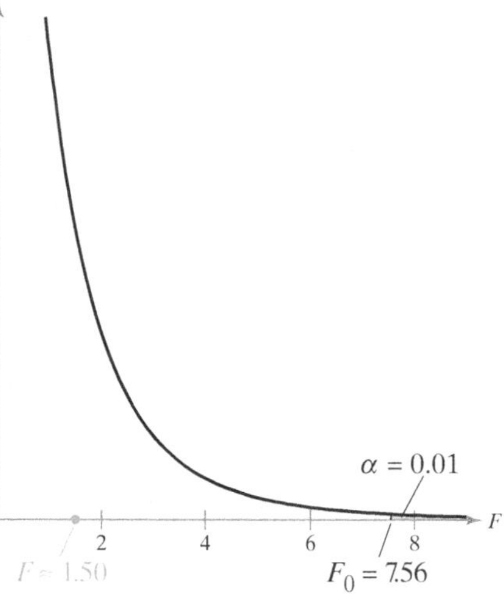


The figure shows the location of the rejection region and the test statistic $F$. Because $F$ is not in the rejection region, you fail to reject the null hypothesis.

***Interpretation*** There is not enough evidence at the 1% level of significance to conclude that there is a difference in the mean length of time it takes the three pain relievers to provide relief from headache pain.

The ANOVA summary table for Example 1 is shown below.

| Variation | Sum of squares | Degrees of freedom | Mean squares | $F$ |
|---|---|---|---|---|
| **Between** | 21.9232 | 2 | 10.9616 | 1.50 |
| **Within** | 73 | 10 | 7.3 | |

### TRY IT YOURSELF 1

A sales analyst wants to determine whether there is a difference in the mean monthly sales of a company's four sales regions. Several salespersons from each region are randomly selected and they provide their sales amounts (in thousands of dollars) for the previous month. The results are shown in the table. At $\alpha = 0.05$, can the analyst conclude that there is a difference in the mean monthly sales among the sales regions? Assume that each population of sales is normally distributed and that the population variances are equal.

| North | East | South | West |
|---|---|---|---|
| 34 | 47 | 40 | 21 |
| 28 | 36 | 30 | 30 |
| 18 | 30 | 41 | 24 |
| 24 | 38 | 29 | 37 |
| | 44 | | 23 |
| $n_1 = 4$ | $n_2 = 5$ | $n_3 = 4$ | $n_4 = 5$ |
| $\bar{x}_1 = 26$ | $\bar{x}_2 = 39$ | $\bar{x}_3 = 35$ | $\bar{x}_4 = 27$ |
| $s_1^2 \approx 45.33$ | $s_2^2 = 45$ | $s_3^2 \approx 40.67$ | $s_4^2 = 42.5$ |

*Answer: Page A43*

Using technology greatly simplifies the one-way ANOVA process. When using technology such as Minitab, Excel, StatCrunch, or the TI-84 Plus to perform a one-way analysis of variance test, you can use $P$-values to decide whether to reject the null hypothesis. If the $P$-value is less than $\alpha$, then reject $H_0$.

## EXAMPLE 2

### Using Technology to Perform a One-Way ANOVA Test

| Compact | Midsize | Large |
|---|---|---|
| 12 | 21 | 18 |
| 23 | 23 | 17 |
| 17 | 19 | 15 |
| 20 | 14 | 17 |
| 25 | 14 | 20 |
| 18 | 21 | 17 |
| 24 | 26 | 17 |
| 27 | 18 | 13 |
| 29 | 25 | |
| 17 | 16 | |
| 31 | 27 | |
| 24 | 22 | |
| 24 | 21 | |
| | 25 | |
| | 21 | |

A researcher believes that for city driving, the fuel economy of compact, midsize, and large cars are the same. The gas mileages (in miles per gallon) for city driving for several randomly selected cars from each category are shown in the table at the left. Assume that the populations are normally distributed, the samples are independent, and the population variances are equal. At $\alpha = 0.05$, can you reject the claim that the mean gas mileages for city driving are the same for the three categories? Use technology to test the claim. *(Source: Fueleconomy.gov)*

#### SOLUTION

Here are the null and alternative hypotheses.

$H_0$: $\mu_1 = \mu_2 = \mu_3$ (Claim)

$H_a$: At least one mean is different from the others.

The results obtained by performing the test using Excel are shown below. From the results, you can see that $P \approx 0.02$. Because $P < \alpha$, you reject the null hypothesis.

**EXCEL**

| | A | B | C | D | E | F |
|---|---|---|---|---|---|---|
| 1 | Anova: Single factor | | | | | |
| 2 | | | | | | |
| 3 | SUMMARY | | | | | |
| 4 | *Groups* | *Count* | *Sum* | *Average* | *Variance* | |
| 5 | compact | 13 | 291 | 22.38462 | 28.75641 | |
| 6 | midsize | 15 | 313 | 20.86667 | 16.69524 | |
| 7 | large | 8 | 134 | 16.75 | 4.214286 | |
| 8 | | | | | | |
| 9 | | | | | | |
| 10 | ANOVA | | | | | |
| 11 | *Source of Variation* | *SS* | *df* | *MS* | *F* | *P-value* |
| 12 | Between Groups | 160.6897 | 2 | 80.34487 | 4.358599 | 0.020906 |
| 13 | Within Groups | 608.3103 | 33 | 18.43364 | | |
| 14 | | | | | | |
| 15 | Total | 769 | 35 | | | |
| 16 | | | | | | |

***Interpretation*** There is enough evidence at the 5% level of significance to reject the claim that the mean gas mileages for city driving are the same.

**Tech Tip**

Here are instructions for performing a one-way analysis of variance test on a TI-84 Plus. Begin by storing the data in L1, L2, and so on.

STAT

Choose the TESTS menu.

H: ANOVA(

Then enter L1, L2, and so on, separated by commas.

#### TRY IT YOURSELF 2

The data shown in the table represent the GPAs of randomly selected freshmen, sophomores, juniors, and seniors. At $\alpha = 0.05$, can you conclude that there is a difference in the means of the GPAs? Assume that the populations of GPAs are normally distributed and that the population variances are equal. Use technology to test the claim.

| | | | | | | | | | | |
|---|---|---|---|---|---|---|---|---|---|---|
| **Freshmen** | 2.34 | 2.38 | 3.31 | 2.39 | 3.40 | 2.70 | 2.34 | | | |
| **Sophomores** | 3.26 | 2.22 | 3.26 | 3.29 | 2.95 | 3.01 | 3.13 | 3.59 | 2.84 | 3.00 |
| **Juniors** | 2.80 | 2.60 | 2.49 | 2.83 | 2.34 | 3.23 | 3.49 | 3.03 | 2.87 | |
| **Seniors** | 3.31 | 2.35 | 3.27 | 2.86 | 2.78 | 2.75 | 3.05 | 3.31 | | |

*Answer: Page A43*

## Two-Way ANOVA

When you want to test the effect of *two* independent variables, or factors, on one dependent variable, you can use a **two-way analysis of variance test.** For instance, suppose a medical researcher wants to test the effect of age *and* type of medication on the mean length of time it takes pain relievers to provide relief. To perform such an experiment, the researcher can use the two-way ANOVA block design shown below.

| Type of medication | Age: 18–64 | Age: 65+ |
|---|---|---|
| I | Adults ages 18–64 taking type I | Adults ages 65+ taking type I |
| II | Adults ages 18–64 taking type II | Adults ages 65+ taking type II |
| III | Adults ages 18–64 taking type III | Adults ages 65+ taking type III |

A two-way ANOVA test has three null hypotheses—one for each main effect and one for the interaction effect. A **main effect** is the effect of one independent variable on the dependent variable, and the **interaction effect** is the effect of both independent variables on the dependent variable. For instance, the hypotheses for the pain reliever experiment are listed below.

**Study Tip**

If age and type of medication have no effect on the length of time it takes a pain reliever to provide relief, then there will be no significant difference in the means of the relief times.

Hypotheses for main effects:

$H_0$: Age has no effect on the mean length of time it takes a pain reliever to provide relief.

$H_a$: Age has an effect on the mean length of time it takes a pain reliever to provide relief.

$H_0$: The type of medication has no effect on the mean length of time it takes a pain reliever to provide relief.

$H_a$: The type of medication has an effect on the mean length of time it takes a pain reliever to provide relief.

Hypotheses for interaction effect:

$H_0$: There is no interaction effect between age and type of medication on the mean length of time it takes a pain reliever to provide relief.

$H_a$: There is an interaction effect between age and type of medication on the mean length of time it takes a pain reliever to provide relief.

To test these hypotheses, you can perform a two-way ANOVA test. Note that the conditions for a two-way ANOVA test are the same as those for a one-way ANOVA test with the additional condition that all samples must be of equal size. Using the *F*-distribution, a two-way ANOVA test calculates an *F*-test statistic for each hypothesis. As a result, it is possible to reject none, one, two, or all of the null hypotheses.

The statistics involved with a two-way ANOVA test is beyond the scope of this course. You can, however, use technology such as Minitab to perform a two-way ANOVA test.

# 10.4 EXERCISES

For Extra Help: MyLab Statistics

## Building Basic Skills and Vocabulary

1. State the null and alternative hypotheses for a one-way ANOVA test.
2. What conditions are necessary in order to use a one-way ANOVA test?
3. Describe the difference between the variance between samples $MS_B$ and the variance within samples $MS_W$.
4. Describe the hypotheses for a two-way ANOVA test.

## Using and Interpreting Concepts

**Performing a One-Way ANOVA Test** *In Exercises 5–14, (a) identify the claim and state $H_0$ and $H_a$, (b) find the critical value and identify the rejection region, (c) find the test statistic F, (d) decide whether to reject or fail to reject the null hypothesis, and (e) interpret the decision in the context of the original claim. Assume the samples are random and independent, the populations are normally distributed, and the population variances are equal.*

5. **Toothpaste** The table shows the costs per ounce (in dollars) for a sample of toothpastes sold in the categories of whitening, cavity prevention, and breath freshening. At $\alpha = 0.05$, can you conclude that at least one mean cost per ounce is different from the others? *(Source: Amazon)*

| **Whitening** | 0.68 | 1.99 | 1.38 | 0.28 | 5.00 | 1.23 |
|---|---|---|---|---|---|---|
| **Cavity prevention** | 0.70 | 0.85 | 0.49 | 1.43 | 0.68 | |
| **Breath freshening** | 0.66 | 0.68 | 1.23 | 0.45 | | |

6. **Dog Lifespan** The table shows the lengths (in years) of the lives of dogs for a sample of three different breeds. At $\alpha = 0.05$, is there enough evidence to conclude that at least one of the dog breeds has a mean lifespan that is different from the others? *(Adapted from American Kennel Club)*

| **Boxer** | 11.6 | 10.8 | 12.9 | 12.3 | 16.1 | 9.9 |
|---|---|---|---|---|---|---|
| **Bulldog** | 10.5 | 13.6 | 12.3 | 11.1 | 11.0 | 10.7 |
| **Rottweiler** | 9.1 | 11.0 | 11.5 | 10.4 | 12.2 | 12.4 |

7. **Vacuum Cleaners** The table shows the weights (in pounds) for a sample of vacuum cleaners. The weights are classified according to vacuum cleaner type. At $\alpha = 0.01$, can you conclude that at least one mean vacuum cleaner weight is different from the others? *(Source: Consumer Reports)*

| **Bagged upright** | 21 | 22 | 23 | 21 | 17 | 19 |
|---|---|---|---|---|---|---|
| **Bagless upright** | 16 | 18 | 19 | 18 | 17 | 20 |
| **Bagged canister** | 26 | 24 | 23 | 25 | 27 | 21 |

 **8. Government Salaries** The table shows the annual salaries (in thousands of dollars) for a sample of individuals from the federal, state, and local levels of government. At $\alpha = 0.01$, can you conclude that at least one mean salary is different from the others? *(Adapted from Bureau of Labor Statistics)*

| Federal | State | Local |
|---|---|---|
| 88.6 | 97.0 | 71.6 |
| 68.5 | 80.9 | 38.6 |
| 57.1 | 69.1 | 46.9 |
| 95.9 | 40.7 | 59.6 |
| 94.2 | 83.6 | 26.3 |
| 87.7 | 98.6 | 62.9 |
| 100.5 | 65.4 | 78.5 |
| 93.8 | 76.9 | 55.5 |
| 80.3 | 67.0 | 60.3 |
| 87.5 | 67.5 | 40.8 |

 **9. Ages of Professional Athletes** The table shows the ages (in years) for a sample of professional athletes from several sports. At $\alpha = 0.05$, can you conclude that at least one mean age is different from the others? *(Source: ESPN)*

| MLB | NBA | NFL | NHL |
|---|---|---|---|
| 30 | 28 | 26 | 29 |
| 25 | 27 | 28 | 23 |
| 26 | 29 | 27 | 26 |
| 31 | 30 | 26 | 30 |
| 27 | 24 | 29 | 27 |
| 29 | 27 | 27 | 25 |
| 27 | 28 | 26 | 24 |
| 25 | 33 | 26 | 26 |
| 27 | 26 | 27 | 29 |
| 23 | 28 | 27 | 32 |
| 26 | 27 | 29 | 28 |
| 34 | 28 | 25 | 25 |
| 29 | 26 | 24 | 27 |

 **10. Cost per Mile** The table shows the costs per mile (in cents) for a sample of automobiles. At $\alpha = 0.01$, can you conclude that at least one mean cost per mile is different from the others? *(Adapted from American Automobile Association)*

| Small sedan | Medium sedan | Large sedan | SUV 4WD | Minivan |
|---|---|---|---|---|
| 44 | 46 | 65 | 56 | 69 |
| 40 | 61 | 67 | 57 | 51 |
| 43 | 42 | 64 | 57 | 56 |
| 39 | 58 | 58 | 61 | 53 |
| 36 | 48 | 63 | | 68 |
| 44 | 53 | | | |

 **11. Well-Being Index** The well-being index is a way to measure how people are faring physically, emotionally, socially, and professionally, as well as to rate the overall quality of their lives and their outlooks for the future. The table shows the well-being index scores for a sample of states from four regions of the United States. At $\alpha = 0.10$, can you reject the claim that the mean score is the same for all regions? *(Adapted from Gallup and Healthways)*

| Northeast | Midwest | South | West |
|---|---|---|---|
| 61.7 | 61.6 | 61.0 | 64.0 |
| 63.6 | 61.8 | 60.8 | 63.0 |
| 62.6 | 61.4 | 63.1 | 63.5 |
| 61.8 | 63.2 | 62.3 | 63.2 |
| 62.1 | 61.7 | 60.5 | 61.8 |
| 63.5 | 62.9 | 62.0 | 62.6 |
| | 62.9 | 61.3 | 62.5 |
| | 63.7 | 60.5 | 62.8 |
| | | 62.3 | 62.5 |
| | | 61.5 | |
| | | 63.1 | |

 **12. Days Spent at the Hospital** In a recent study, a health insurance company investigated the number of days patients spent at the hospital. In part of the study, the company selected a sample of patients from four regions of the United States and recorded the number of days each patient spent at the hospital. The table shows the results of the study. At $\alpha = 0.01$, can the company reject the claim that the mean number of days patients spend at the hospital is the same for all four regions? *(Adapted from National Center for Health Statistics)*

| Northeast | Midwest | South | West |
|---|---|---|---|
| 6 | 6 | 3 | 3 |
| 4 | 6 | 5 | 4 |
| 7 | 7 | 6 | 6 |
| 2 | 3 | 6 | 4 |
| 3 | 5 | 3 | 6 |
| 4 | 4 | 7 | 6 |
| 6 | 4 | 4 | 5 |
| 8 | 3 | | 2 |
| 9 | 2 | | |

 **13. Statistician Salaries** The table shows the salaries of a sample of entry level statisticians from six large metropolitan areas. At $\alpha = 0.05$, can you conclude that the mean salary is different in at least one of the areas? *(Adapted from Salary.com)*

| Boston | Houston | Los Angeles | Phoenix | Seattle | Virginia Beach |
|---|---|---|---|---|---|
| 65,702 | 50,500 | 58,055 | 61,314 | 63,698 | 76,750 |
| 60,095 | 56,237 | 68,451 | 59,400 | 64,917 | 86,660 |
| 71,458 | 53,913 | 69,700 | 56,359 | 58,756 | 55,650 |
| 58,842 | 66,603 | 59,766 | 60,046 | 56,488 | 70,850 |
| 84,477 | 62,818 | 70,970 | 65,200 | 69,756 | 73,170 |
| 51,511 | 56,066 | 60,000 | 58,945 | | |
| | 50,111 | 62,109 | | | |

**14. Housing Prices** The table shows the sale prices (in thousands of dollars) of a sample of one-family houses in three cities. At $\alpha = 0.10$, can you conclude that at least one mean sale price is different from the others? *(Adapted from National Association of Realtors)*

| Kansas City | Ann Arbor | Birmingham |
|---|---|---|
| 209.6 | 603.5 | 309.5 |
| 288.1 | 56.1 | 195.1 |
| 208.0 | 285.7 | 65.3 |
| 61.9 | 367.3 | 524.9 |
| 92.3 | 181.8 | 103.4 |
| 352.9 | 119.3 | 122.2 |
| 196.5 | 380.1 | 221.1 |
| 427.2 | 184.2 | 212.7 |
| 373.9 | 484.6 | 243.0 |
| 500.6 | 322.2 | 420.6 |
| 125.8 | 565.4 | |

## Extending Concepts

**Using Technology to Perform a Two-Way ANOVA Test** *In Exercises 15–18, use technology and the block design to perform a two-way ANOVA test. Use $\alpha = 0.10$. Interpret the results. Assume the samples are random and independent, the populations are normally distributed, and the population variances are equal.*

**15. Advertising** A study was conducted in which a sample of 20 adults was asked to rate the effectiveness of advertisements. Each adult rated a radio or television advertisement that lasted 30 or 60 seconds. The block design shows these ratings (on a scale of 1 to 5, with 5 being extremely effective).

| Length of ad | Advertising medium: Radio | Advertising medium: Television |
|---|---|---|
| 30 sec | 2, 3, 5, 1, 3 | 3, 5, 4, 1, 2 |
| 60 sec | 1, 4, 2, 2, 5 | 2, 5, 3, 4, 4 |

**16. Vehicle Sales** The owner of a car dealership wants to determine whether the gender of a salesperson and the type of vehicle sold affect the number of vehicles sold in a month. The block design shows the numbers of vehicles, listed by type, sold in a month by a sample of eight salespeople.

| Gender | Type of vehicle: Car | Type of vehicle: Truck | Type of vehicle: Van/SUV |
|---|---|---|---|
| Male | 6, 5, 4, 5 | 2, 2, 1, 3 | 4, 3, 4, 2 |
| Female | 5, 7, 8, 7 | 1, 0, 1, 2 | 4, 2, 0, 1 |

**17. Grade Point Average** A study was conducted in which a sample of 24 high school students was asked to give their grade point average (GPA). The block design shows the GPAs of male and female students from four different age groups.

| Gender | Age 15 | Age 16 | Age 17 | Age 18 |
|---|---|---|---|---|
| Male | 2.5, 2.1, 3.8 | 4.0, 1.4, 2.0 | 3.5, 2.2, 2.0 | 3.1, 0.7, 2.8 |
| Female | 4.0, 2.1, 1.9 | 3.5, 3.0, 2.1 | 4.0, 2.2, 1.7 | 1.6, 2.5, 3.6 |

**18. Laptop Repairs** The manager of a computer repair service wants to determine whether there is a difference in the time it takes four technicians to repair different brands of laptops. The block design shows the times (in minutes) it took for each technician to repair three laptops of each brand.

| Brand | Technician 1 | Technician 2 | Technician 3 | Technician 4 |
|---|---|---|---|---|
| Brand A | 67, 82, 64 | 42, 56, 39 | 69, 47, 38 | 70, 44, 50 |
| Brand B | 44, 62, 55 | 47, 58, 62 | 55, 45, 66 | 47, 29, 40 |
| Brand C | 47, 36, 68 | 39, 74, 51 | 74, 80, 70 | 45, 62, 59 |

**The Scheffé Test** *If the null hypothesis is rejected in a one-way ANOVA test of three or more means, then a* ***Scheffé Test*** *can be performed to find which means have a significant difference. In a Scheffé Test, the means are compared two at a time. For instance, with three means you would have these comparisons:* $\overline{x}_1$ *versus* $\overline{x}_2$, $\overline{x}_1$ *versus* $\overline{x}_3$, *and* $\overline{x}_2$ *versus* $\overline{x}_3$. *For each comparison, calculate*

$$\frac{(\overline{x}_a - \overline{x}_b)^2}{\frac{SS_W}{\Sigma(n_i - 1)}\left(\frac{1}{n_a} + \frac{1}{n_b}\right)}$$

*where* $\overline{x}_a$ *and* $\overline{x}_b$ *are the means being compared and* $n_a$ *and* $n_b$ *are the corresponding sample sizes. Calculate the critical value by multiplying the critical value of the one-way ANOVA test by* $k - 1$. *Then compare the value that is calculated using the formula above with the critical value. The means have a significant difference when the value calculated using the formula above is greater than the critical value.*

*Use the information above to solve Exercises 19–22.*

**19.** Refer to the data in Exercise 7. At $\alpha = 0.01$, perform a Scheffé Test to determine which means have a significant difference.

**20.** Refer to the data in Exercise 8. At $\alpha = 0.01$, perform a Scheffé Test to determine which means have a significant difference.

**21.** Refer to the data in Exercise 10. At $\alpha = 0.01$, perform a Scheffé Test to determine which means have a significant difference.

**22.** Refer to the data in Exercise 11. At $\alpha = 0.10$, perform a Scheffé Test to determine which means have a significant difference.

# USES AND ABUSES Statistics in the Real World

## Uses

***One-Way Analysis of Variance (ANOVA)*** ANOVA can help you make important decisions about the allocation of resources. For instance, suppose you work for a large manufacturing company and part of your responsibility is to determine the distribution of the company's sales throughout the world and decide where to focus the company's efforts. Because wrong decisions will cost your company money, you want to make sure that you make the right decisions.

## Abuses

***Preconceived Notions*** There are several ways that the tests presented in this chapter can be abused. For instance, it is easy to allow preconceived notions to affect the results of a chi-square goodness-of-fit test and a chi-square independence test. When testing to see whether a distribution has changed, do not let the existing distribution "cloud" the study results. Similarly, when determining whether two variables are independent, do not let your intuition "get in the way." As with any hypothesis test, you must properly gather appropriate data and perform the corresponding test before you can reach a logical conclusion.

***Incorrect Interpretation of Rejection of Null Hypothesis*** It is important to remember that when you reject the null hypothesis of an ANOVA test, you are simply stating that you have enough evidence to determine that at least one of the population means is different from the others. You are not finding them all to be different. One way to further test which of the population means differs from the others is explained in Extending Concepts in Section 10.4 Exercises.

## EXERCISES

1. ***Preconceived Notions*** ANOVA depends on having independent variables. Describe an abuse that might occur by having dependent variables. Then describe how the abuse could be avoided.
2. ***Incorrect Interpretation of Rejection of Null Hypothesis*** Find an example of the use of ANOVA. In that use, describe what would be meant by "rejection of the null hypothesis." How should rejection of the null hypothesis be correctly interpreted?

# 10 Chapter Summary

| What Did You Learn? | Example(s) | Review Exercises |
|---|---|---|
| **Section 10.1** | | |
| How to use the chi-square distribution to test whether a frequency distribution fits an expected distribution $\chi^2 = \Sigma \frac{(O - E)^2}{E}$ | 2, 3 | 1–4 |
| **Section 10.2** | | |
| How to use a contingency table to find expected frequencies $E_{r,c} = \frac{(\text{Sum of row } r) \cdot (\text{Sum of column } c)}{\text{Sample size}}$ | 1 | 5–8 |
| How to use a chi-square distribution to test whether two variables are independent | 2, 3 | 5–8 |
| **Section 10.3** | | |
| How to interpret the $F$-distribution and use an $F$-table to find critical values | 1, 2 | 9–16 |
| How to perform a two-sample $F$-test to compare two variances | 3, 4 | 17–20 |
| **Section 10.4** | | |
| How to use one-way analysis of variance to test claims involving three or more means | 1, 2 | 21, 22 |

## Study Strategies

**Preparing for the Final Exam** For many of the college classes you take, your score on the final exam has a major impact on your grade for the course. So, it is important to be as prepared as possible for the final exam.

- As with studying for any other test, begin studying well before the final exam. Depending on your comfort level with the material, you may need to begin studying up to three weeks before the final.
- *Do not* try to memorize everything you learned in the course the entire semester. This can cause some students to panic or freeze from information overload during the final exam. Instead, to help you focus on your studying, you can ask your instructor what subject matter you should expect to see on the final.
- Be sure to study all material that will be on the final exam. Include material that will be on the final but has not yet been covered in class.
- You can form a final exam study group. As with any other study group, *do not* use the group for excessive socializing. The group should come up with sample final exam problems. Show the instructor your sample problems to make sure the group is on track. Then work together to make sure that each member of the group knows how to solve these problems.
- As with preparing for any other test, try to get a good night's rest the night before the final exam. *Do not* stay up all night cramming. Eat sensibly before the final.
- Be sure to *show up* for the final exam. Most instructors give failing grades to students who do not take the final, regardless of their grade before the final.
- For tips on taking the final exam, see **Taking a Test** in the Chapter 6 Summary.

For more information, visit Skills for Success in the accompanying MyLab course.

# 10 Review Exercises

## Section 10.1

*In Exercises 1–4, (a) identify the claim and state $H_0$ and $H_a$, (b) find the critical value and identify the rejection region, (c) find the chi-square test statistic, (d) decide whether to reject or fail to reject the null hypothesis, and (e) interpret the decision in the context of the original claim.*

**1.** A researcher claims that the age distribution of U.S. physicians is different from the distribution shown in the pie chart. You randomly select 400 U.S. physicians and ask them their age. The table shows the results. At $\alpha = 0.01$, test the researcher's claim. *(Adapted from Medscape)*

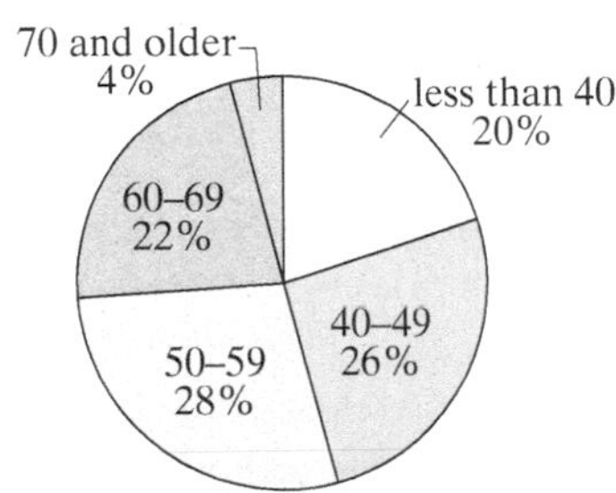


| Survey results | |
|---|---|
| **Age** | **Frequency, *f*** |
| Less than 40 | 100 |
| 40–49 | 85 |
| 50–59 | 125 |
| 60–69 | 70 |
| 70 and older | 20 |

**2.** A researcher claims that the distribution of the amounts that parents give their children per week for an allowance is different from the distribution shown in the pie chart. You randomly select 1509 parents and ask them how much they give their children per week for an allowance. The table shows the results. At $\alpha = 0.10$, test the researcher's claim. *(Adapted from T. Rowe Price)*

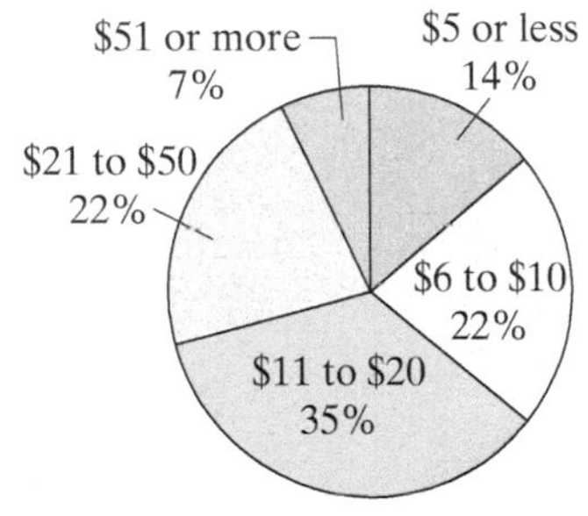


FIGURE FOR EXERCISE 2

| Survey results | |
|---|---|
| **Response** | **Frequency, *f*** |
| $5 or less | 220 |
| $6–$10 | 312 |
| $11–$20 | 539 |
| $21–$50 | 337 |
| $51 or more | 101 |

**3.** A sports website claims that the opinions of golfers about what irritates them the most on the golf course are distributed as shown in the pie chart. You randomly select 1018 golfers and ask them what irritates them the most on the golf course. The table shows the results. At $\alpha = 0.05$, test the sports website's claim. *(Adapted from GOLF.com)*

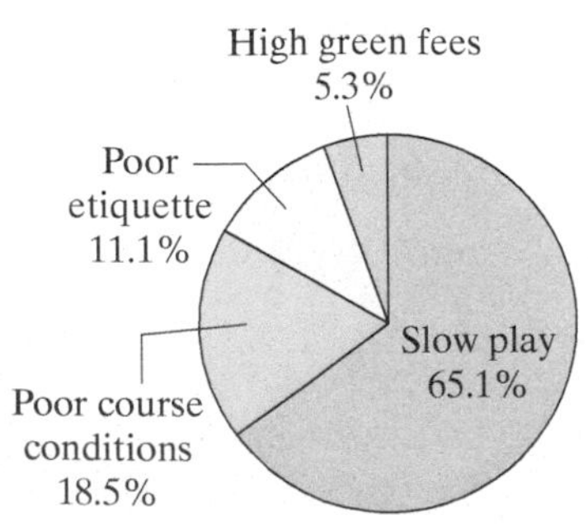


FIGURE FOR EXERCISE 3

| Survey results | |
|---|---|
| **Response** | **Frequency, *f*** |
| Slow play | 646 |
| Poor course conditions | 201 |
| Poor etiquette | 126 |
| High green fees | 45 |

**4.** An education researcher claims that the charges for tuition, fees, room, and board at 4-year degree-granting postsecondary institutions are uniformly distributed. To test this claim, you randomly select 800 4-year degree-granting postsecondary institutions and determine the charges for tuition, fees, room, and board at each. The table shows the results. At $\alpha = 0.05$, test the education researcher's claim. *(Adapted from National Center for Education Statistics)*

| Cost | Frequency, $f$ |
|---|---|
| \$17,000–\$19,499 | 138 |
| \$19,500–\$21,999 | 154 |
| \$22,000–\$24,499 | 246 |
| \$24,500–\$26,999 | 169 |
| \$27,000 or more | 93 |

## Section 10.2

*In Exercises 5–8, (a) find the expected frequency for each cell in the contingency table, (b) identify the claim and state $H_0$ and $H_a$, (c) determine the degrees of freedom, find the critical value, and identify the rejection region, (d) find the chi-square test statistic, (e) decide whether to reject or fail to reject the null hypothesis, and (f) interpret the decision in the context of the original claim.*

**5.** The contingency table shows the results of a random sample of public elementary and secondary school teachers and years of full-time teaching experience. At $\alpha = 0.01$, can you conclude that the level of instruction is related to the years of full-time teaching experience? *(Adapted from U.S. National Center for Education Statistics)*

| | Years of full-time teaching experience | | | |
|---|---|---|---|---|
| **Level of instruction** | **Less than 3 years** | **3–9 years** | **10–20 years** | **20 years or more** |
| Elementary | 99 | 307 | 410 | 235 |
| Secondary | 211 | 670 | 1001 | 567 |

**6.** The contingency table shows the results of a random sample of individuals by generation and type of vehicle owned. At $\alpha = 0.01$, can you conclude that generation is related to the type of vehicle owned?

| | Type of vehicle owned | | | |
|---|---|---|---|---|
| **Generation** | **Car** | **Truck** | **SUV** | **Van** |
| Gen X (ages 41–56) | 85 | 95 | 44 | 8 |
| Millennial (ages 25–40) | 110 | 73 | 61 | 4 |

**7.** The contingency table shows the results of a random sample of endangered and threatened species by status and vertebrate group. At $\alpha = 0.05$, test the hypothesis that the variables are independent. *(Adapted from U.S. Fish and Wildlife Service)*

| | Vertebrate group | | | | |
|---|---|---|---|---|---|
| **Status** | **Mammals** | **Birds** | **Reptiles** | **Amphibians** | **Fish** |
| Endangered | 148 | 132 | 39 | 14 | 55 |
| Threatened | 23 | 20 | 24 | 8 | 38 |

**8.** The contingency table shows the distribution of a random sample of fatal pedestrian and bicyclist motor vehicle collisions by time of day in a recent year. At $\alpha = 0.10$, can you conclude that the type of crash victim and the time of day are related? *(Adapted from National Highway Traffic Safety Administration)*

| | Time of day | | | |
|---|---|---|---|---|
| **Victim** | **12–5:59 A.M.** | **6–11:59 A.M.** | **12–5:59 P.M.** | **6–11:59 P.M.** |
| Pedestrian | 924 | 581 | 617 | 2054 |
| Bicyclist | 72 | 124 | 145 | 213 |

## Section 10.3

*In Exercises 9–12, find the critical F-value for a right-tailed test using the level of significance $\alpha$ and degrees of freedom $d.f._N$ and $d.f._D$.*

**9.** $\alpha = 0.05$, $\text{d.f.}_N = 6$, $\text{d.f.}_D = 50$

**10.** $\alpha = 0.01$, $\text{d.f.}_N = 12$, $\text{d.f.}_D = 10$

**11.** $\alpha = 0.10$, $\text{d.f.}_N = 5$, $\text{d.f.}_D = 12$

**12.** $\alpha = 0.05$, $\text{d.f.}_N = 20$, $\text{d.f.}_D = 25$

*In Exercises 13–16, find the critical F-value for a two-tailed test using the level of significance $\alpha$ and degrees of freedom $d.f._N$ and $d.f._D$.*

**13.** $\alpha = 0.10$, $\text{d.f.}_N = 15$, $\text{d.f.}_D = 27$

**14.** $\alpha = 0.05$, $\text{d.f.}_N = 9$, $\text{d.f.}_D = 8$

**15.** $\alpha = 0.01$, $\text{d.f.}_N = 40$, $\text{d.f.}_D = 60$

**16.** $\alpha = 0.01$, $\text{d.f.}_N = 11$, $\text{d.f.}_D = 13$

*In Exercises 17–20, (a) identify the claim and state $H_0$ and $H_a$, (b) find the critical value and identify the rejection region, (c) find the test statistic F, (d) decide whether to reject or fail to reject the null hypothesis, and (e) interpret the decision in the context of the original claim. Assume the samples are random and independent, and the populations are normally distributed.*

**17.** A travel consultant claims that the standard deviations of hotel room rates for Sacramento, CA, and San Francisco, CA, are the same. A sample of 36 hotel room rates in Sacramento has a standard deviation of \$51 and a sample of 31 hotel room rates in San Francisco has a standard deviation of \$37. At $\alpha = 0.10$, can you reject the travel consultant's claim? *(Adapted from Expedia)*

**18.** An agricultural analyst is comparing the wheat production in Oklahoma counties. The analyst claims that the variation in wheat production is greater in Garfield County than in Kay County. A sample of 21 Garfield County farms has a standard deviation of 0.76 bushel per acre. A sample of 16 Kay County farms has a standard deviation of 0.58 bushel per acre. At $\alpha = 0.10$, can you support the analyst's claim? *(Adapted from Environmental Verification and Analysis Center—University of Oklahoma)*

**19.** An instructor claims that the variance of SAT evidence-based reading and writing scores is different than the variance of SAT math scores. The table shows the SAT evidence-based reading and writing scores for 12 randomly selected students and the SAT math scores for 12 randomly selected students. At $\alpha = 0.01$, can you support the instructor's claim?

| Reading and writing | | Math | |
|---|---|---|---|
| 480 | 600 | 560 | 310 |
| 610 | 800 | 680 | 730 |
| 340 | 540 | 360 | 740 |
| 630 | 750 | 530 | 520 |
| 520 | 650 | 380 | 560 |
| 690 | 630 | 460 | 400 |

 **20.** A quality technician claims that the variance of the insert diameters produced by a plastic company's new injection mold for automobile dashboard inserts is less than the variance of the insert diameters produced by the company's current mold. The table shows samples of insert diameters (in centimeters) for both the current and new molds. At $\alpha = 0.05$, can you support the technician's claim?

| **New** | 9.611 | 9.618 | 9.594 | 9.580 | 9.611 | 9.597 |
|---|---|---|---|---|---|---|
| **Current** | 9.571 | 9.642 | 9.650 | 9.651 | 9.596 | 9.636 |

| **New** | 9.638 | 9.568 | 9.605 | 9.603 | 9.647 | 9.590 |
|---|---|---|---|---|---|---|
| **Current** | 9.570 | 9.537 | 9.641 | 9.625 | 9.626 | 9.579 |

## Section 10.4

*In Exercises 21 and 22, (a) identify the claim and state $H_0$ and $H_a$, (b) find the critical value and identify the rejection region, (c) find the test statistic F, (d) decide whether to reject or fail to reject the null hypothesis, and (e) interpret the decision in the context of the original claim. Assume the samples are random and independent, the populations are normally distributed, and the population variances are equal.*

 **21.** The table shows the monthly electric bills (in dollars) for a sample of households from four regions of the United States. At $\alpha = 0.10$, can you conclude that the mean monthly electric bill is different in at least one of the regions? *(Adapted from U.S. Energy Information Administration)*

| Northeast | Midwest | South | West |
|---|---|---|---|
| 150.71 | 92.37 | 119.16 | 83.07 |
| 100.53 | 100.23 | 97.62 | 95.43 |
| 125.89 | 108.15 | 131.84 | 106.83 |
| 120.04 | 95.52 | 127.92 | 80.04 |
| 121.62 | 113.26 | 144.73 | 75.63 |
| 97.18 | 99.02 | 150.45 | 101.92 |
| 105.07 | 117.82 | 109.46 | 127.29 |
| 115.47 | 120.60 | 134.07 | 168.21 |
| 103.60 | 120.74 | 113.93 | 95.83 |

 **22.** The table shows the annual incomes (in dollars) for a sample of families from four regions of the United States. At $\alpha = 0.05$, can you conclude that the mean annual income of families is different in at least one of the regions? *(Adapted from U.S. Census Bureau)*

| Northeast | Midwest | South | West |
|---|---|---|---|
| 78,123 | 63,930 | 62,623 | 79,496 |
| 71,388 | 73,543 | 64,182 | 77,904 |
| 81,251 | 71,602 | 59,668 | 74,113 |
| 74,379 | 65,357 | 59,373 | 72,191 |
| 75,210 | 62,907 | 61,536 | 75,668 |
| | 70,119 | 63,073 | 76,415 |
| | 66,833 | | |

# 10 Chapter Quiz

*Take this quiz as you would take a quiz in class. After you are done, check your work against the answers given in the back of the book.*

*In each exercise,*

*(a) identify the claim and state $H_0$ and $H_a$,*

*(b) find the critical value and identify the rejection region,*

*(c) find the test statistic,*

*(d) decide whether to reject or fail to reject the null hypothesis, and*

*(e) interpret the decision in the context of the original claim.*

*In Exercises 1 and 2, use the table, which lists the distribution of educational achievement for people in the United States ages 25 and older. It also lists the results of a random survey for two additional age groups. (Adapted from U.S. Census Bureau)*

| | Ages | | |
|---|---|---|---|
| **Educational attainment** | **25 and older** | **30–34** | **65–69** |
| **None–8th grade** | 3.5% | 10 | 23 |
| **9th–11th grade** | 5.5% | 23 | 26 |
| **High school graduate** | 27.6% | 80 | 136 |
| **Some college, no degree** | 15.2% | 56 | 77 |
| **Associate's degree** | 10.6% | 34 | 41 |
| **Bachelor's degree** | 23.4% | 75 | 78 |
| **Master's degree** | 10.6% | 31 | 41 |
| **Professional/doctoral degree** | 3.6% | 11 | 18 |

1. Does the distribution for people in the United States ages 25 and older differ from the distribution for people in the United States ages 30–34? Use $\alpha = 0.05$.

2. Use the data for 30- to 34-year-olds and 65- to 69-year-olds to test whether age and educational attainment are related. Use $\alpha = 0.01$.

*In Exercises 3 and 4, use the data, which list the annual wages (in thousands of dollars) for randomly selected individuals from three metropolitan areas. Assume the wages are normally distributed and that the samples are independent. (Adapted from U.S. Bureau of Economic Analysis)*

**Ithaca, NY:** 53.0, 60.3, 34.6, 37.1, 46.6, 46.8, 41.4, 50.6, 50.8, 49.4, 35.0, 36.7, 57.1

**Little Rock, AR:** 50.7, 43.7, 53.4, 40.0, 45.2, 52.7, 35.2, 60.4, 40.0, 45.9, 45.7, 47.3, 46.5, 44.5, 31.5

**Madison, WI:** 62.4, 53.9, 67.6, 52.9, 67.7, 50.7, 62.1, 58.9, 61.1, 65.0, 60.4, 59.6, 51.3, 44.8, 66.2

3. At $\alpha = 0.01$, is there enough evidence to conclude that the variances of the annual wages for Ithaca, NY, and Little Rock, AR, are different?

4. Are the mean annual wages the same for all three cities? Use $\alpha = 0.10$. Assume that the population variances are equal.

# 10 Chapter Test

*Take this test as you would take a test in class.*

*In each exercise,*

*(a) identify the claim and state $H_0$ and $H_a$,*

*(b) find the critical value and identify the rejection region,*

*(c) find the test statistic,*

*(d) decide whether to reject or fail to reject the null hypothesis, and*

*(e) interpret the decision in the context of the original claim.*

 *In Exercises 1–3, use the data, which list the hourly wages (in dollars) for randomly selected surgical technologists from three states. Assume the wages are normally distributed and that the samples are independent.* (Adapted from U.S. Bureau of Labor Statistics)

**Maine:** 22.76, 27.60, 25.08, 17.01, 30.15, 27.09, 20.95, 25.52, 20.11, 23.67, 24.32

**Oklahoma:** 24.64, 21.66, 19.38, 18.19, 23.14, 20.58, 19.53, 30.77, 27.46, 23.80

**Massachusetts:** 27.07, 24.71, 32.80, 28.34, 33.45, 33.36, 36.81, 30.04, 29.01, 24.30, 29.22, 29.50

**1.** At $\alpha = 0.05$, is there enough evidence to conclude that the variances of the hourly wages for surgical technologists in Maine and Massachusetts are the same?

**2.** At $\alpha = 0.01$, is there enough evidence to conclude that the variance of the hourly wages for surgical technologists in Oklahoma is greater than the variance of the hourly wages for surgical technologists in Massachusetts?

**3.** Are the mean hourly wages of surgical technologists the same for all three states? Use $\alpha = 0.01$. Assume that the population variances are equal.

*In Exercises 4–6, use the table, which lists the distribution of the ages of employees who carpool in Maine. It also lists the results of a random survey for two additional states.* (Adapted from U.S. Census Bureau)

| | State | | |
|---|---|---|---|
| **Ages** | **Maine** | **Oklahoma** | **Massachusetts** |
| 16–19 | 7.1% | 12 | 16 |
| 20–24 | 11.6% | 25 | 21 |
| 25–44 | 43.1% | 95 | 86 |
| 45–54 | 19.6% | 36 | 37 |
| 55–59 | 7.8% | 15 | 15 |
| 60+ | 10.8% | 17 | 25 |

**4.** Does the distribution of the ages of employees who carpool in Maine differ from the distribution of the ages of employees who carpool in Oklahoma? Use $\alpha = 0.10$.

**5.** Is the distribution of the ages of employees who carpool in Maine the same as the distribution of the ages of employees who carpool in Massachusetts? Use $\alpha = 0.01$.

**6.** Use the data for Oklahoma and Massachusetts to test whether state and age are independent. Use $\alpha = 0.05$.

# REAL STATISTICS REAL DECISIONS

## Putting it all together

Fraud.org was created by the National Consumers League (NCL) to combat the growing problem of telemarketing and Internet fraud by improving prevention and enforcement. NCL works to protect and promote social and economic justice for consumers and workers in the United States and abroad.

You work for the NCL as a statistical analyst. You are studying data on fraud. Part of your analysis involves testing the goodness-of-fit, testing for independence, comparing variances, and performing ANOVA.

### EXERCISES

1. ***Goodness-of-Fit***

   The table at the right shows an expected distribution of the ages of fraud victims. The table also shows the results of a survey of 1000 randomly selected fraud victims. Using $\alpha = 0.01$, perform a chi-square goodness-of-fit test. What can you conclude?

2. ***Independence***

   The contingency table below shows the results of a random sample of 2000 fraud victims classified by age and type of fraud. The frauds were committed using bogus sweepstakes or credit card offers.

   (a) Calculate the expected frequency for each cell in the contingency table. Assume the variables *age* and *type of fraud* are independent.

   (b) Can you conclude that the ages of the victims are related to the type of fraud? Use $\alpha = 0.01$.

| Age | Expected distribution | Survey results |
|---|---|---|
| Under 18 | 0.71% | 8 |
| 18–25 | 13.39% | 148 |
| 26–35 | 15.54% | 166 |
| 36–45 | 16.38% | 185 |
| 46–55 | 14.00% | 131 |
| 56–65 | 15.94% | 153 |
| Over 65 | 24.05% | 209 |

TABLE FOR EXERCISE 1

| Type of Fraud | Age | | | | | | | | |
|---|---|---|---|---|---|---|---|---|---|
| | **Under 20** | **20–29** | **30–39** | **40–49** | **50–59** | **60–69** | **70–79** | **80 +** | **Total** |
| Sweepstakes | 10 | 60 | 70 | 130 | 90 | 160 | 280 | 200 | 1000 |
| Credit cards | 20 | 180 | 260 | 240 | 180 | 70 | 30 | 20 | 1000 |
| Total | 30 | 240 | 330 | 370 | 270 | 230 | 310 | 220 | 2000 |

TECHNOLOGY

MINITAB EXCEL TI-84 PLUS

# Teacher Salaries

The Illinois State Board of Education conducts an annual study of the salaries of Illinois teachers. The study looks at how teachers' salaries are distributed based on factors such as degree and experience level, district size, and union membership.

The table shows the beginning salaries of random samples of Illinois teachers from different-sized districts. District size is measured by the number of students enrolled.

| Teacher salaries | | |
|---|---|---|
| **Under 500 students** | **1000–2999 students** | **At least 12,000 students** |
| 37,289 | 43,127 | 38,965 |
| 32,736 | 45,579 | 48,507 |
| 44,076 | 44,279 | 44,030 |
| 41,087 | 46,085 | 43,133 |
| 36,832 | 46,361 | 41,603 |
| 32,227 | 43,888 | 39,167 |
| 41,283 | 40,321 | 51,005 |
| 40,305 | 50,452 | 49,616 |
| 36,430 | 35,945 | 44,521 |
| 43,375 | 37,150 | 46,552 |
| 39,029 | 46,405 | 43,000 |
| 33,561 | 35,348 | 47,186 |
| 34,472 | 40,459 | 45,000 |

## EXERCISES

*In Exercises 1–3, refer to the samples listed below. Use $\alpha = 0.05$.*

*(a) Under 500 students*

*(b) 1000–2999 students*

*(c) At least 12,000 students*

**1.** Are the samples independent of each other? Explain.

**2.** Use technology to determine whether each sample is from a normal, or approximately normal, population.

**3.** Use technology to determine whether the samples were selected from populations having equal variances.

**4.** Using the results of Exercises 1–3, discuss whether the three conditions for a one-way ANOVA test are satisfied. If so, use technology to test the claim that teachers from districts of the three sizes have the same mean salary. Use $\alpha = 0.05$.

**5.** Repeat Exercises 1–4 using the data in the table below. The table displays the beginning salaries of random samples of Illinois teachers with different union memberships.

| Teacher salaries | | |
|---|---|---|
| **IEA-NEA** | **IFT-AFT** | **None/Other** |
| 52,866 | 35,122 | 42,000 |
| 60,708 | 37,989 | 33,083 |
| 34,452 | 28,915 | 40,722 |
| 40,357 | 45,422 | 39,907 |
| 49,828 | 40,459 | 36,400 |
| 48,715 | 35,697 | 34,681 |
| 37,920 | 37,880 | 50,500 |
| 33,561 | 48,095 | 35,034 |
| 39,404 | 41,805 | 35,692 |
| 32,951 | 40,626 | 36,703 |
| 40,525 | 39,690 | 33,833 |
| 40,606 | 35,276 | 42,000 |
| 39,521 | 39,454 | 34,750 |

Extended solutions are given in the technology manuals that accompany this text. Technical instruction is provided for Minitab, Excel, and the TI-84 Plus.

# CHAPTERS 9&10 CUMULATIVE REVIEW

1. The table below shows the winning times (in seconds) for the men's and women's 100-meter runs in the Summer Olympics from 1932 to 2020. *(Source: Olympic Channel Services)*

| **Men, $x$** | 10.30 | 10.30 | 10.30 | 10.40 | 10.50 | 10.20 | 10.00 |
|---|---|---|---|---|---|---|---|
| **Women, $y$** | 11.90 | 11.50 | 11.90 | 11.50 | 11.50 | 11.00 | 11.40 |

| **Men, $x$** | 9.90 | 10.14 | 10.06 | 10.25 | 9.99 | 9.92 | 9.96 |
|---|---|---|---|---|---|---|---|
| **Women, $y$** | 11.00 | 11.07 | 11.08 | 11.06 | 10.97 | 10.54 | 10.82 |

| **Men, $x$** | 9.84 | 9.87 | 9.85 | 9.69 | 9.63 | 9.81 | 9.80 |
|---|---|---|---|---|---|---|---|
| **Women, $y$** | 10.94 | 11.12 | 10.93 | 10.78 | 10.75 | 10.71 | 10.61 |

(a) Display the data in a scatter plot, calculate the correlation coefficient $r$, and describe the type of correlation.

(b) At $\alpha = 0.05$, is there enough evidence to conclude that there is a significant linear correlation between the winning times for the men's and women's 100-meter runs?

(c) Find the equation of the regression line for the data. Draw the regression line on the scatter plot.

(d) Use the regression equation to predict the women's 100-meter time when the men's 100-meter time is 9.90 seconds.

2. The table at the right shows the residential natural gas expenditures (in dollars) in one year for a random sample of households in four regions of the United States. Assume that the populations are normally distributed and the population variances are equal. At $\alpha = 0.10$, can you reject the claim that the mean expenditures are the same for all four regions? *(Adapted from U.S. Energy Information Administration)*

| Northeast | Midwest | South | West |
|---|---|---|---|
| 1091 | 318 | 403 | 499 |
| 529 | 734 | 312 | 425 |
| 654 | 471 | 609 | 853 |
| 884 | 859 | 597 | 391 |
| 775 | 652 | 738 | 229 |
| 1150 | 987 | 455 | 273 |
| 533 | 656 | 417 | 435 |
| 528 | 614 | 868 | 505 |

3. The equation used to predict the annual sweet potato yield (in pounds per acre) is $\hat{y} = 17{,}106 - 0.318x_1 + 0.303x_2$, where $x_1$ is the number of acres planted and $x_2$ is the number of acres harvested. Use the multiple regression equation to predict the annual sweet potato yields for the values of the independent variables. *(Adapted from U.S. Department of Agriculture)*

(a) $x_1 = 110{,}000, x_2 = 100{,}000$ (b) $x_1 = 125{,}000, x_2 = 115{,}000$

**4.** A school administrator claims that the standard deviations of reading test scores for eighth-grade students are the same in Illinois and Georgia. A random sample of 16 test scores from Illinois has a standard deviation of 33.1 points, and a random sample of 15 test scores from Georgia has a standard deviation of 31.8 points. At $\alpha = 0.10$, can you reject the administrator's claim? Assume the samples are independent and each population has a normal distribution. *(Adapted from National Center for Education Statistics)*

**5.** A researcher claims that how families pay for college is distributed as shown in the pie chart. You randomly select 900 families and record how each pays for college. The table shows the results, where $f$ is the frequency of each response. At $\alpha = 0.05$, test the researcher's claim. *(Adapted from Sallie Mae, Inc.)*

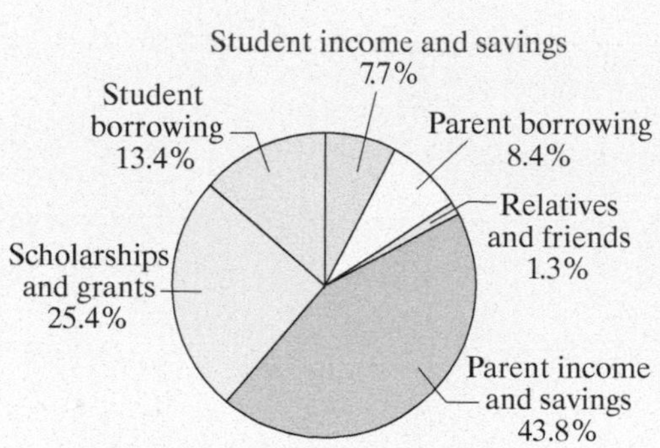


| **Survey results** | |
|---|---|
| **Response** | $f$ |
| Parent income and savings | 393 |
| Scholarships and grants | 222 |
| Student borrowing | 120 |
| Student income and savings | 85 |
| Parent borrowing | 66 |
| Relatives and friends | 14 |

**6. Reviewing a Movie** The contingency table shows how a random sample of adults rated a newly released movie and generation. At $\alpha = 0.05$, can you conclude that the adults' ratings are related to generation?

| | **Rating** | | | |
|---|---|---|---|---|
| **Generation** | **Excellent** | **Good** | **Fair** | **Poor** |
| Gen X (ages 41–56) | 97 | 42 | 26 | 5 |
| Millennial (ages 25–40) | 101 | 33 | 25 | 11 |

**7.** The figure shows the metacarpal bones in the human hand. The table shows the first metacarpal bone lengths (in millimeters) and the heights (in centimeters) of 12 adults. The equation of the regression line is $\hat{y} = 1.746x + 92.536$. *(Adapted from the American Journal of Physical Anthropology)*

| **Metacarpal bone length, $x$** | 45 | 51 | 39 | 41 | 47 | 48 |
|---|---|---|---|---|---|---|
| **Height, $y$** | 171 | 178 | 157 | 163 | 172 | 183 |

| **Metacarpal bone length, $x$** | 47 | 43 | 47 | 42 | 40 | 46 |
|---|---|---|---|---|---|---|
| **Height, $y$** | 173 | 175 | 173 | 169 | 160 | 172 |

(a) Find the coefficient of determination $r^2$ and interpret the results.

(b) Find the standard error of estimate $s_e$ and interpret the results.

(c) Construct a 95% prediction interval for the height of an adult whose first metacarpal bone length is 50 millimeters. Interpret the results.

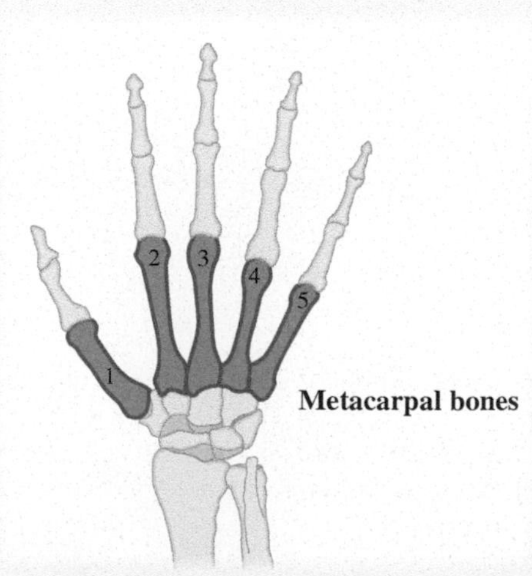


FIGURE FOR EXERCISE 7

# APPENDIX A

In this appendix, we use a 0-to-$z$ table as an alternative development of the standard normal distribution. It is intended that this appendix be used after completion of the "Properties of a Normal Distribution" subsection of Section 5.1 in the text. If used, this appendix should replace the material in the "Standard Normal Distribution" subsection of Section 5.1 except for the exercises.

Standard Normal Distribution (0-to-$z$)

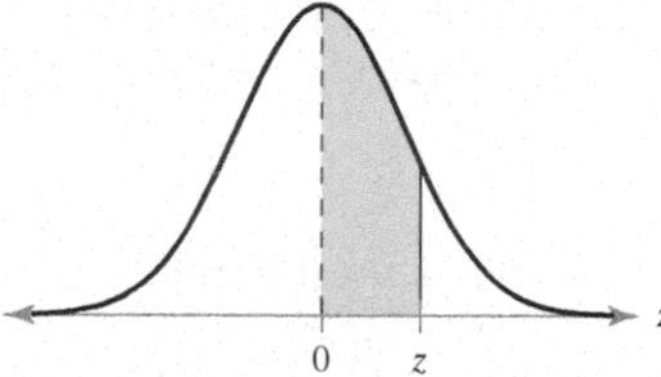


| $z$ | .00 | .01 | .02 | .03 | .04 | .05 | .06 | .07 | .08 | .09 |
|---|---|---|---|---|---|---|---|---|---|---|
| **0.0** | .0000 | .0040 | .0080 | .0120 | .0160 | .0199 | .0239 | .0279 | .0319 | .0359 |
| **0.1** | .0398 | .0438 | .0478 | .0517 | .0557 | .0596 | .0636 | .0675 | .0714 | .0753 |
| **0.2** | .0793 | .0832 | .0871 | .0910 | .0948 | .0987 | .1026 | .1064 | .1103 | .1141 |
| **0.3** | .1179 | .1217 | .1255 | .1293 | .1331 | .1368 | .1406 | .1443 | .1480 | .1517 |
| **0.4** | .1554 | .1591 | .1628 | .1664 | .1700 | .1736 | .1772 | .1808 | .1844 | .1879 |
| **0.5** | .1915 | .1950 | .1985 | .2019 | .2054 | .2088 | .2123 | .2157 | .2190 | .2224 |
| **0.6** | .2257 | .2291 | .2324 | .2357 | .2389 | .2422 | .2454 | .2486 | .2517 | .2549 |
| **0.7** | .2580 | .2611 | .2642 | .2673 | .2704 | .2734 | .2764 | .2794 | .2823 | .2852 |
| **0.8** | .2881 | .2910 | .2939 | .2967 | .2995 | .3023 | .3051 | .3078 | .3106 | .3133 |
| **0.9** | .3159 | .3186 | .3212 | .3238 | .3264 | .3289 | .3315 | .3340 | .3365 | .3389 |
| **1.0** | .3413 | .3438 | .3461 | .3485 | .3508 | .3531 | .3554 | .3577 | .3599 | .3621 |
| **1.1** | .3643 | .3665 | .3686 | .3708 | .3729 | .3749 | .3770 | .3790 | .3810 | .3830 |
| **1.2** | .3849 | .3869 | .3888 | .3907 | .3925 | .3944 | .3962 | .3980 | .3997 | .4015 |
| **1.3** | .4032 | .4049 | .4066 | .4082 | .4099 | .4115 | .4131 | .4147 | .4162 | .4177 |
| **1.4** | .4192 | .4207 | .4222 | .4236 | .4251 | .4265 | .4279 | .4292 | .4306 | .4319 |
| **1.5** | .4332 | .4345 | .4357 | .4370 | .4382 | .4394 | .4406 | .4418 | .4429 | .4441 |
| **1.6** | .4452 | .4463 | .4474 | .4484 | .4495 | .4505 | .4515 | .4525 | .4535 | .4545 |
| **1.7** | .4554 | .4564 | .4573 | .4582 | .4591 | .4599 | .4608 | .4616 | .4625 | .4633 |
| **1.8** | .4641 | .4649 | .4656 | .4664 | .4671 | .4678 | .4686 | .4693 | .4699 | .4706 |
| **1.9** | .4713 | .4719 | .4726 | .4732 | .4738 | .4744 | .4750 | .4756 | .4761 | .4767 |
| **2.0** | .4772 | .4778 | .4783 | .4788 | .4793 | .4798 | .4803 | .4808 | .4812 | .4817 |
| **2.1** | .4821 | .4826 | .4830 | .4834 | .4838 | .4842 | .4846 | .4850 | .4854 | .4857 |
| **2.2** | .4861 | .4864 | .4868 | .4871 | .4875 | .4878 | .4881 | .4884 | .4887 | .4890 |
| **2.3** | .4893 | .4896 | .4898 | .4901 | .4904 | .4906 | .4909 | .4911 | .4913 | .4916 |
| **2.4** | .4918 | .4920 | .4922 | .4925 | .4927 | .4929 | .4931 | .4932 | .4934 | .4936 |
| **2.5** | .4938 | .4940 | .4941 | .4943 | .4945 | .4946 | .4948 | .4949 | .4951 | .4952 |
| **2.6** | .4953 | .4955 | .4956 | .4957 | .4959 | .4960 | .4961 | .4962 | .4963 | .4964 |
| **2.7** | .4965 | .4966 | .4967 | .4968 | .4969 | .4970 | .4971 | .4972 | .4973 | .4974 |
| **2.8** | .4974 | .4975 | .4976 | .4977 | .4977 | .4978 | .4979 | .4979 | .4980 | .4981 |
| **2.9** | .4981 | .4982 | .4982 | .4983 | .4984 | .4984 | .4985 | .4985 | .4986 | .4986 |
| **3.0** | .4987 | .4987 | .4987 | .4988 | .4988 | .4989 | .4989 | .4989 | .4990 | .4990 |
| **3.1** | .4990 | .4991 | .4991 | .4991 | .4992 | .4992 | .4992 | .4992 | .4993 | .4993 |
| **3.2** | .4993 | .4993 | .4994 | .4994 | .4994 | .4994 | .4994 | .4995 | .4995 | .4995 |
| **3.3** | .4995 | .4995 | .4995 | .4996 | .4996 | .4996 | .4996 | .4996 | .4996 | .4997 |
| **3.4** | .4997 | .4997 | .4997 | .4997 | .4997 | .4997 | .4997 | .4997 | .4997 | .4998 |

Reprinted with permission of Frederick Mosteller.

# Alternative Presentation of the Standard Normal Distribution

### What You Should Learn

- How to find areas under the standard normal curve

## The Standard Normal Distribution

There are infinitely many normal distributions, each with its own mean and standard deviation. The normal distribution with a mean of 0 and a standard deviation of 1 is called the **standard normal distribution.** The horizontal scale of the graph of the standard normal distribution corresponds to $z$-scores. In Section 2.5, you learned that a $z$-score is a measure of position that indicates the number of standard deviations a value lies from the mean. Recall that you can transform an $x$-value to a $z$-score using the formula

$$z = \frac{\text{Value} - \text{Mean}}{\text{Standard deviation}} = \frac{x - \mu}{\sigma}.$$

Round to the nearest hundredth.

### Study Tip

Because every normal distribution can be transformed to the standard normal distribution, you can use $z$-scores and the standard normal curve to find areas (and therefore probabilities) under any normal curve.

### DEFINITION

The **standard normal distribution** is a normal distribution with a mean of 0 and a standard deviation of 1. The total area under its normal curve is 1.

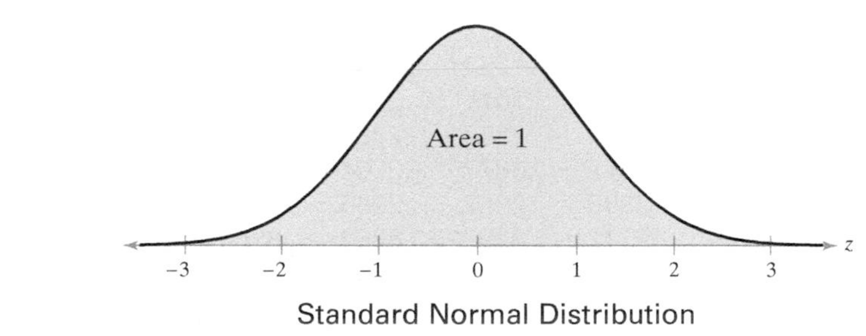


Standard Normal Distribution

When each data value of a normally distributed random variable $x$ is transformed into a $z$-score, the result will be the standard normal distribution. After this transformation takes place, the area that falls in the interval under the nonstandard normal curve is the *same* as that under the standard normal curve within the corresponding $z$-boundaries.

In Section 2.4, you learned to use the Empirical Rule to approximate areas under a normal curve when the values of the random variable $x$ corresponded to −3, −2, −1, 0, 1, 2, or 3 standard deviations from the mean. Now, you will learn to calculate areas corresponding to other $x$-values. After you use the formula above to transform an $x$-value to a $z$-score, you can use the Standard Normal Table (0-to-$z$) on page A1. The table lists the area under the standard normal curve between 0 and the given $z$-score. As you examine the table, notice the following.

### Study Tip

It is important that you know the difference between $x$ and $z$. The random variable $x$ is sometimes called a raw score and represents values in a nonstandard normal distribution, whereas $z$ represents values in the standard normal distribution.

### Properties of the Standard Normal Distribution

1. The distribution is symmetric about the mean $(z = 0)$.
2. The area under the standard normal curve to the left of $z = 0$ is 0.5 and the area to the right of $z = 0$ is 0.5.
3. The area under the standard normal curve increases as the distance between 0 and $z$ increases.

At first glance, the table on page A1 appears to give areas for positive $z$-scores only. However, because of the symmetry of the standard normal curve, the table also gives areas for negative $z$-scores (see Example 1).

## EXAMPLE 1

### Using the Standard Normal Table (0-to-$z$)

1. Find the area under the standard normal curve between $z = 0$ and $z = 1.15$.
2. Find the $z$-scores that correspond to an area of 0.0948.

**SOLUTION**

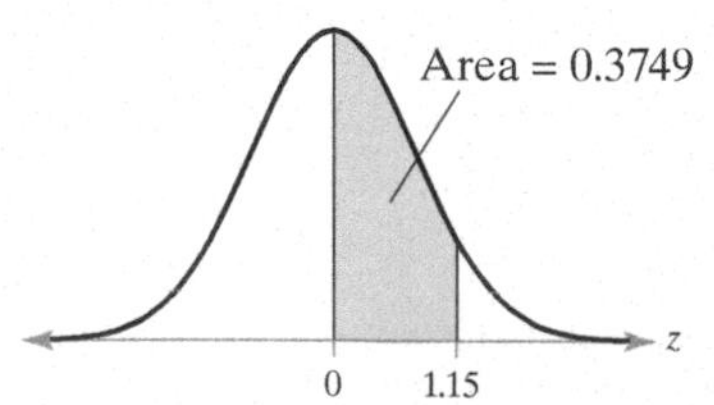


1. Find the area that corresponds to $z = 1.15$ by finding 1.1 in the left column and then moving across the row to the column under 0.05. The number in that row and column is 0.3749. So, the area between $z = 0$ and $z = 1.15$ is 0.3749, as shown in the figure at the left.

| $z$ | .00 | .01 | .02 | .03 | .04 | .05 | .06 |
|---|---|---|---|---|---|---|---|
| 0.0 | .0000 | .0040 | .0080 | .0120 | .0160 | .0199 | .0239 |
| 0.1 | .0398 | .0438 | .0478 | .0517 | .0557 | .0596 | .0636 |
| 0.2 | .0793 | .0832 | .0871 | .0910 | .0948 | .0987 | .1026 |
| 0.3 | .1179 | .1217 | .1255 | .1293 | .1331 | .1368 | .1406 |
| 0.9 | .3159 | .3186 | .3212 | .3238 | .3264 | .3289 | .3315 |
| 1.0 | .3413 | .3438 | .3461 | .3485 | .3508 | .3531 | .3554 |
| 1.1 | .3643 | .3665 | .3686 | .3708 | .3729 | .3749 | .3770 |
| 1.2 | .3849 | .3869 | .3888 | .3907 | .3925 | .3944 | .3962 |
| 1.3 | .4032 | .4049 | .4066 | .4082 | .4099 | .4115 | .4131 |
| 1.4 | .4192 | .4207 | .4222 | .4236 | .4251 | .4265 | .4279 |

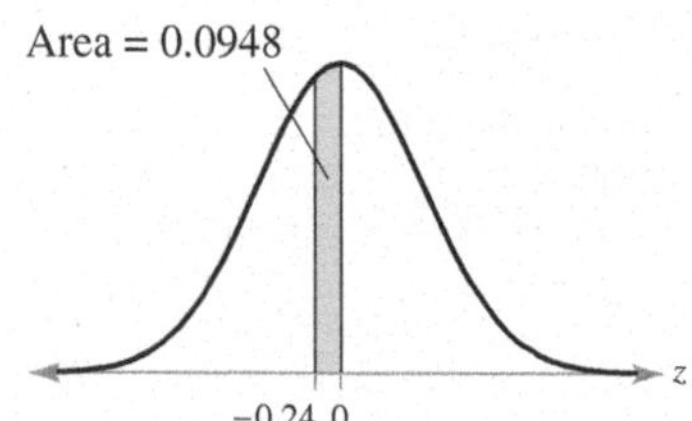


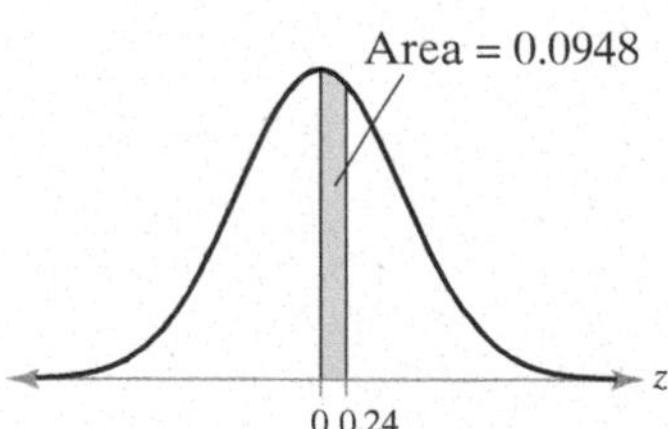


2. Find the $z$-scores that correspond to an area of 0.0948 by locating 0.0948 in the table. The values at the beginning of the corresponding row and at the top of the corresponding column give the $z$-score. For an area of 0.0948, the row value is 0.2 and the column value is 0.04. So, the $z$-scores are $z = -0.24$ and $z = 0.24$, as shown in the figures at the left.

| $z$ | .00 | .01 | .02 | .03 | .04 | .05 | .06 |
|---|---|---|---|---|---|---|---|
| 0.0 | .0000 | .0040 | .0080 | .0120 | .0160 | .0199 | .0239 |
| 0.1 | .0398 | .0438 | .0478 | .0517 | .0557 | .0596 | .0636 |
| 0.2 | .0793 | .0832 | .0871 | .0910 | .0948 | .0987 | .1026 |
| 0.3 | .1179 | .1217 | .1255 | .1293 | .1331 | .1368 | .1406 |
| 0.4 | .1554 | .1591 | .1628 | .1664 | .1700 | .1736 | .1772 |
| 0.5 | .1915 | .1950 | .1985 | .2019 | .2054 | .2088 | .2123 |

**TRY IT YOURSELF 1**

1. Find the area under the standard normal curve between $z = 0$ and $z = 2.19$.
2. Find the $z$-scores that correspond to an area of 0.4850.

*Answer: Page A43*

**TI-84 PLUS**

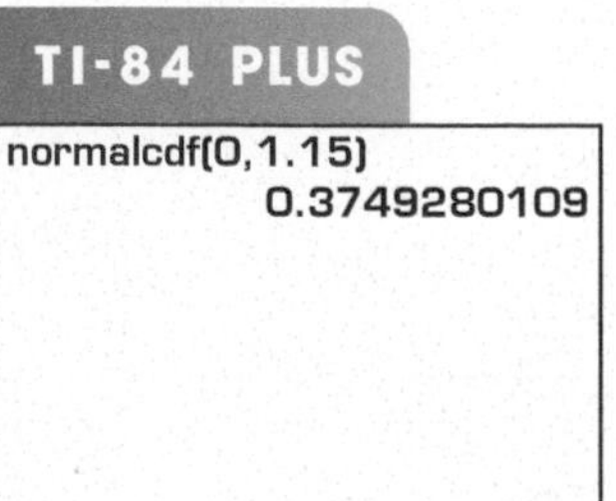


When the $z$-score is not in the table, use the entry closest to it. When the $z$-score is exactly midway between two $z$-scores, use the area midway between the corresponding areas. In addition to using the table, you can use technology to find the area under the standard normal curve that corresponds to a $z$-score, as shown at the left using a TI-84 Plus for Part 1 of Example 1.

You can use the following guidelines to find various types of areas under the standard normal curve.

## GUIDELINES

**Finding Areas Under the Standard Normal Curve**

1. Sketch the standard normal curve and shade the appropriate area under the curve.
2. Use the Standard Normal Table (0-to-$z$) on page A1 to find the area that corresponds to the $z$-score(s).
3. Find the area by following the directions for each case shown.

**a.** Area to the left of $z$

i. When $z < 0$, *subtract* the area from 0.5.

1. The area between $z = 0$ and $z = -1.23$ is 0.3907.
2. Subtract to find the area to the left of $z = -1.23$; $0.5 - 0.3907 = 0.1093$.

−1.23 0 z

ii. When $z > 0$, *add* 0.5 to the area.

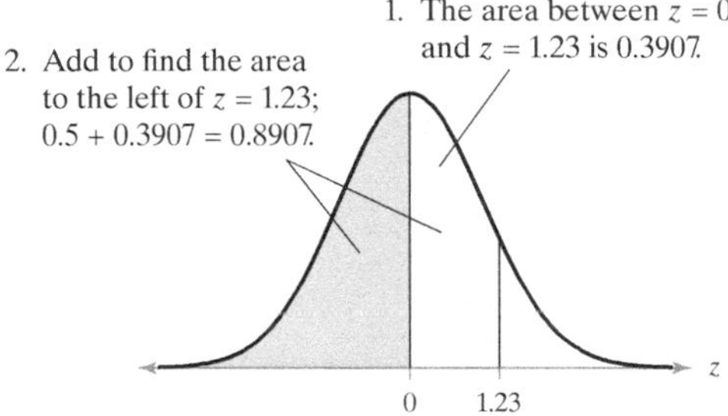
1. The area between z = 0 and z = 1.23 is 0.3907.
2. Add to find the area to the left of z = 1.23; 0.5 + 0.3907 = 0.8907.
0
1.23
z

**b.** Area to the right of $z$

i. When $z < 0$, *add* 0.5 to the area.

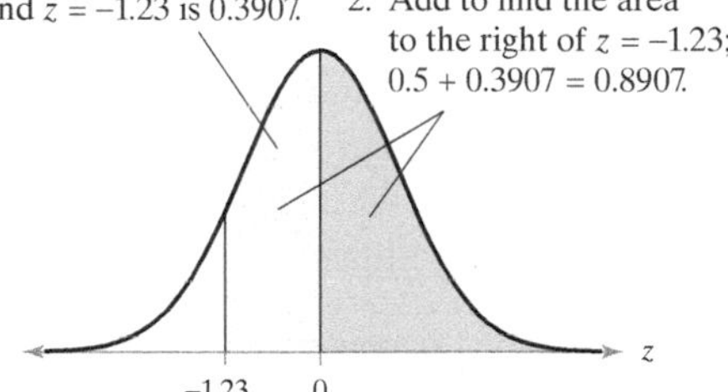
1. The area between z = 0 and z = −1.23 is 0.3907.
2. Add to find the area to the right of z = −1.23; 0.5 + 0.3907 = 0.8907.
−1.23
0
z

ii. When $z > 0$, *subtract* the area from 0.5.

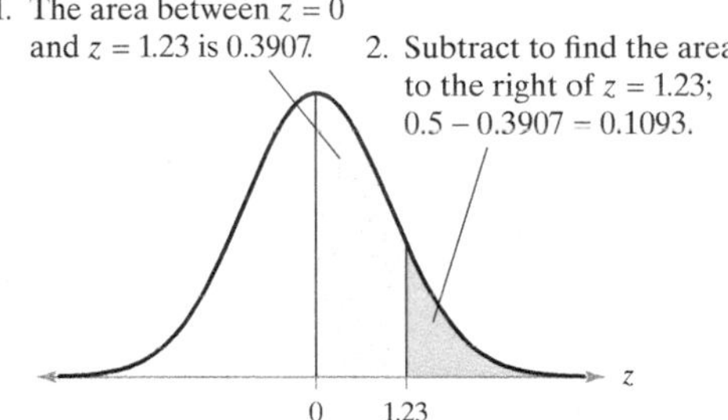
1. The area between z = 0 and z = 1.23 is 0.3907.
2. Subtract to find the area to the right of z = 1.23; 0.5 − 0.3907 = 0.1093.
0
1.23
z

**c.** Area between two $z$-scores

i. When the two $z$-scores have the same sign (both positive or both negative), *subtract* the smaller area from the larger area.

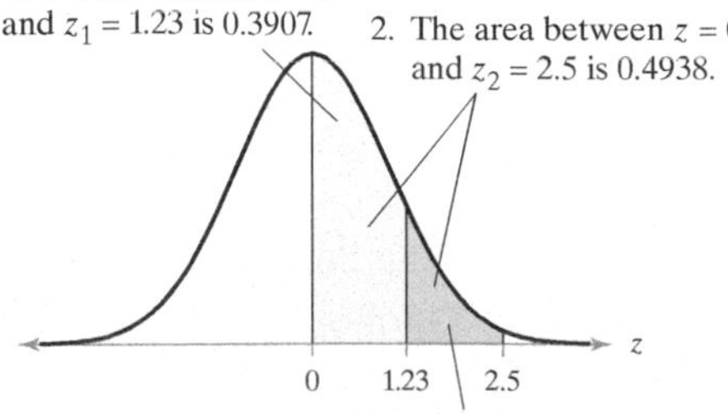
1. The area between z = 0 and z1 = 1.23 is 0.3907.
2. The area between z = 0 and z2 = 2.5 is 0.4938.
0
1.23
2.5
z
3. Subtract to find the area between z1 = 1.23 and z2 = 2.5; 0.4938 − 0.3907 = 0.1031.

ii. When the two $z$-scores have opposite signs (one negative and one positive), *add* the areas.

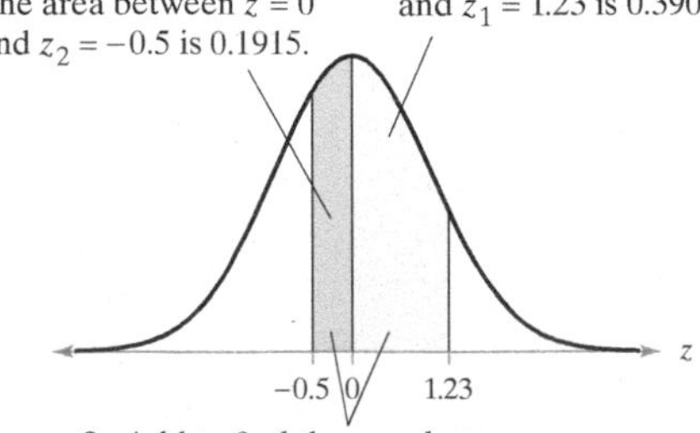
1. The area between z = 0 and z1 = 1.23 is 0.3907.
2. The area between z = 0 and z2 = −0.5 is 0.1915.
−0.5
0
1.23
z
3. Add to find the area between z1 = 1.23 and z2 = −0.5; 0.3907 + 0.1915 = 0.5822.

## EXAMPLE 2

### Finding Area Under the Standard Normal Curve

Find the area under the standard normal curve to the left of $z = -0.99$.

**SOLUTION**

The area under the standard normal curve to the left of $z = -0.99$ is shown.

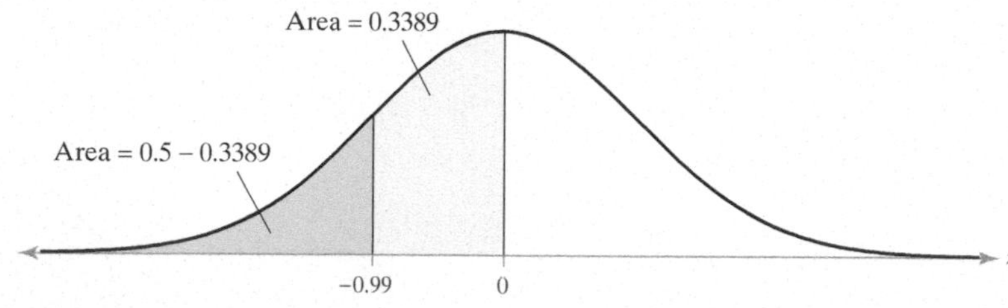


**TI-84 PLUS**

```
0.5-normalcdf(0,0.99)
             0.1610870617
```

From the Standard Normal Table (0-to-$z$), the area corresponding to $z = -0.99$ is 0.3389. Because the area to the left of $z = 0$ is 0.5, the area to the left of $z = -0.99$ is

$$\text{Area} = 0.5 - 0.3389 = 0.1611.$$

You can use technology to find the area to the left of $z = -0.99$, as shown at the left.

**TRY IT YOURSELF 2**

Find the area under the standard normal curve to the left of $z = 2.13$.

*Answer: Page A43*

## EXAMPLE 3

### Finding Area Under the Standard Normal Curve

Find the area under the standard normal curve to the right of $z = 1.06$.

**SOLUTION**

The area under the standard normal curve to the right of $z = 1.06$ is shown.

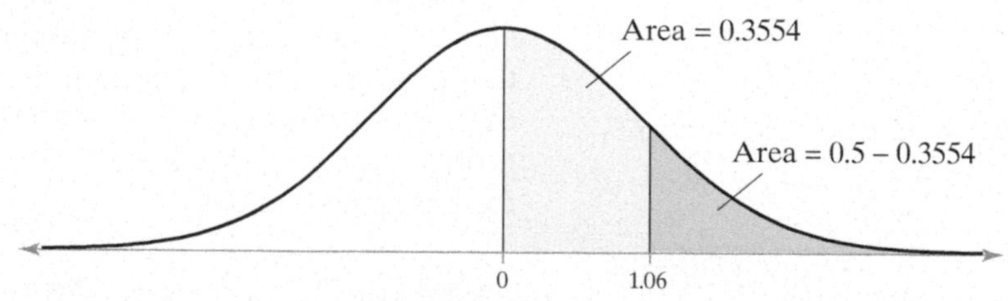


**TI-84 PLUS**

```
0.5-normalcdf(0,1.06)
             0.1445723279
```

From the Standard Normal Table (0-to-$z$), the area corresponding to $z = 1.06$ is 0.3554. Because the area to the right of $z = 0$ is 0.5, the area to the right of $z = 1.06$ is

$$\text{Area} = 0.5 - 0.3554 = 0.1446.$$

You can use technology to find the area to the right of $z = 1.06$, as shown at the left.

**TRY IT YOURSELF 3**

Find the area under the standard normal curve to the right of $z = -2.16$.

*Answer: Page A43*

## EXAMPLE 4

### Finding Area Under the Standard Normal Curve

Find the area under the standard normal curve between $z = -1.5$ and $z = 1.25$.

**SOLUTION**

The area under the standard normal curve between $z = -1.5$ and $z = 1.25$ is shown.

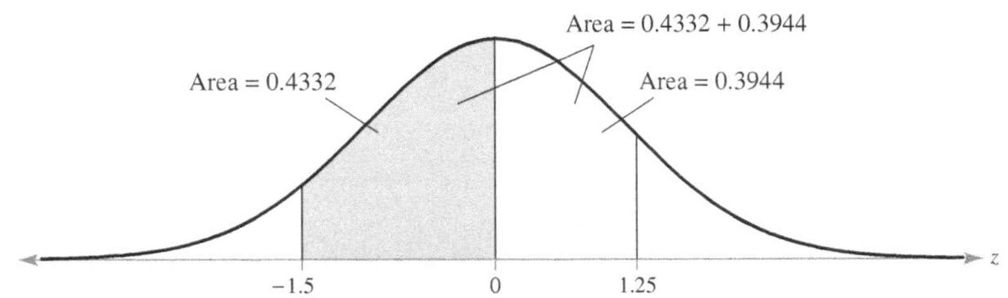


**TI-84 PLUS**

```
normalcdf(-1.5,1.25)
            0.8275429323
```

From the Standard Normal Table (0-to-$z$), the area corresponding to $z = -1.5$ is 0.4332 and the area corresponding to $z = 1.25$ is 0.3944. To find the area between these two $z$-scores, add the resulting areas.

$$\text{Area} = 0.4332 + 0.3944 = 0.8276$$

Note that when you use technology, your answers may differ slightly from those found using the Standard Normal Table. For instance, when finding the area between $z = -1.5$ and $z = 1.25$ on a TI-84 Plus, you get the result shown at the left.

***Interpretation*** So, about 82.76% of the area under the curve falls between $z = -1.5$ and $z = 1.25$.

**TRY IT YOURSELF 4**

Find the area under the standard normal curve between $z = -2.165$ and $z = -1.35$.

*Answer: Page A43*

Because the normal distribution is a continuous probability distribution, the area under the standard normal curve to the left of a $z$-score gives the probability that $z$ is less than that $z$-score. For instance, in Example 2, the area to the left of $z = -0.99$ is 0.1611. So, $P(z < -0.99) = 0.1611$, which is read as "the probability that $z$ is less than −0.99 is 0.1611." The table shows the probabilities for Examples 3 and 4.

| | Area | Probability |
|---|---|---|
| **Example 3** | To the right of $z = 1.06$: 0.1446 | $P(z > 1.06) = 0.1446$ |
| **Example 4** | Between $z = -1.5$ and $z = 1.25$: 0.8276 | $P(-1.5 < z < 1.25) = 0.8276$ |

Recall from Section 2.4 that values lying more than two standard deviations from the mean are considered unusual. Values lying more than three standard deviations from the mean are considered *very* unusual. So, a $z$-score greater than 2 or less than −2 is unusual. A $z$-score greater than 3 or less than −3 is *very* unusual.

You are now ready to continue Section 5.1 on page 242 with the section exercises.

# APPENDIX B

## Table 1—Random Numbers

| 92630 | 78240 | 19267 | 95457 | 53497 | 23894 | 37708 | 79862 | 76471 | 66418 |
|---|---|---|---|---|---|---|---|---|---|
| 79445 | 78735 | 71549 | 44843 | 26104 | 67318 | 00701 | 34986 | 66751 | 99723 |
| 59654 | 71966 | 27386 | 50004 | 05358 | 94031 | 29281 | 18544 | 52429 | 06080 |
| 31524 | 49587 | 76612 | 39789 | 13537 | 48086 | 59483 | 60680 | 84675 | 53014 |
| 06348 | 76938 | 90379 | 51392 | 55887 | 71015 | 09209 | 79157 | 24440 | 30244 |
| 28703 | 51709 | 94456 | 48396 | 73780 | 06436 | 86641 | 69239 | 57662 | 80181 |
| 68108 | 89266 | 94730 | 95761 | 75023 | 48464 | 65544 | 96583 | 18911 | 16391 |
| 99938 | 90704 | 93621 | 66330 | 33393 | 95261 | 95349 | 51769 | 91616 | 33238 |
| 91543 | 73196 | 34449 | 63513 | 83834 | 99411 | 58826 | 40456 | 69268 | 48562 |
| 42103 | 02781 | 73920 | 56297 | 72678 | 12249 | 25270 | 36678 | 21313 | 75767 |
| 17138 | 27584 | 25296 | 28387 | 51350 | 61664 | 37893 | 05363 | 44143 | 42677 |
| 28297 | 14280 | 54524 | 21618 | 95320 | 38174 | 60579 | 08089 | 94999 | 78460 |
| 09331 | 56712 | 51333 | 06289 | 75345 | 08811 | 82711 | 57392 | 25252 | 30333 |
| 31295 | 04204 | 93712 | 51287 | 05754 | 79396 | 87399 | 51773 | 33075 | 97061 |
| 36146 | 15560 | 27592 | 42089 | 99281 | 59640 | 15221 | 96079 | 09961 | 05371 |
| 29553 | 18432 | 13630 | 05529 | 02791 | 81017 | 49027 | 79031 | 50912 | 09399 |
| 23501 | 22642 | 63081 | 08191 | 89420 | 67800 | 55137 | 54707 | 32945 | 64522 |
| 57888 | 85846 | 67967 | 07835 | 11314 | 01545 | 48535 | 17142 | 08552 | 67457 |
| 55336 | 71264 | 88472 | 04334 | 63919 | 36394 | 11196 | 92470 | 70543 | 29776 |
| 10087 | 10072 | 55980 | 64688 | 68239 | 20461 | 89381 | 93809 | 00796 | 95945 |
| 34101 | 81277 | 66090 | 88872 | 37818 | 72142 | 67140 | 50785 | 21380 | 16703 |
| 53362 | 44940 | 60430 | 22834 | 14130 | 96593 | 23298 | 56203 | 92671 | 15925 |
| 82975 | 66158 | 84731 | 19436 | 55790 | 69229 | 28661 | 13675 | 99318 | 76873 |
| 54827 | 84673 | 22898 | 08094 | 14326 | 87038 | 42892 | 21127 | 30712 | 48489 |
| 25464 | 59098 | 27436 | 89421 | 80754 | 89924 | 19097 | 67737 | 80368 | 08795 |
| 67609 | 60214 | 41475 | 84950 | 40133 | 02546 | 09570 | 45682 | 50165 | 15609 |
| 44921 | 70924 | 61295 | 51137 | 47596 | 86735 | 35561 | 76649 | 18217 | 63446 |
| 33170 | 30972 | 98130 | 95828 | 49786 | 13301 | 36081 | 80761 | 33985 | 68621 |
| 84687 | 85445 | 06208 | 17654 | 51333 | 02878 | 35010 | 67578 | 61574 | 20749 |
| 71886 | 56450 | 36567 | 09395 | 96951 | 35507 | 17555 | 35212 | 69106 | 01679 |
| 00475 | 02224 | 74722 | 14721 | 40215 | 21351 | 08596 | 45625 | 83981 | 63748 |
| 25993 | 38881 | 68361 | 59560 | 41274 | 69742 | 40703 | 37993 | 03435 | 18873 |
| 92882 | 53178 | 99195 | 93803 | 56985 | 53089 | 15305 | 50522 | 55900 | 43026 |
| 25138 | 26810 | 07093 | 15677 | 60688 | 04410 | 24505 | 37890 | 67186 | 62829 |
| 84631 | 71882 | 12991 | 83028 | 82484 | 90339 | 91950 | 74579 | 03539 | 90122 |
| 34003 | 92326 | 12793 | 61453 | 48121 | 74271 | 28363 | 66561 | 75220 | 35908 |
| 53775 | 45749 | 05734 | 86169 | 42762 | 70175 | 97310 | 73894 | 88606 | 19994 |
| 59316 | 97885 | 72807 | 54966 | 60859 | 11932 | 35265 | 71601 | 55577 | 67715 |
| 20479 | 66557 | 50705 | 26999 | 09854 | 52591 | 14063 | 30214 | 19890 | 19292 |
| 86180 | 84931 | 25455 | 26044 | 02227 | 52015 | 21820 | 50599 | 51671 | 65411 |
| 21451 | 68001 | 72710 | 40261 | 61281 | 13172 | 63819 | 48970 | 51732 | 54113 |
| 98062 | 68375 | 80089 | 24135 | 72355 | 95428 | 11808 | 29740 | 81644 | 86610 |
| 01788 | 64429 | 14430 | 94575 | 75153 | 94576 | 61393 | 96192 | 03227 | 32258 |
| 62465 | 04841 | 43272 | 68702 | 01274 | 05437 | 22953 | 18946 | 99053 | 41690 |
| 94324 | 31089 | 84159 | 92933 | 99989 | 89500 | 91586 | 02802 | 69471 | 68274 |
| 05797 | 43984 | 21575 | 09908 | 70221 | 19791 | 51578 | 36432 | 33494 | 79888 |
| 10395 | 14289 | 52185 | 09721 | 25789 | 38562 | 54794 | 04897 | 59012 | 89251 |
| 35177 | 56986 | 25549 | 59730 | 64718 | 52630 | 31100 | 62384 | 49483 | 11409 |
| 25633 | 89619 | 75882 | 98256 | 02126 | 72099 | 57183 | 55887 | 09320 | 73463 |
| 16464 | 48280 | 94254 | 45777 | 45150 | 68865 | 11382 | 11782 | 22695 | 41988 |

*A Million Random Digits with 100,000 Normal Deviates* by the Rand Corporation (New York: The Free Press, 1955).

# Table 2—Binomial Distribution

This table shows the probability of $x$ successes in $n$ independent trials, each with probability of success $p$.

| | | *p* | | | | | | | | | | | | | | | | | | | |
|---|---|---|---|---|---|---|---|---|---|---|---|---|---|---|---|---|---|---|---|---|---|
| *n* | *x* | .01 | .05 | .10 | .15 | .20 | .25 | .30 | .35 | .40 | .45 | .50 | .55 | .60 | .65 | .70 | .75 | .80 | .85 | .90 | .95 |
| 2 | 0 | .980 | .902 | .810 | .723 | .640 | .563 | .490 | .423 | .360 | .303 | .250 | .203 | .160 | .123 | .090 | .063 | .040 | .023 | .010 | .002 |
| | 1 | .020 | .095 | .180 | .255 | .320 | .375 | .420 | .455 | .480 | .495 | .500 | .495 | .480 | .455 | .420 | .375 | .320 | .255 | .180 | .095 |
| | 2 | .000 | .002 | .010 | .023 | .040 | .063 | .090 | .123 | .160 | .203 | .250 | .303 | .360 | .423 | .490 | .563 | .640 | .723 | .810 | .902 |
| 3 | 0 | .970 | .857 | .729 | .614 | .512 | .422 | .343 | .275 | .216 | .166 | .125 | .091 | .064 | .043 | .027 | .016 | .008 | .003 | .001 | .000 |
| | 1 | .029 | .135 | .243 | .325 | .384 | .422 | .441 | .444 | .432 | .408 | .375 | .334 | .288 | .239 | .189 | .141 | .096 | .057 | .027 | .007 |
| | 2 | .000 | .007 | .027 | .057 | .096 | .141 | .189 | .239 | .288 | .334 | .375 | .408 | .432 | .444 | .441 | .422 | .384 | .325 | .243 | .135 |
| | 3 | .000 | .000 | .001 | .003 | .008 | .016 | .027 | .043 | .064 | .091 | .125 | .166 | .216 | .275 | .343 | .422 | .512 | .614 | .729 | .857 |
| 4 | 0 | .961 | .815 | .656 | .522 | .410 | .316 | .240 | .179 | .130 | .092 | .062 | .041 | .026 | .015 | .008 | .004 | .002 | .001 | .000 | .000 |
| | 1 | .039 | .171 | .292 | .368 | .410 | .422 | .412 | .384 | .346 | .300 | .250 | .200 | .154 | .112 | .076 | .047 | .026 | .011 | .004 | .000 |
| | 2 | .001 | .014 | .049 | .098 | .154 | .211 | .265 | .311 | .346 | .368 | .375 | .368 | .346 | .311 | .265 | .211 | .154 | .098 | .049 | .014 |
| | 3 | .000 | .000 | .004 | .011 | .026 | .047 | .076 | .112 | .154 | .200 | .250 | .300 | .346 | .384 | .412 | .422 | .410 | .368 | .292 | .171 |
| | 4 | .000 | .000 | .000 | .001 | .002 | .004 | .008 | .015 | .026 | .041 | .062 | .092 | .130 | .179 | .240 | .316 | .410 | .522 | .656 | .815 |
| 5 | 0 | .951 | .774 | .590 | .444 | .328 | .237 | .168 | .116 | .078 | .050 | .031 | .019 | .010 | .005 | .002 | .001 | .000 | .000 | .000 | .000 |
| | 1 | .048 | .204 | .328 | .392 | .410 | .396 | .360 | .312 | .259 | .206 | .156 | .113 | .077 | .049 | .028 | .015 | .006 | .002 | .000 | .000 |
| | 2 | .001 | .021 | .073 | .138 | .205 | .264 | .309 | .336 | .346 | .337 | .312 | .276 | .230 | .181 | .132 | .088 | .051 | .024 | .008 | .001 |
| | 3 | .000 | .001 | .008 | .024 | .051 | .088 | .132 | .181 | .230 | .276 | .312 | .337 | .346 | .336 | .309 | .264 | .205 | .138 | .073 | .021 |
| | 4 | .000 | .000 | .000 | .002 | .006 | .015 | .028 | .049 | .077 | .113 | .156 | .206 | .259 | .312 | .360 | .396 | .410 | .392 | .328 | .204 |
| | 5 | .000 | .000 | .000 | .000 | .000 | .001 | .002 | .005 | .010 | .019 | .031 | .050 | .078 | .116 | .168 | .237 | .328 | .444 | .590 | .774 |
| 6 | 0 | .941 | .735 | .531 | .377 | .262 | .178 | .118 | .075 | .047 | .028 | .016 | .008 | .004 | .002 | .001 | .000 | .000 | .000 | .000 | .000 |
| | 1 | .057 | .232 | .354 | .399 | .393 | .356 | .303 | .244 | .187 | .136 | .094 | .061 | .037 | .020 | .010 | .004 | .002 | .000 | .000 | .000 |
| | 2 | .001 | .031 | .098 | .176 | .246 | .297 | .324 | .328 | .311 | .278 | .234 | .186 | .138 | .095 | .060 | .033 | .015 | .006 | .001 | .000 |
| | 3 | .000 | .002 | .015 | .042 | .082 | .132 | .185 | .236 | .276 | .303 | .312 | .303 | .276 | .236 | .185 | .132 | .082 | .042 | .015 | .002 |
| | 4 | .000 | .000 | .001 | .006 | .015 | .033 | .060 | .095 | .138 | .186 | .234 | .278 | .311 | .328 | .324 | .297 | .246 | .176 | .098 | .031 |
| | 5 | .000 | .000 | .000 | .000 | .002 | .004 | .010 | .020 | .037 | .061 | .094 | .136 | .187 | .244 | .303 | .356 | .393 | .399 | .354 | .232 |
| | 6 | .000 | .000 | .000 | .000 | .000 | .000 | .001 | .002 | .004 | .008 | .016 | .028 | .047 | .075 | .118 | .178 | .262 | .377 | .531 | .735 |
| 7 | 0 | .932 | .698 | .478 | .321 | .210 | .133 | .082 | .049 | .028 | .015 | .008 | .004 | .002 | .001 | .000 | .000 | .000 | .000 | .000 | .000 |
| | 1 | .066 | .257 | .372 | .396 | .367 | .311 | .247 | .185 | .131 | .087 | .055 | .032 | .017 | .008 | .004 | .001 | .000 | .000 | .000 | .000 |
| | 2 | .002 | .041 | .124 | .210 | .275 | .311 | .318 | .299 | .261 | .214 | .164 | .117 | .077 | .047 | .025 | .012 | .004 | .001 | .000 | .000 |
| | 3 | .000 | .004 | .023 | .062 | .115 | .173 | .227 | .268 | .290 | .292 | .273 | .239 | .194 | .144 | .097 | .058 | .029 | .011 | .003 | .000 |
| | 4 | .000 | .000 | .003 | .011 | .029 | .058 | .097 | .144 | .194 | .239 | .273 | .292 | .290 | .268 | .227 | .173 | .115 | .062 | .023 | .004 |
| | 5 | .000 | .000 | .000 | .001 | .004 | .012 | .025 | .047 | .077 | .117 | .164 | .214 | .261 | .299 | .318 | .311 | .275 | .210 | .124 | .041 |
| | 6 | .000 | .000 | .000 | .000 | .000 | .001 | .004 | .008 | .017 | .032 | .055 | .087 | .131 | .185 | .247 | .311 | .367 | .396 | .372 | .257 |
| | 7 | .000 | .000 | .000 | .000 | .000 | .000 | .000 | .001 | .002 | .004 | .008 | .015 | .028 | .049 | .082 | .133 | .210 | .321 | .478 | .698 |
| 8 | 0 | .923 | .663 | .430 | .272 | .168 | .100 | .058 | .032 | .017 | .008 | .004 | .002 | .001 | .000 | .000 | .000 | .000 | .000 | .000 | .000 |
| | 1 | .075 | .279 | .383 | .385 | .336 | .267 | .198 | .137 | .090 | .055 | .031 | .016 | .008 | .003 | .001 | .000 | .000 | .000 | .000 | .000 |
| | 2 | .003 | .051 | .149 | .238 | .294 | .311 | .296 | .259 | .209 | .157 | .109 | .070 | .041 | .022 | .010 | .004 | .001 | .000 | .000 | .000 |
| | 3 | .000 | .005 | .033 | .084 | .147 | .208 | .254 | .279 | .279 | .257 | .219 | .172 | .124 | .081 | .047 | .023 | .009 | .003 | .000 | .000 |
| | 4 | .000 | .000 | .005 | .018 | .046 | .087 | .136 | .188 | .232 | .263 | .273 | .263 | .232 | .188 | .136 | .087 | .046 | .018 | .005 | .000 |
| | 5 | .000 | .000 | .000 | .003 | .009 | .023 | .047 | .081 | .124 | .172 | .219 | .257 | .279 | .279 | .254 | .208 | .147 | .084 | .033 | .005 |
| | 6 | .000 | .000 | .000 | .000 | .001 | .004 | .010 | .022 | .041 | .070 | .109 | .157 | .209 | .259 | .296 | .311 | .294 | .238 | .149 | .051 |
| | 7 | .000 | .000 | .000 | .000 | .000 | .000 | .001 | .003 | .008 | .016 | .031 | .055 | .090 | .137 | .198 | .267 | .336 | .385 | .383 | .279 |
| | 8 | .000 | .000 | .000 | .000 | .000 | .000 | .000 | .000 | .001 | .002 | .004 | .008 | .017 | .032 | .058 | .100 | .168 | .272 | .430 | .663 |
| 9 | 0 | .914 | .630 | .387 | .232 | .134 | .075 | .040 | .021 | .010 | .005 | .002 | .001 | .000 | .000 | .000 | .000 | .000 | .000 | .000 | .000 |
| | 1 | .083 | .299 | .387 | .368 | .302 | .225 | .156 | .100 | .060 | .034 | .018 | .008 | .004 | .001 | .000 | .000 | .000 | .000 | .000 | .000 |
| | 2 | .003 | .063 | .172 | .260 | .302 | .300 | .267 | .216 | .161 | .111 | .070 | .041 | .021 | .010 | .004 | .001 | .000 | .000 | .000 | .000 |
| | 3 | .000 | .008 | .045 | .107 | .176 | .234 | .267 | .272 | .251 | .212 | .164 | .116 | .074 | .042 | .021 | .009 | .003 | .001 | .000 | .000 |
| | 4 | .000 | .001 | .007 | .028 | .066 | .117 | .172 | .219 | .251 | .260 | .246 | .213 | .167 | .118 | .074 | .039 | .017 | .005 | .001 | .000 |
| | 5 | .000 | .000 | .001 | .005 | .017 | .039 | .074 | .118 | .167 | .213 | .246 | .260 | .251 | .219 | .172 | .117 | .066 | .028 | .007 | .001 |
| | 6 | .000 | .000 | .000 | .001 | .003 | .009 | .021 | .042 | .074 | .116 | .164 | .212 | .251 | .272 | .267 | .234 | .176 | .107 | .045 | .008 |
| | 7 | .000 | .000 | .000 | .000 | .000 | .001 | .004 | .010 | .021 | .041 | .070 | .111 | .161 | .216 | .267 | .300 | .302 | .260 | .172 | .063 |
| | 8 | .000 | .000 | .000 | .000 | .000 | .000 | .000 | .001 | .004 | .008 | .018 | .034 | .060 | .100 | .156 | .225 | .302 | .368 | .387 | .299 |
| | 9 | .000 | .000 | .000 | .000 | .000 | .000 | .000 | .000 | .000 | .001 | .002 | .005 | .010 | .021 | .040 | .075 | .134 | .232 | .387 | .630 |

From Brase/Brase, *Understandable Statistics,* Sixth Edition.

## Table 2—Binomial Distribution *(continued)*

| n | x | .01 | .05 | .10 | .15 | .20 | .25 | .30 | .35 | .40 | .45 | .50 | .55 | .60 | .65 | .70 | .75 | .80 | .85 | .90 | .95 |
|---|---|---|---|---|---|---|---|---|---|---|---|---|---|---|---|---|---|---|---|---|---|
| 10 | 0 | .904 | .599 | .349 | .197 | .107 | .056 | .028 | .014 | .006 | .003 | .001 | .000 | .000 | .000 | .000 | .000 | .000 | .000 | .000 | .000 |
| | 1 | .091 | .315 | .387 | .347 | .268 | .188 | .121 | .072 | .040 | .021 | .010 | .004 | .002 | .000 | .000 | .000 | .000 | .000 | .000 | .000 |
| | 2 | .004 | .075 | .194 | .276 | .302 | .282 | .233 | .176 | .121 | .076 | .044 | .023 | .011 | .004 | .001 | .000 | .000 | .000 | .000 | .000 |
| | 3 | .000 | .010 | .057 | .130 | .201 | .250 | .267 | .252 | .215 | .166 | .117 | .075 | .042 | .021 | .009 | .003 | .001 | .000 | .000 | .000 |
| | 4 | .000 | .001 | .011 | .040 | .088 | .146 | .200 | .238 | .251 | .238 | .205 | .160 | .111 | .069 | .037 | .016 | .006 | .001 | .000 | .000 |
| | 5 | .000 | .000 | .001 | .008 | .026 | .058 | .103 | .154 | .201 | .234 | .246 | .234 | .201 | .154 | .103 | .058 | .026 | .008 | .001 | .000 |
| | 6 | .000 | .000 | .000 | .001 | .006 | .016 | .037 | .069 | .111 | .160 | .205 | .238 | .251 | .238 | .200 | .146 | .088 | .040 | .011 | .001 |
| | 7 | .000 | .000 | .000 | .000 | .001 | .003 | .009 | .021 | .042 | .075 | .117 | .166 | .215 | .252 | .267 | .250 | .201 | .130 | .057 | .010 |
| | 8 | .000 | .000 | .000 | .000 | .000 | .000 | .001 | .004 | .011 | .023 | .044 | .076 | .121 | .176 | .233 | .282 | .302 | .276 | .194 | .075 |
| | 9 | .000 | .000 | .000 | .000 | .000 | .000 | .000 | .000 | .002 | .004 | .010 | .021 | .040 | .072 | .121 | .188 | .268 | .347 | .387 | .315 |
| | 10 | .000 | .000 | .000 | .000 | .000 | .000 | .000 | .000 | .000 | .000 | .001 | .003 | .006 | .014 | .028 | .056 | .107 | .197 | .349 | .599 |
| 11 | 0 | .895 | .569 | .314 | .167 | .086 | .042 | .020 | .009 | .004 | .001 | .000 | .000 | .000 | .000 | .000 | .000 | .000 | .000 | .000 | .000 |
| | 1 | .099 | .329 | .384 | .325 | .236 | .155 | .093 | .052 | .027 | .013 | .005 | .002 | .001 | .000 | .000 | .000 | .000 | .000 | .000 | .000 |
| | 2 | .005 | .087 | .213 | .287 | .295 | .258 | .200 | .140 | .089 | .051 | .027 | .013 | .005 | .002 | .001 | .000 | .000 | .000 | .000 | .000 |
| | 3 | .000 | .014 | .071 | .152 | .221 | .258 | .257 | .225 | .177 | .126 | .081 | .046 | .023 | .010 | .004 | .001 | .000 | .000 | .000 | .000 |
| | 4 | .000 | .001 | .016 | .054 | .111 | .172 | .220 | .243 | .236 | .206 | .161 | .113 | .070 | .038 | .017 | .006 | .002 | .000 | .000 | .000 |
| | 5 | .000 | .000 | .002 | .013 | .039 | .080 | .132 | .183 | .221 | .236 | .226 | .193 | .147 | .099 | .057 | .027 | .010 | .002 | .000 | .000 |
| | 6 | .000 | .000 | .000 | .002 | .010 | .027 | .057 | .099 | .147 | .193 | .226 | .236 | .221 | .183 | .132 | .080 | .039 | .013 | .002 | .000 |
| | 7 | .000 | .000 | .000 | .000 | .002 | .006 | .017 | .038 | .070 | .113 | .161 | .206 | .236 | .243 | .220 | .172 | .111 | .054 | .016 | .001 |
| | 8 | .000 | .000 | .000 | .000 | .000 | .001 | .004 | .010 | .023 | .046 | .081 | .126 | .177 | .225 | .257 | .258 | .221 | .152 | .071 | .014 |
| | 9 | .000 | .000 | .000 | .000 | .000 | .000 | .001 | .002 | .005 | .013 | .027 | .051 | .089 | .140 | .200 | .258 | .295 | .287 | .213 | .087 |
| | 10 | .000 | .000 | .000 | .000 | .000 | .000 | .000 | .000 | .001 | .002 | .005 | .013 | .027 | .052 | .093 | .155 | .236 | .325 | .384 | .329 |
| | 11 | .000 | .000 | .000 | .000 | .000 | .000 | .000 | .000 | .000 | .000 | .000 | .001 | .004 | .009 | .020 | .042 | .086 | .167 | .314 | .569 |
| 12 | 0 | .886 | .540 | .282 | .142 | .069 | .032 | .014 | .006 | .002 | .001 | .000 | .000 | .000 | .000 | .000 | .000 | .000 | .000 | .000 | .000 |
| | 1 | .107 | .341 | .377 | .301 | .206 | .127 | .071 | .037 | .017 | .008 | .003 | .001 | .000 | .000 | .000 | .000 | .000 | .000 | .000 | .000 |
| | 2 | .006 | .099 | .230 | .292 | .283 | .232 | .168 | .109 | .064 | .034 | .016 | .007 | .002 | .001 | .000 | .000 | .000 | .000 | .000 | .000 |
| | 3 | .000 | .017 | .085 | .172 | .236 | .258 | .240 | .195 | .142 | .092 | .054 | .028 | .012 | .005 | .001 | .000 | .000 | .000 | .000 | .000 |
| | 4 | .000 | .002 | .021 | .068 | .133 | .194 | .231 | .237 | .213 | .170 | .121 | .076 | .042 | .020 | .008 | .002 | .001 | .000 | .000 | .000 |
| | 5 | .000 | .000 | .004 | .019 | .053 | .103 | .158 | .204 | .227 | .223 | .193 | .149 | .101 | .059 | .029 | .011 | .003 | .001 | .000 | .000 |
| | 6 | .000 | .000 | .000 | .004 | .016 | .040 | .079 | .128 | .177 | .212 | .226 | .212 | .177 | .128 | .079 | .040 | .016 | .004 | .000 | .000 |
| | 7 | .000 | .000 | .000 | .001 | .003 | .011 | .029 | .059 | .101 | .149 | .193 | .223 | .227 | .204 | .158 | .103 | .053 | .019 | .004 | .000 |
| | 8 | .000 | .000 | .000 | .000 | .001 | .002 | .008 | .020 | .042 | .076 | .121 | .170 | .213 | .237 | .231 | .194 | .133 | .068 | .021 | .002 |
| | 9 | .000 | .000 | .000 | .000 | .000 | .000 | .001 | .005 | .012 | .028 | .054 | .092 | .142 | .195 | .240 | .258 | .236 | .172 | .085 | .017 |
| | 10 | .000 | .000 | .000 | .000 | .000 | .000 | .000 | .001 | .002 | .007 | .016 | .034 | .064 | .109 | .168 | .232 | .283 | .292 | .230 | .099 |
| | 11 | .000 | .000 | .000 | .000 | .000 | .000 | .000 | .000 | .000 | .001 | .003 | .008 | .017 | .037 | .071 | .127 | .206 | .301 | .377 | .341 |
| | 12 | .000 | .000 | .000 | .000 | .000 | .000 | .000 | .000 | .000 | .000 | .000 | .001 | .002 | .006 | .014 | .032 | .069 | .142 | .282 | .540 |
| 15 | 0 | .860 | .463 | .206 | .087 | .035 | .013 | .005 | .002 | .000 | .000 | .000 | .000 | .000 | .000 | .000 | .000 | .000 | .000 | .000 | .000 |
| | 1 | .130 | .366 | .343 | .231 | .132 | .067 | .031 | .013 | .005 | .002 | .000 | .000 | .000 | .000 | .000 | .000 | .000 | .000 | .000 | .000 |
| | 2 | .009 | .135 | .267 | .286 | .231 | .156 | .092 | .048 | .022 | .009 | .003 | .001 | .000 | .000 | .000 | .000 | .000 | .000 | .000 | .000 |
| | 3 | .000 | .031 | .129 | .218 | .250 | .225 | .170 | .111 | .063 | .032 | .014 | .005 | .002 | .000 | .000 | .000 | .000 | .000 | .000 | .000 |
| | 4 | .000 | .005 | .043 | .116 | .188 | .225 | .219 | .179 | .127 | .078 | .042 | .019 | .007 | .002 | .001 | .000 | .000 | .000 | .000 | .000 |
| | 5 | .000 | .001 | .010 | .045 | .103 | .165 | .206 | .212 | .186 | .140 | .092 | .051 | .024 | .010 | .003 | .001 | .000 | .000 | .000 | .000 |
| | 6 | .000 | .000 | .002 | .013 | .043 | .092 | .147 | .191 | .207 | .191 | .153 | .105 | .061 | .030 | .012 | .003 | .001 | .000 | .000 | .000 |
| | 7 | .000 | .000 | .000 | .003 | .014 | .039 | .081 | .132 | .177 | .201 | .196 | .165 | .118 | .071 | .035 | .013 | .003 | .001 | .000 | .000 |
| | 8 | .000 | .000 | .000 | .001 | .003 | .013 | .035 | .071 | .118 | .165 | .196 | .201 | .177 | .132 | .081 | .039 | .014 | .003 | .000 | .000 |
| | 9 | .000 | .000 | .000 | .000 | .001 | .003 | .012 | .030 | .061 | .105 | .153 | .191 | .207 | .191 | .147 | .092 | .043 | .013 | .002 | .000 |
| | 10 | .000 | .000 | .000 | .000 | .000 | .001 | .003 | .010 | .024 | .051 | .092 | .140 | .186 | .212 | .206 | .165 | .103 | .045 | .010 | .001 |
| | 11 | .000 | .000 | .000 | .000 | .000 | .000 | .001 | .002 | .007 | .019 | .042 | .078 | .127 | .179 | .219 | .225 | .188 | .116 | .043 | .005 |
| | 12 | .000 | .000 | .000 | .000 | .000 | .000 | .000 | .000 | .002 | .005 | .014 | .032 | .063 | .111 | .170 | .225 | .250 | .218 | .129 | .031 |
| | 13 | .000 | .000 | .000 | .000 | .000 | .000 | .000 | .000 | .000 | .001 | .003 | .009 | .022 | .048 | .092 | .156 | .231 | .286 | .267 | .135 |
| | 14 | .000 | .000 | .000 | .000 | .000 | .000 | .000 | .000 | .000 | .000 | .000 | .002 | .005 | .013 | .031 | .067 | .132 | .231 | .343 | .366 |
| | 15 | .000 | .000 | .000 | .000 | .000 | .000 | .000 | .000 | .000 | .000 | .000 | .000 | .000 | .002 | .005 | .013 | .035 | .087 | .206 | .463 |

## Table 2—Binomial Distribution *(continued)*

| | | *p* | | | | | | | | | | | | | | | | | | | |
|---|---|---|---|---|---|---|---|---|---|---|---|---|---|---|---|---|---|---|---|---|---|
| *n* | *x* | .01 | .05 | .10 | .15 | .20 | .25 | .30 | .35 | .40 | .45 | .50 | .55 | .60 | .65 | .70 | .75 | .80 | .85 | .90 | .95 |
| 16 | 0 | .851 | .440 | .185 | .074 | .028 | .010 | .003 | .001 | .000 | .000 | .000 | .000 | .000 | .000 | .000 | .000 | .000 | .000 | .000 | .000 |
| | 1 | .138 | .371 | .329 | .210 | .113 | .053 | .023 | .009 | .003 | .001 | .000 | .000 | .000 | .000 | .000 | .000 | .000 | .000 | .000 | .000 |
| | 2 | .010 | .146 | .275 | .277 | .211 | .134 | .073 | .035 | .015 | .006 | .002 | .001 | .000 | .000 | .000 | .000 | .000 | .000 | .000 | .000 |
| | 3 | .000 | .036 | .142 | .229 | .246 | .208 | .146 | .089 | .047 | .022 | .009 | .003 | .001 | .000 | .000 | .000 | .000 | .000 | .000 | .000 |
| | 4 | .000 | .006 | .051 | .131 | .200 | .225 | .204 | .155 | .101 | .057 | .028 | .011 | .004 | .001 | .000 | .000 | .000 | .000 | .000 | .000 |
| | 5 | .000 | .001 | .014 | .056 | .120 | .180 | .210 | .201 | .162 | .112 | .067 | .034 | .014 | .005 | .001 | .000 | .000 | .000 | .000 | .000 |
| | 6 | .000 | .000 | .003 | .018 | .055 | .110 | .165 | .198 | .198 | .168 | .122 | .075 | .039 | .017 | .006 | .001 | .000 | .000 | .000 | .000 |
| | 7 | .000 | .000 | .000 | .005 | .020 | .052 | .101 | .152 | .189 | .197 | .175 | .132 | .084 | .044 | .019 | .006 | .001 | .000 | .000 | .000 |
| | 8 | .000 | .000 | .000 | .001 | .006 | .020 | .049 | .092 | .142 | .181 | .196 | .181 | .142 | .092 | .049 | .020 | .006 | .001 | .000 | .000 |
| | 9 | .000 | .000 | .000 | .000 | .001 | .006 | .019 | .044 | .084 | .132 | .175 | .197 | .189 | .152 | .101 | .052 | .020 | .005 | .000 | .000 |
| | 10 | .000 | .000 | .000 | .000 | .000 | .001 | .006 | .017 | .039 | .075 | .122 | .168 | .198 | .198 | .165 | .110 | .055 | .018 | .003 | .000 |
| | 11 | .000 | .000 | .000 | .000 | .000 | .000 | .001 | .005 | .014 | .034 | .067 | .112 | .162 | .201 | .210 | .180 | .120 | .056 | .014 | .001 |
| | 12 | .000 | .000 | .000 | .000 | .000 | .000 | .000 | .001 | .004 | .011 | .028 | .057 | .101 | .155 | .204 | .225 | .200 | .131 | .051 | .006 |
| | 13 | .000 | .000 | .000 | .000 | .000 | .000 | .000 | .000 | .001 | .003 | .009 | .022 | .047 | .089 | .146 | .208 | .246 | .229 | .142 | .036 |
| | 14 | .000 | .000 | .000 | .000 | .000 | .000 | .000 | .000 | .000 | .001 | .002 | .006 | .015 | .035 | .073 | .134 | .211 | .277 | .275 | .146 |
| | 15 | .000 | .000 | .000 | .000 | .000 | .000 | .000 | .000 | .000 | .000 | .000 | .001 | .003 | .009 | .023 | .053 | .113 | .210 | .329 | .371 |
| | 16 | .000 | .000 | .000 | .000 | .000 | .000 | .000 | .000 | .000 | .000 | .000 | .000 | .000 | .001 | .003 | .010 | .028 | .074 | .185 | .440 |
| 20 | 0 | .818 | .358 | .122 | .039 | .012 | .003 | .001 | .000 | .000 | .000 | .000 | .000 | .000 | .000 | .000 | .000 | .000 | .000 | .000 | .000 |
| | 1 | .165 | .377 | .270 | .137 | .058 | .021 | .007 | .002 | .000 | .000 | .000 | .000 | .000 | .000 | .000 | .000 | .000 | .000 | .000 | .000 |
| | 2 | .016 | .189 | .285 | .229 | .137 | .067 | .028 | .010 | .003 | .001 | .000 | .000 | .000 | .000 | .000 | .000 | .000 | .000 | .000 | .000 |
| | 3 | .001 | .060 | .190 | .243 | .205 | .134 | .072 | .032 | .012 | .004 | .001 | .000 | .000 | .000 | .000 | .000 | .000 | .000 | .000 | .000 |
| | 4 | .000 | .013 | .090 | .182 | .218 | .190 | .130 | .074 | .035 | .014 | .005 | .001 | .000 | .000 | .000 | .000 | .000 | .000 | .000 | .000 |
| | 5 | .000 | .002 | .032 | .103 | .175 | .202 | .179 | .127 | .075 | .036 | .015 | .005 | .001 | .000 | .000 | .000 | .000 | .000 | .000 | .000 |
| | 6 | .000 | .000 | .009 | .045 | .109 | .169 | .192 | .171 | .124 | .075 | .036 | .015 | .005 | .001 | .000 | .000 | .000 | .000 | .000 | .000 |
| | 7 | .000 | .000 | .002 | .016 | .055 | .112 | .164 | .184 | .166 | .122 | .074 | .037 | .015 | .005 | .001 | .000 | .000 | .000 | .000 | .000 |
| | 8 | .000 | .000 | .000 | .005 | .022 | .061 | .114 | .161 | .180 | .162 | .120 | .073 | .035 | .014 | .004 | .001 | .000 | .000 | .000 | .000 |
| | 9 | .000 | .000 | .000 | .001 | .007 | .027 | .065 | .116 | .160 | .177 | .160 | .119 | .071 | .034 | .012 | .003 | .000 | .000 | .000 | .000 |
| | 10 | .000 | .000 | .000 | .000 | .002 | .010 | .031 | .069 | .117 | .159 | .176 | .159 | .117 | .069 | .031 | .010 | .002 | .000 | .000 | .000 |
| | 11 | .000 | .000 | .000 | .000 | .000 | .003 | .012 | .034 | .071 | .119 | .160 | .177 | .160 | .116 | .065 | .027 | .007 | .001 | .000 | .000 |
| | 12 | .000 | .000 | .000 | .000 | .000 | .001 | .004 | .014 | .035 | .073 | .120 | .162 | .180 | .161 | .114 | .061 | .022 | .005 | .000 | .000 |
| | 13 | .000 | .000 | .000 | .000 | .000 | .000 | .001 | .005 | .015 | .037 | .074 | .122 | .166 | .184 | .164 | .112 | .055 | .016 | .002 | .000 |
| | 14 | .000 | .000 | .000 | .000 | .000 | .000 | .000 | .001 | .005 | .015 | .037 | .075 | .124 | .171 | .192 | .169 | .109 | .045 | .009 | .000 |
| | 15 | .000 | .000 | .000 | .000 | .000 | .000 | .000 | .000 | .001 | .005 | .015 | .036 | .075 | .127 | .179 | .202 | .175 | .103 | .032 | .002 |
| | 16 | .000 | .000 | .000 | .000 | .000 | .000 | .000 | .000 | .000 | .001 | .005 | .014 | .035 | .074 | .130 | .190 | .218 | .182 | .090 | .013 |
| | 17 | .000 | .000 | .000 | .000 | .000 | .000 | .000 | .000 | .000 | .000 | .001 | .004 | .012 | .032 | .072 | .134 | .205 | .243 | .190 | .060 |
| | 18 | .000 | .000 | .000 | .000 | .000 | .000 | .000 | .000 | .000 | .000 | .000 | .001 | .003 | .010 | .028 | .067 | .137 | .229 | .285 | .189 |
| | 19 | .000 | .000 | .000 | .000 | .000 | .000 | .000 | .000 | .000 | .000 | .000 | .000 | .000 | .002 | .007 | .021 | .058 | .137 | .270 | .377 |
| | 20 | .000 | .000 | .000 | .000 | .000 | .000 | .000 | .000 | .000 | .000 | .000 | .000 | .000 | .000 | .001 | .003 | .012 | .039 | .122 | .358 |

# Table 3—Poisson Distribution

| x | μ 0.1 | 0.2 | 0.3 | 0.4 | 0.5 | 0.6 | 0.7 | 0.8 | 0.9 | 1.0 |
|---|---|---|---|---|---|---|---|---|---|---|
| 0 | .9048 | .8187 | .7408 | .6703 | .6065 | .5488 | .4966 | .4493 | .4066 | .3679 |
| 1 | .0905 | .1637 | .2222 | .2681 | .3033 | .3293 | .3476 | .3595 | .3659 | .3679 |
| 2 | .0045 | .0164 | .0333 | .0536 | .0758 | .0988 | .1217 | .1438 | .1647 | .1839 |
| 3 | .0002 | .0011 | .0033 | .0072 | .0126 | .0198 | .0284 | .0383 | .0494 | .0613 |
| 4 | .0000 | .0001 | .0003 | .0007 | .0016 | .0030 | .0050 | .0077 | .0111 | .0153 |
| 5 | .0000 | .0000 | .0000 | .0001 | .0002 | .0004 | .0007 | .0012 | .0020 | .0031 |
| 6 | .0000 | .0000 | .0000 | .0000 | .0000 | .0000 | .0001 | .0002 | .0003 | .0005 |
| 7 | .0000 | .0000 | .0000 | .0000 | .0000 | .0000 | .0000 | .0000 | .0000 | .0001 |

| x | μ 1.1 | 1.2 | 1.3 | 1.4 | 1.5 | 1.6 | 1.7 | 1.8 | 1.9 | 2.0 |
|---|---|---|---|---|---|---|---|---|---|---|
| 0 | .3329 | .3012 | .2725 | .2466 | .2231 | .2019 | .1827 | .1653 | .1496 | .1353 |
| 1 | .3662 | .3614 | .3543 | .3452 | .3347 | .3230 | .3106 | .2975 | .2842 | .2707 |
| 2 | .2014 | .2169 | .2303 | .2417 | .2510 | .2584 | .2640 | .2678 | .2700 | .2707 |
| 3 | .0738 | .0867 | .0998 | .1128 | .1255 | .1378 | .1496 | .1607 | .1710 | .1804 |
| 4 | .0203 | .0260 | .0324 | .0395 | .0471 | .0551 | .0636 | .0723 | .0812 | .0902 |
| 5 | .0045 | .0062 | .0084 | .0111 | .0141 | .0176 | .0216 | .0260 | .0309 | .0361 |
| 6 | .0008 | .0012 | .0018 | .0026 | .0035 | .0047 | .0061 | .0078 | .0098 | .0120 |
| 7 | .0001 | .0002 | .0003 | .0005 | .0008 | .0011 | .0015 | .0020 | .0027 | .0034 |
| 8 | .0000 | .0000 | .0001 | .0001 | .0001 | .0002 | .0003 | .0005 | .0006 | .0009 |
| 9 | .0000 | .0000 | .0000 | .0000 | .0000 | .0000 | .0001 | .0001 | .0001 | .0002 |

| x | μ 2.1 | 2.2 | 2.3 | 2.4 | 2.5 | 2.6 | 2.7 | 2.8 | 2.9 | 3.0 |
|---|---|---|---|---|---|---|---|---|---|---|
| 0 | .1225 | .1108 | .1003 | .0907 | .0821 | .0743 | .0672 | .0608 | .0550 | .0498 |
| 1 | .2572 | .2438 | .2306 | .2177 | .2052 | .1931 | .1815 | .1703 | .1596 | .1494 |
| 2 | .2700 | .2681 | .2652 | .2613 | .2565 | .2510 | .2450 | .2384 | .2314 | .2240 |
| 3 | .1890 | .1966 | .2033 | .2090 | .2138 | .2176 | .2205 | .2225 | .2237 | .2240 |
| 4 | .0992 | .1082 | .1169 | .1254 | .1336 | .1414 | .1488 | .1557 | .1622 | .1680 |
| 5 | .0417 | .0476 | .0538 | .0602 | .0668 | .0735 | .0804 | .0872 | .0940 | .1008 |
| 6 | .0146 | .0174 | .0206 | .0241 | .0278 | .0319 | .0362 | .0407 | .0455 | .0504 |
| 7 | .0044 | .0055 | .0068 | .0083 | .0099 | .0118 | .0139 | .0163 | .0188 | .0216 |
| 8 | .0011 | .0015 | .0019 | .0025 | .0031 | .0038 | .0047 | .0057 | .0068 | .0081 |
| 9 | .0003 | .0004 | .0005 | .0007 | .0009 | .0011 | .0014 | .0018 | .0022 | .0027 |
| 10 | .0001 | .0001 | .0001 | .0002 | .0002 | .0003 | .0004 | .0005 | .0006 | .0008 |
| 11 | .0000 | .0000 | .0000 | .0000 | .0000 | .0001 | .0001 | .0001 | .0002 | .0002 |
| 12 | .0000 | .0000 | .0000 | .0000 | .0000 | .0000 | .0000 | .0000 | .0000 | .0001 |

| x | μ 3.1 | 3.2 | 3.3 | 3.4 | 3.5 | 3.6 | 3.7 | 3.8 | 3.9 | 4.0 |
|---|---|---|---|---|---|---|---|---|---|---|
| 0 | .0450 | .0408 | .0369 | .0334 | .0302 | .0273 | .0247 | .0224 | .0202 | .0183 |
| 1 | .1397 | .1304 | .1217 | .1135 | .1057 | .0984 | .0915 | .0850 | .0789 | .0733 |
| 2 | .2165 | .2087 | .2008 | .1929 | .1850 | .1771 | .1692 | .1615 | .1539 | .1465 |
| 3 | .2237 | .2226 | .2209 | .2186 | .2158 | .2125 | .2087 | .2046 | .2001 | .1954 |
| 4 | .1734 | .1781 | .1823 | .1858 | .1888 | .1912 | .1931 | .1944 | .1951 | .1954 |
| 5 | .1075 | .1140 | .1203 | .1264 | .1322 | .1377 | .1429 | .1477 | .1522 | .1563 |
| 6 | .0555 | .0608 | .0662 | .0716 | .0771 | .0826 | .0881 | .0936 | .0989 | .1042 |
| 7 | .0246 | .0278 | .0312 | .0348 | .0385 | .0425 | .0466 | .0508 | .0551 | .0595 |
| 8 | .0095 | .0111 | .0129 | .0148 | .0169 | .0191 | .0215 | .0241 | .0269 | .0298 |
| 9 | .0033 | .0040 | .0047 | .0056 | .0066 | .0076 | .0089 | .0102 | .0116 | .0132 |
| 10 | .0010 | .0013 | .0016 | .0019 | .0023 | .0028 | .0033 | .0039 | .0045 | .0053 |
| 11 | .0003 | .0004 | .0005 | .0006 | .0007 | .0009 | .0011 | .0013 | .0016 | .0019 |
| 12 | .0001 | .0001 | .0001 | .0002 | .0002 | .0003 | .0003 | .0004 | .0005 | .0006 |
| 13 | .0000 | .0000 | .0000 | .0000 | .0001 | .0001 | .0001 | .0001 | .0002 | .0002 |
| 14 | .0000 | .0000 | .0000 | .0000 | .0000 | .0000 | .0000 | .0000 | .0000 | .0001 |

W. H. Beyer, *Handbook of Tables for Probability and Statistics,* 2e, CRC Press, Boca Raton, Florida, 1986.

# Table 3—Poisson Distribution *(continued)*

| | $\mu$ | | | | | | | | | |
|---|---|---|---|---|---|---|---|---|---|---|
| $x$ | 4.1 | 4.2 | 4.3 | 4.4 | 4.5 | 4.6 | 4.7 | 4.8 | 4.9 | 5.0 |
| 0 | .0166 | .0150 | .0136 | .0123 | .0111 | .0101 | .0091 | .0082 | .0074 | .0067 |
| 1 | .0679 | .0630 | .0583 | .0540 | .0500 | .0462 | .0427 | .0395 | .0365 | .0337 |
| 2 | .1393 | .1323 | .1254 | .1188 | .1125 | .1063 | .1005 | .0948 | .0894 | .0842 |
| 3 | .1904 | .1852 | .1798 | .1743 | .1687 | .1631 | .1574 | .1517 | .1460 | .1404 |
| 4 | .1951 | .1944 | .1933 | .1917 | .1898 | .1875 | .1849 | .1820 | .1789 | .1755 |
| 5 | .1600 | .1633 | .1662 | .1687 | .1708 | .1725 | .1738 | .1747 | .1753 | .1755 |
| 6 | .1093 | .1143 | .1191 | .1237 | .1281 | .1323 | .1362 | .1398 | .1432 | .1462 |
| 7 | .0640 | .0686 | .0732 | .0778 | .0824 | .0869 | .0914 | .0959 | .1002 | .1044 |
| 8 | .0328 | .0360 | .0393 | .0428 | .0463 | .0500 | .0537 | .0575 | .0614 | .0653 |
| 9 | .0150 | .0168 | .0188 | .0209 | .0232 | .0255 | .0280 | .0307 | .0334 | .0363 |
| 10 | .0061 | .0071 | .0081 | .0092 | .0104 | .0118 | .0132 | .0147 | .0164 | .0181 |
| 11 | .0023 | .0027 | .0032 | .0037 | .0043 | .0049 | .0056 | .0064 | .0073 | .0082 |
| 12 | .0008 | .0009 | .0011 | .0014 | .0016 | .0019 | .0022 | .0026 | .0030 | .0034 |
| 13 | .0002 | .0003 | .0004 | .0005 | .0006 | .0007 | .0008 | .0009 | .0011 | .0013 |
| 14 | .0001 | .0001 | .0001 | .0001 | .0002 | .0002 | .0003 | .0003 | .0004 | .0005 |
| 15 | .0000 | .0000 | .0000 | .0000 | .0001 | .0001 | .0001 | .0001 | .0001 | .0002 |

| | $\mu$ | | | | | | | | | |
|---|---|---|---|---|---|---|---|---|---|---|
| $x$ | 5.1 | 5.2 | 5.3 | 5.4 | 5.5 | 5.6 | 5.7 | 5.8 | 5.9 | 6.0 |
| 0 | .0061 | .0055 | .0050 | .0045 | .0041 | .0037 | .0033 | .0030 | .0027 | .0025 |
| 1 | .0311 | .0287 | .0265 | .0244 | .0225 | .0207 | .0191 | .0176 | .0162 | .0149 |
| 2 | .0793 | .0746 | .0701 | .0659 | .0618 | .0580 | .0544 | .0509 | .0477 | .0446 |
| 3 | .1348 | .1293 | .1239 | .1185 | .1133 | .1082 | .1033 | .0985 | .0938 | .0892 |
| 4 | .1719 | .1681 | .1641 | .1600 | .1558 | .1515 | .1472 | .1428 | .1383 | .1339 |
| 5 | .1753 | .1748 | .1740 | .1728 | .1714 | .1697 | .1678 | .1656 | .1632 | .1606 |
| 6 | .1490 | .1515 | .1537 | .1555 | .1571 | .1584 | .1594 | .1601 | .1605 | .1606 |
| 7 | .1086 | .1125 | .1163 | .1200 | .1234 | .1267 | .1298 | .1326 | .1353 | .1377 |
| 8 | .0692 | .0731 | .0771 | .0810 | .0849 | .0887 | .0925 | .0962 | .0998 | .1033 |
| 9 | .0392 | .0423 | .0454 | .0486 | .0519 | .0552 | .0586 | .0620 | .0654 | .0688 |
| 10 | .0200 | .0220 | .0241 | .0262 | .0285 | .0309 | .0334 | .0359 | .0386 | .0413 |
| 11 | .0093 | .0104 | .0116 | .0129 | .0143 | .0157 | .0173 | .0190 | .0207 | .0225 |
| 12 | .0039 | .0045 | .0051 | .0058 | .0065 | .0073 | .0082 | .0092 | .0102 | .0113 |
| 13 | .0015 | .0018 | .0021 | .0024 | .0028 | .0032 | .0036 | .0041 | .0046 | .0052 |
| 14 | .0006 | .0007 | .0008 | .0009 | .0011 | .0013 | .0015 | .0017 | .0019 | .0022 |
| 15 | .0002 | .0002 | .0003 | .0003 | .0004 | .0005 | .0006 | .0007 | .0008 | .0009 |
| 16 | .0001 | .0001 | .0001 | .0001 | .0001 | .0002 | .0002 | .0002 | .0003 | .0003 |
| 17 | .0000 | .0000 | .0000 | .0000 | .0000 | .0000 | .0001 | .0001 | .0001 | .0001 |

## Table 3—Poisson Distribution *(continued)*

| x | μ 6.1 | 6.2 | 6.3 | 6.4 | 6.5 | 6.6 | 6.7 | 6.8 | 6.9 | 7.0 |
|---|---|---|---|---|---|---|---|---|---|---|
| 0 | .0022 | .0020 | .0018 | .0017 | .0015 | .0014 | .0012 | .0011 | .0010 | .0009 |
| 1 | .0137 | .0126 | .0116 | .0106 | .0098 | .0090 | .0082 | .0076 | .0070 | .0064 |
| 2 | .0417 | .0390 | .0364 | .0340 | .0318 | .0296 | .0276 | .0258 | .0240 | .0223 |
| 3 | .0848 | .0806 | .0765 | .0726 | .0688 | .0652 | .0617 | .0584 | .0552 | .0521 |
| 4 | .1294 | .1249 | .1205 | .1162 | .1118 | .1076 | .1034 | .0992 | .0952 | .0912 |
| 5 | .1579 | .1549 | .1519 | .1487 | .1454 | .1420 | .1385 | .1349 | .1314 | .1277 |
| 6 | .1605 | .1601 | .1595 | .1586 | .1575 | .1562 | .1546 | .1529 | .1511 | .1490 |
| 7 | .1399 | .1418 | .1435 | .1450 | .1462 | .1472 | .1480 | .1486 | .1489 | .1490 |
| 8 | .1066 | .1099 | .1130 | .1160 | .1188 | .1215 | .1240 | .1263 | .1284 | .1304 |
| 9 | .0723 | .0757 | .0791 | .0825 | .0858 | .0891 | .0923 | .0954 | .0985 | .1014 |
| 10 | .0441 | .0469 | .0498 | .0528 | .0558 | .0588 | .0618 | .0649 | .0679 | .0710 |
| 11 | .0245 | .0265 | .0285 | .0307 | .0330 | .0353 | .0377 | .0401 | .0426 | .0452 |
| 12 | .0124 | .0137 | .0150 | .0164 | .0179 | .0194 | .0210 | .0227 | .0245 | .0264 |
| 13 | .0058 | .0065 | .0073 | .0081 | .0089 | .0098 | .0108 | .0119 | .0130 | .0142 |
| 14 | .0025 | .0029 | .0033 | .0037 | .0041 | .0046 | .0052 | .0058 | .0064 | .0071 |
| 15 | .0010 | .0012 | .0014 | .0016 | .0018 | .0020 | .0023 | .0026 | .0029 | .0033 |
| 16 | .0004 | .0005 | .0005 | .0006 | .0007 | .0008 | .0010 | .0011 | .0013 | .0014 |
| 17 | .0001 | .0002 | .0002 | .0002 | .0003 | .0003 | .0004 | .0004 | .0005 | .0006 |
| 18 | .0000 | .0001 | .0001 | .0001 | .0001 | .0001 | .0001 | .0002 | .0002 | .0002 |
| 19 | .0000 | .0000 | .0000 | .0000 | .0000 | .0000 | .0000 | .0001 | .0001 | .0001 |

| x | μ 7.1 | 7.2 | 7.3 | 7.4 | 7.5 | 7.6 | 7.7 | 7.8 | 7.9 | 8.0 |
|---|---|---|---|---|---|---|---|---|---|---|
| 0 | .0008 | .0007 | .0007 | .0006 | .0006 | .0005 | .0005 | .0004 | .0004 | .0003 |
| 1 | .0059 | .0054 | .0049 | .0045 | .0041 | .0038 | .0035 | .0032 | .0029 | .0027 |
| 2 | .0208 | .0194 | .0180 | .0167 | .0156 | .0145 | .0134 | .0125 | .0116 | .0107 |
| 3 | .0492 | .0464 | .0438 | .0413 | .0389 | .0366 | .0345 | .0324 | .0305 | .0286 |
| 4 | .0874 | .0836 | .0799 | .0764 | .0729 | .0696 | .0663 | .0632 | .0602 | .0573 |
| 5 | .1241 | .1204 | .1167 | .1130 | .1094 | .1057 | .1021 | .0986 | .0951 | .0916 |
| 6 | .1468 | .1445 | .1420 | .1394 | .1367 | .1339 | .1311 | .1282 | .1252 | .1221 |
| 7 | .1489 | .1486 | .1481 | .1474 | .1465 | .1454 | .1442 | .1428 | .1413 | .1396 |
| 8 | .1321 | .1337 | .1351 | .1363 | .1373 | .1382 | .1388 | .1392 | .1395 | .1396 |
| 9 | .1042 | .1070 | .1096 | .1121 | .1144 | .1167 | .1187 | .1207 | .1224 | .1241 |
| 10 | .0740 | .0770 | .0800 | .0829 | .0858 | .0887 | .0914 | .0941 | .0967 | .0993 |
| 11 | .0478 | .0504 | .0531 | .0558 | .0585 | .0613 | .0640 | .0667 | .0695 | .0722 |
| 12 | .0283 | .0303 | .0323 | .0344 | .0366 | .0388 | .0411 | .0434 | .0457 | .0481 |
| 13 | .0154 | .0168 | .0181 | .0196 | .0211 | .0227 | .0243 | .0260 | .0278 | .0296 |
| 14 | .0078 | .0086 | .0095 | .0104 | .0113 | .0123 | .0134 | .0145 | .0157 | .0169 |
| 15 | .0037 | .0041 | .0046 | .0051 | .0057 | .0062 | .0069 | .0075 | .0083 | .0090 |
| 16 | .0016 | .0019 | .0021 | .0024 | .0026 | .0030 | .0033 | .0037 | .0041 | .0045 |
| 17 | .0007 | .0008 | .0009 | .0010 | .0012 | .0013 | .0015 | .0017 | .0019 | .0021 |
| 18 | .0003 | .0003 | .0004 | .0004 | .0005 | .0006 | .0006 | .0007 | .0008 | .0009 |
| 19 | .0001 | .0001 | .0001 | .0002 | .0002 | .0002 | .0003 | .0003 | .0003 | .0004 |
| 20 | .0000 | .0000 | .0001 | .0001 | .0001 | .0001 | .0001 | .0001 | .0001 | .0002 |
| 21 | .0000 | .0000 | .0000 | .0000 | .0000 | .0000 | .0000 | .0000 | .0001 | .0001 |

# Table 3—Poisson Distribution *(continued)*

| | $\mu$ | | | | | | | | | |
|---|---|---|---|---|---|---|---|---|---|---|
| $x$ | 8.1 | 8.2 | 8.3 | 8.4 | 8.5 | 8.6 | 8.7 | 8.8 | 8.9 | 9.0 |
| 0 | .0003 | .0003 | .0002 | .0002 | .0002 | .0002 | .0002 | .0002 | .0001 | .0001 |
| 1 | .0025 | .0023 | .0021 | .0019 | .0017 | .0016 | .0014 | .0013 | .0012 | .0011 |
| 2 | .0100 | .0092 | .0086 | .0079 | .0074 | .0068 | .0063 | .0058 | .0054 | .0050 |
| 3 | .0269 | .0252 | .0237 | .0222 | .0208 | .0195 | .0183 | .0171 | .0160 | .0150 |
| 4 | .0544 | .0517 | .0491 | .0466 | .0443 | .0420 | .0398 | .0377 | .0357 | .0337 |
| 5 | .0882 | .0849 | .0816 | .0784 | .0752 | .0722 | .0692 | .0663 | .0635 | .0607 |
| 6 | .1191 | .1160 | .1128 | .1097 | .1066 | .1034 | .1003 | .0972 | .0941 | .0911 |
| 7 | .1378 | .1358 | .1338 | .1317 | .1294 | .1271 | .1247 | .1222 | .1197 | .1171 |
| 8 | .1395 | .1392 | .1388 | .1382 | .1375 | .1366 | .1356 | .1344 | .1332 | .1318 |
| 9 | .1256 | .1269 | .1280 | .1290 | .1299 | .1306 | .1311 | .1315 | .1317 | .1318 |
| 10 | .1017 | .1040 | .1063 | .1084 | .1104 | .1123 | .1140 | .1157 | .1172 | .1186 |
| 11 | .0749 | .0776 | .0802 | .0828 | .0853 | .0878 | .0902 | .0925 | .0948 | .0970 |
| 12 | .0505 | .0530 | .0555 | .0579 | .0604 | .0629 | .0654 | .0679 | .0703 | .0728 |
| 13 | .0315 | .0334 | .0354 | .0374 | .0395 | .0416 | .0438 | .0459 | .0481 | .0504 |
| 14 | .0182 | .0196 | .0210 | .0225 | .0240 | .0256 | .0272 | .0289 | .0306 | .0324 |
| 15 | .0098 | .0107 | .0116 | .0126 | .0136 | .0147 | .0158 | .0169 | .0182 | .0194 |
| 16 | .0050 | .0055 | .0060 | .0066 | .0072 | .0079 | .0086 | .0093 | .0101 | .0109 |
| 17 | .0024 | .0026 | .0029 | .0033 | .0036 | .0040 | .0044 | .0048 | .0053 | .0058 |
| 18 | .0011 | .0012 | .0014 | .0015 | .0017 | .0019 | .0021 | .0024 | .0026 | .0029 |
| 19 | .0005 | .0005 | .0006 | .0007 | .0008 | .0009 | .0010 | .0011 | .0012 | .0014 |
| 20 | .0002 | .0002 | .0002 | .0003 | .0003 | .0004 | .0004 | .0005 | .0005 | .0006 |
| 21 | .0001 | .0001 | .0001 | .0001 | .0001 | .0002 | .0002 | .0002 | .0002 | .0003 |
| 22 | .0000 | .0000 | .0000 | .0000 | .0001 | .0001 | .0001 | .0001 | .0001 | .0001 |

| | $\mu$ | | | | | | | | | |
|---|---|---|---|---|---|---|---|---|---|---|
| $x$ | 9.1 | 9.2 | 9.3 | 9.4 | 9.5 | 9.6 | 9.7 | 9.8 | 9.9 | 10.0 |
| 0 | .0001 | .0001 | .0001 | .0001 | .0001 | .0001 | .0001 | .0001 | .0001 | .0000 |
| 1 | .0010 | .0009 | .0009 | .0008 | .0007 | .0007 | .0006 | .0005 | .0005 | .0005 |
| 2 | .0046 | .0043 | .0040 | .0037 | .0034 | .0031 | .0029 | .0027 | .0025 | .0023 |
| 3 | .0140 | .0131 | .0123 | .0115 | .0107 | .0100 | .0093 | .0087 | .0081 | .0076 |
| 4 | .0319 | .0302 | .0285 | .0269 | .0254 | .0240 | .0226 | .0213 | .0201 | .0189 |
| 5 | .0581 | .0555 | .0530 | .0506 | .0483 | .0460 | .0439 | .0418 | .0398 | .0378 |
| 6 | .0881 | .0851 | .0822 | .0793 | .0764 | .0736 | .0709 | .0682 | .0656 | .0631 |
| 7 | .1145 | .1118 | .1091 | .1064 | .1037 | .1010 | .0982 | .0955 | .0928 | .0901 |
| 8 | .1302 | .1286 | .1269 | .1251 | .1232 | .1212 | .1191 | .1170 | .1148 | .1126 |
| 9 | .1317 | .1315 | .1311 | .1306 | .1300 | .1293 | .1284 | .1274 | .1263 | .1251 |
| 10 | .1198 | .1210 | .1219 | .1228 | .1235 | .1241 | .1245 | .1249 | .1250 | .1251 |
| 11 | .0991 | .1012 | .1031 | .1049 | .1067 | .1083 | .1098 | .1112 | .1125 | .1137 |
| 12 | .0752 | .0776 | .0799 | .0822 | .0844 | .0866 | .0888 | .0908 | .0928 | .0948 |
| 13 | .0526 | .0549 | .0572 | .0594 | .0617 | .0640 | .0662 | .0685 | .0707 | .0729 |
| 14 | .0342 | .0361 | .0380 | .0399 | .0419 | .0439 | .0459 | .0479 | .0500 | .0521 |
| 15 | .0208 | .0221 | .0235 | .0250 | .0265 | .0281 | .0297 | .0313 | .0330 | .0347 |
| 16 | .0118 | .0127 | .0137 | .0147 | .0157 | .0168 | .0180 | .0192 | .0204 | .0217 |
| 17 | .0063 | .0069 | .0075 | .0081 | .0088 | .0095 | .0103 | .0111 | .0119 | .0128 |
| 18 | .0032 | .0035 | .0039 | .0042 | .0046 | .0051 | .0055 | .0060 | .0065 | .0071 |
| 19 | .0015 | .0017 | .0019 | .0021 | .0023 | .0026 | .0028 | .0031 | .0034 | .0037 |
| 20 | .0007 | .0008 | .0009 | .0010 | .0011 | .0012 | .0014 | .0015 | .0017 | .0019 |
| 21 | .0003 | .0003 | .0004 | .0004 | .0005 | .0006 | .0006 | .0007 | .0008 | .0009 |
| 22 | .0001 | .0001 | .0002 | .0002 | .0002 | .0002 | .0003 | .0003 | .0004 | .0004 |
| 23 | .0000 | .0001 | .0001 | .0001 | .0001 | .0001 | .0001 | .0001 | .0002 | .0002 |
| 24 | .0000 | .0000 | .0000 | .0000 | .0000 | .0000 | .0000 | .0001 | .0001 | .0001 |

## Table 3—Poisson Distribution *(continued)*

| | $\mu$ | | | | | | | | | |
|---|---|---|---|---|---|---|---|---|---|---|
| $x$ | 11 | 12 | 13 | 14 | 15 | 16 | 17 | 18 | 19 | 20 |
| 0 | .0000 | .0000 | .0000 | .0000 | .0000 | .0000 | .0000 | .0000 | .0000 | .0000 |
| 1 | .0002 | .0001 | .0000 | .0000 | .0000 | .0000 | .0000 | .0000 | .0000 | .0000 |
| 2 | .0010 | .0004 | .0002 | .0001 | .0000 | .0000 | .0000 | .0000 | .0000 | .0000 |
| 3 | .0037 | .0018 | .0008 | .0004 | .0002 | .0001 | .0000 | .0000 | .0000 | .0000 |
| 4 | .0102 | .0053 | .0027 | .0013 | .0006 | .0003 | .0001 | .0001 | .0000 | .0000 |
| 5 | .0224 | .0127 | .0070 | .0037 | .0019 | .0010 | .0005 | .0002 | .0001 | .0001 |
| 6 | .0411 | .0255 | .0152 | .0087 | .0048 | .0026 | .0014 | .0007 | .0004 | .0002 |
| 7 | .0646 | .0437 | .0281 | .0174 | .0104 | .0060 | .0034 | .0018 | .0010 | .0005 |
| 8 | .0888 | .0655 | .0457 | .0304 | .0194 | .0120 | .0072 | .0042 | .0024 | .0013 |
| 9 | .1085 | .0874 | .0661 | .0473 | .0324 | .0213 | .0135 | .0083 | .0050 | .0029 |
| 10 | .1194 | .1048 | .0859 | .0663 | .0486 | .0341 | .0230 | .0150 | .0095 | .0058 |
| 11 | .1194 | .1144 | .1015 | .0844 | .0663 | .0496 | .0355 | .0245 | .0164 | .0106 |
| 12 | .1094 | .1144 | .1099 | .0984 | .0829 | .0661 | .0504 | .0368 | .0259 | .0176 |
| 13 | .0926 | .1056 | .1099 | .1060 | .0956 | .0814 | .0658 | .0509 | .0378 | .0271 |
| 14 | .0728 | .0905 | .1021 | .1060 | .1024 | .0930 | .0800 | .0655 | .0514 | .0387 |
| 15 | .0534 | .0724 | .0885 | .0989 | .1024 | .0992 | .0906 | .0786 | .0650 | .0516 |
| 16 | .0367 | .0543 | .0719 | .0866 | .0960 | .0992 | .0963 | .0884 | .0772 | .0646 |
| 17 | .0237 | .0383 | .0550 | .0713 | .0847 | .0934 | .0963 | .0936 | .0863 | .0760 |
| 18 | .0145 | .0256 | .0397 | .0554 | .0706 | .0830 | .0909 | .0936 | .0911 | .0844 |
| 19 | .0084 | .0161 | .0272 | .0409 | .0557 | .0699 | .0814 | .0887 | .0911 | .0888 |
| 20 | .0046 | .0097 | .0177 | .0286 | .0418 | .0559 | .0692 | .0798 | .0866 | .0888 |

| | $\mu$ | | | | | | | | | |
|---|---|---|---|---|---|---|---|---|---|---|
| $x$ | 11 | 12 | 13 | 14 | 15 | 16 | 17 | 18 | 19 | 20 |
| 21 | .0024 | .0055 | .0109 | .0191 | .0299 | .0426 | .0560 | .0684 | .0783 | .0846 |
| 22 | .0012 | .0030 | .0065 | .0121 | .0204 | .0310 | .0433 | .0560 | .0676 | .0769 |
| 23 | .0006 | .0016 | .0037 | .0074 | .0133 | .0216 | .0320 | .0438 | .0559 | .0669 |
| 24 | .0003 | .0008 | .0020 | .0043 | .0083 | .0144 | .0226 | .0328 | .0442 | .0557 |
| 25 | .0001 | .0004 | .0010 | .0024 | .0050 | .0092 | .0154 | .0237 | .0336 | .0446 |
| 26 | .0000 | .0002 | .0005 | .0013 | .0029 | .0057 | .0101 | .0164 | .0246 | .0343 |
| 27 | .0000 | .0001 | .0002 | .0007 | .0016 | .0034 | .0063 | .0109 | .0173 | .0254 |
| 28 | .0000 | .0000 | .0001 | .0003 | .0009 | .0019 | .0038 | .0070 | .0117 | .0181 |
| 29 | .0000 | .0000 | .0001 | .0002 | .0004 | .0011 | .0023 | .0044 | .0077 | .0125 |
| 30 | .0000 | .0000 | .0000 | .0001 | .0002 | .0006 | .0013 | .0026 | .0049 | .0083 |
| 31 | .0000 | .0000 | .0000 | .0000 | .0001 | .0003 | .0007 | .0015 | .0030 | .0054 |
| 32 | .0000 | .0000 | .0000 | .0000 | .0001 | .0001 | .0004 | .0009 | .0018 | .0034 |
| 33 | .0000 | .0000 | .0000 | .0000 | .0000 | .0001 | .0002 | .0005 | .0010 | .0020 |
| 34 | .0000 | .0000 | .0000 | .0000 | .0000 | .0000 | .0001 | .0002 | .0006 | .0012 |
| 35 | .0000 | .0000 | .0000 | .0000 | .0000 | .0000 | .0000 | .0001 | .0003 | .0007 |
| 36 | .0000 | .0000 | .0000 | .0000 | .0000 | .0000 | .0000 | .0001 | .0002 | .0004 |
| 37 | .0000 | .0000 | .0000 | .0000 | .0000 | .0000 | .0000 | .0000 | .0001 | .0002 |
| 38 | .0000 | .0000 | .0000 | .0000 | .0000 | .0000 | .0000 | .0000 | .0000 | .0001 |
| 39 | .0000 | .0000 | .0000 | .0000 | .0000 | .0000 | .0000 | .0000 | .0000 | .0001 |

# Table 4—Standard Normal Distribution

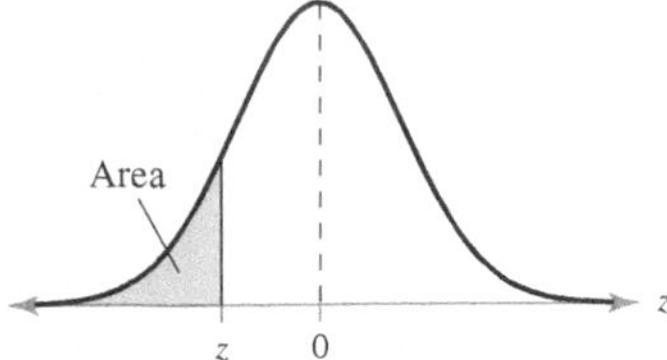


| z | .09 | .08 | .07 | .06 | .05 | .04 | .03 | .02 | .01 | .00 |
|---|---|---|---|---|---|---|---|---|---|---|
| −3.4 | .0002 | .0003 | .0003 | .0003 | .0003 | .0003 | .0003 | .0003 | .0003 | .0003 |
| −3.3 | .0003 | .0004 | .0004 | .0004 | .0004 | .0004 | .0004 | .0005 | .0005 | .0005 |
| −3.2 | .0005 | .0005 | .0005 | .0006 | .0006 | .0006 | .0006 | .0006 | .0007 | .0007 |
| −3.1 | .0007 | .0007 | .0008 | .0008 | .0008 | .0008 | .0009 | .0009 | .0009 | .0010 |
| −3.0 | .0010 | .0010 | .0011 | .0011 | .0011 | .0012 | .0012 | .0013 | .0013 | .0013 |
| −2.9 | .0014 | .0014 | .0015 | .0015 | .0016 | .0016 | .0017 | .0018 | .0018 | .0019 |
| −2.8 | .0019 | .0020 | .0021 | .0021 | .0022 | .0023 | .0023 | .0024 | .0025 | .0026 |
| −2.7 | .0026 | .0027 | .0028 | .0029 | .0030 | .0031 | .0032 | .0033 | .0034 | .0035 |
| −2.6 | .0036 | .0037 | .0038 | .0039 | .0040 | .0041 | .0043 | .0044 | .0045 | .0047 |
| −2.5 | .0048 | .0049 | .0051 | .0052 | .0054 | .0055 | .0057 | .0059 | .0060 | .0062 |
| −2.4 | .0064 | .0066 | .0068 | .0069 | .0071 | .0073 | .0075 | .0078 | .0080 | .0082 |
| −2.3 | .0084 | .0087 | .0089 | .0091 | .0094 | .0096 | .0099 | .0102 | .0104 | .0107 |
| −2.2 | .0110 | .0113 | .0116 | .0119 | .0122 | .0125 | .0129 | .0132 | .0136 | .0139 |
| −2.1 | .0143 | .0146 | .0150 | .0154 | .0158 | .0162 | .0166 | .0170 | .0174 | .0179 |
| −2.0 | .0183 | .0188 | .0192 | .0197 | .0202 | .0207 | .0212 | .0217 | .0222 | .0228 |
| −1.9 | .0233 | .0239 | .0244 | .0250 | .0256 | .0262 | .0268 | .0274 | .0281 | .0287 |
| −1.8 | .0294 | .0301 | .0307 | .0314 | .0322 | .0329 | .0336 | .0344 | .0351 | .0359 |
| −1.7 | .0367 | .0375 | .0384 | .0392 | .0401 | .0409 | .0418 | .0427 | .0436 | .0446 |
| −1.6 | .0455 | .0465 | .0475 | .0485 | .0495 | .0505 | .0516 | .0526 | .0537 | .0548 |
| −1.5 | .0559 | .0571 | .0582 | .0594 | .0606 | .0618 | .0630 | .0643 | .0655 | .0668 |
| −1.4 | .0681 | .0694 | .0708 | .0721 | .0735 | .0749 | .0764 | .0778 | .0793 | .0808 |
| −1.3 | .0823 | .0838 | .0853 | .0869 | .0885 | .0901 | .0918 | .0934 | .0951 | .0968 |
| −1.2 | .0985 | .1003 | .1020 | .1038 | .1056 | .1075 | .1093 | .1112 | .1131 | .1151 |
| −1.1 | .1170 | .1190 | .1210 | .1230 | .1251 | .1271 | .1292 | .1314 | .1335 | .1357 |
| −1.0 | .1379 | .1401 | .1423 | .1446 | .1469 | .1492 | .1515 | .1539 | .1562 | .1587 |
| −0.9 | .1611 | .1635 | .1660 | .1685 | .1711 | .1736 | .1762 | .1788 | .1814 | .1841 |
| −0.8 | .1867 | .1894 | .1922 | .1949 | .1977 | .2005 | .2033 | .2061 | .2090 | .2119 |
| −0.7 | .2148 | .2177 | .2206 | .2236 | .2266 | .2296 | .2327 | .2358 | .2389 | .2420 |
| −0.6 | .2451 | .2483 | .2514 | .2546 | .2578 | .2611 | .2643 | .2676 | .2709 | .2743 |
| −0.5 | .2776 | .2810 | .2843 | .2877 | .2912 | .2946 | .2981 | .3015 | .3050 | .3085 |
| −0.4 | .3121 | .3156 | .3192 | .3228 | .3264 | .3300 | .3336 | .3372 | .3409 | .3446 |
| −0.3 | .3483 | .3520 | .3557 | .3594 | .3632 | .3669 | .3707 | .3745 | .3783 | .3821 |
| −0.2 | .3859 | .3897 | .3936 | .3974 | .4013 | .4052 | .4090 | .4129 | .4168 | .4207 |
| −0.1 | .4247 | .4286 | .4325 | .4364 | .4404 | .4443 | .4483 | .4522 | .4562 | .4602 |
| −0.0 | .4641 | .4681 | .4721 | .4761 | .4801 | .4840 | .4880 | .4920 | .4960 | .5000 |

## Critical Values

| Level of Confidence $c$ | $z_c$ |
|---|---|
| 0.80 | 1.28 |
| 0.90 | 1.645 |
| 0.95 | 1.96 |
| 0.99 | 2.575 |

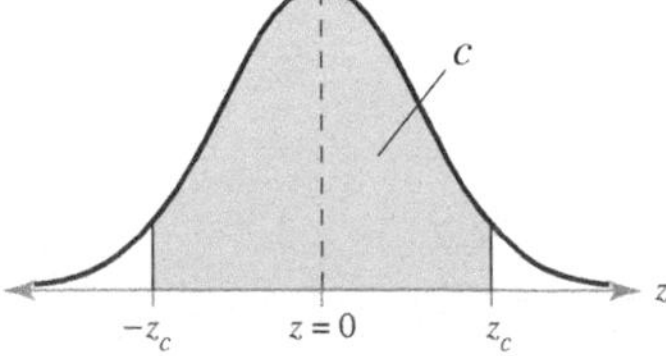


Table A-3, pp. 681–682 from *Probability and Statistics for Engineers and Scientists,* 6e, by Walpole, Myers, and Myers. Copyright 1997. Pearson Prentice Hall, Upper Saddle River, N.J.

# Table 4—Standard Normal Distribution *(continued)*

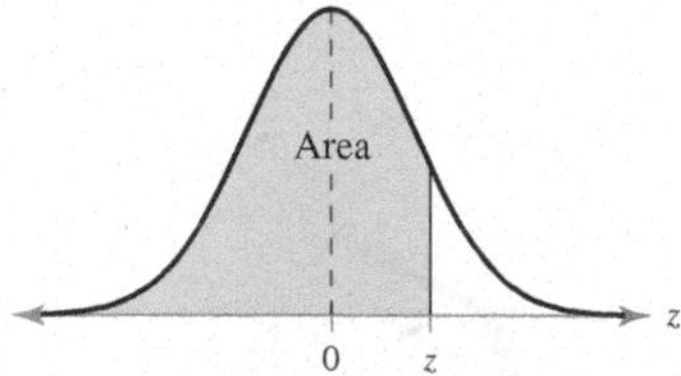


| z | .00 | .01 | .02 | .03 | .04 | .05 | .06 | .07 | .08 | .09 |
|---|---|---|---|---|---|---|---|---|---|---|
| **0.0** | .5000 | .5040 | .5080 | .5120 | .5160 | .5199 | .5239 | .5279 | .5319 | .5359 |
| **0.1** | .5398 | .5438 | .5478 | .5517 | .5557 | .5596 | .5636 | .5675 | .5714 | .5753 |
| **0.2** | .5793 | .5832 | .5871 | .5910 | .5948 | .5987 | .6026 | .6064 | .6103 | .6141 |
| **0.3** | .6179 | .6217 | .6255 | .6293 | .6331 | .6368 | .6406 | .6443 | .6480 | .6517 |
| **0.4** | .6554 | .6591 | .6628 | .6664 | .6700 | .6736 | .6772 | .6808 | .6844 | .6879 |
| **0.5** | .6915 | .6950 | .6985 | .7019 | .7054 | .7088 | .7123 | .7157 | .7190 | .7224 |
| **0.6** | .7257 | .7291 | .7324 | .7357 | .7389 | .7422 | .7454 | .7486 | .7517 | .7549 |
| **0.7** | .7580 | .7611 | .7642 | .7673 | .7704 | .7734 | .7764 | .7794 | .7823 | .7852 |
| **0.8** | .7881 | .7910 | .7939 | .7967 | .7995 | .8023 | .8051 | .8078 | .8106 | .8133 |
| **0.9** | .8159 | .8186 | .8212 | .8238 | .8264 | .8289 | .8315 | .8340 | .8365 | .8389 |
| **1.0** | .8413 | .8438 | .8461 | .8485 | .8508 | .8531 | .8554 | .8577 | .8599 | .8621 |
| **1.1** | .8643 | .8665 | .8686 | .8708 | .8729 | .8749 | .8770 | .8790 | .8810 | .8830 |
| **1.2** | .8849 | .8869 | .8888 | .8907 | .8925 | .8944 | .8962 | .8980 | .8997 | .9015 |
| **1.3** | .9032 | .9049 | .9066 | .9082 | .9099 | .9115 | .9131 | .9147 | .9162 | .9177 |
| **1.4** | .9192 | .9207 | .9222 | .9236 | .9251 | .9265 | .9279 | .9292 | .9306 | .9319 |
| **1.5** | .9332 | .9345 | .9357 | .9370 | .9382 | .9394 | .9406 | .9418 | .9429 | .9441 |
| **1.6** | .9452 | .9463 | .9474 | .9484 | .9495 | .9505 | .9515 | .9525 | .9535 | .9545 |
| **1.7** | .9554 | .9564 | .9573 | .9582 | .9591 | .9599 | .9608 | .9616 | .9625 | .9633 |
| **1.8** | .9641 | .9649 | .9656 | .9664 | .9671 | .9678 | .9686 | .9693 | .9699 | .9706 |
| **1.9** | .9713 | .9719 | .9726 | .9732 | .9738 | .9744 | .9750 | .9756 | .9761 | .9767 |
| **2.0** | .9772 | .9778 | .9783 | .9788 | .9793 | .9798 | .9803 | .9808 | .9812 | .9817 |
| **2.1** | .9821 | .9826 | .9830 | .9834 | .9838 | .9842 | .9846 | .9850 | .9854 | .9857 |
| **2.2** | .9861 | .9864 | .9868 | .9871 | .9875 | .9878 | .9881 | .9884 | .9887 | .9890 |
| **2.3** | .9893 | .9896 | .9898 | .9901 | .9904 | .9906 | .9909 | .9911 | .9913 | .9916 |
| **2.4** | .9918 | .9920 | .9922 | .9925 | .9927 | .9929 | .9931 | .9932 | .9934 | .9936 |
| **2.5** | .9938 | .9940 | .9941 | .9943 | .9945 | .9946 | .9948 | .9949 | .9951 | .9952 |
| **2.6** | .9953 | .9955 | .9956 | .9957 | .9959 | .9960 | .9961 | .9962 | .9963 | .9964 |
| **2.7** | .9965 | .9966 | .9967 | .9968 | .9969 | .9970 | .9971 | .9972 | .9973 | .9974 |
| **2.8** | .9974 | .9975 | .9976 | .9977 | .9977 | .9978 | .9979 | .9979 | .9980 | .9981 |
| **2.9** | .9981 | .9982 | .9982 | .9983 | .9984 | .9984 | .9985 | .9985 | .9986 | .9986 |
| **3.0** | .9987 | .9987 | .9987 | .9988 | .9988 | .9989 | .9989 | .9989 | .9990 | .9990 |
| **3.1** | .9990 | .9991 | .9991 | .9991 | .9992 | .9992 | .9992 | .9992 | .9993 | .9993 |
| **3.2** | .9993 | .9993 | .9994 | .9994 | .9994 | .9994 | .9994 | .9995 | .9995 | .9995 |
| **3.3** | .9995 | .9995 | .9995 | .9996 | .9996 | .9996 | .9996 | .9996 | .9996 | .9997 |
| **3.4** | .9997 | .9997 | .9997 | .9997 | .9997 | .9997 | .9997 | .9997 | .9997 | .9998 |

# Table 5—$t$-Distribution

| | Level of confidence, $c$ | 0.80 | 0.90 | 0.95 | 0.98 | 0.99 |
|---|---|---|---|---|---|---|
| | One tail, $\alpha$ | 0.10 | 0.05 | 0.025 | 0.01 | 0.005 |
| d.f. | Two tails, $\alpha$ | 0.20 | 0.10 | 0.05 | 0.02 | 0.01 |
| 1 | | 3.078 | 6.314 | 12.706 | 31.821 | 63.657 |
| 2 | | 1.886 | 2.920 | 4.303 | 6.965 | 9.925 |
| 3 | | 1.638 | 2.353 | 3.182 | 4.541 | 5.841 |
| 4 | | 1.533 | 2.132 | 2.776 | 3.747 | 4.604 |
| 5 | | 1.476 | 2.015 | 2.571 | 3.365 | 4.032 |
| 6 | | 1.440 | 1.943 | 2.447 | 3.143 | 3.707 |
| 7 | | 1.415 | 1.895 | 2.365 | 2.998 | 3.499 |
| 8 | | 1.397 | 1.860 | 2.306 | 2.896 | 3.355 |
| 9 | | 1.383 | 1.833 | 2.262 | 2.821 | 3.250 |
| 10 | | 1.372 | 1.812 | 2.228 | 2.764 | 3.169 |
| 11 | | 1.363 | 1.796 | 2.201 | 2.718 | 3.106 |
| 12 | | 1.356 | 1.782 | 2.179 | 2.681 | 3.055 |
| 13 | | 1.350 | 1.771 | 2.160 | 2.650 | 3.012 |
| 14 | | 1.345 | 1.761 | 2.145 | 2.624 | 2.977 |
| 15 | | 1.341 | 1.753 | 2.131 | 2.602 | 2.947 |
| 16 | | 1.337 | 1.746 | 2.120 | 2.583 | 2.921 |
| 17 | | 1.333 | 1.740 | 2.110 | 2.567 | 2.898 |
| 18 | | 1.330 | 1.734 | 2.101 | 2.552 | 2.878 |
| 19 | | 1.328 | 1.729 | 2.093 | 2.539 | 2.861 |
| 20 | | 1.325 | 1.725 | 2.086 | 2.528 | 2.845 |
| 21 | | 1.323 | 1.721 | 2.080 | 2.518 | 2.831 |
| 22 | | 1.321 | 1.717 | 2.074 | 2.508 | 2.819 |
| 23 | | 1.319 | 1.714 | 2.069 | 2.500 | 2.807 |
| 24 | | 1.318 | 1.711 | 2.064 | 2.492 | 2.797 |
| 25 | | 1.316 | 1.708 | 2.060 | 2.485 | 2.787 |
| 26 | | 1.315 | 1.706 | 2.056 | 2.479 | 2.779 |
| 27 | | 1.314 | 1.703 | 2.052 | 2.473 | 2.771 |
| 28 | | 1.313 | 1.701 | 2.048 | 2.467 | 2.763 |
| 29 | | 1.311 | 1.699 | 2.045 | 2.462 | 2.756 |
| 30 | | 1.310 | 1.697 | 2.042 | 2.457 | 2.750 |
| 31 | | 1.309 | 1.696 | 2.040 | 2.453 | 2.744 |
| 32 | | 1.309 | 1.694 | 2.037 | 2.449 | 2.738 |
| 33 | | 1.308 | 1.692 | 2.035 | 2.445 | 2.733 |
| 34 | | 1.307 | 1.691 | 2.032 | 2.441 | 2.728 |
| 35 | | 1.306 | 1.690 | 2.030 | 2.438 | 2.724 |
| 36 | | 1.306 | 1.688 | 2.028 | 2.434 | 2.719 |
| 37 | | 1.305 | 1.687 | 2.026 | 2.431 | 2.715 |
| 38 | | 1.304 | 1.686 | 2.024 | 2.429 | 2.712 |
| 39 | | 1.304 | 1.685 | 2.023 | 2.426 | 2.708 |
| 40 | | 1.303 | 1.684 | 2.021 | 2.423 | 2.704 |
| 45 | | 1.301 | 1.679 | 2.014 | 2.412 | 2.690 |
| 50 | | 1.299 | 1.676 | 2.009 | 2.403 | 2.678 |
| 60 | | 1.296 | 1.671 | 2.000 | 2.390 | 2.660 |
| 70 | | 1.294 | 1.667 | 1.994 | 2.381 | 2.648 |
| 80 | | 1.292 | 1.664 | 1.990 | 2.374 | 2.639 |
| 90 | | 1.291 | 1.662 | 1.987 | 2.368 | 2.632 |
| 100 | | 1.290 | 1.660 | 1.984 | 2.364 | 2.626 |
| 500 | | 1.283 | 1.648 | 1.965 | 2.334 | 2.586 |
| 1000 | | 1.282 | 1.646 | 1.962 | 2.330 | 2.581 |
| $\infty$ | | 1.282 | 1.645 | 1.960 | 2.326 | 2.576 |

The critical values in Table 5 were generated using Excel.

$c$-confidence interval

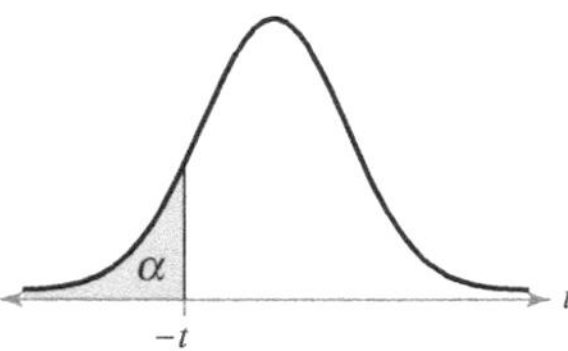

Left-tailed test

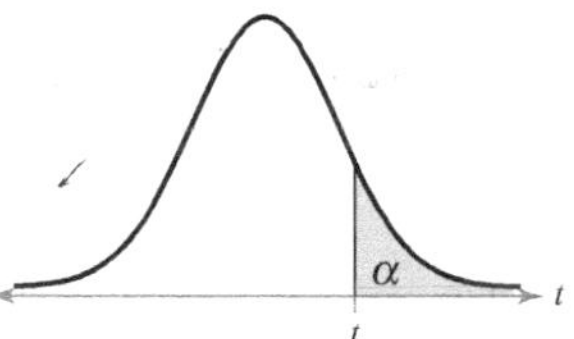

Right-tailed test

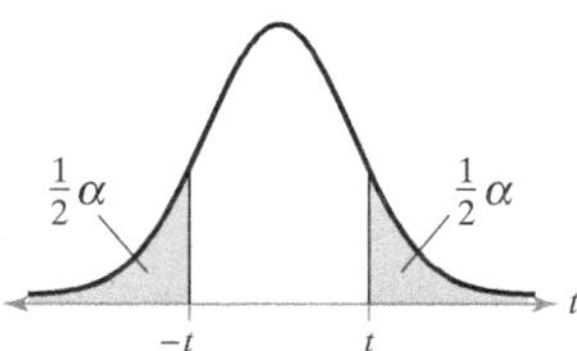

Two-tailed test

## Table 7—*F*-Distribution *(continued)*

| d.f.$_D$: Degrees of freedom, denominator | $\alpha = 0.01$ | | | | | | | | | | | | | | | | | | |
|---|---|---|---|---|---|---|---|---|---|---|---|---|---|---|---|---|---|---|---|
| | d.f.$_N$: Degrees of freedom, numerator | | | | | | | | | | | | | | | | | | |
| | 1 | 2 | 3 | 4 | 5 | 6 | 7 | 8 | 9 | 10 | 12 | 15 | 20 | 24 | 30 | 40 | 60 | 120 | ∞ |
| 1 | 4052 | 4999.5 | 5403 | 5625 | 5764 | 5859 | 5928 | 5982 | 6022 | 6056 | 6106 | 6157 | 6209 | 6235 | 6261 | 6287 | 6313 | 6339 | 6366 |
| 2 | 98.50 | 99.00 | 99.17 | 99.25 | 99.30 | 99.33 | 99.36 | 99.37 | 99.39 | 99.40 | 99.42 | 99.43 | 99.45 | 99.46 | 99.47 | 99.47 | 99.48 | 99.49 | 99.50 |
| 3 | 34.12 | 30.82 | 29.46 | 28.71 | 28.24 | 27.91 | 27.67 | 27.49 | 27.35 | 27.23 | 27.05 | 26.87 | 26.69 | 26.60 | 26.50 | 26.41 | 26.32 | 26.22 | 26.13 |
| 4 | 21.20 | 18.00 | 16.69 | 15.98 | 15.52 | 15.21 | 14.98 | 14.80 | 14.66 | 14.55 | 4.37 | 14.20 | 14.02 | 13.93 | 13.84 | 13.75 | 13.65 | 13.56 | 13.46 |
| 5 | 16.26 | 13.27 | 12.06 | 11.39 | 10.97 | 10.67 | 10.46 | 10.29 | 10.16 | 10.05 | 9.89 | 9.72 | 9.55 | 9.47 | 9.38 | 9.29 | 9.20 | 9.11 | 9.02 |
| 6 | 13.75 | 10.92 | 9.78 | 9.15 | 8.75 | 8.47 | 8.26 | 8.10 | 7.98 | 7.87 | 7.72 | 7.56 | 7.40 | 7.31 | 7.23 | 7.14 | 7.06 | 6.97 | 6.88 |
| 7 | 12.25 | 9.55 | 8.45 | 7.85 | 7.46 | 7.19 | 6.99 | 6.84 | 6.72 | 6.62 | 6.47 | 6.31 | 6.16 | 6.07 | 5.99 | 5.91 | 5.82 | 5.74 | 5.65 |
| 8 | 11.26 | 8.65 | 7.59 | 7.01 | 6.63 | 6.37 | 6.18 | 6.03 | 5.91 | 5.81 | 5.67 | 5.52 | 5.36 | 5.28 | 5.20 | 5.12 | 5.03 | 4.95 | 4.86 |
| 9 | 10.56 | 8.02 | 6.99 | 6.42 | 6.06 | 5.80 | 5.61 | 5.47 | 5.35 | 5.26 | 5.11 | 4.96 | 4.81 | 4.73 | 4.65 | 4.57 | 4.48 | 4.40 | 4.31 |
| 10 | 10.04 | 7.56 | 6.55 | 5.99 | 5.64 | 5.39 | 5.20 | 5.06 | 4.94 | 4.85 | 4.71 | 4.56 | 4.41 | 4.33 | 4.25 | 4.17 | 4.08 | 4.00 | 3.91 |
| 11 | 9.65 | 7.21 | 6.22 | 5.67 | 5.32 | 5.07 | 4.89 | 4.74 | 4.63 | 4.54 | 4.40 | 4.25 | 4.10 | 4.02 | 3.94 | 3.86 | 3.78 | 3.69 | 3.60 |
| 12 | 9.33 | 6.93 | 5.95 | 5.41 | 5.06 | 4.82 | 4.64 | 4.50 | 4.39 | 4.30 | 4.16 | 4.01 | 3.86 | 3.78 | 3.70 | 3.62 | 3.54 | 3.45 | 3.36 |
| 13 | 9.07 | 6.70 | 5.74 | 5.21 | 4.86 | 4.62 | 4.44 | 4.30 | 4.19 | 4.10 | 3.96 | 3.82 | 3.66 | 3.59 | 3.51 | 3.43 | 3.34 | 3.25 | 3.17 |
| 14 | 8.86 | 6.51 | 5.56 | 5.04 | 4.69 | 4.46 | 4.28 | 4.14 | 4.03 | 3.94 | 3.80 | 3.66 | 3.51 | 3.43 | 3.35 | 3.27 | 3.18 | 3.09 | 3.00 |
| 15 | 8.68 | 6.36 | 5.42 | 4.89 | 4.56 | 4.32 | 4.14 | 4.00 | 3.89 | 3.80 | 3.67 | 3.52 | 3.37 | 3.29 | 3.21 | 3.13 | 3.05 | 2.96 | 2.87 |
| 16 | 8.53 | 6.23 | 5.29 | 4.77 | 4.44 | 4.20 | 4.03 | 3.89 | 3.78 | 3.69 | 3.55 | 3.41 | 3.26 | 3.18 | 3.10 | 3.02 | 2.93 | 2.84 | 2.75 |
| 17 | 8.40 | 6.11 | 5.18 | 4.67 | 4.34 | 4.10 | 3.93 | 3.79 | 3.68 | 3.59 | 3.46 | 3.31 | 3.16 | 3.08 | 3.00 | 2.92 | 2.83 | 2.75 | 2.65 |
| 18 | 8.29 | 6.01 | 5.09 | 4.58 | 4.25 | 4.01 | 3.84 | 3.71 | 3.60 | 3.51 | 3.37 | 3.23 | 3.08 | 3.00 | 2.92 | 2.84 | 2.75 | 2.66 | 2.57 |
| 19 | 8.18 | 5.93 | 5.01 | 4.50 | 4.17 | 3.94 | 3.77 | 3.63 | 3.52 | 3.43 | 3.30 | 3.15 | 3.00 | 2.92 | 2.84 | 2.76 | 2.67 | 2.58 | 2.49 |
| 20 | 8.10 | 5.85 | 4.94 | 4.43 | 4.10 | 3.87 | 3.70 | 3.56 | 3.46 | 3.37 | 3.23 | 3.09 | 2.94 | 2.86 | 2.78 | 2.69 | 2.61 | 2.52 | 2.42 |
| 21 | 8.02 | 5.78 | 4.87 | 4.37 | 4.04 | 3.81 | 3.64 | 3.51 | 3.40 | 3.31 | 3.17 | 3.03 | 2.88 | 2.80 | 2.72 | 2.64 | 2.55 | 2.46 | 2.36 |
| 22 | 7.95 | 5.72 | 4.82 | 4.31 | 3.99 | 3.76 | 3.59 | 3.45 | 3.35 | 3.26 | 3.12 | 2.98 | 2.83 | 2.75 | 2.67 | 2.58 | 2.50 | 2.40 | 2.31 |
| 23 | 7.88 | 5.66 | 4.76 | 4.26 | 3.94 | 3.71 | 3.54 | 3.41 | 3.30 | 3.21 | 3.07 | 2.93 | 2.78 | 2.70 | 2.62 | 2.54 | 2.45 | 2.35 | 2.26 |
| 24 | 7.82 | 5.61 | 4.72 | 4.22 | 3.90 | 3.67 | 3.50 | 3.36 | 3.26 | 3.17 | 3.03 | 2.89 | 2.74 | 2.66 | 2.58 | 2.49 | 2.40 | 2.31 | 2.21 |
| 25 | 7.77 | 5.57 | 4.68 | 4.18 | 3.85 | 3.63 | 3.46 | 3.32 | 3.22 | 3.13 | 2.99 | 2.85 | 2.70 | 2.62 | 2.54 | 2.45 | 2.36 | 2.27 | 2.17 |
| 26 | 7.72 | 5.53 | 4.64 | 4.14 | 3.82 | 3.59 | 3.42 | 3.29 | 3.18 | 3.09 | 2.96 | 2.81 | 2.66 | 2.58 | 2.50 | 2.42 | 2.33 | 2.23 | 2.13 |
| 27 | 7.68 | 5.49 | 4.60 | 4.11 | 3.78 | 3.56 | 3.39 | 3.26 | 3.15 | 3.06 | 2.93 | 2.78 | 2.63 | 2.55 | 2.47 | 2.38 | 2.29 | 2.20 | 2.10 |
| 28 | 7.64 | 5.45 | 4.57 | 4.07 | 3.75 | 3.53 | 3.36 | 3.23 | 3.12 | 3.03 | 2.90 | 2.75 | 2.60 | 2.52 | 2.44 | 2.35 | 2.26 | 2.17 | 2.06 |
| 29 | 7.60 | 5.42 | 4.54 | 4.04 | 3.73 | 3.50 | 3.33 | 3.20 | 3.09 | 3.00 | 2.87 | 2.73 | 2.57 | 2.49 | 2.41 | 2.33 | 2.23 | 2.14 | 2.03 |
| 30 | 7.56 | 5.39 | 4.51 | 4.02 | 3.70 | 3.47 | 3.30 | 3.17 | 3.07 | 2.98 | 2.84 | 2.70 | 2.55 | 2.47 | 2.39 | 2.30 | 2.21 | 2.11 | 2.01 |
| 40 | 7.31 | 5.18 | 4.31 | 3.83 | 3.51 | 3.29 | 3.12 | 2.99 | 2.89 | 2.80 | 2.66 | 2.52 | 2.37 | 2.29 | 2.20 | 2.11 | 2.02 | 1.92 | 1.80 |
| 60 | 7.08 | 4.98 | 4.13 | 3.65 | 3.34 | 3.12 | 2.95 | 2.82 | 2.72 | 2.63 | 2.50 | 2.35 | 2.20 | 2.12 | 2.03 | 1.94 | 1.84 | 1.73 | 1.60 |
| 120 | 6.85 | 4.79 | 3.95 | 3.48 | 3.17 | 2.96 | 2.79 | 2.66 | 2.56 | 2.47 | 2.34 | 2.19 | 2.03 | 1.95 | 1.86 | 1.76 | 1.66 | 1.53 | 1.38 |
| ∞ | 6.63 | 4.61 | 3.78 | 3.32 | 3.02 | 2.80 | 2.64 | 2.51 | 2.41 | 2.32 | 2.18 | 2.04 | 1.88 | 1.79 | 1.70 | 1.59 | 1.47 | 1.32 | 1.00 |

# Table 7—*F*-Distribution (continued)

| d.f.$_D$: Degrees of freedom, denominator | $\alpha = 0.025$ | | | | | | | | | | | | | | | | | | |
|---|---|---|---|---|---|---|---|---|---|---|---|---|---|---|---|---|---|---|---|
| | d.f.$_N$: Degrees of freedom, numerator | | | | | | | | | | | | | | | | | | |
| | 1 | 2 | 3 | 4 | 5 | 6 | 7 | 8 | 9 | 10 | 12 | 15 | 20 | 24 | 30 | 40 | 60 | 120 | ∞ |
| 1 | 647.8 | 799.5 | 864.2 | 899.6 | 921.8 | 937.1 | 948.2 | 956.7 | 963.3 | 968.6 | 976.7 | 984.9 | 993.1 | 997.2 | 1001 | 1006 | 1010 | 1014 | 1018 |
| 2 | 38.51 | 39.00 | 39.17 | 39.25 | 39.30 | 39.33 | 39.36 | 39.37 | 39.39 | 39.40 | 39.41 | 39.43 | 39.45 | 39.46 | 39.46 | 39.47 | 39.48 | 39.49 | 39.50 |
| 3 | 17.44 | 16.04 | 15.44 | 15.10 | 14.88 | 14.73 | 14.62 | 14.54 | 14.47 | 14.42 | 14.34 | 14.25 | 14.17 | 14.12 | 14.08 | 14.04 | 13.99 | 13.95 | 13.90 |
| 4 | 12.22 | 10.65 | 9.98 | 9.60 | 9.36 | 9.20 | 9.07 | 8.98 | 8.90 | 8.84 | 8.75 | 8.66 | 8.56 | 8.51 | 8.46 | 8.41 | 8.36 | 8.31 | 8.26 |
| 5 | 10.01 | 8.43 | 7.76 | 7.39 | 7.15 | 6.98 | 6.85 | 6.76 | 6.68 | 6.62 | 6.52 | 6.43 | 6.33 | 6.28 | 6.23 | 6.18 | 6.12 | 6.07 | 6.02 |
| 6 | 8.81 | 7.26 | 6.60 | 6.23 | 5.99 | 5.82 | 5.70 | 5.60 | 5.52 | 5.46 | 5.37 | 5.27 | 5.17 | 5.12 | 5.07 | 5.01 | 4.96 | 4.90 | 4.85 |
| 7 | 8.07 | 6.54 | 5.89 | 5.52 | 5.29 | 5.12 | 4.99 | 4.90 | 4.82 | 4.76 | 4.67 | 4.57 | 4.47 | 4.42 | 4.36 | 4.31 | 4.25 | 4.20 | 4.14 |
| 8 | 7.57 | 6.06 | 5.42 | 5.05 | 4.82 | 4.65 | 4.53 | 4.43 | 4.36 | 4.30 | 4.20 | 4.10 | 4.00 | 3.95 | 3.89 | 3.84 | 3.78 | 3.73 | 3.67 |
| 9 | 7.21 | 5.71 | 5.08 | 4.72 | 4.48 | 4.32 | 4.20 | 4.10 | 4.03 | 3.96 | 3.87 | 3.77 | 3.67 | 3.61 | 3.56 | 3.51 | 3.45 | 3.39 | 3.33 |
| 10 | 6.94 | 5.46 | 4.83 | 4.47 | 4.24 | 4.07 | 3.95 | 3.85 | 3.78 | 3.72 | 3.62 | 3.52 | 3.42 | 3.37 | 3.31 | 3.26 | 3.20 | 3.14 | 3.08 |
| 11 | 6.72 | 5.26 | 4.63 | 4.28 | 4.04 | 3.88 | 3.76 | 3.66 | 3.59 | 3.53 | 3.43 | 3.33 | 3.23 | 3.17 | 3.12 | 3.06 | 3.00 | 2.94 | 2.88 |
| 12 | 6.55 | 5.10 | 4.47 | 4.12 | 3.89 | 3.73 | 3.61 | 3.51 | 3.44 | 3.37 | 3.28 | 3.18 | 3.07 | 3.02 | 2.96 | 2.91 | 2.85 | 2.79 | 2.72 |
| 13 | 6.41 | 4.97 | 4.35 | 4.00 | 3.77 | 3.60 | 3.48 | 3.39 | 3.31 | 3.25 | 3.15 | 3.05 | 2.95 | 2.89 | 2.84 | 2.78 | 2.72 | 2.66 | 2.60 |
| 14 | 6.30 | 4.86 | 4.24 | 3.89 | 3.66 | 3.50 | 3.38 | 3.29 | 3.21 | 3.15 | 3.05 | 2.95 | 2.84 | 2.79 | 2.73 | 2.67 | 2.61 | 2.55 | 2.49 |
| 15 | 6.20 | 4.77 | 4.15 | 3.80 | 3.58 | 3.41 | 3.29 | 3.20 | 3.12 | 3.06 | 2.98 | 2.86 | 2.76 | 2.70 | 2.64 | 2.59 | 2.52 | 2.46 | 2.40 |
| 16 | 6.12 | 4.69 | 4.08 | 3.73 | 3.50 | 3.34 | 3.22 | 3.12 | 3.05 | 2.99 | 2.89 | 2.79 | 2.68 | 2.63 | 2.57 | 2.51 | 2.45 | 2.38 | 2.32 |
| 17 | 6.04 | 4.62 | 4.01 | 3.66 | 3.44 | 3.28 | 3.16 | 3.06 | 2.98 | 2.92 | 2.82 | 2.72 | 2.62 | 2.56 | 2.50 | 2.44 | 2.38 | 2.32 | 2.25 |
| 18 | 5.98 | 4.56 | 3.95 | 3.61 | 3.38 | 3.22 | 3.10 | 3.01 | 2.93 | 2.87 | 2.77 | 2.67 | 2.56 | 2.50 | 2.44 | 2.38 | 2.32 | 2.26 | 2.19 |
| 19 | 5.92 | 4.51 | 3.90 | 3.56 | 3.33 | 3.17 | 3.05 | 2.96 | 2.88 | 2.82 | 2.72 | 2.62 | 2.51 | 2.45 | 2.39 | 2.33 | 2.27 | 2.20 | 2.13 |
| 20 | 5.87 | 4.46 | 3.86 | 3.51 | 3.29 | 3.13 | 3.01 | 2.91 | 2.84 | 2.77 | 2.68 | 2.57 | 2.46 | 2.41 | 2.35 | 2.29 | 2.22 | 2.16 | 2.09 |
| 21 | 5.83 | 4.42 | 3.82 | 3.48 | 3.25 | 3.09 | 2.97 | 2.87 | 2.80 | 2.73 | 2.64 | 2.53 | 2.42 | 2.37 | 2.31 | 2.25 | 2.18 | 2.11 | 2.04 |
| 22 | 5.79 | 4.38 | 3.78 | 3.44 | 3.22 | 3.05 | 2.93 | 2.84 | 2.76 | 2.70 | 2.60 | 2.50 | 2.39 | 2.33 | 2.27 | 2.21 | 2.14 | 2.08 | 2.00 |
| 23 | 5.75 | 4.35 | 3.75 | 3.41 | 3.18 | 3.02 | 2.90 | 2.81 | 2.73 | 2.67 | 2.57 | 2.47 | 2.36 | 2.30 | 2.24 | 2.18 | 2.11 | 2.04 | 1.97 |
| 24 | 5.72 | 4.32 | 3.72 | 3.38 | 3.15 | 2.99 | 2.87 | 2.78 | 2.70 | 2.64 | 2.54 | 2.44 | 2.33 | 2.27 | 2.21 | 2.15 | 2.08 | 2.01 | 1.94 |
| 25 | 5.69 | 4.29 | 3.69 | 3.35 | 3.13 | 2.97 | 2.85 | 2.75 | 2.68 | 2.61 | 2.51 | 2.41 | 2.30 | 2.24 | 2.18 | 2.12 | 2.05 | 1.98 | 1.91 |
| 26 | 5.66 | 4.27 | 3.67 | 3.33 | 3.10 | 2.94 | 2.82 | 2.73 | 2.65 | 2.59 | 2.49 | 2.39 | 2.25 | 2.22 | 2.16 | 2.09 | 2.03 | 1.95 | 1.88 |
| 27 | 5.63 | 4.24 | 3.65 | 3.31 | 3.08 | 2.92 | 2.80 | 2.71 | 2.63 | 2.57 | 2.47 | 2.36 | 2.25 | 2.19 | 2.13 | 2.07 | 2.00 | 1.93 | 1.85 |
| 28 | 5.61 | 4.22 | 3.63 | 3.29 | 3.06 | 2.90 | 2.78 | 2.69 | 2.61 | 2.55 | 2.45 | 2.34 | 2.23 | 2.17 | 2.11 | 2.05 | 1.98 | 1.91 | 1.83 |
| 29 | 5.59 | 4.20 | 3.61 | 3.27 | 3.04 | 2.88 | 2.76 | 2.67 | 2.59 | 2.53 | 2.43 | 2.32 | 2.21 | 2.15 | 2.09 | 2.03 | 1.96 | 1.89 | 1.81 |
| 30 | 5.57 | 4.18 | 3.59 | 3.25 | 3.03 | 2.87 | 2.75 | 2.65 | 2.57 | 2.51 | 2.41 | 2.31 | 2.20 | 2.14 | 2.07 | 2.01 | 1.94 | 1.87 | 1.79 |
| 40 | 5.42 | 4.05 | 3.46 | 3.13 | 2.90 | 2.74 | 2.62 | 2.53 | 2.45 | 2.39 | 2.29 | 2.18 | 2.07 | 2.01 | 1.94 | 1.88 | 1.80 | 1.72 | 1.64 |
| 60 | 5.29 | 3.93 | 3.34 | 3.01 | 2.79 | 2.63 | 2.51 | 2.41 | 2.33 | 2.27 | 2.17 | 2.06 | 1.94 | 1.88 | 1.82 | 1.74 | 1.67 | 1.58 | 1.48 |
| 120 | 5.15 | 3.80 | 3.23 | 2.89 | 2.67 | 2.52 | 2.39 | 2.30 | 2.22 | 2.16 | 2.05 | 1.94 | 1.82 | 1.76 | 1.69 | 1.61 | 1.53 | 1.43 | 1.31 |
| ∞ | 5.02 | 3.69 | 3.12 | 2.79 | 2.57 | 2.41 | 2.29 | 2.19 | 2.11 | 2.05 | 1.94 | 1.83 | 1.71 | 1.64 | 1.57 | 1.48 | 1.39 | 1.27 | 1.00 |

## Table 7—*F*-Distribution *(continued)*

| d.f.$_D$: Degrees of freedom, denominator | $\alpha = 0.05$ | | | | | | | | | | | | | | | | | | |
|---|---|---|---|---|---|---|---|---|---|---|---|---|---|---|---|---|---|---|---|
| | d.f.$_N$: Degrees of freedom, numerator | | | | | | | | | | | | | | | | | | |
| | 1 | 2 | 3 | 4 | 5 | 6 | 7 | 8 | 9 | 10 | 12 | 15 | 20 | 24 | 30 | 40 | 60 | 120 | ∞ |
| 1 | 161.4 | 199.5 | 215.7 | 224.6 | 230.2 | 234.0 | 236.8 | 238.9 | 240.5 | 241.9 | 243.9 | 245.9 | 248.0 | 249.1 | 250.1 | 251.1 | 252.2 | 253.3 | 254.3 |
| 2 | 18.51 | 19.00 | 19.16 | 19.25 | 19.30 | 19.33 | 19.35 | 19.37 | 19.38 | 19.40 | 19.41 | 19.43 | 19.45 | 19.45 | 19.46 | 19.47 | 19.48 | 19.49 | 19.50 |
| 3 | 10.13 | 9.55 | 9.28 | 9.12 | 9.01 | 8.94 | 8.89 | 8.85 | 8.81 | 8.79 | 8.74 | 8.70 | 8.66 | 8.64 | 8.62 | 8.59 | 8.57 | 8.55 | 8.53 |
| 4 | 7.71 | 6.94 | 6.59 | 6.39 | 6.26 | 6.16 | 6.09 | 6.04 | 6.00 | 5.96 | 5.91 | 5.86 | 5.80 | 5.77 | 5.75 | 5.72 | 5.69 | 5.66 | 5.63 |
| 5 | 6.61 | 5.79 | 5.41 | 5.19 | 5.05 | 4.95 | 4.88 | 4.82 | 4.77 | 4.74 | 4.68 | 4.62 | 4.56 | 4.53 | 4.50 | 4.46 | 4.43 | 4.40 | 4.36 |
| 6 | 5.99 | 5.14 | 4.76 | 4.53 | 4.39 | 4.28 | 4.21 | 4.15 | 4.10 | 4.06 | 4.00 | 3.94 | 3.87 | 3.84 | 3.81 | 3.77 | 3.74 | 3.70 | 3.67 |
| 7 | 5.59 | 4.74 | 4.35 | 4.12 | 3.97 | 3.87 | 3.79 | 3.73 | 3.68 | 3.64 | 3.57 | 3.51 | 3.44 | 3.41 | 3.38 | 3.34 | 3.30 | 3.27 | 3.23 |
| 8 | 5.32 | 4.46 | 4.07 | 3.84 | 3.69 | 3.58 | 3.50 | 3.44 | 3.39 | 3.35 | 3.28 | 3.22 | 3.15 | 3.12 | 3.08 | 3.04 | 3.01 | 2.97 | 2.93 |
| 9 | 5.12 | 4.26 | 3.86 | 3.63 | 3.48 | 3.37 | 3.29 | 3.23 | 3.18 | 3.14 | 3.07 | 3.01 | 2.94 | 2.90 | 2.86 | 2.83 | 2.79 | 2.75 | 2.71 |
| 10 | 4.96 | 4.10 | 3.71 | 3.48 | 3.33 | 3.22 | 3.14 | 3.07 | 3.02 | 2.98 | 2.91 | 2.85 | 2.77 | 2.74 | 2.70 | 2.66 | 2.62 | 2.58 | 2.54 |
| 11 | 4.84 | 3.98 | 3.59 | 3.36 | 3.20 | 3.09 | 3.01 | 2.95 | 2.90 | 2.85 | 2.79 | 2.72 | 2.65 | 2.61 | 2.57 | 2.53 | 2.49 | 2.45 | 2.40 |
| 12 | 4.75 | 3.89 | 3.49 | 3.26 | 3.11 | 3.00 | 2.91 | 2.85 | 2.80 | 2.75 | 2.69 | 2.62 | 2.54 | 2.51 | 2.47 | 2.43 | 2.38 | 2.34 | 2.30 |
| 13 | 4.67 | 3.81 | 3.41 | 3.18 | 3.03 | 2.92 | 2.83 | 2.77 | 2.71 | 2.67 | 2.60 | 2.53 | 2.46 | 2.42 | 2.38 | 2.34 | 2.30 | 2.25 | 2.21 |
| 14 | 4.60 | 3.74 | 3.34 | 3.11 | 2.96 | 2.85 | 2.76 | 2.70 | 2.65 | 2.60 | 2.53 | 2.46 | 2.39 | 2.35 | 2.31 | 2.27 | 2.22 | 2.18 | 2.13 |
| 15 | 4.54 | 3.68 | 3.29 | 3.06 | 2.90 | 2.79 | 2.71 | 2.64 | 2.59 | 2.54 | 2.48 | 2.40 | 2.33 | 2.29 | 2.25 | 2.20 | 2.16 | 2.11 | 2.07 |
| 16 | 4.49 | 3.63 | 3.24 | 3.01 | 2.85 | 2.74 | 2.66 | 2.59 | 2.54 | 2.49 | 2.42 | 2.35 | 2.28 | 2.24 | 2.19 | 2.15 | 2.11 | 2.06 | 2.01 |
| 17 | 4.45 | 3.59 | 3.20 | 2.96 | 2.81 | 2.70 | 2.61 | 2.55 | 2.49 | 2.45 | 2.38 | 2.31 | 2.23 | 2.19 | 2.15 | 2.10 | 2.06 | 2.01 | 1.96 |
| 18 | 4.41 | 3.55 | 3.16 | 2.93 | 2.77 | 2.66 | 2.58 | 2.51 | 2.46 | 2.41 | 2.34 | 2.27 | 2.19 | 2.15 | 2.11 | 2.06 | 2.02 | 1.97 | 1.92 |
| 19 | 4.38 | 3.52 | 3.13 | 2.90 | 2.74 | 2.63 | 2.54 | 2.48 | 2.42 | 2.38 | 2.31 | 2.23 | 2.16 | 2.11 | 2.07 | 2.03 | 1.98 | 1.93 | 1.88 |
| 20 | 4.35 | 3.49 | 3.10 | 2.87 | 2.71 | 2.60 | 2.51 | 2.45 | 2.39 | 2.35 | 2.28 | 2.20 | 2.12 | 2.08 | 2.04 | 1.99 | 1.95 | 1.90 | 1.84 |
| 21 | 4.32 | 3.47 | 3.07 | 2.84 | 2.68 | 2.57 | 2.49 | 2.42 | 2.37 | 2.32 | 2.25 | 2.18 | 2.10 | 2.05 | 2.01 | 1.96 | 1.92 | 1.87 | 1.81 |
| 22 | 4.30 | 3.44 | 3.05 | 2.82 | 2.66 | 2.55 | 2.46 | 2.40 | 2.34 | 2.30 | 2.23 | 2.15 | 2.07 | 2.03 | 1.98 | 1.94 | 1.89 | 1.84 | 1.78 |
| 23 | 4.28 | 3.42 | 3.03 | 2.80 | 2.64 | 2.53 | 2.44 | 2.37 | 2.32 | 2.27 | 2.20 | 2.13 | 2.05 | 2.01 | 1.96 | 1.91 | 1.86 | 1.81 | 1.76 |
| 24 | 4.26 | 3.40 | 3.01 | 2.78 | 2.62 | 2.51 | 2.42 | 2.36 | 2.30 | 2.25 | 2.18 | 2.11 | 2.03 | 1.98 | 1.94 | 1.89 | 1.84 | 1.79 | 1.73 |
| 25 | 4.24 | 3.39 | 2.99 | 2.76 | 2.60 | 2.49 | 2.40 | 2.34 | 2.28 | 2.24 | 2.16 | 2.09 | 2.01 | 1.96 | 1.92 | 1.87 | 1.82 | 1.77 | 1.71 |
| 26 | 4.23 | 3.37 | 2.98 | 2.74 | 2.59 | 2.47 | 2.39 | 2.32 | 2.27 | 2.22 | 2.15 | 2.07 | 1.99 | 1.95 | 1.90 | 1.85 | 1.80 | 1.75 | 1.69 |
| 27 | 4.21 | 3.35 | 2.96 | 2.73 | 2.57 | 2.46 | 2.37 | 2.31 | 2.25 | 2.20 | 2.13 | 2.06 | 1.97 | 1.93 | 1.88 | 1.84 | 1.79 | 1.73 | 1.67 |
| 28 | 4.20 | 3.34 | 2.95 | 2.71 | 2.56 | 2.45 | 2.36 | 2.29 | 2.24 | 2.19 | 2.12 | 2.04 | 1.96 | 1.91 | 1.87 | 1.82 | 1.77 | 1.71 | 1.65 |
| 29 | 4.18 | 3.33 | 2.93 | 2.70 | 2.55 | 2.43 | 2.35 | 2.28 | 2.22 | 2.18 | 2.10 | 2.03 | 1.94 | 1.90 | 1.85 | 1.81 | 1.75 | 1.70 | 1.64 |
| 30 | 4.17 | 3.32 | 2.92 | 2.69 | 2.53 | 2.42 | 2.33 | 2.27 | 2.21 | 2.16 | 2.09 | 2.01 | 1.93 | 1.89 | 1.84 | 1.79 | 1.74 | 1.68 | 1.62 |
| 40 | 4.08 | 3.23 | 2.84 | 2.61 | 2.45 | 2.34 | 2.25 | 2.18 | 2.12 | 2.08 | 2.00 | 1.92 | 1.84 | 1.79 | 1.74 | 1.69 | 1.64 | 1.58 | 1.51 |
| 60 | 4.00 | 3.15 | 2.76 | 2.53 | 2.37 | 2.25 | 2.17 | 2.10 | 2.04 | 1.99 | 1.92 | 1.84 | 1.75 | 1.70 | 1.65 | 1.59 | 1.53 | 1.47 | 1.39 |
| 120 | 3.92 | 3.07 | 2.68 | 2.45 | 2.29 | 2.17 | 2.09 | 2.02 | 1.96 | 1.91 | 1.83 | 1.75 | 1.66 | 1.61 | 1.55 | 1.50 | 1.43 | 1.35 | 1.25 |
| ∞ | 3.84 | 3.00 | 2.60 | 2.37 | 2.21 | 2.10 | 2.01 | 1.94 | 1.88 | 1.83 | 1.75 | 1.67 | 1.57 | 1.52 | 1.46 | 1.39 | 1.32 | 1.22 | 1.00 |

## Table 7—*F*-Distribution *(continued)*

| d.f.$_D$: Degrees of freedom, denominator | $\alpha = 0.10$ | | | | | | | | | | | | | | | | | | |
|---|---|---|---|---|---|---|---|---|---|---|---|---|---|---|---|---|---|---|---|
| | d.f.$_N$: Degrees of freedom, numerator | | | | | | | | | | | | | | | | | | |
| | 1 | 2 | 3 | 4 | 5 | 6 | 7 | 8 | 9 | 10 | 12 | 15 | 20 | 24 | 30 | 40 | 60 | 120 | ∞ |
| 1 | 39.86 | 49.50 | 53.59 | 55.83 | 57.24 | 58.20 | 58.91 | 59.44 | 59.86 | 60.19 | 60.71 | 61.22 | 61.74 | 62.00 | 62.26 | 62.53 | 62.79 | 63.06 | 63.33 |
| 2 | 8.53 | 9.00 | 9.16 | 9.24 | 9.29 | 9.33 | 9.35 | 9.37 | 9.38 | 9.39 | 9.41 | 9.42 | 9.44 | 9.45 | 9.46 | 9.47 | 9.47 | 9.48 | 9.49 |
| 3 | 5.54 | 5.46 | 5.39 | 5.34 | 5.31 | 5.28 | 5.27 | 5.25 | 5.24 | 5.23 | 5.22 | 5.20 | 5.18 | 5.18 | 5.17 | 5.16 | 5.15 | 5.14 | 5.13 |
| 4 | 4.54 | 4.32 | 4.19 | 4.11 | 4.05 | 4.01 | 3.98 | 3.95 | 3.94 | 3.92 | 3.90 | 3.87 | 3.84 | 3.83 | 3.82 | 3.80 | 3.79 | 3.78 | 3.76 |
| 5 | 4.06 | 3.78 | 3.62 | 3.52 | 3.45 | 3.40 | 3.37 | 3.34 | 3.32 | 3.30 | 3.27 | 3.24 | 3.21 | 3.19 | 3.17 | 3.16 | 3.14 | 3.12 | 3.10 |
| 6 | 3.78 | 3.46 | 3.29 | 3.18 | 3.11 | 3.05 | 3.01 | 2.98 | 2.96 | 2.94 | 2.90 | 2.87 | 2.84 | 2.82 | 2.80 | 2.78 | 2.76 | 2.74 | 2.72 |
| 7 | 3.59 | 3.26 | 3.07 | 2.96 | 2.88 | 2.83 | 2.78 | 2.75 | 2.72 | 2.70 | 2.67 | 2.63 | 2.59 | 2.58 | 2.56 | 2.54 | 2.51 | 2.49 | 2.47 |
| 8 | 3.46 | 3.11 | 2.92 | 2.81 | 2.73 | 2.67 | 2.62 | 2.59 | 2.56 | 2.54 | 2.50 | 2.46 | 2.42 | 2.40 | 2.38 | 2.36 | 2.34 | 2.32 | 2.29 |
| 9 | 3.36 | 3.01 | 2.81 | 2.69 | 2.61 | 2.55 | 2.51 | 2.47 | 2.44 | 2.42 | 2.38 | 2.34 | 2.30 | 2.28 | 2.25 | 2.23 | 2.21 | 2.18 | 2.16 |
| 10 | 3.29 | 2.92 | 2.73 | 2.61 | 2.52 | 2.46 | 2.41 | 2.38 | 2.35 | 2.32 | 2.28 | 2.24 | 2.20 | 2.18 | 2.16 | 2.13 | 2.11 | 2.08 | 2.06 |
| 11 | 3.23 | 2.86 | 2.66 | 2.54 | 2.45 | 2.39 | 2.34 | 2.30 | 2.27 | 2.25 | 2.21 | 2.17 | 2.12 | 2.10 | 2.08 | 2.05 | 2.03 | 2.00 | 1.97 |
| 12 | 3.18 | 2.81 | 2.61 | 2.48 | 2.39 | 2.33 | 2.28 | 2.24 | 2.21 | 2.19 | 2.15 | 2.10 | 2.06 | 2.04 | 2.01 | 1.99 | 1.96 | 1.93 | 1.90 |
| 13 | 3.14 | 2.76 | 2.56 | 2.43 | 2.35 | 2.28 | 2.23 | 2.20 | 2.16 | 2.14 | 2.10 | 2.05 | 2.01 | 1.98 | 1.96 | 1.93 | 1.90 | 1.88 | 1.85 |
| 14 | 3.10 | 2.73 | 2.52 | 2.39 | 2.31 | 2.24 | 2.19 | 2.15 | 2.12 | 2.10 | 2.05 | 2.01 | 1.96 | 1.94 | 1.91 | 1.89 | 1.86 | 1.83 | 1.80 |
| 15 | 3.07 | 2.70 | 2.49 | 2.36 | 2.27 | 2.21 | 2.16 | 2.12 | 2.09 | 2.06 | 2.02 | 1.97 | 1.92 | 1.90 | 1.87 | 1.85 | 1.82 | 1.79 | 1.76 |
| 16 | 3.05 | 2.67 | 2.46 | 2.33 | 2.24 | 2.18 | 2.13 | 2.09 | 2.06 | 2.03 | 1.99 | 1.94 | 1.89 | 1.87 | 1.84 | 1.81 | 1.78 | 1.75 | 1.72 |
| 17 | 3.03 | 2.64 | 2.44 | 2.31 | 2.22 | 2.15 | 2.10 | 2.06 | 2.03 | 2.00 | 1.96 | 1.91 | 1.86 | 1.84 | 1.81 | 1.78 | 1.75 | 1.72 | 1.69 |
| 18 | 3.01 | 2.62 | 2.42 | 2.29 | 2.20 | 2.13 | 2.08 | 2.04 | 2.00 | 1.98 | 1.93 | 1.89 | 1.84 | 1.81 | 1.78 | 1.75 | 1.72 | 1.69 | 1.66 |
| 19 | 2.99 | 2.61 | 2.40 | 2.27 | 2.18 | 2.11 | 2.06 | 2.02 | 1.98 | 1.96 | 1.91 | 1.86 | 1.81 | 1.79 | 1.76 | 1.73 | 1.70 | 1.67 | 1.63 |
| 20 | 2.97 | 2.59 | 2.38 | 2.25 | 2.16 | 2.09 | 2.04 | 2.00 | 1.96 | 1.94 | 1.89 | 1.84 | 1.79 | 1.77 | 1.74 | 1.71 | 1.68 | 1.64 | 1.61 |
| 21 | 2.96 | 2.57 | 2.36 | 2.23 | 2.14 | 2.08 | 2.02 | 1.98 | 1.95 | 1.92 | 1.87 | 1.83 | 1.78 | 1.75 | 1.72 | 1.69 | 1.66 | 1.62 | 1.59 |
| 22 | 2.95 | 2.56 | 2.35 | 2.22 | 2.13 | 2.06 | 2.01 | 1.97 | 1.93 | 1.90 | 1.86 | 1.81 | 1.76 | 1.73 | 1.70 | 1.67 | 1.64 | 1.60 | 1.57 |
| 23 | 2.94 | 2.55 | 2.34 | 2.21 | 2.11 | 2.05 | 1.99 | 1.95 | 1.92 | 1.89 | 1.84 | 1.80 | 1.74 | 1.72 | 1.69 | 1.66 | 1.62 | 1.59 | 1.55 |
| 24 | 2.93 | 2.54 | 2.33 | 2.19 | 2.10 | 2.04 | 1.98 | 1.94 | 1.91 | 1.88 | 1.83 | 1.78 | 1.73 | 1.70 | 1.67 | 1.64 | 1.61 | 1.57 | 1.53 |
| 25 | 2.92 | 2.53 | 2.32 | 2.18 | 2.09 | 2.02 | 1.97 | 1.93 | 1.89 | 1.87 | 1.82 | 1.77 | 1.72 | 1.69 | 1.66 | 1.63 | 1.59 | 1.56 | 1.52 |
| 26 | 2.91 | 2.52 | 2.31 | 2.17 | 2.08 | 2.01 | 1.96 | 1.92 | 1.88 | 1.86 | 1.81 | 1.76 | 1.71 | 1.68 | 1.65 | 1.61 | 1.58 | 1.54 | 1.50 |
| 27 | 2.90 | 2.51 | 2.30 | 2.17 | 2.07 | 2.00 | 1.95 | 1.91 | 1.87 | 1.85 | 1.80 | 1.75 | 1.70 | 1.67 | 1.64 | 1.60 | 1.57 | 1.53 | 1.49 |
| 28 | 2.89 | 2.50 | 2.29 | 2.16 | 2.06 | 2.00 | 1.94 | 1.90 | 1.87 | 1.84 | 1.79 | 1.74 | 1.69 | 1.66 | 1.63 | 1.59 | 1.56 | 1.52 | 1.48 |
| 29 | 2.89 | 2.50 | 2.28 | 2.15 | 2.06 | 1.99 | 1.93 | 1.89 | 1.86 | 1.83 | 1.78 | 1.73 | 1.68 | 1.65 | 1.62 | 1.58 | 1.55 | 1.51 | 1.47 |
| 30 | 2.88 | 2.49 | 2.28 | 2.14 | 2.05 | 1.98 | 1.93 | 1.88 | 1.85 | 1.82 | 1.77 | 1.72 | 1.67 | 1.64 | 1.61 | 1.57 | 1.54 | 1.50 | 1.46 |
| 40 | 2.84 | 2.44 | 2.23 | 2.09 | 2.00 | 1.93 | 1.87 | 1.83 | 1.79 | 1.76 | 1.71 | 1.66 | 1.61 | 1.57 | 1.54 | 1.51 | 1.47 | 1.42 | 1.38 |
| 60 | 2.79 | 2.39 | 2.18 | 2.04 | 1.95 | 1.87 | 1.82 | 1.77 | 1.74 | 1.71 | 1.66 | 1.60 | 1.54 | 1.51 | 1.48 | 1.44 | 1.40 | 1.35 | 1.29 |
| 120 | 2.75 | 2.35 | 2.13 | 1.99 | 1.90 | 1.82 | 1.77 | 1.72 | 1.68 | 1.65 | 1.60 | 1.55 | 1.48 | 1.45 | 1.41 | 1.37 | 1.32 | 1.26 | 1.19 |
| ∞ | 2.71 | 2.30 | 2.08 | 1.94 | 1.85 | 1.77 | 1.72 | 1.67 | 1.63 | 1.60 | 1.55 | 1.49 | 1.42 | 1.38 | 1.34 | 1.30 | 1.24 | 1.17 | 1.00 |

From M. Merrington and C.M. Thompson, "Table of Percentage Points of the Inverted Beta (F) Distribution," Biometrika 33 (1943), pp. 74-87, Oxford University Press.

## Table 8—Critical Values for the Sign Test

Reject the null hypothesis when the test statistic $x$ is less than or equal to the value in the table.

| | One-tailed, $\alpha = 0.005$ | $\alpha = 0.01$ | $\alpha = 0.025$ | $\alpha = 0.05$ |
|---|---|---|---|---|
| $n$ | Two-tailed, $\alpha = 0.01$ | $\alpha = 0.02$ | $\alpha = 0.05$ | $\alpha = 0.10$ |
| 8 | 0 | 0 | 0 | 1 |
| 9 | 0 | 0 | 1 | 1 |
| 10 | 0 | 0 | 1 | 1 |
| 11 | 0 | 1 | 1 | 2 |
| 12 | 1 | 1 | 2 | 2 |
| 13 | 1 | 1 | 2 | 3 |
| 14 | 1 | 2 | 3 | 3 |
| 15 | 2 | 2 | 3 | 3 |
| 16 | 2 | 2 | 3 | 4 |
| 17 | 2 | 3 | 4 | 4 |
| 18 | 3 | 3 | 4 | 5 |
| 19 | 3 | 4 | 4 | 5 |
| 20 | 3 | 4 | 5 | 5 |
| 21 | 4 | 4 | 5 | 6 |
| 22 | 4 | 5 | 5 | 6 |
| 23 | 4 | 5 | 6 | 7 |
| 24 | 5 | 5 | 6 | 7 |
| 25 | 5 | 6 | 6 | 7 |

Note: Table 8 is for one-tailed or two-tailed tests. The sample size $n$ represents the total number of + and − signs. The test value is the smaller number of + or − signs.

From *Journal of American Statistical Association* Vol. 41 (1946), pp. 557– 566. W. J. Dixon and A. M. Mood.

## Table 9—Critical Values for the Wilcoxon Signed-Rank Test

Reject the null hypothesis when the test statistic $w_s$ is less than or equal to the value in the table.

| | One-tailed, $\alpha = 0.05$ | $\alpha = 0.025$ | $\alpha = 0.01$ | $\alpha = 0.005$ |
|---|---|---|---|---|
| $n$ | Two-tailed, $\alpha = 0.10$ | $\alpha = 0.05$ | $\alpha = 0.02$ | $\alpha = 0.01$ |
| 5 | 1 | — | — | — |
| 6 | 2 | 1 | — | — |
| 7 | 4 | 2 | 0 | — |
| 8 | 6 | 4 | 2 | 0 |
| 9 | 8 | 6 | 3 | 2 |
| 10 | 11 | 8 | 5 | 3 |
| 11 | 14 | 11 | 7 | 5 |
| 12 | 17 | 14 | 10 | 7 |
| 13 | 21 | 17 | 13 | 10 |
| 14 | 26 | 21 | 16 | 13 |
| 15 | 30 | 25 | 20 | 16 |
| 16 | 36 | 30 | 24 | 19 |
| 17 | 41 | 35 | 28 | 23 |
| 18 | 47 | 40 | 33 | 28 |
| 19 | 54 | 46 | 38 | 32 |
| 20 | 60 | 52 | 43 | 37 |
| 21 | 68 | 59 | 49 | 43 |
| 22 | 75 | 66 | 56 | 49 |
| 23 | 83 | 73 | 62 | 55 |
| 24 | 92 | 81 | 69 | 61 |
| 25 | 101 | 90 | 77 | 68 |
| 26 | 110 | 98 | 85 | 76 |
| 27 | 120 | 107 | 93 | 84 |
| 28 | 130 | 117 | 102 | 92 |
| 29 | 141 | 127 | 111 | 100 |
| 30 | 152 | 137 | 120 | 109 |

From *Some Rapid Approximate Statistical Procedures.* Copyright 1949, 1964 Lederle Laboratories, American Cyanamid Co., Wayne, N.J.

## Table 10—Critical Values for the Spearman Rank Correlation Coefficient

Reject $H_0$: $\rho_s = 0$ when the absolute value of $r_s$ is greater than the value in the table.

| $n$ | $\alpha = 0.10$ | $\alpha = 0.05$ | $\alpha = 0.01$ |
|---|---|---|---|
| 5 | 0.900 | — | — |
| 6 | 0.829 | 0.886 | — |
| 7 | 0.714 | 0.786 | 0.929 |
| 8 | 0.643 | 0.738 | 0.881 |
| 9 | 0.600 | 0.700 | 0.833 |
| 10 | 0.564 | 0.648 | 0.794 |
| 11 | 0.536 | 0.618 | 0.818 |
| 12 | 0.497 | 0.591 | 0.780 |
| 13 | 0.475 | 0.566 | 0.745 |
| 14 | 0.457 | 0.545 | 0.716 |
| 15 | 0.441 | 0.525 | 0.689 |
| 16 | 0.425 | 0.507 | 0.666 |
| 17 | 0.412 | 0.490 | 0.645 |
| 18 | 0.399 | 0.476 | 0.625 |
| 19 | 0.388 | 0.462 | 0.608 |
| 20 | 0.377 | 0.450 | 0.591 |
| 21 | 0.368 | 0.438 | 0.576 |
| 22 | 0.359 | 0.428 | 0.562 |
| 23 | 0.351 | 0.418 | 0.549 |
| 24 | 0.343 | 0.409 | 0.537 |
| 25 | 0.336 | 0.400 | 0.526 |
| 26 | 0.329 | 0.392 | 0.515 |
| 27 | 0.323 | 0.385 | 0.505 |
| 28 | 0.317 | 0.377 | 0.496 |
| 29 | 0.311 | 0.370 | 0.487 |
| 30 | 0.305 | 0.364 | 0.478 |

From the Institute of Mathematical Statistics.

## Table 11—Critical Values for the Pearson Correlation Coefficient

The correlation is significant when the absolute value of $r$ is greater than the value in the table.

| $n$ | $\alpha = 0.05$ | $\alpha = 0.01$ |
|---|---|---|
| 4 | 0.950 | 0.990 |
| 5 | 0.878 | 0.959 |
| 6 | 0.811 | 0.917 |
| 7 | 0.754 | 0.875 |
| 8 | 0.707 | 0.834 |
| 9 | 0.666 | 0.798 |
| 10 | 0.632 | 0.765 |
| 11 | 0.602 | 0.735 |
| 12 | 0.576 | 0.708 |
| 13 | 0.553 | 0.684 |
| 14 | 0.532 | 0.661 |
| 15 | 0.514 | 0.641 |
| 16 | 0.497 | 0.623 |
| 17 | 0.482 | 0.606 |
| 18 | 0.468 | 0.590 |
| 19 | 0.456 | 0.575 |
| 20 | 0.444 | 0.561 |
| 21 | 0.433 | 0.549 |
| 22 | 0.423 | 0.537 |
| 23 | 0.413 | 0.526 |
| 24 | 0.404 | 0.515 |
| 25 | 0.396 | 0.505 |
| 26 | 0.388 | 0.496 |
| 27 | 0.381 | 0.487 |
| 28 | 0.374 | 0.479 |
| 29 | 0.367 | 0.471 |
| 30 | 0.361 | 0.463 |
| 35 | 0.334 | 0.430 |
| 40 | 0.312 | 0.403 |
| 45 | 0.294 | 0.380 |
| 50 | 0.279 | 0.361 |
| 55 | 0.266 | 0.345 |
| 60 | 0.254 | 0.330 |
| 65 | 0.244 | 0.317 |
| 70 | 0.235 | 0.306 |
| 75 | 0.227 | 0.296 |
| 80 | 0.220 | 0.286 |
| 85 | 0.213 | 0.278 |
| 90 | 0.207 | 0.270 |
| 95 | 0.202 | 0.263 |
| 100 | 0.197 | 0.256 |

The critical values in Table 11 were generated using Excel.

# Table 12—Critical Values for the Number of Runs

Reject the null hypothesis when the test statistic $G$ is less than or equal to the smaller entry or greater than or equal to the larger entry.

| Value of $n_1$ | Value of $n_2$: 2 | 3 | 4 | 5 | 6 | 7 | 8 | 9 | 10 | 11 | 12 | 13 | 14 | 15 | 16 | 17 | 18 | 19 | 20 |
|---|---|---|---|---|---|---|---|---|---|---|---|---|---|---|---|---|---|---|---|
| 2 | 1 | 1 | 1 | 1 | 1 | 1 | 1 | 1 | 1 | 1 | 2 | 2 | 2 | 2 | 2 | 2 | 2 | 2 | 2 |
|  | 6 | 6 | 6 | 6 | 6 | 6 | 6 | 6 | 6 | 6 | 6 | 6 | 6 | 6 | 6 | 6 | 6 | 6 | 6 |
| 3 | 1 | 1 | 1 | 1 | 2 | 2 | 2 | 2 | 2 | 2 | 2 | 2 | 2 | 3 | 3 | 3 | 3 | 3 | 3 |
|  | 6 | 8 | 8 | 8 | 8 | 8 | 8 | 8 | 8 | 8 | 8 | 8 | 8 | 8 | 8 | 8 | 8 | 8 | 8 |
| 4 | 1 | 1 | 1 | 2 | 2 | 2 | 3 | 3 | 3 | 3 | 3 | 3 | 3 | 3 | 4 | 4 | 4 | 4 | 4 |
|  | 6 | 8 | 9 | 9 | 9 | 10 | 10 | 10 | 10 | 10 | 10 | 10 | 10 | 10 | 10 | 10 | 10 | 10 | 10 |
| 5 | 1 | 1 | 2 | 2 | 3 | 3 | 3 | 3 | 3 | 4 | 4 | 4 | 4 | 4 | 4 | 4 | 5 | 5 | 5 |
|  | 6 | 8 | 9 | 10 | 10 | 11 | 11 | 12 | 12 | 12 | 12 | 12 | 12 | 12 | 12 | 12 | 12 | 12 | 12 |
| 6 | 1 | 2 | 2 | 3 | 3 | 3 | 3 | 4 | 4 | 4 | 4 | 5 | 5 | 5 | 5 | 5 | 5 | 6 | 6 |
|  | 6 | 8 | 9 | 10 | 11 | 12 | 12 | 13 | 13 | 13 | 13 | 14 | 14 | 14 | 14 | 14 | 14 | 14 | 14 |
| 7 | 1 | 2 | 2 | 3 | 3 | 3 | 4 | 4 | 5 | 5 | 5 | 5 | 5 | 6 | 6 | 6 | 6 | 6 | 6 |
|  | 6 | 8 | 10 | 11 | 12 | 13 | 13 | 14 | 14 | 14 | 14 | 15 | 15 | 15 | 16 | 16 | 16 | 16 | 16 |
| 8 | 1 | 2 | 3 | 3 | 3 | 4 | 4 | 5 | 5 | 5 | 6 | 6 | 6 | 6 | 6 | 7 | 7 | 7 | 7 |
|  | 6 | 8 | 10 | 11 | 12 | 13 | 14 | 14 | 15 | 15 | 16 | 16 | 16 | 16 | 17 | 17 | 17 | 17 | 17 |
| 9 | 1 | 2 | 3 | 3 | 4 | 4 | 5 | 5 | 5 | 6 | 6 | 6 | 7 | 7 | 7 | 7 | 8 | 8 | 8 |
|  | 6 | 8 | 10 | 12 | 13 | 14 | 14 | 15 | 16 | 16 | 16 | 17 | 17 | 18 | 18 | 18 | 18 | 18 | 18 |
| 10 | 1 | 2 | 3 | 3 | 4 | 5 | 5 | 5 | 6 | 6 | 7 | 7 | 7 | 7 | 8 | 8 | 8 | 8 | 9 |
|  | 6 | 8 | 10 | 12 | 13 | 14 | 15 | 16 | 16 | 17 | 17 | 18 | 18 | 18 | 19 | 19 | 19 | 20 | 20 |
| 11 | 1 | 2 | 3 | 4 | 4 | 5 | 5 | 6 | 6 | 7 | 7 | 7 | 8 | 8 | 8 | 9 | 9 | 9 | 9 |
|  | 6 | 8 | 10 | 12 | 13 | 14 | 15 | 16 | 17 | 17 | 18 | 19 | 19 | 19 | 20 | 20 | 20 | 21 | 21 |
| 12 | 2 | 2 | 3 | 4 | 4 | 5 | 6 | 6 | 7 | 7 | 7 | 8 | 8 | 8 | 9 | 9 | 9 | 10 | 10 |
|  | 6 | 8 | 10 | 12 | 13 | 14 | 16 | 16 | 17 | 18 | 19 | 19 | 20 | 20 | 21 | 21 | 21 | 22 | 22 |
| 13 | 2 | 2 | 3 | 4 | 5 | 5 | 6 | 6 | 7 | 7 | 8 | 8 | 9 | 9 | 9 | 10 | 10 | 10 | 10 |
|  | 6 | 8 | 10 | 12 | 14 | 15 | 16 | 17 | 18 | 19 | 19 | 20 | 20 | 21 | 21 | 22 | 22 | 23 | 23 |
| 14 | 2 | 2 | 3 | 4 | 5 | 5 | 6 | 7 | 7 | 8 | 8 | 9 | 9 | 9 | 10 | 10 | 10 | 11 | 11 |
|  | 6 | 8 | 10 | 12 | 14 | 15 | 16 | 17 | 18 | 19 | 20 | 20 | 21 | 22 | 22 | 23 | 23 | 23 | 24 |
| 15 | 2 | 3 | 3 | 4 | 5 | 6 | 6 | 7 | 7 | 8 | 8 | 9 | 9 | 10 | 10 | 11 | 11 | 11 | 12 |
|  | 6 | 8 | 10 | 12 | 14 | 15 | 16 | 18 | 18 | 19 | 20 | 21 | 22 | 22 | 23 | 23 | 24 | 24 | 25 |
| 16 | 2 | 3 | 4 | 4 | 5 | 6 | 6 | 7 | 8 | 8 | 9 | 9 | 10 | 10 | 11 | 11 | 11 | 12 | 12 |
|  | 6 | 8 | 10 | 12 | 14 | 16 | 17 | 18 | 19 | 20 | 21 | 21 | 22 | 23 | 23 | 24 | 25 | 25 | 25 |
| 17 | 2 | 3 | 4 | 4 | 5 | 6 | 7 | 7 | 8 | 9 | 9 | 10 | 10 | 11 | 11 | 11 | 12 | 12 | 13 |
|  | 6 | 8 | 10 | 12 | 14 | 16 | 17 | 18 | 19 | 20 | 21 | 22 | 23 | 23 | 24 | 25 | 25 | 26 | 26 |
| 18 | 2 | 3 | 4 | 5 | 5 | 6 | 7 | 8 | 8 | 9 | 9 | 10 | 10 | 11 | 11 | 12 | 12 | 13 | 13 |
|  | 6 | 8 | 10 | 12 | 14 | 16 | 17 | 18 | 19 | 20 | 21 | 22 | 23 | 24 | 25 | 25 | 26 | 26 | 27 |
| 19 | 2 | 3 | 4 | 5 | 6 | 6 | 7 | 8 | 8 | 9 | 10 | 10 | 11 | 11 | 12 | 12 | 13 | 13 | 13 |
|  | 6 | 8 | 10 | 12 | 14 | 16 | 17 | 18 | 20 | 21 | 22 | 23 | 23 | 24 | 25 | 26 | 26 | 27 | 27 |
| 20 | 2 | 3 | 4 | 5 | 6 | 6 | 7 | 8 | 9 | 9 | 10 | 10 | 11 | 12 | 12 | 13 | 13 | 13 | 14 |
|  | 6 | 8 | 10 | 12 | 14 | 16 | 17 | 18 | 20 | 21 | 22 | 23 | 24 | 25 | 25 | 26 | 27 | 27 | 28 |

Note: Table 12 is for a two-tailed test with $\alpha = 0.05$.

From the Institute of Mathematical Statistics.

# APPENDIX C

# C Normal Probability Plots

**What You Should Learn**

- How to construct and interpret a normal probability plot

## Normal Probability Plots

For many of the examples and exercises in this text, it has been assumed that a random sample is selected from a population that has a normal distribution. After selecting a random sample from a population with an unknown distribution, how can you determine whether the sample was selected from a population that has a normal distribution?

You have already learned that a histogram or stem-and-leaf plot can reveal the shape of a distribution and any outliers, clusters, or gaps in a distribution (see Sections 2.1, 2.2, and 2.3). These data displays are useful for assessing large sets of data, but assessing small data sets in this manner can be difficult and unreliable. A reliable method for assessing normality in *any* data set is to use a **normal probability plot.**

**DEFINITION**

A **normal probability plot** (also called a **normal quantile plot**) is a graph that plots each observed value from the data set along with its expected $z$-score. The observed values are usually plotted along the horizontal axis while the expected $z$-scores are plotted along the vertical axis.

The guidelines below can help you determine whether data come from a population that has a normal distribution.

1. If the plotted points in a normal probability plot are approximately linear, then you can conclude that the data come from a normal distribution.
2. If the plotted points are not approximately linear or follow some type of pattern that is not linear, then you can conclude that the data come from a distribution that is not normal.
3. Multiple outliers or clusters of points indicate a distribution that is not normal.

Two normal probability plots are shown below. The normal probability plot on the left is approximately linear. So, you can conclude that the data come from a population that has a normal distribution. The normal probability plot on the right follows a nonlinear pattern. So, you can conclude that the data do not come from a population that has a normal distribution.

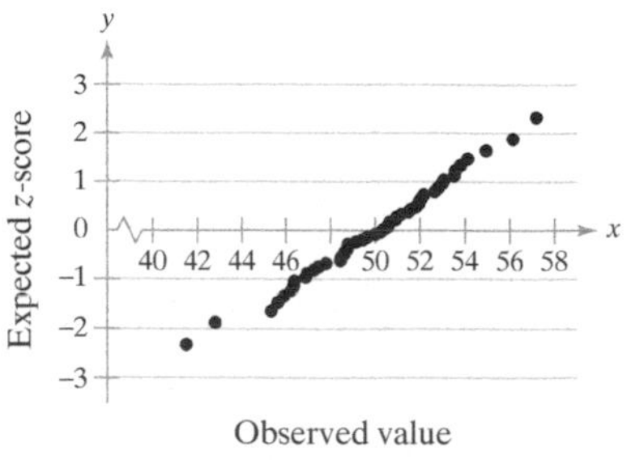


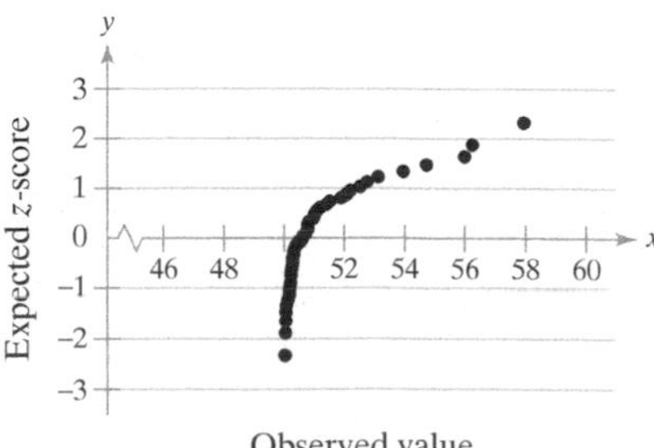

Constructing a normal probability plot by hand can be rather tedious. You can use technology such as Minitab, Excel, StatCrunch, or the TI-84 Plus to construct a normal probability plot, as shown in Example 1.

## EXAMPLE 1

### Constructing a Normal Probability Plot

The heights (in inches) of 12 randomly selected current National Basketball Association players are listed. Use technology to construct a normal probability plot to determine whether the data come from a population that has a normal distribution. *(Source: NBA Media Ventures, LLC)*

74 70 78 75 73 71 80 82 81 76 86 77

**SOLUTION**

Using Minitab, enter the heights into column C1. From the *Graph* menu, select "Probability Plot," choose the option "Single," and click OK. Next, select column C1 as the graph variable. Then click "Distribution" and choose "Normal" from the drop-down menu. Click the *Data Display* tab, select "Symbols only," and click OK. After clicking "Scale," click the *Y-Scale Type* tab, select "Score," and click OK. Click OK to construct the normal probability plot. Your result should be similar to the one shown below. (To construct a normal probability plot using a TI-84 Plus, follow the instructions in the Tech Tip at the left.)

MINITAB

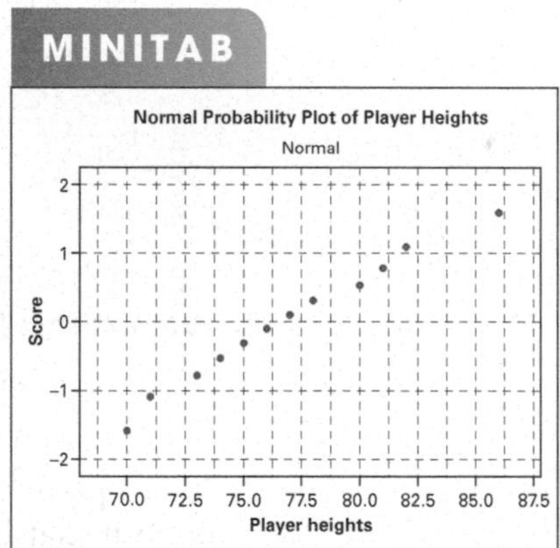


***Interpretation*** Because the points are approximately linear, you can conclude that the sample data come from a population that has a normal distribution.

**TRY IT YOURSELF 1**

The balances (in dollars) on student loans for 18 randomly selected college seniors are listed. Use technology to construct a normal probability plot to determine whether the data come from a population that has a normal distribution.

29,150 16,980 12,470 19,235 15,875 8,960 16,105 14,575 39,860
20,170 9,710 19,650 21,590 8,200 18,100 25,530 9,285 10,075

*Answer: Page A43*

To see that the points are approximately linear, you can graph the regression line for the observed values from the data set and their expected $z$-scores. The regression line for the heights and expected $z$-scores from Example 1 is shown in the graph at the left. From the graph, you can see that the points lie along the regression line. You can also approximate the mean of the data set by determining where the line crosses the $x$-axis.

**Tech Tip**

Here are instructions for constructing a normal probability plot using a TI-84 Plus. First, enter the data into List 1. Then use *Stat Plot* to construct the normal probability plot, as shown below.

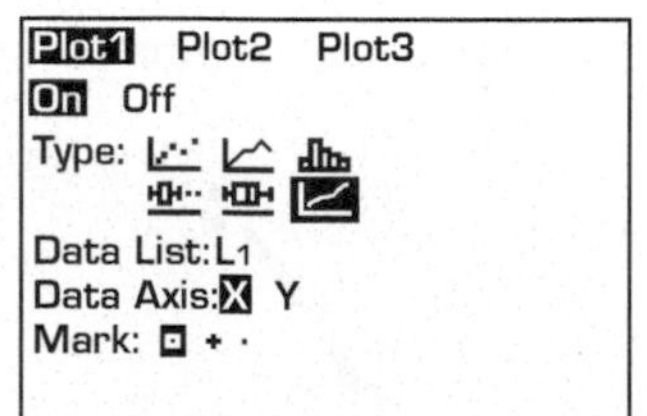


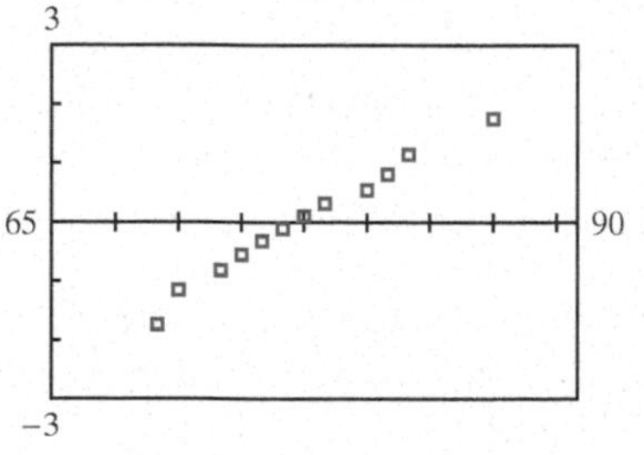


MINITAB

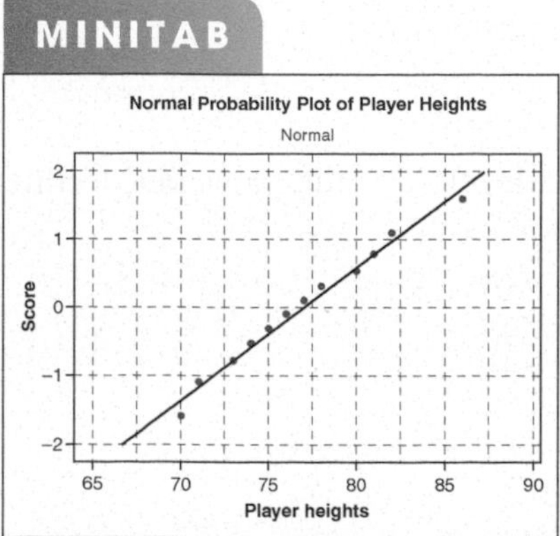

# C EXERCISES

For Extra Help: MyLab Statistics

1. In a normal probability plot, what is usually plotted along the horizontal axis? What is usually plotted along the vertical axis?
2. Describe how you can use a normal probability plot to determine whether data come from a normal distribution.

**Graphical Analysis** *In Exercises 3 and 4, use the histogram and normal probability plot to determine whether the data come from a normal distribution. Explain your reasoning.*

3.

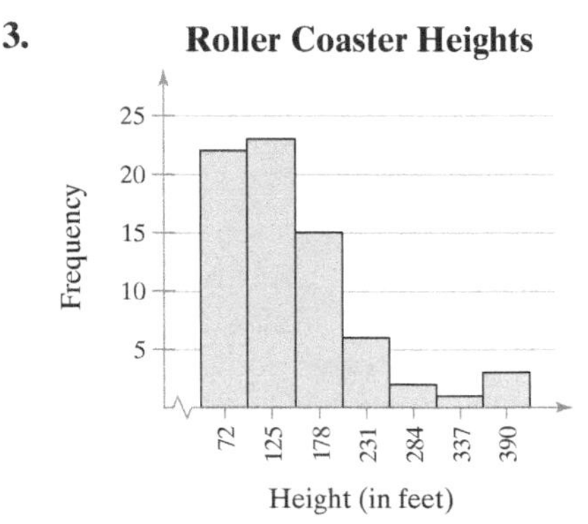


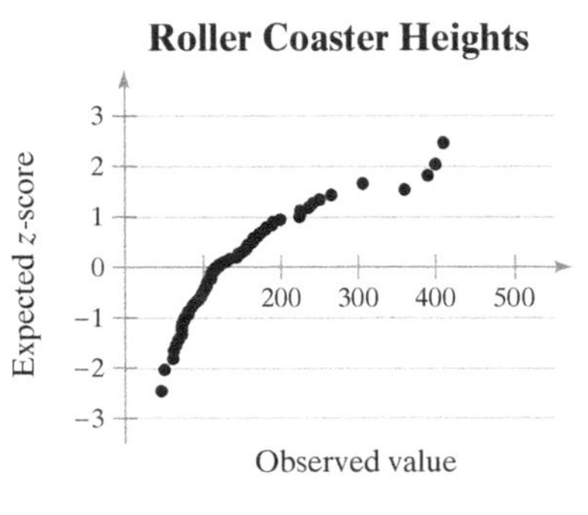


4.

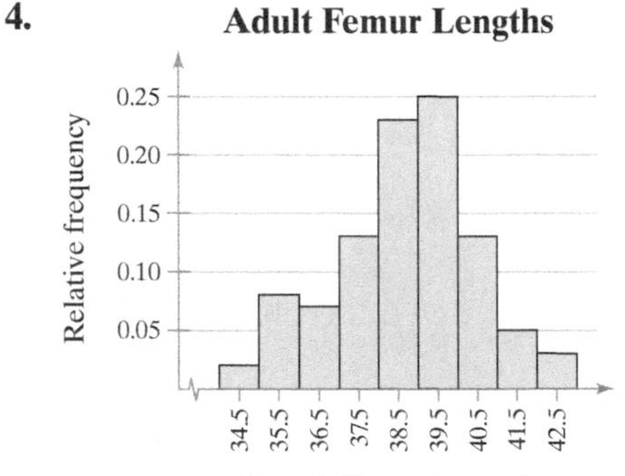


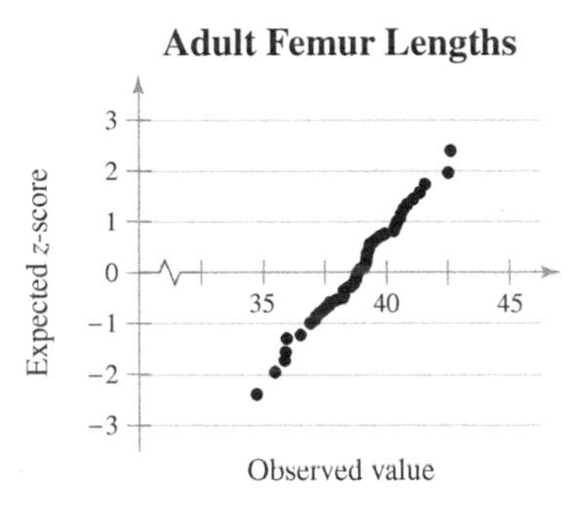


**Constructing a Normal Probability Plot** *In Exercises 5 and 6, use technology to construct a normal probability plot to determine whether the data come from a population that has a normal distribution.*

5. **Reaction Times** The reaction times (in milliseconds) of 30 randomly selected adults to an auditory stimulus

| | | | | | | | |
|---|---|---|---|---|---|---|---|
| 507 | 389 | 305 | 291 | 336 | 310 | 514 | 442 |
| 373 | 428 | 387 | 454 | 323 | 441 | 388 | 426 |
| 411 | 382 | 320 | 450 | 309 | 416 | 359 | 388 |
| 307 | 337 | 469 | 351 | 422 | 413 | | |

6. **Triglyceride Levels** The triglyceride levels (in milligrams per deciliter of blood) of 26 randomly selected patients

| | | | | | | |
|---|---|---|---|---|---|---|
| 209 | 140 | 155 | 170 | 265 | 138 | 180 |
| 295 | 250 | 320 | 270 | 225 | 215 | 390 |
| 420 | 462 | 150 | 200 | 400 | 295 | 240 |
| 200 | 190 | 145 | 160 | 175 | | |

# APPENDIX D

# D Key Formulas

## CHAPTER 2

Class Width $= \dfrac{\text{Range of data}}{\text{Number of classes}}$

(round up to next convenient number)

Midpoint $= \dfrac{(\text{Lower class limit}) + (\text{Upper class limit})}{2}$

Relative Frequency $= \dfrac{\text{Class frequency}}{\text{Sample size}} = \dfrac{f}{n}$

Population Mean: $\mu = \dfrac{\Sigma x}{N}$

Sample Mean: $\bar{x} = \dfrac{\Sigma x}{n}$

Weighted Mean: $\bar{x} = \dfrac{\Sigma xw}{\Sigma w}$

Mean of a Frequency Distribution: $\bar{x} = \dfrac{\Sigma xf}{n}$

Range = (Maximum entry) − (Minimum entry)

Population Variance: $\sigma^2 = \dfrac{\Sigma(x - \mu)^2}{N}$

Population Standard Deviation:

$$\sigma = \sqrt{\sigma^2} = \sqrt{\frac{\Sigma(x - \mu)^2}{N}}$$

Sample Variance: $s^2 = \dfrac{\Sigma(x - \bar{x})^2}{n - 1}$

Sample Standard Deviation: $s = \sqrt{s^2} = \sqrt{\dfrac{\Sigma(x - \bar{x})^2}{n - 1}}$

***Empirical Rule*** (or 68-95-99.7 Rule) For data sets with distributions that are approximately symmetric and bell-shaped:

1. About 68% of the data lie within one standard deviation of the mean.
2. About 95% of the data lie within two standard deviations of the mean.
3. About 99.7% of the data lie within three standard deviations of the mean.

***Chebychev's Theorem*** The portion of any data set lying within $k$ standard deviations ($k > 1$) of the mean is at least $1 - \dfrac{1}{k^2}$.

Sample Standard Deviation of a Frequency Distribution:

$$s = \sqrt{\frac{\Sigma(x - \bar{x})^2 f}{n - 1}}$$

Population Coefficient of Variation: $CV = \dfrac{\sigma}{\mu} \cdot 100\%$

Sample Coefficient of Variation: $CV = \dfrac{s}{\bar{x}} \cdot 100\%$

Interquartile Range: $\text{IQR} = Q_3 - Q_1$

Percentile of $x = \dfrac{\text{number of data entries less than } x}{\text{total number of data entries}} \cdot 100$

Standard Score: $z = \dfrac{\text{Value} - \text{Mean}}{\text{Standard deviation}} = \dfrac{x - \mu}{\sigma}$

## CHAPTER 3

Classical (or Theoretical) Probability:

$$P(E) = \frac{\text{Number of outcomes in event } E}{\text{Total number of outcomes in sample space}}$$

Empirical (or Statistical) Probability:

$$P(E) = \frac{\text{Frequency of event } E}{\text{Total frequency}} = \frac{f}{n}$$

Probability of a Complement: $P(E') = 1 - P(E)$

Probability of occurrence of both events $A$ and $B$:

$P(A \text{ and } B) = P(A) \cdot P(B \mid A)$

$P(A \text{ and } B) = P(A) \cdot P(B)$ if $A$ and $B$ are independent

Probability of occurrence of either $A$ or $B$:

$P(A \text{ or } B) = P(A) + P(B) - P(A \text{ and } B)$

$P(A \text{ or } B) = P(A) + P(B)$ if $A$ and $B$ are mutually exclusive

Permutations of $n$ objects taken $r$ at a time:

$${}_nP_r = \frac{n!}{(n-r)!}, \text{ where } r \le n$$

Distinguishable Permutations: $n_1$ alike, $n_2$ alike, . . . , $n_k$ alike:

$$\frac{n!}{n_1! \cdot n_2! \cdot n_3! \cdots n_k!},$$

where $n_1 + n_2 + n_3 + \cdots + n_k = n$

Combinations of $n$ objects taken $r$ at a time:

$${}_nC_r = \frac{n!}{(n-r)!r!}, \text{ where } r \le n$$

## CHAPTER 4

Mean of a Discrete Random Variable: $\mu = \Sigma x P(x)$

Variance of a Discrete Random Variable:

$$\sigma^2 = \Sigma(x - \mu)^2 P(x)$$

Standard Deviation of a Discrete Random Variable:

$$\sigma = \sqrt{\sigma^2} = \sqrt{\Sigma(x - \mu)^2 P(x)}$$

Expected Value: $E(x) = \mu = \Sigma x P(x)$

Binomial Probability of $x$ successes in $n$ trials:

$$P(x) = {}_nC_x p^x q^{n-x} = \frac{n!}{(n-x)!x!} p^x q^{n-x}$$

Population Parameters of a Binomial Distribution:

Mean: $\mu = np$ Variance: $\sigma^2 = npq$

Standard Deviation: $\sigma = \sqrt{npq}$

Geometric Distribution: The probability that the first success will occur on trial number $x$ is $P(x) = pq^{x-1}$, where $q = 1 - p$.

Poisson Distribution: The probability of exactly $x$ occurrences in an interval is $P(x) = \dfrac{\mu^x e^{-\mu}}{x!}$, where $e \approx 2.71828$ and $\mu$ is the mean number of occurrences per interval unit.

## CHAPTER 5

Standard Score, or $z$-Score:

$$z = \frac{\text{Value} - \text{Mean}}{\text{Standard deviation}} = \frac{x - \mu}{\sigma}$$

Transforming a $z$-Score to an $x$-Value: $x = \mu + z\sigma$

***Central Limit Theorem*** ($n \ge 30$ or population is normally distributed):

Mean of the Sampling Distribution: $\mu_{\bar{x}} = \mu$

Variance of the Sampling Distribution: $\sigma_{\bar{x}}^2 = \dfrac{\sigma^2}{n}$

Standard Deviation of the Sampling Distribution (Standard Error): $\sigma_{\bar{x}} = \dfrac{\sigma}{\sqrt{n}}$

$$z\text{-Score} = \frac{\text{Value} - \text{Mean}}{\text{Standard Error}} = \frac{\bar{x} - \mu_{\bar{x}}}{\sigma_{\bar{x}}} = \frac{\bar{x} - \mu}{\sigma/\sqrt{n}}$$

## Chapter 6

$c$-Confidence Interval for $\mu$: $\bar{x} - E < \mu < \bar{x} + E$, where $E = z_c \dfrac{\sigma}{\sqrt{n}}$ when $\sigma$ is known, the sample is random, and either the population is normally distributed or $n \geq 30$, or $E = t_c \dfrac{s}{\sqrt{n}}$ when $\sigma$ is unknown, the sample is random, and either the population is normally distributed or $n \geq 30$.

If the distribution of a random variable $x$ is approximately normal, then $t = \dfrac{\bar{x} - \mu}{s/\sqrt{n}}$ follows a $t$-distribution.

Minimum Sample Size to Estimate $\mu$: $n = \left(\dfrac{z_c \sigma}{E}\right)^2$

Point Estimate for $p$, the population proportion of successes: $\hat{p} = \dfrac{x}{n}$

$c$-Confidence Interval for Population Proportion $p$ (when $np \geq 5$ and $nq \geq 5$): $\hat{p} - E < p < \hat{p} + E$, where

$$E = z_c \sqrt{\frac{\hat{p}\hat{q}}{n}}$$

Minimum Sample Size to Estimate $p$: $n = \hat{p}\hat{q}\left(\dfrac{z_c}{E}\right)^2$

If a random variable $x$ has a normal distribution, then the distribution of $\chi^2 = \dfrac{(n-1)s^2}{\sigma^2}$ forms a chi-square distribution for samples of any size $n > 1$.

$c$-Confidence Interval for Population Variance $\sigma^2$:

$$\frac{(n-1)s^2}{\chi_R^2} < \sigma^2 < \frac{(n-1)s^2}{\chi_L^2}$$

$c$-Confidence Interval for Population Standard Deviation $\sigma$:

$$\sqrt{\frac{(n-1)s^2}{\chi_R^2}} < \sigma < \sqrt{\frac{(n-1)s^2}{\chi_L^2}}$$

## Chapter 7

$z$-Test for a Mean $\mu$: $z = \dfrac{\bar{x} - \mu}{\sigma/\sqrt{n}}$, when $\sigma$ is known, the sample is random, and either the population is normally distributed or $n \geq 30$.

$t$-Test for a Mean $\mu$: $t = \dfrac{\bar{x} - \mu}{s/\sqrt{n}}$, when $\sigma$ is unknown, the sample is random, and either the population is normally distributed or $n \geq 30$. (d.f. $= n - 1$)

$z$-Test for a Proportion $p$ (when $np \geq 5$ and $nq \geq 5$):

$$z = \frac{\hat{p} - \mu_{\hat{p}}}{\sigma_{\hat{p}}} = \frac{\hat{p} - p}{\sqrt{pq/n}}$$

Chi-Square Test for a Variance $\sigma^2$ or Standard Deviation $\sigma$:

$$\chi^2 = \frac{(n-1)s^2}{\sigma^2} \quad (\text{d.f.} = n - 1)$$

## Chapter 8

Two-Sample $z$-Test for the Difference Between Means ($\sigma_1$ and $\sigma_2$ are known, the samples are random and independent, and either the populations are normally distributed or both $n_1 \geq 30$ and $n_2 \geq 30$):

$$z = \frac{(\bar{x}_1 - \bar{x}_2) - (\mu_1 - \mu_2)}{\sigma_{\bar{x}_1 - \bar{x}_2}},$$

$$\text{where } \sigma_{\bar{x}_1 - \bar{x}_2} = \sqrt{\frac{\sigma_1^2}{n_1} + \frac{\sigma_2^2}{n_2}}$$

Two-Sample $t$-Test for the Difference Between Means ($\sigma_1$ and $\sigma_2$ are unknown, the samples are random and independent, and either the populations are normally distributed or both $n_1 \geq 30$ and $n_2 \geq 30$):

$$t = \frac{(\bar{x}_1 - \bar{x}_2) - (\mu_1 - \mu_2)}{s_{\bar{x}_1 - \bar{x}_2}}$$

If population variances are equal, d.f. $= n_1 + n_2 - 2$ and

$$s_{\bar{x}_1 - \bar{x}_2} = \sqrt{\frac{(n_1 - 1)s_1^2 + (n_2 - 1)s_2^2}{n_1 + n_2 - 2}} \cdot \sqrt{\frac{1}{n_1} + \frac{1}{n_2}}.$$

If population variances are not equal, d.f. is the smaller of $n_1 - 1$ or $n_2 - 1$ and $s_{\bar{x}_1 - \bar{x}_2} = \sqrt{\frac{s_1^2}{n_1} + \frac{s_2^2}{n_2}}$.

$t$-Test for the Difference Between Means (the samples are random and dependent, and either the populations are normally distributed or $n \geq 30$):

$$t = \frac{\bar{d} - \mu_d}{s_d/\sqrt{n}}, \text{ where } \bar{d} = \frac{\Sigma d}{n}, \ s_d = \sqrt{\frac{\Sigma(d - \bar{d})^2}{n - 1}},$$

and d.f. $= n - 1$.

Two-Sample $z$-Test for the Difference Between Proportions (the samples are random and independent, and $n_1\bar{p}$, $n_1\bar{q}$, $n_2\bar{p}$, and $n_2\bar{q}$ are at least 5):

$$z = \frac{(\hat{p}_1 - \hat{p}_2) - (p_1 - p_2)}{\sqrt{\bar{p}\bar{q}\left(\frac{1}{n_1} + \frac{1}{n_2}\right)}}, \text{ where } \bar{p} = \frac{x_1 + x_2}{n_1 + n_2}$$

and $\bar{q} = 1 - \bar{p}$.

## Chapter 9

Correlation Coefficient:

$$r = \frac{n\Sigma xy - (\Sigma x)(\Sigma y)}{\sqrt{n\Sigma x^2 - (\Sigma x)^2}\sqrt{n\Sigma y^2 - (\Sigma y)^2}}$$

$t$-Test for the Correlation Coefficient:

$$t = \frac{r}{\sqrt{\frac{1 - r^2}{n - 2}}} \quad (\text{d.f.} = n - 2)$$

Equation of a Regression Line: $\hat{y} = mx + b$,

$$\text{where } m = \frac{n\Sigma xy - (\Sigma x)(\Sigma y)}{n\Sigma x^2 - (\Sigma x)^2} \text{ and}$$

$$b = \bar{y} - m\bar{x} = \frac{\Sigma y}{n} - m\frac{\Sigma x}{n}.$$

Coefficient of Determination:

$$r^2 = \frac{\text{Explained variation}}{\text{Total variation}} = \frac{\Sigma(\hat{y}_i - \bar{y})^2}{\Sigma(y_i - \bar{y})^2}$$

Standard Error of Estimate: $s_e = \sqrt{\frac{\Sigma(y_i - \hat{y}_i)^2}{n - 2}}$

$c$-Prediction Interval for $y$: $\hat{y} - E < y < \hat{y} + E$, where

$$E = t_c s_e \sqrt{1 + \frac{1}{n} + \frac{n(x_0 - \bar{x})^2}{n\Sigma x^2 - (\Sigma x)^2}} \quad (\text{d.f.} = n - 2)$$

## Chapter 10

Chi-Square: $\chi^2 = \Sigma\frac{(O - E)^2}{E}$

Goodness-of-Fit Test: d.f. $= k - 1$

Independence Test:

d.f. $=$ (no. of rows $-$ 1)(no. of columns $-$ 1)

Expected frequency $E_{r,c} = \frac{(\text{Sum of row } r) \cdot (\text{Sum of column } c)}{\text{Sample size}}$.

Two-Sample $F$-Test for Variances: $F = \frac{s_1^2}{s_2^2}$, where

$s_1^2 \geq s_2^2$, d.f.$_\text{N} = n_1 - 1$, and d.f.$_\text{D} = n_2 - 1$.

One-Way Analysis of Variance Test:

$$F = \frac{MS_B}{MS_W}, \text{ where } MS_B = \frac{SS_B}{\text{d.f.}_\text{N}} = \frac{\Sigma n_i(\bar{x}_i - \bar{\bar{x}})^2}{k - 1}$$

$$\text{and } MS_W = \frac{SS_W}{\text{d.f.}_\text{D}} = \frac{\Sigma(n_i - 1)s_i^2}{N - k}.$$

(d.f.$_\text{N} = k - 1$, d.f.$_\text{D} = N - k$)

# TRY IT YOURSELF ANSWERS

## Chapter 1

### Section 1.1

1. The population consists of the responses of all teens in the United States. The sample consists of the responses of the 1516 teens in the survey. The sample data set consists of the 1228 teens who said mental health is a significant issue for young people in the U.S. and 288 teens who did not.
2. (a) Population parameter, because the total spent on employees' salaries, $5,150,694, is based on the entire company.
   (b) Sample statistic, because 47% is based on a subset of the population.
3. (a) The population consists of the responses of all Internet users, and the sample consists of the responses of the 513 respondents in the study.
   (b) The part of this study that represents the descriptive branch of statistics involves the statement "97% of the respondents said music is important to them, and 83% of the respondents said they actively look for new music."
   (c) A possible inference drawn from the study is that a large majority of Internet users find music to be important to them and actively look for new music.

### Section 1.2

1. The city names are nonnumerical entries, so these are qualitative data. The city populations are numerical entries, so these are quantitative data.
2. (1) Ordinal, because the data can be put in order.
   (2) Nominal, because no mathematical computations can be made.
3. (1) Interval, because the data can be ordered and meaningful differences can be calculated, but it does not make sense to write a ratio using the temperatures.
   (2) Ratio, because the data can be ordered, meaningful differences can be calculated, the data can be written as a ratio, and the data set contains an inherent zero.

### Section 1.3

1. This is an observational study.
2. There is no way to tell why the people quit smoking. They could have quit smoking as a result of either chewing the gum or watching the DVD. The gum and the DVD could be confounding variables. To improve the study, two experiments could be done, one using the gum and the other using the DVD. Or just conduct one experiment using either the gum or the DVD.
3. *Sample answer:* Assign numbers 1 to 79 to the employees of the company. Use the table of random numbers and obtain 63, 7, 40, 19, and 26. The employees assigned these numbers will make up the sample.
4. (1) The sample was selected by using the students in a randomly chosen class. This is cluster sampling.
   (2) The sample was selected by numbering each student in the school, randomly choosing a starting number, and selecting students at regular intervals from the starting number. This is systematic sampling.

## Chapter 2

### Section 2.1

1.

| Class | Frequency, $f$ |
|---|---|
| 13–20 | 9 |
| 21–28 | 16 |
| 29–36 | 18 |
| 37–44 | 7 |
| 45–52 | 4 |
| 53–60 | 1 |

2.

| Class | Frequency, $f$ | Midpoint | Relative frequency | Cumulative frequency |
|---|---|---|---|---|
| 13–20 | 9 | 16.5 | 0.16 | 9 |
| 21–28 | 16 | 24.5 | 0.29 | 25 |
| 29–36 | 18 | 32.5 | 0.33 | 43 |
| 37–44 | 7 | 40.5 | 0.13 | 50 |
| 45–52 | 4 | 48.5 | 0.07 | 54 |
| 53–60 | 1 | 56.5 | 0.02 | 55 |
| | $\Sigma f = 55$ | | $\Sigma \frac{f}{n} = 1$ | |

*Sample answer:* The most common range of points scored by winning teams is 29 to 36. About 9% of the winning teams scored more than 45 points.

3.

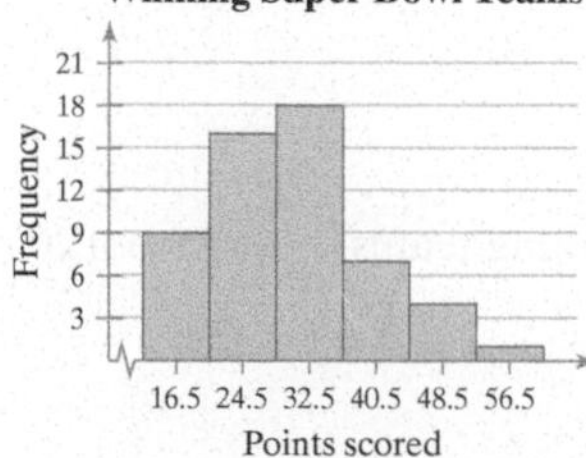


*Sample answer:* The most common range of points scored by winning teams is 29 to 36. About 9% of the winning teams scored more than 45 points.

**4.**

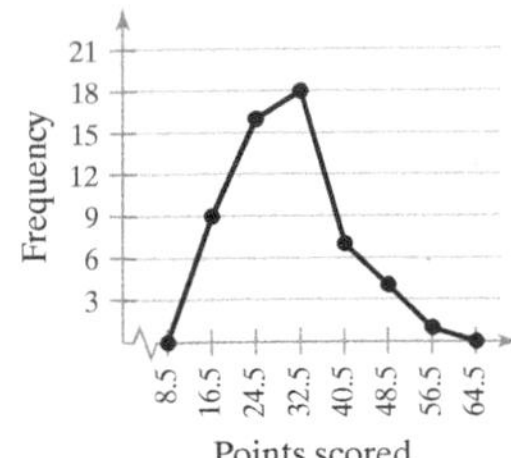


*Sample answer:* The frequency of points scored increases up to 32.5 points and then decreases.

**5.**

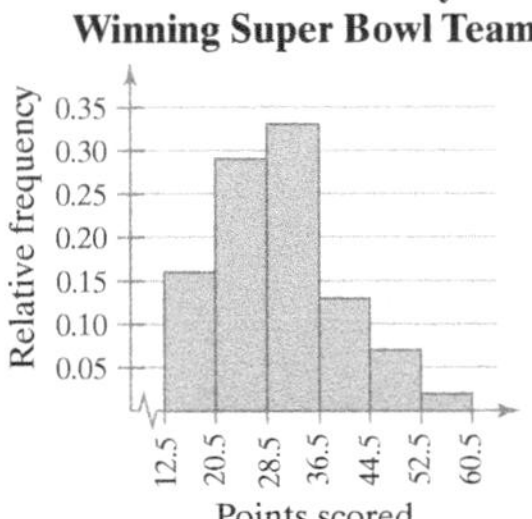


**6.**

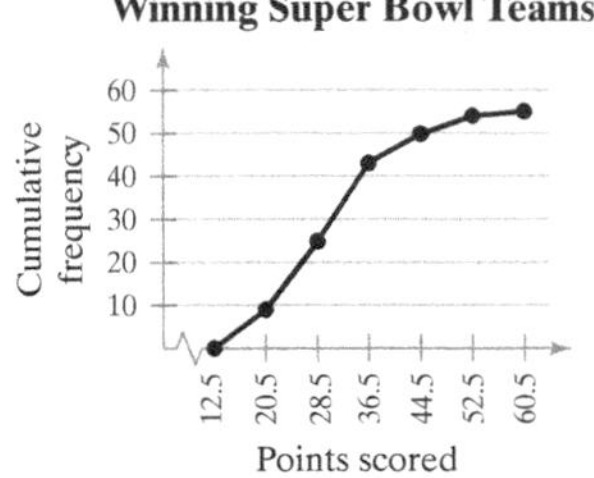


**7.** 21

12.5 0 60.5

## Section 2.2

**1.**

| | | |
|---|---|---|
| 1 | 3 4 6 6 6 7 | Key: 1\|3 = 13 |
| 2 | 0 0 0 1 1 1 3 3 4 4 4 4 6 7 7 7 7 7 8 9 | |
| 3 | 0 1 1 1 1 1 1 2 2 3 4 4 4 4 5 5 5 7 8 8 9 | |
| 4 | 1 2 3 6 8 9 | |
| 5 | 2 5 | |

*Sample answer:* Most of the winning teams scored between 20 and 39 points.

**2.**

| | | |
|---|---|---|
| 1 | 3 4 | Key: 1\|3 = 13 |
| 1 | 6 6 6 7 | |
| 2 | 0 0 0 1 1 1 3 3 4 4 4 4 | |
| 2 | 6 7 7 7 7 7 8 9 | |
| 3 | 0 1 1 1 1 1 1 2 2 3 4 4 4 4 | |
| 3 | 5 5 5 7 8 8 9 | |
| 4 | 1 2 3 | |
| 4 | 6 8 9 | |
| 5 | 2 | |
| 5 | 5 | |

*Sample answer:* Most of the winning teams scored from 20 to 35 points.

**3.**

10 15 20 25 30 35 40 45 50 55

*Sample answer:* Most of the points scored by the winning teams cluster between 20 and 40.

**4.**

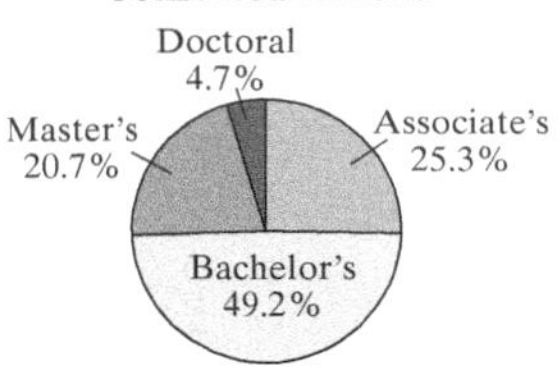


From 2010 to 2019, as percentages of the total degrees conferred, associate's degrees increased by 0.2%, bachelor's degrees decreased by 0.2%, master's degrees decreased by 0.2%, and doctoral degrees decreased by 0.1%.

**5.**

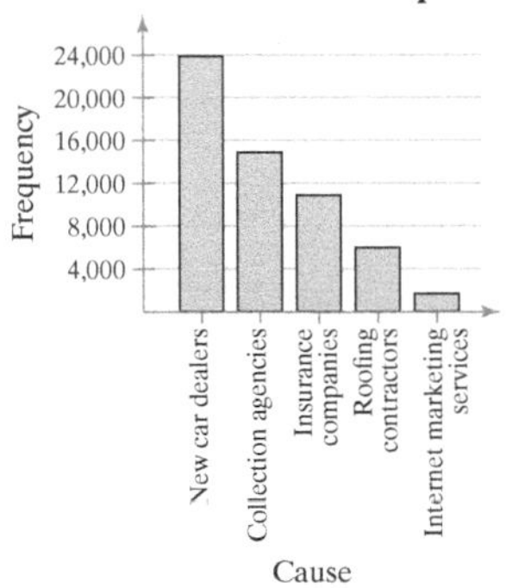


New car dealers are the greatest cause of complaints.

**6.**

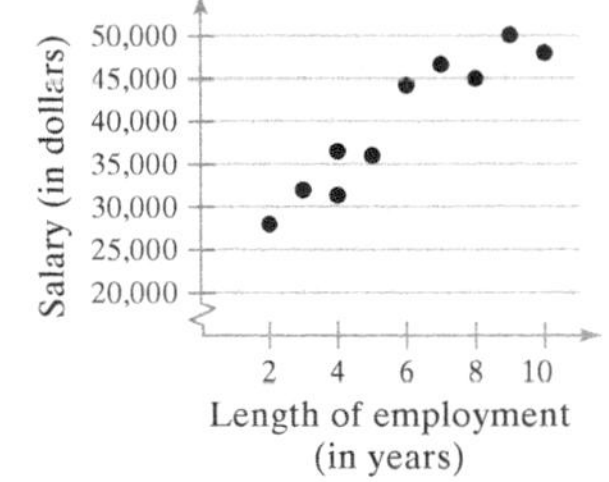


It appears that the longer an employee is with the company, the greater the employee's salary.

**7.**

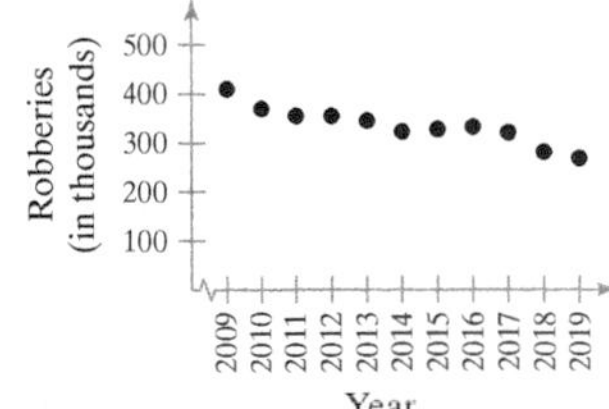


*Sample answer:* The number of robberies decreased between 2009 and 2019.

## Section 2.3

**1.** 28.5 **2.** 31 **3.** 30 **4.** 31 **5.** "not too much"

**6.** $\bar{x} \approx 21.6$; median $= 21$; mode $= 20$

The mean in Example 6 ($\bar{x} \approx 23.8$) was heavily influenced by the entry 65. Neither the median nor the mode was affected as much by the entry 65.

**7.** About 2.6

**8.** About 30.6; This is very close to the mean found using the original data set.

## Section 2.4

1. 35, or \$35,000; The range of the starting salaries for Corporation B, which is \$35,000, is much larger than the range of Corporation A.
2. $\sigma^2 = 110.3$; $\sigma = 10.5$, or \$10,500
3. $s^2 \approx 132.6$; $s \approx 11.5$ **4.** $\bar{x} \approx 20.8$; $s \approx 6.7$
5. *Sample answer:* 7, 7, 7, 7, 7, 13, 13, 13, 13, 13 **6.** 34.13%
7. At least 75% of Iowa's population is between 0 and 87.2 years old. Because $80 < 87.2$, an age of 80 lies within two standard deviations of the mean. So, this age is not unusual.
8. $\bar{x} = 1.7$; $s \approx 1.5$
   Both the mean and sample standard deviation decreased slightly.
9. $\bar{x} \approx 157.0$; $s \approx 147.1$
   Both the mean and sample standard deviation increased.
10. Los Angeles: $CV \approx 41.8\%$
    Dallas: $CV \approx 32.2\%$
    The office rentals are more variable in Los Angeles than in Dallas.

## Section 2.5

1. $Q_1 = 23$, $Q_2 = 31$, $Q_3 = 35$
   About one quarter of the winning scores were 23 points or less. About one half were 31 points or less, and about three quarters were 35 points or less.
2. $Q_1 = 27.5$, $Q_2 = 35$, $Q_3 = 51.5$
   About one quarter of these universities charge tuition of \$27,500 or less, about one half charge \$35,000 or less, and about three quarters charge \$51,500 or less.
3. IQR = 12; 55 is an outlier.
4. **Points Scored by Winning Teams**

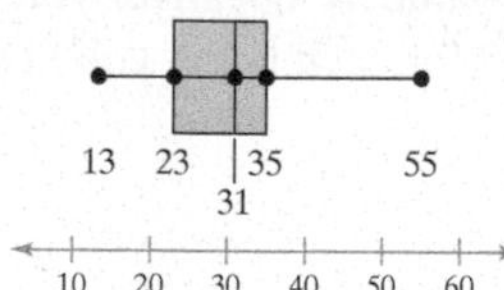


   About 50% of the winning scores were between 23 and 35 points. About 25% of the winning scores were less than 23 points. About 25% of the winning scores were greater than 35 points.
5. 34; About 65% of the winning scores were 34 points or less.
6. 28th percentile
7. For \$60, $z = -1.25$.
   For \$71, $z = 0.125$.
   For \$92, $z = 2.75$.
8. Man: $z = -3.3$; Woman: $z \approx -1.7$
   The $z$-score for the 5-foot-tall man is 3.3 standard deviations below the mean. This is a very unusual height for a man. The $z$-score for the 5-foot-tall woman is 1.7 standard deviations below the mean. This is among the typical heights for a woman.

# Chapter 3

## Section 3.1

1. (1)

Yes No Not sure

M F M F M F

6 outcomes
Let Y = Yes, N = No, NS = Not sure, M = Male, F = Female.
Sample space = {YM, YF, NM, NF, NSM, NSF}

(2)

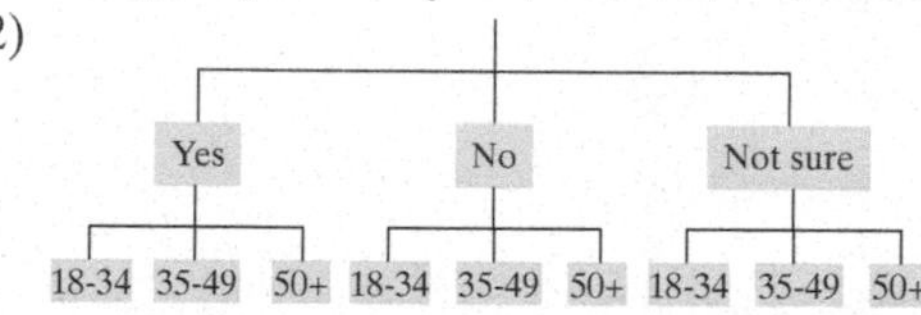


9 outcomes
Let Y = Yes, N = No, NS = Not sure, 50+ = 50 and older.
Sample space = {Y18–34, Y35–49, Y50+, N18–34, N35–49, N50+, NS18–34, NS35–49, NS50+}

(3)

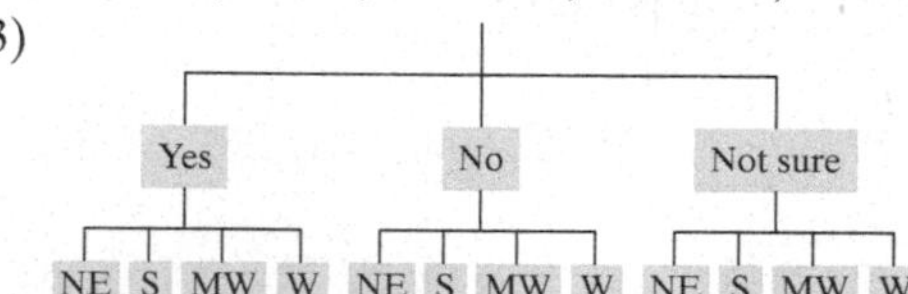


12 outcomes
Let Y = Yes, N = No, NS = Not sure, NE = Northeast, S = South, MW = Midwest, W = West.
Sample space = {YNE, YS, YMW, YW, NNE, NS, NMW, NW, NSNE, NSS, NSMW, NSW}

2. (1) 6. Not a simple event because it is an event that consists of more than a single outcome.
   (2) 1. Simple event because it is an event that consists of a single outcome.

**3.** 40

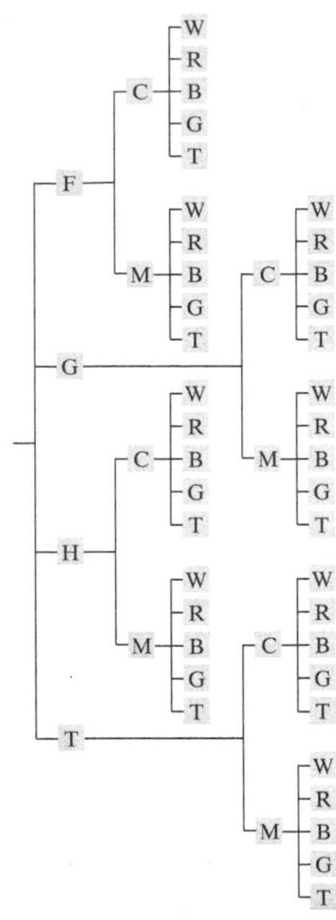


**4.** (1) 308,915,776 (2) 165,765,600 (3) 261,390,272
(4) 106,932,384

**5.** (1) 0.019 (2) 0.25 (3) 1 **6.** 0.072 **7.** 0.182

**8.** Empirical probability **9.** 0.847 **10.** 0.313

**11.** $\dfrac{1}{10{,}000{,}000}$

## Section 3.2

**1.** 0.263

**2.** (1) Dependent (2) Independent

**3.** (1) 0.723 (2) 0.059

**4.** (1) 0.729 (2) 0.001 (3) 0.999

**5.** (1) 0.163 (2) 0.488
Both of the events are not unusual because their probabilities are not less than or equal to 0.05.

## Section 3.3

**1.** (1) Not mutually exclusive; the events can occur at the same time.
(2) Mutually exclusive; the events cannot occur at the same time.

**2.** (1) 0.667 (2) 0.423 **3.** 0.222

**4.** (1) 0.149 (2) 0.149 (3) 0.910 (4) 0.499 **5.** 0.839 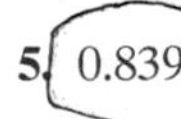

## Section 3.4

**1.** 3,628,800 **2.** 336 **3.** 11,880 **4.** 77,597,520

**5.** 1140 **6.** 0.003 **7.** 0.0009 **8.** 0.045

# Chapter 4

## Section 4.1

**1.** (1) The random variable is continuous because $x$ can be any speed up to the maximum speed of a rocket.
(2) The random variable is discrete because the number of calves born on a farm in one year is countable.
(3) The random variable is discrete because the number of days of rain for the next three days is countable.

**2.**

| $x$ | $f$ | $P(x)$ |
|---|---|---|
| 0 | 16 | 0.16 |
| 1 | 19 | 0.19 |
| 2 | 15 | 0.15 |
| 3 | 21 | 0.21 |
| 4 | 9 | 0.09 |
| 5 | 10 | 0.10 |
| 6 | 8 | 0.08 |
| 7 | 2 | 0.02 |
| | $n = 100$ | $\Sigma P(x) = 1$ |

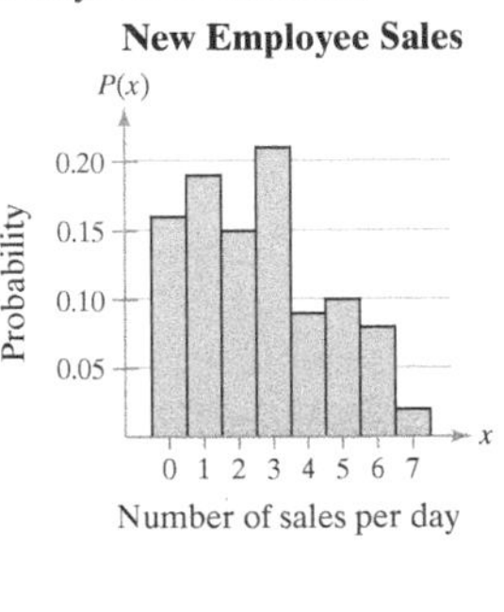


**3.** Each $P(x)$ is between 0 and 1 and $\Sigma P(x) = 1$. Because both conditions are met, the distribution is a probability distribution.

**4.** (1) Probability distribution. The probability of each outcome is between 0 and 1, and the sum of all the probabilities is 1.
(2) Not a probability distribution. The sum of all the probabilities is not 1.

**5.** $\mu = 2.6$. On average, a new employee makes 2.6 sales per day.

**6.** $\sigma^2 \approx 3.7$; $\sigma \approx 1.9$

**7.** −\$3.08. Because the expected value is negative, you can expect to lose an average of \$3.08 for each ticket you buy.

## Section 4.2

**1.** Binomial experiment
$n = 10, p = 0.25, q = 0.75, x = 0, 1, 2, 3, 4, 5, 6, 7, 8, 9, 10$

**2.** 0.088

**3.**

| $x$ | $P(x)$ |
|---|---|
| 0 | 0.156 |
| 1 | 0.351 |
| 2 | 0.316 |
| 3 | 0.142 |
| 4 | 0.032 |
| 5 | 0.003 |
| | $\Sigma P(x) = 1$ |

**4.** 0.006

**5.** (1) 0.152 (2) 0.183 (3) 0.817 **6.** 0.176

**7.**

| $x$ | $P(x)$ |
|---|---|
| 0 | 0.284 |
| 1 | 0.420 |
| 2 | 0.233 |
| 3 | 0.057 |
| 4 | 0.005 |

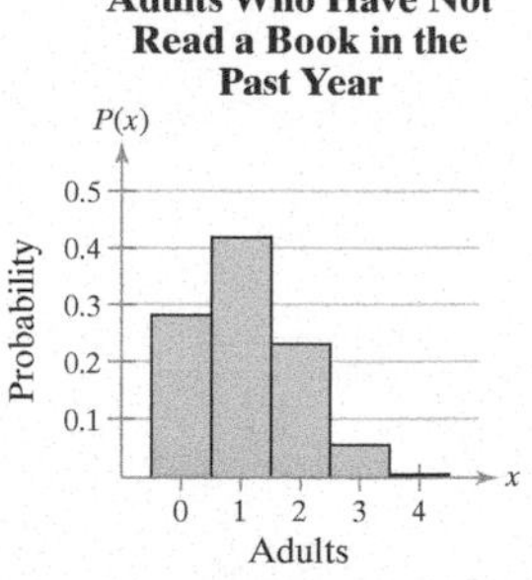


**8.** $\mu \approx 13.6$; $\sigma^2 \approx 7.6$; $\sigma \approx 2.8$; On average, there are about 14 clear days during the month of May. A May with fewer than 8 clear days or more than 19 clear days would be unusual.

## Section 4.3

**1.** 0.066 **2.** 0.185 **3.** 0.0002

# Chapter 5

## Section 5.1

**1.** (1) Curve $B$ has the greatest mean.
(2) Curve $C$ is more spread out, so curve $C$ has the greatest standard deviation.

**2.** $\mu = 18; \sigma = 5.8$ **3.** (1) 0.0143 (2) 0.9850

**4.** 0.9834 **5.** 0.9846 **6.** 0.0733

## Section 5.2

**1.** 0.1957 **2.** 0.7357; 147 **3.** 0.214

## Section 5.3

**1.** (1) −1.77 (2) 1.96

**2.** (1) −1.28 (2) −0.84 (3) 2.33

**3.** (1) 17.05 pounds (2) 97 pounds (3) 60.7 pounds
17.05 pounds is to the left of the mean, 97 pounds is to the right of the mean, and 60.7 pounds is to the right of the mean.

**4.** The longest braking distance one of these cars could have and still be in the bottom 1% is about 120 feet.

**5.** The maximum length of time an employee could have worked and still be laid off is about 8.5 years.

## Section 5.4

**1.**

| Sample | Mean |
|---|---|
| 1, 1, 1 | 1 |
| 1, 1, 3 | 1.67 |
| 1, 1, 5 | 2.33 |
| 1, 3, 1 | 1.67 |
| 1, 3, 3 | 2.33 |
| 1, 3, 5 | 3 |
| 1, 5, 1 | 2.33 |
| 1, 5, 3 | 3 |
| 1, 5, 5 | 3.67 |
| 3, 1, 1 | 1.67 |
| 3, 1, 3 | 2.33 |
| 3, 1, 5 | 3 |
| 3, 3, 1 | 2.33 |
| 3, 3, 3 | 3 |

| Sample | Mean |
|---|---|
| 3, 3, 5 | 3.67 |
| 3, 5, 1 | 3 |
| 3, 5, 3 | 3.67 |
| 3, 5, 5 | 4.33 |
| 5, 1, 1 | 2.33 |
| 5, 1, 3 | 3 |
| 5, 1, 5 | 3.67 |
| 5, 3, 1 | 3 |
| 5, 3, 3 | 3.67 |
| 5, 3, 5 | 4.33 |
| 5, 5, 1 | 3.67 |
| 5, 5, 3 | 4.33 |
| 5, 5, 5 | 5 |

$\mu_{\bar{x}} = 3$; $(\sigma_{\bar{x}})^2 \approx 0.889$; $\sigma_{\bar{x}} \approx 0.943$

$\mu_{\bar{x}} = \mu = 3$

$$(\sigma_{\bar{x}})^2 = \frac{\sigma^2}{n} = \frac{8/3}{3} = \frac{8}{9} \approx 0.889$$

$$\sigma_{\bar{x}} = \frac{\sigma}{\sqrt{n}} = \frac{\sqrt{8/3}}{\sqrt{3}} = \frac{\sqrt{8}}{3} \approx 0.943$$

**2.** $\mu_{\bar{x}} = 6.9$; $\sigma_{\bar{x}} = 0.1875$

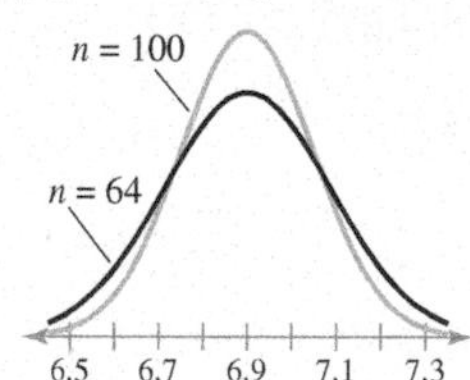


With a smaller sample size, the mean stays the same but the standard deviation increases.

**3.** $\mu_{\bar{x}} = 3.5$, $\sigma_{\bar{x}} = 0.05$

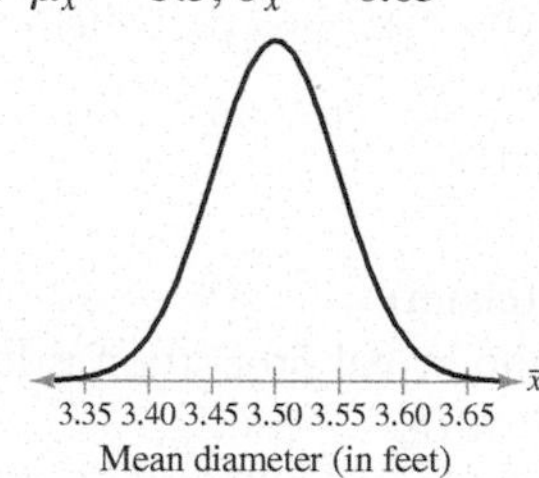


**4.** 0.8324 **5.** 0.9332 (*Tech:* 0.9336)

**6.** 0.4702; 0.4065
There is about a 47% chance that a monitor will cost less than \$200. There is about a 41% chance that the mean of a sample of 10 monitors is less than \$200.

## Section 5.5

**1.** Because $np$ and $nq$ are greater than 5, a normal distribution can be used.

**2.** (1) $56.5 < x < 83.5$ (2) $x < 54.5$

**3.** 0.8264 (*Tech:* 0.8273) **4.** 0.0281 **5.** 0.0479 (*Tech:* 0.0476)

# Chapter 6

## Section 6.1

**1.** 2.85 **2.** 0.43 hour **3.** (2.42, 3.28)

**4.** (19.49, 20.36); (19.38, 20.47); (19.30, 20.55); As the confidence level increases, so does the width of the interval.

**5.** (22.4, 23.4) [*Tech:* (22.5, 23.4)]; Because of the larger sample size, the confidence interval is slightly narrower.

**6.** 40; Because of the larger margin of error, the sample size needed is smaller.

## Section 6.2

**1.** 1.721 **2.** (157.6, 166.4); (154.6, 169.4)

**3.** (9.08, 10.42); (8.94, 10.56); The 90% confidence interval is slightly narrower.

**4.** Use a *t*-distribution because $\sigma$ is not known and the population is normally distributed.

## Section 6.3

**1.** 14% **2.** (0.12, 0.16) **3.** (0.475, 0.565)

**4.** (1) 1692 (2) 1591

## Section 6.4

**1.** 42.557, 17.708

**2.** Population variance: (0.98, 2.36), (0.91, 2.60)
Standard deviation: (0.99, 1.54), (0.96, 1.61)

# Chapter 7

## Section 7.1

**1.** (1) The mean is not 74 months.
$\mu \neq 74$
$H_0$: $\mu = 74$; $H_a$: $\mu \neq 74$ (claim)

(2) The variance is less than or equal to 2.7.
$\sigma^2 \leq 2.7$
$H_0$: $\sigma^2 \leq 2.7$ (claim); $H_a$: $\sigma^2 > 2.7$

(3) The proportion is more than 24%.
$p > 0.24$
$H_0$: $p \leq 0.24$; $H_a$: $p > 0.24$ (claim)

**2.** A type I error will occur when the actual proportion is less than or equal to 0.01, but you reject $H_0$.
A type II error will occur when the actual proportion is greater than 0.01, but you fail to reject $H_0$.
A type II error is more serious because you would be misleading the consumer, possibly causing serious injury or death.

**3.** (1) $H_0$: The mean life of a certain type of automobile battery is 74 months.
$H_a$: The mean life of a certain type of automobile battery is not 74 months.
$H_0$: $\mu = 74$; $H_a$: $\mu \neq 74$
Two-tailed

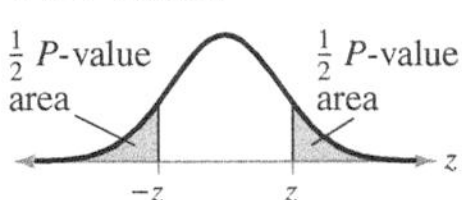


(2) $H_0$: The variance of the life of a manufacturer's home theater systems is less than or equal to 2.7.
$H_a$: The variance of the life of a manufacturer's home theater systems is greater than 2.7.
$H_0$: $\sigma^2 \leq 2.7$; $H_a$: $\sigma^2 > 2.7$
Right-tailed

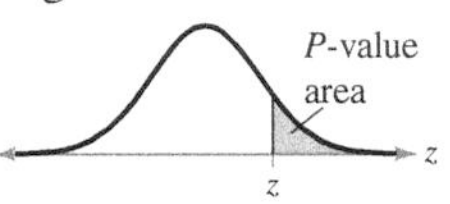


(3) $H_0$: The proportion of homeowners who feel their house is too small for their family is less than or equal to 24%.
$H_a$: The proportion of homeowners who feel their house is too small for their family is greater than 24%.
$H_0$: $p \leq 0.24$; $H_a$: $p > 0.24$
Right-tailed

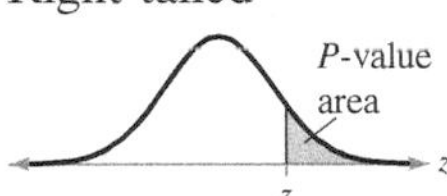


**4.** (1) There is enough evidence to support the claim that the mean life of a certain type of automobile battery is not 74 months.
There is not enough evidence to support the claim that the mean life of a certain type of automobile battery is not 74 months.

(2) There is enough evidence to support the realtor's claim that the proportion of homeowners who feel their house is too small for their family is more than 24%.
There is not enough evidence to support the realtor's claim that the proportion of homeowners who feel their house is too small for their family is more than 24%.

**5.** (1) $H_0$: $\mu \geq 650$; $H_a$: $\mu < 650$ (claim)
If you reject $H_0$, then you will support the claim that the mean repair cost per automobile is less than \$650.

(2) $H_0$: $\mu = 98.6$ (claim); $H_a$: $\mu \neq 98.6$
If you reject $H_0$, then you will reject the claim that the mean temperature is about 98.6°F.

## Section 7.2

**1.** (1) Fail to reject $H_0$. (2) Reject $H_0$.

**2.** 0.0436; Reject $H_0$ because $0.0436 < 0.05$.

**3.** 0.1010; Fail to reject $H_0$ because $0.1010 > 0.01$.

**4.** There is enough evidence at the 5% level of significance to support the claim that the average speed is greater than 35 miles per hour.

5. There is not enough evidence at the 1% level of significance to support the claim that the mean number of workdays missed due to illness or injury in the past 12 months is 3.6 days.
6. Fail to reject $H_0$.
7. $z_0 = -1.28$; Rejection region: $z < -1.28$
8. $-z_0 = -1.75$, $z_0 = 1.75$
   Rejection regions: $z < -1.75$, $z > 1.75$
9. There is enough evidence at the 1% level of significance to support the claim that the mean workday is less than 8.5 hours.
10. There is not enough evidence at the 1% level of significance to reject the claim that the mean cost of raising a child between the ages of 1 and 3 in the United States is $13,350.

### Section 7.3

1. −2.650    2. 1.397    3. −2.131, 2.131
4. There is enough evidence at the 10% level of significance to support the analyst's claim that the mean transaction price of new vehicles sold in the last 12 months is less than $43,500.
5. There is enough evidence at the 1% level of significance to reject the company's claim that the mean conductivity of the river is 1890 milligrams per liter.
6. There is not enough evidence at the 5% level of significance to reject the office's claim that the mean wait time is at most 18 minutes.

### Section 7.4

1. There is not enough evidence at the 1% level of significance to support the researcher's claim that more than 36% of U.S. adults would consider buying a product or service directly from an advertisement that is run during streaming programming.
2. There is enough evidence at the 10% level of significance to reject the researcher's claim that 70% of U.S. adults ages 22 to 59 who have at least one parent with a bachelor's degree or more education have completed a bachelor's degree themselves.

### Section 7.5

1. $\chi^2 = 33.409$    2. $\chi^2 = 17.708$
3. $\chi^2_L = 27.991$, $\chi^2_R = 79.490$
4. There is enough evidence at the 1% level of significance to reject the bottling company's claim that the variance of the amount of sports drink in a 12-ounce bottle is no more than 0.40.
5. There is not enough evidence at the 5% level of significance to support the police chief's claim that the standard deviation of the lengths of response times is less than 3.7 minutes.
6. There is enough evidence at the 10% level of significance to reject the company's claim that the variance of the weight losses of the users is 25.5.

## Chapter 8

### Section 8.1

1. (1) Independent    (2) Dependent
2. There is enough evidence at the 10% level of significance to support the claim that there is a difference in mean annual wages.
3. There is not enough evidence at the 5% level of significance to support the claim that the average monthly rent for a one-bedroom apartment in Atlanta, GA, is greater than the average monthly rent for a one-bedroom apartment in Nashville, TN.

### Section 8.2

1. There is enough evidence at the 5% level of significance to support the claim that there is a difference in the mean annual earnings based on level of education.
2. There is not enough evidence at the 10% level of significance to support the manufacturer's claim that the mean driving cost per mile of its minivans is less than that of its leading competitor.

### Section 8.3

1. There is enough evidence at the 10% level of significance to support the claim that people who play golf can improve (decrease) their average golf scores by using the company's newly designed golf clubs.
2. There is not enough evidence at the 5% level of significance to support the claim that the drug changes the body's temperature.

### Section 8.4

1. There is not enough evidence at the 5% level of significance to support the claim that there is a difference between the proportion of people who use yoga who are 40- to 49-year-olds and the proportion of people who do not use yoga who are 40- to 49-year-olds.
2. There is enough evidence at the 5% level of significance to reject the claim that the proportion of people who use yoga who are from the western region of the United States is greater than or equal to the proportion of people who do not use yoga who are from the western region of the United States.

# Chapter 9

## Section 9.1

1. 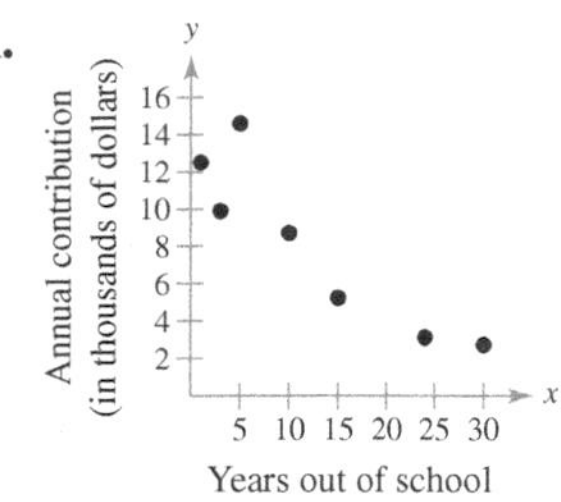


It appears that there is a negative linear correlation. As the number of years out of school increases, the annual contribution tends to decrease.

2. 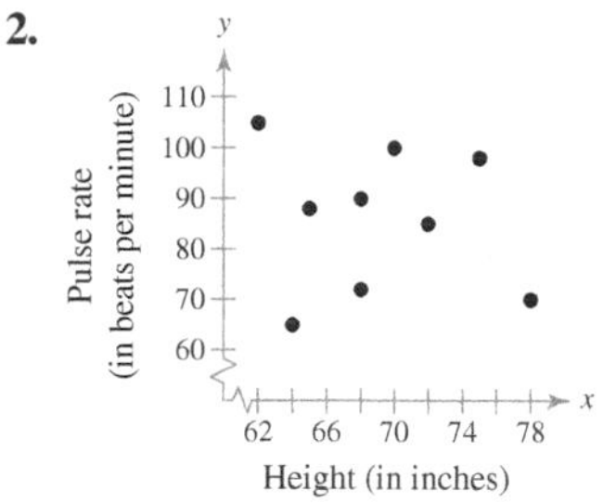


It appears that there is no linear correlation between height and pulse rate.

3. 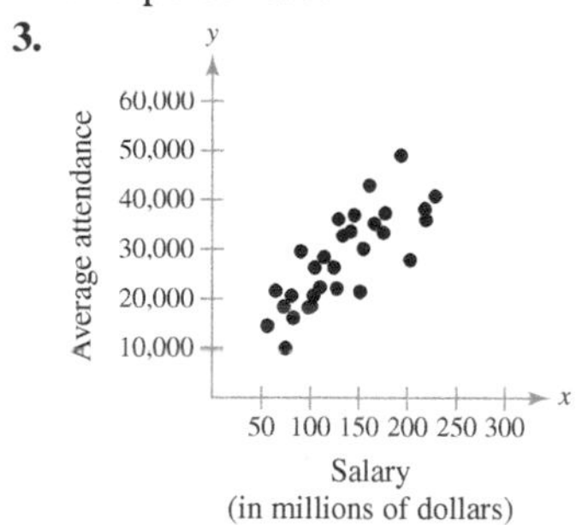


It appears that there is a positive linear correlation. As the team salary increases, the average attendance per home game tends to increase.

4. $-0.908$. Because $r$ is close to $-1$, this suggests a strong negative linear correlation. As the number of years out of school increases, the annual contribution tends to decrease.
5. 0.792. Because $r$ is close to 1, this suggests a strong positive linear correlation. As the team salaries increase, the average attendance per home game tends to increase.
6. $|r| \approx 0.908 > 0.875$. The correlation is significant. There is enough evidence at the 1% level of significance to conclude that there is a significant linear correlation between the number of years out of school and the annual contribution.
7. There is enough evidence at the 1% level of significance to conclude that there is a significant linear correlation between the salaries and average attendances per home game for the teams in Major League Baseball.

## Section 9.2

1. $\hat{y} = -0.380x + 12.876$
2. $\hat{y} = 152.932x + 7811.244$
3. (1) 58.645 minutes (2) 75.120 minutes

## Section 9.3

1. 0.958. About 95.8% of the variation in the times is explained. About 4.2% of the variation is unexplained.
2. 6.218
3. $411.225 < y < 1179.381$
You can be 95% confident that when the gross domestic product is $4 trillion, the carbon dioxide emissions will be between 411.225 and 1179.381 million metric tons.

## Section 9.4

1. $\hat{y} = 46.385 + 0.540x_1 - 4.897x_2$
2. (1) 90 (2) 74 (3) 81

# Chapter 10

## Section 10.1

1.

| Tax preparation method | % of people | Expected frequency |
|---|---|---|
| Accountant | 24% | 120 |
| By hand | 20% | 100 |
| Computer software | 35% | 175 |
| Friend or family | 6% | 30 |
| Tax preparation service | 15% | 75 |

2. There is not enough evidence at the 5% level of significance to support the sociologist's claim that the age distribution differs from the age distribution 10 years ago.
3. There is enough evidence at the 5% level of significance to reject the claim that the distribution of different-colored candies in bags of peanut M&M's is uniform.

## Section 10.2

1. $E_{1,1} \approx 426.549$, $E_{1,2} \approx 75.451$, $E_{1,3} \approx 271.120$, $E_{1,4} \approx 195.669$, $E_{1,5} \approx 35.210$, $E_{2,1} \approx 421.451$, $E_{2,2} \approx 74.549$, $E_{2,3} \approx 267.880$, $E_{2,4} \approx 193.331$, $E_{2,5} \approx 34.790$
2. There is enough evidence at the 1% level of significance to conclude that *student's living arrangement* depends on *borrowing status.*
3. There is enough evidence at the 1% level of significance to conclude that whether or not a tax credit would influence an adult to make a charitable donation is dependent on age.

## Section 10.3

**1.** 2.45 **2.** 18.31

**3.** There is enough evidence at the 1% level of significance to support the researcher's claim that a specially treated intravenous solution decreases the variance of the time required for nutrients to enter the bloodstream.

**4.** There is not enough evidence at the 1% level of significance to reject the biologist's claim that the pH levels of the soil in the two geographic locations have equal standard deviations.

## Section 10.4

**1.** There is enough evidence at the 5% level of significance for the analyst to conclude that there is a difference in the mean monthly sales among the sales regions.

**2.** There is not enough evidence at the 5% level of significance to conclude that there is a difference in the means of the GPAs.

## Appendix A

**1.** (1) 0.4857 (2) $z = \pm 2.17$

**2.** 0.9834 **3.** 0.9846 **4.** 0.0733

## Appendix C

**1.**

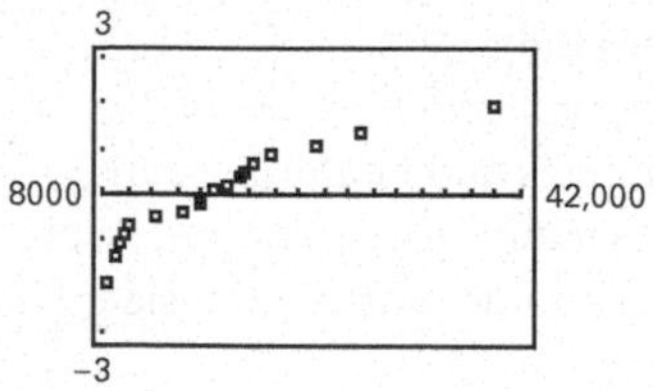

3
8000 42,000
−3

Because the points do not appear to be approximately linear and there is an outlier, you can conclude that the sample data do not come from a population that has a normal distribution.

# ODD ANSWERS

## Chapter 1

### Section 1.1 (page 6)

**1.** A sample is a subset of a population.

**3.** A parameter is a numerical description of a population characteristic. A statistic is a numerical description of a sample characteristic.

**5.** False. A statistic is a numerical description of a sample characteristic.

**7.** True

**9.** False. A population is the collection of *all* outcomes, responses, measurements, or counts that are of interest.

**11.** Population, because it is a collection of the salaries of each employee of an advertising firm.

**13.** Sample, because the collection of 250 people is a subset of the population of 20,000 members of an organized union.

**15.** Sample, because the collection of the 12 people is a subset of the 49 people who escaped a burning building.

**17.** Population, because it is the collection of all the guests in each room of a hotel.

**19.** Population, because it is the collection of the nationalities of every person passing through a customs station.

**21.** Population: Parties of registered voters
Sample: Parties of registered voters who respond to a survey

**23.** Population: Ages of adults in the United States who own motor vehicles
Sample: Ages of adults in the United States who own two-wheeled motor vehicles

**25.** Population: Collection of the responses of all U.S. adults
Sample: Collection of the responses of the 1021 U.S. adults surveyed
Sample data set: 45% of adults who have a favorable view of Cuba and 55% who do not

**27.** Population: Collection of the U.S. adults who have received vaccines
Sample: Collection of responses of 1500 U.S adults who have received vaccines
Sample data set: 59% of U.S. adults who have never had a vaccine reaction and 41% who have

**29.** Population: Collection of responses from small business owners in the U.S.
Sample: Collection of responses of 2111 U.S. small business owners
Sample data set: 54% of small business owners who oppose increasing the minimum wage and 46% who do not

**31.** Population: Collection of all U.S. adults
Sample: Collection of responses of 1001 U.S. adults who were surveyed
Sample data set: 47% of respondents who typically feel well rested on weekdays and 53% who do not

**33.** Population: Collection of all companies listed in the Standard & Poor's 500
Sample: Collection of the responses of 74 Standard & Poor's 500 companies surveyed
Sample data set: Starting salaries of the 74 companies surveyed

**35.** Sample statistic. The value $71,000 is a numerical description of a sample of average salaries.

**37.** Population parameter. The 62 surviving passengers out of 97 total passengers is a numerical description of all of the passengers of the *Hindenburg* who survived.

**39.** Sample statistic. The value of 6% is a numerical description of the sample of automobile owners.

**41.** Sample statistic. The value 79% is a numerical description of a sample of U.S. adults.

**43.** The statement "47% of respondents typically feel well rested on weekdays" is an example of descriptive statistics. Using inferential statistics, you may conclude that an association exists between feeling well rested and the day of the week.

**45.** Answers will vary.

**47.** No, this inference may incorrectly imply that exercise stimulates T cell production for all ages when it was only shown for senior citizens.

**49.** (a) The sample is scores on quizzes and midterm exams by the participants in the study.
(b) The population is the collection of all of the college students' scores on quizzes and midterm exams.
(c) The statement "participants earned higher scores on quizzes and midterm exams with better sleep" is an example of descriptive statistics.
(d) Individuals who sleep better will be more likely to perform better on quizzes and midterm exams than they would with worse sleep.

### Section 1.2 (page 13)

**1.** Nominal and ordinal

**3.** False. Data at the ordinal level can be qualitative or quantitative.

**5.** False. More types of calculations can be performed with data at the interval level than with data at the nominal level.

**7.** Qualitative, because nationalities are nonnumerical entries.

**9.** Quantitative, because age is counted.

**11.** Qualitative, because flower types are labels.

**13.** Quantitative, because distances are numerical measurements.

**15.** Interval. Data can be ordered and meaningful differences can be calculated, but it does not make sense to say that one year is a multiple of another.

**17.** Ratio. A ratio of two data values can be formed, so one data value can be expressed as a multiple of another.

**19.** Ordinal. Data can be arranged in order, but the differences between data entries are not meaningful.

21. Horizontal: Nominal; Vertical: Ratio
23. Horizontal: Nominal; Vertical: Ratio
25. (a) Interval (b) Nominal (c) Ratio (d) Ordinal
27. Qualitative. Ordinal. Data can be arranged in order, but the differences between data entries make no sense.
29. Qualitative. Nominal. No mathematical computations can be made and data are categorized by region.
31. Qualitative. Ordinal. Data can be arranged in order, but the differences between data entries are not meaningful.
33. An inherent zero is a zero that implies "none." Answers will vary.

## Section 1.3 (page 24)

1. In an experiment, a treatment is applied to part of a population and responses are observed. In an observational study, a researcher measures characteristics of interest of a part of a population but does not change existing conditions.
3. In a random sample, every member of the population has an equal chance of being selected. In a simple random sample, every possible sample of the same size has an equal chance of being selected.
5. False. A placebo is a fake treatment.
7. False. Using stratified sampling guarantees that members of each group within a population will be sampled.
9. False. A systematic sample is selected by ordering a population in some way and then selecting members of the population at regular intervals.
11. Experiment. The study applies a treatment (periods of wakeful rest or periods of distraction) to the subjects.
13. Observational study. The study does not apply a treatment to the adults.
15. Answers will vary. 17. Answers will vary.
19. (a) The experimental units are the 500 girls ages 13 to 17 who have acne. The treatment is the new cream used to treat acne.
    (b) *Sample answer:* A problem with the design is that the sample is not representative of the entire population because only girls ages 13 to 17 were used. To increase validity, use a stratified sample.
    (c) For the experiment to be double-blind, neither the subjects nor the company would know whether the subjects are receiving the acne cream or the placebo.
21. *Sample answer:* Treatment group: Jake, Arya, Nyla, Juan, Nia, Bruno, Kayla, Liam, and Kai. Control group: Xavier, Shaniece, Chen, Hana, Ansel, Liam, Mei, Zoey, and Sofia. A random number table was used.
23. Simple random sampling is used because each student has an equal chance of being contacted, and all samples of 300 students have an equal chance of being selected. A possible source of bias is that the random sample may contain a much greater percentage of students from one major than another.
25. Cluster sampling is used because the disaster area is divided into grids, and 30 grids are then entirely selected. A possible source of bias is that certain grids may have been much more severely damaged than others.
27. Stratified sampling is used because a sample is taken from each one-acre subplot.
29. Census, because it is relatively easy to obtain the GPAs of 85 students.
31. The question is biased because it already suggests that eating whole-grain foods improves your health. The question could be rewritten as "How does eating whole-grain foods affect your health?"
33. The survey question is unbiased.
35. Answers will vary.
37. Open Question
    Advantage: Allows respondent to express some depth and shades of meaning in the answer. Allows for new solutions to be introduced.
    Disadvantage: Not easily quantified and difficult to compare surveys.
    Closed Question
    Advantage: Easy to analyze results.
    Disadvantage: May not provide appropriate alternatives and may influence the opinion of the respondent.

## Section 1.3 Activity (page 27)

1. Answers will vary. The list contains one number at least twice.
2. The minimum is 1, the maximum is 731, and the number of samples is 8. Answers will vary.

## Uses and Abuses for Chapter 1 (page 28)

1. Answers will vary. 2. Answers will vary.

## Review Exercises for Chapter 1 (page 30)

1. Population: Collection of responses of all U.S. adults
   Sample: Collection of responses of the 1025 U.S. adults who were sampled
   Sample data set: Those sampled had visited the library an average of 10.5 times in the past 12 months.
3. Population: Collection of responses of all U.S. adults
   Sample: Collection of the responses of the 23,503 U.S. adults who were sampled
   Sample data set: 59% of adults who said if they were single, they would look up someone on the Internet before going on a date with them and 41% who would not
5. Population parameter. The value \$4.8 billion is a numerical description of the amount of personal protective equipment imported.
7. Sample statistic. The value of 39% is a numerical description of a sample of U.S. workers.
9. The statement "59% said that if they were single, they would look up someone on the Internet before going on a date with them" is an example of descriptive statistics. An inference drawn from the sample is that a majority of adults would look someone up on the Internet before going on a date.
11. Quantitative, because ages are numerical measurements.

**13.** Quantitative, because revenues are numerical measurements.

**15.** Interval. The data can be ordered and meaningful differences can be calculated but it does not make sense to say that 87 degrees is 1.09 times as hot as 80 degrees.

**17.** Nominal. The data are qualitative and cannot be arranged in a meaningful order.

**19.** Experiment. The study applied a treatment (medication used to reduce the risk of cardiac events) to the subjects.

**21.** *Sample answer:* The subjects could be split into male and female and then be randomly assigned to each of the five treatment groups.

**23.** Simple random sampling is used because random telephone numbers were generated and called. A potential source of bias is that telephone sampling only samples individuals who have telephones, who are available, and who are willing to respond.

**25.** Cluster sampling is used because each neighborhood is considered a cluster and every pregnant woman in a selected neighborhood is surveyed. A potential source of bias is that the selected neighborhoods may not be representative of the entire area.

**27.** Stratified sampling is used because the population is divided by grade level and then 25 students are randomly selected from each grade level.

**29.** Sampling, because the population of students at the university is too large for their favorite spring break destinations to be easily recorded. Random sampling would be advised because it would be easy to select students randomly and then record their favorite spring break destinations.

## Quiz for Chapter 1 (page 32)

**1.** Population: Collection of grade point averages, SAT scores, and ACT scores of all high school seniors.
Sample: Collection of grade point averages, SAT scores, and ACT scores of 1622 high school seniors from four public high schools in the northeastern United States.

**2.** (a) Sample statistic. The value 42% is a numerical description of a sample of U.S. adults.
(b) Population parameter. The 90% of members that approved the contract of the new president is a numerical description of all Board of Trustees members.
(c) Sample statistic. The value 48% is a numerical description of a sample of small business owners.

**3.** (a) Qualitative, because debit card personal identification numbers are labels and it does not make sense to find differences between numbers.
(b) Quantitative, because final scores are numerical measurements.

**4.** (a) Ordinal, because badge numbers can be ordered and often indicate seniority of service, but no meaningful mathematical computation can be performed.
(b) Ratio, because one data entry can be expressed as a multiple of another.
(c) Ordinal, because data can be arranged in order, but the differences between data entries make no sense.
(d) Interval, because meaningful differences between entries can be calculated but a zero entry is not an inherent zero.

**5.** (a) Observational study. The study does not attempt to influence the responses of the subjects and there is no treatment.
(b) Experiment. The study applies a treatment (video involving smoking) to the subjects.

**6.** Randomized block design

**7.** (a) Convenience sampling, because all of the people sampled are in one convenient location.
(b) Systematic sampling, because every tenth machine part is sampled.
(c) Stratified sampling, because the population is first stratified and then a sample is collected from each stratum.

**8.** Convenience sampling. People at campgrounds may be strongly against air pollution because they are at an outdoor location.

## Real Statistics—Real Decisions for Chapter 1 (page 34)

**1.** (a)–(b) Answers will vary.
(c) *Sample answer:* Use surveys.
(d) *Sample answer:* You may take too large a percentage of your sample from a subgroup of the population that is relatively small.

**2.** (a) *Sample answer:* Qualitative, because questions will ask for demographics and the sample questions have nonnumerical categories.
(b) *Sample answer:* Nominal and ordinal, because the results can be put in categories and the categories can be ranked.
(c) Sample (d) Statistics

**3.** (a) *Sample answer:* Sample includes only members of the population with access to the Internet.
(b) Answers will vary.

# Chapter 2

## Section 2.1 (page 49)

**1.** Organizing the data into a frequency distribution may make patterns within the data more evident. Sometimes it is easier to identify patterns of a data set by looking at a graph of the frequency distribution.

**3.** Class limits determine which numbers can belong to each class. Class boundaries are the numbers that separate classes without forming gaps between them.

**5.** The sum of the relative frequencies must be 1 or 100% because it is the sum of all portions or percentages of the data.

**7.** False. Class width is the difference between lower or upper limits of consecutive classes.

**9.** False. The graph of cumulative frequencies always starts at the lower boundary of the first class and increases to the upper boundary of the last class, therefore always increasing from left to right.

**11.** Class width = 8; Lower class limits: 9, 17, 25, 33, 41, 49, 57; Upper class limits: 16, 24, 32, 40, 48, 56, 64

**13.** Class width = 15; Lower class limits: 17, 32, 47, 62, 77, 92, 107, 122; Upper class limits: 31, 46, 61, 76, 91, 106, 121, 136

**15.** (a) 11
(b) and (c)

| Class | Midpoint | Class boundaries |
|---|---|---|
| 0–10 | 5 | −0.5–10.5 |
| 11–21 | 16 | 10.5–21.5 |
| 22–32 | 27 | 21.5–32.5 |
| 33–43 | 38 | 32.5–43.5 |
| 44–54 | 49 | 43.5–54.5 |
| 55–65 | 60 | 54.5–65.5 |
| 66–76 | 71 | 65.5–76.5 |

**17.**

| Class | Frequency, $f$ | Midpoint | Relative frequency | Cumulative frequency |
|---|---|---|---|---|
| 0–10 | 188 | 5 | 0.15 | 188 |
| 11–21 | 372 | 16 | 0.30 | 560 |
| 22–32 | 264 | 27 | 0.22 | 824 |
| 33–43 | 205 | 38 | 0.17 | 1029 |
| 44–54 | 83 | 49 | 0.07 | 1112 |
| 55–65 | 76 | 60 | 0.06 | 1188 |
| 66–76 | 32 | 71 | 0.03 | 1220 |
| | $\Sigma f = 1220$ | | $\Sigma \frac{f}{n} = 1$ | |

**19.** (a) 7
(b) Greatest frequency: about 300
Least frequency: about 10
(c) 10
(d) *Sample answer:* About half of the employee salaries are between \$50,000 and \$69,000.

**21.** Class with greatest frequency: 506–510
Classes with least frequency: 474–478

**23.** (a) Class with greatest relative frequency: 35–36 centimeters
Class with least relative frequency: 39–40 centimeters
(b) Greatest relative frequency ≈ 0.25
Least relative frequency ≈ 0.01
(c) *Sample answer:* From the graph, 0.25 or 25% of females have a fibula length between 35 and 36 centimeters.

**25.** (a) 75 (b) 158.5–201.5 pounds

**27.** (a) 47 (b) 287.5 pounds (c) 40 (d) 6

**29.**

| Class | Frequency, $f$ | Midpoint | Relative frequency | Cumulative frequency |
|---|---|---|---|---|
| 28–57 | 2 | 42.5 | 0.08 | 2 |
| 58–87 | 4 | 72.5 | 0.17 | 6 |
| 88–117 | 7 | 102.5 | 0.29 | 13 |
| 118–147 | 7 | 132.5 | 0.29 | 20 |
| 148–177 | 4 | 162.5 | 0.17 | 24 |
| | $\Sigma f = 24$ | | $\Sigma \frac{f}{n} \approx 1$ | |

Classes with greatest frequency: 88–117, 118–147
Class with the least frequency: 28–57

**31.**

| Class | Frequency, $f$ | Mid-point | Relative frequency | Cumulative frequency |
|---|---|---|---|---|
| 1000–2019 | 11 | 1509.5 | 0.52 | 11 |
| 2020–3039 | 3 | 2529.5 | 0.14 | 14 |
| 3040–4059 | 2 | 3549.5 | 0.10 | 16 |
| 4060–5079 | 3 | 4569.5 | 0.14 | 19 |
| 5080–6099 | 1 | 5589.5 | 0.05 | 20 |
| 6100–7119 | 1 | 6609.5 | 0.05 | 21 |
| | $\Sigma f = 21$ | | $\Sigma \frac{f}{n} = 1$ | |

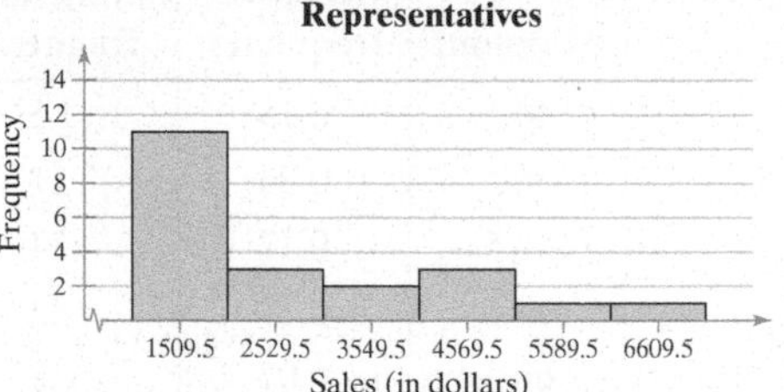


*Sample answer:* The graph shows that most of the sales representatives at the company sold from \$1000 to \$2019.

**33.**

| Class | Frequency, $f$ | Mid-point | Relative frequency | Cumulative frequency |
|---|---|---|---|---|
| 291–318 | 5 | 304.5 | 0.1667 | 5 |
| 319–346 | 4 | 332.5 | 0.1333 | 9 |
| 347–374 | 3 | 360.5 | 0.1000 | 12 |
| 375–402 | 5 | 388.5 | 0.1667 | 17 |
| 403–430 | 6 | 416.5 | 0.2000 | 23 |
| 431–458 | 4 | 444.5 | 0.1333 | 27 |
| 459–486 | 1 | 472.5 | 0.0333 | 28 |
| 487–514 | 2 | 500.5 | 0.0667 | 30 |
| | $\Sigma f = 30$ | | $\Sigma \frac{f}{n} = 1$ | |

Reaction Times for Females

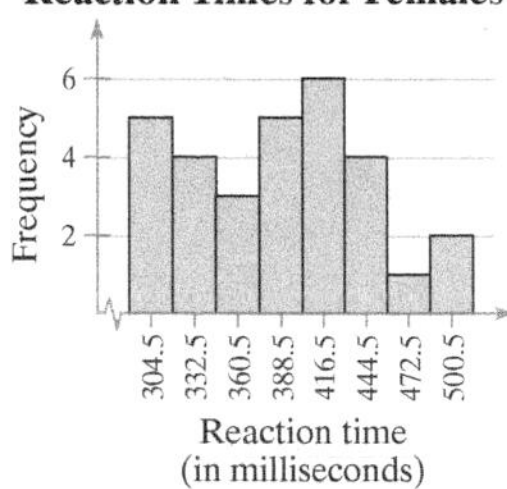


*Sample answer:* The graph shows that the most frequent reaction times were from 403 to 430 milliseconds.

**35.**

| Class | Frequency, $f$ | Midpoint | Relative frequency | Cumulative frequency |
|---|---|---|---|---|
| 42–47 | 6 | 44.5 | 0.13 | 6 |
| 48–53 | 11 | 50.5 | 0.24 | 17 |
| 54–59 | 17 | 56.5 | 0.37 | 34 |
| 60–65 | 8 | 62.5 | 0.17 | 42 |
| 66–71 | 3 | 68.5 | 0.07 | 45 |
| 72–77 | 0 | 74.5 | 0.00 | 45 |
| 78–83 | 1 | 80.5 | 0.02 | 46 |
| | $\Sigma f = 46$ | | $\Sigma \frac{f}{n} \approx 1$ | |

Ages of U.S. Presidents at Inauguration

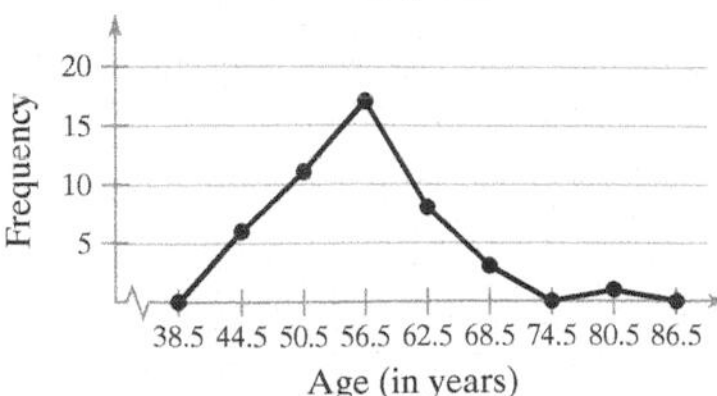


*Sample answer:* The graph shows that the number of U.S. presidents who were 60 or older at inauguration was less than half as many as those who were 59 and younger.

**37.**

| Class | Frequency, $f$ | Midpoint | Relative frequency | Cumulative frequency |
|---|---|---|---|---|
| 1–2 | 7 | 1.5 | 0.19 | 7 |
| 3–4 | 8 | 3.5 | 0.22 | 15 |
| 5–6 | 10 | 5.5 | 0.28 | 25 |
| 7–8 | 2 | 7.5 | 0.06 | 27 |
| 9–10 | 9 | 9.5 | 0.25 | 36 |
| | $\Sigma f = 36$ | | $\Sigma \frac{f}{n} = 1$ | |

Taste Test Ratings

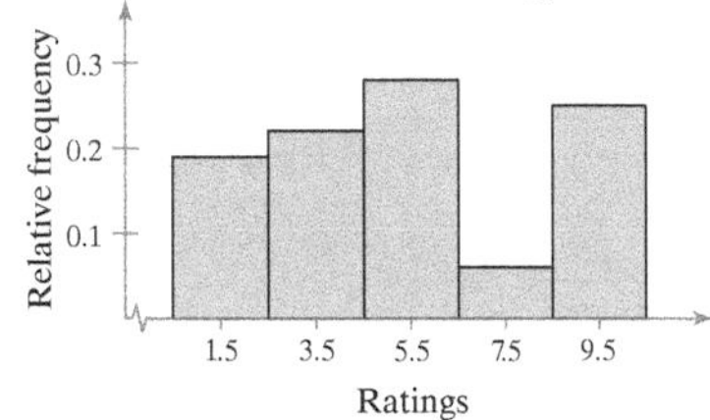


Class with greatest relative frequency: 5–6
Class with least relative frequency: 7–8

**39.**

| Class | Frequency, $f$ | Midpoint | Relative frequency | Cumulative frequency |
|---|---|---|---|---|
| 60–63 | 6 | 61.5 | 0.2143 | 6 |
| 64–67 | 7 | 65.5 | 0.2500 | 13 |
| 68–71 | 9 | 69.5 | 0.3214 | 22 |
| 72–75 | 6 | 73.5 | 0.2143 | 28 |
| 76–79 | 0 | 77.5 | 0.0000 | 28 |
| | $\Sigma f = 28$ | | $\Sigma \frac{f}{n} = 1$ | |

Lengths of Fijian Banded Iguanas

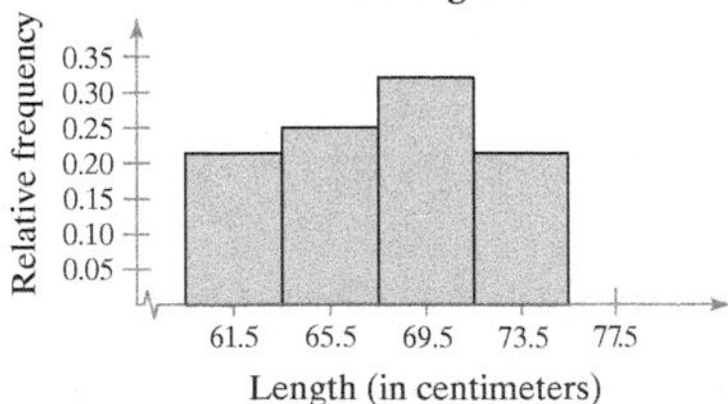


Class with greatest relative frequency: 68–71
Class with least relative frequency: 76–79

**41.**

| Class | Frequency, $f$ | Relative frequency | Cumulative frequency |
|---|---|---|---|
| 52–55 | 6 | 0.1714 | 6 |
| 56–59 | 4 | 0.1143 | 10 |
| 60–63 | 6 | 0.1714 | 16 |
| 64–67 | 10 | 0.2857 | 26 |
| 68–71 | 5 | 0.1429 | 31 |
| 72–75 | 4 | 0.1143 | 35 |
| | $\Sigma f = 35$ | $\Sigma \frac{f}{n} = 1$ | |

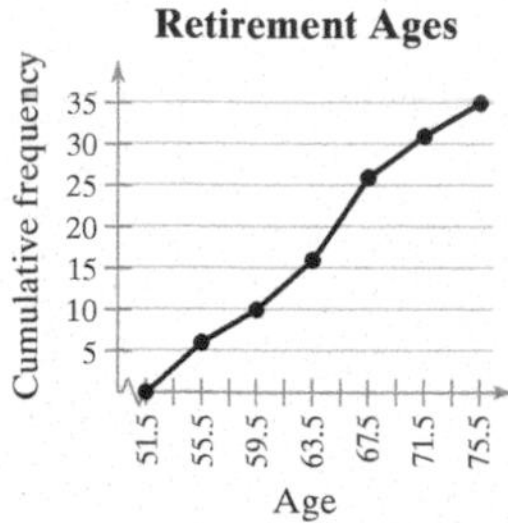


Location of the greatest increase in frequency: 64–67

**43.** (a)

| Class | Frequency, $f$ | Midpoint | Relative frequency | Cumulative frequency |
|---|---|---|---|---|
| 65–74 | 4 | 69.5 | 0.1667 | 4 |
| 75–84 | 7 | 79.5 | 0.2917 | 11 |
| 85–94 | 4 | 89.5 | 0.1667 | 15 |
| 95–104 | 5 | 99.5 | 0.2083 | 20 |
| 105–114 | 3 | 109.5 | 0.1250 | 23 |
| 115–124 | 1 | 119.5 | 0.0417 | 24 |
| | $\Sigma f = 24$ | | $\Sigma \frac{f}{n} \approx 1$ | |

(b)

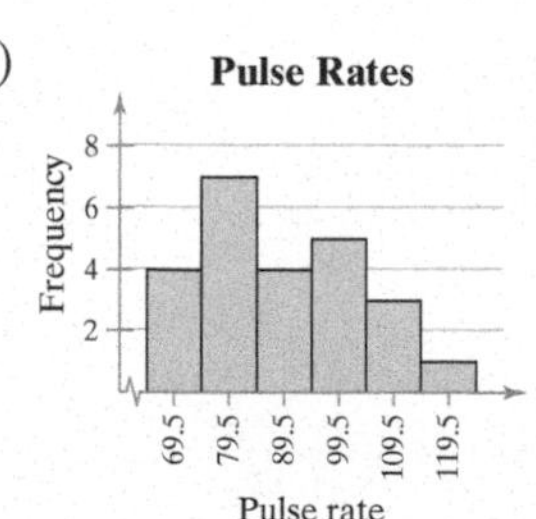


(c)

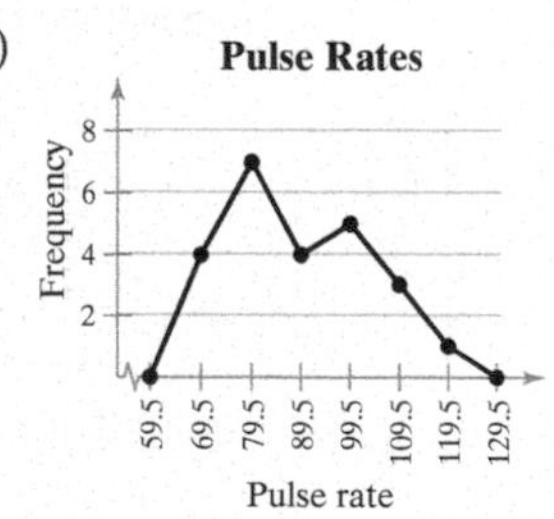


(d)

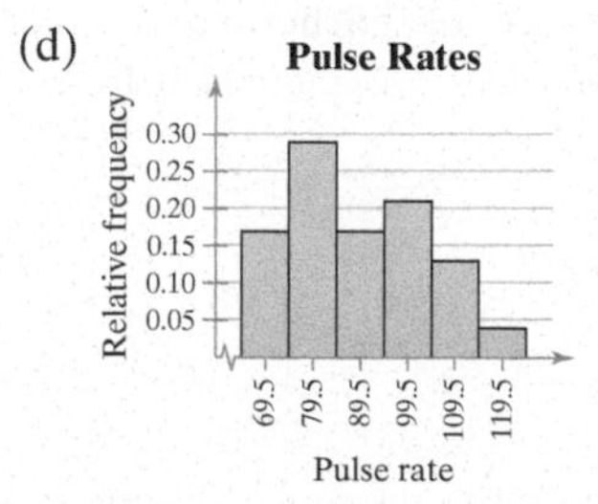


(e)

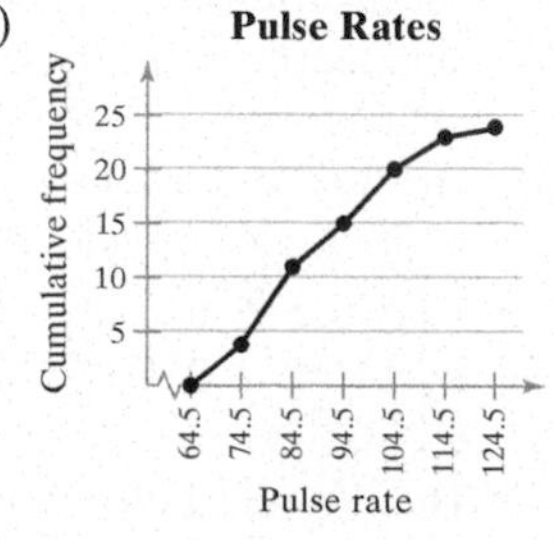


**45.** (a)

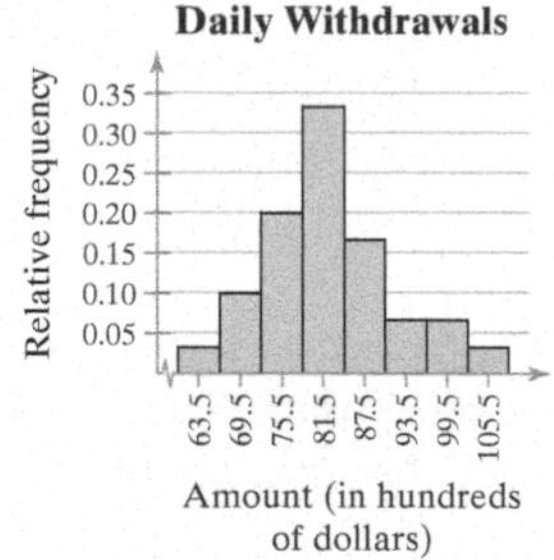


(b) 16.7%, because the sum of the relative frequencies for the last three classes is 0.167.

(c) $9700, because the sum of the relative frequencies for the last two classes is 0.10.

**47.** **Histogram (5 Classes)**

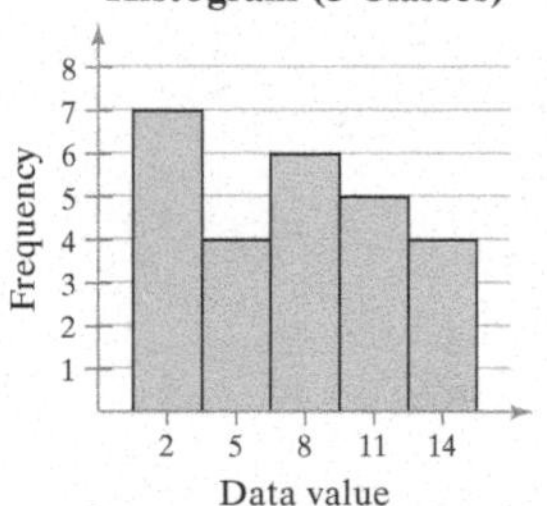


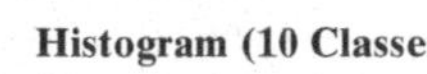


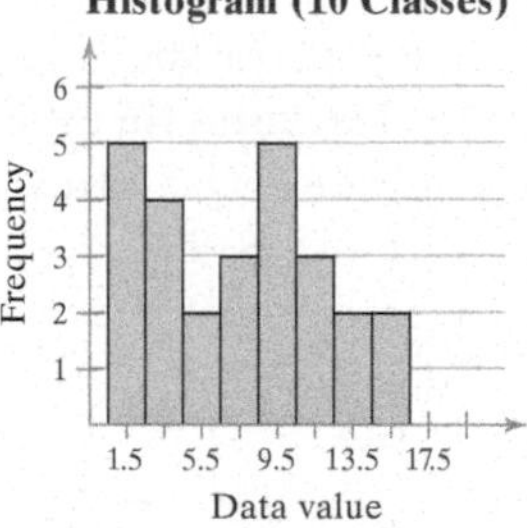


**Histogram (20 Classes)**

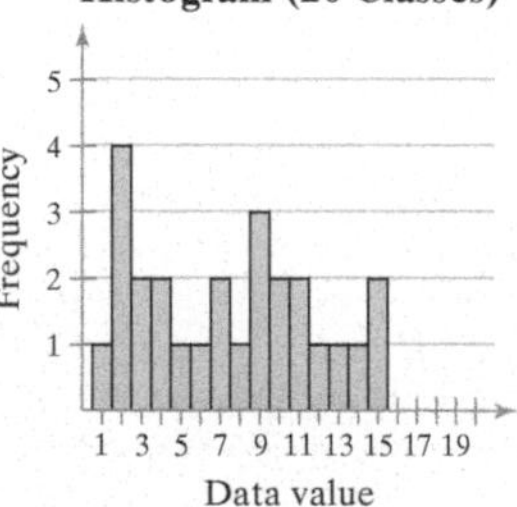


In general, a greater number of classes better preserves the actual values of the data set but is not as helpful for observing general trends and making conclusions. In choosing the number of classes, an important consideration is the size of the data set. For instance, you would not want to use 20 classes if your data set contained 20 entries. In this particular example, as the number of classes increases, the histogram shows more fluctuation. The histograms with 10 and 20 classes have classes with zero frequencies. Not much is gained by using more than five classes. Therefore, it appears that five classes would be best.

## Section 2.2 (page 62)

**1.** Quantitative: stem-and-leaf plot, dot plot, histogram, scatter plot, time series chart
Qualitative: pie chart, Pareto chart

**3.** Both the stem-and-leaf plot and the dot plot allow you to see how data are distributed, to determine specific data entries, and to identify unusual data values.

**5.** b **6.** d **7.** a **8.** c

**9.** 27, 32, 41, 43, 43, 44, 47, 47, 48, 50, 51, 51, 52, 53, 53, 53, 54, 54, 54, 54, 55, 56, 56, 58, 59, 68, 68, 68, 73, 78, 78, 85
Max: 85; Min: 27

**11.** 13, 13, 14, 14, 14, 15, 15, 15, 15, 15, 16, 17, 17, 18, 19
Max: 19; Min: 13

**13.** *Sample answer:* Facebook has the most users, and TikTok has the least. Instagram and WeChat have about the same number of users.

**15.** *Sample answer:* The Texter is the least popular driver. The Left-Lane Hog is tolerated more than the Tailgater. The Speedster and the Drifter have the same popularity.

**17. Exam Scores**

| Stem | Leaves |
|---|---|
| 6 | 7 8 |
| 7 | 3 5 5 6 9 |
| 8 | 0 0 2 3 5 5 7 7 8 |
| 9 | 0 1 1 1 2 4 5 5 |

Key: 6|7 = 67

*Sample answer:* Most grades for the biology midterm were in the 80s or 90s.

**19. Ice Thickness (in centimeters)**

| Stem | Leaves |
|---|---|
| 4 | 3 9 |
| 5 | 1 8 8 8 9 |
| 6 | 4 8 9 9 9 |
| 7 | 0 0 2 2 2 5 |
| 8 | 0 1 |

Key: 4|3 = 4.3

*Sample answer:* Most of the ice had a thickness of 5.8 centimeters to 7.2 centimeters.

**21. Incomes (in millions) of Highest Paid Athletes**

| Stem | Leaves |
|---|---|
| 3 | |
| 3 | 7 7 9 |
| 4 | 0 1 1 2 |
| 4 | 5 5 5 7 7 8 8 8 9 |
| 5 | 2 4 |
| 5 | 6 7 9 |
| 6 | 1 2 4 |
| 6 | |
| 7 | 4 |
| 7 | |
| 8 | |
| 8 | 8 |
| 9 | |
| 9 | 6 |
| 10 | 4 |
| 10 | 5 6 |

Key: 3|7 = 37

*Sample answer:* Most highly paid athletes have an income around $40 million.

**23.**

105 115 125 135 145 155 165 175 185 195 205
Systolic blood pressure (in mmHg)

*Sample answer:* Systolic blood pressure tends to be from 120 to 150 millimeters of mercury.

**25.**

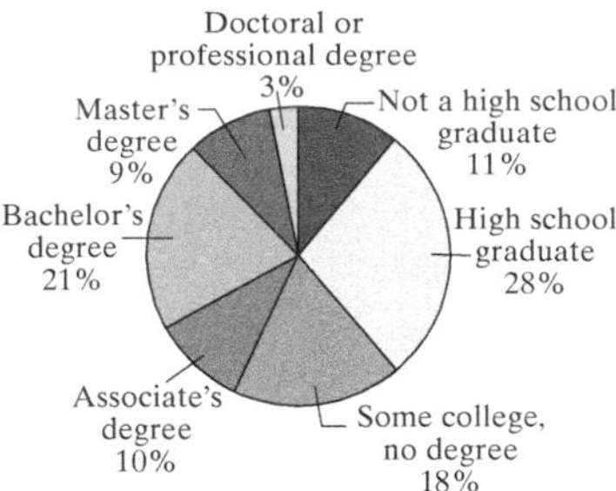


*Sample answer:* The majority of U.S. adults are high school graduates.

**27.**

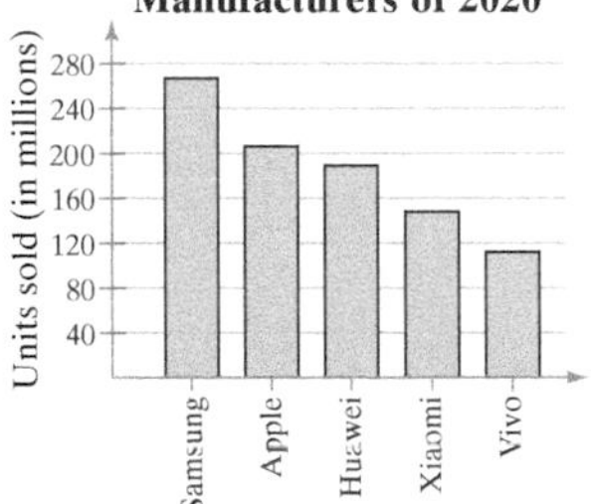


*Sample answer:* Samsung sold the most smartphones out of the five manufacturers and Vivo sold the least.

**29.**

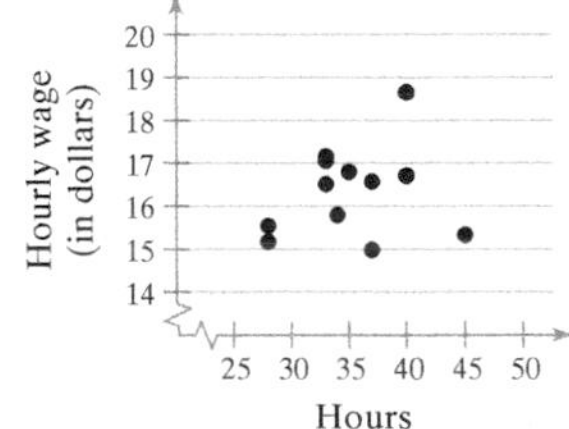


*Sample answer:* It appears that there is no relation between hourly wages and hours worked.

**31.**

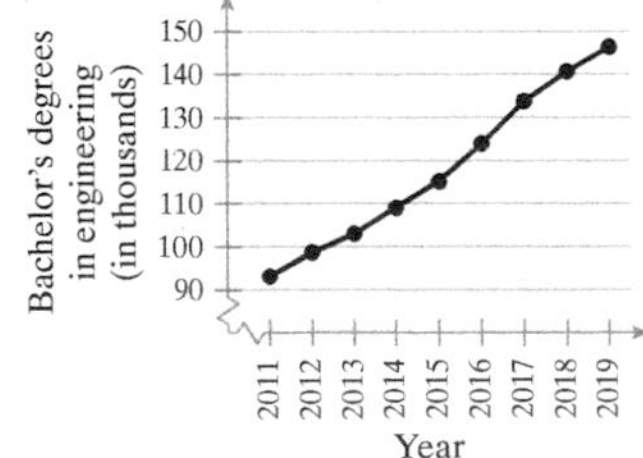


*Sample answer:* The number of bachelor's degrees in engineering conferred in the U.S. has increased from 2011 to 2019.

**33. Heights (in inches)**

| Stem | Leaves |
|---|---|
| 7 | 2 2 4 |
| 7 | 5 5 5 5 6 |
| 8 | 1 1 2 2 2 4 |
| 8 | |

Key: 7|2 = 72

The dot plot helps you see that the data are clustered from 72 to 76 and 81 to 84, with 75 being the most frequent value. The stem-and-leaf plot helps you see that most values are 75 or greater.

35. 

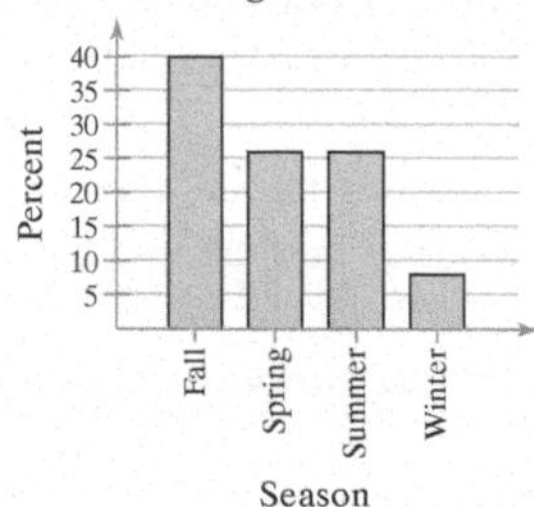


The pie chart helps you to see the percentages as parts of a whole, with fall being the largest. It also shows that while fall is the largest percentage, it makes up less than half of the pie chart. That means that a majority of U.S. adults ages 18 and older prefer a season other than fall. This means it would not be a fair statement to say that most U.S. adults ages 18 and older prefer fall. The Pareto chart helps you to see the rankings of the seasons.

37. (a) The graph is misleading because the large gap from 0 to 90 makes it appear that the sales for the 3rd quarter are disproportionately larger than sales for the other quarters.

(b)

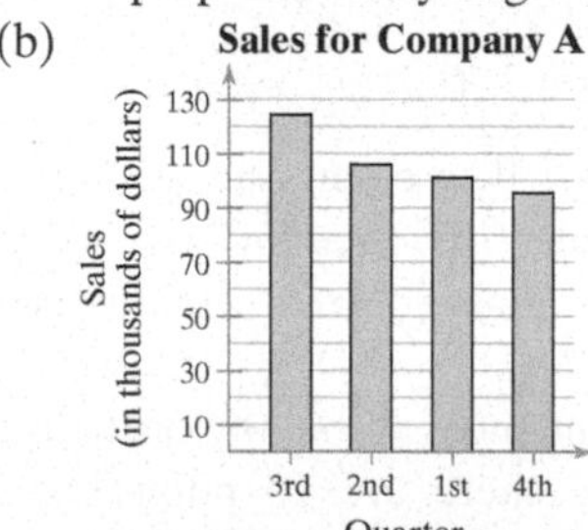


39. (a) The graph is misleading because the angle makes it appear as though the 3rd quarter had a larger percent of sales than the others, when the 1st and 3rd quarters have the same percent.

(b)

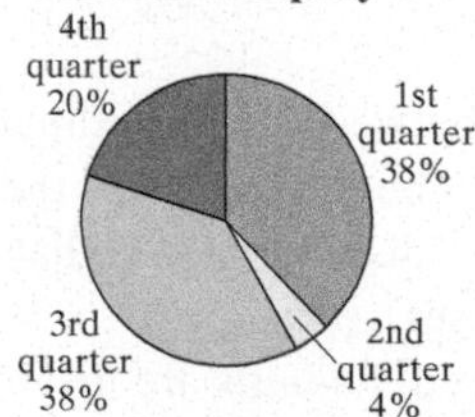


41. (a) At Law Firm A, the lowest salary was $90,000 and the highest salary was $203,000. At Law Firm B, the lowest salary was $90,000 and the highest salary was $190,000. There are 30 lawyers at Law Firm A and 32 lawyers at Law Firm B.

(b) At Law Firm A, the salaries are clustered at the far ends of the distribution range. At Law Firm B, the salaries are spread out.

43. (a) Key: 2|6 = 26

| Stem | Leaves |
|---|---|
| 2 | 6 |
| 3 | 1 |
| 4 | 0 4 4 5 6 7 9 9 |
| 5 | 5 5 5 |
| 6 | 3 4 4 |
| 7 | 0 1 2 2 |

(b) 25 30 35 40 45 50 55 60 65 70

(c) (d)

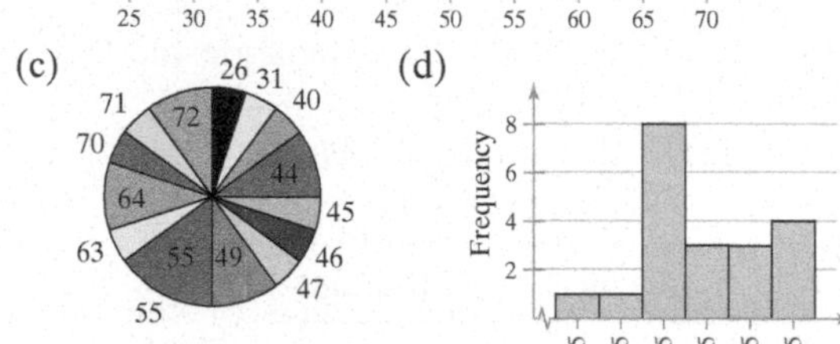


(e)

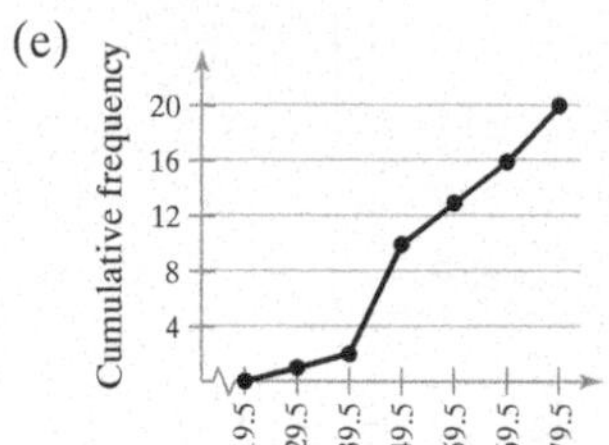


*Sample answer:* The stem-and-leaf plot, dot plot, frequency histogram, and ogive display the data best because the data are quantitative.

## Section 2.3 (page 74)

1. True 3. True 5. *Sample answer:* 2, 4, 5, 5, 6, 8

7. *Sample answer:* 2, 5, 7, 9, 35

9. The shape of the distribution is skewed right because the bars have a "tail" to the right.

11. The shape of the distribution is uniform because the bars are approximately the same height.

13. (11), because the distribution of values ranges from 1 to 12 and has (approximately) equal frequencies.

14. (9), because the distribution has values in the thousands and is skewed right due to the few vehicles that have much higher mileages than the majority of the vehicles.

15. (12), because the distribution has a maximum value of 90 and is skewed left due to a few students scoring much lower than the majority of the students.

16. (10), because the distribution is approximately symmetric and the weights range from 80 to 160 pounds.

17. $\bar{x} \approx 14.9$; median $= 15$; mode $= 16$

19. $\bar{x} \approx 74.6$; median $= 67$; The mode cannot be found because no data entry is repeated.

21. $\bar{x} \approx 58$; median $= 58.5$; mode $= 54, 59$

23. $\bar{x} \approx 7.1$; median $= 6.5$; mode $= 10$

25. $\bar{x} \approx 59.1$; median $= 49$; mode $= 80, 125$; The modes do not represent the center of the data set because they are large values compared to the rest of the data.

27. $\bar{x}$ is not possible; median is not possible; mode = "Social media site"; The mean and median cannot be found because the data are at the nominal level of measurement.

**29.** $\bar{x}$ is not possible; median is not possible; mode = "Junior"; The mean and median cannot be found because the data are at the nominal level of measurement.

**31.** $\bar{x} \approx 29.2$; median = 30.5; mode = 23, 34

**33.** $\bar{x} \approx 19.5$; median = 20; mode = 15

**35.** Cluster around 475–525, gap between 225 and 275

**37.** Mode, because the data are at the nominal level of measurement.

**39.** Mean, because the distribution is symmetric and there are no outliers.

**41.** 90.5 **43.** \$612.73 **45.** 84 **47.** 87

**49.** 53.5 minutes **51.** 42.3 years old

**53.**

| Class | Frequency, $f$ | Midpoint |
|---|---|---|
| 127–161 | 7 | 144 |
| 162–196 | 6 | 179 |
| 197–231 | 3 | 214 |
| 232–266 | 3 | 249 |
| 267–301 | 1 | 284 |

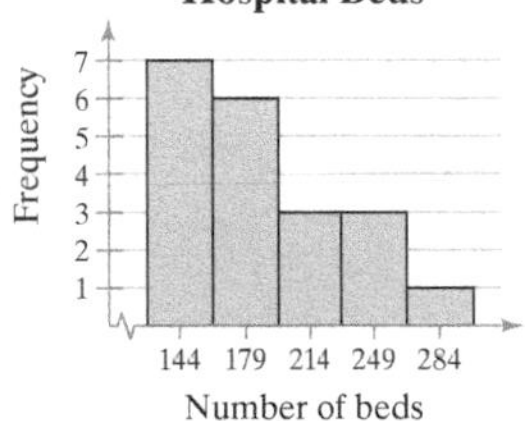


Positively skewed

**55.**

| Class | Frequency, $f$ | Midpoint |
|---|---|---|
| 62–64 | 3 | 63 |
| 65–67 | 7 | 66 |
| 68–70 | 9 | 69 |
| 71–73 | 8 | 72 |
| 74–76 | 3 | 75 |

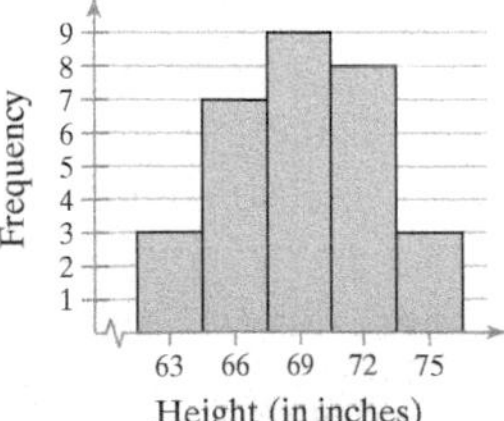


Symmetric

**57.** (a) $\bar{x} \approx 1518.2$, median = 1520.5
(b) $\bar{x} \approx 1521.2$, median = 1522.5
(c) Mean

**59.** The data are skewed right.
A = mode, because it is the data entry that occurred most often.
B = median, because the median is to the left of the mean in a skewed right distribution.
C = mean, because the mean is to the right of the median in a skewed right distribution.

**61.** Increase one of the three-credit B classes to an A. The three-credit class is weighted more than the two-credit classes, so it will have a greater effect on the grade point average.

**63.** (a) Mean, because Car A has the highest mean of the three.
(b) Median, because Car B has the highest median of the three.
(c) Mode, because Car C has the highest mode of the three.

**65.** (a) $\bar{x} \approx 49.2$; median = 46.5
(b) **Test Scores**

```
1 | 1 3          Key: 3|6 = 36
2 | 2 8
3 | 6 6 6 7 7 7 8
4 | 1 3 4 6 7 —— mean
5 | 1 1 1 3
6 | 1 2 3 4         median
7 | 2 2 4 6
8 | 5
9 | 0
```

(c) Positively skewed

## Section 2.3 Activity (page 81)

1. The distribution is symmetric. The mean and median both decrease slightly. Over time, the median will decrease dramatically and the mean will also decrease, but to a lesser degree.
2. Neither the mean nor the median can be any of the points that were plotted. Because there are 10 points in each region, the mean will fall somewhere between the two regions. By the same logic, the median will be the average of the greatest point between 0 and 0.75 and the least point between 20 and 25.

## Section 2.4 (page 93)

**1.** The range is the difference between the maximum and minimum values of a data set. The advantage of the range is that it is easy to calculate. The disadvantage is that it uses only two entries from the data set.

**3.** The units of variance are squared. Its units are meaningless (example: dollars$^2$). The units of standard deviation are the same as the data.

**5.** When calculating the population standard deviation, you divide the sum of the squared deviations by $N$, then take the square root of that value. When calculating the sample standard deviation, you divide the sum of the squared deviations by $n - 1$, then take the square root of that value.

**7.** Similarity: Both estimate proportions of the data contained within $k$ standard deviations of the mean.
Difference: The Empirical Rule assumes the distribution is approximately symmetric and bell-shaped and Chebychev's Theorem makes no such assumption.

**9.** Approximately 50, or \$50,000 **11.** (a) 17.8 (b) 39.8

**13.** Range = 1.1; $\mu \approx 10.33$; $\sigma^2 \approx 0.16$; $\sigma \approx 0.4$

**15.** Range = 6; $\bar{x} = 19$; $s^2 \approx 3.5$; $s \approx 1.9$

**17.** The data set in (a) has a standard deviation of 2.4 and the data set in (b) has a standard deviation of 5 because the data in (b) have more variability.

**19.** Company B; An offer of $43,000 is two standard deviations from the mean of Company A's starting salaries, which makes it unlikely. The same offer is within one standard deviation of the mean of Company B's starting salaries, which makes the offer likely.

**21.** (a) Greatest sample standard deviation: (ii)
Data set (ii) has more entries that are farther away from the mean.
Least sample standard deviation: (iii)
Data set (iii) has more entries that are close to the mean.
(b) The three data sets have the same mean, median, and mode, but have a different standard deviation.
(c) Estimates will vary; (i) $s \approx 1.1$; (ii) $s \approx 1.3$; (iii) $s \approx 0.8$

**23.** (a) Greatest sample standard deviation: (i)
Data set (i) has more entries that are farther away from the mean.
Least sample standard deviation: (iii)
Data set (iii) has more entries that are close to the mean.
(b) The three data sets have the same mean, median, and mode, but have a different standard deviation.
(c) Estimates will vary; (i) $s \approx 9.6$; (ii) $s \approx 9.0$; (iii) $s \approx 5.1$

**25.** *Sample answer:* 3, 3, 3, 7, 7, 7

**27.** *Sample answer:* 9, 9, 9, 9, 9, 9, 9

**29.** 68%   **31.** (a) 51 (b) 17

**33.** 78, 76, and 82 are unusual; 82 is very unusual because it is more than 3 standard deviations from the mean.

**35.** 30

**37.** At least 93.75% of the exam scores are from 70 to 94.

**39.**

| $x$ | $f$ | $xf$ |
|---|---|---|
| 0 | 3 | 0 |
| 1 | 4 | 4 |
| 2 | 3 | 6 |
| 3 | 9 | 27 |
| 4 | 3 | 12 |
| 5 | 3 | 15 |
| 6 | 8 | 48 |
| 7 | 5 | 35 |
| 8 | 6 | 48 |
| 9 | 6 | 54 |
| | $\Sigma = 50$ | $\Sigma = 249$ |

| $x - \bar{x}$ | $(x - \bar{x})^2$ | $(x - \bar{x})^2 f$ |
|---|---|---|
| −5 | 25 | 75 |
| −4 | 16 | 64 |
| −3 | 9 | 27 |
| −2 | 4 | 36 |
| −1 | 1 | 3 |
| 0 | 0 | 0 |
| 1 | 1 | 8 |
| 2 | 4 | 20 |
| 3 | 9 | 54 |
| 4 | 16 | 96 |
| | | $\Sigma = 383$ |

$\bar{x} \approx 5.0$, $s \approx 2.8$

**41.**

| Class | $x$ | $f$ | $xf$ |
|---|---|---|---|
| 17,000–19,499 | 18,249.5 | 9 | 155,245.5 |
| 19,500–21,999 | 20,749.5 | 10 | 207,495 |
| 22,000–24,499 | 23,249.5 | 16 | 371,992 |
| 24,500–26,999 | 25,749.5 | 11 | 283,244.5 |
| 27,000 or more | 28,249.5 | 6 | 169,497 |
| | | $n = 52$ | $\Sigma xf = 1{,}187{,}474$ |

| $x - \bar{x}$ | $(x - \bar{x})^2$ | $(x - \bar{x})^2 f$ |
|---|---|---|
| −5586.54 | 31,209,429.17 | 280,884,862.5 |
| −2086.54 | 4,353,649.17 | 43,536,491.72 |
| 413.46 | 170,949.17 | 2,735,186.75 |
| 2913.46 | 8,488,249.17 | 93,370,740.89 |
| 5413.46 | 29,305,549.17 | 175,833,295 |
| | $\Sigma(x - \bar{x})^2 f = 596{,}360{,}576.9$ | |

$\bar{x} \approx \$22{,}836.04$; $s \approx \$3419.55$

**43.**

| $x$ | $f$ | $xf$ | $x - \bar{x}$ | $(x - \bar{x})^2$ | $(x - \bar{x})^2 f$ |
|---|---|---|---|---|---|
| 1 | 2 | 2 | −1.9 | 3.61 | 7.22 |
| 2 | 18 | 36 | −0.9 | 0.81 | 14.58 |
| 3 | 24 | 72 | 0.1 | 0.01 | 0.24 |
| 4 | 16 | 64 | 1.1 | 1.21 | 19.36 |
| | $n = 60$ | $\Sigma xf = 174$ | | $\Sigma(x - \bar{x})^2 f = 41.4$ | |

$\bar{x} \approx 2.9$; $s \approx 0.8$

**45.** $CV_{\text{Denver}} \approx 8.1\%$, $CV_{\text{LA}} \approx 7.2\%$
Salaries for entry level architects are more variable in Denver than in Los Angeles.

**47.** $CV_{\text{ages}} \approx 16.3\%$, $CV_{\text{caps}} \approx 95.3\%$
Caps are more variable than ages for all members of the 2021 Women's U.S. soccer team.

**49.** $CV_{\text{males}} \approx 20.7\%$, $CV_{\text{females}} \approx 17.6\%$
SAT scores are more variable for males than for females.

**51.** (a)
$$SS_x = \Sigma(x - \bar{x})^2$$
$$SS_x = \Sigma(x^2 - 2x\bar{x} + \bar{x}^2)$$
$$SS_x = \Sigma x^2 - 2\bar{x}\Sigma x + \bar{x}^2\Sigma 1$$
$$SS_x = \Sigma x^2 - 2\bar{x}\Sigma x + \bar{x}^2 n$$
$$SS_x = \Sigma x^2 - 2\bar{x}^2 n + \bar{x}^2 n$$
$$SS_x = \Sigma x^2 - \bar{x}^2 n$$
$$SS_x = \Sigma x^2 - \frac{(\Sigma x)^2}{n}$$
(b) $s \approx 1.9$
(c) They are the same.

**53.** (a) $\bar{x} \approx 42.1$; $s \approx 5.6$ (b) $\bar{x} \approx 44.3$; $s \approx 5.9$
(c) 3.5, 3, 3, 4, 4, 2.75, 4.25, 3.25, 3.25, 3.5, 3.25, 3.75, 3.5, 4.17
$\bar{x} \approx 3.5$; $s \approx 0.47$
(d) When each entry is multiplied by a constant $k$, the new sample mean is $k \cdot x$, and the new sample standard deviation is $k \cdot s$.

**55.** (a) $P \approx -2.61$
The data are skewed left.
(b) $P \approx 4.12$
The data are skewed right.
(c) $P = 0$
The data are symmetric.
(d) $P = 1$
The data are skewed right.
(e) $P = -3$
The data are skewed left.

## Section 2.4 Activity (page 100)

1. When a point with a value of 15 is added, the mean remains constant or changes very little, and the standard deviation decreases. When a point with a value of 20 is added, the mean is raised and the standard deviation increases.
2. To get the largest standard deviation, plot four of the points at 30 and four of the points at 40.
To get the smallest standard deviation, plot all of the points at the same number. That way, each $x - \bar{x}$ is 0, so the standard deviation will be 0.

## Section 2.5 (page 109)

**1.** The talk is longer in length than 75% of the lectures in the series.

**3.** The student's grade on the Fundamentals of Engineering exam was below the average.

**5.** The interquartile range of a data set can be used to identify outliers because data entries that are greater than $Q_3 + 1.5(\text{IQR})$ or less than $Q_1 - 1.5(\text{IQR})$ are considered outliers.

**7.** True

**9.** False. An outlier is any number above $Q_3 + 1.5(\text{IQR})$ or below $Q_1 - 1.5(\text{IQR})$.

**11.** (a) $Q_1 = 57, Q_2 = 60, Q_3 = 63$ (b) $\text{IQR} = 6$ (c) 80

**13.** $\text{Min} = 0, Q_1 = 2, Q_2 = 5, Q_3 = 8, \text{Max} = 10$

**15.** (a) $\text{Min} = 24, Q_1 = 28, Q_2 = 35, Q_3 = 41, \text{Max} = 60$
(b)

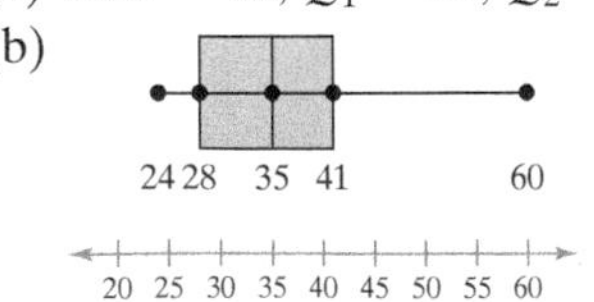


**17.** (a) $\text{Min} = 1, Q_1 = 4.5, Q_2 = 6, Q_3 = 7.5, \text{Max} = 9$
(b)

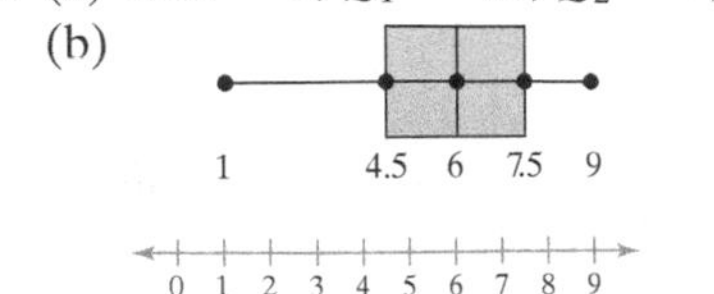


**19.** None. The data are not skewed or symmetric.

**21.** Skewed left. Most of the data lie to the right on the box plot.

**23.** Studying

1 2 3 6.5 8

Number of hours

**25.** Commuting Distances

1 3 7 12 45

Distance (in miles)

**27.** (a) 6.5 hours (b) about 50% (c) about 25%

**29.** About 158; About 65% of quantitative reasoning scores on the Graduate Record Examination are less than 158.

**31.** About 7th percentile; About 7% of quantitative reasoning scores on the Graduate Record Examination are less than 140.

**33.** 10th percentile **35.** 57, 57, 61, 61, 65, 66

**37.**

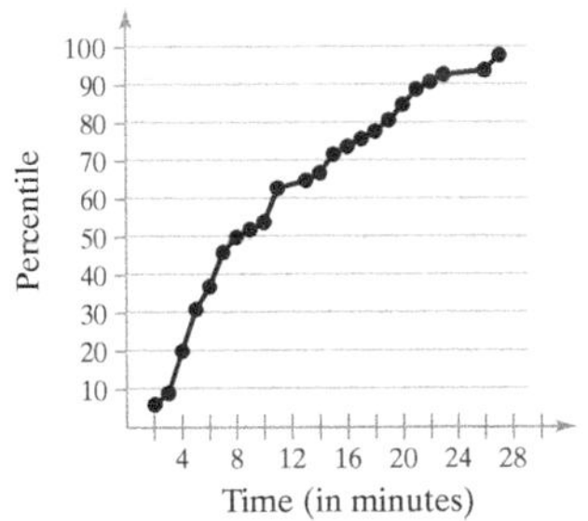


**39.** About 85th percentile

**41.** $A \rightarrow z = -1.43$
$B \rightarrow z = 0$
$C \rightarrow z = 2.14$
A $z$-score of 2.14 would be unusual.

**43.** Not unusual; The $z$-score is 0.91, so the age of 31 is about 0.91 standard deviation above the mean.

**45.** Not unusual; The $z$-score is $-0.26$, so the age of 27 is about 0.26 standard deviation below the mean.

**47.** Unusual; The $z$-score is $-2.32$, so the age of 20 is about 2.38 standard deviations below the mean.

**49.** (a) For 34,000, $z \approx -0.44$; For 37,000, $z \approx 0.89$;
For 30,000, $z \approx -2.22$
The tire with a life span of 30,000 miles has an unusually short life span.
(b) For 30,500, about 2.5th percentile;
For 37,250, about 84th percentile;
For 35,000, about 50th percentile

**51.** Gary Oldman: $z \approx 1.75$; Sam Rockwell: $z \approx -0.09$; The age of Gary Oldman was between 1 and 2 standard deviations above the mean age of Best Actor winners, and the age of Sam Rockwell was less than 1 standard deviation below the mean age of Best Supporting Actor winners. Neither actor's age is unusual.

**53.** John Wayne: $z \approx 2.09$; Gig Young: $z \approx 0.43$; The age of John Wayne was more than 2 standard deviations above the mean age of Best Actor winners, which is unusual. The age of Gig Young was less than one standard deviation above the mean age of Best Supporting Actor winners, which is not unusual.

**55.** 5

**57.** (a) The distribution of the Punk Rock Concert is symmetric. The distribution of the Jazz Concert is skewed right. The Punk Rock Concert has less variation.
(b) The Jazz Concert is more likely to have outliers because it has more variation.
(c) The Punk Rock Concert, because 68% of the data should be between $\pm 16.3$ of the mean.
(d) No, you do not know the number of songs played at either concert or the actual lengths of the songs.

**59.** (a) 24, 2 (b)

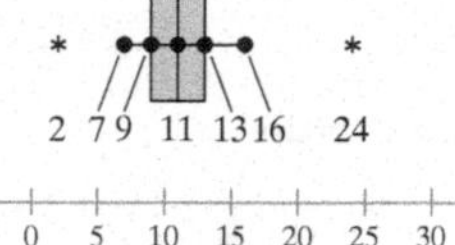


**61.** (a) 1 (b)

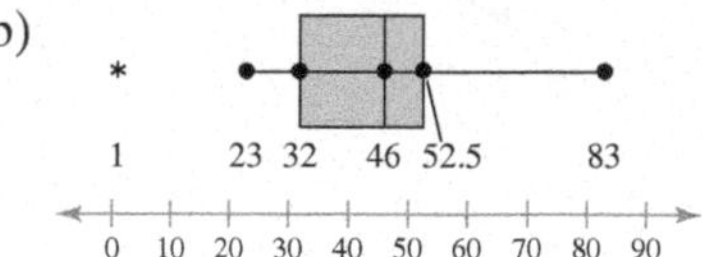


**63.** Answers will vary.

## Uses and Abuses for Chapter 2 (page 114)

**1.** Answers will vary.

**2.** No, it is not ethical because it misleads the consumer to believe that drinking red wine is more effective at preventing heart disease than it may actually be.

## Review Exercises for Chapter 2 (page 116)

**1.**

| Class | Midpoint | Class boundaries |
|---|---|---|
| 26–31 | 28.5 | 25.5–31.5 |
| 32–37 | 34.5 | 31.5–37.5 |
| 38–43 | 40.5 | 37.5–43.5 |
| 44–49 | 46.5 | 43.5–49.5 |
| 50–55 | 52.5 | 49.5–55.5 |

| Frequency, $f$ | Relative frequency | Cumulative frequency |
|---|---|---|
| 5 | 0.25 | 5 |
| 4 | 0.20 | 9 |
| 6 | 0.30 | 15 |
| 3 | 0.15 | 18 |
| 2 | 0.10 | 20 |
| $\Sigma f = 20$ | $\Sigma \frac{f}{n} = 1$ | |

**3.**

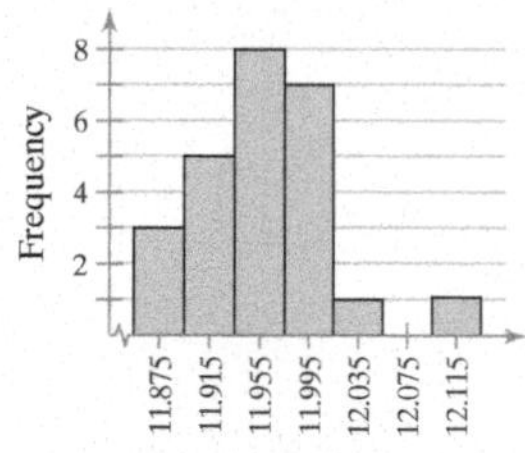


**5.**

| Class | Midpoint | Frequency, $f$ |
|---|---|---|
| 79–93 | 86 | 9 |
| 94–108 | 101 | 12 |
| 109–123 | 116 | 5 |
| 124–138 | 131 | 4 |
| 139–153 | 146 | 2 |
| 154–168 | 161 | 1 |
| | | $\Sigma f = 33$ |

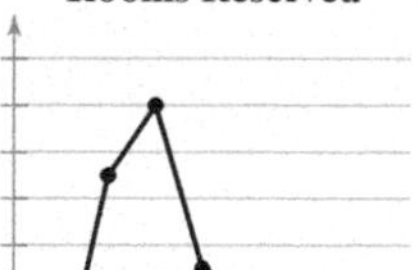


**7.** **Pollution Indices of U.S. Cities**

2 | 0 3 5 7 9 Key: 2|0 = 20
3 | 0 0 1 1 2 6 7 9 9
4 | 2 3 4 5 5 5 7
5 | 0 2
6 | 3

*Sample answer:* Most U.S. cities have a pollution index from 30 to 47.

**9.**

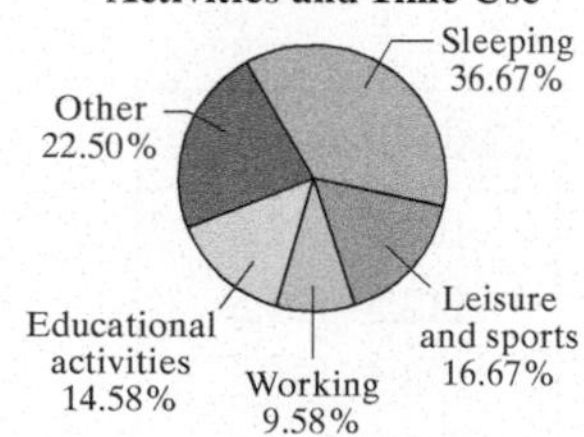


*Sample answer:* Full-time university and college students spend the least amount of time working.

**11.**

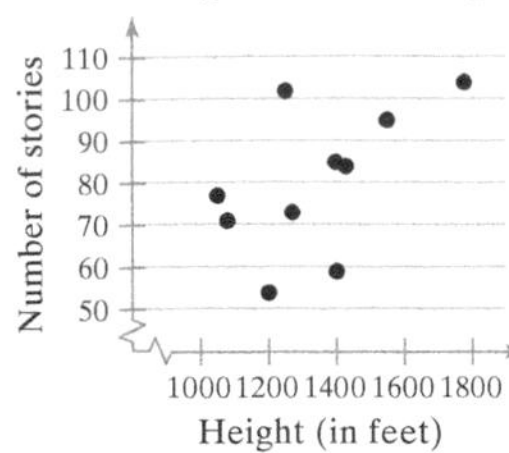


*Sample answer:* The number of stories appears to increase with height.

**13.** $\bar{x} = 29.85$; median $= 29.75$; mode $= 30.0$

**15.** 82.1 **17.** 38.4 **19.** Skewed right **21.** Skewed right

**23.** Mean; When a distribution is skewed right, the mean is to the right of the median.

**25.** Range $= 14$; $\mu \approx 6.9$; $\sigma^2 \approx 21.1$; $\sigma \approx 4.6$

**27.** Range $= \$2044$; $\bar{x} \approx \$6266.81$; $s^2 \approx 455{,}944.30$; $s \approx \$675.24$

**29.** \$75 and \$145 **31.** 30 customers

**33.** $\bar{x} \approx 2.5$; $s \approx 1.2$

**35.** $CV_{\text{freshmen}} \approx 41.3\%$; $CV_{\text{seniors}} \approx 24.2\%$
Grade point averages are more variable for freshmen than seniors.

**37.** Min $= 22$, $Q_1 = 30$, $Q_2 = 35.5$, $Q_3 = 58$, Max $= 141$

**39.**

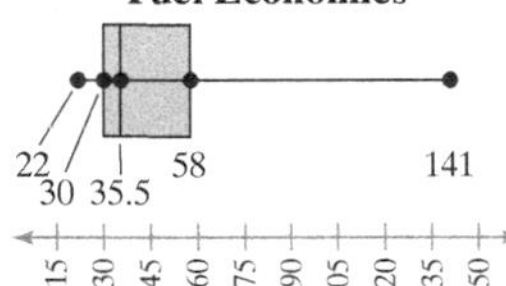


**41.** 1 inch **43.** 35%

**45.** Not unusual; The $z$-score is 1.97, so a towing capacity of 16,500 pounds is about 1.97 standard deviations above the mean.

**47.** Unusual; The $z$-score is 2.60, so a towing capacity of 18,000 pounds is about 2.60 standard deviations above the mean.

## Quiz for Chapter 2 (page 120)

**1.** (a)

| Class | Midpoint | Class boundaries |
|---|---|---|
| 101–112 | 106.5 | 100.5–112.5 |
| 113–124 | 118.5 | 112.5–124.5 |
| 125–136 | 130.5 | 124.5–136.5 |
| 137–148 | 142.5 | 136.5–148.5 |
| 149–160 | 154.5 | 148.5–160.5 |

| Frequency, $f$ | Relative frequency | Cumulative frequency |
|---|---|---|
| 3 | 0.11 | 3 |
| 11 | 0.41 | 14 |
| 8 | 0.30 | 22 |
| 3 | 0.11 | 25 |
| 2 | 0.07 | 27 |

(b)

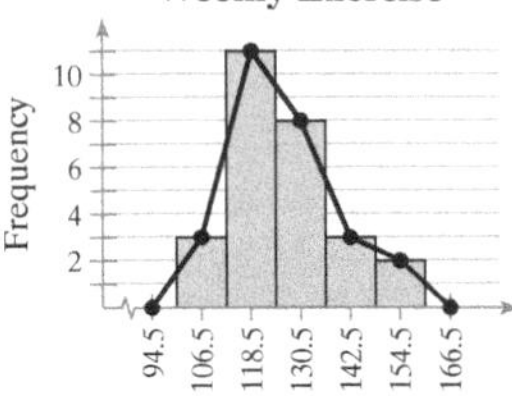


(c)

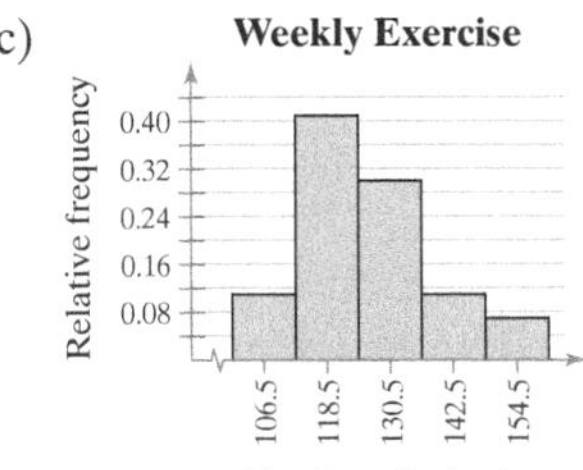


(d) Skewed right

(e)

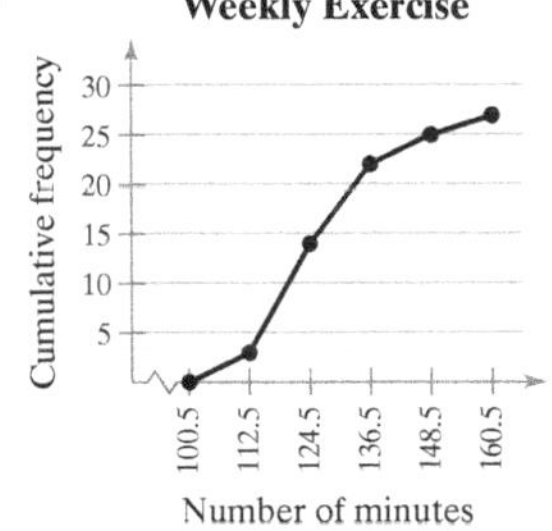


(f) **Weekly Exercise (in minutes)**

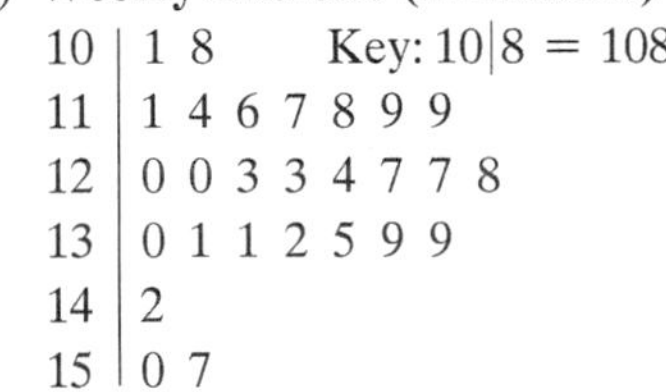

| | | |
|---|---|---|
| 10 | 1 8 | Key: 10\|8 = 108 |
| 11 | 1 4 6 7 8 9 9 | |
| 12 | 0 0 3 3 4 7 7 8 | |
| 13 | 0 1 1 2 5 9 9 | |
| 14 | 2 | |
| 15 | 0 7 | |

(g)

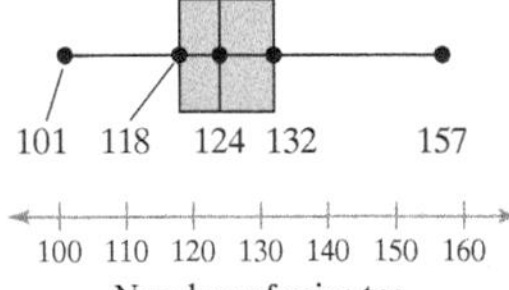


**2.** $\bar{x} \approx 126.1$; $s \approx 13.0$

**3.** (a)

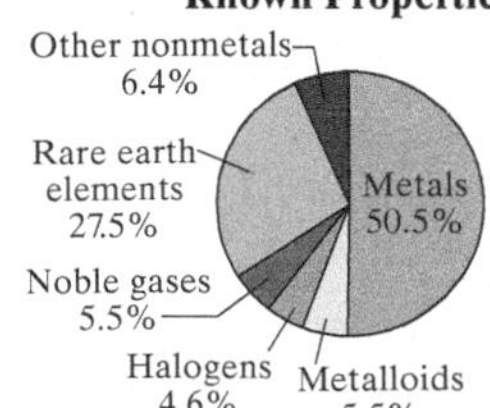

(b) Elements with Known Properties

Number of elements

Metals, Rare earth elements, Other nonmetals, Metalloids, Noble gases, Halogens

Element

4. (a) $\bar{x} \approx 1016.4$; median = 1019; mode = 1100; The mean or median best describes a typical salary because there are no outliers.
   (b) Range = 666; $s^2 \approx 47{,}120.9$; $s \approx 217.1$
   (c) $CV \approx 21.4\%$
5. $150,000 and $210,000
6. (a) Unusual; The $z$-score is 3, so a new home price of $225,000 is about 3 standard deviations above the mean.
   (b) Unusual; The $z$-score is −6.67, so a new home price of $80,000 is about 6.67 standard deviations below the mean.
   (c) Not unusual; The $z$-score is 1.33, so a new home price of $200,000 is about 1.33 standard deviations above the mean.
   (d) Unusual; The $z$-score is −2.2, so a new home price of $147,000 is about 2.2 standard deviations below the mean.
7. 

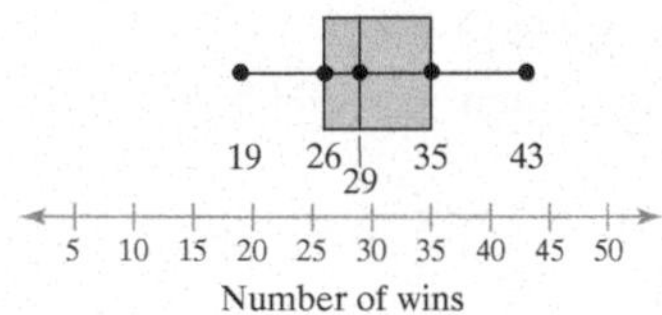


## Real Statistics—Real Decisions for Chapter 2 (page 122)

1. (a) Find the average cost of renting an apartment for each area and do a comparison.
   (b) The mean would best represent the data sets for the four areas of the city.
   (c) Area A: $\bar{x}$ = $1131.58
   Area B: $\bar{x}$ = $998.33
   Area C: $\bar{x}$ = $991.58
   Area D: $\bar{x}$ = $1064.17
2. (a) Construct a Pareto chart, because the data are quantitative and a Pareto chart positions data in order of decreasing height, with the tallest bar positioned at the left.
   (b)

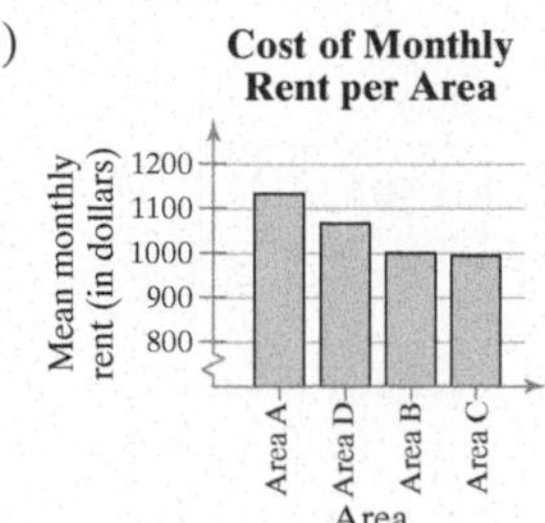

   (c) Yes. From the Pareto chart, you can see that Area A has the highest average cost of monthly rent, followed by Area D, Area B, and Area C.
3. *Sample answer:*
   (a) You could use the range and sample standard deviation for each area.
   (b)

| **Area A** | **Area B** |
|---|---|
| range = $467 | range = $474 |
| $s \approx$ $138.45 | $s \approx$ $163.11 |
| **Area C** | **Area D** |
| range = $518 | range = $560 |
| $s \approx$ $164.51 | $s \approx$ $156.26 |

   (c) No. Area A has the lowest range and standard deviation, so the rents in Areas B–D are more spread out. There could be one or two inexpensive rents that lower the means for these areas. It is possible that the population means of Areas B–D are close to the population mean of Area A.
4. (a) Answers will vary.
   (b) Location, weather, population

## Cumulative Review for Chapters 1–2 (page 126)

1. Systematic sampling is used because every fortieth toothbrush from each assembly line is tested. It is possible for bias to enter into the sample if, for some reason, an assembly line makes a consistent error.
2. Simple random sampling is used because each telephone number has an equal chance of being dialed, and all samples of 1090 phone numbers have an equal chance of being selected. The sample may be biased because telephone sampling only samples those individuals who have telephones, who are available, and who are willing to respond.
3. Workplace Fraud

Percent

Tip, Internal audit, Management review, Other means, By accident, Account reconciliation, External audit, Document examination, Surveillance/monitoring, Notified by law enforcement, IT controls, Confession

Fraud detection

4. Parameter. The median salary is based on all first-year chemists.
5. Statistic. The percent, 64%, is based on a subset of the population.
6. (a) 95%
   (b) For $93,500, $z \approx 4.67$; For $85,600, $z \approx -0.6$; For $82,750, $z \approx -2.5$.
   The salaries of $93,500 and $82,750 are unusual.
7. Population: Collection of opinions of all college students in bachelor's degree programs.
   Sample: Collection of opinions of the 3941 college students in bachelor's degree programs surveyed.

8. Population: Collection of responses of all undergraduate and graduate students.
Sample: Collection of responses of the 182 undergraduate and graduate students surveyed.
9. Experiment. The study applies a treatment (digital device) to the subjects.
10. Observational study. The study does not attempt to influence the responses of the subjects.
11. Quantitative; Ratio
12. Qualitative; Nominal
13. (a)

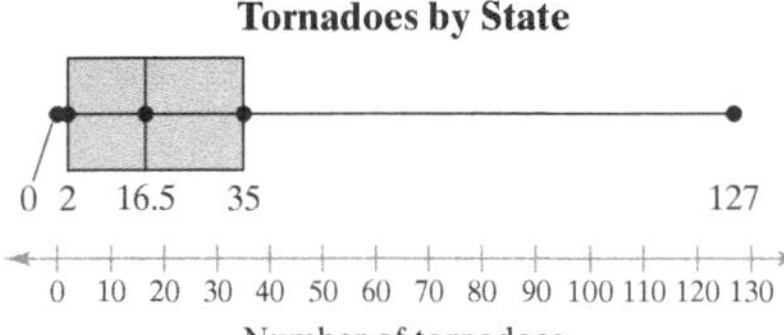


(b) Skewed right
14. 88.9
15. (a) $\bar{x} \approx 5.49$; median = 5.4; mode = none; Both the mean and the median accurately describe a typical American alligator tail length.
(b) Range = 4.1; $s^2 \approx 2.34$; $s \approx 1.53$
16. (a) An inference drawn from the study is that the life expectancies for Americans will continue to increase or remain stable.
(b) This inference may incorrectly imply that Americans will have higher life expectancies in the future.
17.

| Class | Midpoint | Class boundaries | Frequency, $f$ | Relative frequency | Cumulative frequency |
|---|---|---|---|---|---|
| 0–9 | 4.5 | −0.5–9.5 | 18 | 0.56 | 18 |
| 10–19 | 14.5 | 9.5–19.5 | 5 | 0.16 | 23 |
| 20–29 | 24.5 | 19.5–29.5 | 2 | 0.06 | 25 |
| 30–39 | 34.5 | 29.5–39.5 | 1 | 0.03 | 26 |
| 40–49 | 44.5 | 39.5–49.5 | 1 | 0.03 | 27 |
| 50–59 | 54.5 | 49.5–59.5 | 1 | 0.03 | 28 |
| 60–69 | 64.5 | 59.5–69.5 | 2 | 0.06 | 30 |
| 70–79 | 74.5 | 69.5–79.5 | 2 | 0.06 | 32 |

18. Skewed right
19.

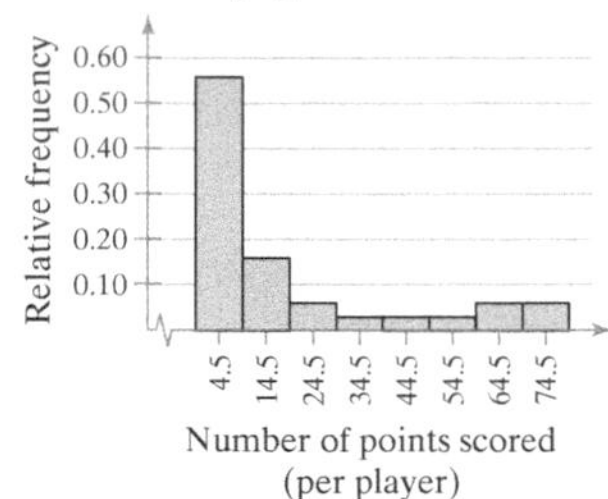


Class with greatest frequency: 0–9
Classes with the least frequency: 30–39, 40–49, and 50–59

# Chapter 3

## Section 3.1 (page 140)

1. An outcome is the result of a single trial in a probability experiment, whereas an event is a set of one or more outcomes.
3. The probability of an event cannot exceed 100%.
5. The law of large numbers states that as an experiment is repeated over and over, the probabilities found in the experiment will approach the actual probabilities of the event. Examples will vary.
7. False. The event "choosing false on a true or false question and choosing A or B on a multiple choice question" is not simple because it consists of two possible outcomes and can be represented as $A = \{FA, FB\}$.
9. False. A probability of less than $\frac{1}{20} = 0.05$ indicates an unusual event.
11. d 12. f 13. b 14. c 15. a 16. e
17. $\frac{1}{6}$ 19. 0.97 21. 0.05 23. $\frac{1}{4}$
25. {A, B, C, D, E, F, G, H, I, J, K, L, M, N, O, P, Q, R, S, T, U, V, W, X, Y, Z}; 26
27. {A♥, K♥, Q♥, J♥, 10♥, 9♥, 8♥, 7♥, 6♥, 5♥, 4♥, 3♥, 2♥, A♦, K♦, Q♦, J♦, 10♦, 9♦, 8♦, 7♦, 6♦, 5♦, 4♦, 3♦, 2♦, A♠, K♠, Q♠, J♠, 10♠, 9♠, 8♠, 7♠, 6♠, 5♠, 4♠, 3♠, 2♠, A♣, K♣, Q♣, J♣, 10♣, 9♣, 8♣, 7♣, 6♣, 5♣, 4♣, 3♣, 2♣}; 52
29.

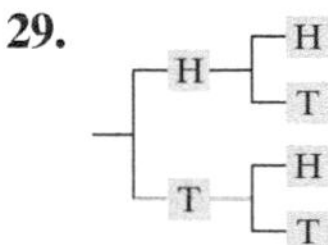


{HH, HT, TH, TT}; 4
31.

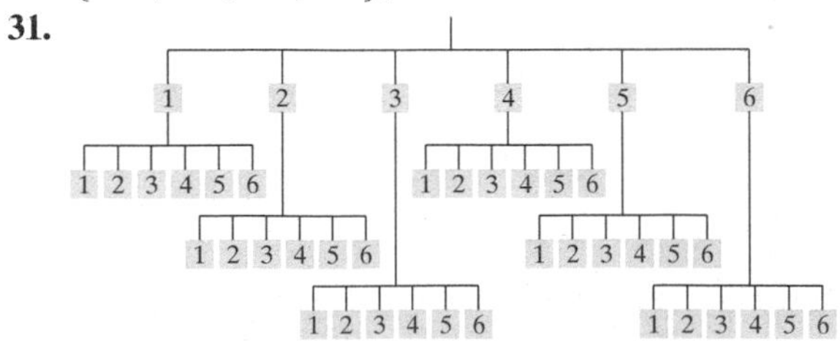


{(1, 1), (1, 2), (1, 3), (1, 4), (1, 5), (1, 6), (2, 1), (2, 2), (2, 3), (2, 4), (2, 5), (2, 6), (3, 1), (3, 2), (3, 3), (3, 4), (3, 5), (3, 6), (4, 1), (4, 2), (4, 3), (4, 4), (4, 5), (4, 6), (5, 1), (5, 2), (5, 3), (5, 4), (5, 5), (5, 6), (6, 1), (6, 2), (6, 3), (6, 4), (6, 5), (6, 6)}; 36

**33.** 1. Simple event because it is an event that consists of a single outcome

**35.** 13. Not a simple event because it is an event that consists of more than a single outcome

**37.** 576 **39.** 4500 **41.** 0.083 **43.** 0.667 **45.** 0.333

**47.** 0.700 **49.** 0.092 **51.** 0.254

**53.** Empirical probability because company records were used to calculate the frequency of a car needing repairs

**55.** Subjective probability because it is most likely based on an educated guess

**57.** Classical probability because each outcome in the sample space is equally likely to occur

**59.** 0.457 **61.** 0.921 **63.** 0.648

**65.** (a) 0.001 (b) 0.999 **67.** 0.042; unusual

**69.** 0.208; not unusual **71.** 0.125 **73.** 0.375

**75.** 0.033 **77.** 0.275

**79.** No. None of the events has a probability of 0.05 or less.

**81.** (a) 0.5 (b) 0.25 (c) 0.25 **83.** 0.091 **85.** 0.201

**87.** (a) 0.047 (b) 0.370

(c) 0.039. Both a and c are unusual because the probability is less than or equal to 0.05.

**89.** The probability of randomly choosing a smoker whose mother did not smoke

**91.** No. The odds of winning a prize are 1 : 6 (one winning cap and six losing caps). So, the statement should read, "one in seven game pieces wins a prize."

**93.** (a) 0.444 (b) 0.556 **95.** 39 : 13 = 3 : 1

**97.** (a)

| Sum | Probability |
|---|---|
| 2 | 0.028 |
| 3 | 0.056 |
| 4 | 0.083 |
| 5 | 0.111 |
| 6 | 0.139 |
| 7 | 0.167 |
| 8 | 0.139 |
| 9 | 0.111 |
| 10 | 0.083 |
| 11 | 0.056 |
| 12 | 0.028 |

(b) Answers will vary.

(c) Answers will vary.

## Section 3.1 Activity (page 146)

**1–2.** Answers will vary.

## Section 3.2 (page 152)

**1.** Two events are independent when the occurrence of one of the events does not affect the probability of the occurrence of the other event, whereas two events are dependent when the occurrence of one of the events does affect the probability of the occurrence of the other event.

**3.** The notation $P(B|A)$ means the probability of event $B$ occurring, given that event $A$ has occurred.

**5.** False. If two events are independent, then $P(A|B) = P(A)$.

**7.** (a) 0.530 (b) 0.160

**9.** Independent. The outcome of the first draw does not affect the outcome of the second draw.

**11.** Dependent. The outcome of returning a movie after its due date affects the outcome of receiving a late fee.

**13.** Dependent. The sum of the rolls depends on which numbers came up on the first and second rolls.

**15.** Events: achievements in math and achievements in music; Dependent. There is a relationship between achievements in math and music.

**17.** Events: playing violent video games, aggressive or bullying behavior; Independent. Playing violent video games does not cause aggressive or bullying behavior in teens.

**19.** 0.063 **21.** 0.0016

**23.** (a) 0.563 (b) 0.063 (c) 0.938

**25.** (a) 0.032 (b) 0.672 (c) 0.328

(d) Both adults saying that Barack Obama was the best president in U.S. history is unusual because the probability is less than or equal to 0.05.

**27.** (a) 0.004 (b) 0.052 (c) 0.948

(d) The probability that all six people have type O+ blood is unusual because the probability is less than or equal to 0.05.

**29.** (a) 0.005 (b) 0.995

(c) Yes, this is unusual because the probability is less than or equal to 0.05.

**31.** 0.612 **33.** 0.444 **35.** 0.167 **37.** 0.792

**39.** (a) 0.074 (b) 0.999 **41.** 0.954

## Section 3.3 (page 162)

**1.** $P(A \text{ and } B) = 0$ because $A$ and $B$ cannot occur at the same time.

**3.** True

**5.** False. The probability that event $A$ or event $B$ will occur is $P(A \text{ or } B) = P(A) + P(B) - P(A \text{ and } B)$.

**7.** Not mutually exclusive. People can wear a polo shirt while wearing Bermuda shorts.

**9.** Not mutually exclusive. A freshman music major can be 20 years old.

**11.** Mutually exclusive. A voter cannot be both a Republican and a Democrat.

**13.** 0.625 **15.** 0.126

**17.** (a) 0.308 (b) 0.538 (c) 0.308

**19.** (a) 0.121 (b) 0.366 (c) 0.750 (d) 0.732

**21.** (a) 0.730 (b) 0.320 (c) 0.760 (d) 0.410

**23.** (a) 0.819 (b) 0.470 (c) 0.959

**25.** (a) 0.718 (b) 0.645 (c) 0.584 (d) 0.809

**27.** 0.63

**29.** If events $A$, $B$, and $C$ are not mutually exclusive, then $P(A \text{ and } B \text{ and } C)$ must be added because $P(A) + P(B) + P(C)$ counts the intersection of all three events three times and $-P(A \text{ and } B) - P(A \text{ and } C) - P(B \text{ and } C)$ subtracts the intersection of all three events three times. So, if $P(A \text{ and } B \text{ and } C)$ is not added at the end, then it will not be counted.

## Section 3.3 Activity (page 166)

**1.** Answers will vary.

**2.** The theoretical probability is 0.5, so the green line should be placed there.

## Section 3.4 (page 174)

**1.** The number of ordered arrangements of $n$ objects taken $r$ at a time
*Sample answer:* An example of a permutation is the number of seating arrangements of you and three of your friends.

**3.** False. A permutation is an ordered arrangement of objects.

**5.** True **7.** 15,120 **9.** 56 **11.** 0.076 **13.** 0.462

**15.** Permutation. The order of the 16 floats in line matters.

**17.** Combination. The order does not matter because the position of one captain is the same as the other.

**19.** 5040 **21.** 720 **23.** 357,840 **25.** 39,070,080

**27.** 2,042,040 **29.** 50,400 **31.** 184,756 **33.** 9880

**35.** 3640 **37.** 86,296,950 **39.** 0.024 **41.** 0.008

**43.** (a) 0.016 (b) 0.385 **45.** 0.001 **47.** 0.210 or 0.213

**49.** 0.0000015 **51.** 0.166 **53.** 0.070 **55.** 0.933

**57.** 0.086 **59.** 0.066 **61.** 0.001

## Uses and Abuses for Chapter 3 (page 178)

**1.** 0.000001 **2.** 0.001 **3.** 0.001

## Review Exercises for Chapter 3 (page 180)

**1.**

```
            ┌─H─┬─H
            │   └─T
       ┌─H──┤
       │    └─T─┬─H
       │        └─T
  ┌─H──┤
  │    │    ┌─H─┬─H
  │    │    │   └─T
  │    └─T──┤
  │         └─T─┬─H
  │             └─T
──┤
  │         ┌─H─┬─H
  │         │   └─T
  │    ┌─H──┤
  │    │    └─T─┬─H
  │    │        └─T
  └─T──┤
       │    ┌─H─┬─H
       │    │   └─T
       └─T──┤
            └─T─┬─H
                └─T
```

{HHHH, HHHT, HHTH, HHTT, HTHH, HTHT, HTTH, HTTT, THHH, THHT, THTH, THTT, TTHH, TTHT, TTTH, TTTT}; 4

**3.** {January, February, March, April, May, June, July, August, September, October, November, December}; 3

**5.** 84

**7.** Empirical probability because prior counts were used to calculate the frequency of a part being defective

**9.** Subjective probability because it is based on opinion

**11.** Classical probability because all of the outcomes in the event and the sample space can be counted

**13.** 0.215 **15.** $1.25 \times 10^{-7}$ **17.** 0.315

**19.** Independent. The outcomes of the first four coin tosses do not affect the outcome of the fifth coin toss.

**21.** Dependent. The outcome of taking a driver's education course affects the outcome of passing the driver's license exam.

**23.** 0.025. Yes, the event is unusual because its probability is less than or equal to 0.05.

**25.** Mutually exclusive. A jelly bean cannot be both completely red and completely yellow.

**27.** 0.9 **29.** 0.538 **31.** 0.583 **33.** 0.579 **35.** 0.180

**37.** 0.722

**39.** No. You do not know whether events $A$ and $B$ are mutually exclusive.

**41.** 110 **43.** 35 **45.** 2730 **47.** 2380 **49.** 0.000009

**51.** (a) 0.955 (b) 0.0000008 (c) 0.045 (d) 0.9999992

**53.** (a) 0.071 (b) 0.005 (c) 0.429 (d) 0.114

## Quiz for Chapter 3 (page 184)

**1.** 450,000

**2.** (a) 0.700 (b) 0.650 (c) 0.774 (d) 0.948
(e) 0.038 (f) 0.587 (g) 0.310 (h) 0.557

**3.** The event in part (e) is unusual because its probability is less than or equal to 0.05.

**4.** Not mutually exclusive. A bowler can have the highest game in a 40-game tournament and still lose the tournament.
Dependent. One event can affect the occurrence of the second event.

**5.** 2,193,360

**6.** (a) 2,481,115 (b) 1 (c) 2,572,999

**7.** (a) 0.964 (b) 0.0000004 (c) 0.9999996

## Real Statistics—Real Decisions for Chapter 3 (page 186)

**1.** (a) *Sample answer:* Investigate the number of possible passwords when different sets of characters, such as lowercase and capital letters, numbers, and special characters, are used.
(b) You could use the definition of theoretical probability, the Fundamental Counting Principle, and the Multiplication Rule.

**2.** (a) *Sample answer:* Allow lowercase letters, uppercase letters, and numerical digits.
(b) *Sample answer:* Because there are 26 lowercase letters, 26 uppercase letters, and 10 numerical digits, there are $26 + 26 + 10 = 62$ choices for each digit. So, there are $62^8$ 8-digit passwords and the probability of guessing a password correctly on one try is $\frac{1}{62^8}$, which is less than $\frac{1}{60^8}$.

3. (a) Without the requirement, the number of possible PINs is $10^5 = 100{,}000$. With the requirement, the number of possible PINs is ${}_{10}P_5 = 10 \cdot 9 \cdot 8 \cdot 7 \cdot 6 = 30{,}240$.
(b) *Sample answer:* No, although the requirement would likely discourage customers from choosing predictable PINs, the numbers of possible PINs would significantly decrease, and the most popular PIN, 12345, would still be allowed.

# Chapter 4

## Section 4.1 (page 197)

1. A random variable represents a value associated with each outcome of a probability experiment.
Examples: Answers will vary.
3. No. The expected value may not be a possible value of $x$ for one trial, but it represents the average value of $x$ over a large number of trials.
5. False. In most applications, discrete random variables represent counted data, while continuous random variables represent measured data.
7. False. The mean of the random variable of a probability distribution describes a typical outcome. The variance and standard deviation of the random variable of a probability distribution describe how the outcomes vary.
9. Discrete. Attendance is a random variable that is countable.
11. Continuous. Distance traveled is a random variable that must be measured.
13. Discrete. The number of cars in a university parking lot is a random variable that is countable.
15. Continuous. The volume of blood drawn for a blood test is a random variable that must be measured.
17. Discrete. The fitted sizes of hats is a random variable that can be measured.
19. (a)

| $x$ | $P(x)$ |
|---|---|
| 0 | 0.028 |
| 1 | 0.256 |
| 2 | 0.340 |
| 3 or more | 0.376 |

(b)

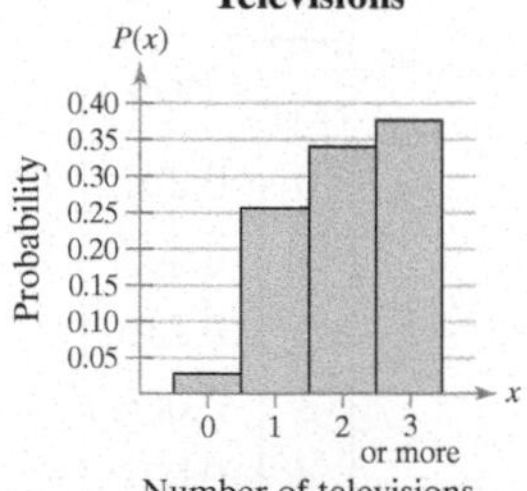


Skewed left

21. (a) 0.596 (b) 0.716 (c) 0.972 (d) 0.624
23. Yes, it would be unusual for a household to have no HD televisions because the probability is less than or equal to 0.05.
25. 0.34 27. Yes
29. (a) $\mu \approx 0.5$; $\sigma^2 \approx 0.8$; $\sigma \approx 0.9$
(b) The mean is 0.5, so the average number of dogs per household is about 0 or 1 dog. The standard deviation is 0.9, so most of the households differ from the mean by no more than about 1 dog.
31. (a) $\mu \approx 1.5$; $\sigma^2 \approx 1.5$; $\sigma \approx 1.2$
(b) The mean is 1.5, so the average batch of 1000 machine parts has 1 or 2 defects. The standard deviation is 1.2, so most of the batches of 1000 differ from the mean by no more than about 1 defect.
33. (a) mean = 2.01 variance = 1.07
standard deviation = 1.03
(b) The mean is 2.01, so the average category of hurricane is about 2. The standard deviation is 1.03, so most hurricanes differ from the mean by no more than about 1 category.
35. An expected value of 0 means that the money gained is equal to the money spent, representing the break-even point.
37. −\$0.05
39. Area of bar 1 = 0.028, area of bar 2 = 0.256, area of bar 3 = 0.340, area of bar 4 = 0.376, sum = 1. The area of each of the bars is the probability of each outcome because the width is one. The sum is 1 is because all of the probabilities should add up to 1, as they are between 0 and 1.
41. \$47,980 43. mean = 1047; standard deviation ≈ 164.9

## Section 4.2 (page 210)

1. Each trial is independent of the other trials when the outcome of one trial does not affect the outcome of any of the other trials.
3. c. Because the probability is greater than 0.5, the distribution is skewed left.
4. b. Because the probability is 0.5, the distribution is symmetric.
5. a. Because the probability is less than 0.5, the distribution is skewed right.
6. c. The histogram shows probabilities for 12 trials.
7. a. The histogram shows probabilities for 4 trials.
8. b. The histogram shows probabilities for 8 trials.
As $n$ increases, the distribution becomes more symmetric.
9. Combinations Rule
11. $\mu = 20$; $\sigma^2 = 12$; $\sigma \approx 3.5$
13. $\mu \approx 32.2$; $\sigma^2 \approx 23.9$; $\sigma \approx 4.9$
15. Binomial experiment, Success: frequent gamers who own a virtual reality device
$n = 10$; $p = 0.29$; $q = 0.71$; $x = 0, 1, 2, 3, 4, 5, 6, 7, 8, 9, 10$
17. Not a binomial experiment because the probability of a success is not the same for each trial
19. (a) 0.037 (b) 0.281
21. (a) 0.188 (b) 0.207 (c) 0.329
23. (a) 0.341 (b) 0.998 (c) 0.056
25. (a) 0.123 (b) 0.030 (c) 0.153

**27.** (a)

| $x$ | $P(x)$ |
|---|---|
| 0 | 0.009 |
| 1 | 0.060 |
| 2 | 0.174 |
| 3 | 0.279 |
| 4 | 0.268 |
| 5 | 0.154 |
| 6 | 0.049 |
| 7 | 0.007 |

(b)

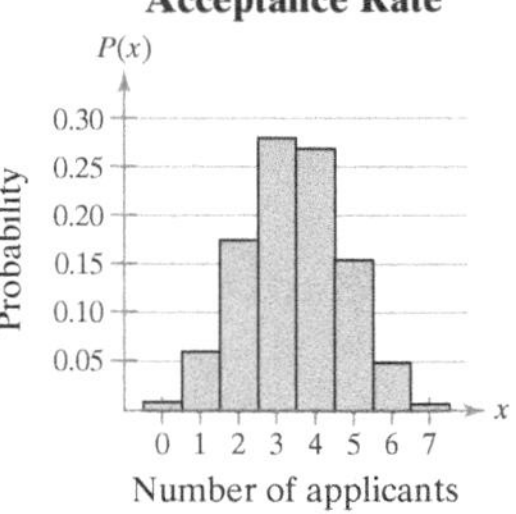


Bell Shape

(c) The following values are unusual: 0, 6 and 7. This is because their probabilities are all less than or equal to 0.05.

**29.** (a)

| $x$ | $P(x)$ |
|---|---|
| 0 | 0.00064 |
| 1 | 0.01077 |
| 2 | 0.07214 |
| 3 | 0.24151 |
| 4 | 0.40426 |
| 5 | 0.27068 |

(b)

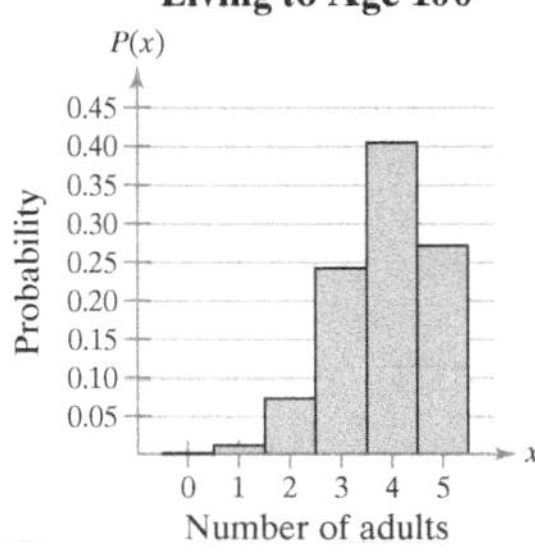


Skewed left

(c) The values 0 and 1 are unusual because their probabilities are less than 0.05.

**31.** $\mu \approx 1.98$, $\sigma^2 \approx 1.33$, $\sigma \approx 1.15$. On average, 1.98 out of every 6 penalty shots are converted. The standard deviation is 1.15, so most samples of 6 penalty shots would differ from the mean by at most 1.15. Unusual values would be any above 4.28.

**33.** $\mu \approx 6.3$; $\sigma^2 \approx 1.3$; $\sigma \approx 1.2$. On average, 6.3 out of every 8 adults believe that life on other planets is possible. The standard deviation is 1.2, so most samples of 8 adults would differ from the mean by at most 1.2 adults. Unusual values would be any under 3.9.

**35.** $\mu \approx 3.72$, $\sigma^2 \approx 2.57$, $\sigma \approx 1.60$. On average, 3.72 out of every 12 U.S. employees who are late for work blame oversleeping. The standard deviation is 1.60, so most samples of 12 U.S. employees who are late for work would differ from the mean by at most 1.60. Unusual values would be any under 0.52 or over 6.92.

**37.** (a) 0.102
(b) 0.042; unusual because it is less than or equal to 0.05
(c) 0.143

**39.** 0.033

**41.** (a) 0.107 (b) 0.107 (c) The results are the same.

## Section 4.2 Activity (page 214)

**1–3.** Answers will vary.

## Section 4.3 (page 220)

**1.** 0.080 **3.** 0.062 **5.** 0.175 **7.** 0.223

**9.** In a binomial distribution, the value of $x$ represents the number of successes in $n$ trials. In a geometric distribution, the value of $x$ represents the first trial that results in a success.

**11.** (a) 0.190 (b) 0.154 (c) 0.082
**13.** (a) 0.195 (b) 0.433 (c) 0.567
**15.** (a) 0.227 (b) 0.878 (c) 0.122
**17.** (a) 0.232 (b) 0.406 (c) 0.950
**19.** (a) 0.298 (b) 0.463 (c) 0.537
**21.** (a) 0.064 (b) 0.556 (c) 0.016; unusual
**23.** (a) 0.071 (b) 0.827 (c) 0.173
**25.** (a) 0.002; unusual (b) 0.006; unusual (c) 0.980
**27.** (a) 0.12542
(b) 0.12541. The results are approximately the same.

**29.** (a) $\mu = 1000$; $\sigma^2 = 999{,}000$; $\sigma \approx 999.5$ (b) 1000 times
(c) Lose money. On average, you would win \$500 once in every 1000 times you play the lottery. So, the net gain would be $-\$500$.

**31.** (a) $\sigma^2 = 3.9$, $\sigma \approx 1.97$. The standard deviation is about 1.97, so most of the scores will differ from the mean by no more than 2 strokes.
(b) More than 8 strokes would be unusual.

## Uses and Abuses for Chapter 4 (page 223)

**1.** 11 incidents. The probability of 11 incidents is about 0.119, while the probability of at least 16 is about 0.093.

**2.** 10 to 12. The probability of 10 to 12 incidents is about 0.348, while the probability of less than ten incidents is about 0.341.

**3.** Yes. On holidays the fire department should adjust the guidelines because more people are out.

## Review Exercises for Chapter 4 (page 225)

**1.** Discrete. The grade of an exam is a random variable that can be counted.

**3.** (a)

| $x$ | $P(x)$ |
|---|---|
| 0 | 0.207 |
| 1 | 0.443 |
| 2 | 0.236 |
| 3 | 0.086 |
| 4 | 0.021 |
| 5 | 0.007 |

(b)

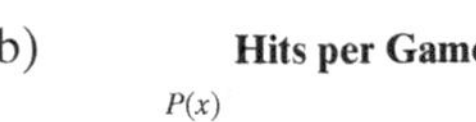


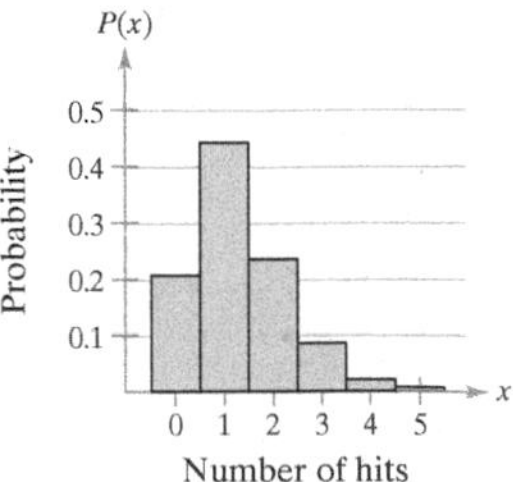


Skewed right

**5.** Yes

**7.** (a) $\mu \approx 2.8$; $\sigma^2 \approx 1.7$; $\sigma \approx 1.3$
(b) The mean is 2.8, so the average number of cell phones per household is about 3. The standard deviation is 1.3, so most of the households differ from the mean by no more than about 1 cell phone.

**9.** $-\$3.13$

**11.** Binomial experiment; Success: a green candy is selected; $n = 12$, $p = 0.125$, $q = 0.875$, $x = 0, 1, 2, 3, 4, 5, 6, 7, 8, 9, 10, 11, 12$

**13.** (a) 0.191 (b) 0.891 (c) 0.700

**15.** (a) 0.257 (b) 0.774 (c) 0.517

**17.** (a)

| $x$ | $P(x)$ |
|---|---|
| 0 | 0.002 |
| 1 | 0.022 |
| 2 | 0.114 |
| 3 | 0.293 |
| 4 | 0.376 |
| 5 | 0.193 |

(b)

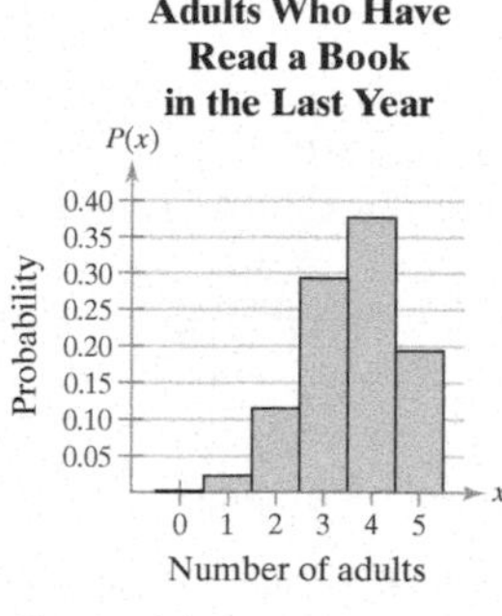


Skewed left

(c) The values 0 and 1 are unusual because they have a probability of less than or equal to 0.05.

**19.** $\mu \approx 1.0$; $\sigma^2 \approx 0.9$; $\sigma \approx 1.0$. On average, 1 out of every 8 drivers is uninsured. The standard deviation is 1.0, so most samples of 8 drivers would differ from the mean by at most 1 driver. Unusual values would be any above 3.

**21.** (a) 0.104 (b) 0.166 (c) 0.405

**23.** (a) 0.154 (b) 0.217 (c) 0.011; unusual

**25.** (a) 0.073 (b) 0.458 (c) 0.384

## Quiz for Chapter 4 (page 228)

**1.** (a) Discrete. The number of lightning strikes that occur in Wyoming during the month of June is a random variable that is countable.

(b) Continuous. The fuel (in gallons) used by a jet during takeoff is a random variable that has an infinite number of possible outcomes and cannot be counted.

(c) Discrete. The final score in a game of bowling is a random variable that is countable.

**2.** (a)

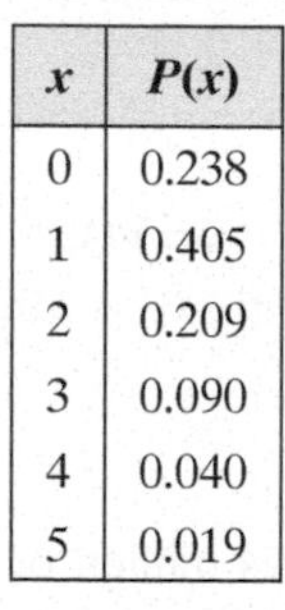

| $x$ | $P(x)$ |
|---|---|
| 0 | 0.238 |
| 1 | 0.405 |
| 2 | 0.209 |
| 3 | 0.090 |
| 4 | 0.040 |
| 5 | 0.019 |

(b)

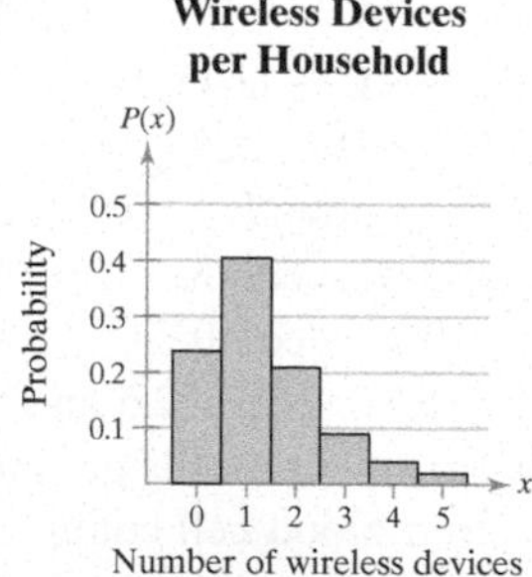


Skewed right

(c) $\mu \approx 1.3$; $\sigma^2 \approx 1.4$; $\sigma \approx 1.2$. The mean is 1.3, so the average number of wireless devices per household is 1.3. The standard deviation is 1.2, so most households will differ from the mean by no more than 1.2 wireless devices.

(d) 0.058

**3.** (a) 0.273 (b) 0.860 (c) 0.040

**4.** (a)

| $x$ | $P(x)$ |
|---|---|
| 0 | 0.0002 |
| 1 | 0.004 |
| 2 | 0.033 |
| 3 | 0.132 |
| 4 | 0.297 |
| 5 | 0.356 |
| 6 | 0.178 |

(b)

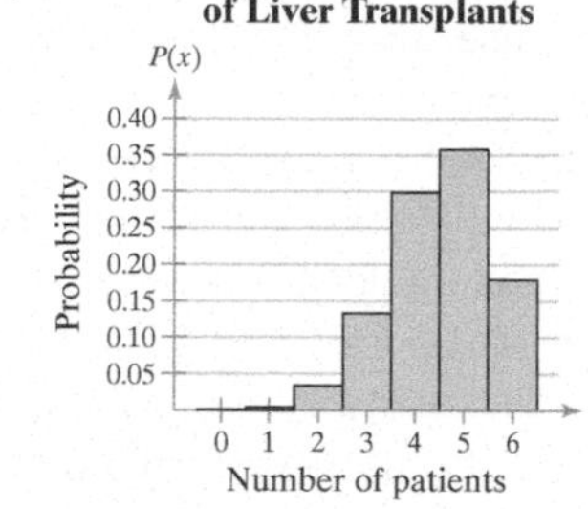


Skewed left

(c) mean = 4.5; variance = 1.12; standard deviation = 1.06. On average 4.5 out of every 6 patients survive to five years. The standard deviation is 1.06, so most samples of 6 patients would differ from the mean by at most 1.06 survivors.

**5.** (a) 0.175 (b) 0.440 (c) 0.007

**6.** (a) 0.140 (b) 0.125 (c) 0.034

**7.** Event (c) in problem 5 and event (c) in problem 6 are both unusual because the probabilities are less than 0.05.

## Real Statistics—Real Decisions for Chapter 4 (page 230)

**1.** (a) *Sample answer:* Calculate the probability of obtaining 0 live births out of 6 randomly selected ART cycles.

(b) Binomial. The distribution is discrete because the number of live births is countable.

**2.** $n = 6$, $p = 0.52$

| $x$ | $P(x)$ |
|---|---|
| 0 | 0.012 |
| 1 | 0.079 |
| 2 | 0.215 |
| 3 | 0.311 |
| 4 | 0.253 |
| 5 | 0.109 |
| 6 | 0.020 |

*Sample answer:* Because $P(0) = 0.12$, this event is unusual but not impossible.

**3.** (a) Not suspicious, because the probability is more than 0.05

(b) Suspicious, because the probability is less than 0.05

# Chapter 5

## Section 5.1 (page 242)

**1.** When it is a normal distribution, the mean is equal to the median.

**3.** Inflection points are where the curve changes concavity. Inflection points occur one standard deviation away from the mean on both the right and left. The $x$-values would be $\mu - \sigma$ and $\mu + \sigma$.

**5.** Answers will vary.
Similarities: The two curves will have the same line of symmetry.
Differences: The curve with the larger standard deviation will be more spread out than the curve with the smaller standard deviation.

**7.** $\mu = 0, \sigma = 1$

**9.** "The" standard normal distribution is used to describe one specific normal distribution $(\mu = 0, \sigma = 1)$. "A" normal distribution is used to describe a normal distribution with any mean and standard deviation.

**11.** No, the graph is skewed left.

**13.** No, the graph is symmetric but it is not bell shaped.

**15.** Yes, the graph fulfills the properties of the normal distribution.
$\mu \approx 11.5, \sigma \approx 1.5$

**17.** 0.7257 **19.** 0.0228 **21.** 0.4878 **23.** 0.6293
**25.** 0.0470 **27.** 0.7422 **29.** 0.6387 **31.** 0.4979
**33.** 0.8788 **35.** 0.2006 (*Tech:* 0.2005)

**37.** (a)

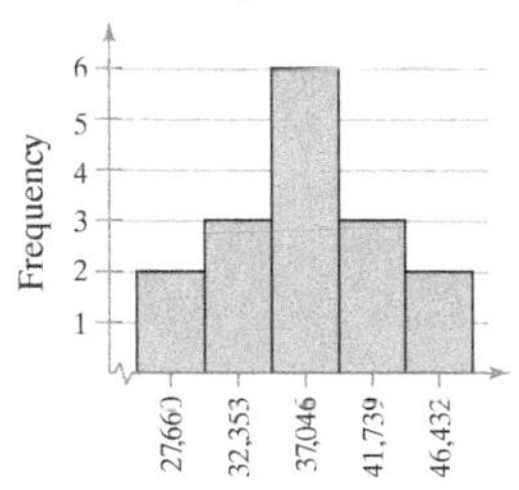


It is reasonable to assume that the life spans are normally distributed because the histogram is symmetric and bell shaped.
(b) 37,234.7; 6259.2
(c) The sample mean of 37,234.7 hours is less than the claimed mean, 40,000 on average; the tires in the sample lasted for a shorter time. The sample standard deviation of 6259.2 is greater than the claimed standard deviation, so the tires in the sample had a greater variation in life span than the manufacturer's claim.

**39.** (a) $x = 98 \rightarrow z \approx -0.125$
$x = 65 \rightarrow z \approx -2.188$
$x = 106 \rightarrow z \approx 0.375$
$x = 124 \rightarrow z \approx 1.50$
(b) $x = 65$ is unusual because the corresponding $z$-score $(-2.188)$ lies more than 2 standard deviations away from the mean.

**41.** 0.2660 **43.** 0.9832 **45.** 0.6826 (*Tech:* 0.6827)
**47.** 0.7019 **49.** 0.0148 **51.** 0.3133
**53.** 0.9250 (*Tech:* 0.9249) **55.** 0.0098 (*Tech:* 0.0099)

**57.**

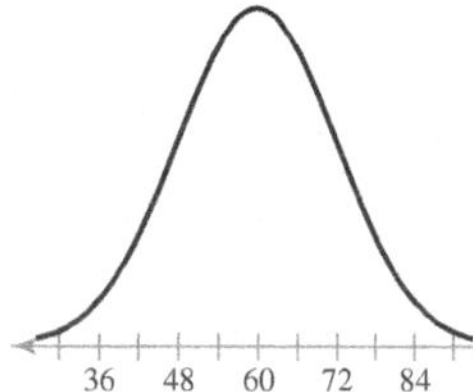


The normal distribution curve is centered at its mean (60) and has 2 points of inflection (48 and 72) representing $\mu \pm \sigma$.

**59.** (1) The area under the curve is
$$(b - a)\left(\frac{1}{b - a}\right) = \frac{b - a}{b - a} = 1.$$
(Because $a < b$, you do not have to worry about division by 0.)
(2) All of the values of the probability density function are positive because $\frac{1}{b - a}$ is positive when $a < b$.

## Section 5.2 (page 249)

**1.** 0.4207 **3.** 0.3446 **5.** 0.1787 (*Tech:* 0.1788)

**7.** (a) 0.0183 (b) 0.5103 (*Tech:* 0.5119) (c) 0.0228
The events a and c are both unusual because the probability is less than 0.05.

**9.** (a) 0.1515 (b) 0.6536 (*Tech:* 0.6528) (c) 0.0918
None of the events are unusual because none of the probabilities are less than 0.05.

**11.** (a) 0.0062 (b) 0.7492 (*Tech:* 0.7499) (c) 0.0004

**13.** 0.3288 (*Tech:* 0.3276) **15.** 0.0324 (*Tech:* 0.0325)

**17.** (a) 86.86% (*Tech:* 86.96%)
(b) 464 scores (*Tech:* 465 scores)

**19.** (a) 98.93% (b) 75.75% (*Tech:* 75.76%)
(c) 6 mothers

**21.** Out of control, because there is a point more than three standard deviations beyond the mean

**23.** Out of control, because there are nine consecutive points below the mean, and two out of three consecutive points lie more than two standard deviations from the mean

## Section 5.3 (page 257)

**1.** −0.81 **3.** 0.45 **5.** −1.645 **7.** 1.04 **9.** −0.44
**11.** 1.96 **13.** −0.67 **15.** 1.34 **17.** −0.38
**19.** 1.99 **21.** −1.645, 1.645 **23.** −1.18 **25.** −0.35
**27.** −2.00 **29.** 1.28

**31.** (a) 247.8 pounds (b) 158.1 pounds (c) 133.42 pounds

**33.** (a) 133.94 seconds (b) 156.74 seconds (*Tech:* 156.60)
(c) 210.04 seconds

**35.** (a) 664.5 (b) 432.5 and 567.5

**37.** (a) 5.67 million cells per microliter
(b) Red blood cell counts less than 4.74 million or greater than 6.06 million

**39.** 32.61 ounces **41.** 7.93 ounces

## Section 5.4 (page 269)

**1.** 150, 3.571 **3.** 790, 3.036

**5.** False. As the size of a sample increases, the mean of the distribution of sample means does not change.

**7.** False. A sampling distribution is normal when either $n \geq 30$ or the population is normal.

**9.** (c), because $\mu_{\bar{x}} = 16.5$, $\sigma_{\bar{x}} = 1.19$, and the graph approximates a normal curve.

**11.** (a) $\mu = 53.2, \sigma \approx 19.9$
(b)

| Sample | Mean |
|---|---|
| 19, 19 | 19 |
| 19, 48 | 33.5 |
| 19, 56 | 37.5 |
| 19, 64 | 41.5 |
| 19, 79 | 49 |
| 48, 19 | 33.5 |
| 48, 48 | 48 |
| 48, 56 | 52 |
| 48, 64 | 56 |
| 48, 79 | 63.5 |
| 56, 19 | 37.5 |
| 56, 48 | 52 |
| 56, 56 | 56 |
| 56, 64 | 60 |
| 56, 79 | 67.5 |
| 64, 19 | 41.5 |
| 64, 48 | 56 |
| 64, 56 | 60 |
| 64, 64 | 64 |
| 64, 79 | 71.5 |
| 79, 19 | 49 |
| 79, 48 | 63.5 |
| 79, 56 | 67.5 |
| 79, 64 | 71.5 |
| 79, 79 | 79 |

(c) $\mu_{\bar{x}} = 53.2, \sigma_{\bar{x}} \approx 14.1$
The means are equal, but the standard deviation of the sampling distribution is smaller.

**13.** (a) $\mu = 389, \sigma \approx 28.65$
(b)

| Sample | Mean |
|---|---|
| 350, 350, 350 | 350 |
| 350, 350, 399 | 366.33 |
| 350, 350, 418 | 372.67 |
| 350, 399, 350 | 366.33 |
| 350, 399, 399 | 382.67 |
| 350, 399, 418 | 389 |
| 350, 418, 350 | 372.67 |
| 350, 418, 399 | 389 |
| 350, 418, 418 | 395.33 |
| 399, 350, 350 | 366.33 |
| 399, 350, 399 | 382.67 |
| 399, 350, 418 | 389 |
| 399, 399, 350 | 382.67 |
| 399, 399, 399 | 399 |
| 399, 399, 418 | 405.33 |
| 399, 418, 350 | 389 |
| 399, 418, 399 | 405.33 |
| 399, 418, 418 | 411.67 |
| 418, 350, 350 | 372.67 |
| 418, 350, 399 | 389 |
| 418, 350, 418 | 395.33 |
| 418, 399, 350 | 389 |
| 418, 399, 399 | 405.33 |
| 418, 399, 418 | 411.67 |
| 418, 418, 350 | 395.33 |
| 418, 418, 399 | 411.67 |
| 418, 418, 418 | 418 |

(c) $\mu_{\bar{x}} = 389, \sigma_{\bar{x}} \approx 16.54$
The means are equal, but the standard deviation of the sampling distribution is smaller.

**15.** 0.9726; not unusual

**17.** 0.0351 (*Tech:* 0.0349); unusual

**19.** $\mu_{\bar{x}} = 31.58, \sigma_{\bar{x}} = 1.419$

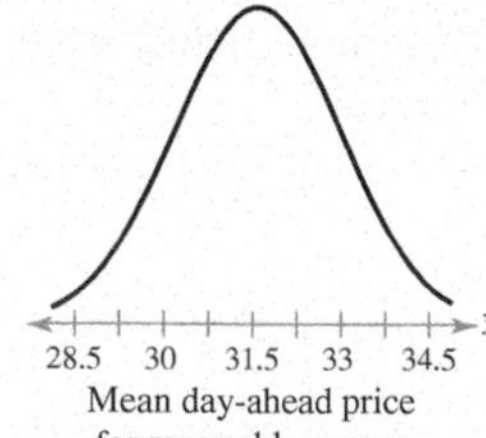


**21.** $\mu_{\bar{x}} = 97.2, \sigma_{\bar{x}} = 0.138$

96.92 97.06 97.2 97.34 97.48
Mean female body temperature (in Fahrenheit)

**23.** $\mu_{\bar{x}} = 54{,}000, \sigma_{\bar{x}} = 1886.48$

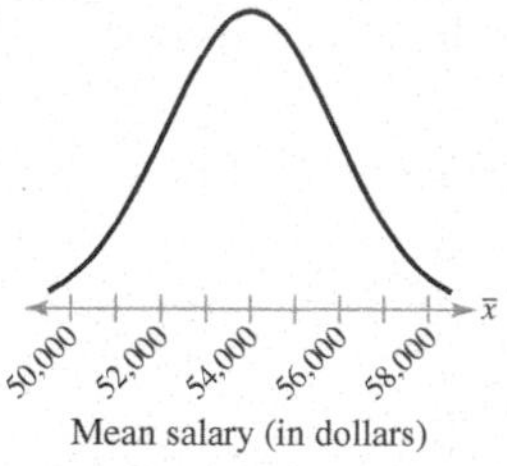


**25.** $\mu_{\bar{x}} = 603, \sigma_{\bar{x}} = 27.75$

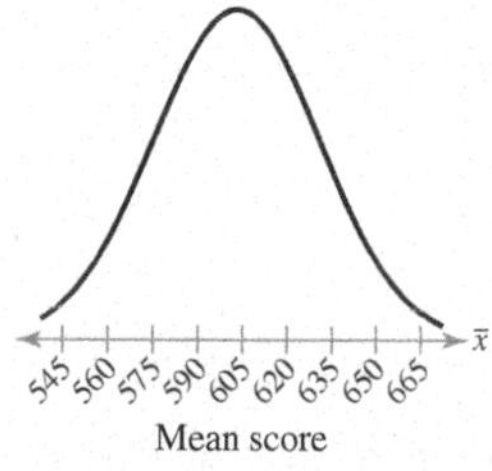


**27.** $n = 40$: $\mu_{\bar{x}} = 603, \sigma_{\bar{x}} = 17.55$
$n = 60$: $\mu_{\bar{x}} = 603, \sigma_{\bar{x}} = 14.33$

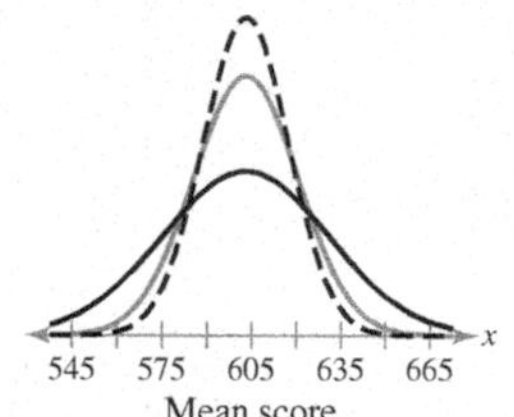


As the sample size increases, the standard deviation of the sample means decreases, while the mean of the sample means remains constant.

**29.** 0.3939 (*Tech:* 0.3927). About 39% of samples of 32 years will have an annual mean gain between 400 and 700.

**31.** 0.0110 (*Tech:* 0.0109). About 1.1% of samples of 30 U.S. states will have a mean asthma rate greater than 10%.

**33.** It is more likely to select a sample of 10 states with a mean asthma prevalence of less than 10% because the sample of 10 states has a higher probability.

**35.** Yes, it is very unlikely that you would have randomly sampled 40 cans with a mean equal to 127.9 ounces because it is more than 3 standard deviations from the mean of the sample means.

**37.** (a) 0.3085 (b) 0.0008

**39.** Yes, the finite correction factor should be used. 0.06615 (*Tech:* 0.06614)

**41.** 0.0446 (*Tech:* 0.0448). The probability that less than 55% of a sample of 105 residents are in favor of building a new high school is about 4.5%. Because the probability is less than 0.05, this is an unusual event.

## Section 5.4 Activity (page 274)

**1–2.** Answers will vary.

## Section 5.5 (page 281)

**1.** Cannot use normal distribution

**3.** Cannot use normal distribution

**5.** a **6.** d **7.** c **8.** b

**9.** The probability of getting fewer than 25 successes; $P(x < 24.5)$

**11.** The probability of getting exactly 33 successes; $P(32.5 < x < 33.5)$

**13.** The probability of getting at most 150 successes; $P(x < 150.5)$

**15.** Binomial: $P(5 \le x \le 7) \approx 0.549$
Normal: $P(4.5 < x < 7.5) = 0.5463$ (*Tech:* 0.5466)
The results are about the same.

**17.** Cannot use normal distribution because $np < 5$

**19.** Can use normal distribution
(a) 0.1308 (*Tech:* 0.1291)

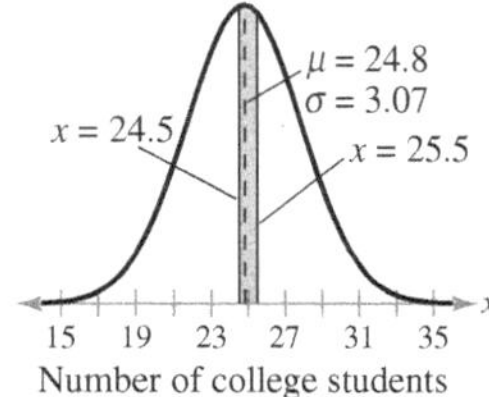


(b) 0.0630 (*Tech:* 0.0629)

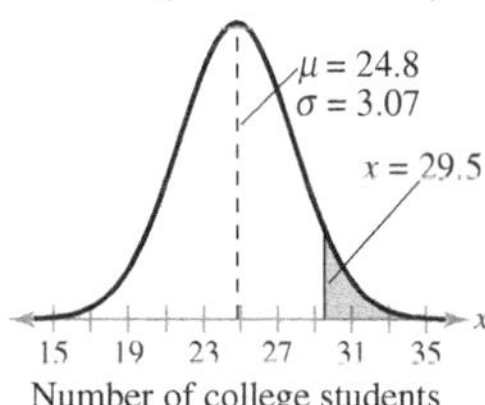


(c) 0.4602 (*Tech:* 0.4611)

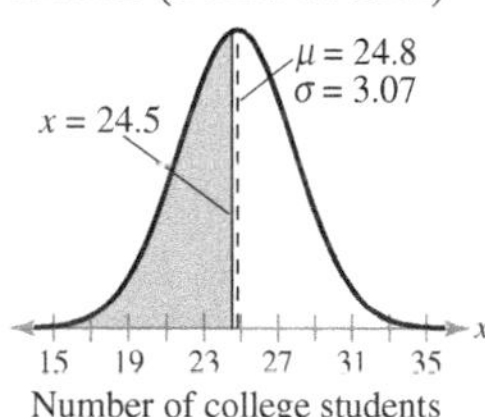


**21.** Can use normal distribution
(a) 0.0649

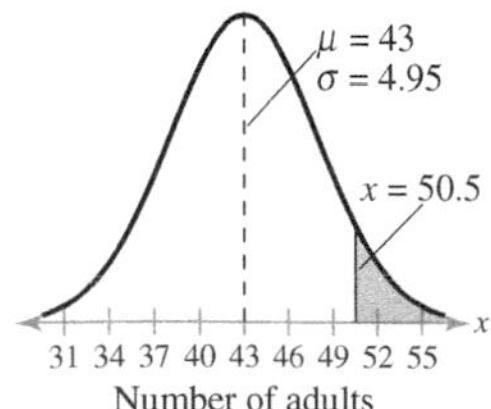


(b) 0.9351

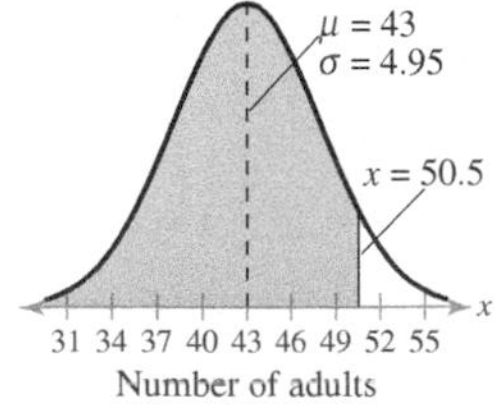


(c) 0.4544 (*Tech:* 0.4534)

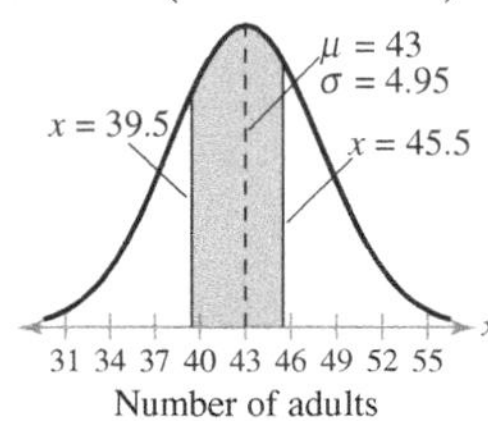


**23.** Cannot use normal distribution $nq < 5$
(a) 0.0737 (b) 0.7870 (c) 0.7509

**25.** Can use normal distribution
(a) 0.9370 (*Tech:* 0.9373)

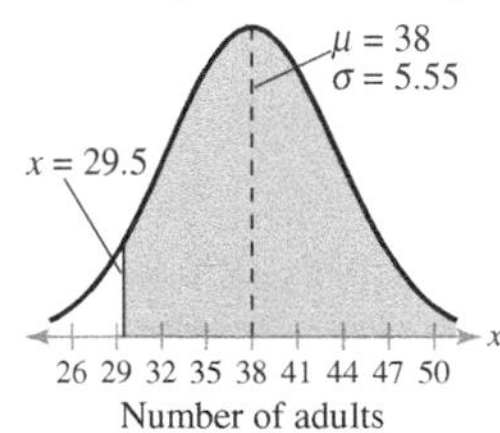


(b) 0.3264 (*Tech:* 0.3261)

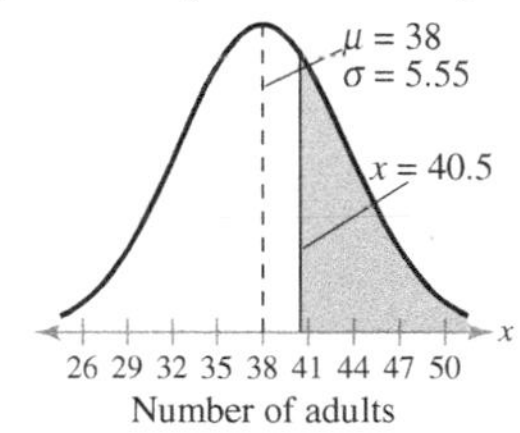


(c) 0.6472 (*Tech:* 0.6477)

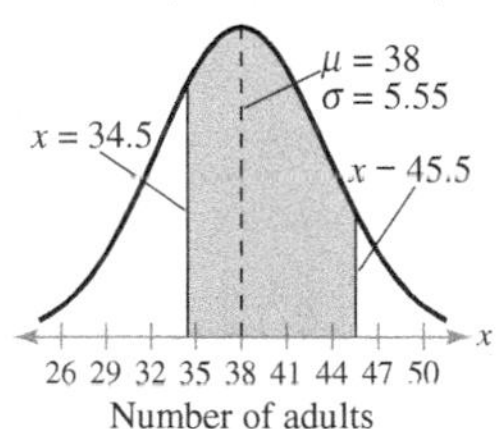


**27.** (a) 0.0098 (b) 0.7794 (*Tech:* 0.7805) (c) 1

**29.** Highly unlikely. Answers will vary. **31.** 0.1020

## Uses and Abuses for Chapter 5 (page 284)

**1.** (a) Not unusual. A sample mean of 112 is less than 2 standard deviations from the population mean.
(b) Unusual. A sample mean of 105 is more than 2 standard deviations from the population mean.

**2.** The ages of students at a high school may not be normally distributed.

**3.** Answers will vary.

## Review Exercises for Chapter 5 (page 286)

**1.** $\mu = 15, \sigma = 3$

**3.** Curve $B$ has the greatest mean because its line of symmetry occurs the farthest to the right.

**5.** 0.6772 **7.** 0.6293 **9.** 0.7157

**11.** 0.00235 (*Tech:* 0.00236) **13.** 0.4495

**15.** 0.4365 (*Tech:* 0.4364) **17.** 0.1336

**19.** $x = 17 \rightarrow z \approx -0.61$
$x = 29 \rightarrow z \approx 1.13$
$x = 8 \rightarrow z \approx -1.91$
$x = 23 \rightarrow z \approx 0.26$

**21.** 0.8997

**23.** 0.9236 (*Tech:* 0.9237) **25.** 0.0124 **27.** 0.8944

**29.** 0.2266 **31.** 0.2684 (*Tech:* 0.2685)

**33.** (a) 0.2061 (*Tech:* 0.2053) (b) 0.2337 (*Tech:* 0.2340)
(c) 0.3520 (*Tech:* 0.3526)

**35.** No unusual events because all of the probabilities are greater than 0.05

**37.** −0.07 **39.** 2.455 (*Tech:* 2.457) **41.** 1.04 **43.** 0.51

**45.** 119.54 feet **47.** 137.80 feet (*Tech:* 137.81 feet)

**49.** 136.71 feet (*Tech:* 136.70 feet)

**51.** (a) $\mu = 1.5, \sigma \approx 1.118$

(b)

| Sample | Mean |
|---|---|
| 0, 0 | 0 |
| 0, 1 | 0.5 |
| 0, 2 | 1 |
| 0, 3 | 1.5 |
| 1, 0 | 0.5 |
| 1, 1 | 1 |
| 1, 2 | 1.5 |
| 1, 3 | 2 |
| 2, 0 | 1 |
| 2, 1 | 1.5 |
| 2, 2 | 2 |
| 2, 3 | 2.5 |
| 3, 0 | 1.5 |
| 3, 1 | 2 |
| 3, 2 | 2.5 |
| 3, 3 | 3 |

(c) $\mu_{\bar{x}} = 1.5, \sigma_{\bar{x}} \approx 0.791$
The means are equal, but the standard deviation of the sampling distribution is smaller.

**53.** mean = 199.6, standard deviation = 44.86

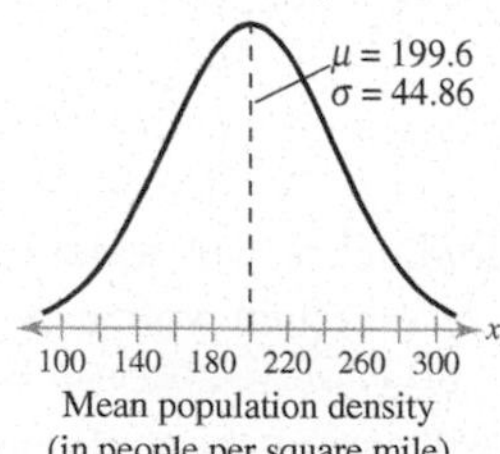


**55.** (a) 0.1230 (*Tech:* 0.1223) (b) 0.1675 (*Tech:* 0.1676)
(c) 0.2964 (*Tech:* 0.2963)
The probabilities are smaller.

**57.** (a) 0.9066 (*Tech:* 0.9069) (b) 0.0096 (*Tech:* 0.0097)
(c) 0.5521 (*Tech:* 0.5538)

**59.** (a) 0.9664 (*Tech:* 0.9663) (b) 0.9927 (*Tech:* 0.9926)

**61.** You cannot use normal distribution because $nq < 5$.

**63.** The probability of getting at least 25 successes; $P(x > 24.5)$

**65.** The probability of getting exactly 45 successes; $P(44.5 < x < 45.5)$

**67.** The probability of getting less than 60 successes; $P(x < 59.5)$

**69.** Can use normal distribution
(a) 0.0043 (*Tech:* 0.0042)

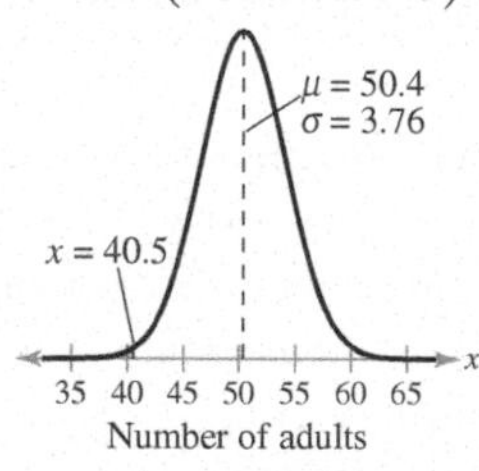


(b) 0.1068 (*Tech:* 0.1053)

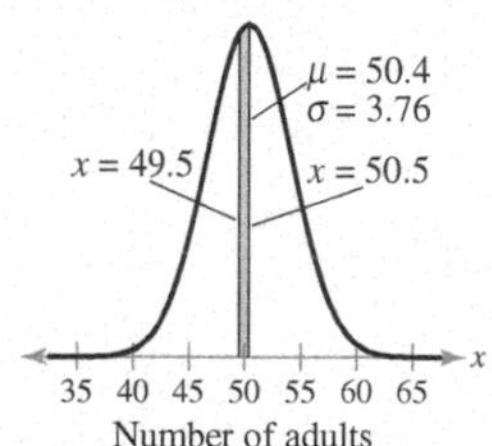


(c) 0.0036

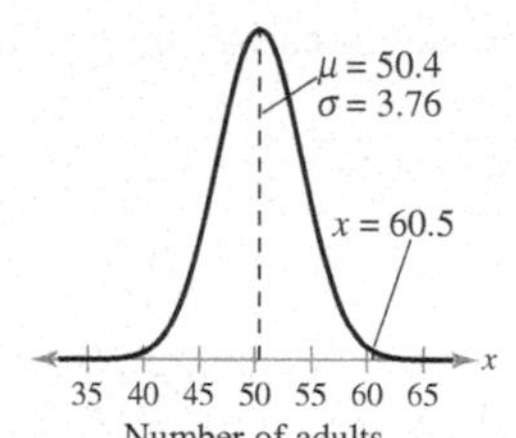


## Quiz for Chapter 5 (page 290)

**1.** (a) 0.9535 (b) 0.9871 (c) 0.3616
(d) 0.7703 (*Tech:* 0.7702)

**2.** (a) 0.0233 (*Tech:* 0.0231) (b) 0.9929 (*Tech:* 0.9928)
(c) 0.9198 (*Tech:* 0.9199) (d) 0.3607 (*Tech:* 0.3610)

**3.** 0.0475 (*Tech:* 0.0478). Yes, the event is unusual because its probability is less than 0.05.

**4.** 0.2586 (*Tech:* 0.2611). No, the event is not unusual because its probability is greater than 0.05.

**5.** 21.19% **6.** 503 people (*Tech:* 505 people)

**7.** 125 **8.** 80

**9.** 0.0049. About 0.5% of samples of 60 people will have a mean IQ score greater than 105. This is a very unusual event.

**10.** More likely to select one person with an IQ score greater than 105 because the standard error of the mean is less than the standard deviation

**11.** Can use normal distribution; $\mu = 202.5, \sigma \approx 6.203$

**12.** (a) 0.3745 (b) 0.8708 (c) 0.0636
No unusual events because all of the probabilities are greater than 0.05

## Real Statistics—Real Decisions for Chapter 5 (page 292)

**1.** (a) 0.4207 (b) 0.9988

**2.** (a) 0.3264 (*Tech:* 0.3274) (b) 0.6944 (*Tech:* 0.6957)
(c) randomly selected sample mean

**3.** Answers will vary.

## Cumulative Review for Chapters 3–5 (page 294)

**1.** (a) $np = 18.3 \geq 5, nq = 11.7 \geq 5$
(b) 0.0778 (*Tech:* 0.0775)
(c) Yes, because the probability is less than 0.05.

**2.** (a) 2.458 (b) 2.00 (c) 1.42 (d) 2.458
The size of an average household is about 2.5 persons. The standard deviation is 1.42, so most households differ from the mean by no more than about 1 person.

**3.** (a) 2.65 (b) 1.73 (c) 1.32 (d) 2.65
The number of fouls per game for DeMar DeRozan is about 2.65 fouls. The standard deviation is 1.32, so most of DeRozan's games differ from the mean by no more than about 1 or 2 fouls.

**4.** (a) 0.795 (b) 0.574 (c) 0.692

**5.** (a) 43,680 (b) 0.019

**6.** 0.7642 **7.** 0.0010 **8.** 0.7995 **9.** 0.4984

**10.** 0.2862 **11.** 0.5905

**12.** (a) 0.1573 (b) 0.3556 (c) 0.000001
(d) The event in part (c) is unusual because the probability is less than 0.05.

**13.** (a) 0.0049 (b) 0.0149 (c) 0.9046

**14.** (a) 0.3288 (b) 0.8685
(c) Dependent
$P$(Being a public school teacher | having 20 years or more of full-time teaching experience) $\neq$ $P$(Being a public school teacher)
(d) 0.3730

**15.** (a) $\mu_{\bar{x}} = 70, \sigma_{\bar{x}} \approx 0.190$ (b) 0.0006

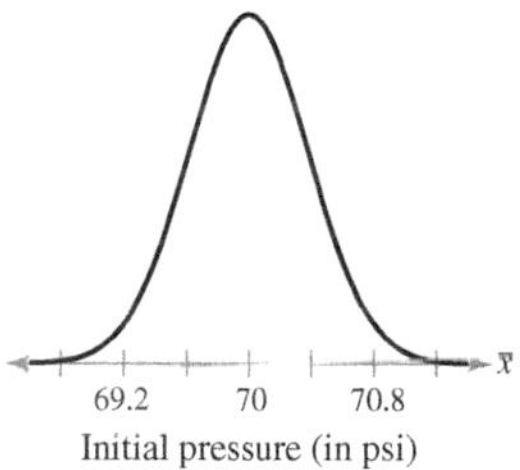


**16.** (a) 0.0548 (b) 0.6547 (c) 52.2 months

**17.** (a) 495 (b) 0.002

**18.** (a)

| $x$ | $P(x)$ |
|---|---|
| 0 | 0.00002 |
| 1 | 0.00031 |
| 2 | 0.00284 |
| 3 | 0.01538 |
| 4 | 0.05465 |
| 5 | 0.13315 |
| 6 | 0.22528 |
| 7 | 0.26136 |
| 8 | 0.19899 |
| 9 | 0.08978 |
| 10 | 0.01823 |

(b)

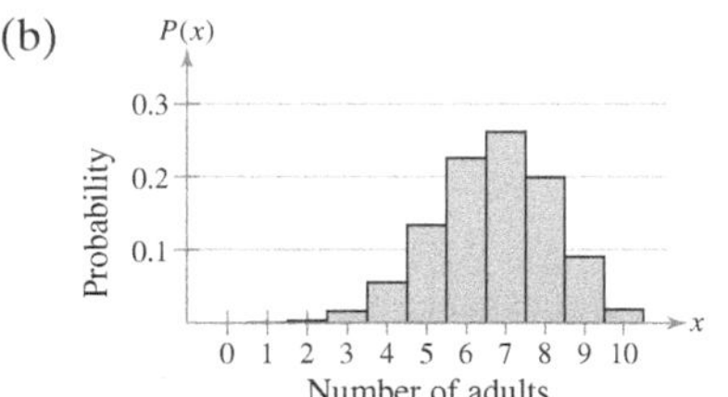


Skewed Left

(c) The values 0, 1, 2, 3, and 10 are unusual because their probabilities are less than or equal to 0.05.

# Chapter 6

## Section 6.1 (page 305)

**1.** You are more likely to be correct using an interval estimate because it is unlikely that a point estimate will exactly equal the population mean.

**3.** d. As the level of confidence increases, $z_c$ increases, causing wider intervals.

**5.** 1.28 **7.** 1.15 **9.** −0.47 **11.** 1.76 **13.** 1.861

**15.** 0.192 **17.** c **18.** d **19.** b **20.** a

**21.** (12.0, 12.6) **23.** (9.7, 11.3) **25.** $E = 1.4, \bar{x} = 13.4$

**27.** $E = 0.17, \bar{x} = 1.88$ **29.** 126 **31.** 7

**33.** $E = 1.95, \bar{x} = 28.15$

**35.** (1348.98, 1459.20); (1338.43, 1469.75)
With 90% confidence, you can say that the population mean price is between \$1348.98 and \$1459.20. With 95% confidence, you can say that the population mean price is between \$1338.43 and \$1469.75. The 95% CI is wider.

**37.** (43.70, 66.24); (41.55, 68.39)
With 90% confidence, you can say that the population mean price is between \$43.70 and \$66.24. With 95% confidence, you can say that the population mean price is between \$41.55 and \$68.39. The 95% CI is wider.

**39.** Yes. The right endpoint of the 95% confidence interval is 1469.75.

**41.** No. The right endpoint of the 95% confidence interval is 68.39.

**43.** (a) An increase in the level of confidence will widen the confidence interval and the less certain you can be about a point estimate.
(b) An increase in the sample size will narrow the confidence interval because it decreases the standard error.
(c) An increase in the population standard deviation will widen the confidence interval because small standard deviations produce more precise intervals, which are smaller.

**45.** (32.1, 40.8); (29.7, 43.3)
With 90% confidence, you can say that the population mean commute time is between 32.1 and 40.8 minutes. With 99% confidence, you can say that the population mean commute time is between 29.7 and 43.3 minutes. The 99% CI is wider.

**47.** 89

**49.** (a) 66 servings
(b) No. Yes. The 95% CI is (28.252, 29.748). If the population mean is within 3% of the sample mean, then it falls outside the CI. If the population mean is within 0.3% of the sample mean, then it falls within the CI.

**51.** (a) 7 cans
(b) Yes. The 90% CI is (127.3, 128.2) and 128 ounces falls within that interval.

**53.** (a) 74 balls
(b) Yes. The 99% CI is (27.360, 27.640) and there are amounts less than 27.6 inches that fall within that interval.

**55.** *Sample answer:* A 99% CI may not be practical to use in all situations. It may produce a CI so wide that it has no practical application.

**57.** (a) 0.707 (b) 0.949 (c) 0.962 (d) 0.975
(e) 0.711 (f) 0.937 (g) 0.964 (h) 0.979
The finite population correction factor approaches 1 as the sample size decreases and the population size remains the same.
The finite population correction factor approaches 1 as the population size increases and the sample size remains the same.

**59.** *Sample answer:*

$$E = \frac{z_c \sigma}{\sqrt{n}} \quad \text{Write the original equation.}$$

$$E\sqrt{n} = z_c \sigma \quad \text{Multiply each side by } \sqrt{n}.$$

$$\sqrt{n} = \frac{z_c \sigma}{E} \quad \text{Divide each side by } E.$$

$$n = \left(\frac{z_c \sigma}{E}\right)^2 \quad \text{Square each side.}$$

## Section 6.2 (page 315)

**1.** The mean, median, and mode are all equal to 0. The distribution is bell-shaped and symmetric about the mean. The total area under the curve is equal to 1.

**3.** 1.833 **5.** 2.947 **7.** 2.664 **9.** (10.9, 14.1)

**11.** (4.1, 4.5) **13.** $E = 3.7, \bar{x} = 18.4$ **15.** $t = 3.10$

**17.** 6.0; (29.5, 41.5). With 95% confidence, you can say that the population mean commute time is between 29.5 and 41.5 minutes.

**19.** 153.83; (372.67, 680.33). With 95% confidence, you can say that the population mean cell phone price is between \$372.67 and \$680.33.

**21.** 6.4; (29.1, 41.9). With 95% confidence, you can say that the population mean commute time is between 29.1 and 41.9 minutes. This confidence interval is slightly wider than the one found in Exercise 17.

**23.** Yes **25.** (a) 1185 (b) 168.1 (c) (1034.3, 1335.7)

**27.** (a) 7.49 (b) 1.64 (c) (6.28, 8.70) **29.** Yes

**31.** (a) 68,757.94 (b) 15,834.18 (c) (61,892.21, 75,623.67)

**33.** Yes

**35.** Use a $t$-distribution because $\sigma$ is unknown and $n \geq 30$. (26.0, 29.4). With 95% confidence, you can say that the population mean BMI is between 26.0 and 29.4.

**37.** Use standard normal distribution because $\sigma$ is known and the weights are known to be normally distributed. (12.14, 15.22). With 95% confidence, you can say that the population mean weight of two-year-old males is between 12.14 pounds and 15.22 pounds.

**39.** Neither distribution can be used because $n < 30$ and the mileages are not normally distributed.

**41.** No. They are not making good tennis balls because the $t$-value for the sample is $t = 10$, which is not between $-t_{0.99} = -2.797$ and $t_{0.99} = 2.797$.

## Section 6.2 Activity (page 318)

**1–2.** Answers will vary.

## Section 6.3 (page 325)

**1.** True **3.** 0.060, 0.940 **5.** 0.330, 0.670

**7.** $E = 0.014, \hat{p} = 0.919$ **9.** $E = 0.042, \hat{p} = 0.554$

**11.** (0.723, 0.757); (0.720, 0.761)
With 90% confidence, you can say that the population proportion of U.S. adults who say they have made a New Year's resolution is between 72.3% and 75.7%. With 95% confidence, you can say it is between 72.0% and 76.1%. The 95% confidence interval is slightly wider.

**13.** (0.321, 0.399)
With 99% confidence, we can say that the population proportion of U.S. adults who say they worry a great deal about the possibility of a future terrorist attack is between 32.1% and 39.9%.

**15.** (0.052, 0.060)

**17.** (a) 601 adults (b) 399 adults
(c) Having an estimate of the population proportion reduces the minimum sample size needed.

**19.** (a) 752 families (b) 425 families
(c) Having an estimate of the population proportion reduces the minimum sample size needed.

**21.** No. It falls within both confidence intervals.

**23.** Yes. The minimum sample size needed is 399 adults.

**25.** France: (0.283, 0.357)
Germany: (0.215, 0.285)
United Kingdom: (0.272, 0.348)
United States: (0.311, 0.389)

**27.** Cyberterrorism: (0.796, 0.844)
Development of nuclear weapons by Iran: (0.723, 0.777)
The spread of infectious diseases throughout the world: (0.692, 0.748)
Global warming or climate change: (0.550, 0.610)
The military power of Russia: (0.410, 0.470)
The conflict between the Israelis and the Palestinians: (0.291, 0.349)

**29.** (0.281, 0.339) is approximately a 98.5% CI.

**31.** (0.68, 0.74) is approximately a 96.3% CI.

**33.** (0.534, 0.606) is approximately a 99.9% CI.

**35.** If $n\hat{p} < 5$ or $n\hat{q} < 5$, the sampling distribution of $\hat{p}$ may not be normally distributed, so $z_c$ cannot be used to calculate the confidence interval.

**37.**

| $\hat{p}$ | $\hat{q} = 1 - \hat{p}$ | $\hat{p}\hat{q}$ |
|---|---|---|
| 0.0 | 1.0 | 0.00 |
| 0.1 | 0.9 | 0.09 |
| 0.2 | 0.8 | 0.16 |
| 0.3 | 0.7 | 0.21 |
| 0.4 | 0.6 | 0.24 |
| 0.5 | 0.5 | 0.25 |
| 0.6 | 0.4 | 0.24 |
| 0.7 | 0.3 | 0.21 |
| 0.8 | 0.2 | 0.16 |
| 0.9 | 0.1 | 0.09 |
| 1.0 | 0.0 | 0.00 |

| $\hat{p}$ | $\hat{q} = 1 - \hat{p}$ | $\hat{p}\hat{q}$ |
|---|---|---|
| 0.45 | 0.55 | 0.2475 |
| 0.46 | 0.54 | 0.2484 |
| 0.47 | 0.53 | 0.2491 |
| 0.48 | 0.52 | 0.2496 |
| 0.49 | 0.51 | 0.2499 |
| 0.50 | 0.50 | 0.2500 |
| 0.51 | 0.49 | 0.2499 |
| 0.52 | 0.48 | 0.2496 |
| 0.53 | 0.47 | 0.2491 |
| 0.54 | 0.46 | 0.2484 |
| 0.55 | 0.45 | 0.2475 |

$\hat{p} = 0.5$ gives the maximum value of $\hat{p}\hat{q}$.

## Section 6.3 Activity (page 329)

**1–2.** Answers will vary.

## Section 6.4 (page 334)

**1.** Yes **3.** $\chi^2_R = 14.067, \chi^2_L = 2.167$
**5.** $\chi^2_R = 32.852, \chi^2_L = 8.907$
**7.** $\chi^2_R = 52.336, \chi^2_L = 13.121$
**9.** (a) (7.33, 20.89) (b) (2.71, 4.57)
**11.** (a) (755, 2401) (b) (27, 49)
**13.** (a) (0.0426, 0.1699) (b) (0.2063, 0.4122)
With 95% confidence, you can say that the population variance is between 0.0426 and 0.1699, and the population standard deviation is between 0.2063 and 0.4122 inch.
**15.** (a) (52.41, 281.98) (b) (7.24, 16.79)
With 99% confidence, you can say that the population variance is between 52.41 and 281.98, and the population standard deviation is between 7.24 and 16.79 thousand dollars.
**17.** (a) (5.46, 45.70) (b) (2.34, 6.76)
With 99% confidence, you can say that the population variance is between 5.46 and 45.70, and the population standard deviation is between 2.34 and 6.76 days.
**19.** (a) (128, 492) (b) (11, 22)
With 95% confidence, you can say that the population variance is between 128 and 492, and the population standard deviation is between 11 and 22 grains per gallon.
**21.** (a) (0.04, 0.11) (b) (0.21, 0.32)
With 80% confidence, you can say that the population variance is between 0.04 and 0.11, and the population standard deviation is between 0.21 and 0.32 day.
**23.** (a) (1809.40, 6597.92) (b) (42.54, 81.23)
With 98% confidence, you can say that the population variance is between 1809.40 and 6597.92, and the population standard deviation is between 42.54 and 81.23 seconds.
**25.** Yes, because all of the values in the confidence interval are less than 0.5.
**27.** No, because 0.25 is contained in the confidence interval.
**29.** *Sample answer:* Unlike a confidence interval for a population mean or proportion, a confidence interval for a population variance does not have a margin of error. The left and right endpoints must be calculated separately.

## Uses and Abuses for Chapter 6 (page 336)

**1–2.** Answers will vary. **3.** (a) No (b) Yes

## Review Exercises for Chapter 6 (page 338)

**1.** (a) 103.5 (b) 11.7
**3.** (a) (91.8, 115.2). With 90% confidence, you can say that the population mean waking time is between 91.8 and 115.2 minutes past 5:00 A.M.
(b) Yes. If the population mean is within 10% of the sample mean, then it falls inside the confidence interval.
**5.** $E = 1.675, \bar{x} = 22.425$ **7.** 78 people **9.** 1.383
**11.** 2.624 **13.** (a) 11.2 (b) (60.9, 83.3)
**15.** (a) 0.7 (b) (6.1, 7.5)
**17.** (146, 184). With 90% confidence, you can say that the population mean height is between 146 and 184 feet.
**19.** (a) 0.420, 0.580 (b) (0.393, 0.447); (0.388, 0.452)
(c) The 95% interval is slightly wider.
**21.** (a) 0.325, 0.675 (b) (0.322, 0.327); (0.321, 0.328)
(c) The 95% interval is slightly wider.
**23.** Yes. It would be unusual because it is outside both confidence intervals.
**25.** (a) 385 adults (b) 335 adults
(c) Having an estimate of the population proportion reduces the minimum sample size needed.
**27.** $\chi^2_R = 23.337, \chi^2_L = 4.404$ **29.** $\chi^2_R = 24.996, \chi^2_L = 7.261$
**31.** (a) (13.28, 70.38) (b) (3.64, 8.39)
With 95% confidence, you can say that the population variance is between 13.28 and 70.38, and the population standard deviation is between 3.64 and 8.39.

## Quiz for Chapter 6 (page 340)

**1.** (a) 2.46 (b) 0.030
(c) (2.43, 2.49). With 95% confidence, you can say that the population mean winning time is between 2.439 and 2.499 hours.
(d) No. It falls outside the confidence interval.
**2.** 28 champions
**3.** (a) $\bar{x} = 6.61, s \approx 3.38$
(b) (4.65, 8.57). With 90% confidence, you can say that the population mean amount of time is between 4.65 and 8.57 minutes.
(c) (4.79, 8.43). With 90% confidence, you can say that the population mean amount of time is between 4.79 and 8.43 minutes. This confidence interval is narrower than the one in part (b).
**4.** (109,990, 156,662). With 95% confidence, you can say that the population mean annual earnings is between \$109,990 and \$156,662.
**5.** Yes

6. (a) 0.830
   (b) (0.810, 0.849). With 90% confidence, you can say that the population proportion of U.S. adults who say that the energy situation in the United States is very or fairly serious is between 81.1% and 84.9%.
   (c) Yes. The values fall outside the confidence intervals.
   (d) 585 adults
7. (a) (5.41, 38.08)
   (b) (2.32, 6.17). With 95% confidence, you can say that the population standard deviation is between 2.32 and 6.17 minutes.

## Real Statistics—Real Decisions for Chapter 6 (page 342)

1. (a) Yes, there has been a change in the mean concentration level because the confidence interval for Year 1 does not overlap the confidence interval for Year 2.
   (b) No, there has not been a change in the mean concentration level because the confidence interval for Year 2 overlaps the confidence interval for Year 3.
   (c) Yes, there has been a change in the mean concentration level because the confidence interval for Year 1 does not overlap the confidence interval for Year 3.
2. The concentrations of cyanide in the drinking water have increased over the three-year period.
3. The width of the confidence interval for Year 2 may have been caused by greater variation in the levels of cyanide than in other years, which may be the result of outliers.
4. Increase the sample size.
5. Answers will vary.
   (a) *Sample answer:* The sampling distribution of the sample means was used because the "mean concentration" was used. The sample mean is the most unbiased point estimate of the population mean.
   (b) *Sample answer:* No, because typically $\sigma$ is unknown. They could have used the sample standard deviation.

# Chapter 7

## Section 7.1 (page 359)

1. The two types of hypotheses used in a hypothesis test are the null hypothesis and the alternative hypothesis.
   The alternative hypothesis is the complement of the null hypothesis.
3. You can reject the null hypothesis, or you can fail to reject the null hypothesis.
5. False. In a hypothesis test, you assume the null hypothesis is true.
7. True
9. False. A small $P$-value in a test will favor rejection of the null hypothesis.
11. $H_0$: $\mu \le 645$ (claim); $H_a$: $\mu > 645$
13. $H_0$: $\sigma = 5$; $H_a$: $\sigma \ne 5$ (claim)
15. $H_0$: $p \ge 0.45$; $H_a$: $p < 0.45$ (claim)
17. c; $H_0$: $\mu \le 3$
18. d; $H_0$: $\mu \ge 3$
19. b; $H_0$: $\mu = 3$
20. a; $H_0$: $\mu \le 2$
21. Right-tailed
23. Two-tailed
25. $\mu > 8$
    $H_0$: $\mu \le 8$; $H_a$: $\mu > 8$ (claim)
27. $\sigma \le 320$
    $H_0$: $\sigma \le 320$ (claim); $H_a$: $\sigma > 320$
29. $p = 0.54$
    $H_0$: $p = 0.54$ (claim); $H_a$: $p \ne 0.54$
31. A type I error will occur when the actual proportion of new customers who return to buy their next textbook is at least 0.60, but you reject $H_0$: $p \ge 0.60$.
    A type II error will occur when the actual proportion of new customers who return to buy their next textbook is less than 0.60, but you fail to reject $H_0$: $p \ge 0.60$.
33. A type I error will occur when the actual standard deviation of the length of time to play a game is less than or equal to 12 minutes, but you reject $H_0$: $\sigma \le 12$.
    A type II error will occur when the actual standard deviation of the length of time to play a game is greater than 12 minutes, but you fail to reject $H_0$: $\sigma \le 12$.
35. A type I error will occur when the actual proportion of applicants who become campus security officers is at most 0.25, but you reject $H_0$: $p \le 0.25$.
    A type II error will occur when the actual proportion of applicants who become campus security officers is greater than 0.25, but you fail to reject $H_0$: $p \le 0.25$.
37. $H_0$: The proportion of homeowners who have a home security alarm is greater than or equal to 14%.
    $H_a$: The proportion of homeowners who have a home security alarm is less than 14%.
    $H_0$: $p \ge 0.14$; $H_a$: $p < 0.14$
    Left-tailed because the alternative hypothesis contains $<$.

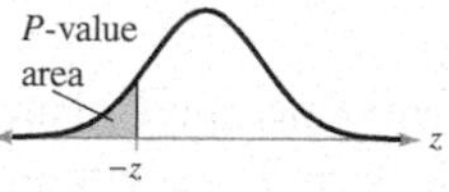


39. $H_0$: The standard deviation of the 18-hole scores for a golfer is greater than or equal to 2.1 strokes.
    $H_a$: The standard deviation of the 18-hole scores for a golfer is less than 2.1 strokes.
    $H_0$: $\sigma \ge 2.1$; $H_a$: $\sigma < 2.1$
    Left-tailed because the alternative hypothesis contains $<$.

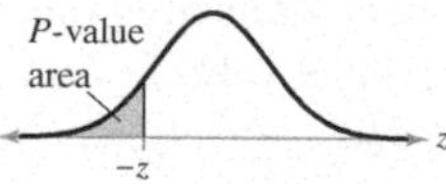


41. $H_0$: The percentage of responses to a survey is 100%.
    $H_a$: The percentage of responses to a survey is not 100%.
    $H_0$: $p = 1$; $H_a$: $p \ne 1$
    Two-tailed because the alternative hypothesis contains $\ne$.

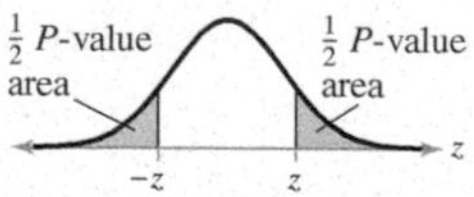

**43.** Alternative hypothesis
(a) There is enough evidence to support the scientist's claim that the mean incubation period for swan eggs is less than 40 days.
(b) There is not enough evidence to support the scientist's claim that the mean incubation period for swan eggs is less than 40 days.

**45.** Null hypothesis
(a) There is enough evidence to reject the researcher's claim that the standard deviation of the life of the lawn mower is at most 2.8 years.
(b) There is not enough evidence to reject the researcher's claim that the standard deviation of the life of the lawn mower is at most 2.8 years.

**47.** Alternative hypothesis
(a) There is enough evidence to support the fitness equipment company's claim that its competitor's home gym does not have a customer satisfaction rate of 99%.
(b) There is not enough evidence to support the fitness equipment company's claim that its competitor's home gym does not have a customer satisfaction rate of 99%.

**49.** $H_0$: $\mu \geq 60$; $H_a$: $\mu < 60$

**51.** (a) $H_0$: $\mu \geq 5$; $H_a$: $\mu < 5$
(b) $H_0$: $\mu \leq 5$; $H_a$: $\mu > 5$

**53.** If you decrease $\alpha$, then you are decreasing the probability that you will reject $H_0$. Therefore, you are increasing the probability of failing to reject $H_0$. This could increase $\beta$, the probability of failing to reject $H_0$ when $H_0$ is false.

**55.** Yes; If the $P$-value is less than $\alpha = 0.05$, then it is also less than $\alpha = 0.10$.

**57.** (a) Fail to reject $H_0$ because the confidence interval includes 70.
(b) Reject $H_0$ because the confidence interval does not include 70.
(c) Fail to reject $H_0$ because the confidence interval includes 70.

**59.** (a) Reject $H_0$ because the confidence interval is located entirely to the right of 0.20.
(b) Fail to reject $H_0$ because the confidence interval includes values less than 0.20.
(c) Fail to reject $H_0$ because the confidence interval includes values less than 0.20.

## Section 7.2 (page 373)

**1.** The $z$-test using a $P$-value compares the $P$-value with the level of significance $\alpha$. In the $z$-test using rejection region(s), the test statistic is compared with critical values.

**3.** (a) Fail to reject $H_0$. (b) Reject $H_0$. (c) Reject $H_0$.

**5.** (a) Fail to reject $H_0$. (b) Fail to reject $H_0$.
(c) Fail to reject $H_0$.

**7.** (a) Fail to reject $H_0$. (b) Fail to reject $H_0$.
(c) Reject $H_0$.

**9.** (b). The smaller $P$-value corresponds to the smaller area.

**11.** (a). The smaller $z$-statistic corresponds to the smaller area.

**13.** $P = 0.0934$. Reject $H_0$. **15.** $P = 0.0069$. Reject $H_0$.

**17.** $P = 0.0930$. Fail to reject $H_0$.

**19.** Fail to reject $H_0$.

**21.** (a) Fail to reject $H_0$ because $z < 1.285$.
(b) Fail to reject $H_0$ because $z < 1.285$.
(c) Fail to reject $H_0$ because $z < 1.285$.
(d) Reject $H_0$ because $z > 1.285$.

**23.** Critical value: $z_0 = -1.88$; Rejection region: $z < -1.88$

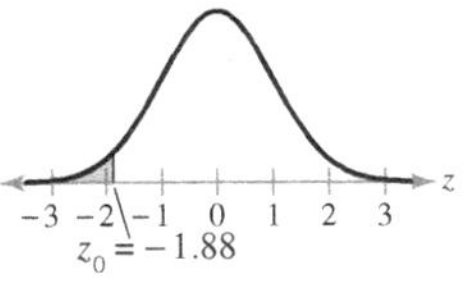


**25.** Critical value: $z_0 = 1.645$; Rejection region: $z > 1.645$

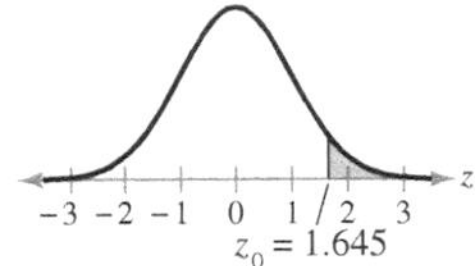


**27.** Critical values: $-z_0 = -2.33$, $z_0 = 2.33$
Rejection regions: $z < -2.33$, $z > 2.33$

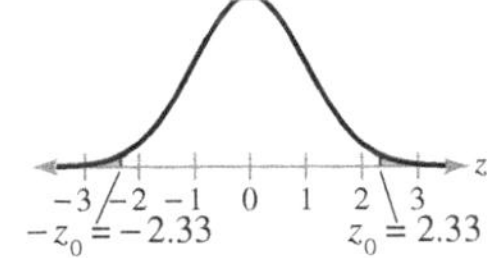


**29.** Reject $H_0$. There is enough evidence at the 5% level of significance to reject the claim.

**31.** Fail to reject $H_0$. There is not enough evidence at the 3% level of significance to support the claim.

**33.** (a) The claim is "the mean total score for the school's applicants is more than 503."
$H_0$: $\mu \leq 503$; $H_a$: $\mu > 503$ (claim)
(b) 1.89 (c) 0.0294 (d) Fail to reject $H_0$.
(e) There is not enough evidence at the 1% level of significance to support the report's claim that the mean total score for the school's applicants is more than 503.

**35.** (a) The claim is "the mean winning times for Boston Marathon women's open division champions is at least 2.6 hours."
$H_0$: $\mu \geq 2.6$ (claim); $H_a$: $\mu < 2.6$
(b) $-2.43$ (c) 0.0075 (d) Reject $H_0$.
(e) There is enough evidence at the 5% level of significance to reject the statistician's claim that the mean winning times for Boston Marathon women's open division champions is at least 2.6 hours.

**37.** (a) The claim is "the mean vertical drop of top-rated roller coasters is 163 feet."
$H_0$: $\mu = 163$ (claim); $H_a$: $\mu \neq 163$
(b) $-1.66$ (c) 0.097 (d) Fail to reject $H_0$.
(e) There is not enough evidence at the 5% level of significance to reject the claim that the mean vertical drop of top-rated roller coasters is 163 feet.

**39.** (a) The claim is "the mean caffeine content per 12-ounce bottle of a population of caffeinated soft drinks is 37.7 milligrams."
$H_0$: $\mu = 37.7$ (claim); $H_a$: $\mu \neq 37.7$
(b) $-z_0 = -2.575$, $z_0 = 2.575$
Rejection regions: $z < -2.575$, $z > 2.575$
(c) $-0.72$ (d) Fail to reject $H_0$.
(e) There is not enough evidence at the 1% level of significance to reject the consumer research organization's claim that the mean caffeine content per 12-ounce bottle of a population of caffeinated soft drinks is 37.7 milligrams.

**41.** (a) The claim is "the mean sodium content in one of its breakfast sandwiches is less than 920 milligrams."
$H_0$: $\mu \geq 920$; $H_a$: $\mu < 920$ (claim)
(b) $z_0 = 1.645$; Rejection region: $z > 1.645$
(c) 1.76 (d) Reject $H_0$.
(e) There is enough evidence at the 5% level of significance to support the claim that the mean sodium content in one of its breakfast sandwiches is less than 920 milligrams.

**43.** (a) The claim is "the mean life of a CFL bulb is at least 10,000 hours."
$H_0$: $\mu \geq 10{,}000$ (claim); $H_a$: $\mu < 10{,}000$
(b) $z_0 = -1.23$; Rejection region: $z < -1.23$
(c) $-1.28$ (d) Reject $H_0$.
(e) There is enough evidence at the 11% level of significance to reject the lamp manufacturer's claim that the mean life of a CFL bulb is at least 10,000 hours.

**45.** Outside. When the standardized test statistic is inside the rejection region, $P < \alpha$.

## Section 7.3 (page 383)

**1.** Specify the level of significance $\alpha$ and the degrees of freedom, d.f. $= n - 1$. Find the critical value(s) using the $t$-distribution table in the row with $n - 1$ d.f. When the hypothesis test is
(1) left-tailed, use the "One Tail, $\alpha$" column with a negative sign.
(2) right-tailed, use the "One Tail, $\alpha$" column with a positive sign.
(3) two-tailed, use the "Two Tails, $\alpha$" column with a negative and a positive sign.

**3.** Critical value: $t_0 = -1.328$; Rejection region: $t < -1.328$

**5.** Critical value: $t_0 = 1.717$; Rejection region: $t > 1.717$

**7.** Critical values: $-t_0 = -2.056$, $t_0 = 2.056$
Rejection regions: $t < -2.056$, $t > 2.056$

**9.** (a) Fail to reject $H_0$ because $t > -2.086$.
(b) Fail to reject $H_0$ because $t > -2.086$.
(c) Reject $H_0$ because $t < -2.086$.

**11.** (a) Reject $H_0$ because $t < -1.725$.
(b) Fail to reject $H_0$ because $-1.725 < t < 1.725$.
(c) Reject $H_0$ because $t > 1.725$.

**13.** Fail to reject $H_0$. There is not enough evidence at the 1% level of significance to reject the claim.

**15.** Reject $H_0$. There is enough evidence at the 1% level of significance to reject the claim.

**17.** Fail to reject $H_0$. There is not enough evidence at the 2% level of significance to reject the claim.

**19.** (a) The claim is "Apple AirPods have a mean listening time of at least 5.0 hours on a single charge."
$H_0$: $\mu \geq 5.0$ (claim); $H_a$: $\mu < 5.0$
(b) $t_0 = -2.567$; Rejection region: $t < -2.567$
(c) $-2.31$ (d) Fail to reject $H_0$.
(e) There is not enough evidence at the 1% level to reject the claim that Apple AirPods have a mean listening time of at least 5.0 hours on a single charge.

**21.** (a) The claim is "the mean credit card debt in Colorado is greater than \$5540 per borrower."
$H_0$: $\mu \leq 5540$; $H_a$: $\mu > 5540$ (claim)
(b) $t_0 = 1.699$; Rejection region: $t > 1.699$
(c) 0.495 (d) Fail to reject $H_0$.
(e) There is not enough evidence to support the claim that the mean credit card debt in Colorado is greater than \$5540 per borrower.

**23.** (a) The claim is "the mean amount of carbon monoxide in the air in U.S. cities is less than 1.80 parts per million."
$H_0$: $\mu \geq 1.80$; $H_a$: $\mu < 1.80$ (claim)
(b) $t_0 = -1.295$; Rejection region: $t < -1.295$
(c) 0.691 (d) Fail to reject $H_0$.
(e) There is not enough evidence at the 10% level of significance to support the claim that the mean amount of carbon monoxide in the air in U.S. cities is less than 1.80 parts per million.

**25.** (a) The claim is "the mean annual salary for mid-level product engineers is \$86,000."
$H_0$: $\mu = 86{,}000$ (claim); $H_a$: $\mu \neq 86{,}000$
(b) $-t_0 = -2.131$, $t_0 = 2.131$
Rejection region: $t < -2.131$, $t > 2.131$
(c) $-2.152$ (d) Reject $H_0$.
(e) There is enough evidence at the 5% level of significance to reject the claim that the mean annual salary for mid-level product engineers is \$86,000.

**27.** (a) The claim is "the mean minimum time it takes for a sedan to travel a quarter mile is greater than 15.3 seconds."
$H_0$: $\mu \leq 15.3$; $H_a$: $\mu > 15.3$ (claim)
(b) 0.166 (c) Fail to reject $H_0$.
(d) There is not enough evidence at the 10% level of significance to support the consumer group's claim that the mean minimum time it takes for a sedan to travel a quarter mile is greater than 15.3 seconds.

**29.** (a) The claim is "the mean number of classroom hours per week for full-time faculty is 11.0."
$H_0$: $\mu = 11.0$ (claim); $H_a$: $\mu \neq 11.0$
(b) 0.3155 (c) Fail to reject $H_0$.
(d) There is not enough evidence at the 1% level of significance to reject the dean's claim that the mean number of classroom hours per week for full-time faculty is 11.0.

31. Use the $t$-distribution because $\sigma$ is unknown, the sample is random, and the population is normally distributed.
Fail to reject $H_0$. There is not enough evidence at the 5% level of significance to reject the car company's claim that the mean gas mileage for the luxury sedan is at least 23 miles per gallon.

33. More likely. The tails of a $t$-distribution curve are thicker than those of a standard normal distribution curve. So, if you incorrectly use a standard normal sampling distribution instead of a $t$-sampling distribution, then the area under the curve at the tails will be smaller than what it would be for the $t$-test, meaning the critical value(s) will lie closer to the mean. This makes it more likely for the test statistic to be in the rejection region(s). This result is the same regardless of whether the test is left-tailed, right-tailed, or two-tailed; in each case, the tail thickness affects the location of the critical value(s).

## Section 7.3 Activity (page 386)

1–3. Answers will vary.

## Section 7.4 (page 391)

1. If $np \geq 5$ and $nq \geq 5$, then the normal distribution can be used.

3. Cannot use normal distribution

5. Can use normal distribution
Fail to reject $H_0$. There is not enough evidence at the 5% level of significance to support the claim.

7. (a) The claim is "more than 80% of U.S. adults feel children should be vaccinated to attend school."
$H_0$: $p \leq 0.8$; $H_a$: $p > 0.8$ (claim)
(b) $z_0 = 2.33$; Rejection region: $z > 2.33$
(c) 1.414 (d) Fail to reject $H_0$.
(e) There is not enough evidence at the 1% level of significance to support the claim that more than 80% of U.S. adults feel children should be vaccinated to attend school.

9. (a) The claim is "at least 60% of tax filers are expecting a tax refund."
$H_0$: $p \geq 0.60$ (claim); $H_a$: $p < 0.60$
(b) $z_0 = -1.645$; Rejection region: $z < -1.645$
(c) $-4.078$ (d) Reject $H_0$.
(e) There is enough evidence at the 5% level of significance to reject the analyst's claim that at least 60% of tax filers are expecting a tax refund.

11. (a) The claim is "more than half of all nurses feel they became better professionals during the coronavirus pandemic."
$H_0$: $p \leq 0.5$; $H_a$: $p > 0.5$ (claim)
(b) $z_0 = 2.33$; Rejection region: $z > 2.33$
(c) 2.771 (d) Reject $H_0$.
(e) At the 1% level of significance, there is enough evidence to support the manager's claim that more than half of all nurses feel they became better professionals during the coronavirus pandemic.

13. (a) The claim is "27% of U.S. adults would travel into space on a commercial flight if they could afford it."
$H_0$: $p = 0.27$ (claim); $H_a$: $p \neq 0.27$
(b) 0.03 (c) Reject $H_0$.
(d) There is enough evidence at the 5% level of significance to reject the research center's claim that 27% of U.S. adults would travel into space on a commercial flight if they could afford it.

15. (a) The claim is "more than 25% of U.S. adults believe moral values in the country are getting better."
$H_0$: $p \leq 0.25$; $H_a$: $p > 0.25$ (claim)
(b) 0.071 (c) Reject $H_0$.
(d) At the 10% level of significance, there is enough evidence to support the politician's claim that more than 25% of U.S. adults believe moral values in the country are getting better.

17. Fail to reject $H_0$. There is not enough evidence at the 5% level of significance to reject the claim that at least 64% of adults make an effort to live in ways that help protect the environment some of the time.

19. (a) The claim is "more than 80% of U.S. adults feel children should be vaccinated to attend school."
$H_0$: $p \leq 0.08$; $H_a$: $p > 0.8$ (claim)
(b) $z_0 = 2.33$; Rejection region: $z > 2.33$
(c) 1.414 (d) Fail to reject $H_0$.
(e) There is not enough evidence at the 1% level of significance to support the claim that more than 80% of U.S. adults feel children should be vaccinated to attend school. Results are the same.

## Section 7.4 Activity (page 393)

1–2. Answers will vary.

## Section 7.5 (page 400)

1. Specify the level of significance $\alpha$. Determine the degrees of freedom. Determine the critical values using the $\chi^2$-distribution. For a right-tailed test, use the value that corresponds to d.f. and $\alpha$; for a left-tailed test, use the value that corresponds to d.f. and $1 - \alpha$; for a two-tailed test, use the values that correspond to d.f. and $\frac{1}{2}\alpha$, and d.f. and $1 - \frac{1}{2}\alpha$.

3. As $\alpha$ decreases, the right critical value for a two-tailed test increases and the left critical value for a two-tailed test decreases.

5. The requirement of a normal distribution is more important when testing a standard deviation than when testing a mean. When the population is not normal, the results of a chi-square test can be misleading because the chi-square test is not as robust as the tests for the population mean.

7. Critical value: $\chi_0^2 = 38.885$; Rejection region: $\chi^2 > 38.885$

9. Critical value: $\chi_0^2 = 0.872$; Rejection region: $\chi^2 < 0.872$

11. Critical values: $\chi_L^2 = 60.391$, $\chi_R^2 = 101.879$
Rejection regions: $\chi^2 < 60.391$, $\chi^2 > 101.879$

13. (a) Fail to reject $H_0$ because $\chi^2 < 6.251$.
(b) Fail to reject $H_0$ because $\chi^2 < 6.251$.
(c) Reject $H_0$ because $\chi^2 > 6.251$.

**15.** Fail to reject $H_0$. There is not enough evidence at the 5% level of significance to reject the claim.

**17.** Fail to reject $H_0$. There is not enough evidence at the 5% level of significance to reject the claim.

**19.** Fail to reject $H_0$. There is not enough evidence at the 1% level of significance to support the claim.

**21.** Reject $H_0$. There is enough evidence at the 10% level of significance to support the claim.

**23.** (a) The claim is "the variance of the diameters in a certain tire model is 8.6."
$H_0$: $\sigma^2 = 8.6$ (claim); $H_a$: $\sigma^2 \neq 8.6$
(c) 4.5 (d) Fail to reject $H_0$.
(e) There is not enough evidence at the 1% level of significance to reject the tire manufacturer's claim that the variance of the diameters in a certain tire model is 8.6.

**25.** (a) The claim is "the standard deviation for grade 12 students on a mathematics assessment test is less than 37."
$H_0$: $\sigma \geq 37$; $H_a$: $\sigma < 37$ (claim)
(b) $\chi_0^2 = 18.114$; Rejection region: $\chi^2 < 18.114$
(c) 22.799 (d) Fail to reject $H_0$.
(e) There is not enough evidence at the 10% level of significance to support the school administrator's claim that the standard deviation for grade 12 students on a mathematics assessment test is less than 37 points.

**27.** (a) The claim is "the standard deviation of the waiting times for patients is no more than 0.5 minute."
$H_0$: $\sigma \leq 0.5$ (claim); $H_a$: $\sigma > 0.5$
(b) $\chi_0^2 = 33.196$; Rejection region: $\chi^2 > 33.196$
(c) 47.04 (d) Reject $H_0$.
(e) There is enough evidence at the 10% level of significance to reject the hospital's claim that the standard deviation of the waiting times for patients is no more than 0.5 minute.

**29.** (a) The claim is "the standard deviation of the annual salaries of senior level graphic design specialists is different from \$13,056."
$H_0$: $\sigma = 13{,}056$ (claim); $H_a$: $\sigma \neq 13{,}056$
(b) $\chi_L^2 = 5.629$, $\chi_R^2 = 26.119$
Rejection region: $\chi^2 < 5.629$, $\chi^2 > 26.119$
(c) 27.464 (d) Reject $H_0$.
(e) There is enough evidence at the 5% level of significance to support the claim that the standard deviation of the annual salaries of senior level graphic design specialists is different from \$13,056.

**31.** $P$-value $= 0.304$; Fail to reject $H_0$.

**33.** $P$-value $= 0.0033$; Reject $H_0$.

## Uses and Abuses for Chapter 7 (page 404)

**1.** $H_0$: $p = 0.5$; Answers will vary. **2–3.** Answers will vary.

## Review Exercises for Chapter 7 (page 406)

**1.** $H_0$: $\mu \leq 375$ (claim); $H_a$: $\mu > 375$

**3.** $H_0$: $p \geq 0.205$; $H_a$: $p < 0.205$ (claim)

**5.** $H_0$: $\sigma \leq 1.9$; $H_a$: $\sigma > 1.9$ (claim)

**7.** (a) $H_0$: $p = 0.81$ (claim); $H_a$: $p \neq 0.81$
(b) A type I error will occur when the actual proportion of U.S. adults who believe that Earth's temperature has been increasing over the past 100 years is 81%, but you reject $H_0$: $p = 0.81$. A type II error will occur when the actual proportion is not 81%, but you fail to reject $H_0$: $p = 0.81$.
(c) Two-tailed because the alternative hypothesis contains $\neq$.
(d) There is enough evidence to reject the polling organization's claim that the proportion of U.S. adults who believe that Earth's temperature has been increasing over the past 100 years is 81%.
(e) There is not enough evidence to reject the polling organization's claim that the proportion of U.S. adults who believe that Earth's temperature has been increasing over the past 100 years is 81%.

**9.** (a) $H_0$: $\sigma \leq 2900$ (claim); $H_a$: $\sigma > 2900$
(b) A type I error will occur when the actual standard deviation of the starting prices of its top-rated vehicles for a recent year is no more than \$2900, but you reject $H_0$: $\sigma \leq 2900$. A type II error will occur when the actual standard deviation of the starting prices of its top-rated vehicles for a recent year is more than \$2900, but you fail to reject $H_0$: $\sigma \leq 2900$.
(c) Right-tailed because the alternative hypothesis contains $>$.
(d) There is enough evidence to reject the nonprofit consumer organization's claim that the standard deviation of the starting prices of its top-rated vehicles for a recent year is no more than \$2900.
(e) There is not enough evidence to reject the nonprofit consumer organization's claim that the standard deviation of the starting prices of its top-rated vehicles for a recent year is no more than \$2900.

**11.** 0.1736. Fail to reject $H_0$.

**13.** Critical value: $z_0 = -2.05$; Rejection region: $z < -2.05$

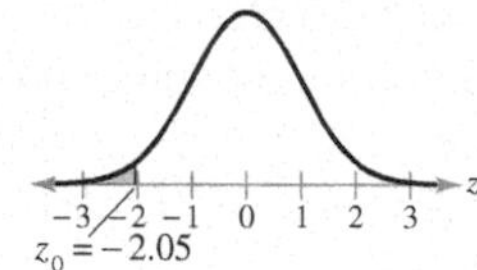


**15.** Critical value: $z_0 = 1.96$; Rejection region: $z > 1.96$

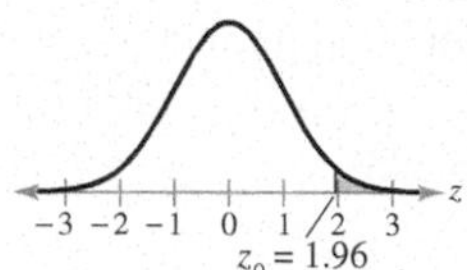


**17.** Fail to reject $H_0$ because $-1.645 < z < 1.645$.

**19.** Fail to reject $H_0$ because $-1.645 < z < 1.645$.

**21.** Fail to reject $H_0$. There is not enough evidence at the 5% level of significance to reject the claim.

**23.** Fail to reject $H_0$. There is not enough evidence at the 1% level of significance to support the claim.

**25.** (a) The claim is "the mean air concentration of nitrogen dioxide in U.S. cities is 9 parts per billion."
$H_0$: $\mu = 9$ (claim); $H_a$: $\mu \neq 9$
(b) $-1.15$ (c) 0.2502 (d) Fail to reject $H_0$.
(e) There is not enough evidence at the 5% level of significance to reject the researcher's claim that the mean air concentration of nitrogen dioxide in U.S. cities is 9 parts per billion.

**27.** (a) The claim is "the mean annual drug overdose death rate for the 50 states is at least 25 deaths per 100,000 people."
$H_0$: $\mu \geq 25$ (claim); $H_a$: $\mu < 25$
(b) $z_0 = -2.33$; Rejection region: $z_0 < -2.33$
(c) $-1.29$ (d) Fail to reject $H_0$.
(e) At the 1% level of significance there is not enough evidence to reject the claim that the mean annual drug overdose death rate for the 50 states is at least 25 deaths per 100,000 people.

**29.** Critical values: $-t_0 = -2.093$, $t_0 = 2.093$
Rejection regions: $t < -2.093$, $t > 2.093$

**31.** Critical value: $t_0 = 2.098$; Rejection region: $t > 2.098$

**33.** Critical value: $t_0 = -2.977$; Rejection region: $t < -2.977$

**35.** Reject $H_0$. There is enough evidence at the 0.5% level of significance to support the claim.

**37.** Reject $H_0$. There is enough evidence at the 1% level of significance to reject the claim.

**39.** Fail to reject $H_0$. There is not enough evidence at the 10% level of significance to reject the claim.

**41.** (a) The claim is "the mean monthly cost of joining a health club is \$25."
$H_0$: $\mu = 25$ (claim); $H_a$: $\mu \neq 25$
(b) $-t_0 = -1.740$, $t_0 = 1.740$
Rejection regions: $t < -1.740$, $t > 1.740$
(c) 1.64 (d) Fail to reject $H_0$.
(e) There is not enough evidence at the 10% level of significance to reject the advertisement's claim that the mean monthly cost of joining a health club is \$25.

**43.** (a) The claim is "the mean score for grade 12 students on a science achievement test is more than 145."
$H_0$: $\mu \leq 145$; $H_a$: $\mu > 145$ (claim)
(b) 0.0824 (c) Reject $H_0$.
(d) There is enough evidence at the 10% level of significance to support the education publication's claim that the mean score for grade 12 students on a science achievement test is more than 145.

**45.** Can use normal distribution
Fail to reject $H_0$. There is not enough evidence at the 5% level of significance to reject the claim.

**47.** Can use normal distribution
Reject $H_0$. There is enough evidence at the 1% level of significance to support the claim.

**49.** (a) The claim is "over 56% of U.S. adults think it is likely that robots and computers will do most jobs 25 years from now."
$H_0$: $p \leq 0.56$; $H_a$: $p > 0.56$ (claim)
(b) $z_0 = 2.33$; Rejection region: $z > 2.33$
(c) 1.911 (d) Fail to reject $H_0$.
(e) There is not enough evidence at the 1% level to support the claim that over 56% of U.S. adults think it is likely that robots and computers will do most jobs 25 years from now.

**51.** Critical value: $\chi_0^2 = 30.144$; Rejection region: $\chi^2 > 30.144$

**53.** Critical values: $\chi_L^2 = 26.509$, $\chi_R^2 = 55.758$
Rejection regions: $\chi^2 < 26.509$, $\chi^2 > 55.758$

**55.** Reject $H_0$. There is enough evidence at the 10% level of significance to support the claim.

**57.** Fail to reject $H_0$. There is not enough evidence at the 5% level of significance to reject the claim.

**59.** (a) The claim is "the variance of the bolt widths is at most 0.01."
$H_0$: $\sigma^2 \leq 0.01$ (claim); $H_a$: $\sigma^2 > 0.01$
(b) $\chi_0^2 = 49.645$; Rejection region: $\chi^2 > 49.645$
(c) 172.8 (d) Reject $H_0$.
(e) There is enough evidence at the 0.5% level of significance to reject the bolt manufacturer's claim that the variance is at most 0.01.

**61.** You can reject $H_0$ at the 1% level of significance because $\chi^2 = 172.8 > 46.963$.

## Quiz for Chapter 7 (page 410)

**1.** (a) The claim is "the mean hat size for a male is at least 7.25."
$H_0$: $\mu \geq 7.25$ (claim); $H_a$: $\mu < 7.25$
(b) Left-tailed because the alternative hypothesis contains $<$; $z$-test because $\sigma$ is known and the population is normally distributed.
(c) *Sample answer:* $z_0 = -2.33$;
Rejection region: $z < -2.33$; $-1.28$
(d) Fail to reject $H_0$.
(e) There is not enough evidence at the 1% level of significance to reject the company's claim that the mean hat size for a male is at least 7.25.

**2.** (a) The claim is "the mean daily base price for renting a full-size or less expensive vehicle in Vancouver, British Columbia, is more than \$86."
$H_0$: $\mu \leq 86$; $H_a$: $\mu > 86$ (claim)
(b) Right-tailed because the alternative hypothesis contains $>$; $z$-test because $\sigma$ is known and $n \geq 30$.
(c) *Sample answer:* $z_0 = 1.28$; Rejection region: $z > 1.28$; 1.582
(d) Reject $H_0$.
(e) There is enough evidence at the 10% level of significance to support the travel analyst's claim that that the mean daily base price for renting a full-size or less expensive vehicle in Vancouver, British Columbia, is more than \$86.

**3.** (a) The claim is "the mean amount of earnings for full-time workers ages 18 to 24 with a bachelor's degree in a recent year is \$52,133."
$H_0$: $\mu = 52{,}133$ (claim); $H_a$: $\mu \neq 52{,}133$
(b) Two-tailed because the alternative hypothesis contains $\neq$; $t$-test because $\sigma$ is unknown and population is normally distributed.
(c) *Sample answer:* $-t_0 = -2.145$, $t_0 = 2.145$
Rejection region $t < -2.145$, $t > 2.145$; $-2.165$

(d) Reject $H_0$.

(e) There is enough evidence at the 5% level of significance to reject the government agency's claim that the mean amount of earnings for full-time workers ages 18 to 24 with a bachelor's degree in a recent year is \$52,133.

**4.** (a) The claim is "program participants have a mean weight loss of at least 10.5 pounds after 1 month."
$H_0$: $\mu \geq 10.5$ (claim); $H_a$: $\mu < 10.5$

(b) Left-tailed because the alternative hypothesis contains <; *t*-test because $\sigma$ is unknown and $n \geq 30$.

(c) *Sample answer:* $t_0 = -2.462$;
Rejection region: $t < -2.462$; $-3.09$

(d) Reject $H_0$.

(e) There is enough evidence at the 1% level of significance to reject the weight loss program's claim that program participants have a mean weight loss of at least 10.5 pounds after 1 month.

**5.** (a) The claim is "less than 25% of the televisions the organization rated in a recent year have an overall score of 70 or more."
$H_0$: $p \geq 0.25$; $H_a$: $p < 0.25$ (claim)

(b) Left-tailed because the alternative hypothesis contains <; *z*-test because $np \geq 5$ and $nq \geq 5$.

(c) *Sample answer:* $z_0 = -1.645$
Rejection region: $z_0 < -1.645$; $-0.273$

(d) Fail to reject $H_0$.

(e) There is not enough evidence at the 5% level of significance to support the claim that less than 25% of the televisions the organization rated in a recent year have an overall score of 70 or more.

**6.** (a) The claim is "the standard deviation of the television rating scores is 10.1."
$H_0$: $\sigma = 10.1$ (claim); $H_a$: $\sigma \neq 10.1$

(b) Two-tailed because the alternative hypothesis contains ≠; chi-square test because the test is for a standard deviation and the population is normally distributed.

(c) *Sample answer:* $\chi^2_L = 18.493$, $\chi^2_R = 43.773$
Rejection region: $\chi^2 < 18.493$, $\chi^2 > 43.773$; 39.599

(d) Fail to reject $H_0$.

(e) There is not enough evidence at the 10% level of significance to reject the claim that the standard deviation of the TV rating scores is 10.1.

## Real Statistics—Real Decisions for Chapter 7 (page 412)

**1.** Answers will vary.

**2.** (a) Not random; *Sample answer:* Randomly select students from the student directory.

(b) Random (c) Random

**3.** Alternative hypothesis because you cannot use a hypothesis test to support your claim if your claim is the null hypothesis.

**4.** No **5.** No **6.** Answers will vary.

# Chapter 8

## Section 8.1 (page 424)

**1.** Two samples are dependent when each member of one sample corresponds to a member of the other sample. Example: The weights of 22 people before starting an exercise program and the weights of the same 22 people 6 weeks after starting the exercise program.
Two samples are independent when the sample selected from one population is not related to the sample selected from the other population. Example: The weights of 25 cats and the weights of 20 dogs.

**3.** Use *P*-values.

**5.** Dependent because the same football players were sampled.

**7.** Independent because different boats were sampled.

**9.** Reject $H_0$.

**11.** Reject $H_0$. There is enough evidence at the 1% level of significance to reject the claim.

**13.** Fail to reject $H_0$. There is not enough evidence at the 5% level of significance to support the claim.

**15.** (a) The claim is "the mean braking distances are different for the two categories of SUVs."
$H_0$: $\mu_1 = \mu_2$; $H_a$: $\mu_1 \neq \mu_2$ (claim)

(b) $-z_0 = -1.645$, $z_0 = 1.645$
Rejection region: $z < -1.645$, $z > 1.645$

(c) $-0.409$ (d) Fail to reject $H_0$.

(e) There is not enough evidence at the 10% level of significance to support the claim that the mean braking distances are different for the two categories of SUVs.

**17.** (a) The claim is "the wind speed in Region A is less than the wind speed in Region B."
$H_0$: $\mu_1 \geq \mu_2$; $H_a$: $\mu_1 < \mu_2$ (claim)

(b) $z_0 = -1.645$; Rejection region: $z < -1.645$

(c) $-1.94$ (d) Reject $H_0$.

(e) There is enough evidence at the 5% level of significance to support the claim that the wind speed in Region A is less than the wind speed in Region B.

**19.** (a) The claim is "ACT mathematics and science scores are equal."
$H_0$: $\mu_1 = \mu_2$ (claim); $H_a$: $\mu_1 \neq \mu_2$

(b) $-z_0 = -2.575$, $z_0 = 2.575$
Rejection region: $z < -2.575$, $z > 2.575$

(c) $-0.399$ (d) Fail to reject $H_0$.

(e) There is not enough evidence at the 1% level of significance to reject the claim that ACT mathematics and science scores are equal.

**21.** (a) The claim is "the mean home sales price in Casper, Wyoming, is the same as in Cheyenne, Wyoming."
$H_0$: $\mu_1 = \mu_2$ (claim); $H_a$: $\mu_1 \neq \mu_2$

(b) $-z_0 = -2.575$, $z_0 = 2.575$
Rejection region: $z < -2.575$, $z > 2.575$

(c) $-2.388$ (d) Fail to reject $H_0$.

(e) There is not enough evidence at the 1% level of significance to reject the claim that the mean home sales price in Casper, Wyoming, is the same as in Cheyenne, Wyoming.

**23.** (a) The claim is "the precipitation in Seattle, Washington, was greater than in Birmingham, Alabama."
$H_0$: $\mu_1 \le \mu_2$; $H_a$: $\mu_1 > \mu_2$ (claim)
(b) $z_0 = 1.645$; Rejection region: $z > 1.645$
(c) 1.019 (d) Fail to reject $H_0$.
(e) There is not enough evidence at the 5% level of significance to support the claim that the precipitation in Seattle, Washington, was greater than in Birmingham, Alabama.

**25.** They are equivalent through algebraic manipulation of the equation.
$\mu_1 = \mu_2 \Rightarrow \mu_1 - \mu_2 = 0$

**27.** $H_0$: $\mu_1 - \mu_2 \le 4000$; $H_a$: $\mu_1 - \mu_2 > 4000$ (claim)
Fail to reject $H_0$. There is not enough evidence at the 5% level of significance to support the claim that the difference between the mean annual salaries of entry level software engineers in Santa Clara, California and Greenwich, Connecticut is more than \$4000.

**29.** $\$1359 < \mu_1 - \mu_2 < \$13{,}241$

## Section 8.2 (page 432)

**1.** (1) The population standard deviations are unknown.
(2) The samples are randomly selected.
(3) The samples are independent.
(4) The populations are normally distributed or each sample size is at least 30.

**3.** (a) $-t_0 = -1.714$, $t_0 = 1.714$
(b) $-t_0 = -1.812$, $t_0 = 1.812$

**5.** (a) $t_0 = -1.746$ (b) $t_0 = -1.943$

**7.** (a) $t_0 = 1.729$ (b) $t_0 = 1.895$

**9.** Fail to reject $H_0$. There is not enough evidence at the 1% level of significance to reject the claim.

**11.** Reject $H_0$. There is enough evidence at the 5% level of significance to reject the claim.

**13.** (a) The claim is "the mean annual costs of food for dogs and cats are the same."
$H_0$: $\mu_1 = \mu_2$ (claim); $H_a$: $\mu_1 \ne \mu_2$
(b) $-t_0 = -1.694$, $t_0 = 1.694$
Rejection region: $t < -1.694$, $t > 1.694$
(c) 2.412 (d) Reject $H_0$.
(e) There is enough evidence at the 10% level of significance to reject the pet association's claim that the mean costs of food for dogs and cats are the same.

**15.** (a) The claim is "the stomachs of blue crabs from one location contain more fish than the stomachs of blue crabs from another location."
$H_0$: $\mu_1 \le \mu_2$; $H_a$: $\mu_1 > \mu_2$ (claim)
(b) $t_0 = 2.429$; Rejection region: $t > 2.429$
(c) 1.80 (d) Fail to reject $H_0$.
(e) There is not enough evidence at the 1% level of significance to support the claim that the stomachs of blue crabs from one location contain more fish than the stomachs of blue crabs from another location.

**17.** (a) The claim is "the mean household income in a recent year is greater in York County, South Carolina, than it is in Elmore County, Alabama."
$H_0$: $\mu_1 \le \mu_2$; $H_a$: $\mu_1 > \mu_2$ (claim)
(b) $t_0 = 1.734$; Rejection region: $t > 1.734$
(c) 0.849 (d) Fail to reject $H_0$.
(e) There is not enough evidence at the 5% level of significance to support the claim that the mean household income in a recent year is greater in York County, South Carolina, than it is in Elmore County, Alabama.

**19.** (a) The claim is "an experimental method makes a difference in the tensile strength of steel bars."
$H_0$: $\mu_1 = \mu_2$; $H_a$: $\mu_1 \ne \mu_2$ (claim)
(b) $-t_0 = -2.819$, $t_0 = 2.819$
Rejection regions: $t < -2.819$, $t > 2.819$
(c) $-2.64$ (d) Fail to reject $H_0$.
(e) There is not enough evidence at the 1% level of significance to support the claim that an experimental method makes a difference in the tensile strength of steel bars.

**21.** (a) The claim is "the new method of teaching reading produces higher reading test scores than the old method."
$H_0$: $\mu_1 \ge \mu_2$; $H_a$: $\mu_1 < \mu_2$ (claim)
(b) $t_0 = -1.303$; Rejection region: $t < -1.303$
(c) $-4.286$ (d) Reject $H_0$.
(e) There is enough evidence at the 10% level of significance to support the claim that the new method of teaching reading produces higher reading test scores than the old method.

**23.** $-11.1 < \mu_1 - \mu_2 < 12.1$ **25.** $-20.8 < \mu_1 - \mu_2 < 24.8$

## Section 8.3 (page 442)

**1.** (1) The samples are randomly selected.
(2) The samples are dependent.
(3) The populations are normally distributed or the number $n$ of pairs of data is at least 30.

**3.** Fail to reject $H_0$. There is not enough evidence at the 5% level of significance to support the claim.

**5.** Reject $H_0$. There is enough evidence at the 10% level of significance to reject the claim.

**7.** Reject $H_0$. There is enough evidence at the 1% level of significance to reject the claim.

**9.** (a) The claim is "injections of onabotulinumtoxinA reduce the number of days per month that chronic migraine sufferers have headaches."
$H_0$: $\mu_d \le 0$; $H_a$: $\mu_d > 0$ (claim)
(b) $t_0 = 2.567$; Rejection region: $t > 2.567$
(c) $\bar{d} \approx 13.33$; $s_d \approx 7.146$ (d) 7.914 (e) Reject $H_0$.
(f) There is enough evidence at the 1% level of significance to support the claim that injections of onabotulinumtoxinA reduce the number of days per month that chronic migraine sufferers have headaches.

**11.** (a) The claim is "an SAT preparation course will improve the test scores of students."
$H_0$: $\mu_d \geq 0$; $H_a$: $\mu_d < 0$ (claim)
(b) $t_0 = -2.821$; Rejection region: $t < -2.821$
(c) $\overline{d} = -60$; $s_d \approx 27.889$ (d) $-6.803$ (e) Reject $H_0$.
(f) There is enough evidence at the 1% level of significance to support the SAT preparation course's claim that its course will improve the test scores of students.

**13.** (a) The claim is "a baseball clinic will help players raise their batting averages."
$H_0$: $\mu_d \geq 0$; $H_a$: $\mu_d < 0$ (claim)
(b) $t_0 = -1.771$; Rejection region: $t < -1.771$
(c) $\overline{d} \approx -0.002$; $s_d \approx 0.015$
(d) $-0.499$ (e) Fail to reject $H_0$.
(f) There is not enough evidence at the 5% level of significance to support the claim that the baseball clinic will help players raise their batting averages.

**15.** (a) The claim is "U.S. gasoline prices increased from May to June of 2021."
$H_0$: $\mu_d \geq 0$; $H_a$: $\mu_d < 0$ (claim)
(b) $t_0 = -3.106$; Rejection region: $t < -3.106$
(c) $\overline{d} \approx -0.029$; $s_d \approx 0.0303$ (d) $-3.315$
(e) Reject $H_0$.
(f) There is enough evidence at the 0.5% level of significance to support the claim that U.S. gasoline prices increased from May to June of 2021.

**17.** (a) The claim is "the product ratings have changed from last year to this year."
$H_0$: $\mu_d = 0$; $H_a$: $\mu_d \neq 0$ (claim)
(b) $-t_0 = -2.365$, $t_0 = 2.365$
Rejection regions: $t < -2.365$, $t > 2.365$
(c) $\overline{d} = -1$; $s_d \approx 1.309$ (d) $-2.161$ (*Tech:* $-2.160$)
(e) Fail to reject $H_0$.
(f) There is not enough evidence at the 5% level of significance to support the claim that the product ratings have changed from last year to this year.

**19.** (a) The claim is "eating a new cereal as part of a daily diet lowers total blood cholesterol levels."
$H_0$: $\mu_d \leq 0$; $H_a$: $\mu_d > 0$ (claim)
(b) $t_0 = 1.943$; Rejection region: $t > 1.943$
(c) $\overline{d} \approx 2.857$; $s_d \approx 4.451$ (d) 1.698
(e) Fail to reject $H_0$.
(f) There is not enough evidence at the 5% level of significance to support the claim that the new cereal lowers total blood cholesterol levels.

**21.** Yes. $P \approx 0.0058 < 0.05$, so you reject $H_0$.

**23.** $-1.76 < \mu_d < -1.29$

## Section 8.4 (page 451)

**1.** (1) The samples are randomly selected.
(2) The samples are independent.
(3) $n_1\overline{p} \geq 5$, $n_1\overline{q} \geq 5$, $n_2\overline{p} \geq 5$, and $n_2\overline{q} \geq 5$

**3.** Can use normal sampling distribution. Fail to reject $H_0$. There is not enough evidence at the 1% level of significance to support the claim.

**5.** Can use normal sampling distribution. Reject $H_0$. There is enough evidence at the 10% level of significance to reject the claim.

**7.** (a) The claim is "there is a difference in the proportion of subjects who had no 12-week confirmed disability progression."
$H_0$: $p_1 = p_2$; $H_a$: $p_1 \neq p_2$ (claim)
(b) $-z_0 = -2.575$, $z_0 = 2.575$
Rejection regions: $z < -2.575$, $z > 2.575$
(c) $-1.70$ (d) Fail to reject $H_0$.
(e) There is not enough evidence at the 1% level of significance to support the claim that there is a difference in the proportion of subjects who had no 12-week confirmed disability progression.

**9.** (a) The claim is "there is a difference in the proportion of those employed between the two groups."
$H_0$: $p_1 = p_2$; $H_a$: $p_1 \neq p_2$ (claim)
(b) $-z_0 = -2.575$, $z_0 = 2.575$
Rejection region: $z < -2.575$, $z > 2.575$
(c) $-5.821$ (d) Reject $H_0$.
(e) There is enough evidence at the 1% level of significance to support the claim there is a difference in the proportion of those employed between the two groups.

**11.** (a) The claim is "the proportion of drivers who wear seat belts is greater in the West than in the Northeast."
$H_0$: $p_1 \leq p_2$; $H_a$: $p_1 > p_2$ (claim)
(b) $z_0 = 1.645$; Rejection region: $z > 1.645$
(c) 2.08 (d) Reject $H_0$.
(e) There is enough evidence at the 5% level of significance to support the claim that the proportion of drivers who wear seat belts is greater in the West than in the Northeast.

**13.** No, there is not enough evidence at the 10% level of significance to reject the claim that the proportion of 18- to 24-year-olds who benefit mentally from exercising in parks is the same as the proportion who benefit mentally from socializing in parks.

**15.** Yes, there is enough evidence at the 10% level of significance to support the claim that the proportion of 18- to 24-year-olds who benefit mentally from socializing in parks is greater than the proportion who benefit mentally from enjoying nature in parks.

**17.** Yes, there is enough evidence at the 1% level of significance to support the claim that the proportion of 18- to 24-year-olds who benefit mentally from enjoying nature in parks is less than the proportion who benefit mentally from exercising in parks.

**19.** Yes, there is enough evidence at the 1% level of significance to support the claim that the proportion of men who work is greater than the proportion of men who socialize and communicate on an average day.

**21.** Yes, there is enough evidence at the 1% level of significance to support the claim that the proportion of women who work is less than the proportion of men who work on an average day.

**23.** $-0.0178 < p_1 - p_2 < -0.0022$

**25.** $0.0638 < p_1 - p_2 < 0.1362$. Answers will vary.

## Uses and Abuses for Chapter 8 (page 454)

1. Answers will vary.
2. Blind: The patients do not know which group (medicine or placebo) they belong to.
Double-blind: Both the researcher and patient do not know which group (medicine or placebo) that the patient belongs to.

## Review Exercises for Chapter 8 (page 456)

1. Dependent because the same children were sampled.
3. Independent because different vehicles were sampled.
5. Fail to reject $H_0$. There is not enough evidence at the 5% level of significance to reject the claim.
7. Reject $H_0$. There is enough evidence at the 10% level of significance to support the claim.
9. (a) The claim is "the mean sodium content of chicken sandwiches at Restaurant A is less than the mean sodium content of chicken sandwiches at Restaurant B."
$H_0$: $\mu_1 \geq \mu_2$; $H_a$: $\mu_1 < \mu_2$ (claim)
(b) $z_0 = -1.645$; Rejection region: $z < -1.645$
(c) $-2.82$ (d) Reject $H_0$.
(e) There is enough evidence at the 5% level of significance to support the researcher's claim that the mean sodium content of chicken sandwiches at Restaurant A is less than the mean sodium content of chicken sandwiches at Restaurant B.
11. Reject $H_0$. There is enough evidence at the 5% level of significance to reject the claim.
13. Fail to reject $H_0$. There is not enough evidence at the 10% level of significance to reject the claim.
15. Reject $H_0$. There is enough evidence at the 1% level of significance to support the claim.
17. (a) The claim is "the new method of teaching mathematics produces higher mathematics test scores than the old method does."
$H_0$: $\mu_1 \leq \mu_2$; $H_a$: $\mu_1 > \mu_2$ (claim)
(b) $t_0 = 1.667$; Rejection region: $t > 1.667$
(c) 2.313 (d) Reject $H_0$.
(e) There is enough evidence at the 5% level of significance to support the claim that the new method of teaching mathematics produces higher mathematics test scores than the old method does.
19. Reject $H_0$. There is enough evidence at the 1% level of significance to reject the claim.
21. Reject $H_0$. There is enough evidence at the 10% level of significance to reject the claim.
23. (a) The claim is "the numbers of runs scored in a season by NCAA Division 1 baseball teams changed from 2019 to 2021."
$H_0$: $\mu_d = 0$; $H_a$: $\mu_d \neq 0$ (claim)
(b) $-t_0 = -2.262$, $t_0 = 2.262$
Rejection region: $z < -2.262$, $z > 2.262$
(c) $\bar{d} = 38.1$; $s_d \approx 66.10$ (d) 1.823
(e) Fail to reject $H_0$.
(f) There is not enough evidence at the 5% level of significance to support the claim that the numbers of runs scored in a season by NCAA Division 1 baseball teams changed from 2019 to 2021.
25. Can use normal sampling distribution. Fail to reject $H_0$. There is not enough evidence at the 5% level of significance to reject the claim.
27. Can use normal sampling distribution. Reject $H_0$. There is enough evidence at the 10% level of significance to support the claim.
29. (a) The claim is "the proportion of subjects who had at least 24 weeks of accrued remission is the same for the two groups."
$H_0$: $p_1 = p_2$ (claim); $H_a$: $p_1 \neq p_2$
(b) $-z_0 = -1.96$, $z_0 = 1.96$
Rejection regions: $z < -1.96$, $z > 1.96$
(c) 4.03 (d) Reject $H_0$.
(e) There is enough evidence at the 5% level of significance to reject the medical research team's claim that the proportion of subjects who had at least 24 weeks of accrued remission is the same for the two groups.

## Quiz for Chapter 8 (page 460)

1. (a) The claim is "the mean score on the reading assessment test for male high school students is less than the mean score for female high school students"
$H_0$: $\mu_1 \geq \mu_2$; $H_a$: $\mu_1 < \mu_2$ (claim)
(b) Left-tailed because $H_a$ contains $<$; $z$-test because $\sigma_1$ and $\sigma_2$ are known, the samples are random samples, samples are independent, and $n_1 \geq 30$ and $n_2 \geq 30$.
(c) $z_0 = -1.645$; Rejection region: $z < -1.645$
(d) $-1.616$ (e) Fail to reject $H_0$.
(f) There is not enough evidence at the 5% level of significance to support the claim that the mean score on the reading assessment test for male high school students is less than the mean score for female high school students.
2. (a) The claim is "the mean scores on a music assessment test for eighth grade students in public and private schools are equal."
$H_0$: $\mu_1 = \mu_2$ (claim); $H_a$: $\mu_1 \neq \mu_2$
(b) Two-tailed because $H_a$ contains $\neq$; $t$-test because $\sigma_1$ and $\sigma_2$ are unknown, the samples are random samples, the samples are independent, and the populations are normally distributed.
(c) $-t_0 = -1.706$, $t_0 = 1.706$
Rejection region: $t < -1.706$, $t > 1.706$
(d) $-0.814$ (e) Fail to reject $H_0$.
(f) There is not enough evidence at the 10% level of significance to reject the claim that the mean scores on a music assessment test for eighth grade students in public and private schools are equal.
3. (a) The claim is "the seminar helps adults increase their credit scores."
$H_0$: $\mu_d \geq 0$; $H_a$: $\mu_d < 0$ (claim)

(b) Left-tailed because $H_a$ contains $<$; $t$-test because both populations are normally distributed and the samples are dependent.
(c) $t_0 = -2.718$; Rejection region: $t < -2.718$
(d) $-5.07$ (e) Reject $H_0$.
(f) There is enough evidence at the 1% level of significance to support the claim that the seminar helps adults increase their credit scores.

4. (a) The claim is "the proportion of U.S. adults who approve of the job the Supreme Court is doing is greater than it was 3 years prior."
$H_0$: $p_1 \leq p_2$; $H_a$: $p_1 > p_2$ (claim)
(b) Right-tailed because $H_a$ contains $>$; $z$-test because you are testing proportions, the samples are random, samples are independent, and $n_1\bar{p}$, $n_2\bar{p}$, $n_1\bar{q}$, and $n_2\bar{q}$ are at least 5.
(c) $z_0 = 1.645$; Rejection region: $z > 1.645$
(d) 4.051 (e) Reject $H_0$.
(f) There is not enough evidence at the 5% level of significance to support the claim that the proportion of U.S. adults who approve of the job the Supreme Court is doing is greater than it was 3 years prior.

## Real Statistics—Real Decisions for Chapter 8 (page 462)

1. (a) *Sample answer:* Divide the records into groups according to the inpatients' ages, and then randomly select records from each group.
(b) *Sample answer:* Divide the records into groups according to geographic regions, and then randomly select records from each group.
(c) *Sample answer:* Assign a different number to each record, randomly choose a starting number, and then select every 50th record.
(d) *Sample answer:* Assign a different number to each record, and then use a table of random numbers to generate a sample of numbers.
2. (a)–(b) Answers will vary.
3. Use a $t$-test. Independent. Yes, you need to know if the population distributions are normal or not; yes, you need to know if the population variances are equal or not.
4. There is enough evidence at the 5% level of significance to support the claim that there is a difference in the mean length of hospital stays for inpatients.
This decision supports the claim.

## Cumulative Review for Chapters 6–8 (page 466)

1. (a) (0.758, 0.782)
(b) There is enough evidence at the 5% level of significance to support the claim that more than 75% of U.S. adults say they would date or have already dated someone whose religion was different from theirs.
2. There is enough evidence at the 10% level of significance to support the claim that the fuel additive improved gas mileage.
3. (25.94, 28.00); $z$-distribution
4. (2.59, 4.33); $t$-distribution
5. (10.7, 13.5); $t$-distribution
6. (7.85, 8.57); $z$-distribution
7. $H_0$: $\mu \geq 33$; $H_a$: $\mu < 33$ (claim)
8. $H_0$: $p \geq 0.19$ (claim); $H_a$: $p < 0.19$
9. $H_0$: $\sigma = 0.63$ (claim); $H_a$: $\sigma \neq 0.63$
10. $H_0$: $\mu = 2.28$; $H_a$: $\mu \neq 2.28$ (claim)
11. There is enough evidence at the 10% level of significance to support the pediatrician's claim that the mean birth weight of a single-birth baby is greater than the mean birth weight of a baby that has a twin.
12. (a) (511.95, 2283.75) (b) (22.63, 47.79)
(c) There is not enough evidence at the 1% level of significance to reject the travel analyst's claim that the standard deviation of the mean room rate for two adults at three-star hotels in Cincinnati is at most $30.
13. There is enough evidence at the 5% level of significance to support the organization's claim that the mean SAT scores for male athletes and male non-athletes at a college are different.
14. (a) (54,793.65, 61,542.41)
(b) There is not enough evidence at the 5% level of significance to reject the claim that the mean annual earnings for locksmiths is $55,000.
15. There is enough evidence at the 10% level of significance to support the medical research team's claim that the proportion of monthly convulsive seizure reduction is greater for the group that received the extract than for the group that received the placebo.
16. (a) (41.5, 42.5)
(b) There is enough evidence at the 5% level of significance to reject the zoologist's claim that the mean incubation period for ostriches is at least 45 days.
17. A type I error will occur when the actual proportion of people who purchase their eyeglasses online is 0.05, but you reject $H_0$. A type II error will occur when the actual proportion of people who purchase their eyeglasses online is different from 0.05, but you fail to reject $H_0$.

# Chapter 9

## Section 9.1 (page 481)

1. Increase. Decrease
3. The sample correlation coefficient $r$ measures the strength and direction of a linear relationship between two variables; $r = -0.932$ indicates a stronger correlation because $|-0.932| = 0.932$ is closer to 1 than $|0.918| = 0.918$.
5. A table can be used to compare $r$ with a critical value, or a hypothesis test can be performed using a $t$-test.
7. $H_0$: $\rho = 0$ (no significant correlation)
$H_a$: $\rho \neq 0$ (significant correlation)
Reject the null hypothesis if $t$ is in the rejection region.
9. Explanatory variable: Amount of water consumed
Response variable: Weight loss
11. Strong negative linear correlation
13. No linear correlation
15. c. You would expect a positive linear correlation between age and income.

**16.** d. You would not expect age and height to be correlated.

**17.** b. You would expect a negative linear correlation between age and balance on student loans.

**18.** a. You would expect the relationship between age and body temperature to be fairly constant.

**19.** *Sample answer:* People who can afford more valuable homes will live longer because they have more money to take care of themselves.

**21.** *Sample answer:* Ice cream sales are higher when the weather is warm and people are outside more often. This is when homicide rates go up as well.

**23.** (a)

(b) 0.979

(c) Strong positive correlation. As age increases, the number of words in children's vocabulary tends to increase.

(d) There is enough evidence at the 1% level of significance to conclude that there is a significant linear correlation between children's ages and number of words in their vocabulary.

**25.** (a)

(b) 0.756

(c) Strong positive linear correlation. As the maximum weight for one repetition of a half squat increases, the jump height tends to increase.

(d) There is enough evidence at the 1% level of significance to conclude that there is a significant linear correlation between maximum weight for one repetition of a half squat and jump height.

**27.** (a)

(b) 0.7257

(c) Strong positive linear correlation. As the earnings per share increase, the dividends per share tend to increase.

(d) There is not enough evidence at the 1% level of significance to conclude that there is a significant linear correlation between earnings per share for the companies and their dividends per share.

**29.** The correlation coefficient gets weaker, going from $r \approx 0.979$ to $r \approx 0.863$.

**31.** The correlation coefficient gets stronger, going from $r \approx 0.756$ to $r \approx 0.908$.

**33.** There is not enough evidence at the 1% level of significance to conclude that there is a significant linear correlation between vehicle weight and the variability in braking distance on a dry surface.

**35.** There is enough evidence at the 5% level of significance to conclude that there is a significant linear correlation between the maximum weight for one repetition of a half squat and the jump height.

**37.** $r \approx -0.975$. The correlation coefficient remains unchanged when the $x$-values and $y$-values are switched.

## Section 9.1 Activity (page 485)

**1–4.** Answers will vary.

## Section 9.2 (page 490)

**1.** A residual is the difference between the observed $y$-value of a data point and the predicted $y$-value on the regression line for the $x$-coordinate of the data point. A residual is positive when the data point is above the line, negative when the point is below the line, and zero when the observed $y$-value equals the predicted $y$-value.

**3.** Substitute a value of $x$ into the equation of a regression line and solve for $\hat{y}$.

**5.** The correlation between variables must be significant.

**7.** b **8.** a **9.** e **10.** c **11.** f

**12.** d **13.** b **14.** c **15.** d **16.** a

**17.** $\hat{y} = 0.092x - 18.834$

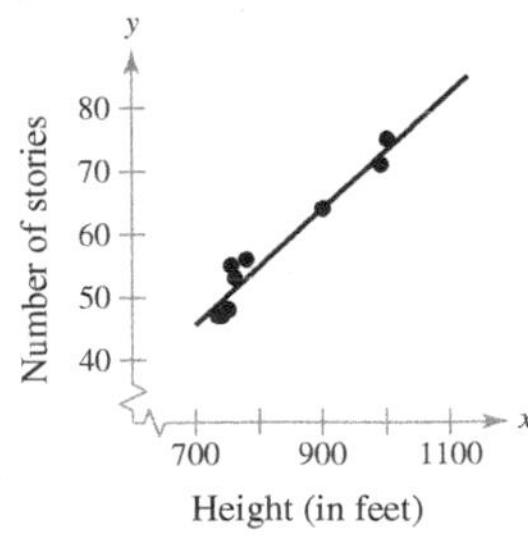


(a) 69 stories (b) 59 stories (c) 55 stories

(d) It is not meaningful to predict the value of $y$ for $x = 650$ feet because $x = 650$ feet is outside the range of the original data.

**19.** $\hat{y} = 7.451x + 37.449$

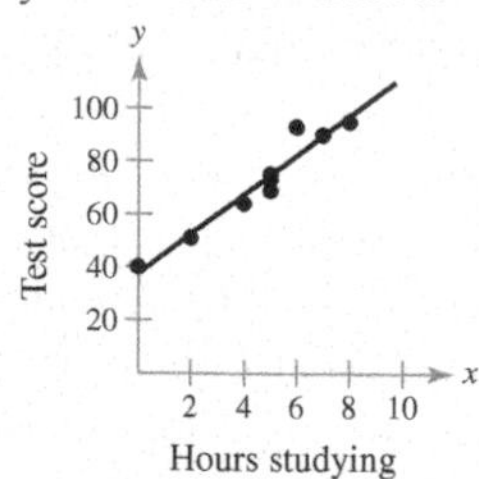


(a) 60 (b) 86
(c) It is not meaningful to predict the value of $y$ for $x = 13$ because $x = 13$ is outside the range of the original data.
(d) 71

**21.** $\hat{y} = -2.044x + 520.668$

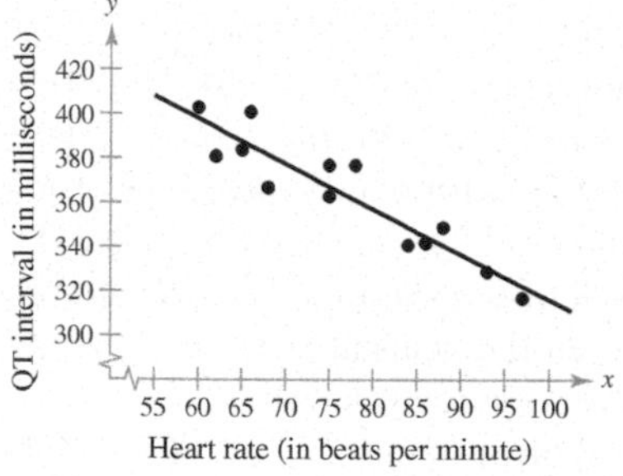


(a) It is not meaningful to predict the value of $y$ for $x = 120$ because $x = 120$ is outside the range of the original data.
(b) 384 milliseconds (c) 337 milliseconds
(d) 351 milliseconds

**23.** $\hat{y} = 2.979x + 52.476$

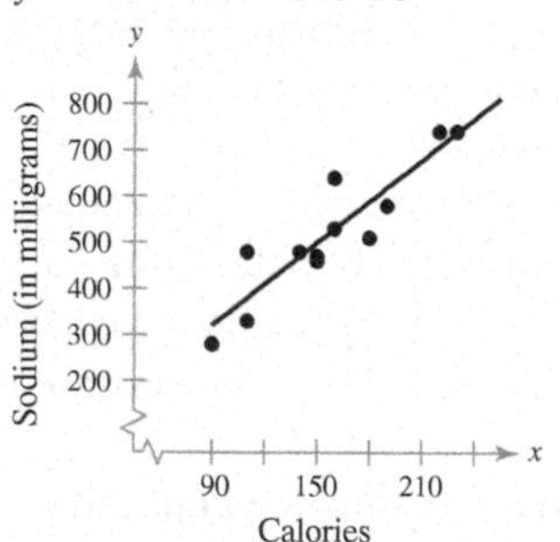


(a) 559 milligrams (b) 350 milligrams
(c) It is not meaningful to predict the value of $y$ for $x = 260$ because $x = 260$ is outside the range of the original data.
(d) 678 milligrams

**25.** $\hat{y} = 1.870x + 51.360$

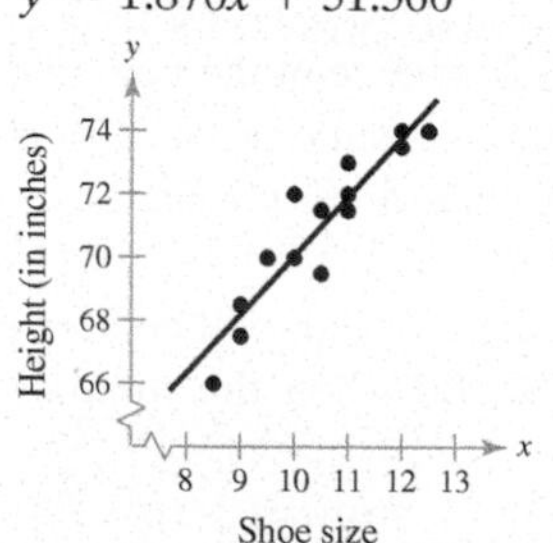


(a) 72.865 inches (b) 66.320 inches
(c) It is not meaningful to predict the value of $y$ for $x = 15.5$ because $x = 15.5$ is outside the range of the original data.
(d) 70.060 inches

**27.** Strong positive linear correlation. As the years of experience of the registered nurses increase, their salaries tend to increase.

**29.** No, it is not meaningful to predict a salary for a registered nurse with 28 years of experience because $x = 28$ is outside the range of the original data.

**31.** (a) $\hat{y} = -4.297x + 94.200$

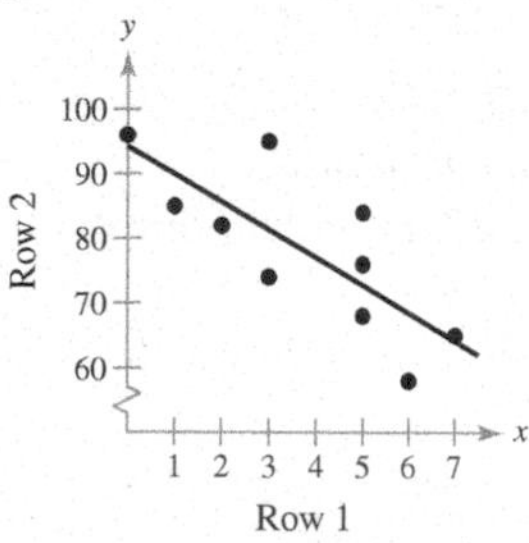


(b) $\hat{y} = -0.141x + 14.763$

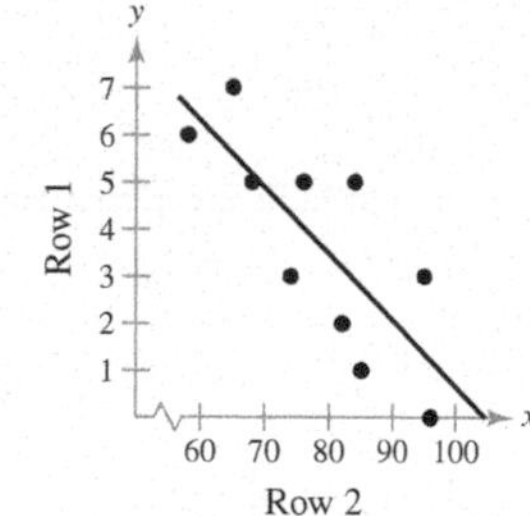


(c) The slope of the line keeps the same sign, but the values of $m$ and $b$ change.

**33.** (a) $\hat{y} = 0.139x + 21.024$

(b)

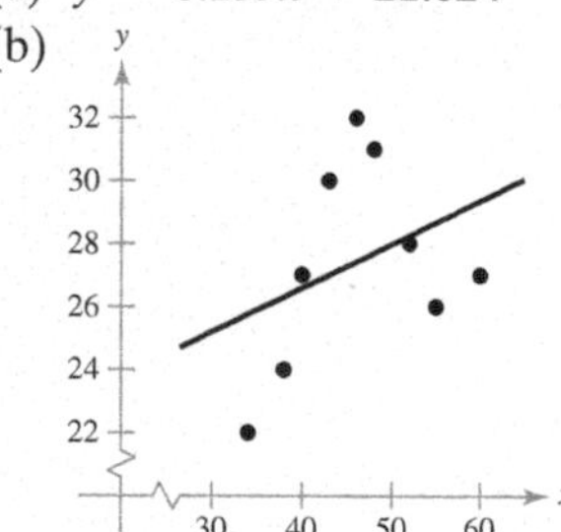

(c) Residual

(d) The residual plot shows a pattern because the residuals do not fluctuate about 0. This implies that the regression line is not a good representation of the relationship between the two variables.

**35.** (a)

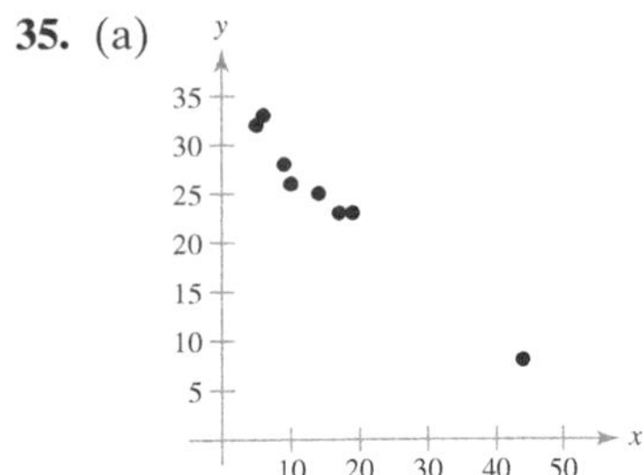


(b) The point (44, 8) may be an outlier.

(c) The point (44, 8) is not an influential point because the slopes and $y$-intercepts of the regression lines with the point included and without the point included are not significantly different.

**37.** $\hat{y} = 654.536x - 1214.857$

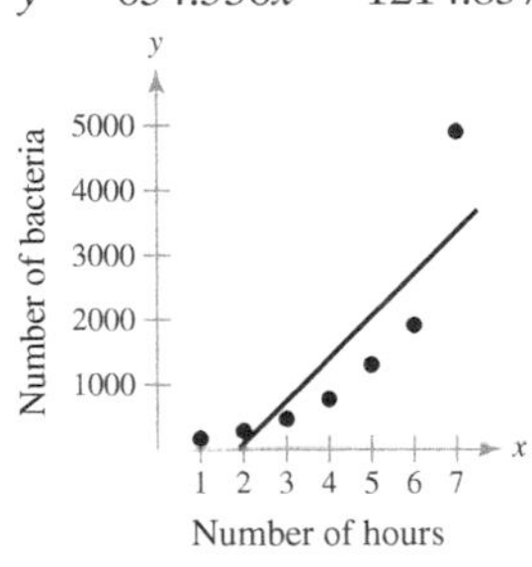


**39.** $y = 93.028(1.712)^x$

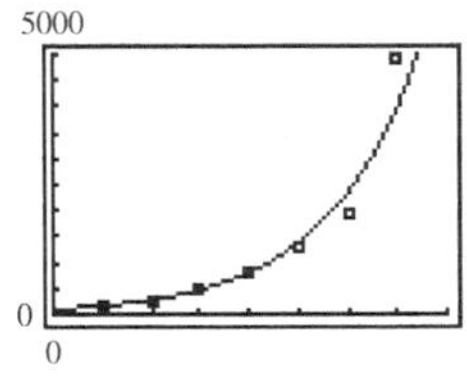


**41.** $\hat{y} = -78.929x + 576.179$

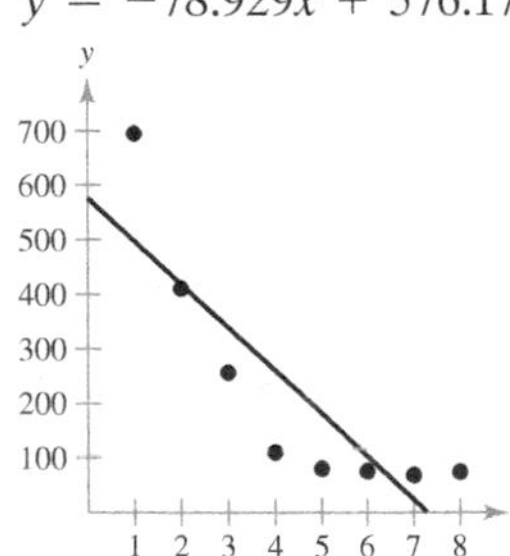


**43.** $y = 782.300x^{-1.251}$

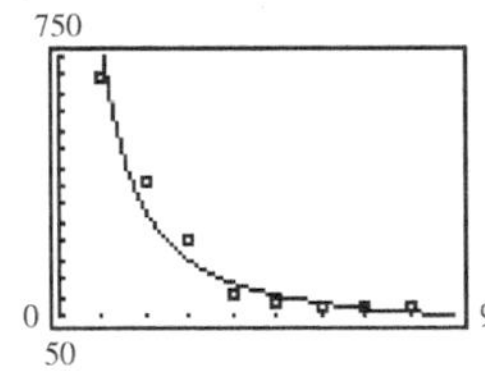


**45.** $y = 25.035 + 19.599 \ln x$

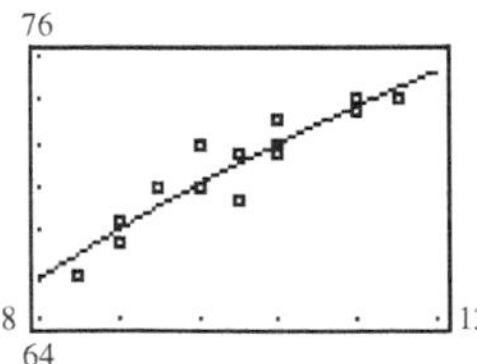


**47.** The logarithmic equation is a better model for the data. The graph of the logarithmic equation fits the data better than the regression line.

## Section 9.2 Activity (page 496)

**1–4.** Answers will vary.

## Section 9.3 (page 504)

**1.** The total variation is the sum of the squares of the differences between the $y$-values of each ordered pair and the mean of the $y$-values of the ordered pairs, or $\Sigma(y_i - \bar{y})^2$.

**3.** The unexplained variation is the sum of the squares of the differences between the observed $y$-values and the predicted $y$-values, or $\Sigma(y_i - \hat{y}_i)^2$.

**5.** Two variables that have perfect positive or perfect negative linear correlation have a correlation coefficient of 1 or $-1$, respectively. In either case, the coefficient of determination is 1, which means that 100% of the variation in the response variable is explained by the variation in the explanatory variable.

**7.** 0.216. About 21.6% of the variation is explained. About 78.4% of the variation is unexplained.

**9.** 0.916. About 91.6% of the variation is explained. About 8.4% of the variation is unexplained.

**11.** (a) 0.592. About 59.2% of the variation is explained by the relationship between the number of offerings and proceeds and about 40.8% of the variation is unexplained.

(b) 9270.785. The standard error of estimate of the proceeds for a specific number of offerings is about 9,270,785,000.

**13.** (a) 0.764. About 76.4% of the variation is explained by the relationship between the goals allowed and points and about 23.6% of the variation is unexplained.

(b) 6.593. The standard error of estimate of the points for a specific number of goals allowed is about 6.593.

**15.** (a) 0.845. About 84.5% of the variation is explained by the relationship between the percentage of employment in STEM occupations and mean annual wage and about 15.5% of the variation is unexplained.

(b) 4.427. The standard error of estimate of the mean annual wage for a specific percentage of employment in STEM occupations is about $4427.

**17.** (a) 0.902. About 90.2% of the variation is explained by the relationship between the marketed productions of natural gas in the U.S. and the exports of natural gas from the U.S. and about 9.8% of the variation is unexplained.

(b) 488.612. The standard error of estimate of the exports of natural gas for a specific marketed production of natural gas is about 488,612,000,000 cubic feet.

**19.** (a) 0.700. About 70% of the variation is explained by the relationship between the new vehicle sales of Ford and General Motors and about 30% of the variation is unexplained.

(b) 199.143. The standard error of estimate of the new vehicle sales of General Motors for a specific amount of new vehicle sales of Ford is about 199,143 new vehicles.

**21.** $25{,}681.536 < y < 73{,}259.544$

You can be 95% confident that the proceeds will be between $25,681,536,000 and $73,259,544,000 when the number of initial offerings is 200 issues.

**23.** $62.72 < y < 87.99$

You can be 90% confident that the total points earned will be between 63 and 88 when the number of goals allowed is 140.

25. $83.332 < y < 111.788$
You can be 99% confident that the mean annual wage will be between \$83,332 and \$111,788 when the percentage of employment in STEM occupations is 13% in the industry.

27. $1714.764 < y < 4402.104$
You can be 95% confident that the export of natural gas from the United States will be between 1,714,764,000,000 and 4,402,104,000,000 cubic feet when the production of natural gas in the United States is 31 trillion cubic feet.

29. $2060.436 < y < 3015.384$
You can be 95% confident that the new vehicle sales of General Motors will be between 2,060,436 and 3,015,384 when the new vehicle sales of Ford are 2,028,000.

31.

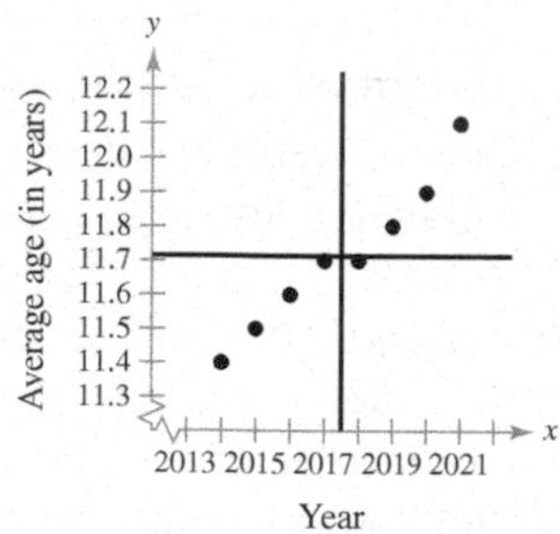


33. 0.960. About 96.0% of the variation in the average age of vehicles can be explained by the relationship between the year and the average age of vehicles and about 4% of the variation is unexplained.

35. Fail to reject $H_0$. There is not enough evidence at the 1% level of significance to support the claim that there is a linear relationship between weight and number of hours slept.

37. $-199.553 < B < 288.879$; $102.795 < M < 272.526$

## Section 9.4 (page 512)

1. The predicted $y$-value, $\hat{y}$, will change by $-8.2$ when the variable $x_2$ is changed by one unit and $x_1$ and $x_3$ are held constant.
3. (a) 18,832.7 pounds per acre
(b) 18,016.4 pounds per acre
(c) 17,350.6 pounds per acre
(d) 16,190.3 pounds per acre
5. (a) 7.5 cubic feet
(b) 16.8 cubic feet
(c) 51.9 cubic feet
(d) 62.1 cubic feet
7. (a) $\hat{y} = 27{,}641.224 - 1597.534x_1 - 80.171x_2$
(b) 1915.046 (c) 0.860
The standard error of estimate of the predicted price given specific age and mileage of pre-owned Honda Civic sedans is about \$1915.05. The multiple regression model explains about 86.0% of the variation.
9. 0.838

## Uses and Abuses for Chapter 9 (page 514)

1–2. Answers will vary.

## Review Exercises for Chapter 9 (page 516)

1. (a)

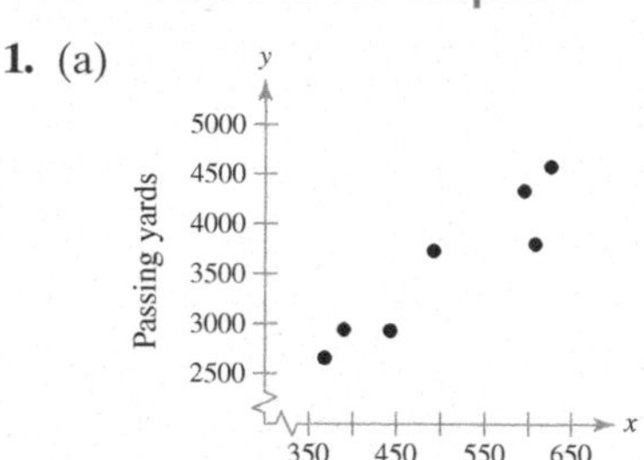


(b) 0.937
(c) Strong positive linear correlation. As the number of pass attempts increase, the number of passing yards tends to increase.

3. (a)

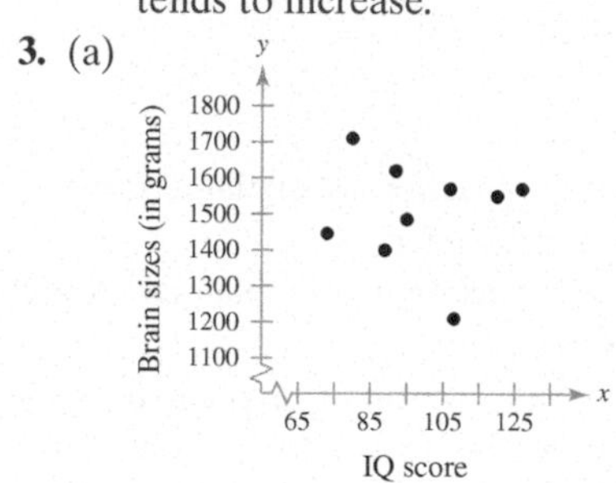


(b) $-0.068$
(c) No linear correlation. The IQ does not appear to be related to brain size.

5. There is enough evidence at the 5% level of significance to conclude that there is a significant linear correlation between a quarterback's pass attempts and passing yards.
7. There is not enough evidence at the 1% level of significance to conclude that there is a significant linear correlation between the IQ scores and brain sizes.
9. $\hat{y} = 0.097x - 695.161$

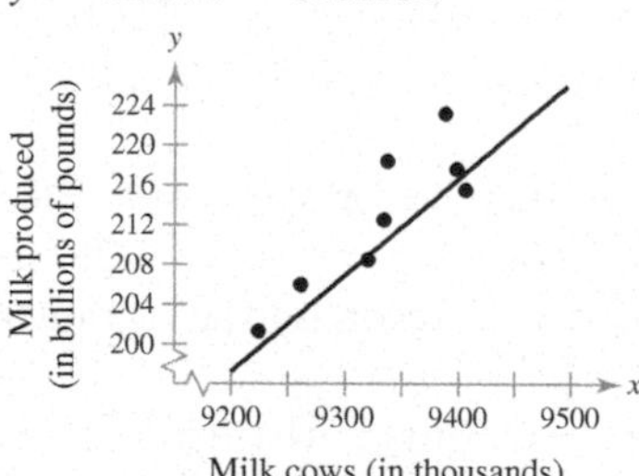


(a) It is not meaningful to predict the value of $y$ for $x = 9080$ because $x = 9080$ is outside the range of the original data.
(b) 202.806 billions of pounds
(c) 213.507 billions of pounds
(d) 219.345 billions of pounds

11. $\hat{y} = -0.086x + 10.450$

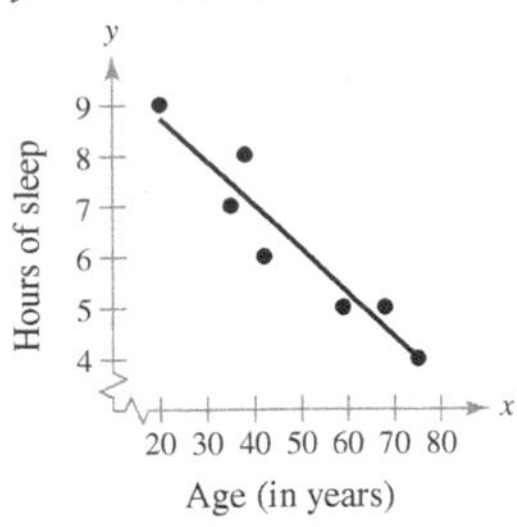


(a) It is not meaningful to predict the value of $y$ when $x = 16$ because $x = 16$ is outside the range of the original data.
(b) 8.3 hours
(c) It is not meaningful to predict the value of $y$ when $x = 85$ because $x = 85$ is outside the range of the original data.
(d) 6.15 hours

13. 0.203. About 20.3% of the variation is explained. About 79.7% of the variation is unexplained.

15. 0.412. About 41.2% of the variation is explained. About 58.8% of the variation is unexplained.

17. (a) 0.876. About 87.6% of the variation is explained by the relationship between the time to accelerate from 0 to 60 miles per hour and top speed for electric cars and about 12.4% of the variation is unexplained.
(b) 9.411. The standard error of estimate of the top speed for a specific time to accelerate from 0 to 60 miles per hour is about 9.411 miles per hour.

19. $196.393 < y < 212.635$
You can be 90% confident that the total amount of milk produced will be between 196.393 billion pounds and 212.635 billion pounds when the average number of cows is 9275.

21. $4.866 < y < 8.294$
You can be 95% confident that the hours slept will be between 4.866 and 8.294 hours for an adult who is 45 years old.

23. $73.727 < y < 150.357$
You can be 99% confident that the top speed of an electric car will be between 73.727 miles per hour and 150.357 miles per hour when it has a time of 5.9 seconds to accelerate from 0 to 60 miles per hour.

25. (a) $\hat{y} = 1.639 + 3.469x_1 - 32.326x_2$ (b) 0.838
(c) 0.943
The standard error of estimate of the carbon monoxide content given specific contents of tar and nicotine is about 0.838 milligram. The multiple regression model explains about 94.3% of the variation.

27. (a) 21.705 miles per gallon
(b) 25.21 miles per gallon
(c) 30.1 miles per gallon
(d) 25.86 miles per gallon

## Quiz for Chapter 9 (page 520)

1. The data appear to have a positive linear correlation. As $x$ increases, $y$ tends to increase.

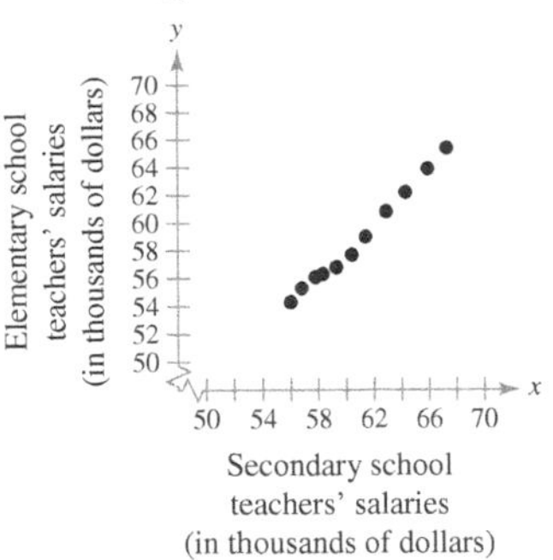


2. 0.995. Strong positive linear correlation. As the average annual salaries of secondary school teachers increase, the average annual salaries of elementary school teachers tend to increase.

3. Reject $H_0$. There is enough evidence at the 5% level of significance to conclude that there is a significant linear correlation between the average annual salaries of secondary school teachers and the average annual salaries of elementary school teachers.

4. $\hat{y} = 0.976x - 0.604$

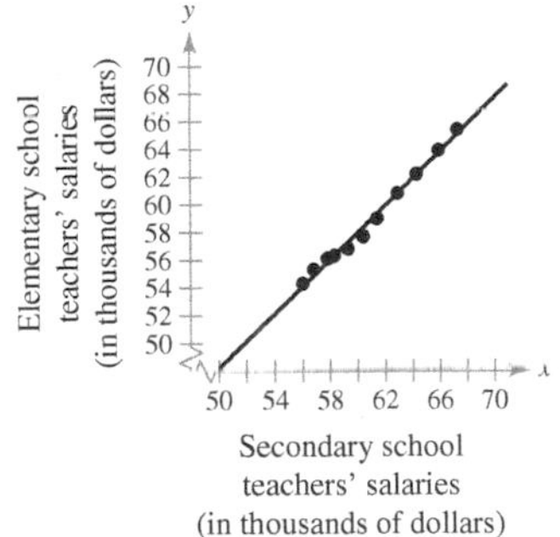


5. $61,372

6. 0.991. About 99.1% of the variation in the average annual salaries of elementary school teachers can be explained by the relationship between the average annual salary of secondary school teachers and elementary school teachers and about 0.9% of the variation is unexplained.

7. 0.372. The standard error of estimate of the average annual salaries of elementary school teachers for a specific average annual salary of secondary school teachers is about $372.

8. $60.486 < y < 62.283$
You can be 95% confident that the average annual salary of elementary school teachers will be between $60,486 and $62,283 when the average annual salary of secondary school teachers is $63,500.

9. (a) $95.26 (b) $70.28 (c) $67.74 (d) $59.46

## Real Statistics—Real Decisions for Chapter 9 (page 522)

1. (a) The data appear to have a positive linear correlation. As the annual average of the daily maximum sulfur dioxide concentration increases, the annual average of the daily maximum nitrogen dioxide concentration tends to increase.

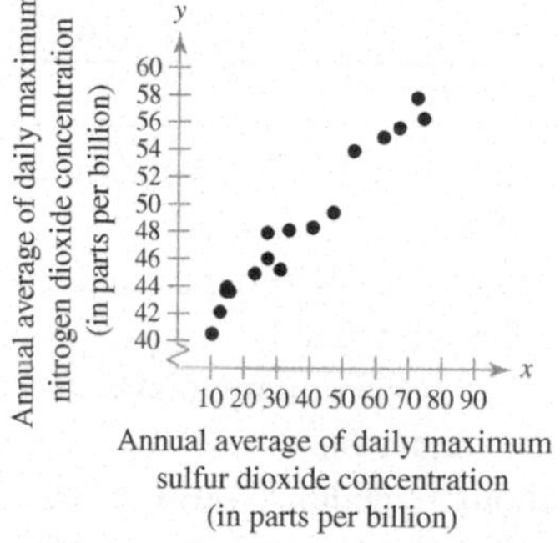


(b) 0.980. There is a strong positive linear correlation.

(c) There is enough evidence at the 5% level of significance to conclude that there is a significant linear correlation between annual averages of the daily maximum concentrations of sulfur dioxide and nitrogen dioxide.

(d) $\hat{y} = 0.242x + 39.403$

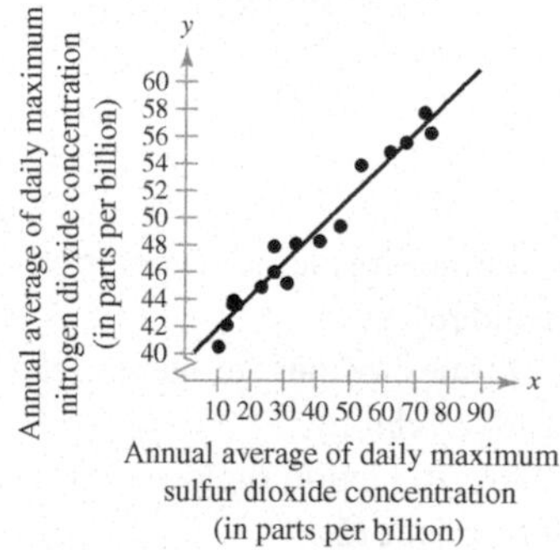


(e) Yes, for $x$-values that are within the range of the data set.

(f) $r^2 \approx 0.961$. About 96.1% of the variation in nitrogen dioxide concentrations can be explained by the variation in sulfur dioxide concentrations, and about 3.9% of the variation is unexplained.

$s_e \approx 1.106$. The standard error of estimate of the annual averages of the daily maximum concentration of nitrogen dioxide for a specififc annual average of the daily maximum concentration of sulfur dioxide is about 1.106 parts per billion.

2. $43.742 < y < 48.616$

You can be 95% confident that the annual average of the daily maximum nitrogen dioxide concentration will be between 43.742 and 48.616 parts per billion when the annual average of the daily maximum sulfur dioxide concentration is 28 parts per billion.

# Chapter 10

## Section 10.1 (page 532)

1. A multinomial experiment is a probability experiment consisting of a fixed number of independent trials in which there are more than two possible outcomes for each trial. The probability of each outcome is fixed, and each outcome is classified into categories.

3. 45 **5.** 57.5

7. (a) $H_0$: The distribution of the ages of moviegoers is 15% ages 2–11, 11% ages 12–17, 11% ages 18–24, 25% ages 25–39, 13% ages 40–49, and 25% ages 50+. (claim)

$H_a$: The distribution of ages differs from the expected distribution.

(b) $\chi_0^2 = 9.236$; Rejection region: $\chi^2 > 9.236$

(c) 7.295 (d) Fail to reject $H_0$.

(e) There is not enough evidence at the 10% level of significance to reject the claim that the distribution of the ages of moviegoers and the expected distribution are the same.

9. (a) $H_0$: The distribution of the days people order pizza is 14% Sunday, 10% Monday, 11% Tuesday, 12% Wednesday, 13% Thursday, 21% Friday, and 19% Saturday.

$H_a$: The distribution of the days differs from the expected distribution. (claim)

(b) $\chi_0^2 = 16.812$; Rejection region: $\chi^2 > 16.812$

(c) 25.086 (d) Reject $H_0$.

(e) There is enough evidence at the 1% level of significance to conclude that the distribution of days differs from the expected distribution.

11. (a) $H_0$: The distribution of the number of homicide crimes in California by county is uniform. (claim)

$H_a$: The distribution of homicides by county is not uniform.

(b) $\chi_0^2 = 30.578$; Rejection region: $\chi^2 > 30.578$

(c) 214.848 (d) Reject $H_0$.

(e) There is enough evidence at the 1% level of significance to reject the claim that the distribution of the number of homicide crimes in California by county is uniform.

13. (a) $H_0$: The distribution of the opinions of Democrat U.S. parents on what path they would prefer their child take after high school is 46% four-year college, 7% two-year college, 19% non-college training program, and 28% all other pathways.

$H_a$: The distribution of opinions differs from the expected distribution. (claim)

(b) $\chi_0^2 = 7.815$; Rejection region: $\chi^2 > 7.815$

(c) 63.059 (d) Reject $H_0$.

(e) There is enough evidence at the 5% level to support the claim that the distribution of opinions of Democrats and Republicans is different.

**15.** (a) $H_0$: The distribution of prospective home buyers by the size they want their next house to be is uniform.
$H_a$: The distribution of prospective home buyers by the size they want their next house to be is not uniform. (claim)
(b) $\chi_0^2 = 5.991$; Rejection region: $\chi^2 > 5.991$
(c) 10.308 (d) Reject $H_0$.
(e) There is enough evidence at the 5% level of significance to conclude that the distribution of prospective home buyers by the size they want their next house to be is not uniform.

**17.** (a) The expected frequencies are 17, 63, 79, 34, and 5.
(b) $\chi_0^2 = 13.277$; Rejection region: $\chi^2 > 13.277$
(c) 0.613 (d) Fail to reject $H_0$.
(e) There is not enough evidence at the 1% level of significance to reject the claim that the test scores are normally distributed.

## Section 10.2 (page 542)

**1.** Find the sum of the row and the sum of the column in which the cell is located. Find the product of these sums. Divide the product by the sample size.

**3.** *Sample answer:* For both the chi-square independence test and the chi-square goodness-of-fit test, you are testing a claim about data that are in categories. However, the chi-square goodness-of-fit test has only one data value per category, while the chi-square independence test has multiple data values per category.
Both tests compare observed and expected frequencies. However, the chi-square goodness-of-fit test simply compares the distributions, whereas the chi-square independence test compares them and then draws a conclusion about the dependence or independence of the variables.

**5.** False. If the two variables of a chi-square independence test are dependent, then you can expect a large difference between the observed frequencies and the expected frequencies.

**7.** (a)–(b)

| | Athlete has | | |
|---|---|---|---|
| **Result** | **Stretched** | **Not stretched** | **Total** |
| Injury | 18 (20.82) | 22 (19.18) | 40 |
| No injury | 211 (208.18) | 189 (191.82) | 400 |
| Total | 229 | 211 | 440 |

**9.** (a)–(b)

| | Preference | | | |
|---|---|---|---|---|
| **Bank employee** | **New procedure** | **Old procedure** | **No preference** | **Total** |
| Teller | 92 (133.80) | 351 (313.00) | 50 (46.19) | 493 |
| Customer service representative | 76 (34.20) | 42 (80.00) | 8 (11.81) | 126 |
| Total | 168 | 393 | 58 | 619 |

**11.** (a)–(b)

| | Type of car | | | | |
|---|---|---|---|---|---|
| **Gender** | **Compact** | **Full-size** | **SUV** | **Truck/van** | **Total** |
| Male | 28 (28.6) | 39 (39.05) | 21 (22.55) | 22 (19.8) | 110 |
| Female | 24 (23.4) | 32 (31.95) | 20 (18.45) | 14 (16.2) | 90 |
| Total | 52 | 71 | 41 | 36 | 200 |

**13.** (a) $H_0$: An athlete's injury result is independent of whether or not the athlete has stretched. (claim)
$H_a$: An athlete's injury result is dependent on whether or not an athlete has stretched.
(b) d.f. = 1; $\chi_0^2 = 6.635$; Rejection region: $\chi^2 > 6.635$
(c) 0.875 (d) Fail to reject $H_0$.
(e) There is not enough evidence at the 1% level of significance to reject the claim that an athlete's injury result is independent of whether or not the athlete has stretched.

**15.** (a) $H_0$: The result is independent of the type of treatment.
$H_a$: The result is dependent on the type of treatment. (claim)
(b) d.f. = 1; $\chi_0^2 = 2.706$; Rejection region: $\chi^2 > 2.706$
(c) 12.478 (d) Reject $H_0$.
(e) There is enough evidence at the 10% level of significance to conclude that the result is dependent on the type of treatment.

**17.** (a) $H_0$: The number of times former smokers tried to quit is independent of gender.
$H_a$: The number of times former smokers tried to quit is dependent on gender. (claim)
(b) d.f. = 2; $\chi_0^2 = 5.991$; Rejection region: $\chi^2 > 5.991$
(c) 0.002 (d) Fail to reject $H_0$.
(e) There is not enough evidence at the 5% level of significance to conclude that the number of times former smokers tried to quit is dependent on gender.

**19.** (a) $H_0$: Reasons are independent of the type of worker.
$H_a$: Reasons are dependent on the type of worker. (claim)
(b) d.f. = 2; $\chi_0^2 = 9.210$; Rejection region: $\chi^2 > 9.210$
(c) 7.326 (d) Fail to reject $H_0$.
(e) There is not enough evidence at the 1% level of significance to conclude that reasons for continuing education are dependent on the type of worker.

**21.** (a) $H_0$: A family's choice to visit colleges before enrolling is independent of their income.
$H_a$: A family's choice to visit colleges before enrolling is dependent on their income. (claim)
(b) d.f. = 6; $\chi_0^2 = 16.812$; Rejection region: $\chi_0^2 > 16.812$
(c) 53.012 (d) Reject $H_0$.
(e) There is enough evidence at the 1% level of significance to conclude that a family's choice to visit colleges before enrolling is dependent on their income.

**23.** (a) $H_0$: Point of initial impact of crashes with occupant fatalities is independent from type of vehicle.
$H_a$: Point of initial impact of crashes with occupant fatalities is dependent on type of vehicle. (claim)
(b) d.f. = 2; $\chi_0^2 = 5.991$; Rejection region: $\chi_0^2 > 5.991$
(c) 30.947 (d) Reject $H_0$.
(e) There is enough evidence at the 5% level of significance to conclude that point of initial impact of crashes with occupant fatalities is dependent on type of vehicle.

**25.** (a) $H_0$: Procedure preference is independent of bank employee.
$H_a$: Procedure preference is dependent on bank employee. (claim)
(b) d.f. = 2; $\chi_0^2 = 5.991$; Rejection region: $\chi^2 > 5.991$
(c) 88.361 (d) Reject $H_0$.
(e) There is enough evidence at the 5% level of significance to conclude that procedure preference is dependent on bank employee.

**27.** (a) $H_0$: Type of car is independent of gender. (claim)
$H_a$: Type of car is dependent on gender.
(b) d.f. = 3; $\chi_0^2 = 6.251$; Rejection region: $\chi^2 > 6.251$
(c) 0.808 (d) Fail to reject $H_0$.
(e) There is not enough evidence at the 10% level of significance to conclude that type of car is dependent on gender.

**29.** Fail to reject $H_0$. There is not enough evidence at the 5% level of significance to reject the claim that the proportions of motor vehicle crash deaths involving males or females are the same for each age group.

**31.** Right-tailed

**33.**

| | Educational attainment | | | |
|---|---|---|---|---|
| **Status** | **Not a high school graduate** | **High school graduate** | **Some college, no degree** | **Associate's, bachelor's, or advanced degree** |
| Employed | 0.037 | 0.148 | 0.088 | 0.335 |
| Unemployed | 0.004 | 0.009 | 0.005 | 0.011 |
| Not in the labor force | 0.050 | 0.119 | 0.059 | 0.136 |

**35.** (a) 1.1% (b) 5.9%

**37.**

| | Educational attainment | | | |
|---|---|---|---|---|
| **Status** | **Not a high school graduate** | **High school graduate** | **Some college, no degree** | **Associate's, bachelor's, or advanced degree** |
| Employed | 0.061 | 0.243 | 0.145 | 0.551 |
| Unemployed | 0.127 | 0.317 | 0.175 | 0.381 |
| Not in the labor force | 0.137 | 0.328 | 0.163 | 0.373 |

**39.** 16.3% **41.** 28.2 %

## Section 10.3 (page 555)

**1.** Specify the level of significance $\alpha$. Determine the degrees of freedom for the numerator and denominator. Use Table 7 in Appendix B to find the critical value $F$.

**3.** (1) The samples must be random, (2) the samples must be independent, and (3) each population must have a normal distribution.

**5.** 2.54 **7.** 2.06 **9.** 9.16 **11.** 1.80

**13.** Fail to reject $H_0$. There is not enough evidence at the 10% level of significance to support the claim.

**15.** Fail to reject $H_0$. There is not enough evidence at the 1% level of significance to reject the claim.

**17.** Reject $H_0$. There is enough evidence at the 1% level of significance to reject the claim.

**19.** (a) $H_0$: $\sigma_1^2 \le \sigma_2^2$; $H_a$: $\sigma_1^2 > \sigma_2^2$ (claim)
(b) $F_0 = 2.45$; Rejection region: $F > 2.45$
(c) 2.17 (d) Fail to reject $H_0$.
(e) There is not enough evidence at the 2.5% level of significance to support Company A's claim that the variance of the life of its appliances is less than the variance of the life of Company B's appliances.

**21.** (a) $H_0$: $\sigma_1^2 = \sigma_2^2$; $H_a$: $\sigma_1^2 \ne \sigma_2^2$ (claim)
(b) $F_0 = 3.18$; Rejection region: $F > 3.18$
(c) 7.31 (d) Reject $H_0$.
(e) There is enough evidence at the 10% level of significance to conclude that the variances of the driving distances differ between the two golfers.

**23.** (a) $H_0$: $\sigma_1^2 = \sigma_2^2$ (claim); $H_a$: $\sigma_1^2 \ne \sigma_2^2$
(b) $F_0 = 2.635$; Rejection region: $F > 2.635$
(c) 1.282 (d) Fail to reject $H_0$.
(e) There is not enough evidence at the 10% level of significance to reject the administrator's claim that the standard deviations of science assessment test scores for eighth-grade students are the same in Districts 1 and 2.

**25.** (a) $H_0$: $\sigma_1^2 \le \sigma_2^2$; $H_a$: $\sigma_1^2 > \sigma_2^2$ (claim)
(b) $F_0 = 1.59$; Rejection region: $F > 1.59$
(c) 2.240 (d) Reject $H_0$.
(e) There is enough evidence at the 5% level of significance to conclude that the standard deviation of the annual salaries for actuaries is less in California than in New York.

**27.** Right-tailed: 14.73; Left-tailed: 0.15 **29.** (0.340, 3.422)

## Section 10.4 (page 565)

**1.** $H_0$: $\mu_1 = \mu_2 = \mu_3 = \cdots = \mu_k$
$H_a$: At least one of the means is different from the others.

**3.** The $MS_B$ measures the differences related to the treatment given to each sample. The $MS_W$ measures the differences related to entries within the same sample.

**5.** (a) $H_0$: $\mu_1 = \mu_2 = \mu_3$
$H_a$: At least one mean is different from the others. (claim)
(b) $F_0 = 3.89$; Rejection region: $F > 3.89$
(c) 1.325 (d) Fail to reject $H_0$.
(e) There is not enough evidence at the 5% level of significance to conclude that at least one mean cost per ounce is different from the others.

**7.** (a) $H_0: \mu_1 = \mu_2 = \mu_3$
$H_a$: At least one mean is different from the others. (claim)
(b) $F_0 = 6.36$; Rejection region: $F > 6.36$
(c) 16.11 (d) Reject $H_0$.
(e) There is enough evidence at the 1% level of significance to conclude that at least one mean vacuum cleaner weight is different from the others.

**9.** (a) $H_0: \mu_1 = \mu_2 = \mu_3 = \mu_4$
$H_a$: At least one mean is different from the others. (claim)
(b) $F_0 = 2.84$; Rejection region: $F > 2.84$
(c) 0.62 (d) Fail to reject $H_0$.
(e) There is not enough evidence at the 5% level of significance to conclude that at least one mean age is different from the others.

**11.** (a) $H_0: \mu_1 = \mu_2 = \mu_3 = \mu_4$ (claim)
$H_a$: At least one mean is different from the others.
(b) $F_0 = 2.28$; Rejection region: $F > 2.28$
(c) 3.67 (d) Reject $H_0$.
(e) There is enough evidence at the 10% level of significance to reject the claim that the mean scores are the same for all regions.

**13.** (a) $H_0: \mu_1 = \mu_2 = \mu_3 = \mu_4 = \mu_5 = \mu_6$
$H_a$: At least one mean is different from the others. (claim)
(b) $F_0 = 2.53$; Rejection region: $F > 2.53$
(c) 2.913 (d) Reject $H_0$.
(e) There is enough evidence at the 5% level of significance to conclude that at least one mean salary is different from the others.

**15.** Fail to reject all null hypotheses. The interaction between the advertising medium and the length of the ad has no effect on the rating and therefore there is no significant difference in the means of the ratings.

**17.** Fail to reject all null hypotheses. The interaction between age and gender has no effect on GPA and therefore there is no significant difference in the means of the GPAs.

**19.** $CV_{\text{Scheffé}} = 12.72$
$(1, 2) \to 4.95 \to$ No difference
$(1, 3) \to 11.61 \to$ No difference
$(2, 3) \to 31.73 \to$ Significant difference

**21.** $CV_{\text{Scheffé}} = 17.48$
$(1, 2) \to 10.06 \to$ No difference
$(1, 3) \to 42.99 \to$ Significant difference
$(1, 4) \to 21.15 \to$ Significant difference
$(1, 5) \to 29.00 \to$ Significant difference
$(2, 3) \to 12.47 \to$ No difference
$(2, 4) \to 3.10 \to$ No difference
$(2, 5) \to 5.58 \to$ No difference
$(3, 4) \to 2.23 \to$ No difference
$(3, 5) \to 1.26 \to$ No difference
$(4, 5) \to 0.19 \to$ No difference

## Uses and Abuses for Chapter 10 (page 570)

**1–2.** Answers will vary.

## Review Exercises for Chapter 10 (page 572)

**1.** (a) $H_0$: The age distribution of U.S. physicians is 20% are less than 40, 26% are 40–49, 28% are 50–59, 22% are 60–69, and 4% are 70 and older.
$H_a$: The age distribution of U.S. physicians differs from the expected distribution. (claim)
(b) $\chi^2_0 = 13.277$; Rejection region: $\chi^2 > 13.277$
(c) 14.662 (d) Reject $H_0$.
(e) There is enough evidence at the 1% level of significance to conclude that the distribution of the ages differs from the expected distribution.

**3.** (a) $H_0$: The distribution of opinions of golfers about what irritates them the most is 65.1% slow play, 18.5% poor course conditions, 11.1% poor etiquette, 5.3% high green fees. (claim)
$H_a$: The distribution of opinions of golfers about what irritates them the most differs from the expected distribution.
(b) $\chi^2_0 = 7.815$; Rejection region: $\chi^2 > 7.815$
(c) 4.256 (d) Fail to reject $H_0$.
(e) There is not enough evidence at the 5% level of significance to conclude that the distribution of opinions of golfers about what irritates them the most differs from the expected distribution.

**5.** (a)

| | Years of full-time teaching experience | | | |
|---|---|---|---|---|
| | **Less than 3 years** | **3–9 years** | **10–20 years** | **20 years or more** |
| Elementary | 93.1 | 293.4 | 423.7 | 240.8 |
| Secondary | 216.9 | 683.6 | 987.3 | 561.2 |

(b) $H_0$: The years of full-time teaching experience is independent of level of instruction.
$H_a$: The years of full-time teaching experience is dependent on level of instruction. (claim)
(c) d.f. = 3; $\chi^2_0 = 11.345$; Rejection region: $\chi^2 > 11.345$
(d) 2.275 (e) Fail to reject $H_0$.
(f) There is not enough evidence at the 1% level of significance to conclude that the years of full-time teaching experience is dependent on level of instruction.

**7.** (a)

| | Vertebrate group | | | | |
|---|---|---|---|---|---|
| **Status** | **Mammals** | **Birds** | **Reptiles** | **Amphibians** | **Fish** |
| Endangered | 132.43 | 117.72 | 48.79 | 17.04 | 72.02 |
| Threatened | 38.57 | 34.28 | 14.21 | 4.96 | 20.98 |

(b) $H_0$: A species' status is independent of vertebrate group. (claim)
$H_a$: A species' status is dependent on vertebrate group.
(c) d.f. = 4; $\chi^2_0 = 9.488$; Rejection region: $\chi^2 > 9.488$
(d) 44.751 (e) Reject $H_0$.
(f) There is enough evidence at the 5% level of significance to reject the claim that a species' status (endangered or threatened) is independent of vertebrate group.

**9.** 2.295 **11.** 2.39 **13.** 2.06 **15.** 2.08

**17.** (a) $H_0$: $\sigma_1 = \sigma_2$ (claim); $H_a$: $\sigma_1 \neq \sigma_2$
(b) $F_0 = 1.81$; Rejection region: $F > 1.81$
(c) 1.900 (d) Reject $H_0$.
(e) There is enough evidence at the 10% level of significance to reject the claim that the standard deviations of hotel room rates in Sacramento, CA, and San Francisco, CA, are the same.

**19.** (a) $H_0$: $\sigma_1^2 = \sigma_2^2$
$H_a$: $\sigma_1^2 \neq \sigma_2^2$ (claim)
(b) $F_0 = 5.32$; Rejection region: $F > 5.32$
(c) 1.37 (d) Fail to reject $H_0$.
(e) There is not enough evidence at the 1% level of significance to support the claim that the test score variance for reading and writing is different from that for math.

**21.** (a) $H_0$: $\mu_1 = \mu_2 = \mu_3 = \mu_4$
$H_a$: At least one mean is different from the others. (claim)
(b) $F_0 = 2.26$; Rejection region: $F > 2.26$
(c) 2.18 (d) Fail to reject $H_0$.
(e) There is not enough evidence at the 10% level of significance to conclude that at least one monthly electric bill is different from the others.

## Quiz for Chapter 10 (page 576)

**1.** (a) $H_0$: The distribution of educational attainment for people in the United States ages 30–34 is 3.5% none–8th grade, 5.5% 9th–11th grade, 27.6% high school graduates, 15.2% some college, no degree, 10.6% associate's degree, 23.4% bachelor's degree, 10.6% master's degree, and 3.6% professional/doctoral degree.
$H_a$: The distribution of educational attainment for people in the United States ages 30–34 differs from the distribution for people ages 25 and older. (claim)
(b) $\chi_0^2 = 14.067$; Rejection region: $\chi^2 > 14.067$
(c) 3.958 (d) Fail to reject $H_0$.
(e) There is not enough evidence at the 5% level of significance to conclude that the distribution for people in the United States ages 30–34 differs from the distribution for people ages 25 and older.

**2.** (a) $H_0$: Age and educational attainment are independent.
$H_a$: Age and educational attainment are dependent. (claim)
(b) $\chi_0^2 = 18.475$; Rejection region: $\chi^2 > 18.475$
(c) 8.187 (d) Fail to reject $H_0$.
(e) There is not enough evidence at the 1% level of significance to conclude that educational attainment is dependent on age.

**3.** (a) $H_0$: $\sigma_1^2 = \sigma_2^2$
$H_a$: $\sigma_1^2 \neq \sigma_2^2$ (claim)
(b) $F_0 = 4.43$; Rejection region: $F > 4.43$
(c) 1.38 (d) Fail to reject $H_0$.
(e) There is not enough evidence at the 1% level of significance to conclude that the variances in annual wages for Ithaca, NY, and Little Rock, AR, are different.

**4.** (a) $H_0$: $\mu_1 = \mu_2 = \mu_3$ (claim)
$H_a$: At least one mean is different from the others.
(b) $F_0 = 2.44$; Rejection region: $F > 2.44$
(c) 15.02 (d) Reject $H_0$.
(e) There is enough evidence at the 10% level of significance to reject the claim that the mean annual wages are the same for all three cities.

## Real Statistics—Real Decisions for Chapter 10 (page 578)

**1.** Fail to reject $H_0$. There is not enough evidence at the 1% level of significance to conclude that the distribution of responses differs from the expected distribution.

**2.** (a) $E_{1,1} = 15$, $E_{1,2} = 120$, $E_{1,3} = 165$, $E_{1,4} = 185$,
$E_{1,5} = 135$, $E_{1,6} = 115$, $E_{1,7} = 155$, $E_{1,8} = 110$,
$E_{2,1} = 15$, $E_{2,2} = 120$, $E_{2,3} = 165$, $E_{2,4} = 185$,
$E_{2,5} = 135$, $E_{2,6} = 115$, $E_{2,7} = 155$, $E_{2,8} = 110$
(b) There is enough evidence at the 1% level of significance to conclude that the ages of the victims are related to the type of fraud.

## Cumulative Review for Chapters 9 and 10 (page 580)

**1.** (a)

$r \approx 0.774$; strong positive linear correlation
(b) There is enough evidence at the 5% level of significance to conclude that there is a significant linear correlation between the men's and women's 100-meter times.
(c) $y = 1.2283x - 1.2253$

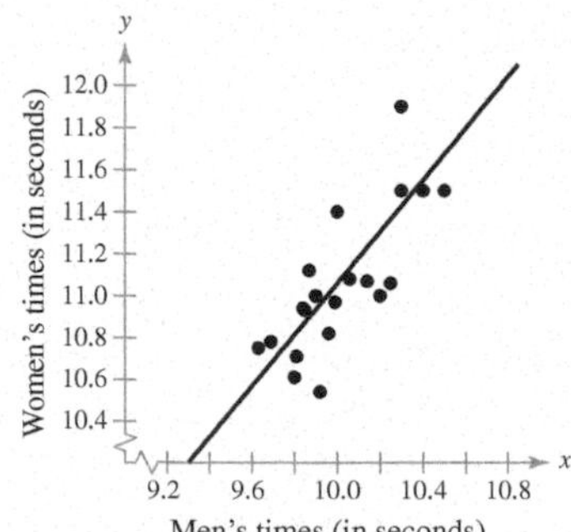


(d) 10.93

**2.** There is enough evidence at the 10% level of significance to reject the claim that the mean expenditures are the same for all four regions.

**3.** (a) 12,426 pounds per acre
(b) 12,201 pounds per acre

4. There is not enough evidence at the 10% level of significance to reject the administrator's claim that the standard deviations of reading test scores for eighth-grade students are the same in Illinois and Georgia.
5. There is not enough evidence at the 5% level of significance to reject the claim that the distributions are the same.
6. There is not enough evidence at the 5% level of significance to conclude that the adults' ratings of the movie are dependent on generation.
7. (a) 0.743; About 74.3% of the variation in height can be explained by the relationship between metacarpal bone length and height, and about 25.7% of the variation is unexplained.
   (b) 3.93; The standard error of estimate of the height for a specific metacarpal bone length is about 3.93 centimeters.
   (c) $169.95 < y < 189.72$; You can be 95% confident that the height will be between 169.95 and 189.72 centimeters when the metacarpal bone length is 50 millimeters.

# Appendix C

## Appendix C (page A30)

1. The observed values are usually plotted along the horizontal axis. The expected $z$-scores are plotted along the vertical axis.
3. Because the points appear to follow a nonlinear pattern, you can conclude that the data do not come from a population that has a normal distribution.
5. 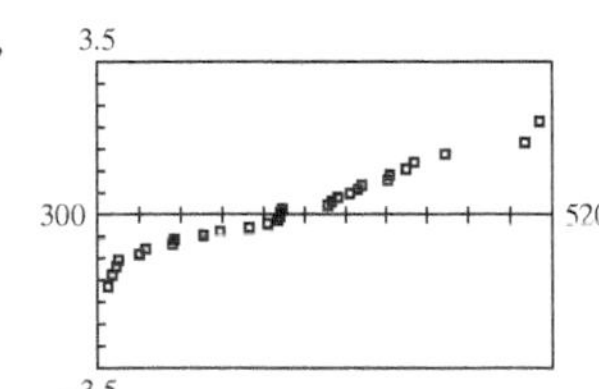


   Because the points are approximately linear, you can conclude that the data come from a population that has a normal distribution.

# INDEX

## R



## S

# T



# U



# V



# W



# X



# Y



# Z

# CREDITS

**Cover Image Credits:** Tuareg with camels walk thru the desert: MondoRidz/Shutterstock; Aurora Borealis: Mike Mumemories/Shutterstock; Taj Mahal: Kalyan Boorla/Shutterstock; Buildings on Damrak canal, Amsterdam: Mistervlad/Shutterstock; Toucan with green background: Michiel Scheerhoorn/Shutterstock; Colorful coral reef with many fishes and sea turtle: stockphoto-graf/Shutterstock; Hand and rolling dices: Marco Martins/Shutterstock; Double decker on London Bridge: William Perugini/Shutterstock; Ripe rice field and sky landscape on the farm: ABCDstock/Shutterstock; Water splashing sphere on blue sky: klyaksun/Shutterstock.

**Multiple Uses:** Girl with red backpack: Sze Fei/Shutterstock; cross-legged boy with laptop: Hans Kim/Shutterstock; girl with orange shirt and books: Hugo Felix/Shutterstock; girl with plaid shirt and red backpack: Elnur/Shutterstock; boy with blue shirt, backpack, and books: Odua Images/Shutterstock; girl with white shirt and books: Hugo Felix/123RF; boy with gray shirt and backpack: Odua Images/Shutterstock; girl with white shirt and laptop: Lenetstan/Shutterstock; boy with aqua shirt and backpack: Viktor Gladkov/Shutterstock; cross-legged girl with book: Lithian/Shutterstock; boy with beard: Antoniodiaz/Shutterstock; boy with blue shirt and backpack: Viktor Gladkov/Shutterstock.

All TI screenshots courtesy of Texas Instruments.

**Front Matter Image Credits:** **v** Shutterstock: Charles Knowles/Shutterstock; Alamy Stock Photo: Mike Segar/Reuters/Alamy Stock Photo; **vi** Getty Images: Steve Powell/Staff/Getty Images; Shutterstock: Beeboys/Shutterstock; **vii** Shutterstock: Smereka/Shutterstock; 123RF: WavebreakMediaMicro/123RF; **viii** Getty Images: Fuse/Corbis/Getty Images; Shutterstock: Kite_rin/Shutterstock; **ix** Getty Images: Stephen Dunn/Staff/Getty Images; Shutterstock: Benoist/Shutterstock.

**Chapter 1 Image Credits:** **1** Shutterstock: Charles Knowles/Shutterstock; **4** Shutterstock: Red shine studio/Shutterstock; **20** Shutterstock: Olinchuk/Shutterstock; **22** Shutterstock: Michael Jung/Shutterstock; **27** Shutterstock: Icojam/Shutterstock.

**Chapter 1 Text Credits:** **2** Pew Research Center: Pew Research Center; **2** Americans for the Arts: Americans for the Arts; **10** Pew Research Center: World Wildlife Fund; **14** Pew Research Center: Pew Research Center; **14** Marriott Bonvoy Bold from Chase: Marriott Bonvoy Bold from Chase; **14** Center for American Women and Politics: Center for American Women and Politics; **14** National Highway Traffic Safety Administrator: National Highway Traffic Safety Administrator; **16** Apple Inc.: Source: The Harris Poll; Amazon.com; Apple, Inc.; Netflix, Inc.; The Kraft Heinz Co.; Facebook, Inc.; Ford Motor Co.; Chipotle Mexican Grill, Inc.; Comcast Corp.; Exxon Mobil Corp.; Wells Fargo & Co.; **34** Fluent Pulse: Fluent Pulse.

**Chapter 2 Image Credits:** **38** Alamy Stock Photo: Mike Segar/Reuters/Alamy Stock Photo; **41** Shutterstock: Antoniodiaz/Shutterstock; **48** Minitab, LLC: Portions of information contained in this publication/book are printed with permission of Minitab, LLC. All such material remains the exclusive property and copyright of Minitab, LLC. All rights reserved; **57** Minitab, LLC: Portions of information contained in this publication/book are printed with permission of Minitab, LLC. All such material remains the exclusive property and copyright of Minitab, LLC. All rights reserved; **73** Shutterstock: Michael Jung/Shutterstock; **86** Minitab, LLC: Portions of information contained in this publication/book are printed with permission of Minitab, LLC. All such material remains the exclusive property and copyright of Minitab, LLC. All rights reserved; **87** Shutterstock: Antoniodiaz/Shutterstock; **101** Shutterstock: Michaeljung/Shutterstock; **103** Minitab, LLC: Portions of information contained in this publication/book are printed with permission of Minitab, LLC. All such material remains the exclusive property and copyright of Minitab, LLC. All rights reserved; **106** Shutterstock: lnur/Shutterstock; **124** Minitab, LLC: Portions of information contained in this publication/book are printed with permission of Minitab, LLC. All such material remains the exclusive property and copyright of Minitab, LLC. All rights reserved.

**Chapter 2 Text Credits:** **39** Disney: Source: ESPN.com; **42** United States Census Bureau: U.S. Census Bureau; **46** Yellowstone National Park: Yellowstone National Park; **52** The White House: Source: The White House; **52** The U.S. National Archives and Records Administration: Source: The U.S. National Archives & Records Administration; **54** American Hospital Directory, Inc: Source: American Hospital Directory; **55** Pew Research Center: Adapted from Pew Research; **58** National Center for Education and Statistics: U.S. National Center for Education Statistics; **59** U.S Department of Health and Human Services: Health, United States, 2015, Table 19; **59** U.S. Bureau of Labor Statistics: Based on U.S. Bureau of Labor Statistics; **59** Council of Better Business Bureaus: Council of Better Business Bureaus; **60** Larson, Ron: Fisher, R. A., 1936; **61** Federal Bureau of Investigation: Federal Bureau of

Investigation, Crime in the United States; **63** Statista: Source: Statista; **63** U.S. Bureau of Economic Analysis: Source: U.S. Bureau of Economic Analysis; **63** Expedia: Source: Expedia; **63** American Pet Products Association: Source: American Pet Products Association; **64** Forbes Media LLC: Source: Forbes Media LLC; **64** U.S. Census Bureau: Source: U.S. Census Bureau; **64** Britannica: Source: Britannica; **64** International Data Corporation: Source: International Data Corporation; **64** Institute for Health Metrics and Evaluation: Source: Institute for Health Metrics and Evaluation; **65** U.S. Department of Education: Source: U.S. Department of Education; **65** U.S. Bureau of Economic Analysis: Source: U.S. Bureau of Economic Analysis; **65** Ipsos: Ipsos Public Affairs; **66** U.S. Energy Information Administration: Source: U.S. Energy Information Administration; **69** Pew Research Center: Adapted from Pew Research Center; **70** National Association of Realtors: Source: National Association of Realtors; **75** Public Broadcasting Service (PBS): Source: PBS; **75** Amazon: Source: Amazon; **75** U.S. News & World Report L.P.: Source: *U.S. News & World Report*; **75** U.S. Customs and Border Protection: Source: U.S. Customs and Border Protection; **75** Bipolar Network News: Source: Adapted from Bipolar Network News; **75** Billboard Media, LLC.: Source: Billboard; **76** Pew Research Center: Source: Adapted from Pew Research; **76** User Voice: Adapted from User Voice; **76** Buffer: Source: Buffer; **76** United States Environmental Protection Agency: Source: United States Environmental Protection Agency; **77** Jobvite, Inc: Source: Jobvite; **78** U.S. Census Bureau: Source: U.S. Census Bureau; **79** U.S. Department of Commerce: Source: U.S. Department of Commerce; **85** SAGE Publications: Adapted from *The American Journal of Sports Medicine*; **86** CoStar Group, Inc.: Adapted from LoopNet.com; **88** National Center for Health Statistics: Adapted from National Center for Health Statistics; **89** U.S Census Bureau: Based on U.S. Census Bureau; **91** National Association of REALTORS: Adapted from National Association of Realtors; **91** Move, Inc: Adapted from Move, Inc; **93** United States Census Bureau: U.S. Census Bureau; **93** National Highway Traffic Safety Administration: Source: National Highway Traffic Safety Administration; **96** Geyser Times: Adapted from Geyser Times; **96** Major League Baseball: Source: Major League Baseball; **98** Ages and Caps: Source: U.S. Soccer; **98** Disney: Source: ESPN; **101** U.S. Census Bureau: U.S. Census Bureau; **102** Texas A&M Transportation Institute: Based on 2015 Urban Mobility Scorecard; **103** U.S. News & World Report L.P.: *U.S. News & World Report*; **105** National Weather Service: National Weather Service; **106** The College Board: The College Board; **111** Educational Testing Service: Adapted from Educational Testing Service; **112** ASO: Source: Le Tour de France; **114** Procter & Gamble: Source: Procter & Gamble Corporation; **114** Public University Honors: Adapted from Public University Honors; **116** Public University Honors: Adapted from Public University Honors; **116** Numbeo: Adapted from Numbeo; **116** Bureau of Labor Statistics: Source: Bureau of Labor Statistics; **117** STR GERMANY GMBH: Source: Emporis; **117** U.S. Bureau of Labor Statistics: Source: U.S. Bureau of Labor Statistics; **117** National Basketball Association: Source: National Basketball Association; **117** Gallup, Inc: Adapted from Gallup; **118** Supreme Court of the United States: Source: Supreme Court of the United States; **118** National Aeronautics and Space Administration: Source: NASA; **119** U.S. Environmental Protection Agency: Source: U.S. Environmental Protection Agency; **119** Theodric Technologies LLC.: Source: Radio-Locator .com; **120** MLB Advanced Media, LP.: Source: Major League Baseball; **121** Recording Industry Association of America: Source: Recording Industry Association of America; **122** FortuneBuilders: Source: FortuneBuilders; **123** City of Toronto: Source: City of Toronto; **126** Association of Certified Fraud Examiners, Inc: Source: Association of Certified Fraud Examiners; **126** Pew Research Center: Source: Pew Research Center; **126** Gallup, Inc: Source: Gallup; **126** The JED Foundation: Source: The JED Foundation; **126** Massachusetts Institute of Technology: Source: Massachusetts Institute of Technology; **126** SAGE Publications: Source: *Journal of Attention Disorders*; **127** U.S. Census Bureau: Source: U.S. Census Bureau; **127** National Oceanic and Atmospheric Administration: Source: National Oceanic and Atmospheric Administration; **127** National Hockey League: Source: National Hockey League.

**Chapter 3 Image Credits: 128** Getty Images: Steve Powell/Staff/Getty Images; **128** Shutterstock: Prostock-studio/Shutterstock; **149** Shutterstock: Michaeljung/ Shutterstock; **150** Getty Images: DNY59/E+/Getty Images.

**Chapter 3 Text Credits: 135** Cornell University Press: Adapted from Life: The Odds; **135** Pew Research Center: Adapted from Pew Research Center; **136** Pew Research Center: Adapted from Pew Research Center; **136** Statista: Adapted from Statista; **137** U.S. Army Corps of Engineers: Army Corps of Engineers; **142** Ipsos: Ipsos; **142** U.S Census Bureau: U.S Census Bureau; **143** West Virginia State: West Virginia State; **143** Texas Secretary of State: Texas Secretary of State; **144** National Collegiate Athletic Association: Source: National Collegiate Athletic Association; **144** U.S. Bureau of Labor Statistics: U.S. Bureau of Labor Statistics; **147** The Harris Poll: Adapted from The Harris Poll; **150** The Orthopedic Centre of St. Louis: The Orthopedic Center of St. Louis; **150** The Orthopedic Center of St. Louis: The Orthopedic Center of St. Louis; **151** National Resident Matching Program: National Resident Matching Program; **152** National Center for Educational Statistics: National Center for Educational Statistics; **153** University of Kansas: Source: University of Kansas; **153** *JAMA*: Source: *JAMA*; **153** The Royal Society Publishing: Source: The Royal Society Publishing; **153** Pollack Peacebuilding Systems: Source: Pollack Peacebuilding Systems; **153** National

Cancer Institute: Source: National Cancer Institute; **154** *The Hollywood Reporter*: *The Hollywood Reporter*; **154** University of New Hampshire: Adapted from University of New Hampshire; **154** YouGov: Adapted from YouGov; **155** American National Red Cross: American National Red Cross; **155** U.S. Department of Health & Human Services: *Morbidity and Mortality Weekly Report*; **155** Niche: Adapted from Niche; **155** Inside Higher Ed: Adapted from Niche; **159** Pew Research Center: Pew Research; **161** National Football League: National Football League; **163** U.S. Census Bureau: U.S. Census Bureau; **163** American College Health Association: American College Health Association; **164** YouGov: Adapted from YouGov; **164** Ipsos: Adapted from Ipsos; **164** National Center for Educational Statistics: National Center for Educational Statistics; **164** Kaiser Family Foundation: Adapted from Kaiser Family Foundation; **176** City of Saratoga Springs: City of Saratoga Springs; **176** University of Colorado: University of Colorado; **176** The Sound of AI: The Sound of AI; **180** U.S. Census Bureau: U.S. Census Bureau; **180** North American Industry Classification System: Adapted from North American Industry Classification System; **181** National Council Licensure Examinations: Adapted from National Council Licensure Examinations; **182:** U.S. National Center for Education Statistics: U.S. National Center for Education Statistics; **182** American College Health Association: American College Health Association; **184** U.S. National Center for Education Statistics: U.S. National Center for Education Statistics; **185** U.S. National Center for Education Statistics: U.S. National Center for Education Statistics; **186** Datagenetics: Datagenetics.com.

**Chapter 4 Image Credits: 188** Shutterstock: Beeboys/Shutterstock; **203** Shutterstock: Michael Jung/Shutterstock; **205** Minitab, LLC: Portions of information contained in this publication/book are printed with permission of Minitab, LLC. All such material remains the exclusive property and copyright of Minitab, LLC. All rights reserved; **207** Minitab, LLC: Portions of information contained in this publication/book are printed with permission of Minitab, LLC. All such material remains the exclusive property and copyright of Minitab, LLC. All rights reserved; **215** Newscom: Mark Lomoglio/Icon Smi Ccx/Newscom; **231** Minitab, LLC: Portions of information contained in this publication/book are printed with permission of Minitab, LLC. All such material remains the exclusive property and copyright of Minitab, LLC. All rights reserved.

**Chapter 4 Text Credits: 193** YouGov PLC: Adapted from YouGov Plc; **197** U.S. Department of Justice: U.S. Department of Justice; **199** National Oceanic and Atmospheric Administration: National Oceanic & Atmospheric Administration; **199** Best Buy: Best Buy; **200** College Board: Adapted from The College Board; **202** Pew Research Center: Adapted from Pew Research Center; **205** The Harris Poll Hard Data: The Harris Poll; **206** Ipsos: Source: Ipsos; **207** U.S. Census Bureau: American Community Survey; **208** U.S. Census Bureau: American Cancer Society; **208** Pew Research Center: Pew Research Center; **209** National Oceanic and Atmospheric Administration: National Oceanic and Atmospheric Administration; **209** National Oceanic and Atmospheric Administration: National Oceanic and Atmospheric Administration; **210** Entertainment Software Association: Entertainment Software Association; **211** NBA Media Ventures, LLC.: Women's National Basketball Association; **211** Gallup, Inc.: Gallup; **211** Source of Actuaries: Society of Actuaries; **211** Transfermarkt GmbH & Co. KG: Transfermarkt; **211** Fashion Revolution Foundation: Fashion Revolution; **211** Quest Diagnostics Incorporated: Quest Diagnostics; **211** American Pecan Council: American Pecans; **212** U.S. News & World Report L.P.: *US News & World Report*; **212** Migration Policy Institute: Migration Policy Institute; **212** Stanford Center on Longevity: Stanford Center on Longevity; **212** Adecco Group AG: Adecco; **212** Sports Reference LLC: Hockey Reference; **212** Ipsos: Ipsos; **212** Gallup, Inc.: Gallup; **212** CareerBuilder, LLC: CareerBuilder; **212** Cable News Network: CNN; **213** Pew Research Center: Pew Research; **216** U.S. Bureau of Labor Statistics: U.S. Bureau of Labor Statistics; **217** U.S. Bureau of Labor Statistics: U.S. Bureau of Labor Statistics; **218** Washington State Department of Transportation: Adapted from Washington State Department of Transportation; **220** U.S. Census Bureau: U.S. Census Bureau; **220** NFL Enterprises LLC.: National Football League; **221** Gallup, Inc.: Gallup; **221** U.S. Department of Health & Human Services: Organ Procurement and Transplantation Network; **221** National Oceanic & Atmospheric Administration: National Oceanic & Atmospheric Administration; **221** Pew Research Center: Pew Research; **221** WTA Tour, Inc.: Women's Tennis Association; **221** National Oceanic and Atmospheric Administration: National Oceanic and Atmospheric Administration; **221** T. Rowe Price: T. Rowe Price Group, Inc.; **222** PGA Tour, Inc: PGATour.com; **222** U.S. Courts: Administrative Office of the U.S. Courts; **226** Gallup, Inc.: Gallup; **226** U.S. Bureau of Labor Statistics: U.S. Bureau of Labor Statistics; **226** National Conference of Bar Examiners: National Conference of Bar Examiners; **226** Pew Research Center: Pew Research; **226** Proofpoint, Inc.: Proofpoint; **227** Insurance Research Council: Insurance Research Council; **227** Gallup, Inc.: Gallup; **227** National Center for Health Statistics: National Center for Health Statistics; **227** National Weather Service: National Weather Service; **227** Rasmussen Reports, LLC: Rasmussen Reports; **227** NHL.com: National Hockey League; **227** Florida Museum of Natural History: International Shark Attack File; **227** Pew Research Center: Pew Research; **228** Gallup, Inc.: Gallup; **228** Mayo Foundation for Medical Education and Research: Mayo Clinic; **228** ESPN Sports Media Ltd.: ESPN; **229** The Kiplinger Washington Editors: Kiplinger; **229** U.S. National Library of Medicine: National Center for Biotechnology Information; **229** U.S. Census Bureau: U.S. Census Bureau; **229** U.S. Department of Education: U.S. Department of Education; **230** U.S. Department of Health and Human Services: Centers for Disease Control and Prevention; **230** U.S. Department of Health and Human Services: Centers for Disease Control and Prevention.

**Chapter 5 Image Credits: 232** Shutterstock: Smereka/Shutterstock; **234** Shutterstock: Ingram/Shutterstock; **237** Getty Images: Szefei/Getty Images; **262** Getty Images: Hexvivo/Getty Images; **263** Shutterstock: Michael Jung/Shutterstock; **277** Shutterstock: Viktor Gladkov/Shutterstock.

**Chapter 5 Text Credits: 235** U.S. Department of Health and Human Services: Adapted from National Center for Health Statistics; **236** New York State Department of Education: Adapted from New York State Education Department; **256** U.S. Department of Health and Human Services: Adapted from National Center for Health Statistics; **265** U.S. Census Bureau: Adapted from U.S. Census Bureau; **267** U.S. Department of Health and Human Services: Adapted from National Center for Education Statistics.

**Chapter 6 Image Credits: 296** 123RF: WavebreakMediaMicro/123RF; **300** Shutterstock: Redshinestudio/Shutterstock; **301** Getty Images: Szefei/istock/Getty Images; Minitab, LLC: Portions of information contained in this publication/book are printed with permission of Minitab, LLC. All such material remains the exclusive property and copyright of Minitab, LLC. All rights reserved; **311** Shutterstock: Michael Jung/Shutterstock; **314** Shutterstock: Redshinestudio/Shutterstock; **319** Shutterstock: Hquality/Shutterstock; **320** Shutterstock: Antoniodiaz/Shutterstock; Shutterstock: Redshinestudio/Shutterstock; **330** Getty Images: Hexvivo/istock/Getty Images; **332** Shutterstock: Redshinestudio/Shutterstock; **333** Minitab, LLC: Portions of information contained in this publication/book are printed with permission of Minitab, LLC. All such material remains the exclusive property and copyright of Minitab, LLC. All rights reserved; **344** Minitab, LLC: Portions of information contained in this publication/book are printed with permission of Minitab, LLC. All such material remains the exclusive property and copyright of Minitab, LLC. All rights reserved.

**Chapter 6 Text Credits: 300** TechJury.net: Adapted from TechJury; **306:** National Oceanic & Atmospheric Administration: NOAA; **321** Pew Research Center: Adapted from Pew Research Center; **323** Pew Research Center: Adapted from Pew Research Center; **324** U.S. Department of Health and Human Services: NCHS, National Health Interview Survey; **327** Pew Research Center: Source: Pew Research Center; Gallup, Inc.: Gallup; **334** NASA: NASA; **335** National Oceanic & Atmospheric Administration: NOAA.

**Chapter 7 Image Credits: 346** Getty Images: Fuse/Corbis/Getty Images; **349** Shutterstock: Redshinestudio/Shutterstock; **354** Shutterstock: Michael Jung/Shutterstock; **371** Shutterstock: 1000 Words/Shutterstock; Shutterstock: Redshinestudio/Shutterstock; **372** Minitab: Minitab; **379** Shutterstock: Redshinestudio/Shutterstock; **381** Minitab: Minitab; **390** Shutterstock: Redshinestudio/Shutterstock; **395** Minitab: Minitab; **399** Shutterstock: Redshinestudio/Shutterstock; **413** Minitab: Minitab.

**Chapter 7 Text Credits: 349** Rhythm Pharmaceuticals, Inc.: Adapted from Rhythm Pharmaceuticals, Inc.; **371** U.S. Department of Energy: U.S. Department of Energy; **392** Pew Research Center: Adapted from Pew Research Center; **399** American Pool Supply, Inc.: Adapted from American Pool Supply; **404** Gallup, Inc.: Gallup.

**Chapter 8 Image Credits: 416** Shutterstock: Kite_rin/Shutterstock; **419** Getty Images: hexvivo/Getty Images; **420** Shutterstock: Michael Jung/Shutterstock; **421** Shutterstock: Redshinestudio/Shutterstock; **429** Alamy Stock Photo: Emily Lai/Alamy Stock Photo; Shutterstock: Redshinestudio/Shutterstock; **433** Shutterstock: Kletr/Shutterstock; **436** Shutterstock: ESB Professional/Shutterstock; **438** Shutterstock: Redshinestudio/Shutterstock; **463** Minitab, LLC: Minitab; **464** Minitab, LLC: Minitab.

**Chapter 8 Text Credits: 421** National Education Association: Adapted from National Education Association; **427** Salary.com: Adapted from Salary.com; **444** BioMed Central: Adapted from BioMed Central, Ltd.; **444** U.S. Energy Information Administration: Adapted from U.S. Energy Information Administration; **448** Cardiorenal Medicine: Cardiorenal Medicine; **451** *New England Journal of Medicine*: Adapted from *The New England Journal of Medicine*; **452** National Recreation and Park Association: Adapted from National Recreation and Park Association; **453** U.S. Bureau of Labor Statistics: Adapted from U.S. Bureau of Labor Statistics; **458** NCAA: NCAA; **459** *New England Journal of Medicine*: *The New England Journal of Medicine*; **459** National Highway Traffic Safety Administration: Adapted from National Highway Traffic Safety Administration.

**Chapter 9 Image Credits: 468** Getty Images: Stephen Dunn/Staff/Getty Images; **473** Shutterstock: Michael Jung/Shutterstock; Minitab, LLC: Portions of information contained in this publication/book are printed with permission of Minitab, LLC. All such material remains the exclusive property and copyright of Minitab, LLC. All rights reserved; **480** Shutterstock: Redshinestudio/Shutterstock; **486** Shutterstock: Szefei/Shutterstock;

Minitab, LLC: Portions of information contained in this publication/book are printed with permission of Minitab, LLC. All such material remains the exclusive property and copyright of Minitab, LLC. All rights reserved; **489** Shutterstock: Redshinestudio/Shutterstock; **499** Shutterstock: Redshinestudio/Shutterstock; **510** Shutterstock: Michael Jung/Shutterstock; Minitab, LLC: Portions of information contained in this publication/book are printed with permission of Minitab, LLC. All such material remains the exclusive property and copyright of Minitab, LLC. All rights reserved; **511** Shutterstock: Redshinestudio/Shutterstock; **522** Shutterstock: Smileus/Shutterstock.

**Chapter 9 Text Credits: 489** U.S. Department of Agriculture: Source: U.S. Department of Agriculture; **497** American College of Sports Medicine: "Generalized Body Composition Prediction Equation for Men Using Simple Measurement Techniques" by K.W. Penrose et al. (1985). *Medicine and Science in Sports and Exercise*, vol. 17, no. 2, p. 189; Wolters Kluwer Health, Inc: Source: "Generalized Body Composition Prediction Equation for Men Using Simple Measurement Techniques" by K.W. Penrose et al. (1985). *Medicine and Science in Sports and Exercise*, vol. 17, no. 2, p. 189; **505** U.S. Census Bureau: Source: U.S. Census Bureau; **506** U.S. Energy Information Administration: U.S. Energy Information Administration; **507** Bureau of Transportation Statistics: Bureau of Transportation Statistics, IHS Markit; **517** U.S. Department of Agriculture: U.S. Department of Agriculture; **517** U.S. Bureau of Labor Statistics: U.S. Bureau of Labor Statistics; **519** United States Department of Agriculture: United States Department of Agriculture; **520** U.S. Bureau of Labor Statistics: U.S. Bureau of Labor Statistics; **520** U.S. Bureau of Labor Statistics: Source: U.S. Bureau of Labor Statistics; **522** Environmental Protection Agency: Environmental Protection Agency.

**Chapter 10 Image Credits: 524** Shutterstock: Benoist/Shutterstock; **536** Getty Images: hexvivo/iStock/Getty Images; **541** Shutterstock: Szefei/iStock/Getty Images; **541** Minitab: Minitab; **564** Shutterstock: Michael Jung/Shutterstock; **570** Shutterstock: Bogdan Vasilescu/Shutterstock.

**Chapter 10 Text Credits: 527** National Center for Health Statistics: National Center for Health Statistics; **535** National Center for Health Statistics: Adapted from National Center for Health Statistics; **536** Sallie Mae Bank: Adapted from Sallie Mae/Ipsos; **537** Sallie Mae Bank: Adapted from Sallie Mae/Ipsos; **538** U.S. Bureau of Labor Statistics: U.S. Bureau of Labor Statistics; **545** Sallie Mae Bank: Adapted from Sallie Mae; **545** Insurance Institute for Highway Safety, Highway Loss Data Institute: Adapted from Insurance Institute for Highway Safety; **546** Insurance Institute for Highway Safety, Highway Loss Data Institute: Adapted from Insurance Institute for Highway Safety; **547** U.S Census Bureau: Adapted from U.S. Census Bureau; **566** U.S. Bureau of Labor Statistics: Adapted from Bureau of Labor Statistics; **567** National Center for Health Statistics: Adapted from National Center for Health Statistics; **573** U.S. Department of Education: Adapted from National Center for Education Statistics; **575** U.S. Energy Information Administration: Adapted from U.S. Energy Information Administration; **575** U.S Census Bureau: Adapted from U.S. Census Bureau; **576** U.S Census Bureau: Adapted from U.S. Census Bureau; **576** U.S. Bureau of Economic Analysis: Adapted from U.S. Bureau of Economic Analysis; **577** U.S. Bureau of Labor Statistics: Adapted from U.S. Bureau of Labor Statistics; **577** U.S Census Bureau: Adapted from U.S. Census Bureau; **580** US Department of Agriculture: Adapted from U.S. Department of Agriculture; **580** U.S. Energy Information Administration: Adapted from U.S. Energy Information Administration; **581** U.S. Department of Education: Adapted from National Center for Education Statistics.

**Appendix A Image Credits: A2** Shutterstock: Szefei/Shutterstock.

**Appendix A Text Credits: A1** Mosteller, Gale: Reprinted with permission of Frederick Mosteller

**Appendix B Text Credits: A7** RAND Corporation: A Million Random Digits with 100,000 Normal Deviates by the Rand Corporation (New York: The Free Press, 1955); **A8–A10** Cengage Learning: From Brase/Brase, *Understandable Statistics*, Sixth Edition; **A11–A15** CRC Press: W. H. Beyer, *Handbook of Tables for Probability and Statistics*, 2e, CRC Press, Boca Raton, Florida, 1986; **A16** Pearson Education, Inc: Table A-3, pp. 681– 682 from *Probability and Statistics for Engineers and Scientists*, 6e by Walpole, Myers, and Myers. Copyright 1997. Pearson Prentice Hall, Upper Saddle River, N.J.; **A19** Pearson Education, Inc: D. B. Owen, *Handbook of Statistical Tables*, A.5, Published by Addison Wesley Longman, Inc.; **A20–A24** Oxford University Press: From M. Merrington and C.M. Thompson, "Table of Percentage Points of the Inverted Beta (F) Distribution," *Biometrika* 33 (1943), pp. 74–87, Oxford University Press; **A25** American Statistical Association: From *Journal of American Statistical Association* Vol. 41 (1946), pp. 557–566. W. J. Dixon and A. M. Mood; **A25** American Cyanamid Company: From *Some Rapid Approximate Statistical Procedures*. Copyright 1949, 1964 Lederle Laboratories, American Cyanamid Co., Wayne, N.J.; **A26** Institute of Mathematical Statistics: From the Institute of Mathematical Statistics; **A27** Institute of Mathematical Statistics: From the Institute of Mathematical Statistics.

## Applet Correlation

| Applet | Concept Illustrated | Descriptor | Applet Activity |
|---|---|---|---|
| Random numbers | This applet investigates how a sample of random numbers is distributed, and how to use randomly generated numbers to select a random sample from a numbered list of values. | This applet generates random numbers from a range of integers specified by the user. The random sample of numbers can be generated with or without replacement. | 1.3 |
| Mean versus median | The mean and the median of a data set respond differently to changes in the data. This applet investigates how skewedness and outliers affect measures of central tendency. | This applet allows the user to visualize the relationship between the mean and median of a data set. The user may easily add and delete data points. The applet automatically updates the mean and median for each change in the data. | 2.3 |
| Standard deviation | Standard deviation measures the spread of a data set. This applet investigates how the shape and spread of a distribution affect the standard deviation. | This applet allows the user to visualize the relationship between the mean and standard deviation of a data set. The user may easily add and delete data points. The applet automatically updates the mean and standard deviation for each change in the data. | 2.4 |
| Simulating the stock market | An "up" day is a day in which the stock market shows a net gain. This applet investigates how the proportion of "up" days will tend to approach the theoretical probability of an "up" day over time. | This applet simulates fluctuation in the stock market, where on any given day going up is equally likely as going down. The user specifies the number of days and the applet reports whether the stock market goes up or down each day and creates a bar graph for the outcomes. It also calculates and plots the proportion of days that the stock market goes up during the simulation. | 3.1 |
| Simulating the probability of rolling a 3 or 4 | This applet investigates how the proportion of times a 3 or 4 is rolled will tend to approach the theoretical probability of rolling a 3 or 4 over time. | This applet simulates rolling a fair die. The user specifies the number of rolls and the applet reports the outcome of each roll and creates a bar graph for the outcomes. It also calculates and plots the proportion of times a 3 or 4 is rolled during the simulation. | 3.3 |
| Binomial distribution | This applet investigates how estimates of binomial probabilities obtained using the outcomes of $N$ samples of a binomial distribution tend to improve with larger values of $N$. | This applet simulates values from a binomial distribution. The user specifies the parameters for the binomial distribution ($n$ and $p$) and the number of values to be simulated ($N$). The applet plots $N$ values from the specified binomial distribution in a bar graph and reports the frequency of each outcome. | 4.2 |
| Sampling distributions | The mean and standard deviation of the distribution of sample means are unbiased estimators of the mean and standard deviation of the population distribution. This applet compares the means and standard deviations of the distributions and assesses the effect of sample size. | This applet simulates repeatedly choosing samples of a fixed size $n$ from a population. The user specifies the shape of the population distribution, the two sample statistics to be analyzed, the sample size $n$, and the number $N$ of samples. The applet plots the value of each specified sample statistic for each sample, and shows the mean, median, and standard deviation of these values for all the samples. | 5.4 |

*(continued on next page)*

| Applet | Concept Illustrated | Descriptor | Applet Activity |
|---|---|---|---|
| Confidence intervals for a mean | Confidence intervals obtained using the sample standard deviation are different from those obtained using the population standard deviation. This applet compares the proportions of $z$ confidence intervals and $t$ confidence intervals that contain the mean for randomly generated samples from the same population. | This applet generates confidence intervals for a population mean. The user specifies the sample size, the shape of the distribution, the population mean, the population standard deviation, and the interval type ($t$ or $z$). The applet simulates selecting 100 random samples from the population and finds the 95% $z$- or $t$-interval for each sample. The confidence intervals are plotted and the number and proportion containing the true mean are reported. | 6.2 |
| Confidence intervals for a proportion | This applet investigates the properties of confidence intervals for a population proportion. | This applet generates confidence intervals for a population proportion. The user specifies the population proportion and the sample size. The applet simulates selecting 100 random samples from the population and finds the 95% confidence interval for each sample. The confidence intervals are plotted and the number and proportion containing the true proportion are reported. The user can input a different confidence interval for the given samples. | 6.3 |
| Hypothesis tests for a mean | Not all tests of hypotheses lead correctly to either rejecting or failing to reject the null hypothesis. This applet investigates the relationship between the level of confidence and the probabilities of making Type I and Type II errors. | This applet performs hypotheses tests for a population mean. The user specifies the shape of the population distribution, the population mean and standard deviation, the sample size, and the null and alternative hypotheses. The user can also adjust the confidence level. The applet simulates selecting a random sample from the population and calculates and plots the $t$-statistic or $P$-value for each sample. The applet reports the number and proportion of times the null hypothesis is rejected at the given confidence level. | 7.3 |
| Hypothesis tests for a proportion | Not all tests of hypotheses lead correctly to either rejecting or failing to reject the null hypothesis. This applet investigates the relationship between the level of confidence and the probabilities of making Type I and Type II errors. | This applet performs hypotheses tests for a population proportion. The user specifies the population proportion, the sample size, and the null and alternative hypotheses. The user can also adjust the confidence level. The applet simulates selecting a random sample from the population and calculates and plots the $z$-statistic or $P$-value for each sample. The applet reports the number and proportion of times the null hypothesis is rejected at the given confidence level. | 7.4 |
| Correlation by eye | The correlation coefficient measures the strength of a linear relationship between two variables. This applet teaches the user how to assess the strength of a linear relationship from a scatter plot. | This applet computes the correlation coefficient $r$ for a set of bivariate data plotted on a scatter plot. The user can easily add or delete points and guess the value of $r$. The applet then compares the guess to its calculated value. | 9.1 |
| Regression by eye | The least squares regression line has a smaller SSE than any other line that might approximate a set of bivariate data. This applet teaches the user how to approximate the location of a regression line on a scatter plot. | This applet shows the $y$-intercept, slope, and SSE of the least squares regression line for a set of bivariate data plotted on a scatter plot. The user can easily add or delete points and guess the location of the regression line by manipulating a line provided on the scatter plot. The applet shows the $y$-intercept, slope, and SSE of this line. The applet will plot the least squares line. | 9.2 |